Frequently Used Symbols and Formulas

SYMBOLS

$=$	Is equal to
$\approx$	Is approximately equal to
$>$	Is greater than
$<$	Is less than
$\geq$	Is greater than or equal to
$\leq$	Is less than or equal to
$\|x\|$	The absolute value of x
$\{x\mid x\ldots\}$	The set of all x such that $x\ldots$
$-x$	The opposite of x
$\sqrt{x}$	The square root of x
$\sqrt[n]{x}$	The nth root of x
LCM	Least Common Multiple
LCD	Least Common Denominator
π	Pi
i	$\sqrt{-1}$
$f(x)$	f of x, or f at x

FORMULAS

$m = \dfrac{y_2 - y_1}{x_2 - x_1}$	Slope of a line
$y = mx + b$	Slope–intercept form of a linear equation
$y - y_1 = m(x - x_1)$	Point–slope form of a linear equation
$(A + B)(A - B) = A^2 - B^2$	Product of the sum and difference of the same two terms
$\left.\begin{array}{l}(A + B)^2 = A^2 + 2AB + B^2,\\ (A - B)^2 = A^2 - 2AB + B^2\end{array}\right\}$	Square of a binomial
$d = rt$	Formula for distance traveled
$\dfrac{1}{a} \cdot t + \dfrac{1}{b} \cdot t = 1$	Work principle
$s = 16t^2$	Free-fall distance
$y = kx$	Direct variation
$y = \dfrac{k}{x}$	Inverse variation
$x = \dfrac{-b \pm \sqrt{b^2 - 4ac}}{2a}$	Quadratic formula

GEOMETRIC FORMULAS*

$A = lw$	Area of a rectangle
$P = 2l + 2w$	Perimeter of a rectangle
$A = \frac{1}{2}bh$	Area of a triangle
$a^2 + b^2 = c^2$	Pythagorean theorem
$A = bh$	Area of a parallelogram
$A = \pi r^2$	Area of a circle
$C = 2\pi r$	Circumference of a circle
$V = lwh$	Volume of a rectangular solid
$V = \pi r^2 h$	Volume of a right circular cylinder
$S = 2\pi rh + 2\pi r^2$	Surface area of a right circular cylinder

*These and other geometric formulas can be found in Table 3.

MyMathLab Starter Guide by Dr. G.

Welcome to the MyMathLab Starter Guide. The following pages will assist you in registering for your course using MyMathLab. There will also be several helpful hints along the way to make your learning experience successful!

MyMathLab does NOT work on the MACINTOSH or APPLE PC's nor does it work within AOL. AOL members need to connect to the internet via AOL. Decrease the size of the AOL window and then click on the Internet Explorer Icon. You MUST connect to MyMathLab through the Internet Explorer outside of AOL.

What do you need to get started?

☑	**A Valid Email Address**	***Don't have it yet?*** Contact your school's technology center for a university e-mail account, or set up an e-mail account through a free service such as Hotmail or Yahoo.
☑	**Course ID**	***The Course ID for your section is:*** (This is given to you by your instructor.)
☑	**Student Access Code**	*Don't have it yet?* There are three ways to get access to MyMathLab: 1. Purchase the package at the bookstore that includes your textbook and a Student Access Kit to MyMathLab (the Access Code is free when packaged with your text). 2. Purchase the stand-alone Student Access Kit from the bookstore. 3. Purchase online access using a credit card at the following website: http://students.pearsoned.com (click on the "Register" button to access the online payment option).

How to Register for a course with an Access Code

This section explains registering with an Access Code.

Connect to MyMathLab using the following URL: http://students.pearsoned.com

1) Click Register, have your access code and course ID available; click next.
2) Enter your Access code and click Next.
3) Enter Course ID. **XXXX**; click Next.
4) Enter your contact information. The school's zip code is 06515. Click Next.
5) Choose Southern Connecticut State University. Click Next.
6) Choose a login name, password and security question. The login name and password must be at least 4 characters. I recommend you use your SCSU login name.
7) Read the license agreement and click "I Agree" and then click Next.

For MAT100/MAT101/MAT102 students:
MyMathLab for Rockswold - Intermediate Algebra through Modeling and Visualization, 1e
For MAT095 students:
Elementary Algebra: Concepts and Applications, 7/E

How to Register for a course with an Access Code.

Connect to MyMathLab using the following URL: http://students.pearsoned.com

1) Click Register,
2) Then click on "purchase online access".
3) Enter the course code: **XXXX**; click Next.
4) Click on:

For MAT100/MAT101/MAT102 students:
MyMathLab for Rockswold - Intermediate Algebra through Modeling and Visualization, 1e

For MAT095 students:
Elementary Algebra: Concepts and Applications, 7/E

5) Enter your contact information. The school's zip code is 06515. Click Next.
6) Choose Southern Connecticut State University. Click Next.
7) Choose a login name, password and security question. The login name and password must be at least 4 characters. I recommend you use your SCSU login name.
8) Read the license agreement and click "I Agree" and then click Next.
9) Enter your Credit Card information; click Next.
10) I suggest you printout your login info so that you have it.

MyMathLab Installation Wizard Guide

This installation guide assumes you have completed the student or instructor registration. If you have not already registered with MyMathLab ensure you have your Access Code, Course ID, and title of your textbook in hand and go to www.mymathlab.com.

About the online MyMathLab Installation Wizard:

Plug-ins and players let you view and interact with the multimedia content in each MyMathLab course. Depending on your course's content, you may need to download some or all of the following plug-ins and players using the MyMathLab installation wizard:

- Adobe Acrobat Reader
- Real Networks RealPlayer
- InterAct Math plug-in (created by Addison-Wesley)
- TestGen-EQ plug-in (created by Addison-Wesley)
- Macromedia Flash Player
- Shockwave Player

The MyMathLab installation wizard determines whether you have each plug-in installed on your computer and walks you through an easy installation process for any plug-ins that may be missing.

The installation wizard is updated as new versions of the plug-ins become available, so it is a good idea to bookmark the wizard and revisit it periodically to make sure you have the latest plug-ins installed.

Step 1. Locate the MyMathLab Installation Wizard:

Go to the MyMathLab web site. Type in your browser's address bar: www.mymathlab.com. Next, click on "Student Login" and then select Step 4. Installing Plug-Ins. On this screen you will see a link labeled, MyMathLab installation wizard. Go ahead and click on this link to navigate to the start of the MyMathLab installation wizard.

Note: *Alternatively, you could login to your MyMathLab course by typing www.coursecompass.com in your browser's address bar. Once you are logged in and have entered your course, you can click on Announcements to see a message entitled,* "MyMathLab Software Installation Wizard." *You can click on the link in this message as another method of accessing the installation wizard.*

Step 2. The System Requirements Checkpoint:

- Windows Pentium class PC or better (95, 98 2000, NT, XP).
- Internet Explorer 5.0 or above.
- Monitor resolution 1024 x 768 (use the ruler on the page to check your resolution).
- Internet connection: 56k modem for tutorials and testing. T1 or better for multimedia textbook.
- Plug-ins installed.

Monitor Resolution

If you aren't able to view the 970 mark on the ruler without having to scroll across, follow these instructions.

To change your screen resolution to 1024 x 768, click the Windows Start button, choose Settings and Control Panel (Windows XP users simply click on Control Panel), and then Display. Click the Settings tab and choose 1024 x 768 pixels for the desktop area.

Note: *Also make sure that "small fonts" or "normal size" is selected for the font size. To see font selection, select the Advanced button.*

When you return to your browser, click the icon in the upper right-hand corner to maximize the window.

Step 3: Browser Plug-In Installation:

Each plug-in has a function within MyMathLab and you will want to ensure that all of the plug-ins are installed so you can take full advantage of all of the features of MyMathLab.

Each box represents a different plug-in for different MyMathLab content. You may already have a few of the more common plug-ins already installed, such as; Adobe Acrobat, Real Player, or Flash.

If you think you already have a plug-in, you can click on the DETECT button. If the plug-in is installed and detected in most instances you will see a preview of some sample content or a detection banner.

IMPORTANT! After you have installed all of the plug-ins close your browser window and restart it in order for the newly installed plug-ins to be recognized.

INTERACT MATH PLUG-IN INSTALLATION

The InterAct Math plug-in is the Internet version of Addison-Wesley's InterAct Math Tutorial software. When properly installed into your Netscape or Internet Explorer browser, the plug-in enables you to take free-response tests and work practice exercises found in MyMathLab.

Click INSTALL to automatically start the plug-in installation. The "Installation Complete" box will come up indicating that the installation was successful.

Note: *If for any reason your browser does not automatically install the plug-in, click on the link option to go through the standard installation.*

TESTGEN PLUG-IN INSTALLATION

The TestGen-EQ plug-in allows students and instructors to access multiple-choice quizzes and tests over the Internet that have been created with Addison-Wesley's TestGen-EQ software. When properly installed into your Netscape and/or Internet Explorer browsers, the plug-in displays the test questions, answer selections, and summary information for each test.

Click INSTALL to automatically start the plug-in installation.

Installation for Internet Explorer users is automatic and is happening behind the scenes. The "Installation Complete" box will come up indicating that the installation was successful.

Note: *If for any reason your browser does not automatically install the plug-in, click on the link option to go through the standard installation.*

When the TestGen plug-in is properly installed you will be able to click the DETECT button to view a screen with an example.

ADOBE ACROBAT PLUG IN INSTALLATION

The Adobe Acrobat plug-in allows you to view the multimedia textbook and other print supplements. This is a common plug-in and it may be already installed on your system through your use of other software. Click on DETECT and see if the sample PDF file is viewable.

If you don't see the screen with a PDF file click the INSTALL button to install the Adobe Acrobat Reader plug-in.

Note: *Unlike the InterAct Math and TestGen plug-ins, the Adobe Acrobat installation is not automatic for Internet Explorer users. Please follow the installation instructions.*

REAL PLAYER INSTALLATION

The Real Player plug-in allows you to view streaming video lectures over the Internet. You will want to install the Real Player plug-in if you want to be able to view these video clips. The Real Player is a common plug-in and it may be already installed on your system through your use of other software. Click on DETECT and see if a sample video clip file is viewable.

If you have Real Player already installed insure that is the current player, if it is not, follow the instructions to download the latest player.

Note: *Unlike the InterAct Math and TestGen plug-ins, the Real Player installation is not automatic for Internet Explorer users. Please follow the installation instructions.*

MACROMEDIA FLASH PLUG-IN INSTALLATION

The Flash plug-in allows you to view streaming some of the animations that available in the online text. The Flash plug-in is a common plug-in and it may be already installed on your system through your use of other software. Click on DETECT and see if the following screen is viewable.

If you have Flash already installed insure that it is the current version. If it is not, follow the instructions to download the latest plug-in.

Installation for Internet Explorer users is automatic and is happening behind the scenes. The "Installation Complete" box will come up indicating that the installation was successful.

Note: *If for any reason your browser does not automatically install the plug-in, click on the link option to go through the standard installation. You will need to close and reopen your browser in order for it to detect any newly installed plug-ins, but do so AFTER completing the entire plug-in installation process.*

Step 4: Detecting Plug-In Installation:

Once you have completed the installation of all of the necessary plug-ins. Close all browser windows and restart your browser. Navigate back to the MyMathLab Installation Wizard page and click on DETECT for each plug-in to assure each has been installed properly.

If you encounter a problem:

1. Restart your computer and try again.
2. Reinstall the plug-in one more time.
3. Write down the following information;
    a. Browser and version number (ex. Internet Explorer 5.5 SP2)
    b. Version of Windows.
    c. Method of connecting to the Internet.
    d. The plug-in you are having a problem with.
    e. Any error messages or error indications.
4. Please be armed with the above information and call or email technical support

Technical Support
Hours: 9AM - 5PM Central Time
Phone: 1-800-677-6337
Fax: 847-486-2595
Email: online.support@pearsoned.com
URL: http://www.mymathlab.com/contactus.html

After you have completed the installation wizard, if you receive the following *error message stating that the fonts are missing or not installed properly* you will need to:

You may experience a problem Installing TestGen Fonts on Windows NT and Windows 2000

Locate the Plugins folder for your browser and see if it contains the TestGen-EQ Plug-in font files listed below.

tgeqa.ttf	tgeqasi.ttf
tgeqas.ttf	tgeqm.ttf
tgeqab.ttf	tgeqai.ttf
tgeqs.ttf	

If all the necessary files are listed in the Plugins folder, check that the .ttf files exist in the winnt\fonts folder

* If the font files are in the Plugins folder and not in the winnt\fonts folder, copy the fonts from the Plugins folder to the winnt\fonts folder

* If the font files are NOT in the Plugins folder, then you will need to run the setup/installer program again to reinstall the TestGen-EQ Plug-in

Additional Features within MyMathLab

You will also have access to MathXL. Within MathXL you have the following resources:

1) Confirm Answer – You can input an answer and get immediate feedback (correct or wrong with a hint).
2) Guided Solution – A tutorial will ask certain questions while you are working on a problem. You will input answers to the questions to solve the problems.
3) Sample Problems – You can view a detailed explanation of a similar problem to the one that was asked.
4) Video Lectures – You can view detailed video clips for each section of your textbook.

Watching the Video Lectures

Once you are logged into MyMathLab and in our course choose the Chapter Contents button on the left hand side menu. You will then see a detailed list of the chapters of our text. Click on chapter 2 and then scroll to section 2.1 and click on the 2.1 heading. A new window will appear and the very first item is the "Video Lecture", click on that and wait for the video to load. You can control the video just like a DVD movie and back up on the tracks if the need be to review what was said.

Summary of Steps:

1. Chapter Contents
2. Select your chapter
3. Open the desired section
4. Click on Video. …. You're now ready for the lecture/s.

On the Chapter Contents page you **ALSO** have access to the tutorial center, tracked tutorial examples, and practice examples. Take advantage of all that his website has to offer! The more additional components you use from MyMathLab will only increase your comprehension and mastery of the skills. I know several of you have stated that math is not your best subject. Please take these words to heart!!

To Login to MathXL:

1) Go to http://www.mathxl.com
2) Click MyMathLab Login on the right hand side.
3) Enter your login name and password, click Login.
4) Click enter MathXL. If this is your first time you may need to install the plug-ins. Follow the directions on the screen. (This is explained above)

Other Resources:

1) Learning Center (Library 3rd floor) – There are video cds.
2) Tutoring Center – First floor Wintergreen.
3) One-to-one tutoring via phone calls, faxes, e-mails, and the Internet at http://www.aw.com/tutorcenter.

SCSU labs equipped with the plug-ins are found in the following locations on campus:

- the Buley Library computers on the third floor, room 314 (NOT THE MACINTOSH OR APPLE COMPUTERS)
- the computer lab of Jennings Hall Room 130,
- the computers in the North Campus computer lab,
- Use the computers in the Math Department Lab (Engleman D124),
- the Campus Tutorial and Writing Center computers of Wintergreen,
- the Student Center Computer lab.

If you have further problems please see your instructor; myself, Dr. C.B. Gubitose or Dr. E. Dennis in the EN D Wing.

References

My Mathlab Website	www.mymathlab.com
CourseCompass Website	www.coursecompass.com

BITTINGER | ELLENBOGEN

ELEMENTARY ALGEBRA
Concepts and Applications

Custom Edition for
Southern Connecticut State University

Taken from:

Elementary Algebra: Concepts and Applications, Seventh Edition
by Marvin L. Bittinger and David J. Ellenbogen

PEARSON Custom Publishing

PEARSON Addison Wesley

Cover Art: *Seashell 01*, by Michael Lary

Excerpts taken from:

Elementary Algebra: Concepts and Applications, Seventh Edition
by Marvin L. Bittinger and David J. Ellenbogen

A Pearson Education Company
Boston, Massachusetts, 02116

Printed in the United States of America

10 9 8 7 6 5 4 3 2

ISBN 0-536-97112-9

2005360399

AK

Please visit our web site at *www.pearsoncustom.com*

PEARSON CUSTOM PUBLISHING
75 Arlington Street, Suite 300, Boston, MA 02116
A Pearson Education Company

Contents

3 Introduction to Graphing

4 Polynomials

5 Polynomials and Factoring

6 Rational Expressions and Equations

7 Systems and More Graphing

8 Radical Expressions and Equations

9 Quadratic Equations

Preface

It is with great pleasure that we introduce you to the seventh edition of *Elementary Algebra: Concepts and Applications*. Every time we work on a new edition, it's a balancing act. On the one hand, we want to preserve the features, applications, and explanations that faculty have come to rely on and expect. On the other hand, we want to blend our own ideas for improvement with the many insights that we receive from faculty and students throughout North America. The result is a living document in which new features and applications are developed at the same time that successful features and popular applications from previous editions are updated and refined. Our goal, as always, is to present content that is easy to understand and has the depth required for success in this and future courses.

Appropriate for a one-term course in elementary algebra, this text is intended for those students who have a firm background in arithmetic. It is the first of three texts in an algebra series that also includes *Intermediate Algebra: Concepts and Applications*, Seventh Edition, by Bittinger/Ellenbogen and *Elementary and Intermediate Algebra: Concepts and Applications*, Fourth Edition, by Bittinger/Ellenbogen/Johnson.

Approach

Our goal, quite simply, is to help today's students both learn and retain mathematical concepts. To achieve this goal, we feel that we must prepare developmental-mathematics students for the transition from "skills-oriented" elementary algebra courses to more "concept-oriented" college-level mathematics courses. This requires that we teach these same students critical thinking skills: to reason mathematically, to communicate mathematically, and to identify and solve mathematical problems. Following are three aspects of our approach that we use to help meet the challenges we all face when teaching developmental mathematics.

Problem Solving

One distinguishing feature of our approach is our treatment of and emphasis on problem solving. We use problem solving and applications to motivate the material wherever possible, and we include real-life applications and problem-solving techniques throughout the text. Problem solving not only encourages students to think about how mathematics can be used, it helps to prepare them for more advanced material in future courses.

In Chapter 2, we introduce our five-step process for solving problems: (1) Familiarize, (2) Translate, (3) Carry out, (4) Check, and (5) State the answer. These steps are then used consistently throughout the text when encountering a problem-solving situation. Repeated use of this problem-solving strategy helps provide students with a starting point for any type of problem they encounter, and frees them to focus on the unique aspects of the particular problem situation. We often use estimation and carefully checked guesses to help with the *Familiarize* and *Check* steps (see pp. 115 and 412–413). We also use dimensional analysis as a quick check of certain problems (see pp. 179 and 415).

Applications

Interesting applications of mathematics help motivate both students and instructors. Solving applied problems gives students the opportunity to see their conceptual understanding put to use in a real way. In the Seventh Edition of *Elementary Algebra: Concepts and Applications*, we have increased the number of applications, the number of real-data problems, and the number of reference lines that specify the sources of the real-world data. As in the past, art is integrated into the applications and exercises to aid the student in visualizing the mathematics. (See pp. 116, 193, 251, 349, and 419.)

Pedagogy

New! **CONCEPT REINFORCEMENT EXERCISES.** This feature is designed to help students build their confidence and comprehension through true/false, matching, and fill-in-the-blank exercises at the beginning of most exercise sets. When appropriate, special attention is devoted to increasing student understanding of the new vocabulary and notation developed in that section. (See pp. 109, 154, 194, and 240.)

New! **STUDY SKILLS.** These remarks, located in the margin near the beginning of each section, provide suggestions for successful study habits that can be applied to both this and other college courses. Ranging from ideas for better time management to suggestions for test preparation, these comments can be useful to even experienced college students. (See pp. 8, 90, and 202.)

New! **STUDENT NOTES.** These comments, strategically located in the margin within each section, are specific to the mathematics appearing on that page. Remarks are more casual in format than the typical exposition and range from suggestions on how to avoid common mistakes to how to best read new mathematical notation. (See pp. 106, 191, and 313.)

New! **STUDY SUMMARY.** Each chapter closes with a Study Summary in which the authors have written notes that highlight the most important concepts and terminology from that chapter. Page numbers are provided so students can reference where the terminology is first introduced, important properties and formulas are listed, and examples of specific types of problems are often listed.

In short, the Study Summary provides a terrific point from which to begin reviewing for a chapter test. (See pp. 143, 294, and 359.)

New!

THE ALGEBRAIC–GRAPHICAL CONNECTION. Because many of us master concepts more easily when provided with visual information, we now include a feature that offers students the opportunity to visualize algebraic concepts that might otherwise prove elusive. (See pp. 344 and 407.)

CONNECTING THE CONCEPTS. To help students understand the "big picture," Connecting the Concepts subsections within each chapter (and highlighted in the table of contents) relate the concept at hand to previously learned and upcoming concepts. Because students may occasionally "lose sight of the forest because of the trees," this feature helps them to better keep their bearings as they encounter new material. (See pp. 340, 402, and 453.)

AHA! EXERCISES. Designated by Aha!, these exercises can be solved quickly if the student has the proper insight. The Aha! designation is used the first time a new insight can be used on a particular type of exercise and indicates to the student that there is a simpler way to complete the exercise than the more routine approach. It's then up to the student to find the simpler approach and, in subsequent exercises, to determine if and when that particular insight can be used again. The Aha! exercises are not more difficult than the neighboring exercises, but are designed to reward students who "look before they leap" into a problem. (See pp. 87, 233, 276, and 394.)

TECHNOLOGY CONNECTIONS. Throughout each chapter, optional Technology Connection boxes help students use graphing calculator technology to better visualize a concept that they have just learned. To connect this feature to the exercise sets, certain exercises are marked with a graphing calculator icon and reinforce the use of this optional technology. (See pp. 92, 258, 306, and 400.)

SKILL MAINTENANCE EXERCISES. Retention of skills is critical to a student's success in this and future courses. To this end, beginning in Section 1.2, every exercise set includes Skill Maintenance exercises that review skills and concepts from preceding sections of the text. Whenever possible, these six to eight exercises provide extra practice with specific skills that may be "rusty" but are needed for the next section of the text. (See pp. 185, 243, and 333.)

SYNTHESIS EXERCISES. Following the Skill Maintenance section, every exercise set ends with a group of Synthesis exercises that offer opportunities for students to synthesize skills and concepts from earlier sections with the present material, and often provide students with deeper insights into the current topic. Synthesis exercises are generally more challenging than those in the main body of the exercise set and occasionally include Aha! exercises. (See pp. 142, 200, 234, and 277.)

WRITING EXERCISES. Every set of exercises includes at least four writing exercises. Two of these are more basic and appear just before the Skill Maintenance exercises. The other writing exercises are more challenging and appear as Synthesis exercises. All writing exercises are marked with and require answers that are one or more complete sentences. This type of problem has been found to aid in student comprehension, critical thinking, and conceptualization. Because some instructors may collect answers to writing exercises, and because more than one answer may be correct, answers to writing exercises are listed at the back of the text only for Review Exercises. (See pp. 157, 315, 357, and 386.)

COLLABORATIVE CORNERS. Studies have shown that students who study together generally outperform those who do not. Throughout the text, we continue to provide optional Collaborative Corner activities that require students to work in groups to explore and solve mathematical problems. There are typically two to three Collaborative Corners per chapter, each one appearing after the appropriate exercise set. (See pp. 12, 114, 158, and 316.) Additional Collaborative Corner activities and suggestions for directing collaborative learning appear in the *Printed Test Bank/Instructor's Resource Guide.*

CUMULATIVE REVIEW. After Chapters 3, 6, and 9, we have included a Cumulative Review, which reviews skills and concepts from all preceding chapters of the text. (See pp. 223, 427, and 587.)

What's New in the Seventh Edition?

We have rewritten many key topics in response to user and reviewer feedback and have made significant improvements in design, art, pedagogy, and an expanded supplements package. Detailed information about the content changes is available in the form of a conversion guide. Please ask your local Addison-Wesley sales consultant for more information. Following is a list of the major changes in this edition.

New Design

While incorporating a new layout, a fresh palette of colors, and new features, we have maintained the larger page dimension for an open look, and a typeface that is easy to read. As always, it is our goal to make the text look mature without being intimidating. In addition, we continue to pay close attention to the pedagogical use of color to make sure that it is used to present concepts in the clearest possible manner.

Content Changes

A variety of content changes have been made throughout the text. Some of the more significant changes are listed below.

- Chapter 1 now includes more emphasis on translating English to mathematics.
- Chapter 2 includes new material on how to choose between the multiplication or addition principles when solving an equation. There is also new material on how to decide which principle to use first when solving linear equations of a more general variety.
- Chapter 3 now includes new material on how to choose an appropriate range and scale for the axes when graphing real-world data. There is also increased emphasis on visualizing the connection between rate and slope.
- Chapter 4 now makes greater use of prime factorizations as a tool for finding the largest common factor.

Ancillaries

The following ancillaries are available to help both instructors and students use this text more effectively:

STUDENT SUPPLEMENTS

Student's Solutions Manual

- By Judith A. Penna, *Indiana University Purdue University Indianapolis*
- Contains completely worked-out solutions with step-by-step annotations for all the odd-numbered exercises in the text, with the exception of the writing exercises.

  ISBN: 0-321-26954-3

Videotapes

- Present a series of lectures correlated directly to the content of each section of the text.
- Feature an engaging team of instructors who present material using examples and exercises from the text in a format that stresses student interaction.

  ISBN: 0-321-26952-7

Digital Video Tutor

- Complete set of digitized videos on CD-ROMs for student use at home or on campus.
- Ideal for distance learning or supplemental instruction.

  ISBN: 0-321-26951-9

Addison-Wesley Math Tutor Center

- The Addison-Wesley Math Tutor Center is staffed by qualified mathematics instructors who provide students with tutoring on examples and odd-numbered exercises from the textbook. Tutoring is available via toll-free telephone, toll-free fax, e-mail, or the Internet. White Board technology allows tutors and students to actually see problems worked while they "talk" in real time over the Internet during tutoring sessions. For more information, go to www.aw-bc/tutorcenter

INSTRUCTOR SUPPLEMENTS

Instructor's Solutions Manual

- By Judith A. Penna, *Indiana University Purdue University Indianapolis*
- Contains fully worked-out solutions to the odd-numbered exercises and brief solutions to the even-numbered exercises in the exercise sets.

  ISBN: 0-321-26955-1

Answer Book

- By Judith A. Penna, *Indiana University Purdue University Indianapolis*
- Contains answers to all the section exercises in the text.

  ISBN: 0-321-26953-5

Printed Test Bank/Instructor's Resource Guide

- By Sybil MacBeth
- Contains two multiple-choice tests per chapter; six free-response tests per chapter; eight final exams; extra practice exercises on selected topics from the text; extra Collaborative Corners; correlation guide; video index; and transparency masters.

  ISBN: 0-321-26956-X

New! *Adjunct Support Manual*

- Includes resources designed to help both new and adjunct faculty with course preparation and classroom management.
- Offers helpful teaching tips.

  ISBN: 0-321-29446-7

TestGen with Quizmaster

- Enables instructors to build, edit, print, and administer tests.
- Features a computerized bank of questions developed to cover all text objectives.
- Available on a dual-platform Windows/Macintosh CD-ROM.

  ISBN: 0-321-26948-9

MathXL® Tutorials on CD (ISBN 0-321-26950-0)

This interactive tutorial CD-ROM provides algorithmically generated practice exercises that are correlated to the exercises in the textbook. Every practice exercise is accompanied by an example and a guided solution designed to involve students in the solution process. Selected exercises may also include a video clip to help students visualize concepts. The software can generate printed summaries of students' progress.

MathXL®: www.mathxl.com (ISBN 0-201-72611-4)

MathXL is a powerful, online homework, tutorial, and assessment system that accompanies your Addison-Wesley textbook. With MathXL, instructors can create, edit, and assign online homework and tests using algorithmically generated exercises correlated to your textbook. All student work is tracked in MathXL's online gradebook. Students can take chapter tests in MathXL and receive personalized study plans based on their test results. The study plan diagnoses weaknesses and links students directly to tutorial exercises for the objectives they need to study and retest. Students can also access supplemental video clips and animations directly from selected exercises.

MyMathLab

MyMathLab is a series of text-specific, easily customizable online courses for Addison-Wesley textbooks in mathematics and statistics. MyMathLab is powered by CourseCompass™—Pearson Education's online teaching and learning environment—and by MathXL—our online homework, tutorial, and assessment system. MyMathLab gives instructors the tools they need to deliver all or a portion of their course online, whether students are in a lab setting or working from home. MyMathLab provides a rich and flexible set of course materials, featuring free-response exercises that are algorithmically generated for unlimited practice and mastery. Students can also use online tools, such as video lectures, animations, and a multimedia textbook, to independently improve their understanding and performance. Instructors can use MyMathLab's homework and test managers to select and assign online exercises correlated directly to the textbook, and they can import TestGen tests into MyMathLab for added flexibility. MyMathLab's online gradebook—designed specifically for mathematics and statistics—automatically tracks students' homework and test results and gives the instructor control over how to calculate final grades. Instructors can also add offline (paper-and-pencil) grades to the gradebook. MyMathLab is available to qualified adopters. For more information, visit our Web site at www.mymathlab.com or contact your Addison-Wesley sales representative.

InterActMath® Tutorial Web site www.interactmath.com

Get practice and tutorial help online! This interactive tutorial Web site provides algorithmically generated practice exercises that correlate directly to the exercises in your textbook. You can retry an exercise as many times as you like with new values each time for unlimited practice and mastery. Every exercise is accompanied by an interactive guided solution that gives you helpful feedback if you enter an incorrect answer, and you can also view a worked-out sample problem that steps you through an exercise similar to the one you're working on.

Acknowledgments

No book can be produced without a team of professionals who take pride in their work and are willing to put in long hours. Barbara Johnson, in particular, deserves extra thanks for her work as developmental editor. Without Barbara's tireless devotion and her many fine suggestions, this book simply would not have been possible. Laurie Hurley, Sybil MacBeth, Elina Niemelä, Dawn Mulheron, Daphne Bell, Louise Jarvis, and Bill Saler also deserve special thanks for their careful accuracy checks, well-thought-out suggestions, and uncanny eye for detail. Judy Penna's outstanding work in organizing and preparing the printed supplements amounts to an inspection of the text that goes far beyond the call of duty and for which we are always extremely grateful. Thanks to Sybil MacBeth for also authoring the *Printed Test Bank*.

We are also indebted to Chris Burditt and Jann MacInnes for their many fine ideas that appear in our Collaborative Corners and Vince McGarry and Janet Wyatt for their recommendations for Teaching Tips featured in the *Annotated Instructor's Edition*.

Martha Morong, of Quadrata, Inc., provided editorial and production services of the highest quality imaginable—she is amazing and a joy to work with. Geri Davis, of the Davis Group, Inc., performed superb work as designer, art editor, and photo researcher, and is always a pleasure to work with. Network Graphics generated the graphs, charts, and many of the illustrations. Not only are the people at Network reliable, but they clearly take pride in their work. The many illustrations appear thanks to Jim Bryant and Bill Melvin, both of whom are artists with insights and creativity.

Our team at Addison-Wesley deserves special thanks. Project Editor Suzanne Alley coordinated all the reviews, helped with a wide variety of tasks, and gently prodded us to stay on schedule, always in a pleasant manner. Associate Editor Katie Nopper and Editorial Assistant Elizabeth Bernardi helped with a variety of jobs and always in a timely way. Senior Acquisitions Editor Jenny Crum provided many fine suggestions and is superb at remaining involved and helpful throughout the project. Senior Production Supervisor Kathy Manley exhibited patience when others would have shown frustration. Designer Dennis Schaefer's willingness to listen and then creatively respond resulted in a book that is beautiful to look at. Senior Marketing Manager Dona Kenly and Marketing Coordinator Tracy Rabinowitz skillfully kept us in touch with the needs of faculty. Our Editor in Chief, Maureen O'Connor, and our Publisher, Greg Tobin, deserve credit for assembling this fine team.

We also thank the students at the Community College of Vermont and the following professors for their thoughtful reviews and insightful comments.

Prerevision Diary Reviewers (Sixth Edition)

Susan Caldiero, *Cosumnes River College*
Paulette Kirkpatrick, *Wharton County Junior College*
Diane Trimble, *Tulsa Community College—West Campus*
Jennifer Vanden Eynden, *Grossmont College*

Manuscript Reviewers

Paul Blankenship, *Lexington Community College*
David Casey, *Citrus College*
Beth Fraser, *Middlesex Community College*
Gary Glaze, *Spokane Falls Community College*
Jeff Koleno, *Lorain County Community College*
Rogers Martin, *Louisiana State University—Shreveport*
Ben Mayo, *Yakima Valley Community College*
Laurie McManus, *St. Louis Community College—Meramac*
Anne Marie Mosher, *St. Louis Community College—Florissant Valley*
Kim Nunn, *Northeast State Technical College*
Michael Oppedisano, *Morrisville College SUNY*
Terri Seiver, *San Jacinto College—Central*
Timothy Thompson, *Oregon Institute of Technology*
Beverly Vredevelt, *Spokane Falls Community College*

Finally, a special thank you to all those who so generously agreed to discuss their professional use of mathematics in our chapter openers. These dedicated people all share a desire to make math more meaningful to students. We cannot imagine a finer set of role models.

M.L.B.
D.J.E.

Feature Walkthrough

9 Quadratic Equations

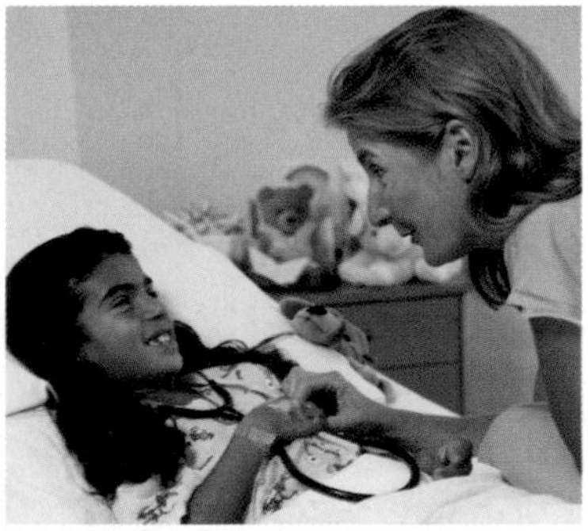

AN APPLICATION

Young's rule for determining the size of a particular child's medicine dosage c is

$$c = \frac{a}{a + 12} \cdot d,$$

where a is the child's age and d is the typical adult dosage (*Source*: Olsen, June Looby, Leon J. Ablon, and Anthony Patrick Giangrasso, *Medical Dosage Calculations*, 6th ed). If a child receives 8 mg of antihistamine when the typical adult dosage is 24 mg, how old is the child?

This problem appears as Exercise 65 in Section 9.4.

Rena J. Webster
REGISTERED NURSE
Indianapolis, Indiana

Nurses dispense medicine on a regular basis. Since medicine often comes in a dosage different from what a doctor prescribes, I must calculate the correct dosage. Math also helps in critical thinking, such as determining dosage on the basis of body weight.

Chapter Openers

Each chapter opens with a list of sections covered and a real-life application that includes a testimonial from a person in that field to show how important mathematics is in everyday problem solving. Real data often appear in these applications, in many other exercises, and in "on the job" examples similar to what students might find in the workplace.

NEW!

To clear an equation of decimals, we count the greatest number of decimal places in any one number. If the greatest number of decimal places is 1, we multiply both sides by 10; if it is 2, we multiply by 100; and so on. This procedure is the same as multiplying by the least common denominator after converting the decimals to fractions.

EXAMPLE 7 Solve: $16.3 - 7.2y = -8.18$.

Solution The greatest number of decimal places in any one number is *two.* Multiplying by 100 will clear all decimals.

$100(16.3 - 7.2y) = 100(-8.18)$	Multiplying both sides by 100
$100(16.3) - 100(7.2y) = 100(-8.18)$	Using the distributive law
$1630 - 720y = -818$	Simplifying
$-720y = -818 - 1630$	Subtracting 1630 from both sides
$-720y = -2448$	Combining like terms
$y = \frac{-2448}{-720}$	Dividing both sides by -720
$y = 3.4$	

In Example 4, the same solution was found without clearing decimals. Finding the same answer in two ways is a good check. The solution is 3.4.

Student Notes

Compare the steps of Examples 4 and 7. Note that although the two approaches differ, they yield the same solution. Whenever you can use two approaches to solve a problem, try to do so, both as a check and as a valuable learning experience.

Student Notes

These comments, strategically located in the margin within each section, are specific to the mathematics appearing on that page. Remarks are more casual in format than the typical exposition and range from suggestions on how to avoid common mistakes to how to properly read new notation.

NEW!

When denominators are different, we use the identity property of 1 and multiply to find a common denominator. Then we add, as in Example 9.

EXAMPLE 10 Add or subtract as indicated: **(a)** $\frac{7}{8} + \frac{5}{12}$; **(b)** $\frac{9}{8} - \frac{4}{5}$.

Solution

a) The number 24 is d
$\frac{5}{12}$ by suitable form
of 24:

$\frac{7}{8} + \frac{5}{12} = \frac{7}{8} \cdot \frac{3}{3} \cdot$

$= \frac{21}{24} + \frac{10}{24}$

$= \frac{31}{24}.$

b) $\frac{9}{8} - \frac{4}{5} = \frac{9}{8} \cdot \frac{5}{5} - \frac{4}{5}$

$= \frac{45}{40} - \frac{32}{40} =$

Study Skills

Do the Exercises

- Usually an instructor assigns some odd-numbered exercises. When you complete these, you can check your answers at the back of the book. If you miss any, closely examine your work, and if necessary, consult the *Student's Solutions Manual* or your instructor for guidance.
- Whether or not your instructor assigns the even-numbered exercises, try to do some on your own. There are no answers given for them, so you will gain practice doing exercises that are similar to quiz or test problems. Check your answers later with a friend or your instructor.

Study Skills

These remarks, located in the margin near the beginning of each section, provide suggestions for successful study habits and can be extended to courses other than algebra. Ranging from ideas for better time management to how to prepare for tests, these comments can be useful to even experienced college students.

technology connection

Most graphing calculators have a TABLE feature that enables the calculator to evaluate a variable expression for different choices of x. For example, to evaluate $6x + 5 - 7x$ for $x = 0, 1, 2, \ldots,$ we first use (Y=) to enter $6x + 5 - 7x$ as y_1. We then use (2ND) (TBLSET) to specify which x-values will be used. Using TblStart = 0, ΔTbl = 1, and selecting AUTO twice, we can generate a table in which the value of $6x + 5 - 7x$ is listed for values of x starting at 0 and increasing by ones.

X	Y1	
0	5	
1	4	
2	3	
3	2	
4	1	
5	0	
6	−1	

X = 0

1. Create the above table on your graphing calculator. Scroll up and down to extend the table.
2. Enter $10 - 4x + 7$ as y_2. Your table should now have three columns.
3. For what x-value is y_1 the same as y_2? Compare this with the solution of Example 5(c). Is this a reliable way to solve equations? Why or why not?

in one step

Isolate variable terms on one side and constant terms on the other side.

$2x - 4 = -3x + 1$	
$2x + 3x - 4 = -3x + 3x + 1$	Adding $3x$ to both sides
$5x - 4 = 1$	Simplifying
$5x - 4 + 4 = 1 + 4$	Adding 4 to both sides
$5x = 5$	Combining like terms
$\frac{5x}{5} = \frac{5}{5}$	Dividing both sides by 5
$x = 1$	

Check:

$2x - 4 = -3x + 1$

$2 \cdot 1 - 4 \mid -3 \cdot 1 + 1$

$2 - 4 \mid -3 + 1$

$-2 \stackrel{?}{=} -2$ TRUE

The solution is 1.

c) $6x + 5 - 7x = 10 - 4x + 7$

$-x + 5 = 17 - 4x$	Con
$-x + 5 + 4x = 17 - 4x + 4x$	Add
$5 + 3x = 17$	Simp
$3x = 12$	Subt
$\frac{3x}{3} = \frac{12}{3}$	Divi
$x = 4$	

Check:

$6x + 5 - 7x = 10 - 4x$

$6 \cdot 4 + 5 - 7 \cdot 4 \mid 10 - 4$

$24 + 5 - 28 \mid 10 - 16$

$1 \stackrel{?}{=} 1$

The solution is 4.

d) $2 - 5(x + 5) = 3(x - 2) - 1$

$2 - 5x - 25 = 3x - 6 - 1$	Using simila
$-5x - 23 = 3x - 7$	Combining like terms on each side
$-5x - 23 + 7 = 3x$ $-23 + 7 = 3x + 5x$	Adding 7 and $5x$ to both sides. This isolates the x-terms on one side and the constant terms on the other.
$-16 = 8x$	Simplifying
$\frac{-16}{8} = \frac{8x}{8}$	Dividing both sides by 8

Technology Connections

Optional Technology Connections appear throughout each chapter to help students visualize, through the use of technology, a concept that they have just learned. This feature is reinforced in many exercise sets through exercises marked with a graphing calculator icon.

that is traveling 39 mph in the same direction. How fast is the jet traveling, in minutes per mile, with respect to the sea?

55. *Running.* Annette ran from the 4-km mark to the 7-km mark of a 10-km race in 15.5 min. At this rate, how long would it take Annette to run a 5-mi race?

Assuming a constant production rate, at what time did they make their 82nd candle?

58. Marcy picks apples twice as fast as Ryan. By 4:30, Ryan had already picked 4 bushels of apples. Fifty minutes later, his total reached $5\frac{1}{2}$ bushels. Find Marcy's picking rate. Give your answer in number of bushels per hour.

COLLABORATIVE CORNER

Determining Depreciation Rates

Focus: Modeling, graphing, and rates
Time: 30 minutes
Group size: 3
Materials: Graph paper and straightedges

From the minute a new car is driven out of the dealership, it *depreciates*, or drops in value with the passing of time. The Kelley Blue Book Auto Market Report is a periodic listing of the trade-in values of used cars. The data below are taken from two such reports from 2003.

ACTIVITY

1. Each group member should select a different one of the cars listed in the table below as his or her own. Assuming that the values are dropping linearly, each student should draw a line representing the trade-in value of his or her car. Draw all three lines on the same graph. Let the horizontal axis represent the time, in months, since April 2003, and let the vertical axis represent the trade-in value of each car. Decide as a group how many months or dollars each square should represent. Make the drawings as neat as possible.
2. At what *rate* is each car depreciating and how are the different rates illustrated in the graph of part (1)?
3. If one of the three cars had to be sold in April 2004, which one would your group sell and why? Compare answers with other groups.

Car	Trade-in Value in April 2003	Trade-in Value in October 2003
2001 Chevrolet Camaro convertible V6	$14,650	$13,600
2001 Ford Mustang convertible V6	$12,550	$11,450
2001 Mitsubishi Eclipse convertible V6	$15,250	$13,800

Collaborative Corners

Optional Collaborative Corners are found throughout the text to give students the opportunity to work as a group to solve problems or to perform specially designed activities. There are two or three Collaborative Corners per chapter, each one appearing after the appropriate exercise set.

n the
at a

Source: Based on data from the Bureau of Justice Statistics

16. *Fire fighting.* In 2000, there were approximately 1.7 million fires in the United States, and the figure was dropping at a rate of about 0.1 million per year.
Source: Based on data from the *Statistical Abstract of the United States*, 2002

17. *Train travel.* At 3:00 P.M., the Boston–Washington Metroliner had traveled 230 mi and was cruising at a rate of 90 miles per hour.

18. *Plane travel.* At 4:00 P.M., the Seattle–Los Angeles shuttle had traveled 400 mi and was cruising at a rate of 300 miles per hour.

19. *Wages.* By 2:00 P.M., Diane had earned $50. She continued earning money at a rate of $15 per hour.

20. *Wages.* By 3:00 P.M., Arnie had earned $70. He continued earning money at a rate of $12 per hour.

21. *Telephone bills.* Roberta's phone bill was already $7.50 when she made a call for which she was charged at a rate of $0.10 per minute.

22. *Telephone bills.* At 3:00 P.M., Larry's phone bill was $6.50 and increasing at a rate of 7¢ per minute.

In Exercises 23–32, use the graph provided to calculate a rate of change in which the units of the horizontal axis are used in the denominator.

23. *Hairdresser.* Eve's Custom Cuts has a graph displaying data from a recent day of work. At what rate does Eve work?

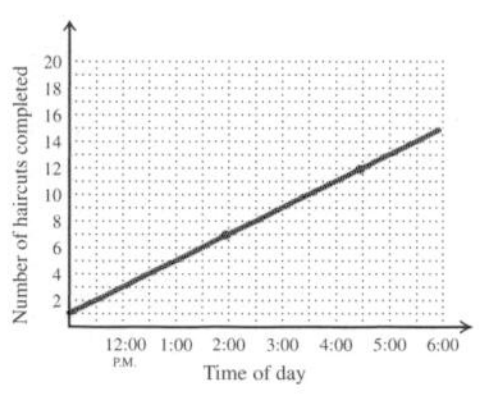

24. *Manicures.* The following graph shows data from a recent day's work at the O'Hara School of Cosmetology. At what rate do they work?

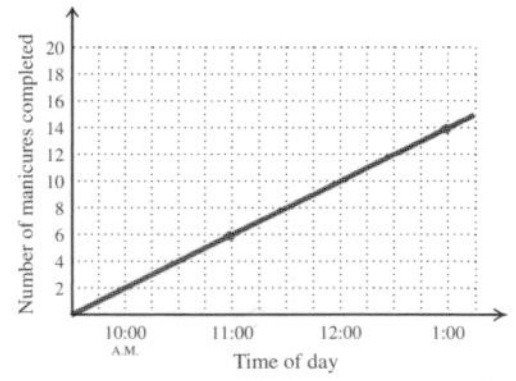

25. *Train travel.* The following graph shows data from a recent train ride from Chicago to St. Louis. At what rate did the train travel?

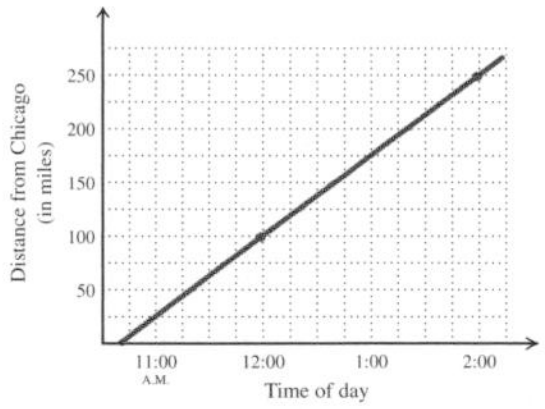

26. *Train travel.* The following graph shows data from a recent train ride from Denver to Kansas City. At what rate did the train travel?

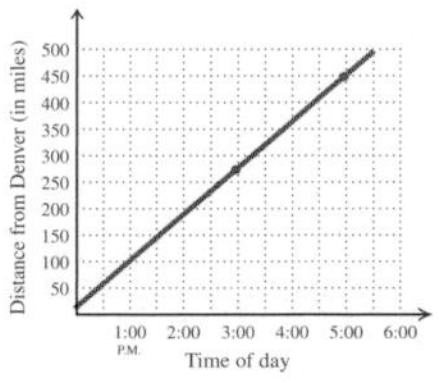

Real-Data Applications

Real-data applications have always been a strength of this text, helping students to see realistic uses of data and math in the world around them.

NEW!

3.6 Exercise Set

FOR EXTRA HELP

Student's Solutions Manual | Digital Video Tutor CD 2 Videotape 6 | AW Math Tutor Center | MathXL Tutorials on CD

Concept Reinforcement *In each of Exercises 1–6, match the phrase with the most appropriate choice from the column on the right.*

1. ___ The y-intercept of the graph of $y = 2x - 3$ **a)** $\left(0, \frac{3}{4}\right)$

2. ___ The y-intercept of the graph of $y = 3x - 2$ **b)** 2

3. ___ The slope of the graph of $y = 3x - 2$ **c)** $(0, -3)$

4. ___ The slope of the graph of $y = 2x - 3$ **d)** $\frac{2}{3}$

Concept Reinforcement Exercises

This feature is designed to help students build their confidence and comprehension through true/false, matching, and fill-in-the-blank exercises at the start of nearly all exercise sets. Where appropriate, special attention is devoted to increasing student understanding of the new vocabulary and notation developed in that section.

Connecting the Concepts

This feature highlights the importance of connecting concepts and invites students to pause and check that they understand the "big picture." This helps assure that students understand how concepts work together in several sections at once.

CONNECTING THE CONCEPTS

We now have three distinctly different ways to solve a system. Each method has certain strengths and weaknesses.

Method	Strengths	Weaknesses
Graphical	Solutions are displayed visually. Works with any system that can be graphed.	Inexact when solutions involve numbers that are not integers or are very large and off the graph.
Substitution	Always yields exact solutions. Easy to use when a variable is alone on one side of an equation.	Introduces extensive computations with fractions when solving more complicated systems. Solutions are not graphically displayed.
Elimination	Always yields exact solutions. Easy to use when fractions or decimals appear in the system.	Solutions are not graphically displayed.

Exercises

100. Jake keys $18/2 \cdot 3$ into his calculator and expects the result to be 3. What mistake is he probably making?

SKILL MAINTENANCE

Translate to an algebraic expression. [1.1]

101. Nine more than twice a number

102. Half of the sum of two numbers

SYNTHESIS

103. Write the sentence $(-x)^2 \neq -x^2$ in words. Explain why $(-x)^2$ and $-x^2$ are not equivalent.

104. Write the sentence $-|x| \neq -x$ in words. Explain why $-|x|$ and $-x$ are not equivalent.

Simplify.

105. $5t - \{7t - [4r - 3(t - 7)] + 6r\} - 4r$

106. $z - \{2z - [3z - (4z - 5z) - 6z] - 7z\} - 8z$

107. $\{x - [f - (f - x)] + [x - f]\} - 3x$

108. Is it true that for all real numbers a and b,
$$ab = (-a)(-b)?$$
Why or why not?

109. Is it true that for all real numbers a, b, and c,
$$a|b - c| = ab - ac?$$
Why or why not?

If $n > 0$, $m > 0$, and $n \neq m$, classify each of the following as either true or false.

110. $-n + m = -(n + m)$

111. $m - n = -(n - m)$

112. $n(-n - m) = -n^2 + nm$

113. $-m(n - m) = -(mn + m^2)$

114. $-n(-n - m) = n(n + m)$

Evaluate.

Aha! **115.** $[x + 3(2 - 5x) \div 7 + x](x - 3)$, for $x = 3$

Aha! **116.** $[x + 2 \div 3x] \div [x + 2 \div 3x]$, for $x = -7$

117. In Mexico, between 500 B.C. and 600 A.D., the Mayans represented numbers using powers of 20 and certain symbols. For example, the symbols

represent $4 \cdot 20^3 + 17 \cdot 20^2 + 10 \cdot 20^1 + 0 \cdot 20^0$. Evaluate this number.

Source: National Council of Teachers of Mathematics, 1906 Association Drive, Reston, VA 22091

118. Examine the Mayan symbols and the numbers in Exercise 117. What numbers do

•, ▬, and ⬭ each represent?

119. Calculate the volume of the tower shown below.

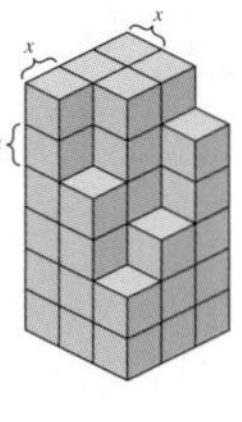

SKILL MAINTENANCE EXERCISES Skill Maintenance exercises appear in all exercise sets as a means of keeping past concepts fresh and as a way of reviewing previously covered skills to prepare students for upcoming topics.

SYNTHESIS EXERCISES Synthesis exercises guarantee an extensive and wide-ranging variety of problems in every exercise set. The Synthesis exercises allow students to combine concepts from more than one section and provide challenge for even the strongest students.

WRITING EXERCISES Writing exercises, indicated by [icon], provide opportunities for students to answer problems with one or more sentences. Often, these questions have more than one correct response and ask students to explain *why* a certain concept works as it does.

AHA! EXERCISES In many exercise sets, students will see the **Aha!** icon. This icon indicates that there is a simpler way to complete the exercise without going through a lengthy computation. It's then up to the student to discover that simpler approach. The **Aha!** icon appears the first time a new insight can be used on a particular type of exercise. After that, the student must determine if and when that particular insight can be reused.

Chapter 3: REVIEW EXERCISES 219

3 Study Summary

Information can be communicated quickly and effectively in a visual form through the use of graphs. **Bar graphs, circle graphs**, and **line graphs** are three of the most commonly used types of graphs (pp. 148–150)

When information is given as **ordered pairs**, like $(-3, 2)$ or $(5, 17)$, the pairs can be **plotted** or **graphed** using a **coordinate system** that uses two **axes**, which are most often labeled x and y. The axes intersect at the **origin**, $(0, 0)$ (p. 151).

When an equation contains two variables, any solution is an ordered pair. When all ordered pairs that are solutions of an equation are graphed, we say that we have **graphed the equation** (p. 160). Some equations are said to be **linear**, like $y = 2x - 7$ or $2x + 3y = 12$, because their graphs are lines (p. 160). Other equations have **nonlinear graphs** (p. 165). When a graph crosses the y-axis, the point at which the axis is crossed is called a ***y*-intercept.** Similarly, an ***x*-intercept** is any point at which a graph crosses the x-axis (p. 169)

A line's slant is measured as its **slope.** Slope measures the **rate** at which the quantity measured on the vertical axis changes with respect to the quantity measured on the horizontal axis (p. 190).

$$\text{Slope} = m = \frac{\text{change in } y}{\text{change in } x} = \frac{\text{rise}}{\text{run}} = \frac{y_2 - y_1}{x_2 - x_1}$$

An equation in **slope–intercept form**, $y = mx + b$, represents a line with slope m and y-intercept $(0, b)$ (p. 203). An equation in **point–slope form**, $y - y_1 = m(x - x_1)$, represents a line with slope m passing through (x_1, y_1) (p. 211)

3 Review Exercises

Classify each statement as either true or false.

1. Not every ordered pair lies in one of the four quadrants. [3.1]
2. The equa… slope–int…

NEW!

Study Summary

Each chapter closes with a Study Summary in which the authors provide study notes highlighting the most important concepts and terminology from that chapter. Page numbers are provided to reference where the concepts and terminology first appear.

CUMULATIVE REVIEW: CHAPTERS 1–6 427

1–6 Cumulative Review

1. Use the commutative law of addition to write an expression equivalent to $a + 2b$. [1.2]
2. Write a true sentence using either $<$ or $>$: $-3.1 \;\square\; -3.15$. [1.4]
3. Evaluate $(y - 1)^2$ for $y = -4$. [1.8]
4. Simplify: $-4[2(x - 3) - 1]$. [1.8]

Simplify.

5. $-\frac{1}{2} + \frac{3}{8} + (-6) + \frac{3}{4}$ [1.5]
6. $-\frac{72}{108} \div \left(-\frac{2}{3}\right)$ [1.7]
7. $-6.262 \div 1.01$ [1.7]
8. $4 \div (-2) \cdot 2 + 3 \cdot 4$ [1.8]

Solve.

$5(x - 2) = 40$ [2.2]

10. $49 = x^2$ [5.6]

$-6t = 20$ [2.1]

12. $3x - 4 = 7x + 8$ [2.2]

$4(y - 5) = -2(y + 2)$ [2.2]

14. $x^2 + 11x + 10 = 0$ [5.6]

$\frac{4}{9}t + \frac{2}{3} = \frac{1}{3}t - \frac{2}{9}$ [2.2]

16. $\frac{4}{x} + x = 5$ [6.6]

$6 - y \geq 2y + 8$ [2.6]

18. $\frac{2}{x - 3} = \frac{5}{3x + 1}$ [6.6]

$2x^2 + 7x = 4$ [5.6]

20. $4(x + 7) < 5(x - 3)$ [2.6]

$\frac{t^2}{t + 5} = \frac{25}{t + 5}$ [6.6]

22. $(2x + 7)(x - 5) = 0$ [5.6]

23. $\frac{2}{x^2 - 9} + \frac{5}{x - 3} = \frac{3}{x + 3}$ [6.6]

Solve each formula. [2.3]

24. $3a - b + 9 = c$, for b
25. $\frac{3}{4}(x + 2y) = z$, for y

Combine like terms. [1.6]

26. $x + 2y - 2z + \frac{1}{2}x - z$
27. $2x^3 - 7 + \frac{3}{7}x^2 - 6x^3 - \frac{4}{7}x^2 + 5$

Graph. [3.2], [3.3]

28. $y = \frac{3}{4}x + 5$
29. $x = -3$
30. $4x + 5y = 20$
31. $y = 6$
32. Find the slope of the line containing the points $(1, 5)$ and $(2, 3)$. [3.5]

Simplify.

33. $\frac{x^{-5}}{x^{-3}}$ [4.8]
34. $y^2 \cdot y^{-8}$ [4.8]
35. $-(2a^2b^7)^2$ [4.1]
36. Subtract: [4.3] $(-8y^2 - y + 2) - (y^3 - 6y^2 + y - 5)$.

Multiply.

37. $5(3a - 2b + c)$ [1.2]
38. $(2x^2 - 1)(x^3 + x - 3)$ [4.4]
39. $(6x - 5y)^2$ [4.5]
40. $(x + 8)(2x - 5)$ [4.5]
41. $(2x^3 + 1)(2x^3 - 1)$ [4.5]

Factor.

42. $6x - 2x^2 - 24x^4$ [5.1]
43. $16x^2 - 81$ [5.4]
44. $t^2 - 10t + 24$ [5.2]
45. $8x^2 + 10x + 3$ [5.3]
46. $6x^2 - 28x + 16$ [5.3]

Cumulative Review

A Cumulative Review is found after Chapters 3, 6, and 9 to help students review skills and concepts from all preceding chapters of the text. The final Cumulative Review is an excellent guide in preparing for a final exam.

1 Introduction to Algebraic Expressions

AN APPLICATION

During the Northeast's electrical blackout of August 14, 2003, residents of Bloomfield, New Jersey, lost power at 4:00 P.M. One resident returned from vacation at 3:00 P.M. the following day to find the clocks in her apartment reading 8:00 A.M. At what time, and on what day, was power restored?

This problem appears as Exercise 147 in Section 1.6.

Rodney E. Johnson
TECHNICIAN
Indianapolis, Indiana

Math is one of the key elements enabling me to perform my job well. Although I often use calculators and computer software, I need a good understanding of math in order to interpret and apply the results.

Problem solving is the focus of this text. Chapter 1 presents important preliminaries that are needed for the problem-solving approach that is developed in Chapter 2 and used throughout the rest of the book. These preliminaries include a review of arithmetic, a discussion of real numbers and their properties, and an examination of how real numbers are added, subtracted, multiplied, divided, and raised to powers.

1.1 Introduction to Algebra

Algebraic Expressions • Translating to Algebraic Expressions • Translating to Equations

This section introduces some basic concepts and expressions used in algebra. Solving real-world problems is an important part of algebra, so we will focus on the wordings and mathematical expressions that often arise in applications.

Algebraic Expressions

Probably the greatest difference between arithmetic and algebra is the use of *variables* in algebra. When a letter can be any one of a set of numbers, that letter is a **variable**. For example, if n represents the number of tickets purchased for a Radiohead concert, then n will vary, depending on factors like price and day of the week. This makes n a variable. If each ticket costs \$25, then 3 tickets cost $25 \cdot 3$ dollars, 4 tickets cost $25 \cdot 4$ dollars, and n tickets cost $25 \cdot n$ dollars. Note that $25 \cdot n$ means 25 *times* n. The number 25 is an example of a **constant** because it does not change.

Price per Ticket (in dollars)	Number of Tickets Purchased	Total Paid (in dollars)
25	n	$25 \cdot n$

The expression $25 \cdot n$ is a **variable expression** because its value varies with the replacement for n. In this case, the total amount paid, $25 \cdot n$, will change with the number of tickets purchased. In the following chart, we replace n with a variety of values and compute the total amount paid. In doing so, we are **evaluating the expression** $25 \cdot n$.

Price per Ticket (in dollars), 25	Number of Tickets Purchased, n	Total Paid (in dollars), $25 \cdot n$
25	400	\$10,000
25	500	12,500
25	600	15,000

Variable expressions are examples of *algebraic expressions*. An **algebraic expression** consists of variables and/or numerals, often with operation signs and grouping symbols. Examples are

$$t + 97, \quad 5 \cdot x, \quad 3a - b, \quad 18 \div y, \quad \frac{9}{7}, \quad \text{and} \quad 4r(s + t).$$

Recall that a fraction bar is a division symbol: $\frac{9}{7}$, or 9/7, means $9 \div 7$. Similarly, multiplication can be written in several ways. For example, "5 times x" can be written as $5 \cdot x$, $5 \times x$, $5(x)$, or simply $5x$. On many calculators, this appears as $5 * x$.

To **evaluate** an algebraic expression, we substitute a number for each variable in the expression. This replaces each variable with a number. We then calculate the result.

EXAMPLE 1 Evaluate each expression for the given values.

a) $x + y$ for $x = 37$ and $y = 28$

b) $5ab$ for $a = 2$ and $b = 3$

Solution

a) We substitute 37 for x and 28 for y and carry out the addition:

$$x + y = 37 + 28 = 65.$$

The number 65 is called the **value** of the expression.

b) We substitute 2 for a and 3 for b and multiply:

$$5ab = 5 \cdot 2 \cdot 3 = 10 \cdot 3 = 30. \qquad 5ab \text{ means 5 times } a \text{ times } b.$$

EXAMPLE 2 The area A of a rectangle of length l and width w is given by the formula $A = lw$. Find the area when l is 17 in. and w is 10 in.

Solution We evaluate, using 17 in. for l and 10 in. for w, and carry out the multiplication:

$$\begin{aligned} A = lw &= (17 \text{ in.})(10 \text{ in.}) \\ &= (17)(10)(\text{in.})(\text{in.}) \\ &= 170 \text{ in}^2, \text{ or } 170 \text{ square inches.} \end{aligned}$$

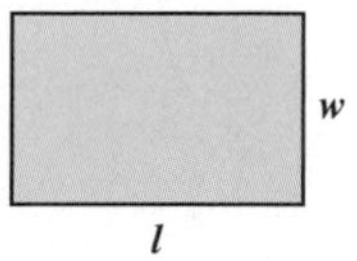

Note that we always use square units for area and $(\text{in.})(\text{in.}) = \text{in}^2$. Exponents like the 2 within the expression in^2 are discussed further in Section 1.8.

EXAMPLE 3 The area of a triangle with a base of length b and a height of length h is given by the formula $A = \frac{1}{2}bh$. Find the area when b is 8 m and h is 6.4 m.

Solution We substitute 8 m for b and 6.4 m for h and then multiply:

$$\begin{aligned} A = \tfrac{1}{2}bh &= \tfrac{1}{2}(8\text{ m})(6.4\text{ m}) \\ &= \tfrac{1}{2}(8)(6.4)(\text{m})(\text{m}) \\ &= 4(6.4)\text{ m}^2 \\ &= 25.6\text{ m}^2,\ \text{or 25.6 square meters.} \end{aligned}$$

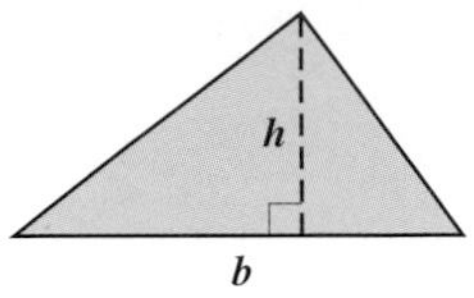

Translating to Algebraic Expressions

Before attempting to translate problems to equations, we need to be able to translate certain phrases to algebraic expressions.

Important Words	Sample Phrase or Sentence	Translation
Addition (+)		
added to	700 lb was added to the car's weight.	$w + 700$
sum of	The sum of a number and 12	$n + 12$
plus	53 plus some number	$53 + x$
more than	8 more than Biloxi's population	$p + 8$
increased by	Jake's original guess, increased by 4	$n + 4$
Subtraction (−)		
subtracted from	2 oz was subtracted from the bag's weight.	$w - 2$
difference of	The difference of two scores	$m - n$
minus	A team of size s, minus 2 injured players	$s - 2$
less than	9 less than the given population	$p - 9$
decreased by	The car's speed, decreased by 8 mph	$s - 8$
Multiplication (·)		
multiplied by	The number of reservations, multiplied by 3	$r \cdot 3$
product of	The product of two numbers	$m \cdot n$
times	5 times the dog's weight	$5w$
twice	Twice Jackie's age	$2a$
of	$\frac{1}{2}$ of Amelia's salary	$\frac{1}{2}s$
Division (÷)		
divided by	A 2-lb coffee cake, divided by 3	$2 \div 3$
quotient of	The quotient of 14 and 7	$14 \div 7$
divided into	4 divided into the delivery fee	$f \div 4$
ratio of	The ratio of \$500 to the cost of a new car	$500/n$
per	There were 18 models per class of size s.	$18/s$

EXAMPLE 4 Translate each phrase to an algebraic expression.

a) Four less than Jean's height, in inches

b) Eighteen more than a number

c) A day's pay, in dollars, divided by eight

Solution To help think through a translation, we sometimes begin with a specific number in place of a variable.

a) If the height were 60, then 4 less than 60 would mean $60 - 4$. If the height were 70, the translation would be $70 - 4$. If we use h to represent "Jean's height, in inches," the translation of "Four less than Jean's height, in inches" is $h - 4$.

b) If we knew the number to be 10, the translation would be $10 + 18$, or $18 + 10$. If we use t to represent "a number," the translation of "Eighteen more than a number" is

$$t + 18, \quad \text{or} \quad 18 + t.$$

c) We let d represent "a day's pay, in dollars." If the pay were \$78, the translation would be $78 \div 8$, or $\frac{78}{8}$. Thus our translation of "a day's pay, in dollars, divided by eight" is

$$d \div 8, \quad \text{or} \quad \frac{d}{8}.$$

Caution! The order in which we subtract and divide affects the answer! Answering $4 - h$ or $8 \div d$ in Examples 4(a) and 4(c) is incorrect.

EXAMPLE 5 Translate each of the following.

a) Kate's age increased by five

b) Half of some number

c) Three more than twice a number

d) Six less than the product of two numbers

e) Forty-seven percent of the town's population

Solution

Phrase	*Algebraic Expression*
a) Kate's age increased by five	$a + 5$, or $5 + a$
b) Half of some number	$\frac{1}{2}t$, or $\frac{t}{2}$, or $t/2$, or $t \div 2$
c) Three more than twice a number	$2x + 3$, or $3 + 2x$
d) Six less than the product of two numbers	$mn - 6$
e) Forty-seven percent of the town's population	47% of p, or $0.47p$

Translating to Equations

The symbol = ("equals") indicates that the expressions on either side of the equals sign represent the same number. An **equation** is a number sentence with the verb =. Equations may be true, false, or neither true nor false.

EXAMPLE 6 Determine whether each equation is true, false, or neither.

a) $8 \cdot 4 = 32$ **b)** $7 - 2 = 4$ **c)** $x + 6 = 13$

Solution

a) $8 \cdot 4 = 32$ The equation is *true*.

b) $7 - 2 = 4$ The equation is *false*.

c) $x + 6 = 13$ The equation is *neither* true nor false, because we do not know what number x represents.

Solution

A replacement or substitution that makes an equation true is called a *solution*. Some equations have more than one solution, and some have no solution. When all solutions have been found, we have *solved* the equation.

To see if a number is a solution, we evaluate all expressions in the equation. If the values on both sides of the equation are the same, the number is a solution.

EXAMPLE 7 Determine whether 7 is a solution of $x + 6 = 13$.

Solution We evaluate $x + 6$ and compare both sides of the equation:

$x + 6 = 13$		Writing the equation
$7 + 6$	13	Substituting 7 for x
$13 \stackrel{?}{=} 13$		$13 = 13$ is TRUE.

Since the left-hand and the right-hand sides are the same, 7 is a solution.

Although we do not study solving equations until Chapter 2, we can translate certain problem situations to equations now. The words "is the same as," "equal," "is," and "are" translate to "=."

Words indicating equality, = : "is the same as," "equal," "is," "are"

EXAMPLE 8 Translate the following problem to an equation.

What number plus 478 is 1019?

Solution We let y represent the unknown number. The translation then comes almost directly from the English sentence.

What number plus 478 is 1019?

$$y + 478 = 1019$$

Note that "plus" translates to "+" and "is" translates to "=."

Sometimes it helps to reword a problem before translating.

EXAMPLE 9 Translate the following problem to an equation.

The Petronas Twin Towers in Kuala Lumpur are the world's tallest buildings. At 1483 ft, they are 33 ft taller than the Sears Tower. (*Source: New York Times*) How tall is the Sears Tower?

Solution We let h represent the height, in feet, of the Sears Tower. A rewording and translation follow:

Rewording: The height of the Twin Towers is 33 ft more than the height of the Sears Tower.

Translating: $1483 = h + 33$

technology connection

Technology Connections are activities that make use of the graphing calculator as a tool for learning algebra. These activities use only basic features that are common to most graphing calculators. **(Henceforth in this text we will refer to all graphing utilities as graphing calculators.)** In some cases, students may find the user's manual for their particular calculator helpful for exact keystrokes.

Although all graphing calculators are not the same, most share the following characteristics.

Screen. The large screen can show graphs and tables as well as the keystrokes used. The screen has a different layout for different functions. Computations are performed in the **home screen**. On many calculators, the home screen is accessed by pressing 2ND QUIT. The **cursor** shows location on the screen, and the **contrast** determines how dark the characters appear.

Keypad. There are options written above the keys as well as on them. To access those above the keys, we press 2ND or ALPHA and then the key. Expressions are usually entered as they would appear in print. For example, to evaluate $3xy + x$ for $x = 65$ and $y = 92$, we press 3 × 65 × 92 + 65 and then ENTER. The value of the expression, 18005, will appear at the right of the screen.

```
3*65*92+65
                    18005
```

Evaluate each of the following.

1. $27a - 18b$, for $a = 136$ and $b = 13$
2. $19xy - 9x + 13y$, for $x = 87$ and $y = 29$

Study Skills

Get the Facts

Throughout this textbook, you will find a feature called Study Skills. These tips are intended to help improve your math study skills. On the first day of class, you should complete this chart.

Instructor: Name ____________________

Office hours and location ____________________

Phone number ____________________

Fax number ____________________

E-mail address ____________________

Find the names of two students whom you could contact for information or study questions:

1. Name ____________________

Phone number ____________________

E-mail address ____________________

2. Name ____________________

Phone number ____________________

E-mail address ____________________

Math lab on campus:

Location ____________________

Hours ____________________

Phone ____________________

Tutoring:

Campus location ____________________

Hours ____________________

Addison-Wesley Tutor Center ____________________

To order, call ____________________

(See the preface for important information concerning this tutoring.)

Important supplements:

(See the preface for a complete list of available supplements.)

Supplements recommended by the instructor.

____

____

1.1 Exercise Set

FOR EXTRA HELP

Student's Solutions Manual | Digital Video Tutor CD 1 Videotape 1 | AW Math Tutor Center | MathXL Tutorials on CD | MathXL | MyMathLab

Concept Reinforcement *Classify each of the following as either an expression or an equation.*

1. $4x + 7$
2. $3x = 21$
3. $2x - 5 = 9$
4. $8x - 3$
5. $38 = 2t$
6. $45 = a - 1$
7. $4a - 5b$
8. $3t + 4 = 19$
9. $2x - 3y = 8$
10. $12 - 4xy$
11. $7 - 4rt$
12. $9a + b$

Evaluate.

13. $4a$, for $a = 9$
14. $\frac{x - y}{6}$, for $x = 23$ and $y = 5$
15. $8x$, for $x = 7$
16. $t + 8$, for $t = 2$
17. $\frac{a}{b}$, for $a = 45$ and $b = 9$
18. $13 - r$, for $r = 9$
19. $\frac{x + y}{4}$, for $x = 2$ and $y = 14$
20. $\frac{m}{n}$, for $m = 54$ and $n = 9$
21. $\frac{p + q}{7}$, for $p = 15$ and $q = 20$
22. $\frac{9m}{q}$, for $m = 6$ and $q = 18$
23. $\frac{m - n}{2}$, for $m = 20$ and $n = 8$
24. $\frac{5z}{y}$, for $z = 9$ and $y = 15$

Substitute to find the value of each expression.

25. *Hockey.* The area of a rectangle with base b and height h is bh. A regulation hockey goal is 6 ft wide and 4 ft high. Find the area of the opening.

26. *Orbit time.* A communications satellite orbiting 300 mi above the earth travels about 27,000 mi in one orbit. The time, in hours, for an orbit is

$$\frac{27{,}000}{v},$$

where v is the velocity, in miles per hour. How long will an orbit take at a velocity of 1125 mph?

27. *Zoology.* A great white shark has triangular teeth. Each tooth measures about 5 cm across the base and has a height of 6 cm. Find the surface area of the front side of one such tooth. (See Example 3.)

28. *Work time.* Enrico takes five times as long to do a job as Rosa does. Suppose t represents the time it takes Rosa to do the job. Then $5t$ represents the time it takes Enrico. How long does it take Enrico if Rosa takes **(a)** 30 sec? **(b)** 90 sec? **(c)** 2 min?

29. *Olympic softball.* A softball player's batting average is h/a, where h is the number of hits and a is the number of "at bats." In the 2004 Summer Olympics, Laura Berg had 7 hits in 19 at bats. What was her batting average? Round to the nearest thousandth.

30. *Area of a parallelogram.* The area of a parallelogram with base b and height h is bh. Find the area of the parallelogram when the height is 6 cm (centimeters) and the base is 7.5 cm.

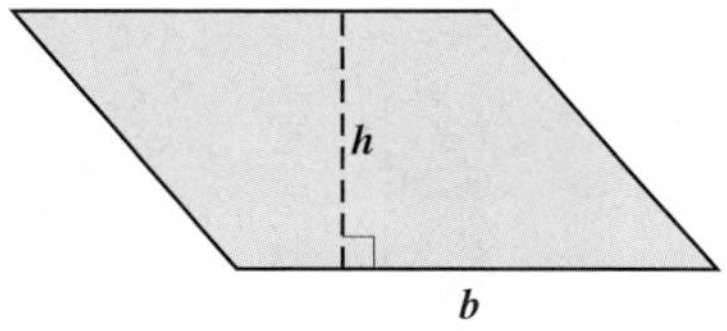

Translate to an algebraic expression.

31. 5 more than Ron's age

32. The product of 4 and a

33. 6 more than b

34. 7 more than Lou's weight

35. 9 less than c

36. 4 less than d

37. 6 increased by q

38. 11 increased by z

39. 9 times Phil's speed

40. c more than d

41. x less than y

42. 2 less than Lorrie's age

43. x divided by w

44. The quotient of two numbers

45. m subtracted from n

46. p subtracted from q

47. The sum of the box's length and height

48. The sum of d and f

49. The product of 9 and twice m

50. Penny's speed minus twice the wind speed

51. One quarter of some number

52. One third of the sum of two numbers

53. 64% of the women attending

54. 38% of a number

Determine whether the given number is a solution of the given equation.

55. 15; $x + 17 = 32$

56. 75; $y + 28 = 93$

57. 93; $a - 28 = 75$

58. 12; $8t = 96$

59. 63; $\frac{t}{7} = 9$

60. 52; $\frac{x}{8} = 6$

61. 3; $\frac{108}{x} = 36$

62. 7; $\frac{94}{y} = 12$

Translate each problem to an equation. Do not solve.

63. What number added to 73 is 201?

64. Seven times what number is 1596?

65. When 42 is multiplied by a number, the result is 2352. Find the number.

66. When 345 is added to a number, the result is 987. Find the number.

67. *Chess.* A chess board has 64 squares. If pieces occupy 19 squares, how many squares are unoccupied?

68. *Hours worked.* A carpenter charges $25 an hour. How many hours did she work if she billed a total of $53,400?

69. *Recycling.* Currently, Americans recycle or compost 27% of all municipal solid waste. This is the same as recycling or composting 56 million tons. What is the total amount of waste generated?

70. *Travel to work.* In the Northeast, the average commute to work is 24.5 min. The average commuting time in the West is 1.8 min less. How long is the average commute in the West?

In each of Exercises 71–78, match the phrase or sentence with the appropriate expression or equation from the column on the right.

71. ____	Twice the sum of two numbers	**a)** $\frac{x}{y} + 6$
72. ____	Five less than a number is nine.	**b)** $2(x + y) = 48$
73. ____	Two more than a number is five.	**c)** $\frac{1}{2} \cdot a \cdot b$
74. ____	Half of the product of two numbers	**d)** $t + 2 = 5$
75. ____	Three times the sum of a number and five	**e)** $ab - 1 = 49$
76. ____	Twice the sum of two numbers is 48.	**f)** $2(m + n)$
77. ____	One less than the product of two numbers is 49.	**g)** $3(t + 5)$
78. ____	Six more than the quotient of two numbers	**h)** $x - 5 = 9$

To the student and the instructor: Writing exercises, *denoted by* ▯, *should be answered using one or more English sentences. Because answers to many writing exercises will vary, solutions are not listed in the answers at the back of the book.*

79. What is the difference between a variable, a variable expression, and an equation?

80. What does it mean to evaluate an algebraic expression?

SYNTHESIS

To the student and the instructor: Synthesis exercises *are designed to challenge students to extend the concepts or skills studied in each section. Many synthesis exercises will require the assimilation of skills and concepts from several sections.*

81. If the lengths of the sides of a square are doubled, is the area doubled? Why or why not?

82. Write a problem that translates to $1998 + t = 2006$.

83. Signs of Distinction charges $90 per square foot for handpainted signs. The town of Belmar commissioned a triangular sign with a base of 3 ft and a height of 2.5 ft. How much will the sign cost?

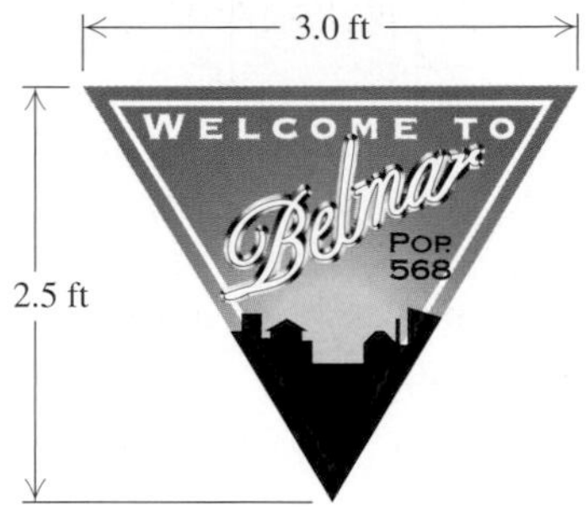

84. Find the area that is shaded.

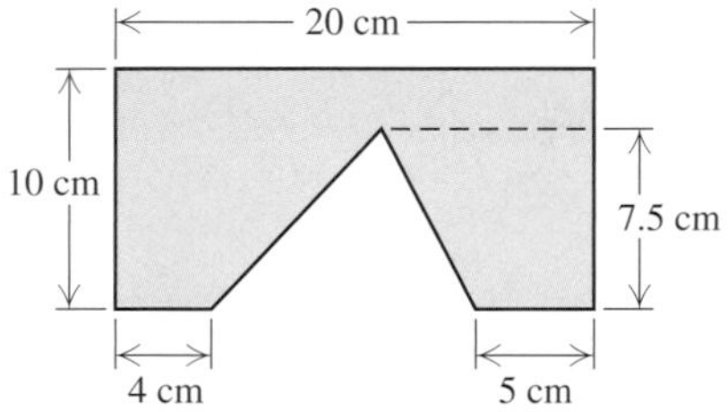

85. Evaluate $\frac{x - y}{3}$ when x is twice y and $x = 12$.

86. Evaluate $\frac{x + y}{2}$ when y is twice x and $x = 6$.

87. Evaluate $\frac{a + b}{4}$ when a is twice b and $a = 16$.

88. Evaluate $\frac{a - b}{3}$ when a is three times b and $a = 18$.

Answer each question with an algebraic expression.

89. If $w + 3$ is a whole number, what is the next whole number after it?

90. If $d + 2$ is an odd number, what is the preceding odd number?

Translate to an algebraic expression.

91. The perimeter of a rectangle with length l and width w (perimeter means distance around)

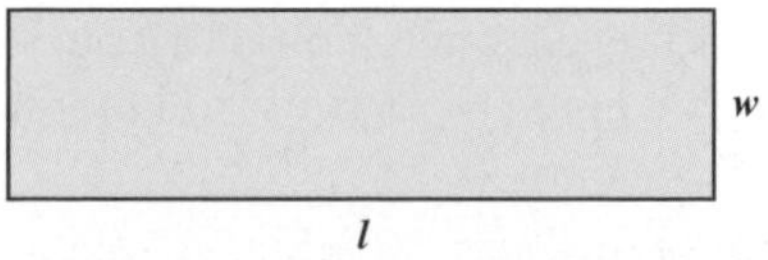

92. The perimeter of a square with side s (perimeter means distance around)

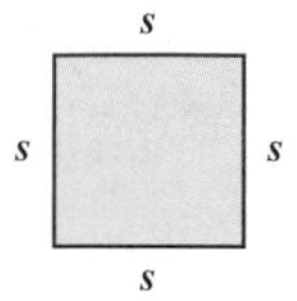

93. Ellie's race time, assuming she took 5 sec longer than Joe and Joe took 3 sec longer than Molly. Assume that Molly's time was t seconds.

94. Ray's age 7 yr from now if he is 2 yr older than Monique and Monique is a years old

95. If the length of the height of a triangle is doubled, is its area also doubled? Why or why not?

COLLABORATIVE CORNER

Teamwork

Focus: Group problem solving; working collaboratively

Time: 15 minutes

Group size: 2

Working and studying as a team often enables students to solve problems that are difficult to solve alone.

ACTIVITY

1. The left-hand column below contains the names of 12 colleges. A scrambled list of the names of their sports teams is on the right. As a group, match the names of the colleges to the teams.

1. University of Texas	**a)** Antelopes
2. Western State College of Colorado	**b)** Fighting Banana Slugs
3. University of North Carolina	**c)** Sea Warriors
4. University of Massachusetts	**d)** Gators
5. Hawaii Pacific University	**e)** Mountaineers
6. University of Nebraska	**f)** Sailfish
7. University of California, Santa Cruz	**g)** Longhorns
8. University of Louisiana at Lafayette	**h)** Tar Heels
9. Grand Canyon University	**i)** Seawolves
10. Palm Beach Atlantic University	**j)** Ragin' Cajuns
11. University of Alaska, Anchorage	**k)** Cornhuskers
12. University of Florida	**l)** Minutemen

2. After working for 5 min, confer with another group and reach mutual agreement.
3. Does the class agree on all 12 pairs?
4. Do you agree that group collaboration enhances our ability to solve problems?

1.2 The Commutative, Associative, and Distributive Laws

Equivalent Expressions • The Commutative Laws • The Associative Laws • The Distributive Law • The Distributive Law and Factoring

In order to solve equations, we must be able to manipulate algebraic expressions. The commutative, associative, and distributive laws discussed in this section enable us to write *equivalent expressions* that will simplify our work. Indeed, much of this text is devoted to finding equivalent expressions.

Equivalent Expressions

The expressions $4 + 4 + 4$, $3 \cdot 4$, and $4 \cdot 3$ all represent the same number, 12. Expressions that represent the same number are said to be **equivalent**. The equivalent expressions $t + 18$ and $18 + t$ were used on p. 5 when we translated "eighteen more than a number." To check that these expressions are equivalent, we make some choices for t:

When $t = 3$, $\quad t + 18 = 3 + 18 = 21 \quad$ and $\quad 18 + t = 18 + 3 = 21.$

When $t = 40$, $\quad t + 18 = 40 + 18 = 58 \quad$ and $\quad 18 + t = 18 + 40 = 58.$

Study Skills

Learn by Example

The examples in each section are designed to prepare you for success with the exercise set. Study the step-by-step solutions of the examples, noting that color is used to indicate substitutions and to call attention to the new steps in multistep examples. The time you spend studying the examples will save you valuable time when you do your assignment.

The Commutative Laws

Recall that changing the order in addition or multiplication does not change the result. Equations like $3 + 78 = 78 + 3$ and $5 \cdot 14 = 14 \cdot 5$ illustrate this idea and show that addition and multiplication are **commutative**.

The Commutative Laws

For Addition. For any numbers a and b,

$$a + b = b + a.$$

(Changing the order of addition does not affect the answer.)

For Multiplication. For any numbers a and b,

$$ab = ba.$$

(Changing the order of multiplication does not affect the answer.)

EXAMPLE 1 Use the commutative laws to write an expression equivalent to each of the following: **(a)** $y + 5$; **(b)** $9x$; **(c)** $7 + ab$.

Solution

a) $y + 5$ is equivalent to $5 + y$ by the commutative law of addition.

b) $9x$ is equivalent to $x \cdot 9$ by the commutative law of multiplication.

c) $7 + ab$ is equivalent to $ab + 7$ by the commutative law of *addition*.

$7 + ab$ is also equivalent to $7 + ba$ by the commutative law of *multiplication*.

$7 + ab$ is also equivalent to $ba + 7$ by the two commutative laws, used together.

The Associative Laws

Parentheses are used to indicate groupings. We normally simplify within the parentheses first. For example,

$$3 + (8 + 4) = 3 + 12 \quad \text{and} \quad (3 + 8) + 4 = 11 + 4$$
$$= 15 \qquad\qquad\qquad\qquad = 15.$$

Similarly,

$$4 \cdot (2 \cdot 3) = 4 \cdot 6 \quad \text{and} \quad (4 \cdot 2) \cdot 3 = 8 \cdot 3$$
$$= 24 \qquad\qquad\qquad\qquad = 24.$$

Note that, so long as only addition or only multiplication appears in an expression, changing the grouping does not change the result. Equations such as $3 + (7 + 5) = (3 + 7) + 5$ and $4(5 \cdot 3) = (4 \cdot 5)3$ illustrate that addition and multiplication are **associative**.

The Associative Laws

For Addition. For any numbers a, b, and c,

$$a + (b + c) = (a + b) + c.$$

(Numbers can be grouped in any manner for addition.)

For Multiplication. For any numbers a, b, and c,

$$a \cdot (b \cdot c) = (a \cdot b) \cdot c.$$

(Numbers can be grouped in any manner for multiplication.)

EXAMPLE 2 Use an associative law to write an expression equivalent to each of the following: **(a)** $y + (z + 3)$; **(b)** $(8x)y$.

Solution

a) $y + (z + 3)$ is equivalent to $(y + z) + 3$ by the associative law of addition.

b) $(8x)y$ is equivalent to $8(xy)$ by the associative law of multiplication.

When only addition or only multiplication is involved, parentheses do not change the result. For that reason, we sometimes omit them altogether. Thus,

$$x + (y + 7) = x + y + 7, \quad \text{and} \quad l(wh) = lwh.$$

A sum such as $(5 + 1) + (3 + 5) + 9$ can be simplified by pairing numbers that add to 10. The associative and commutative laws allow us to do this:

$$\begin{aligned}(5 + 1) + (3 + 5) + 9 &= 5 + 5 + 9 + 1 + 3\\ &= 10 + 10 + 3 = 23.\end{aligned}$$

EXAMPLE 3 Use the commutative and/or associative laws of addition to write two expressions equivalent to $(7 + x) + 3$. Then simplify.

Solution

$(7 + x) + 3 = (x + 7) + 3$	Using the commutative law; $(x + 7) + 3$ is one equivalent expression.
$= x + (7 + 3)$	Using the associative law; $x + (7 + 3)$ is another equivalent expression.
$= x + 10$	Simplifying

EXAMPLE 4 Use the commutative and/or associative laws of multiplication to write two expressions equivalent to $2(x \cdot 3)$.

Solution

$2(x \cdot 3) = 2(3x)$	Using the commutative law; $2(3x)$ is one equivalent expression.
$= (2 \cdot 3)x$	Using the associative law; $(2 \cdot 3)x$ is another equivalent expression.
$= 6x$	Simplifying

The Distributive Law

The *distributive law* is probably the single most important law for manipulating algebraic expressions. Unlike the commutative and associative laws, the distributive law uses multiplication together with addition.

You have already used the distributive law although you may not have realized it at the time. To illustrate, try to multiply $3 \cdot 21$ mentally. Many people find the product, 63, by thinking of 21 as $20 + 1$ and then multiplying 20 by 3 and 1 by 3. The sum of the two products, $60 + 3$, is 63. Note that if the 3 does not multiply both 20 and 1, the result will not be correct.

EXAMPLE 5 Compute in two ways: $4(7 + 2)$.

Student Notes

To remember the names *commutative, associative,* and *distributive,* first understand the concept. Next, use everyday life to link the word to the concept. For example, think of commuting to and from work as changing the order of appearance.

Solution

a) As in the discussion of $3(20 + 1)$ above, to compute $4(7 + 2)$, we can multiply both 7 and 2 by 4 and add the results:

$$4(7 + 2) = 4 \cdot 7 + 4 \cdot 2 \quad \text{Multiplying both 7 and 2 by 4}$$
$$= 28 + 8 = 36. \quad \text{Adding}$$

b) By first adding inside the parentheses, we get the same result in a different way:

$$4(7 + 2) = 4(9) \quad \text{Adding; } 7 + 2 = 9$$
$$= 36. \quad \text{Multiplying}$$

The Distributive Law

For any numbers a, b, and c,

$$a(b + c) = ab + ac.$$

(The product of a number and a sum can be written as the sum of two products.)

EXAMPLE 6 Multiply: $3(x + 2)$.

Solution Since $x + 2$ cannot be simplified unless a value for x is given, we use the distributive law:

$$3(x + 2) = 3 \cdot x + 3 \cdot 2 \quad \text{Using the distributive law}$$
$$= 3x + 6. \quad \text{Note that } 3 \cdot x \text{ is the same as } 3x.$$

The expression $3x + 6$ has two *terms*, $3x$ and 6. In general, a **term** is a number, a variable, or a product or quotient of numbers and/or variables. Thus, t, 29, $5ab$, and $2x/y$ are terms in $t + 29 + 5ab + 2x/y$. Note that terms are separated by plus signs.

EXAMPLE 7 List the terms in the expression $7s + st + \frac{3}{t}$.

Solution Terms are separated by plus signs, so the terms in $7s + st + 3/t$ are $7s$, st, and $3/t$.

The distributive law can also be used when more than two terms are inside the parentheses.

EXAMPLE 8 Multiply: $6(s + 2 + 5w)$.

Solution

$$6(s + 2 + 5w) = 6 \cdot s + 6 \cdot 2 + 6 \cdot 5w$$ Using the distributive law

$$= 6s + 12 + (6 \cdot 5)w$$ Using the associative law for multiplication

$$= 6s + 12 + 30w$$

Because of the commutative law of multiplication, the distributive law can be used on the "right": $(b + c)a = ba + ca$.

EXAMPLE 9 Multiply: $(c + 4)5$.

Solution

$$(c + 4)5 = c \cdot 5 + 4 \cdot 5$$ Using the distributive law on the right

$$= 5c + 20$$

Caution! To use the distributive law for removing parentheses, be sure to multiply *each* term inside the parentheses by the multiplier outside:

~~$a(b + c) = ab + c$.~~

The Distributive Law and Factoring

If we use the distributive law in reverse, we have the basis of a process called **factoring**: $ab + ac = a(b + c)$. To **factor** an expression means to write an equivalent expression that is a product. The parts of the product are called **factors**. Note that "factor" can be used as either a verb or a noun. Thus in the expression $5t$, the factors are 5 and t. In the expression $4(m + n)$, the factors are 4 and $(m + n)$.

EXAMPLE 10 Use the distributive law to factor each of the following.

a) $3x + 3y$ **b)** $7x + 21y + 7$

Solution

a) By the distributive law,

$$3x + 3y = 3(x + y).$$ The *common factor* for $3x$ and $3y$ is 3.

b) $7x + 21y + 7 = 7 \cdot x + 7 \cdot 3y + 7 \cdot 1$ The common factor is 7.

$$= 7(x + 3y + 1)$$ Using the distributive law

Be sure to include both the 1 and the common factor, 7.

To check our factoring, we multiply to see if the original expression is obtained. For example, to check the **factorization** in Example 10(b), note that

$$\begin{aligned} 7(x + 3y + 1) &= 7 \cdot x + 7 \cdot 3y + 7 \cdot 1 \\ &= 7x + 21y + 7. \end{aligned}$$

Since $7x + 21y + 7$ is what we started with in Example 10(b), we have a check.

1.2 Exercise Set

FOR EXTRA HELP

Student's Solutions Manual | Digital Video Tutor CD 1 Videotape 1 | AW Math Tutor Center | MathXL Tutorials on CD | MathXL | MyMathLab

Concept Reinforcement *Complete each sentence using one of these terms: commutative, associative, or distributive.*

1. $8 + t$ is equivalent to $t + 8$ by the ______________ law for addition.
2. $3(xy)$ is equivalent to $(3x)y$ by the ______________ law for multiplication.
3. $(5b)c$ is equivalent to $5(bc)$ by the ______________ law for multiplication.
4. mn is equivalent to nm by the ______________ law for multiplication.
5. $x(y + z)$ is equivalent to $xy + xz$ by the ______________ law.
6. $(9 + a) + b$ is equivalent to $9 + (a + b)$ by the ______________ law for addition.
7. $a + (6 + d)$ is equivalent to $(a + 6) + d$ by the ______________ law for addition.
8. $t + 4$ is equivalent to $4 + t$ by the ______________ law for addition.
9. $x \cdot 7$ is equivalent to $7 \cdot x$ by the ______________ law for multiplication.
10. $2(a + b)$ is equivalent to $2 \cdot a + 2 \cdot b$ by the ______________ law.

Use the commutative law of addition to write an equivalent expression.

11. $7 + x$
12. $a + 2$
13. $ab + c$
14. $x + 3y$
15. $9x + 3y$
16. $3a + 7b$
17. $5(a + 1)$
18. $9(x + 5)$

Use the commutative law of multiplication to write an equivalent expression.

19. $2 \cdot a$
20. xy
21. st
22. $4x$
23. $5 + ab$
24. $x + 3y$
25. $5(a + 1)$
26. $9(x + 5)$

Use the associative law of addition to write an equivalent expression.

27. $(a + 5) + b$
28. $(5 + m) + r$
29. $r + (t + 7)$
30. $x + (2 + y)$
31. $(ab + c) + d$
32. $(m + np) + r$

Use the associative law of multiplication to write an equivalent expression.

33. $(8x)y$
34. $(9a)b$
35. $2(ab)$
36. $9(rp)$
37. $3[2(a + b)]$
38. $5[x(2 + y)]$

Use the commutative and/or associative laws to write two equivalent expressions. Answers may vary.

39. $r + (t + 6)$

40. $5 + (v + w)$

41. $(17a)b$

42. $x(3y)$

Use the commutative and/or associative laws to show why the expression on the left is equivalent to the expression on the right. Write a series of steps with labels, as in Example 4.

43. $(5 + x) + 2$ is equivalent to $x + 7$

44. $(2a)4$ is equivalent to $8a$

45. $(m \cdot 3)7$ is equivalent to $21m$

46. $4 + (9 + x)$ is equivalent to $x + 13$

Multiply.

47. $4(a + 3)$

48. $3(x + 5)$

49. $6(1 + x)$

50. $6(v + 4)$

51. $3(x + 1)$

52. $9(x + 3)$

53. $8(3 + y)$

54. $7(s + 5)$

55. $9(2x + 6)$

56. $9(6m + 7)$

57. $5(r + 2 + 3t)$

58. $4(5x + 8 + 3p)$

59. $(a + b)2$

60. $(x + 2)7$

61. $(x + y + 2)5$

62. $(2 + a + b)6$

List the terms in each expression.

63. $x + xyz + 19$

64. $9 + 17a + abc$

65. $2a + \frac{a}{b} + 5b$

66. $3xy + 20 + \frac{4a}{b}$

Use the distributive law to factor each of the following. Check by multiplying.

67. $2a + 2b$

68. $5y + 5z$

69. $7 + 7y$

70. $13 + 13x$

71. $18x + 3$

72. $20a + 5$

73. $5x + 10 + 15y$

74. $3 + 27b + 6c$

75. $12x + 9$

76. $6x + 6$

77. $3a + 9b$

78. $5a + 15b$

79. $44x + 11y + 22z$

80. $14a + 56b + 7$

List the factors in each expression.

81. st

82. $5x$

83. $3(x + y)$

84. $(a + b)6$

85. $7 \cdot a$

86. $m \cdot 2$

87. $(a - b)(x - y)$

88. $(3 - a)(b + c)$

89. Is subtraction commutative? Why or why not?

90. Is division associative? Why or why not?

SKILL MAINTENANCE

To the student and the instructor: Exercises included for Skill Maintenance review skills previously studied in the text. Often these exercises provide preparation for the next section of the text. The numbers in brackets immediately following the directions or exercise indicate the section in which the skill was introduced. The answers to all Skill Maintenance exercises appear at the back of the book. If a Skill Maintenance exercise gives you difficulty, review the material in the indicated section of the text.

Translate to an algebraic expression. [1.1]

91. Twice Kara's salary

92. Half of m

SYNTHESIS

93. Are terms and factors the same thing? Why or why not?

94. Explain how the distributive, commutative, and associative laws can be used to show that $2(3x + 4y)$ is equivalent to $6x + 8y$.

Tell whether the expressions in each pairing are equivalent. Then explain why or why not.

95. $8 + 4(a + b)$ and $4(2 + a + b)$

96. $7 \div 3m$ and $m \cdot 3 \div 7$

97. $(rt + st)5$ and $5t(r + s)$

98. $yax + ax$ and $xa(1 + y)$

99. $30y + x15$ and $5[2(x + 3y)]$

100. $[c(2 + 3b)]5$ and $10c + 15bc$

101. Evaluate the expressions $3(2 + x)$ and $6 + x$ for $x = 0$. Do your results indicate that $3(2 + x)$ and $6 + x$ are equivalent? Why or why not?

102. Factor $15x + 40$. Then evaluate both $15x + 40$ and the factorization for $x = 4$. Do your results *guarantee* that the factorization is correct? Why or why not? (*Hint*: See Exercise 101.)

COLLABORATIVE CORNER

Mental Addition

Focus: Application of commutative and associative laws

Time: 10 minutes

Group size: 2–3

Legend has it that while still in grade school, the mathematician Carl Friedrich Gauss (1777–1855) was able to add the numbers from 1 to 100 mentally. Gauss did not add them sequentially, but rather paired 1 with 99, 2 with 98, and so on.

ACTIVITY

1. Use a method similar to Gauss's to simplify the following:

$$1 + 2 + 3 + 4 + 5 + 6 + 7 + 8 + 9 + 10.$$

One group member should add from left to right as a check.

2. Use Gauss's method to find the sum of the first 25 counting numbers:

$$1 + 2 + 3 + \cdots + 23 + 24 + 25.$$

Again, one student should add from left to right as a check.

3. How were the associative and commutative laws applied in parts (1) and (2) above?

4. Now use a similar approach involving both addition and division to find the sum of the first 10 counting numbers:

$$\begin{array}{r} 1 + 2 + 3 + \cdots + 10 \\ \underline{+\ 10 + 9 + 8 + \cdots + 1} \end{array}$$

5. Use the approach in step (4) to find the sum of the first 100 counting numbers. Are the associative and commutative laws applied in this method, too? How is the distributive law used in this approach?

1.3 Fraction Notation

Factors and Prime Factorizations • Fraction Notation • Multiplication, Division, and Simplification • More Simplifying • Addition and Subtraction

This section covers multiplication, addition, subtraction, and division with fractions. Although much of this may be review, note that fraction expressions that contain variables are also included.

Factors and Prime Factorizations

In preparation for work with fraction notation, we first review how *natural numbers* are factored. **Natural numbers** can be thought of as the counting numbers:

$$1, 2, 3, 4, 5, \ldots.^*$$

(The dots indicate that the established pattern continues without ending.)

---

*A similar collection of numbers, the **whole numbers,** includes 0: 0, 1, 2, 3, ...

To factor a number, we simply express it as a product of two or more numbers.

EXAMPLE 1 Write several factorizations of 12. Then list all factors of 12.

Solution The number 12 can be factored in several ways:

$$1 \cdot 12, \qquad 2 \cdot 6, \qquad 3 \cdot 4, \qquad 2 \cdot 2 \cdot 3.$$

The factors of 12 are 1, 2, 3, 4, 6, and 12.

Some numbers have only two factors, the number itself and 1. Such numbers are called **prime**.

> **Prime Number**
>
> A *prime number* is a natural number that has exactly two different factors: the number itself and 1. The first several primes are 2, 3, 5, 7, 11, 13, 17, 19, and 23.

EXAMPLE 2 Which of these numbers are prime? 29, 4, 1

Solution

29 is prime. It has exactly two different factors, 29 and 1.

4 is not prime. It has three different factors, 1, 2, and 4.

1 is not prime. It does not have two *different* factors.

If a natural number, other than 1, is not prime, we call it **composite**. Every composite number can be factored into a product of prime numbers. Such a factorization is called the **prime factorization** of that composite number.

EXAMPLE 3 Find the prime factorization of 36.

Solution We first factor 36 in any way that we can. One way is like this:

$$36 = 4 \cdot 9.$$

The factors 4 and 9 are not prime, so we factor them:

$$\begin{aligned} 36 &= 4 \cdot 9 \\ &= 2 \cdot 2 \cdot 3 \cdot 3. \end{aligned} \qquad \text{2 and 3 are both prime.}$$

The prime factorization of 36 is $2 \cdot 2 \cdot 3 \cdot 3$.

Student Notes

When writing a factorization, you are writing an equivalent expression for the original number. Some students do this with a tree diagram:

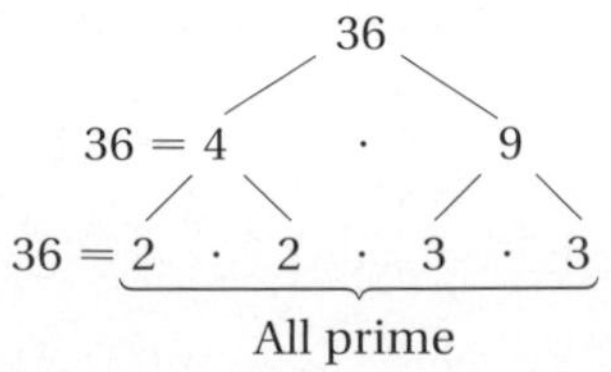

Fraction Notation

An example of **fraction notation** for a number is

$$\frac{2}{3}. \quad \begin{matrix} \leftarrow \text{Numerator} \\ \leftarrow \text{Denominator} \end{matrix}$$

The top number is called the **numerator**, and the bottom number is called the **denominator**. When the numerator and the denominator are the same nonzero number, we have fraction notation for the number 1.

Fraction Notation for 1

For any number a, except 0,

$$\frac{a}{a} = 1.$$

(Any nonzero number divided by itself is 1.)

Multiplication, Division, and Simplification

Recall from arithmetic that fractions are multiplied as follows.

Multiplication of Fractions

For any two fractions a/b and c/d,

$$\frac{a}{b} \cdot \frac{c}{d} = \frac{ac}{bd}.$$

(The numerator of the product is the product of the two numerators. The denominator of the product is the product of the two denominators.)

EXAMPLE 4 Multiply: **(a)** $\frac{2}{3} \cdot \frac{7}{5}$; **(b)** $\frac{4}{x} \cdot \frac{8}{y}$.

Solution We multiply numerators as well as denominators.

a) $\frac{2}{3} \cdot \frac{7}{5} = \frac{2 \cdot 7}{3 \cdot 5} = \frac{14}{15}$

b) $\frac{4}{x} \cdot \frac{8}{y} = \frac{4 \cdot 8}{x \cdot y} = \frac{32}{xy}$

Two numbers whose product is 1 are **reciprocals**, or **multiplicative inverses**, of each other. All numbers, except zero, have reciprocals. For example,

the reciprocal of $\frac{2}{3}$ is $\frac{3}{2}$ because $\frac{2}{3} \cdot \frac{3}{2} = \frac{6}{6} = 1$;

the reciprocal of 9 is $\frac{1}{9}$ because $9 \cdot \frac{1}{9} = \frac{9}{9} = 1$; and

the reciprocal of $\frac{1}{4}$ is 4 because $\frac{1}{4} \cdot 4 = 1$.

Reciprocals are used to rewrite division in an equivalent form that uses multiplication.

Division of Fractions

To divide two fractions, multiply by the reciprocal of the divisor:

$$\frac{a}{b} \div \frac{c}{d} = \frac{a}{b} \cdot \frac{d}{c}.$$

EXAMPLE 5 Divide: $\frac{1}{2} \div \frac{3}{5}$.

Solution

$$\frac{1}{2} \div \frac{3}{5} = \frac{1}{2} \cdot \frac{5}{3} \qquad \frac{5}{3} \text{ is the reciprocal of } \frac{3}{5}.$$

$$= \frac{5}{6}$$

When one of the fractions being multiplied is 1, multiplying yields an equivalent expression because of the *identity property of* 1. A similar property could be stated for division, but there is no need to do so here.

The Identity Property of 1

For any number a,

$$a \cdot 1 = a.$$

(Multiplying a number by 1 gives that same number.)

EXAMPLE 6 Multiply $\frac{4}{5} \cdot \frac{6}{6}$ to find an expression equivalent to $\frac{4}{5}$.

Solution Since $\frac{6}{6} = 1$, the expression $\frac{4}{5} \cdot \frac{6}{6}$ is equivalent to $\frac{4}{5} \cdot 1$, or simply $\frac{4}{5}$. We have

$$\frac{4}{5} \cdot \frac{6}{6} = \frac{4 \cdot 6}{5 \cdot 6} = \frac{24}{30}.$$

Thus, $\frac{24}{30}$ is equivalent to $\frac{4}{5}$.

The steps of Example 6 are reversed by "removing a factor equal to 1"—in this case, $\frac{6}{6}$. By removing a factor that equals 1, we can *simplify* an expression like $\frac{24}{30}$ to an equivalent expression like $\frac{4}{5}$.

To simplify, we factor the numerator and the denominator, looking for the largest factor common to both. This is sometimes made easier by writing prime factorizations. After identifying common factors, we can express the fraction as a product of two fractions, one of which is in the form a/a.

EXAMPLE 7 Simplify: **(a)** $\frac{15}{40}$; **(b)** $\frac{36}{24}$.

Solution

a) Note that 5 is a factor of both 15 and 40:

$$\frac{15}{40} = \frac{3 \cdot 5}{8 \cdot 5}$$ Factoring the numerator and the denominator, using the common factor, 5

$$= \frac{3}{8} \cdot \frac{5}{5}$$ Rewriting as a product of two fractions; $\frac{5}{5} = 1$

$$= \frac{3}{8} \cdot 1 = \frac{3}{8}.$$ Using the identity property of 1 (removing a factor equal to 1)

b) $$\frac{36}{24} = \frac{2 \cdot 2 \cdot 3 \cdot 3}{2 \cdot 2 \cdot 2 \cdot 3}$$ Writing the prime factorizations and identifying common factors; 12/12 could also be used.

$$= \frac{3}{2} \cdot \frac{2 \cdot 2 \cdot 3}{2 \cdot 2 \cdot 3}$$ Rewriting as a product of two fractions; $\frac{2 \cdot 2 \cdot 3}{2 \cdot 2 \cdot 3} = 1$

$$= \frac{3}{2} \cdot 1 = \frac{3}{2}$$ Using the identity property of 1

It is always wise to check your result to see if any common factors of the numerator and the denominator remain. (This will never happen if prime factorizations are used correctly.) If common factors remain, repeat the process by removing another factor equal to 1 to simplify your result.

More Simplifying

"Canceling" is a shortcut that you may have used for removing a factor equal to 1 when working with fraction notation. With *great* concern, we mention it as a possible way to speed up your work. Canceling can be used only when removing common factors in numerators and denominators. Canceling *cannot* be used in sums or differences. Our concern is that "canceling" be used with understanding. Example 7(b) might have been done faster as follows:

$$\frac{36}{24} = \frac{\cancel{2} \cdot \cancel{2} \cdot 3 \cdot \cancel{3}}{\cancel{2} \cdot \cancel{2} \cdot 2 \cdot \cancel{3}} = \frac{3}{2}, \quad \text{or} \quad \frac{36}{24} = \frac{3 \cdot \cancel{12}}{2 \cdot \cancel{12}} = \frac{3}{2}, \quad \text{or} \quad \frac{\overset{3}{\cancel{\overset{18}{\cancel{36}}}}}{\underset{2}{\cancel{\underset{12}{\cancel{24}}}}} = \frac{3}{2}.$$

> ***Caution!*** Unfortunately, canceling is often performed incorrectly:
>
> $$\frac{\cancel{2} + 3}{\cancel{2}} = 3, \qquad \frac{\cancel{4} - 1}{\cancel{4} - 2} = \frac{1}{2}, \qquad \frac{1\cancel{5}}{\cancel{5}4} = \frac{1}{4},$$
>
> The above cancellations are incorrect because the expressions canceled are *not* factors. For example, in 2 + 3, the 2 and 3 are not factors. Correct simplifications are as follows:
>
> $$\frac{2 + 3}{2} = \frac{5}{2}, \qquad \frac{4 - 1}{4 - 2} = \frac{3}{2}, \qquad \frac{15}{54} = \frac{5 \cdot \cancel{3}}{18 \cdot \cancel{3}} = \frac{5}{18}.$$
>
> ***Remember*: If you can't factor, you can't cancel! If in doubt, don't cancel!**

Sometimes it is helpful to use 1 as a factor in the numerator or the denominator when simplifying.

EXAMPLE 8 Simplify: $\frac{9}{72}$.

Solution

$\frac{9}{72} = \frac{1 \cdot 9}{8 \cdot 9}$ Factoring and using the identity property of 1 to write 9 as $1 \cdot 9$

$= \frac{1 \cdot \cancel{9}}{8 \cdot \cancel{9}} = \frac{1}{8}$ Simplifying by removing a factor equal to 1: $\frac{9}{9} = 1$

Addition and Subtraction

When denominators are the same, fractions are added or subtracted by adding or subtracting numerators and keeping the same denominator.

Addition and Subtraction of Fractions

For any two fractions a/d and b/d,

$$\frac{a}{d} + \frac{b}{d} = \frac{a+b}{d} \quad \text{and} \quad \frac{a}{d} - \frac{b}{d} = \frac{a-b}{d}.$$

EXAMPLE 9 Add and simplify: $\frac{4}{8} + \frac{5}{8}$.

Solution The common denominator is 8. We add the numerators and keep the common denominator:

$$\frac{4}{8} + \frac{5}{8} = \frac{4+5}{8} = \frac{9}{8}.$$

You can think of this as $4 \cdot \frac{1}{8} + 5 \cdot \frac{1}{8} = 9 \cdot \frac{1}{8}$, or $\frac{9}{8}$.

In arithmetic, we often write $1\frac{1}{8}$ rather than the "improper" fraction $\frac{9}{8}$. In algebra, $\frac{9}{8}$ is generally more useful and is quite "proper" for our purposes.

When denominators are different, we use the identity property of 1 and multiply to find a common denominator. Then we add, as in Example 9.

EXAMPLE 10 Add or subtract as indicated: **(a)** $\frac{7}{8} + \frac{5}{12}$; **(b)** $\frac{9}{8} - \frac{4}{5}$.

Solution

a) The number 24 is divisible by both 8 and 12. We multiply both $\frac{7}{8}$ and $\frac{5}{12}$ by suitable forms of 1 to obtain two fractions with denominators of 24:

$$\frac{7}{8} + \frac{5}{12} = \frac{7}{8} \cdot \frac{3}{3} + \frac{5}{12} \cdot \frac{2}{2}$$ Multiplying by 1. Since $8 \cdot 3 = 24$, we multiply $\frac{7}{8}$ by $\frac{3}{3}$. Since $12 \cdot 2 = 24$, we multiply $\frac{5}{12}$ by $\frac{2}{2}$.

$$= \frac{21}{24} + \frac{10}{24}$$ Performing the multiplication

$$= \frac{31}{24}.$$ Adding fractions

b) $$\frac{9}{8} - \frac{4}{5} = \frac{9}{8} \cdot \frac{5}{5} - \frac{4}{5} \cdot \frac{8}{8}$$ Using 40 as a common denominator

$$= \frac{45}{40} - \frac{32}{40} = \frac{13}{40}$$ Subtracting fractions

Study Skills

Do the Exercises

- Usually an instructor assigns some odd-numbered exercises. When you complete these, you can check your answers at the back of the book. If you miss any, closely examine your work, and if necessary, consult the *Student's Solutions Manual* or your instructor for guidance.
- Whether or not your instructor assigns the even-numbered exercises, try to do some on your own. There are no answers given for them, so you will gain practice doing exercises that are similar to quiz or test problems. Check your answers later with a friend or your instructor.

After adding, subtracting, multiplying, or dividing, we may still need to simplify the answer.

EXAMPLE 11 Perform the indicated operation and, if possible, simplify.

a) $\dfrac{7}{10} - \dfrac{1}{5}$ **b)** $8 \cdot \dfrac{5}{12}$ **c)** $\dfrac{\frac{5}{6}}{\frac{25}{9}}$

Solution

a) $\dfrac{7}{10} - \dfrac{1}{5} = \dfrac{7}{10} - \dfrac{1}{5} \cdot \dfrac{2}{2}$ Using 10 as the common denominator

$= \dfrac{7}{10} - \dfrac{2}{10}$

$= \dfrac{5}{10} = \dfrac{1 \cdot \cancel{5}}{2 \cdot \cancel{5}} = \dfrac{1}{2}$ Removing a factor equal to 1: $\dfrac{5}{5} = 1$

b) $8 \cdot \dfrac{5}{12} = \dfrac{8 \cdot 5}{12}$ Multiplying numerators and denominators. Think of 8 as $\frac{8}{1}$.

$= \dfrac{2 \cdot 2 \cdot 2 \cdot 5}{2 \cdot 2 \cdot 3}$ Factoring; $\dfrac{4 \cdot 2 \cdot 5}{4 \cdot 3}$ can also be used.

$= \dfrac{\cancel{2} \cdot \cancel{2} \cdot 2 \cdot 5}{\cancel{2} \cdot \cancel{2} \cdot 3}$ Removing a factor equal to 1: $\dfrac{2 \cdot 2}{2 \cdot 2} = 1$

$= \dfrac{10}{3}$ Simplifying

c) $\dfrac{\frac{5}{6}}{\frac{25}{9}} = \dfrac{5}{6} \div \dfrac{25}{9}$ Rewriting horizontally. Remember that a fraction bar indicates division.

$= \dfrac{5}{6} \cdot \dfrac{9}{25}$ Multiplying by the reciprocal of $\frac{25}{9}$

$= \dfrac{5 \cdot 3 \cdot 3}{2 \cdot 3 \cdot 5 \cdot 5}$ Writing as one fraction and factoring

$= \dfrac{\cancel{5} \cdot \cancel{3} \cdot 3}{2 \cdot \cancel{3} \cdot \cancel{5} \cdot 5}$ Removing a factor equal to 1: $\dfrac{5 \cdot 3}{3 \cdot 5} = 1$

$= \dfrac{3}{10}$ Simplifying

---

technology connection

Some graphing calculators can perform operations using fraction notation. Others may be able to convert answers given in decimal notation to fraction notation. Often this conversion is done using a command found in a **menu**, or a list of options that appears when a key is pressed. To select an item from a menu, we highlight its number and press ENTER or simply press the number of the item.

For example, to find fraction notation for $\frac{2}{15} + \frac{7}{12}$, we enter the expression as 2/15 + 7/12. The answer is given in decimal notation. To convert this to fraction notation, we press MATH and select the Frac option. In this case, the notation Ans▶ Frac shows that the graphing calculator will convert .7166666667 to fraction notation.

```
2/15+7/12
              .7166666667
Ans▶Frac
                    43/60
```

We see that $\frac{2}{15} + \frac{7}{12} = \frac{43}{60}$.

1.3 Exercise Set

FOR EXTRA HELP

Student's Solutions Manual | Digital Video Tutor CD 1 Videotape 1 | AW Math Tutor Center | MathXL Tutorials on CD | MathXL | MyMathLab

To the student and the instructor: Beginning in this section, selected exercises are marked with the icon **Aha!**. *These "Aha!" exercises can be answered most easily if the student pauses to inspect the exercise rather than proceed mechanically. This is done to discourage rote memorization. Some later "Aha!" exercises in this exercise set are unmarked, to encourage students to always pause before working a problem.*

Concept Reinforcement *Label each of the following numbers as prime, composite, or neither.*

1. 9 **2.** 15 **3.** 31 **4.** 35

5. 25 **6.** 37 **7.** 2 **8.** 1

9. 0 **10.** 4

Concept Reinforcement *In each of Exercises 11–14, match the description with a number from the list on the right.*

11. ____ A factor of 35 **a)** 2

12. ____ A number that has 3 as a factor **b)** 7

13. ____ An odd composite number **c)** 60

14. ____ The only even prime number **d)** 65

Write at least two factorizations of each number. Then list all the factors of the number.

15. 50 **16.** 70 **17.** 42 **18.** 60

Find the prime factorization of each number. If the number is prime, state this.

19. 26 **20.** 15 **21.** 30

22. 55 **23.** 27 **24.** 98

25. 18 **26.** 54 **27.** 40

28. 56 **29.** 43 **30.** 120

31. 210 **32.** 79 **33.** 115

34. 143

Simplify.

35. $\frac{14}{21}$ **36.** $\frac{10}{14}$ **37.** $\frac{16}{56}$

38. $\frac{72}{27}$ **39.** $\frac{6}{48}$ **40.** $\frac{12}{70}$

41. $\frac{49}{7}$ **42.** $\frac{132}{11}$ **43.** $\frac{19}{76}$

44. $\frac{17}{51}$ **45.** $\frac{150}{25}$ **46.** $\frac{170}{34}$

47. $\frac{42}{50}$ **48.** $\frac{75}{80}$ **49.** $\frac{120}{82}$

50. $\frac{75}{45}$ **51.** $\frac{210}{98}$ **52.** $\frac{140}{350}$

Perform the indicated operation and, if possible, simplify.

53. $\frac{1}{2} \cdot \frac{3}{7}$ **54.** $\frac{11}{10} \cdot \frac{8}{5}$ **55.** $\frac{9}{2} \cdot \frac{3}{4}$

Aha! **56.** $\frac{11}{12} \cdot \frac{12}{11}$ **57.** $\frac{1}{8} + \frac{3}{8}$ **58.** $\frac{1}{2} + \frac{1}{8}$

59. $\frac{4}{9} + \frac{13}{18}$ **60.** $\frac{4}{5} + \frac{8}{15}$ **61.** $\frac{3}{a} \cdot \frac{b}{7}$

62. $\frac{x}{5} \cdot \frac{y}{z}$ **63.** $\frac{4}{a} + \frac{3}{a}$ **64.** $\frac{7}{a} - \frac{5}{a}$

65. $\frac{3}{10} + \frac{8}{15}$ **66.** $\frac{7}{8} + \frac{5}{12}$ **67.** $\frac{9}{7} - \frac{2}{7}$

68. $\frac{12}{5} - \frac{2}{5}$ **69.** $\frac{13}{18} - \frac{4}{9}$ **70.** $\frac{13}{15} - \frac{8}{45}$

Aha! **71.** $\frac{20}{30} - \frac{2}{3}$ **72.** $\frac{5}{7} - \frac{5}{21}$ **73.** $\frac{7}{6} \div \frac{3}{5}$

74. $\frac{7}{5} \div \frac{3}{4}$ **75.** $\frac{8}{9} \div \frac{4}{15}$ **76.** $\frac{9}{4} \div 9$

77. $12 \div \frac{3}{7}$ **78.** $\frac{1}{10} \div \frac{1}{5}$ Aha! **79.** $\frac{7}{13} \div \frac{7}{13}$

80. $\frac{17}{8} \div \frac{5}{6}$ **81.** $\frac{\frac{2}{7}}{\frac{5}{3}}$ **82.** $\frac{\frac{3}{8}}{\frac{1}{5}}$

83. $\frac{9}{\frac{1}{2}}$ **84.** $\frac{\frac{7}{3}}{5}$

85. Under what circumstances would the sum of two fractions be easier to compute than the product of the same two fractions?

86. Under what circumstances would the product of two fractions be easier to compute than the sum of the same two fractions?

SKILL MAINTENANCE

Use a commutative law to write an equivalent expression. There can be more than one correct answer. [1.2]

87. $5(x + 3)$ **88.** $7 + (a + b)$

SYNTHESIS

89. Bryce insists that $(2 + x)/8$ is equivalent to $(1 + x)/4$. What mistake do you think is being made and how could you demonstrate to Bryce that the two expressions are not equivalent?

90. Why are 0 and 1 considered neither prime nor composite?

91. In the following table, the top number can be factored in such a way that the sum of the factors is the bottom number. For example, in the first column, 56 is factored as $7 \cdot 8$, since $7 + 8 = 15$, the bottom number. Find the missing numbers in each column.

Product	56	63	36	72	140	96	168
Factor	7						
Factor	8						
Sum	15	16	20	38	24	20	29

92. *Packaging.* Tritan Candies uses two sizes of boxes, 6 in. long and 8 in. long. These are packed end to end in bigger cartons to be shipped. What is the shortest-length carton that will accommodate boxes of either size without any room left over? (Each carton must contain boxes of only one size; no mixing is allowed.)

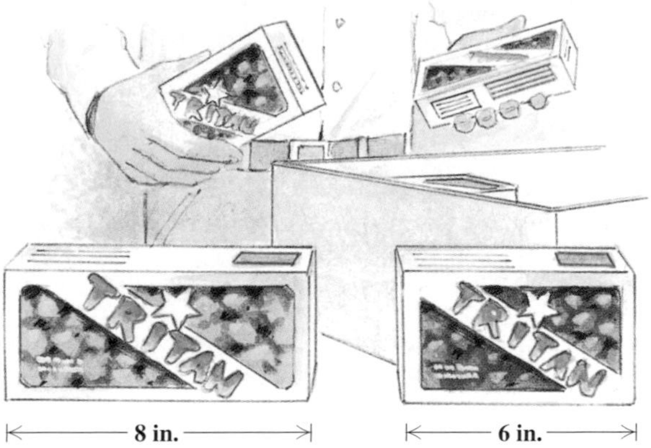

Simplify.

93. $\frac{16 \cdot 9 \cdot 4}{15 \cdot 8 \cdot 12}$ **94.** $\frac{9 \cdot 8xy}{2xy \cdot 36}$

95. $\frac{27pqrs}{9prst}$ **96.** $\frac{512}{192}$

97. $\frac{15 \cdot 4xy \cdot 9}{6 \cdot 25x \cdot 15y}$ **98.** $\frac{10x \cdot 12 \cdot 25y}{2 \cdot 30x \cdot 20y}$

99. $\frac{\frac{27ab}{15mn}}{\frac{18bc}{25np}}$ **100.** $\frac{\frac{45xyz}{24ab}}{\frac{30xz}{32ac}}$

101. $\frac{5\frac{3}{4}rs}{4\frac{1}{2}st}$ **102.** $\frac{3\frac{5}{7}mn}{2\frac{4}{5}np}$

Find the area of each figure.

103.

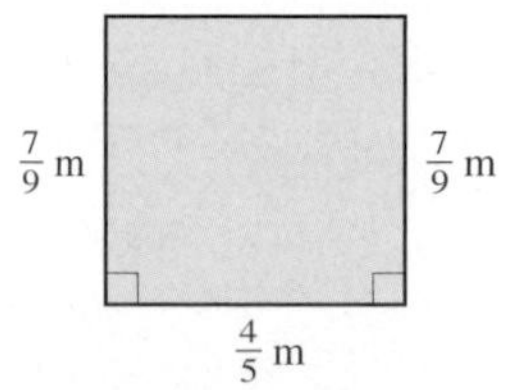

104.

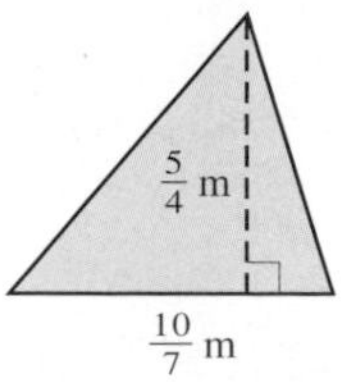

105. Find the perimeter of a square with sides of length $3\frac{5}{9}$ m.

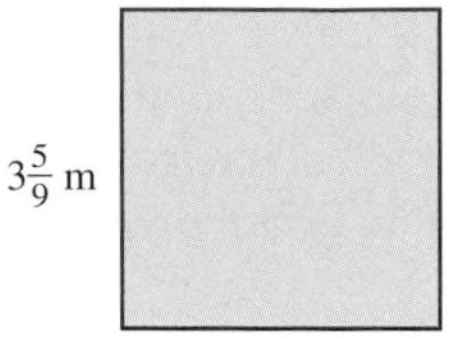

106. Find the perimeter of the rectangle in Exercise 103.

107. Find the total length of the edges of a cube with sides of length $2\frac{3}{10}$ cm.

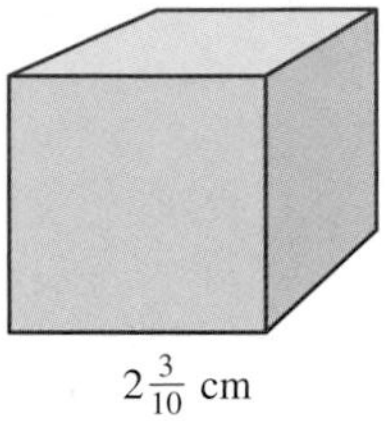

1.4 Positive and Negative Real Numbers

The Integers • The Rational Numbers • Real Numbers and Order • Absolute Value

A **set** is a collection of objects. The set containing 1, 3, and 7 is usually written $\{1, 3, 7\}$. In this section, we examine some important sets of numbers. More on sets can be found in Appendix C.

The Integers

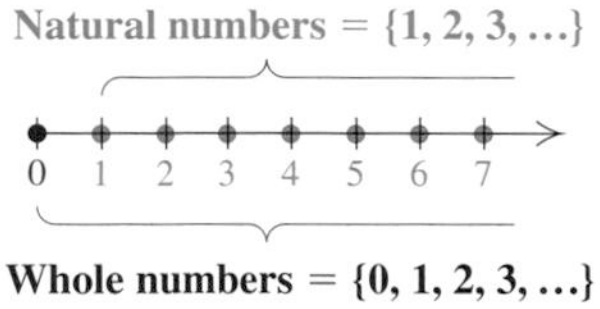

Two sets of numbers were mentioned in Section 1.3. We represent these sets using dots on a number line, as shown at left.

To create the set of *integers,* we include all whole numbers, along with their *opposites.* To find the opposite of a number, we locate the number that is the same distance from 0 but on the other side of the number line. For example,

the opposite of 1 is negative 1, written -1;

and

the opposite of 3 is negative 3, written -3.

The **integers** consist of all whole numbers and their opposites.

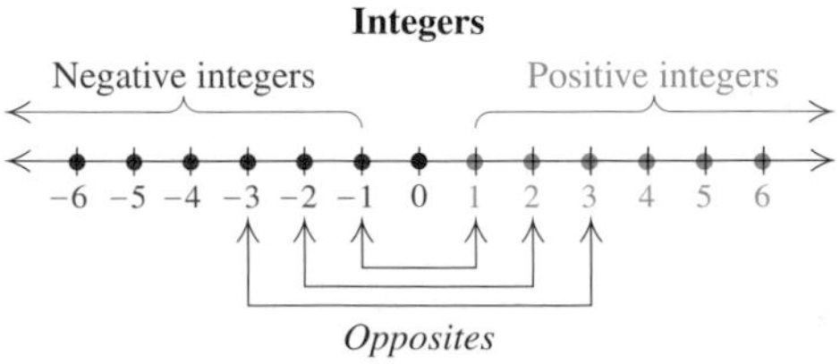

Opposites are discussed in more detail in Section 1.6. Note that, except for 0, opposites occur in pairs. Thus, 5 is the opposite of -5, just as -5 is the opposite of 5. Note that 0 acts as its own opposite.

Set of Integers

The set of integers = {..., −4, −3, −2, −1, 0, 1, 2, 3, 4, ...}.

Integers are associated with many real-world problems and situations.

EXAMPLE 1 State which integer(s) corresponds to each situation.

a) In 2003, the Colonial Pipeline Company was fined a record $34 million for pollution crimes. (*Source*: GreenConsumerGuide.com)

b) The lowest point in New Orleans is 8 ft below sea level.

c) To lose one pound of fat, it is necessary for most people to create a 3500-calorie deficit. (*Source*: World Health Organization)

Solution

a) The integer −34,000,000 corresponds to a fine of $34 million.

b) The integer −8 corresponds to 8 ft below sea level.

c) The integer −3500 corresponds to a deficit of 3500 calories.

Study Skills

Try to Get Ahead

Try to keep one section ahead of your instructor. If you study ahead of your lectures, you can concentrate on what is being explained in them, rather than trying to write everything down. You can then write notes on only special points or questions related to what is happening in class.

The Rational Numbers

Although numbers like $\frac{5}{9}$ are built out of integers, these numbers are not themselves integers. Another set, the **rational numbers**, contains fractions and decimals, as well as the integers. Some examples of rational numbers are

$$\frac{5}{9}, \quad -\frac{4}{7}, \quad 95, \quad -16, \quad 0, \quad \frac{-35}{8}, \quad 2.4, \quad -0.31.$$

In Section 1.7, we show that $-\frac{4}{7}$ can be written as $\frac{-4}{7}$ or $\frac{4}{-7}$. Indeed, every number listed above can be written as an integer over an integer. For example, 95 can be written as $\frac{95}{1}$ and 2.4 can be written as $\frac{24}{10}$. In this manner, any *ratio*nal number can be expressed as the *ratio* of two integers. Rather than attempt to list all rational numbers, we use this idea of ratio to describe the set as follows.

Set of Rational Numbers

The set of rational numbers $= \left\{ \frac{a}{b} \,\middle|\, a \text{ and } b \text{ are integers and } b \neq 0 \right\}$.

This is read "the set of all numbers $\frac{a}{b}$, where a and b are integers and b does not equal zero."

In Section 1.7, we explain why b cannot equal 0.

To *graph* a number is to mark its location on a number line.

EXAMPLE 2 Graph each of the following rational numbers: **(a)** $\frac{5}{2}$; **(b)** -3.2; **(c)** $\frac{11}{8}$.

Solution

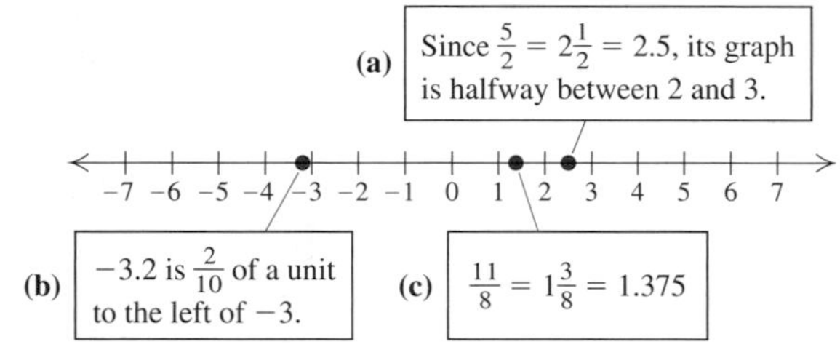

It is important to remember that every rational number can be written as a fraction or a decimal.

EXAMPLE 3 Convert to decimal notation: $-\frac{5}{8}$.

Solution We first find decimal notation for $\frac{5}{8}$. Since $\frac{5}{8}$ means $5 \div 8$, we divide.

$$\begin{array}{r} 0.625 \\ 8\overline{)5.000} \\ \underline{4\,800} \\ 200 \\ \underline{160} \\ 40 \\ \underline{40} \\ 0 \end{array} \leftarrow \text{The remainder is 0.}$$

Thus, $\frac{5}{8} = 0.625$, so $-\frac{5}{8} = -0.625$.

Because the division in Example 3 ends with the remainder 0, we consider -0.625 a **terminating decimal**. If we are "bringing down" zeros and a remainder reappears, we have a **repeating decimal**, as shown in the next example.

EXAMPLE 4 Convert to decimal notation: $\frac{7}{11}$.

Solution We divide:

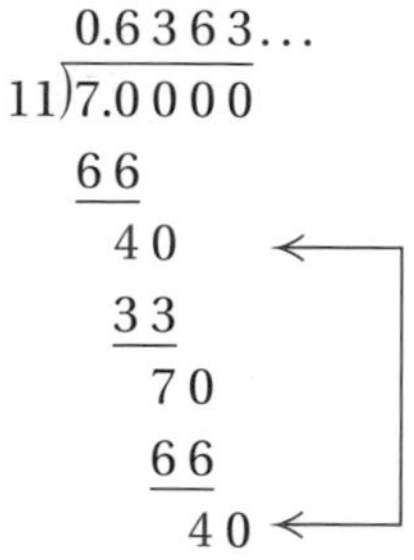

4 reappears as a remainder, so the pattern of 6's and 3's in the quotient will continue.

We abbreviate repeating decimals by writing a bar over the repeating part—in this case, $0.\overline{63}$. Thus, $\frac{7}{11} = 0.\overline{63}$.

Although we do not prove it here, every rational number can be expressed as either a terminating or repeating decimal, and every terminating or repeating decimal can be expressed as a ratio of two integers.

Real Numbers and Order

Some numbers, when written in decimal form, neither terminate nor repeat. Such numbers are called **irrational numbers**.

What sort of numbers are irrational? One example is π (the Greek letter *pi*, read "pie"), which is used to find the area and the circumference of a circle: $A = \pi r^2$ and $C = 2\pi r$.

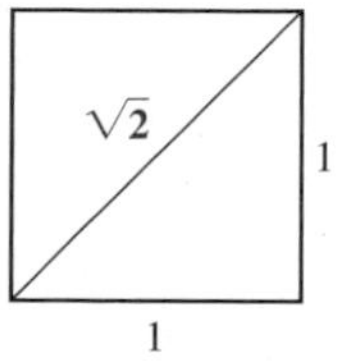

Another irrational number, $\sqrt{2}$ (read "the square root of 2"), is the length of the diagonal of a square with sides of length 1. It is also the number that, when multiplied by itself, gives 2. No rational number can be multiplied by itself to get 2, although some approximations come close:

1.4 is an *approximation* of $\sqrt{2}$ because $(1.4)(1.4) = 1.96$;

1.41 is a better approximation because $(1.41)(1.41) = 1.9881$;

1.4142 is an even better approximation because $(1.4142)(1.4142) = 1.99996164$.

To approximate $\sqrt{2}$ on some calculators, simply press (2) and then (√). With other calculators, press (√) (2), and (ENTER), or consult a manual.

EXAMPLE 5 Graph the real number $\sqrt{3}$ on a number line.

Solution We use a calculator and approximate: $\sqrt{3} \approx 1.732$ ("$\approx$" means "approximately equals"). Then we locate this number on a number line.

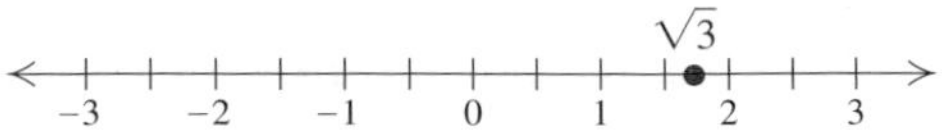

technology connection

To approximate $\sqrt{3}$ on most graphing calculators, we press (√) and then enter 3 enclosed by parentheses. Some graphing calculators will supply the left parenthesis automatically when (√) is pressed.

Approximate each of the following to nine decimal places.

1. $\sqrt{5}$
2. $\sqrt{7}$
3. $\sqrt{13}$
4. $\sqrt{27}$
5. $\sqrt{38}$
6. $\sqrt{50}$

The rational numbers and the irrational numbers together correspond to all the points on a number line and make up what is called the **real-number system**.

Set of Real Numbers

The set of real numbers = The set of all numbers corresponding to points on the number line.

The following figure shows the relationships among various kinds of numbers.

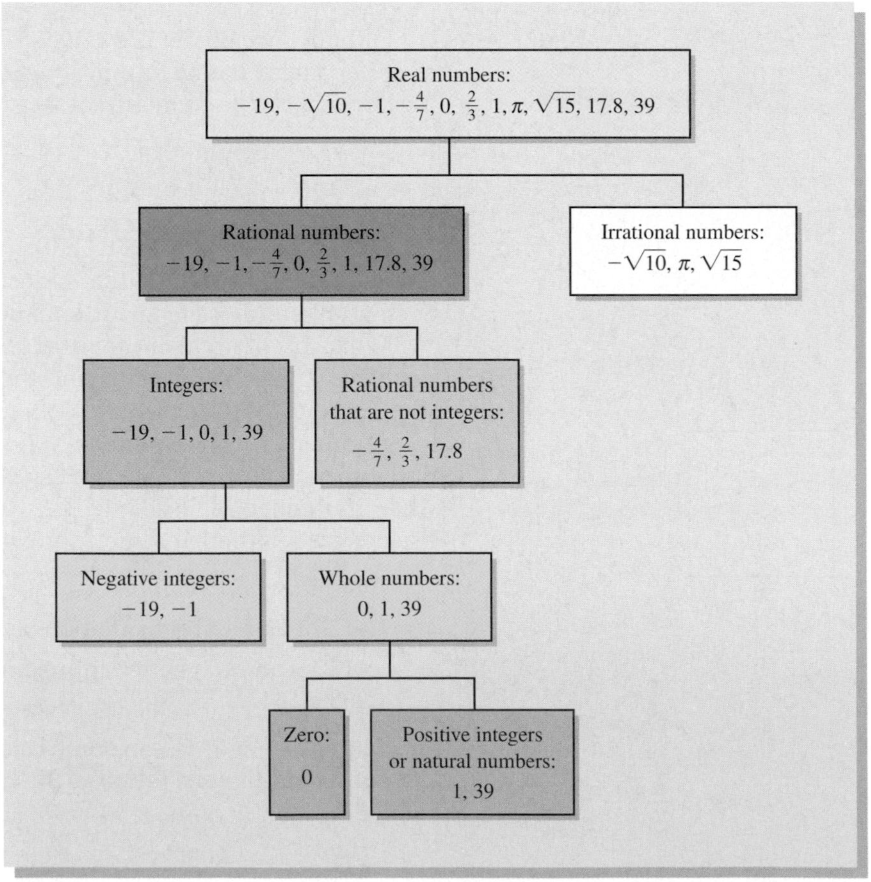

EXAMPLE 6 Which numbers in the following list are **(a)** whole numbers? **(b)** integers? **(c)** rational numbers? **(d)** irrational numbers? **(e)** real numbers?

$$-38, \quad -\frac{8}{5}, \quad 0, \quad 3, \quad 4.5, \quad \sqrt{30}, \quad 52$$

Solution

a) 0, 3, and 52 are whole numbers.

b) -38, 0, 3, and 52 are integers.

c) -38, $-\frac{8}{5}$, 0, 3, 4.5, and 52 are rational numbers.

d) $\sqrt{30}$ is an irrational number.

e) -38, $-\frac{8}{5}$, 0, 3, 4.5, $\sqrt{30}$, and 52 are real numbers.

Real numbers are named in order on the number line, with larger numbers further to the right. For any two numbers, the one to the left is less than the one to the right. We use the symbol **<** to mean "**is less than**." The sentence $-8 < 6$ means "-8 is less than 6." The symbol **>** means "**is greater than**." The sentence $-3 > -7$ means "-3 is greater than -7."

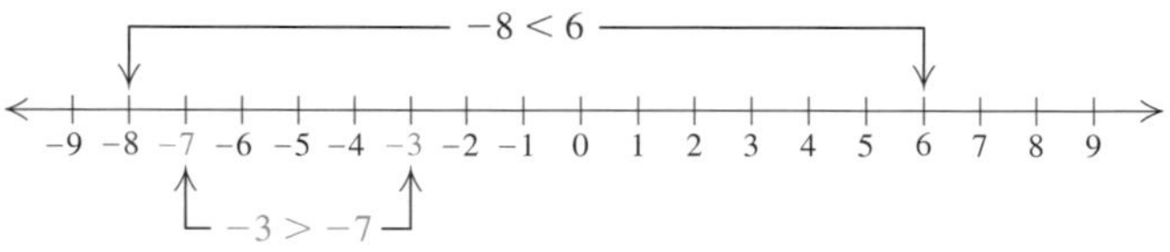

EXAMPLE 7 Use either $<$ or $>$ for ■ to write a true sentence.

a) 2 ■ 9 **b)** -3.45 ■ 1.32 **c)** 6 ■ -12

d) -18 ■ -5 **e)** $\frac{7}{11}$ ■ $\frac{5}{8}$

Solution

a) Since 2 is to the left of 9 on a number line, we know that 2 is less than 9, so $2 < 9$.

b) Since -3.45 is to the left of 1.32, we have $-3.45 < 1.32$.

c) Since 6 is to the right of -12, we have $6 > -12$.

d) Since -18 is to the left of -5, we have $-18 < -5$.

e) We convert to decimal notation: $\frac{7}{11} = 0.\overline{63}$ and $\frac{5}{8} = 0.625$. Thus, $\frac{7}{11} > \frac{5}{8}$.
We also could have used a common denominator: $\frac{7}{11} = \frac{56}{88} > \frac{55}{88} = \frac{5}{8}$.

Sentences like "$a < -5$" and "$-3 > -8$" are **inequalities**. It is useful to remember that every inequality can be written in two ways. For example,

$$-3 > -8 \quad \text{has the same meaning as} \quad -8 < -3.$$

It may be helpful to think of an inequality sign as an "arrow" with the smaller side pointing to the smaller number.

Note that $a > 0$ means that a represents a positive real number and $a < 0$ means that a represents a negative real number.

Statements like $a \le b$ and $b \ge a$ are also inequalities. We read $a \le b$ as "a **is less than or equal to** b" and $a \ge b$ as "a **is greater than or equal to** b."

EXAMPLE 8

Classify each inequality as true or false.

a) $-3 \le 5$ **b)** $-3 \le -3$ **c)** $-5 \ge 4$

Solution

a) $-3 \le 5$ is *true* because $-3 < 5$ is true.

b) $-3 \le -3$ is *true* because $-3 = -3$ is true.

c) $-5 \ge 4$ is *false* since neither $-5 > 4$ nor $-5 = 4$ is true.

Student Notes

It is important to remember that just because an equation or inequality is written or printed, it is not necessarily *true*. For instance, $6 = 7$ is an equation and $2 > 5$ is an inequality. Of course, both statements are *false*.

Absolute Value

There is a convenient terminology and notation for the distance a number is from 0 on a number line. It is called the **absolute value** of the number.

Absolute Value

We write $|a|$, read "the absolute value of a," to represent the number of units that a is from zero.

EXAMPLE 9

Find each absolute value: **(a)** $|-3|$; **(b)** $|7.2|$; **(c)** $|0|$.

Solution

a) $|-3| = 3$ since -3 is 3 units from 0.

b) $|7.2| = 7.2$ since 7.2 is 7.2 units from 0.

c) $|0| = 0$ since 0 is 0 units from itself.

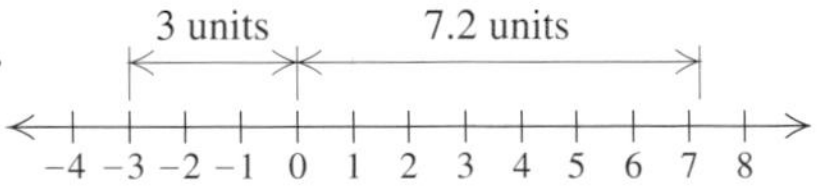

Distance is never negative, so numbers that are opposites have the same absolute value. If a number is nonnegative, its absolute value is the number itself. If a number is negative, its absolute value is its opposite.

technology connection

Most graphing calculators use the notation abs (2) to indicate the absolute value of 2. This is often accessed using the NUM option of the MATH key. When using a graphing calculator for this, be sure to distinguish between the (−) and ((−)) keys (see p. 49 in Section 1.6).

1.4 Exercise Set

FOR EXTRA HELP

Student's Solutions Manual | Digital Video Tutor CD 1 Videotape 1 | AW Math Tutor Center | MathXL Tutorials on CD | MathXL | MyMathLab

Concept Reinforcement *In each of Exercises 1–8, fill in the blank using one of the following words: natural number, whole number, integer, rational number, terminating, repeating, irrational number, absolute value.*

1. Division can be used to show that $\frac{4}{7}$ can be written as a(n) ______________ decimal.

2. Division can be used to show that $\frac{3}{20}$ can be written as a(n) ______________ decimal.

3. If a number is a(n) ______________, it is either a whole number or the opposite of a whole number.

4. 0 is the only ______________ that is not a natural number.

5. Any number of the form a/b, where a and b are integers, with $b \neq 0$, is an example of a(n) ______________.

6. A number like $\sqrt{5}$, which cannot be written precisely in fraction or decimal notation, is an example of a(n) ______________.

7. If a number is a(n) ______________, then it can be thought of as a counting number.

8. When two numbers are opposites, they have the same ______________.

State which real number(s) correspond to each situation.

9. The Dead Sea is 1349 feet below sea level, whereas Mt. Everest is 29,035 feet above sea level.

10. Using a NordicTrack exercise machine, Kit burned 150 calories. She then drank an isotonic drink containing 65 calories.

11. The highest temperature ever reached on the earth was 950 million degrees Fahrenheit (F). The lowest temperature ever reached on the earth was approximately 460°F below zero.

Source: *Guinness World Records* 2001

12. In Burlington, Vermont, the record low temperature for Washington's Birthday is 19°F below zero. The record high for the date is 59°F above zero.

13. In the 2003 Masters Tournament, golfer Tiger Woods finished two over par. In the 2003 Nissan Open, he finished six under par.

14. Ignition occurs 10 seconds before liftoff. A spent fuel tank is detached 235 seconds after liftoff.

15. Janice deposited \$750 in a savings account. Two weeks later, she withdrew \$125.

16. *Birth and death rates.* Recently, the world birth rate was 2043 per hundred thousand. The death rate was 883 per hundred thousand.

Source: Central Intelligence Agency, 2003

17. In bowling, the Jets are 34 pins behind the Strikers after one game. Describe the situation from the viewpoint of each team.

18. The halfback gained 8 yd on the first play. The quarterback was tackled for a 5-yd loss on the second play.

Graph each rational number on a number line.

19. $\frac{10}{3}$

20. $-\frac{17}{5}$

21. -4.3

22. 3.87

23. -2

24. 5

Write decimal notation for each number.

25. $\frac{7}{8}$

26. $-\frac{1}{8}$

27. $-\frac{3}{4}$

28. $\frac{5}{6}$

29. $\frac{7}{6}$

30. $\frac{5}{12}$

31. $\frac{2}{3}$

32. $\frac{1}{4}$

33. $-\frac{1}{2}$

34. $-\frac{3}{8}$

Aha! **35.** $\frac{13}{100}$

36. $-\frac{7}{20}$

Write a true sentence using either $<$ or $>$.

37. $-9 \;\square\; 4$

38. $9 \;\square\; 0$

39. $7 \;\square\; 0$

40. $8 \;\square\; -8$

41. $-6 \;\square\; 6$

42. $0 \;\square\; -7$

43. $-8 \;\square\; -5$

44. $-4 \;\square\; -3$

45. $-5 \;\square\; -11$

46. $-3 \;\square\; -4$

47. $-12.5 \;\square\; -9.4$

48. $-10.3 \;\square\; -14.5$

49. $\frac{5}{12} \;\square\; \frac{11}{25}$

50. $-\frac{14}{17} \;\square\; -\frac{27}{35}$

For each of the following, write a second inequality with the same meaning.

51. $-7 > x$

52. $a > 9$

53. $-10 \leq y$

54. $12 \geq t$

Classify each inequality as either true or false.

55. $-3 \geq -11$

56. $5 \leq -5$

57. $0 \geq 8$

58. $-5 \leq 7$

59. $-8 \leq -8$

60. $8 \geq 8$

Find each absolute value.

61. $|-58|$

62. $|-47|$

63. $|17|$

64. $|3.1|$

65. $|5.6|$

66. $\left|-\frac{2}{5}\right|$

67. $|329|$

68. $|-456|$

69. $\left|-\frac{9}{7}\right|$

70. $|8.02|$

71. $|0|$

72. $|-1.07|$

73. $|x|$, for $x = -8$

74. $|a|$, for $a = -5$

For Exercises 75–80, consider the following list:

$$-83, \quad -4.7, \quad 0, \quad \frac{5}{9}, \quad \pi, \quad \sqrt{17}, \quad 8.31, \quad 62.$$

75. List all rational numbers.

76. List all natural numbers.

77. List all integers.

78. List all irrational numbers.

79. List all real numbers.

80. List all nonnegative integers.

81. Is every integer a rational number? Why or why not?

82. Is every integer a natural number? Why or why not?

SKILL MAINTENANCE

83. Evaluate $3xy$ for $x = 2$ and $y = 7$. [1.1]

84. Use a commutative law to write an expression equivalent to $ab + 5$. [1.2]

SYNTHESIS

85. Is the absolute value of a number always positive? Why or why not?

86. How many rational numbers are there between 0 and 1? Justify your answer.

87. Does "nonnegative" mean the same thing as "positive"? Why or why not?

List in order from least to greatest.

88. $13, -12, 5, -17$

89. $-23, 4, 0, -17$

90. $-\frac{2}{3}, \frac{1}{2}, -\frac{3}{4}, -\frac{5}{6}, \frac{3}{8}, \frac{1}{6}$

91. $\frac{4}{5}, \frac{4}{3}, \frac{4}{8}, \frac{4}{6}, \frac{4}{9}, \frac{4}{2}, -\frac{4}{3}$

Write a true sentence using either $<$, $>$, *or* $=$.

92. $|-5| \;\square\; |-2|$

93. $|4| \;\square\; |-7|$

94. $|-8| \;\square\; |8|$

95. $|23| \;\square\; |-23|$

96. $|-3| \;\square\; |5|$

Solve. Consider only integer replacements.

Aha! **97.** $|x| = 7$

98. $|x| < 3$

99. $2 < |x| < 5$

Given that $0.3\overline{3} = \frac{1}{3}$ *and* $0.6\overline{6} = \frac{2}{3}$, *express each of the following as a ratio of two integers.*

100. $0.1\overline{1}$

101. $0.9\overline{9}$

102. $5.5\overline{5}$

103. $7.7\overline{7}$

To the student and instructor: The calculator icon, ▦, is used to indicate those exercises designed to be solved with a calculator.

104. When Helga's calculator gives a decimal value for $\sqrt{2}$ and that value is promptly squared, the result is 2. Yet when that same decimal approximation is entered by hand and then squared, the result is not exactly 2. Why do you suppose this is?

105. Is the following statement true? Why or why not?

$$\sqrt{a^2} = |a| \quad \text{for any real number } a.$$

1.5 Addition of Real Numbers

Adding with a Number Line • Adding Without a Number Line • Problem Solving • Combining Like Terms

We now consider addition of real numbers. To gain understanding, we will use a number line first. After observing the principles involved, we will develop rules that allow us to work more quickly without a number line.

Adding with a Number Line

To add $a + b$ on a number line, we start at a and move according to b.

a) If b is positive, we move to the right (the positive direction).

b) If b is negative, we move to the left (the negative direction).

c) If b is 0, we stay at a.

EXAMPLE 1 Add: $-4 + 9$.

Solution To add on a number line, we locate the first number, -4, and then move 9 units to the right. Note that it requires 4 units to reach 0. The difference between 9 and 4 is where we finish.

$-4 + 9 = 5$

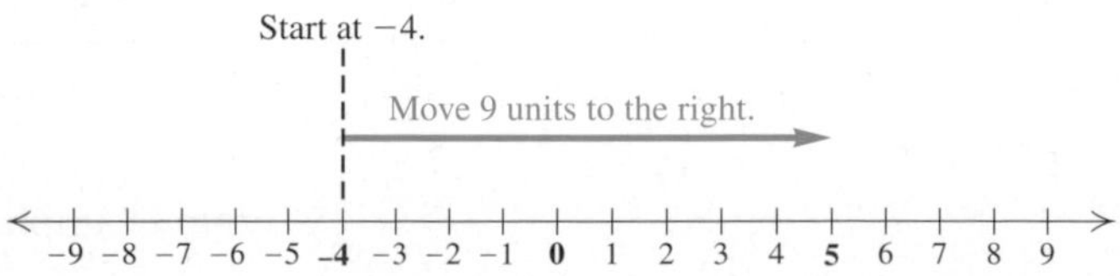

EXAMPLE 2 Add: $3 + (-5)$.

Student Notes

Parentheses are essential when a negative sign follows an operation. Just as we would never write $8 \div \times 2$, it is improper to write $3 + -5$.

Solution We locate the first number, 3, and then move 5 units to the left. Note that it requires 3 units to reach 0. The difference between 5 and 3 is 2, so we finish 2 units to the left of 0.

$$3 + (-5) = -2$$

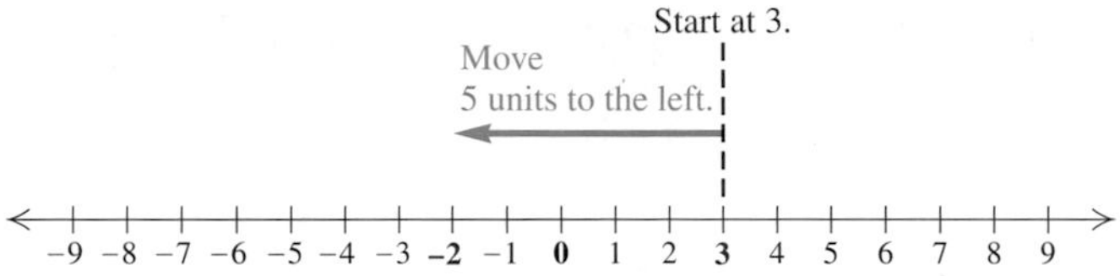

EXAMPLE 3 Add: $-4 + (-3)$.

Solution After locating -4, we move 3 units to the left. We finish a total of 7 units to the left of 0.

$$-4 + (-3) = -7$$

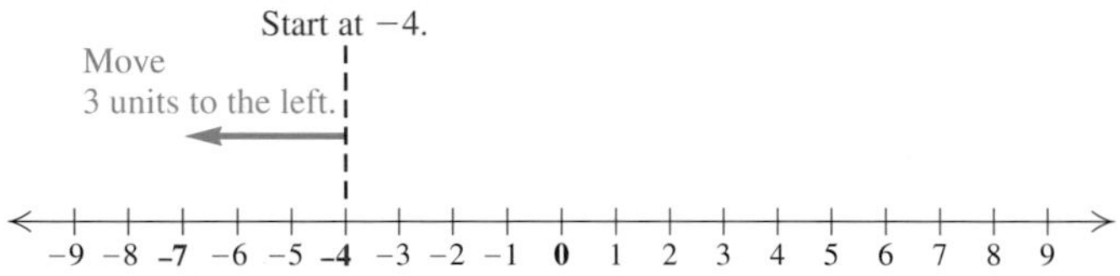

EXAMPLE 4 Add: $-5.2 + 0$.

Solution We locate -5.2 and move 0 units. Thus we finish where we started, at -5.2.

$$-5.2 + 0 = -5.2$$

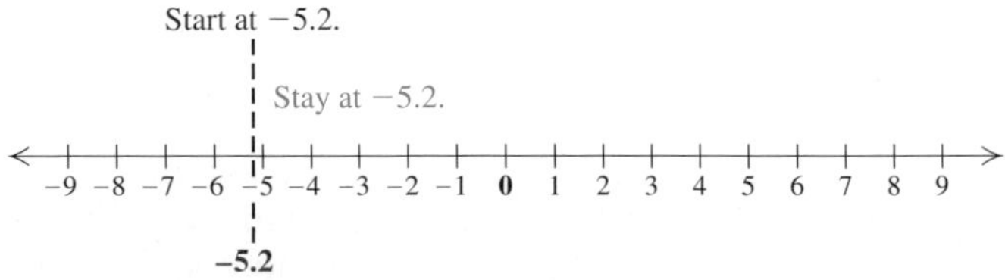

From Examples 1–4, the following rules emerge.

Rules for Addition of Real Numbers

1. *Positive numbers*: Add as usual. The answer is positive.
2. *Negative numbers*: Add absolute values and make the answer negative (see Example 3).
3. *A positive number and a negative number*: Subtract the smaller absolute value from the greater absolute value. Then:
   a) If the positive number has the greater absolute value, the answer is positive (see Example 1).
   b) If the negative number has the greater absolute value, the answer is negative (see Example 2).
   c) If the numbers have the same absolute value, the answer is 0.
4. *One number is zero*: The sum is the other number (see Example 4).

Rule 4 is known as the **identity property of 0**. It says that for any real number a, we have $a + 0 = a$.

Adding Without a Number Line

The rules listed above can be used without drawing a number line.

EXAMPLE 5 Add without using a number line.

a) $-12 + (-7)$ **b)** $-1.4 + 8.5$

c) $-36 + 21$ **d)** $1.5 + (-1.5)$

e) $-\frac{7}{8} + 0$ **f)** $\frac{2}{3} + \left(-\frac{5}{8}\right)$

Solution

a) $-12 + (-7) = -19$ Two negatives. *Think:* Add the absolute values, 12 and 7, to get 19. Make the answer *negative*, -19.

b) $-1.4 + 8.5 = 7.1$ A negative and a positive. *Think:* The difference of absolute values is $8.5 - 1.4$, or 7.1. The positive number has the larger absolute value, so the answer is *positive*, 7.1.

c) $-36 + 21 = -15$ A negative and a positive. *Think:* The difference of absolute values is $36 - 21$, or 15. The negative number has the larger absolute value, so the answer is *negative*, -15.

d) $1.5 + (-1.5) = 0$ A negative and a positive. *Think:* Since the numbers are opposites, they have the same absolute value and the answer is 0.

e) $-\frac{7}{8} + 0 = -\frac{7}{8}$ One number is zero. The sum is the other number, $-\frac{7}{8}$.

Study Skills

Two (or More) Heads Are Better Than One

Consider forming a study group with some of your fellow students. Exchange telephone numbers, schedules, and any e-mail addresses so that you can coordinate study time for homework and tests.

f) $\frac{2}{3} + \left(-\frac{5}{8}\right) = \frac{16}{24} + \left(-\frac{15}{24}\right)$ This is similar to part (b) above. We find a common denominator and then add.

$= \frac{1}{24}$

If we are adding several numbers, some positive and some negative, the commutative and associative laws allow us to add all the positives, then add all the negatives, and then add the results. Of course, we can also add from left to right, if we prefer.

EXAMPLE 6 Add: $15 + (-2) + 7 + 14 + (-5) + (-12)$.

Solution

$15 + (-2) + 7 + 14 + (-5) + (-12)$

$= 15 + 7 + 14 + (-2) + (-5) + (-12)$ Using the commutative law of addition

$= (15 + 7 + 14) + [(-2) + (-5) + (-12)]$ Using the associative law of addition

$= 36 + (-19)$ Adding the positives; adding the negatives

$= 17$ Adding a positive and a negative

Problem Solving

Addition of real numbers occurs in many real-world applications.

EXAMPLE 7 Lake level. Between early June 2001 through the first week of June 2003, the south end of the Great Salt Lake dropped $2\frac{1}{4}$ ft, rose $\frac{3}{4}$ ft, and dropped 2 ft (*Source*: U.S. Geological Survey). By how much did the level change over 2 yr?

Solution The problem translates to a sum:

Rewording: The 1st change plus the 2nd change plus the 3rd change is the total change.

Translating: $-2\frac{1}{4} \quad + \quad \frac{3}{4} \quad + \quad (-2) \quad = \text{Total change.}$

Adding from left to right, we have

$$-2\frac{1}{4} + \frac{3}{4} + (-2) = -\frac{9}{4} + \frac{3}{4} + (-2) = -\frac{6}{4} + (-2) = -1\frac{1}{2} + (-2) = -3\frac{1}{2}.$$

The lake level dropped $3\frac{1}{2}$ ft between early June 2001 and the first week of June 2003.

Combining Like Terms

When two terms have variable factors that are exactly the same, like $5ab$ and $7ab$, the terms are called **like**, or **similar, terms**.* The distributive law enables us to **combine**, or **collect, like terms**. The above rules for addition will again apply.

EXAMPLE 8 Combine like terms.

a) $-7x + 9x$

b) $2a + (-3b) + (-5a) + 9b$

c) $6 + y + (-3.5y) + 2$

Solution

a) $-7x + 9x = (-7 + 9)x$ Using the distributive law
$= 2x$ Adding -7 and 9

b) $2a + (-3b) + (-5a) + 9b$
$= 2a + (-5a) + (-3b) + 9b$ Using the commutative law of addition
$= (2 + (-5))a + (-3 + 9)b$ Using the distributive law
$= -3a + 6b$ Adding

c) $6 + y + (-3.5y) + 2 = y + (-3.5y) + 6 + 2$ Using the commutative law of addition
$= (1 + (-3.5))y + 6 + 2$ Using the distributive law
$= -2.5y + 8$ Adding

With practice we can leave out some steps, combining like terms mentally. Note that numbers like 6 and 2 in the expression $6 + y + (-3.5y) + 2$ are constants and are also considered to be like terms.

*Like terms are discussed in greater detail in Section 1.8.

1.5 Exercise Set

FOR EXTRA HELP

Student's Solutions Manual | Digital Video Tutor CD 1 Videotape 2 | AW Math Tutor Center | MathXL Tutorials on CD | MathXL | MyMathLab

Concept Reinforcement *In each of Exercises 1–6, match the term with a like term from the column on the right.*

1. ____ $8n$ **a)** $-3z$

2. ____ $7m$ **b)** $5x$

3. ____ 43 **c)** $2t$

4. ____ $28z$ **d)** $-4m$

5. ____ $-2x$ **e)** 9

6. ____ $-9t$ **f)** $-3n$

Add using a number line.

7. $5 + (-8)$ **8.** $2 + (-5)$

9. $-5 + 9$ **10.** $-3 + 8$

11. $8 + (-8)$ **12.** $6 + (-6)$

13. $-3 + (-5)$ **14.** $-4 + (-6)$

Add. Do not use a number line except as a check.

15. $-27 + 0$ **16.** $-6 + 0$

17. $0 + (-8)$ **18.** $0 + (-2)$

19. $12 + (-12)$ **20.** $17 + (-17)$

21. $-24 + (-17)$ **22.** $-17 + (-25)$

23. $-13 + 13$ **24.** $-18 + 18$

25. $18 + (-11)$ **26.** $8 + (-5)$

27. $10 + (-12)$ **28.** $9 + (-13)$

29. $-3 + 14$ **30.** $13 + (-6)$

31. $-14 + (-19)$ **32.** $11 + (-9)$

33. $19 + (-19)$ **34.** $-20 + (-6)$

35. $23 + (-5)$ **36.** $-15 + (-7)$

37. $-31 + (-14)$ **38.** $40 + (-8)$

39. $40 + (-40)$ **40.** $-25 + 25$

41. $85 + (-65)$ **42.** $63 + (-18)$

43. $-3.6 + 1.9$ **44.** $-6.5 + 4.7$

45. $-5.4 + (-3.7)$ **46.** $-3.8 + (-9.4)$

47. $\frac{-3}{5} + \frac{4}{5}$ **48.** $\frac{-2}{7} + \frac{3}{7}$

49. $\frac{-4}{7} + \frac{-2}{7}$ **50.** $\frac{-5}{9} + \frac{-2}{9}$

51. $-\frac{2}{5} + \frac{1}{3}$ **52.** $-\frac{4}{13} + \frac{1}{2}$

53. $\frac{-4}{9} + \frac{2}{3}$ **54.** $\frac{-1}{6} + \frac{1}{3}$

55. $35 + (-14) + (-19) + (-5)$

56. $28 + (-44) + 17 + 31 + (-94)$

Aha! **57.** $-4.9 + 8.5 + 4.9 + (-8.5)$

58. $24 + 3.1 + (-44) + (-8.2) + 63$

Solve. Write your answer as a complete sentence.

59. *Gas prices.* In a recent year, the price of a gallon of 87-octane gasoline was \$1.69. The price then rose 5¢, dropped 3¢, and then rose 7¢. By how much did the price change during that period?

60. *Oil prices.* In a recent year, the price of a gallon of home heating oil was \$1.28. The price then rose 6¢, dropped 2¢, and then rose 5¢. By how much did the price change during that period?

61. *Telephone bills.* Maya's cell-phone bill for July was \$82. She sent a check for \$50 and then ran up \$63 in charges for August. What was her new balance?

62. *Profits and losses.* The following table shows the profits and losses of Fitness City over a 3-yr period. Find the profit or loss after this period of time.

Year	*Profit or loss*
2002	−\$26,500
2003	−\$10,200
2004	+\$32,400

63. *Yardage gained.* In an intramural football game, the quarterback attempted passes with the following results.

First try	13-yd gain
Second try	12-yd loss
Third try	21-yd gain

Find the total gain (or loss).

64. *Account balance.* Leah has \$350 in a checking account. She writes a check for \$530, makes a deposit of \$75, and then writes a check for \$90. What is the balance in the account?

65. *Credit-card bills.* Lyle's credit-card bill indicates that he owes \$470. He sends a check to the credit-card company for \$45, charges another \$160 in merchandise, and then pays off another \$500 of his bill. What is Lyle's new balance?

66. *Stock growth.* In the course of one day, the value of a share of America Online rose \$0.82, fell \$0.90, and then rose \$0.25. How much had the stock's value risen or fallen at the end of the day?

67. *Peak elevation.* The tallest mountain in the world, as measured from base to peak, is Mauna Kea in Hawaii. From a base 19,684 ft below sea level, it rises 33,480 ft. What is the elevation of its peak?
Source: *The Guinness Book of Records*, 1999

68. *Class size.* During the first two weeks of the semester, 5 students withdrew from Elisa's algebra class, 8 students were added to the class, and 6 students were dropped as "no-shows." By how many students did the original class size change?

Combine like terms.

69. $8a + 6a$

70. $3x + 8x$

71. $-3x + 12x$

72. $2m + (-7m)$

73. $5t + 8t$

74. $5a + 8a$

75. $7m + (-9m)$

76. $-4x + 4x$

77. $-5a + (-2a)$

78. $10n + (-17n)$

79. $-3 + 8x + 4 + (-10x)$

80. $8a + 5 + (-a) + (-3)$

Find the perimeter of each figure.

81.

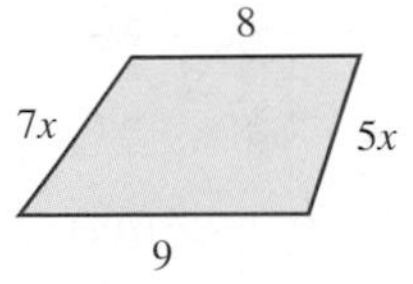

82.

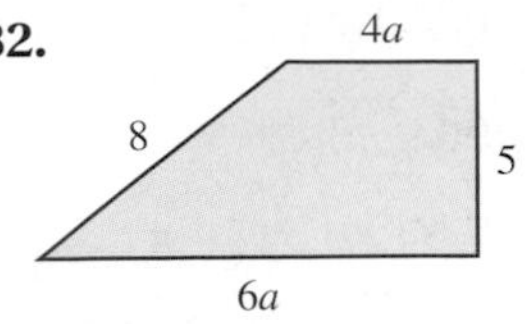

83.

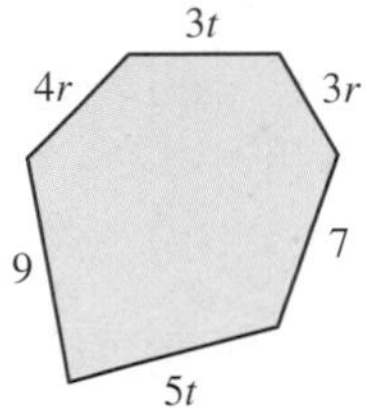

84.

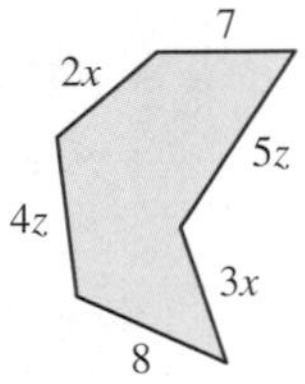

85.

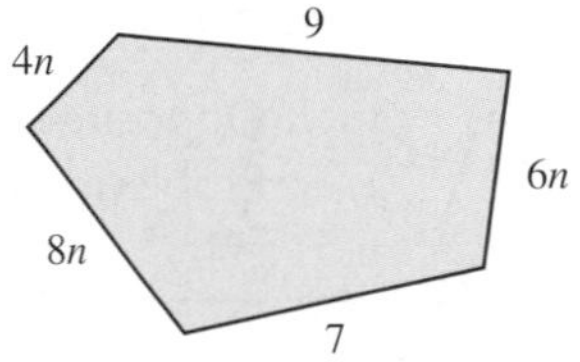

86.

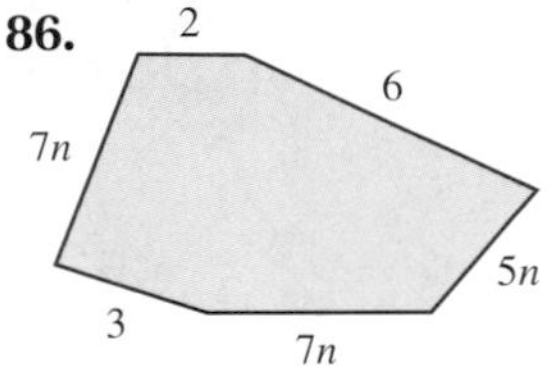

87. Explain in your own words why the sum of two negative numbers is negative.

88. Without performing the actual addition, explain why the sum of all integers from -10 to 10 is 0.

SKILL MAINTENANCE

89. Multiply: $7(3z + y + 2)$. [1.2]

90. Divide and simplify: $\frac{7}{2} \div \frac{3}{8}$. [1.3]

SYNTHESIS

91. Under what circumstances will the sum of one positive number and several negative numbers be positive?

92. Is it possible to add real numbers without knowing how to calculate $a - b$ with a and b both nonnegative and $a \geq b$? Why or why not?

93. *Stock prices.* The value of EKB stock rose \$2.38 and then dropped \$3.25 before finishing at \$64.38. What was the stock's original value?

94. *Sports-card values.* The value of a sports card dropped \$12 and then rose \$17.50 before settling at \$61. What was the original value of the card?

Find the missing term or terms.

95. $4x + \underline{\qquad} + (-9x) + (-2y) = -5x - 7y$

96. $-3a + 9b + \underline{\qquad} + 5a = 2a - 6b$

97. $3m + 2n + \underline{\qquad} + (-2m) = 2n + (-6m)$

98. $\underline{\qquad} + 9x + (-4y) + x = 10x - 7y$

Aha! **99.** $7t + 23 + \underline{\qquad} + \underline{\qquad} = 0$

100. *Geometry.* The perimeter of a rectangle is $7x + 10$. If the length of the rectangle is 5, express the width in terms of x.

101. *Golfing.* After five rounds of golf, a golf pro was 3 under par twice, 2 over par once, 2 under par once, and 1 over par once. On average, how far above or below par was the golfer?

1.6 Subtraction of Real Numbers

Opposites and Additive Inverses • Subtraction • Problem Solving

In arithmetic, when a number b is subtracted from another number a, the difference, $a - b$, is the number that when added to b gives a. For example, $45 - 17 = 28$ because $28 + 17 = 45$. We will use this approach to develop an efficient way of finding the value of $a - b$ for any real numbers a and b. Before doing so, however, we must develop some terminology.

Opposites and Additive Inverses

Numbers such as 6 and -6 are *opposites,* or *additive inverses,* of each other. Whenever opposites are added, the result is 0; and whenever two numbers add to 0, those numbers are opposites.

EXAMPLE 1 Find the opposite of each number: **(a)** 34; **(b)** -8.3; **(c)** 0.

Solution

a) The opposite of 34 is -34: $34 + (-34) = 0.$

b) The opposite of -8.3 is 8.3: $-8.3 + 8.3 = 0.$

c) The opposite of 0 is 0: $0 + 0 = 0.$

To write the opposite, we use the symbol $-$, as follows.

Opposite

The *opposite,* or *additive inverse,* of a number a is written $-a$ (read "the opposite of a" or "the additive inverse of a").

Note that if we take a number, say 8, and find its opposite, -8, and then find the opposite of the result, we will have the original number, 8, again.

> *The Opposite of an Opposite*
>
> For any real number a,
>
> $$-(-a) = a.$$
>
> (The opposite of the opposite of a is a.)

EXAMPLE 2 Find $-x$ and $-(-x)$ when $x = 16$.

Solution

If $x = 16$, then $-x = -16$. The opposite of 16 is -16.

If $x = 16$, then $-(-x) = -(-16) = 16$. The opposite of the opposite of 16 is 16.

EXAMPLE 3 Find $-x$ and $-(-x)$ when $x = -3$.

Solution

If $x = -3$, then $-x = -(-3) = 3$. The opposite of -3 is 3.

If $x = -3$, then $-(-x) = -(-(-3)) = -(\ 3\ ) = -3$.

Student Notes

As you read mathematics, it is important to verbalize correctly the words and symbols to yourself. Consistently reading the expression $-x$ as "the opposite of x" is a good step in this direction.

Note in Example 3 that an extra set of parentheses is used to show that we are substituting the negative number -3 for x. The notation $- \ -x$ is not used.

A symbol such as -8 is usually read "negative 8." It could be read "the additive inverse of 8," because the additive inverse of 8 is negative 8. It could also be read "the opposite of 8," because the opposite of 8 is -8.

A symbol like $-x$, which has a variable, should be read "the opposite of x" or "the additive inverse of x" and *not* "negative x," since to do so suggests that $-x$ represents a negative number.

The symbol "$-$" is read differently depending on where it appears. For example, $-5 - (-x)$ is read "negative five minus the opposite of x."

EXAMPLE 4 Write each of the following in words.

a) $2 - 8$ **b)** $5 - (-4)$ **c)** $6 - (-x)$

Solution

a) $2 - 8$ is read "two minus eight."

b) $5 - (-4)$ is read "five minus negative four."

c) $6 - (-x)$ is read "six minus the opposite of x."

As we saw in Example 3, $-x$ can represent a positive number. This notation can be used to restate a result from Section 1.5 as *the law of opposites*:

The Law of Opposites

For any two numbers a and $-a$,

$$a + (-a) = 0.$$

(When opposites are added, their sum is 0.)

A negative number is said to have a "negative *sign*." A positive number is said to have a "positive *sign*." If we change a number to its opposite, or additive inverse, we say that we have "changed or reversed its sign."

EXAMPLE 5 Change the sign (find the opposite) of each number: **(a)** -3; **(b)** -10; **(c)** 14.

Solution

a) When we change the sign of -3, we obtain 3.

b) When we change the sign of -10, we obtain 10.

c) When we change the sign of 14, we obtain -14.

Subtraction

Opposites are helpful when subtraction involves negative numbers. To see why, look for a pattern in the following:

Subtracting		*Adding the Opposite*
$9 - 5 = 4$	since $4 + 5 = 9$	$9 + (-5) = 4$
$5 - 8 = -3$	since $-3 + 8 = 5$	$5 + (-8) = -3$
$-6 - 4 = -10$	since $-10 + 4 = -6$	$-6 + (-4) = -10$
$-7 - (-10) = 3$	since $3 + (-10) = -7$	$-7 + 10 = 3$
$-7 - (-2) = -5$	since $-5 + (-2) = -7$	$-7 + 2 = -5$

The matching results suggest that we can subtract by adding the opposite of the number being subtracted. This can always be done and often provides the easiest way to subtract real numbers.

Subtraction of Real Numbers

For any real numbers a and b,

$$a - b = a + (-b).$$

(To subtract, add the opposite, or additive inverse, of the number being subtracted.)

EXAMPLE 6 Subtract each of the following and then check with addition.

a) $2 - 6$ **b)** $4 - (-9)$ **c)** $-4.2 - (-3.6)$
d) $-1.8 - (-7.5)$ **e)** $\frac{1}{5} - \left(-\frac{3}{5}\right)$

Solution

a) $2 - 6 = 2 + (-6) = -4$ The opposite of 6 is -6. We change the subtraction to addition and add the opposite. *Check*: $-4 + 6 = 2$.

b) $4 - (-9) = 4 + 9 = 13$ The opposite of -9 is 9. We change the subtraction to addition and add the opposite. *Check*: $13 + (-9) = 4$.

c) $-4.2 - (-3.6) = -4.2 + 3.6$ Adding the opposite of -3.6. *Check*: $-0.6 + (-3.6) = -4.2$.
$= -0.6$

d) $-1.8 - (-7.5) = -1.8 + 7.5$ Adding the opposite
$= 5.7$ *Check*: $5.7 + (-7.5) = -1.8$.

e) $\frac{1}{5} - \left(-\frac{3}{5}\right) = \frac{1}{5} + \frac{3}{5}$ Adding the opposite

$= \frac{1 + 3}{5}$ A common denominator exists so we add in the numerator.

$= \frac{4}{5}$

Check: $\frac{4}{5} + \left(-\frac{3}{5}\right) = \frac{4}{5} + \frac{-3}{5} = \frac{4 + (-3)}{5} = \frac{1}{5}$.

technology connection

On nearly all graphing calculators, it is essential to distinguish between the key for negation and the key for subtraction. To enter a negative number, we use (–) and to subtract, we use –. This said, be careful not to rely on a calculator for computations that you will be expected to do by hand.

EXAMPLE 7 Simplify: $8 - (-4) - 2 - (-5) + 3$.

Solution

$$8 - (-4) - 2 - (-5) + 3 = 8 + 4 + (-2) + 5 + 3$$ To subtract, we add the opposite.
$$= 18$$

Recall from Section 1.2 that the terms of an algebraic expression are separated by plus signs. This means that the terms of $5x - 7y - 9$ are $5x$, $-7y$, and -9, since $5x - 7y - 9 = 5x + (-7y) + (-9)$.

EXAMPLE 8 Identify the terms of $4 - 2ab + 7a - 9$.

Solution We have

$$4 - 2ab + 7a - 9 = 4 + (-2ab) + 7a + (-9),$$ Rewriting as addition

so the terms are 4, $-2ab$, $7a$, and -9.

EXAMPLE 9 Combine like terms.

a) $1 + 3x - 7x$

b) $-5a - 7b - 4a + 10b$

c) $4 - 3m - 9 + 7m$

Study Skills

Indicate the Highlights

Most students find it helpful to draw a star or use a color, felt-tipped highlighter to indicate important concepts or trouble spots that require further study. Most campus bookstores carry a variety of highlighters that permit you to brightly color written material while keeping it easy to read.

Solution

a) $1 + 3x - 7x = 1 + 3x + (-7x)$ Adding the opposite

$= 1 + (3 + (-7))x$
$= 1 + (-4)x$ Using the distributive law. Try to do this mentally.

$= 1 - 4x$ Rewriting as subtraction to be more concise

b) $-5a - 7b - 4a + 10b = -5a + (-7b) + (-4a) + 10b$ Adding the opposite

$= -5a + (-4a) + (-7b) + 10b$ Using the commutative law of addition

$= -9a + 3b$ Combining like terms mentally

c) $4 - 3m - 9 + 7m = 4 + (-3m) + (-9) + 7m$ Rewriting as addition

$= 4 + (-9) + (-3m) + 7m$ Using the commutative law of addition

$= -5 + 4m$

Problem Solving

We use subtraction to solve problems involving differences. These include problems that ask "How much more?" or "How much higher?"

EXAMPLE 10 Temperature extremes. The highest temperature ever recorded in the United States is 134°F in Greenland Ranch, California, on July 10, 1913. The lowest temperature ever recorded is −80°F in Prospect Creek, Alaska, on January 23, 1971. (*Source*: National Oceanographic and Atmospheric Administration) How much higher was the temperature in Greenland Ranch than that in Prospect Creek?

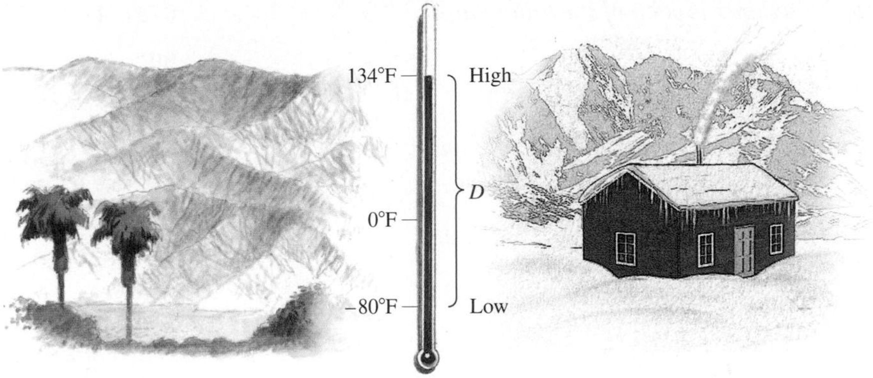

Solution To find the difference between two temperatures, we always subtract the lower temperature from the higher temperature:

$$\underbrace{\text{Higher temperature}}_{134} - \underbrace{\text{Lower temperature}}_{(-80)}$$

$$= 134 + 80$$

$$= 214.$$

The temperature in Greenland Ranch was 214°F higher than the temperature in Prospect Creek.

1.6 Exercise Set

FOR EXTRA HELP

Student's Solutions Manual | Digital Video Tutor CD 1 Videotape 2 | AW Math Tutor Center | MathXL Tutorials on CD | MathXL | MyMathLab

Concept Reinforcement *In each of Exercises 1–8, match the expression with the appropriate wording from the column on the right.*

1. ____ $-x$	**a)** x minus negative twelve
2. ____ $12 - x$	**b)** The opposite of x minus x
3. ____ $12 - (-x)$	**c)** The opposite of x minus twelve
4. ____ $x - 12$	**d)** The opposite of x
5. ____ $x - (-12)$	**e)** The opposite of x minus negative twelve
6. ____ $-x - 12$	**f)** Twelve minus the opposite of x
7. ____ $-x - x$	**g)** Twelve minus x
8. ____ $-x - (-12)$	**h)** x minus twelve

Write each of the following in words.

9. $4 - 10$

10. $5 - 13$

11. $2 - (-9)$

12. $4 - (-1)$

13. $9 - (-t)$

14. $8 - (-m)$

15. $-x - y$

16. $-a - b$

17. $-3 - (-n)$

18. $-7 - (-m)$

Find the opposite, or additive inverse.

19. 39

20. -17

21. -9

22. $\frac{7}{2}$

23. -3.14

24. 48.2

Find $-x$ when x is each of the following.

25. 23 **26.** -26 **27.** $-\frac{14}{3}$

28. $\frac{1}{328}$ **29.** 0.101 **30.** 0

Find $-(-x)$ when x is each of the following.

31. 72 **32.** 29

33. $-\frac{2}{5}$ **34.** -9.1

Change the sign. (Find the opposite.)

35. -1 **36.** -7

37. 7 **38.** 10

Subtract.

39. $6 - 8$ **40.** $4 - 13$

41. $0 - 5$ **42.** $0 - 8$

43. $3 - 9$ **44.** $3 - 13$

45. $0 - 10$ **46.** $0 - 7$

47. $-9 - (-3)$ **48.** $-9 - (-5)$

Aha! **49.** $-8 - (-8)$ **50.** $-10 - (-10)$

51. $14 - 19$ **52.** $12 - 16$

53. $30 - 40$ **54.** $20 - 27$

55. $-7 - (-9)$ **56.** $-8 - (-3)$

57. $-9 - (-9)$ **58.** $-40 - (-40)$

59. $5 - 5$ **60.** $7 - 7$

61. $4 - (-4)$ **62.** $6 - (-6)$

63. $-7 - 4$ **64.** $-6 - 8$

65. $6 - (-10)$ **66.** $3 - (-12)$

67. $-4 - 15$ **68.** $-14 - 2$

69. $-6 - (-5)$ **70.** $-4 - (-3)$

71. $5 - (-12)$ **72.** $5 - (-6)$

73. $0 - 5$ **74.** $0 - 6$

75. $-5 - (-2)$ **76.** $-3 - (-1)$

77. $-7 - 14$ **78.** $-9 - 16$

79. $0 - (-5)$ **80.** $0 - (-1)$

81. $-8 - 0$ **82.** $-9 - 0$

83. $3 - (-7)$ **84.** $12 - (-5)$

85. $2 - 25$ **86.** $18 - 63$

87. $-42 - 26$ **88.** $-18 - 63$

89. $-51 - 7$ **90.** $-45 - 4$

91. $3.2 - 8.7$ **92.** $1.5 - 9.4$

93. $0.072 - 1$ **94.** $0.825 - 1$

95. $\frac{2}{11} - \frac{9}{11}$ **96.** $\frac{3}{7} - \frac{5}{7}$

97. $\frac{-1}{5} - \frac{3}{5}$ **98.** $\frac{-2}{9} - \frac{5}{9}$

99. $-\frac{4}{17} - \left(-\frac{9}{17}\right)$ **100.** $-\frac{2}{13} - \left(-\frac{5}{13}\right)$

In each of Exercises 101–104, translate the phrase to mathematical language and simplify. See Example 10.

101. The difference between 3.8 and -5.2

102. The difference between -2.1 and -5.9

103. The difference between 114 and -79

104. The difference between 23 and -17

105. Subtract 37 from -21.

106. Subtract 19 from -7.

107. Subtract -25 from 9.

108. Subtract -31 from -5.

Simplify.

109. $25 - (-12) - 7 - (-2) + 9$

110. $22 - (-18) + 7 + (-42) - 27$

111. $-31 + (-28) - (-14) - 17$

112. $-43 - (-19) - (-21) + 25$

113. $-34 - 28 + (-33) - 44$

114. $39 + (-88) - 29 - (-83)$

Aha! **115.** $-93 + (-84) - (-93) - (-84)$

116. $84 + (-99) + 44 - (-18) - 43$

Identify the terms in each expression.

117. $-7x - 4y$

118. $7a - 9b$

119. $9 - 5t - 3st$

120. $-4 - 3x + 2xy$

Combine like terms.

121. $4x - 7x$

122. $3a - 14a$

123. $7a - 12a + 4$

124. $-9x - 13x + 7$

125. $-8n - 9 + n$

126. $-7 + 9n - 8$

127. $3x + 5 - 9x$

128. $2 + 3a - 7$

129. $2 - 6t - 9 - 2t$

130. $-5 + 3b - 7 - 5b$

131. $5y + (-3x) - 9x + 1 - 2y + 8$

132. $14 - (-5x) + 2z - (-32) + 4z - 2x$

133. $13x - (-2x) + 45 - (-21) - 7x$

134. $8x - (-2x) - 14 - (-5x) + 53 - 9x$

Solve.

135. *Changes in temperature.* The Viking 2 Lander spacecraft has determined that temperatures on Mars range from $-125°$ Celsius (C) to 25°C. Find the temperature range on Mars.
Source: The Lunar and Planetary Institute

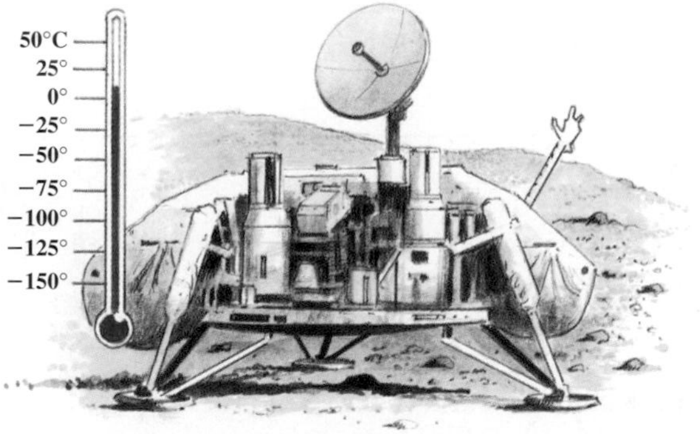

136. *Record temperature drop.* The greatest recorded temperature change in one day occurred in Browning, Montana, when the temperature fell from 44°F to -56°F. How much did the temperature drop?
Source: *The Guinness Book of Records*, 1999

137. *Elevation extremes.* The lowest elevation in Asia, the Dead Sea, is 1349 ft below sea level. The highest elevation in Asia, Mount Everest, is 29,035 ft. Find the difference in elevation.
Source: *Time Almanac* 2004

138. *Elevation extremes.* The elevation of Mount Whitney, the highest peak in California, is 14,776 ft more than the elevation of Death Valley, California. If Death Valley is 282 ft below sea level, find the elevation of Mount Whitney.
Source: 1999 *Information Please Almanac*

139. *Changes in elevation.* The lowest point in Africa is Lake Assal, which is 156 m below sea level. The lowest point in South America is the Valdes Peninsula, which is 40 m below sea level. How much lower is Lake Assal than the Valdes Peninsula?

140. *Underwater elevation.* The deepest point in the Pacific Ocean is the Marianas Trench, with a depth of 10,415 m. The deepest point in the Atlantic Ocean is the Puerto Rico Trench, with a depth of 8648 m. What is the difference in elevation of the two trenches?

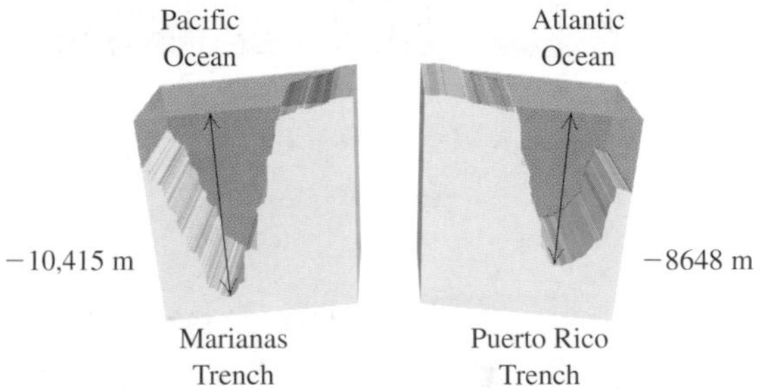

141. Jeremy insists that if you can *add* real numbers, then you can also *subtract* real numbers. Do you agree? Why or why not?

142. Are the expressions $-a + b$ and $a + (-b)$ opposites of each other? Why or why not?

SKILL MAINTENANCE

143. Find the area of a rectangle when the length is 36 ft and the width is 12 ft. [1.1]

144. Find the prime factorization of 864. [1.3]

SYNTHESIS

145. Why might it be advantageous to rewrite a long series of additions and subtractions as all additions?

146. If a and b are both negative, under what circumstances will $a - b$ be negative?

147. *Power outages.* During the Northeast's electrical blackout of August 14, 2003, residents of Bloomfield, New Jersey, lost power at 4:00 P.M. One resident returned from vacation at 3:00 P.M. the following day to find the clocks in her apartment reading 8:00 A.M. At what time, and on what day, was power restored?

Tell whether each statement is true or false for all real numbers m and n. Use various replacements for m and n to support your answer.

148. If $m > n$, then $m - n > 0$.

149. If $m > n$, then $m + n > 0$.

150. If m and n are opposites, then $m - n = 0$.

151. If $m = -n$, then $m + n = 0$.

152. A gambler loses a wager and then loses "double or nothing" (meaning the gambler owes twice as much) twice more. After the three losses, the gambler's assets are $-\$20$. Explain how much the gambler originally bet and how the $20 debt occurred.

153. List the keystrokes needed to compute $-9 - (-7)$.

154. If n is positive and m is negative, what is the sign of $n + (-m)$? Why?

1.7 Multiplication and Division of Real Numbers

Multiplication • Division

We now develop rules for multiplication and division of real numbers. Because multiplication and division are closely related, the rules are quite similar.

Multiplication

We already know how to multiply two nonnegative numbers. To see how to multiply a positive number and a negative number, consider the following pattern in which multiplication is regarded as repeated addition:

This number → (decreases by 1 each time.)

$$\begin{aligned} 4(-5) &= (-5) + (-5) + (-5) + (-5) = -20 \\ 3(-5) &= (-5) + (-5) + (-5) = -15 \\ 2(-5) &= (-5) + (-5) = -10 \\ 1(-5) &= (-5) = -5 \\ 0(-5) &= 0 = 0 \end{aligned}$$

← This number increases by 5 each time.

This pattern illustrates that the product of a negative number and a positive number is negative.

The Product of a Negative Number and a Positive Number

To multiply a positive number and a negative number, multiply their absolute values. The answer is negative.

EXAMPLE 1 Multiply: **(a)** $8(-5)$; **(b)** $-\frac{1}{3} \cdot \frac{5}{7}$.

Solution

a) $8(-5) = -40$ *Think*: $8 \cdot 5 = 40$; make the answer negative.

b) $-\frac{1}{3} \cdot \frac{5}{7} = -\frac{5}{21}$ *Think*: $\frac{1}{3} \cdot \frac{5}{7} = \frac{5}{21}$; make the answer negative.

Study Skills

Help Is Just a Phone Call Away

The Addison-Wesley Tutor Center provides tutoring to students using this text. Assisted by qualified mathematics instructors via telephone, fax, e-mail, or Internet, you can receive live tutoring on examples and odd-numbered exercises. This valuable resource provides you with immediate assistance when additional instruction is needed.

The pattern developed above includes not just products of positive and negative numbers, but a product involving zero as well.

The Multiplicative Property of Zero

For any real number a,

$$0 \cdot a = a \cdot 0 = 0.$$

(The product of 0 and any real number is 0.)

EXAMPLE 2 Multiply: $173(-452)0$.

Solution We have

$173(-452)0 = 173[(-452)0]$	Using the associative law of multiplication
$= 173[0]$	Using the multiplicative property of zero
$= 0.$	Using the multiplicative property of zero again

Note that whenever 0 appears as a factor, the product is 0.

We can extend the above pattern still further to examine the product of two negative numbers.

This number → decreases by 1 each time.	$2(-5) =$	$(-5) + (-5) = -10$	← This number increases by 5 each time.
	$1(-5) =$	$(-5) = -5$	
	$0(-5) =$	$0 = 0$	
	$-1(-5) =$	$-(-5) = 5$	
	$-2(-5) =$	$-(-5) - (-5) = 10$	

According to the pattern, the product of two negative numbers is positive.

The Product of Two Negative Numbers

To multiply two negative numbers, multiply their absolute values. The answer is positive.

EXAMPLE 3 Multiply: **(a)** $(-6)(-8)$; **(b)** $(-1.2)(-3)$.

Solution

a) The absolute value of -6 is 6 and the absolute value of -8 is 8. Thus,

$(-6)(-8) = 6 \cdot 8$ Multiplying absolute values. The answer is positive.

$= 48.$

b) $(-1.2)(-3) = (1.2)(3)$ Multiplying absolute values. The answer is positive.

$= 3.6$ Try to go directly to this step.

When three or more numbers are multiplied, we can order and group the numbers as we please, because of the commutative and associative laws.

EXAMPLE 4 Multiply: **(a)** $-3(-2)(-5)$; **(b)** $-4(-6)(-1)(-2)$.

Solution

a) $-3(-2)(-5) = 6(-5)$ Multiplying the first two numbers. The product of two negatives is positive.

$= -30$ The product of a positive and a negative is negative.

b) $-4(-6)(-1)(-2) = 24 \cdot 2$ Multiplying the first two numbers and the last two numbers

$= 48$

We can see the following pattern in the results of Example 4.

The product of an even number of negative numbers is positive.

The product of an odd number of negative numbers is negative.

Division

Recall that $a \div b$, or $\frac{a}{b}$, is the number, if one exists, that when multiplied by b gives a. For example, to show that $10 \div 2$ is 5, we need only note that $5 \cdot 2 = 10$. Thus division can always be checked with multiplication.

EXAMPLE 5 Divide, if possible, and check your answer.

a) $14 \div (-7)$

b) $\dfrac{-32}{-4}$

c) $\dfrac{-10}{9}$

d) $\dfrac{-17}{0}$

Solution

a) $14 \div (-7) = -2$ — We look for a number that when multiplied by -7 gives 14. That number is -2. *Check*: $(-2)(-7) = 14$.

b) $\dfrac{-32}{-4} = 8$ — We look for a number that when multiplied by -4 gives -32. That number is 8. *Check*: $8(-4) = -32$.

c) $\dfrac{-10}{9} = -\dfrac{10}{9}$ — We look for a number that when multiplied by 9 gives -10. That number is $-\frac{10}{9}$. *Check*: $-\frac{10}{9} \cdot 9 = -10$.

d) $\dfrac{-17}{0}$ is **undefined.** — We look for a number that when multiplied by 0 gives -17. There is no such number because if 0 is a factor, the product is 0, not -17.

Student Notes

Try to regard "undefined" as a mathematical way of saying "we do not give any meaning to this expression."

The sign rules for division are the same as those for multiplication: The quotient of a positive number and a negative number is negative; the quotient of two negative numbers is positive.

Rules for Multiplication and Division

To multiply or divide two nonzero real numbers:

1. Using the absolute values, multiply or divide, as indicated.
2. If the signs are the same, the answer is positive.
3. If the signs are different, the answer is negative.

Had Example 5(a) been written as $-14 \div 7$ or $-\frac{14}{7}$, rather than $14 \div (-7)$, the result would still have been -2. Thus from Examples 5(a)–5(c), we have the following:

$$\frac{-a}{b} = \frac{a}{-b} = -\frac{a}{b} \quad \text{and} \quad \frac{-a}{-b} = \frac{a}{b}.$$

EXAMPLE 6 Rewrite each of the following in two equivalent forms: **(a)** $\frac{5}{-2}$; **(b)** $-\frac{3}{10}$.

Solution We use one of the properties just listed.

a) $\frac{5}{-2} = \frac{-5}{2}$ and $\frac{5}{-2} = -\frac{5}{2}$

b) $-\frac{3}{10} = \frac{-3}{10}$ and $-\frac{3}{10} = \frac{3}{-10}$

Since $\frac{-a}{b} = \frac{a}{-b} = -\frac{a}{b}$

When a fraction contains a negative sign, it can be helpful to rewrite (or simply visualize) the fraction in an equivalent form.

EXAMPLE 7 Perform the indicated operation: **(a)** $\left(-\frac{4}{5}\right)\left(\frac{-7}{3}\right)$; **(b)** $-\frac{2}{7} + \frac{9}{-7}$.

Solution

a) $\left(-\frac{4}{5}\right)\left(\frac{-7}{3}\right) = \left(-\frac{4}{5}\right)\left(-\frac{7}{3}\right)$ Rewriting $\frac{-7}{3}$ as $-\frac{7}{3}$

$= \frac{28}{15}$ Try to go directly to this step.

b) Given a choice, we generally choose a positive denominator:

$-\frac{2}{7} + \frac{9}{-7} = \frac{-2}{7} + \frac{-9}{7}$ Rewriting both fractions with a common denominator of 7

$= \frac{-11}{7}$, or $-\frac{11}{7}$.

To divide with fraction notation, it is usually easiest to find a reciprocal and then multiply.

EXAMPLE 8 Find the reciprocal of each number, if it exists.

a) -27 **b)** $\frac{-3}{4}$ **c)** $-\frac{1}{5}$ **d)** 0

Solution Recall from Section 1.3 that we can check that two numbers are reciprocals of each other by confirming that their product is 1.

a) The reciprocal of -27 is $\frac{1}{-27}$. More often, this number is written as $-\frac{1}{27}$.
Check: $(-27)\left(-\frac{1}{27}\right) = \frac{27}{27} = 1$.

b) The reciprocal of $\frac{-3}{4}$ is $\frac{4}{-3}$, or, equivalently, $-\frac{4}{3}$. *Check*: $\frac{-3}{4} \cdot \frac{4}{-3} = \frac{-12}{-12} = 1$.

c) The reciprocal of $-\frac{1}{5}$ is -5. *Check*: $-\frac{1}{5}(-5) = \frac{5}{5} = 1$.

d) The reciprocal of 0 does not exist. To see this, recall that there is no number r for which $0 \cdot r = 1$.

EXAMPLE 9 Divide: **(a)** $-\frac{2}{3} \div \left(-\frac{5}{4}\right)$; **(b)** $-\frac{3}{4} \div \frac{3}{10}$.

Solution We divide by multiplying by the reciprocal of the divisor.

a) $-\dfrac{2}{3} \div \left(-\dfrac{5}{4}\right) = -\dfrac{2}{3} \cdot \left(-\dfrac{4}{5}\right) = \dfrac{8}{15}$ Multiplying by the reciprocal

Be careful not to change the sign when taking a reciprocal!

b) $-\dfrac{3}{4} \div \dfrac{3}{10} = -\dfrac{3}{4} \cdot \left(\dfrac{10}{3}\right) = -\dfrac{30}{12} = -\dfrac{5}{2} \cdot \dfrac{6}{6} = -\dfrac{5}{2}$ Removing a factor equal to 1: $\frac{6}{6} = 1$

To divide with decimal notation, it is usually easiest to carry out the division.

EXAMPLE 10 Divide: $27.9 \div (-3)$.

Solution

$$27.9 \div (-3) = \frac{27.9}{-3} = -9.3$$

Dividing: $3\overline{)27.9}$ gives 9.3.
The answer is negative.

In Example 5(d), we explained why we cannot divide -17 by 0. To see why *no* nonzero number b can be divided by 0, remember that $b \div 0$ would have to be the number that when multiplied by 0 gives b. But since the product of 0 and any number is 0, not b, we say that $b \div 0$ is **undefined** for $b \neq 0$. In the special case of $0 \div 0$, we look for a number r such that $0 \div 0 = r$ and $r \cdot 0 = 0$. But, $r \cdot 0 = 0$ for *any* number r. For this reason, we say that $b \div 0$ is undefined for any choice of b.*

Finally, note that $0 \div 7 = 0$ since $0 \cdot 7 = 0$. This can be written $0/7 = 0$. It is important not to confuse division *by* 0 with division *into* 0.

EXAMPLE 11 Divide, if possible: **(a)** $\frac{0}{-2}$; **(b)** $\frac{5}{0}$.

Solution

a) $\dfrac{0}{-2} = 0$ *Check*: $0(-2) = 0$.

b) $\dfrac{5}{0}$ is undefined.

*Sometimes $0 \div 0$ is said to be *indeterminate*.

Division Involving Zero

For any real number a,

$$\frac{a}{0} \text{ is undefined,}$$

and for $a \neq 0$,

$$\frac{0}{a} = 0.$$

Caution! It is important *not* to confuse *opposite* with *reciprocal*. Keep in mind that the opposite, or additive inverse, of a number is what we add to the number to get 0. The reciprocal, or multiplicative inverse, is what we multiply the number by to get 1.

Compare the following.

Number	Opposite (Change the sign.)	Reciprocal (Invert but do not change the sign.)
$-\frac{3}{8}$	$\frac{3}{8}$	$-\frac{8}{3}$
19	-19	$\frac{1}{19}$
$\frac{18}{7}$	$-\frac{18}{7}$	$\frac{7}{18}$
-7.9	7.9	$-\frac{1}{7.9}$, or $-\frac{10}{79}$
0	0	Not defined

$\left(-\frac{3}{8}\right)\left(-\frac{8}{3}\right) = 1$

$-\frac{3}{8} + \frac{3}{8} = 0$

1.7 Exercise Set

FOR EXTRA HELP

Student's Solutions Manual | Digital Video Tutor CD 1 Videotape 2 | AW Math Tutor Center | MathXL Tutorials on CD | MathXL | MyMathLab

Concept Reinforcement In each of Exercises 1–10, replace the blank with either 0 *or* 1 *to match the description given.*

1. The product of two reciprocals ____
2. The sum of a pair of opposites ____
3. The sum of a pair of additive inverses ____
4. The product of two multiplicative inverses ____
5. This number has no reciprocal. ____

6. This number is its own reciprocal. ____

7. This number is the multiplicative identity. ____

8. This number is the additive identity. ____

9. A nonzero number divided by itself ____

10. Division by this number is undefined. ____

Multiply.

11. $-3 \cdot 8$

12. $-3 \cdot 7$

13. $-8 \cdot 7$

14. $-9 \cdot 2$

15. $8 \cdot (-3)$

16. $9 \cdot (-5)$

17. $-9 \cdot 8$

18. $-10 \cdot 3$

19. $-6 \cdot (-7)$

20. $-2 \cdot (-5)$

21. $-5 \cdot (-9)$

22. $-9 \cdot (-2)$

23. $-19 \cdot (-10)$

24. $-12 \cdot (-10)$

25. $-12 \cdot 12$

26. $-13 \cdot (-15)$

27. $-25 \cdot (-48)$

28. $39 \cdot (-43)$

29. $-3.5 \cdot (-28)$

30. $97 \cdot (-2.1)$

31. $6 \cdot (-13)$

32. $7 \cdot (-9)$

33. $-7 \cdot (-3.1)$

34. $-4 \cdot (-3.2)$

35. $\frac{2}{3} \cdot \left(-\frac{3}{5}\right)$

36. $\frac{5}{7} \cdot \left(-\frac{2}{3}\right)$

37. $-\frac{3}{8} \cdot \left(-\frac{2}{9}\right)$

38. $-\frac{5}{8} \cdot \left(-\frac{2}{5}\right)$

39. $(-5.3)(2.1)$

40. $(-4.3)(9.5)$

41. $-\frac{5}{9} \cdot \frac{3}{4}$

42. $-\frac{8}{3} \cdot \frac{9}{4}$

43. $3 \cdot (-7) \cdot (-2) \cdot 6$

44. $9 \cdot (-2) \cdot (-6) \cdot 7$

Aha! 45. $-27 \cdot (-34) \cdot 0$

46. $-43 \cdot (-74) \cdot 0$

47. $-\frac{1}{3} \cdot \frac{1}{4} \cdot \left(-\frac{3}{7}\right)$

48. $-\frac{1}{2} \cdot \frac{3}{5} \cdot \left(-\frac{2}{7}\right)$

49. $-2 \cdot (-5) \cdot (-3) \cdot (-5)$

50. $-3 \cdot (-5) \cdot (-2) \cdot (-1)$

51. $(-31) \cdot (-27) \cdot 0$

52. $7 \cdot (-6) \cdot 5 \cdot (-4) \cdot 3 \cdot (-2) \cdot 1 \cdot 0$

53. $(-8)(-9)(-10)$

54. $(-7)(-8)(-9)(-10)$

55. $(-6)(-7)(-8)(-9)(-10)$

56. $(-5)(-6)(-7)(-8)(-9)(-10)$

Divide, if possible, and check. If a quotient is undefined, state this.

57. $14 \div (-2)$

58. $\frac{24}{-3}$

59. $\frac{36}{-9}$

60. $26 \div (-13)$

61. $\frac{-56}{8}$

62. $-32 \div (-4)$

63. $\frac{-48}{-12}$

64. $-63 \div (-9)$

65. $\frac{-72}{9}$

66. $\frac{-50}{25}$

67. $-100 \div (-50)$

68. $\frac{-200}{8}$

69. $-108 \div 9$

70. $\frac{-64}{-7}$

71. $\frac{400}{-50}$

72. $-300 \div (-13)$

73. $\frac{28}{0}$

74. $\frac{0}{-5}$

75. $-4.8 \div 1.2$

76. $-3.9 \div 1.3$

77. $\frac{0}{-9}$

78. $0 \div (-47)$

Aha! 79. $\frac{9.7(-2.8)0}{4.3}$

80. $\frac{(-4.9)(7.2)}{0}$

Write each number in two equivalent forms, as in Example 6.

81. $\frac{-8}{3}$

82. $\frac{-12}{7}$

83. $\frac{29}{-35}$

84. $\frac{9}{-14}$

85. $-\frac{7}{3}$

86. $-\frac{4}{15}$

87. $\frac{-x}{2}$

88. $\frac{9}{-a}$

Find the reciprocal of each number, if it exists.

89. $\dfrac{4}{-5}$

90. $\dfrac{2}{-9}$

91. $-\dfrac{47}{13}$

92. $-\dfrac{31}{12}$

93. -10

94. 34

95. 4.3

96. -1.7

97. $\dfrac{-9}{4}$

98. $\dfrac{-6}{11}$

99. 0

100. -1

Perform the indicated operation and, if possible, simplify. If a quotient is undefined, state this.

101. $\left(\frac{-7}{4}\right)\left(-\frac{3}{5}\right)$

102. $\left(-\frac{5}{6}\right)\left(\frac{-1}{3}\right)$

103. $\left(\frac{-6}{5}\right)\left(\frac{2}{-11}\right)$

104. $\left(\frac{7}{-2}\right)\left(\frac{-5}{6}\right)$

105. $\frac{-3}{8} + \frac{-5}{8}$

106. $\frac{-4}{5} + \frac{7}{5}$

Aha! **107.** $\left(\frac{-9}{5}\right)\left(\frac{5}{-9}\right)$

108. $\left(-\frac{2}{7}\right)\left(\frac{5}{-8}\right)$

109. $\left(-\frac{3}{11}\right) + \left(-\frac{6}{11}\right)$

110. $\left(-\frac{4}{7}\right) + \left(-\frac{2}{7}\right)$

111. $\frac{7}{8} \div \left(-\frac{1}{2}\right)$

112. $\frac{3}{4} \div \left(-\frac{2}{3}\right)$

113. $\frac{9}{5} \cdot \frac{-20}{3}$

114. $\frac{-5}{12} \cdot \frac{7}{15}$

115. $\left(-\frac{18}{7}\right) + \left(-\frac{3}{7}\right)$

116. $\left(-\frac{12}{5}\right) + \left(-\frac{3}{5}\right)$

Aha! **117.** $-\frac{5}{9} \div \left(-\frac{5}{9}\right)$

118. $-\frac{5}{4} \div \left(-\frac{3}{4}\right)$

119. $-44.1 \div (-6.3)$

120. $-6.6 \div 3.3$

121. $\frac{5}{9} - \frac{7}{9}$

122. $\frac{2}{7} - \frac{6}{7}$

123. $\frac{-3}{10} + \frac{2}{5}$

124. $\frac{-5}{9} + \frac{2}{3}$

125. $\frac{7}{10} \div \left(\frac{-3}{5}\right)$

126. $\left(\frac{-3}{5}\right) \div \frac{6}{15}$

127. $\frac{5}{7} - \frac{1}{-7}$

128. $\frac{4}{9} - \frac{1}{-9}$

129. $\frac{-4}{15} + \frac{2}{-3}$

130. $\frac{3}{-10} + \frac{-1}{5}$

131. Most calculators have a key, often appearing as [1/x], for finding reciprocals. To use this key, enter a number and then press [1/x] to find its reciprocal. What should happen if you enter a number and then press the reciprocal key twice? Why?

132. Multiplication can be regarded as repeated addition. Using this idea and a number line, explain why $3 \cdot (-5) = -15$.

SKILL MAINTENANCE

133. Simplify: $\dfrac{264}{468}$. [1.3]

134. Combine like terms: $x + 12y + 11x - 14y - 9$. [1.5]

SYNTHESIS

135. If two nonzero numbers are opposites of each other, are their reciprocals opposites of each other? Why or why not?

136. If two numbers are reciprocals of each other, are their opposites reciprocals of each other? Why or why not?

137. Show that the reciprocal of a sum is *not* the sum of the two reciprocals.

138. Which real numbers are their own reciprocals?

Tell whether each expression represents a positive number or a negative number when m and n are negative.

139. $\dfrac{m}{-n}$

140. $\dfrac{-n}{-m}$

141. $-m \cdot \left(\dfrac{-n}{m}\right)$

142. $-\left(\dfrac{n}{-m}\right)$

143. $(m + n) \cdot \dfrac{m}{n}$

144. $(-n - m)\dfrac{n}{m}$

145. What must be true of m and n if $-mn$ is to be **(a)** positive? **(b)** zero? **(c)** negative?

146. The following is a proof that a positive number times a negative number is negative. Provide a reason for each step. Assume that $a > 0$ and $b > 0$.

$$\begin{aligned} a(-b) + ab &= a[-b + b] \\ &= a(0) \\ &= 0 \end{aligned}$$

Therefore, $a(-b)$ is the opposite of ab.

147. Is it true that for any numbers a and b, if a is larger than b, then the reciprocal of a is smaller than the reciprocal of b? Why or why not?

1.8 Exponential Notation and Order of Operations

Exponential Notation • Order of Operations • Simplifying and the Distributive Law • The Opposite of a Sum

Algebraic expressions often contain *exponential notation.* In this section, we learn how to use exponential notation as well as rules for the *order of operations* in performing certain algebraic manipulations.

Study Skills

A Journey of 1000 Miles Starts with a Single Step

It is extremely important to include steps when working problems. Doing so allows you and others to follow your thought process. It also helps you to avoid careless errors and to identify specific areas in which you may have made mistakes.

Exponential Notation

A product like $3 \cdot 3 \cdot 3 \cdot 3$, in which the factors are the same, is called a **power**. Powers occur often enough that a simpler notation called **exponential notation** is used. For

$\underbrace{3 \cdot 3 \cdot 3 \cdot 3}_{\text{4 factors}}$, we write 3^4. Because $3^4 = 81$, we sometimes say that 81 "is a power of 3."

This is read "three to the fourth power," or simply, "three to the fourth." The number 4 is called an **exponent** and the number 3 a **base**.

Expressions like s^2 and s^3 are usually read "s squared" and "s cubed," respectively. This comes from the fact that a square with sides of length s has an area A given by $A = s^2$ and a cube with sides of length s has a volume V given by $V = s^3$.

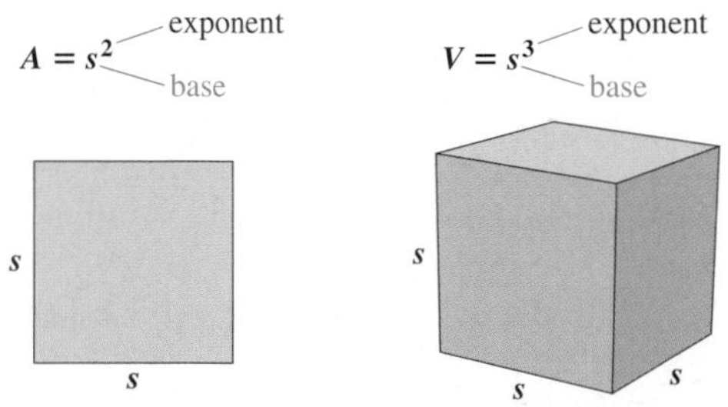

EXAMPLE 1 Write exponential notation for $10 \cdot 10 \cdot 10 \cdot 10 \cdot 10$.

Solution

Exponential notation is 10^5. 5 is the exponent. 10 is the base.

EXAMPLE 2 Evaluate: **(a)** 5^2; **(b)** $(-5)^3$; **(c)** $(2n)^3$.

Solution

a) $5^2 = 5 \cdot 5 = 25$ The exponent 2 indicates two factors of 5.

b) $(-5)^3 = (-5)(-5)(-5)$ The exponent 3 indicates three factors of -5.

$= 25(-5)$ Using the associative law of multiplication

$= -125$

c) $(2n)^3 = (2n)(2n)(2n)$ The exponent 3 indicates three factors of $2n$.

$= 2 \cdot 2 \cdot 2 \cdot n \cdot n \cdot n$ Using the associative and commutative laws of multiplication

$= 8n^3$

To determine what the exponent 1 will mean, look for a pattern in the following:

$$7 \cdot 7 \cdot 7 \cdot 7 = 7^4$$
$$7 \cdot 7 \cdot 7 = 7^3$$
$$7 \cdot 7 = 7^2$$
$$7 = 7^?$$

We divide by 7 each time.

The exponents decrease by 1 each time. To extend the pattern, we say that

$$7 = 7^1.$$

Exponential Notation

For any natural number n,

$$b^n \quad \text{means} \quad \overbrace{b \cdot b \cdot b \cdot b \cdots b}^{n \text{ factors}}.$$

technology connection

On most graphing calculators, grouping symbols, such as a fraction bar, must be replaced with parentheses. For example, to calculate

$$\frac{12(9 - 7) + 4 \cdot 5}{2^4 + 3^2},$$

we enter $(12(9 - 7) + 4 \cdot 5) \div (2^4 + 3^2)$. To enter an exponential expression, we enter the base, press ^ and then enter the exponent. The x^2 key can be used to enter an exponent of 2. We can also convert to fraction notation if we wish.

```
(12(9−7)+4*5)/(2^4+3²)
                  1.76
Ans►Frac
                 44/25
```

Order of Operations

How should $4 + 2 \times 5$ be computed? If we multiply 2 by 5 and then add 4, the result is 14. If we add 2 and 4 first and then multiply by 5, the result is 30. Since these results differ, the order in which we perform operations matters. If grouping symbols such as parentheses ( ), brackets [ ], braces { }, absolute-value symbols | |, or fraction bars appear, they tell us what to do first. For example,

$(4 + 2) \times 5$ indicates 6×5, resulting in 30,

and

$4 + (2 \times 5)$ indicates $4 + 10$, resulting in 14.

Besides grouping symbols, the following conventions exist for determining the order in which operations should be performed.

Rules for Order of Operations

1. Calculate within the innermost grouping symbols, ( ), [ ], { }, | |, and above or below fraction bars.
2. Simplify all exponential expressions.
3. Perform all multiplication and division, working from left to right.
4. Perform all addition and subtraction, working from left to right.

Thus the correct way to compute $4 + 2 \times 5$ is to first multiply 2 by 5 and then add 4. The result is 14.

EXAMPLE 3 Simplify: $15 - 2 \times 5 + 3$.

Solution When no groupings or exponents appear, we *always* multiply or divide before adding or subtracting:

$$15 - 2 \times 5 + 3 = 15 - 10 + 3 \quad \text{Multiplying}$$
$$= 5 + 3$$
$$= 8. \quad \text{Subtracting and adding from left to right}$$

Always calculate within parentheses first. When there are exponents and no parentheses, simplify powers before multiplying or dividing.

EXAMPLE 4 Simplify: **(a)** $(3 \cdot 4)^2$; **(b)** $3 \cdot 4^2$.

Solution

a) $(3 \cdot 4)^2 = (12)^2$ Working within parentheses first
$= 144$

b) $3 \cdot 4^2 = 3 \cdot 16$ Simplifying the power
$= 48$ Multiplying

Note that $(3 \cdot 4)^2 \neq 3 \cdot 4^2$.

Caution! Example 4 illustrates that, in general, $(ab)^2 \neq ab^2$.

EXAMPLE 5 Evaluate for $x = 5$: **(a)** $(-x)^2$; **(b)** $-x^2$.

Solution

a) $(-x)^2 = (-5)^2 = (-5)(-5) = 25$ We square the opposite of 5.

b) $-x^2 = -5^2 = -25$ We square 5 and then find the opposite.

> ***Caution!*** Example 5 illustrates that, in general, $(-x)^2 \neq -x^2$.

EXAMPLE 6 Evaluate $-15 \div 3(6 - a)^3$ for $a = 4$.

Solution

$-15 \div 3(6 - a)^3 = -15 \div 3(6 - 4)^3$	Substituting 4 for a
$= -15 \div 3(2)^3$	Working within parentheses first
$= -15 \div 3 \cdot 8$	Simplifying the exponential expression
$= -5 \cdot 8$ $= -40$	Dividing and multiplying from left to right

---

Student Notes

The symbols ( ), [ ], and { } are all used in the same way. Used inside or next to each other, they make it easier to locate the left and right sides of a grouping. Try doing this in your own work to minimize mistakes.

When combinations of grouping symbols are used, the rules still apply within those grouping symbols. We begin with the innermost grouping symbols and work to the outside.

EXAMPLE 7 Simplify: $8 \div 4 + 3[9 + 2(3 - 5)^3]$.

Solution

$8 \div 4 + 3[9 + 2(3 - 5)^3] = 8 \div 4 + 3[9 + 2(-2)^3]$	Doing the calculations in the innermost parentheses first
$= 8 \div 4 + 3[9 + 2(-8)]$	$(-2)^3 = (-2)(-2)(-2)$ $= -8$
$= 8 \div 4 + 3[9 + (-16)]$	
$= 8 \div 4 + 3[-7]$	Completing the calculations within the brackets
$= 2 + (-21)$	Multiplying and dividing from left to right
$= -19$	

EXAMPLE 8 Calculate: $\dfrac{12(9-7)+4\cdot 5}{3^4+2^3}$.

Solution An equivalent expression with brackets is

$$[12(9-7)+4\cdot 5] \div [3^4+2^3].$$

In effect, we need to simplify the numerator, simplify the denominator, and then divide the results:

$$\frac{12(9-7)+4\cdot 5}{3^4+2^3} = \frac{12(2)+4\cdot 5}{81+8} = \frac{24+20}{89} = \frac{44}{89}.$$

Simplifying and the Distributive Law

Sometimes we cannot simplify within grouping symbols. When a sum or difference is being grouped, the distributive law provides a method for removing the grouping symbols.

EXAMPLE 9 Simplify: $5x - 9 + 2(4x + 5)$.

Solution

$5x - 9 + 2(4x + 5) = 5x - 9 + 8x + 10$ Using the distributive law

$= 13x + 1$ Combining like terms

Now that exponents have been introduced, we can make our definition of *like* or *similar terms* more precise. **Like**, or **similar**, **terms** are either constant terms or terms containing the same variable(s) raised to the same power(s). Thus, 5 and -7, $19xy$ and $2yx$, and $4a^3b$ and a^3b are all pairs of like terms.

EXAMPLE 10 Simplify: $7x^2 + 3[x^2 + 2x] - 5x$.

Solution

$7x^2 + 3[x^2 + 2x] - 5x = 7x^2 + 3x^2 + 6x - 5x$ Using the distributive law

$= 10x^2 + x$ Combining like terms

The Opposite of a Sum

When a number is multiplied by -1, the result is the opposite of that number. For example, $-1(7) = -7$ and $-1(-5) = 5$.

The Property of -1

For any real number a,

$$-1 \cdot a = -a.$$

(Negative one times a is the opposite of a.)

When grouping symbols are preceded by a "$-$" symbol, we can multiply the grouping by -1 and use the distributive law. In this manner, we can find the *opposite*, or *additive inverse*, of a sum.

EXAMPLE 11 Write an expression equivalent to $-(3x + 2y + 4)$ without using parentheses.

Solution

$-(3x + 2y + 4)$	$= -1(3x + 2y + 4)$	Using the property of -1
	$= -1(3x) + (-1)(2y) + (-1)4$	Using the distributive law
	$= -3x - 2y - 4$	Using the associative law and the property of -1

Example 11 illustrates an important property of real numbers.

The Opposite of a Sum

For any real numbers a and b,

$$-(a + b) = -a + (-b) = -a - b.$$

(The opposite of a sum is the sum of the opposites.)

To remove parentheses from an expression like $-(x - 7y + 5)$, we can first rewrite the subtraction as addition:

$-(x - 7y + 5)$	$= -(x + (-7y) + 5)$	Rewriting as addition
	$= -x + 7y - 5.$	Taking the opposite of a sum

This procedure is normally streamlined to one step in which we find the opposite by "removing parentheses and changing the sign of every term":

$$-(x - 7y + 5) = -x + 7y - 5.$$

EXAMPLE 12 Simplify: $3x - (4x + 2)$.

Solution

$$\begin{aligned}
3x - (4x + 2) &= 3x + [-(4x + 2)] && \text{Adding the opposite of } 4x + 2\\
&= 3x + [-4x - 2] && \text{Taking the opposite of } 4x + 2\\
&= 3x + (-4x) + (-2)\\
&= 3x - 4x - 2 && \text{Try to go directly to this step.}\\
&= -x - 2 && \text{Combining like terms}
\end{aligned}$$

In practice, the first three steps of Example 12 are generally skipped.

EXAMPLE 13 Simplify: $5t^2 - 2t - (4t^2 - 9t)$.

Solution

$$\begin{aligned}
5t^2 - 2t - (4t^2 - 9t) &= 5t^2 - 2t - 4t^2 + 9t && \text{Removing parentheses and changing the sign of each term inside}\\
&= t^2 + 7t && \text{Combining like terms}
\end{aligned}$$

Expressions such as $7 - 3(x + 2)$ can be simplified as follows:

$$\begin{aligned}
7 - 3(x + 2) &= 7 + [-3(x + 2)] && \text{Adding the opposite of } 3(x + 2)\\
&= 7 + [-3x - 6] && \text{Multiplying } x + 2 \text{ by } -3\\
&= 7 - 3x - 6 && \text{Try to go directly to this step.}\\
&= 1 - 3x. && \text{Combining like terms}
\end{aligned}$$

EXAMPLE 14 Simplify: **(a)** $3n - 2(4n - 5)$; **(b)** $7x^3 + 2 - [5(x^3 - 1) + 8]$.

Solution

a)
$$\begin{aligned}
3n - 2(4n - 5) &= 3n - 8n + 10 && \text{Multiplying each term inside the parentheses by } -2\\
&= -5n + 10 && \text{Combining like terms}
\end{aligned}$$

b)
$$\begin{aligned}
7x^3 + 2 - [5(x^3 - 1) + 8] &= 7x^3 + 2 - [5x^3 - 5 + 8] && \text{Removing parentheses}\\
&= 7x^3 + 2 - [5x^3 + 3]\\
&= 7x^3 + 2 - 5x^3 - 3 && \text{Removing brackets}\\
&= 2x^3 - 1 && \text{Combining like terms}
\end{aligned}$$

CONNECTING THE CONCEPTS

Algebra is a tool that is used to solve problems. We have seen in this chapter that certain problems can be translated to algebraic expressions that can in turn be simplified (see Section 1.6). In Chapter 2, we will solve problems that require us to solve an equation.

As we progress through our study of algebra, it is important that we be able to distinguish between the two tasks of **simplifying an expression** and **solving an equation.** In Chapter 1, we did not solve equations, but we did simplify expressions. This enabled us to write *equivalent expressions* that were simpler than the given expression. In Chapter 2, we will continue to simplify expressions, but we will also begin to solve equations.

1.8 Exercise Set

FOR EXTRA HELP

Student's Solutions Manual | Digital Video Tutor CD 1 Videotape 2 | AW Math Tutor Center | MathXL Tutorials on CD | MathXL | MyMathLab

Concept Reinforcement In each part of Exercises 1 and 2, name the operation that should be performed first. Do not perform the calculations.

1. a) $4 + 8 \div 2 \cdot 2$
b) $7 - 9 + 15$
c) $5 - 2(3 + 4)$
d) $6 + 7 \cdot 3$
e) $18 - 2[4 + (3 - 2)]$
f) $\dfrac{5 - 6 \cdot 7}{2}$

2. a) $9 - 3 \cdot 4 \div 2$
b) $8 + 7(6 - 5)$
c) $5 \cdot [2 - 3(4 + 1)]$
d) $8 - 7 + 2$
e) $4 + 6 \div 2 \cdot 3$
f) $\dfrac{37}{8 - 2 \cdot 2}$

Write exponential notation.

3. $2 \cdot 2 \cdot 2$
4. $6 \cdot 6 \cdot 6 \cdot 6$
5. $x \cdot x \cdot x \cdot x \cdot x \cdot x \cdot x$
6. $y \cdot y \cdot y \cdot y \cdot y \cdot y$
7. $3t \cdot 3t \cdot 3t \cdot 3t \cdot 3t$
8. $5m \cdot 5m \cdot 5m \cdot 5m \cdot 5m$

Simplify.

9. 3^2
10. 5^3
11. $(-4)^2$
12. $(-7)^2$
13. -4^2
14. -7^2
15. 4^3
16. 9^1
17. $(-5)^4$
18. 5^4
19. 7^1
20. $(-1)^7$
21. $(3t)^4$
22. $(5t)^2$
23. $(-7x)^3$
24. $(-5x)^4$
25. $5 + 3 \cdot 7$
26. $3 - 4 \cdot 2$
27. $8 \cdot 7 + 6 \cdot 5$
28. $10 \cdot 5 + 1 \cdot 1$
29. $19 - 5 \cdot 3 + 3$
30. $14 - 2 \cdot 6 + 7$
31. $9 \div 3 + 16 \div 8$
32. $32 - 8 \div 4 - 2$
Aha! **33.** $14 \cdot 19 \div (19 \cdot 14)$
34. $18 - 6 \div 3 \cdot 2 + 7$
35. $3(-10)^2 - 8 \div 2^2$
36. $9 - 3^2 \div 9(-1)$
37. $8 - (2 \cdot 3 - 9)$

38. $(8 - 2 \cdot 3) - 9$

39. $(8 - 2)(3 - 9)$

40. $32 \div (-2)^2 \cdot 4$

41. $13(-10)^2 + 45 \div (-5)$

42. $5 \cdot 3^2 - 4^2 \cdot 2$

43. $2^4 + 2^3 - 10 \div (-1)^4$

44. $112 \div 28 - 112 \div 28$

45. $5 + 3(2 - 9)^2$

46. $9 - (3 - 5)^3 - 4$

47. $[2 \cdot (5 - 8)]^2$

48. $3(5 - 7)^4 \div 4$

49. $\dfrac{7 + 2}{5^2 - 4^2}$

50. $\dfrac{5^2 - 3^2}{2 \cdot 6 - 4}$

51. $8(-7) + |6(-5)|$

52. $|10(-5)| + 1(-1)$

53. $\dfrac{(-2)^3 + 4^2}{3 - 5^2 + 3 \cdot 6}$

54. $\dfrac{7^2 - (-1)^5}{3 - 2 \cdot 3^2 + 5}$

55. $\dfrac{27 - 2 \cdot 3^2}{8 \div 2^2 - (-2)^2}$

56. $\dfrac{(-5)^2 - 4 \cdot 5}{3^2 + 4 \cdot 2(-1)^5}$

Evaluate.

57. $9 - 4x$, for $x = 5$

58. $1 + x^3$, for $x = -2$

59. $24 \div t^3$, for $t = -2$

60. $20 \div a \cdot 4$, for $a = 5$

61. $45 \div 3 \cdot a$, for $a = -1$

62. $50 \div 2 \cdot t$, for $t = -5$

63. $5x \div 15x^2$, for $x = 3$

64. $6a \div 12a^3$, for $a = 2$

65. $45 \div 3^2x(x - 1)$, for $x = 3$

66. $-30 \div t(t + 4)^2$, for $t = -6$

67. $-x^2 - 5x$, for $x = -3$

68. $(-x)^2 - 5x$, for $x = -3$

69. $\dfrac{3a - 4a^2}{a^2 - 20}$, for $a = 5$

70. $\dfrac{a^3 - 4a}{a(a - 3)}$, for $a = -2$

Write an equivalent expression without using grouping symbols.

71. $-(9x + 1)$

72. $-(3x + 5)$

73. $-[5 - 6x]$

74. $-(6x - 7)$

75. $-(4a - 3b + 7c)$

76. $-[5x - 2y - 3z]$

77. $-(3x^2 + 5x - 1)$

78. $-(8x^3 - 6x + 5)$

Simplify.

79. $8x - (6x + 7)$

80. $7y - (2y + 9)$

81. $2a - (5a - 9)$

82. $11n - (3n - 7)$

83. $2x + 7x - (4x + 6)$

84. $2a + 5a - (6a + 8)$

85. $9t - 5r - 2(3r + 6t)$

86. $4m - 9n - 3(2m - n)$

87. $15x - y - 5(3x - 2y + 5z)$

88. $4a - b - 4(5a - 7b + 8c)$

89. $3x^2 + 7 - (2x^2 + 5)$

90. $5x^4 + 3x - (5x^4 + 3x)$

91. $5t^3 + t - 3(t + 2t^3)$

92. $8n^2 + n - 2(n + 3n^2)$

93. $12a^2 - 3ab + 5b^2 - 5(-5a^2 + 4ab - 6b^2)$

94. $-8a^2 + 5ab - 12b^2 - 6(2a^2 - 4ab - 10b^2)$

95. $-7t^3 - t^2 - 3(5t^3 - 3t)$

96. $9t^4 + 7t - 5(9t^3 - 2t)$

97. $5(2x - 7) - [4(2x - 3) + 2]$

98. $3(6x - 5) - [3(1 - 8x) + 5]$

99. Some students use the mnemonic device PEMDAS to help remember the rules for the order of operations. Explain how this can be done and whether it is a valid approach.

100. Jake keys $18/2 \cdot 3$ into his calculator and expects the result to be 3. What mistake is he probably making?

SKILL MAINTENANCE

Translate to an algebraic expression. [1.1]

101. Nine more than twice a number

102. Half of the sum of two numbers

SYNTHESIS

103. Write the sentence $(-x)^2 \neq -x^2$ in words. Explain why $(-x)^2$ and $-x^2$ are not equivalent.

104. Write the sentence $-|x| \neq -x$ in words. Explain why $-|x|$ and $-x$ are not equivalent.

Simplify.

105. $5t - \{7t - [4r - 3(t - 7)] + 6r\} - 4r$

106. $z - \{2z - [3z - (4z - 5z) - 6z] - 7z\} - 8z$

107. $\{x - [f - (f - x)] + [x - f]\} - 3x$

108. Is it true that for all real numbers a and b,

$$ab = (-a)(-b)?$$

Why or why not?

109. Is it true that for all real numbers a, b, and c,

$$a|b - c| = ab - ac?$$

Why or why not?

If $n > 0$, $m > 0$, and $n \neq m$, classify each of the following as either true or false.

110. $-n + m = -(n + m)$

111. $m - n = -(n - m)$

112. $n(-n - m) = -n^2 + nm$

113. $-m(n - m) = -(mn + m^2)$

114. $-n(-n - m) = n(n + m)$

Evaluate.

Aha! **115.** $[x + 3(2 - 5x) \div 7 + x](x - 3)$, for $x = 3$

Aha! **116.** $[x + 2 \div 3x] \div [x + 2 \div 3x]$, for $x = -7$

117. In Mexico, between 500 B.C. and 600 A.D., the Mayans represented numbers using powers of 20 and certain symbols. For example, the symbols

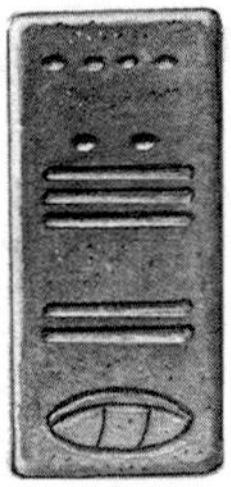

represent $4 \cdot 20^3 + 17 \cdot 20^2 + 10 \cdot 20^1 + 0 \cdot 20^0$. Evaluate this number.

Source: National Council of Teachers of Mathematics, 1906 Association Drive, Reston, VA 22091

118. Examine the Mayan symbols and the numbers in Exercise 117. What numbers do

, , and 

each represent?

119. Calculate the volume of the tower shown below.

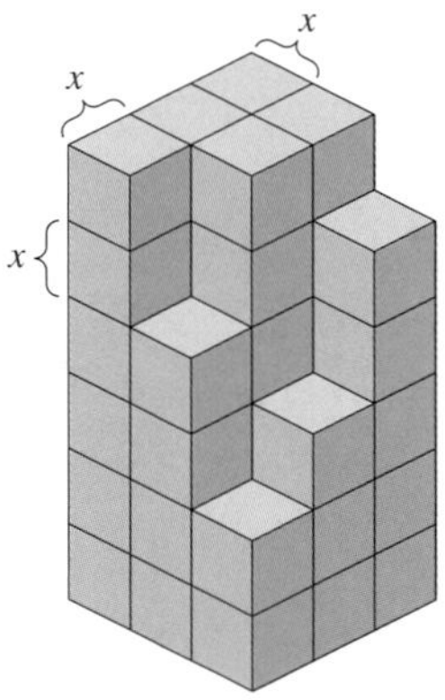

COLLABORATIVE CORNER

Select the Symbols

Focus: Order of operations

Time: 15 minutes

Group size: 2

One way to master the rules for the order of operations is to insert symbols within a display of numbers in order to obtain a predetermined result. For example, the display

$$1 \quad 2 \quad 3 \quad 4 \quad 5$$

can be used to obtain the result 21 as follows:

$$(1 + 2) \div 3 + 4 \cdot 5.$$

Note that without an understanding of the rules for the order of operations, solving a problem of this sort is impossible.

ACTIVITY

1. Each group should prepare an exercise similar to the example shown above. (Exponents are not allowed.) To do so, first select five single-digit numbers for display. Then insert operations and grouping symbols and calculate the result.
2. Pair with another group. Each group should give the other its result along with its five-number display, and challenge the other group to insert symbols that will make the display equal the result given.
3. Share with the entire class the various mathematical statements developed by each group.

1 Study Summary

In a **variable expression** like $5ab^3$, the number 5 is a **constant** and a and b are **variables** (p. 2). When numbers are **substituted** for a and b, we say that we are **evaluating** the **algebraic expression** (p. 3). A substitution that makes an **equation** true is called a **solution** of the equation (p. 6).

Expressions like $5x + 2$ and $2 + x \cdot 5$ are **equivalent expressions** because, for any replacement of the variable, they will represent the same **value** (pp. 3, 13). The following laws are often used to create or **simplify** equivalent expressions (pp. 13–16, 23, 41):

Commutative laws:	$a + b = b + a$; $ab = ba$
Associative laws:	$a + (b + c) = (a + b) + c$; $a(bc) = (ab)c$
Distributive law:	$a(b + c) = ab + ac$
Identity property of 1:	$1 \cdot a = a \cdot 1 = a$
Identity property of 0:	$a + 0 = 0 + a = a$

Important **sets** of numbers are (p. 34)

Natural numbers:	$\{1, 2, 3, \ldots\}$
Whole numbers:	$\{0, 1, 2, 3, \ldots\}$
Integers:	$\{\ldots, -3, -2, -1, 0, 1, 2, 3, \ldots\}$
Rational numbers:	$\left\{\frac{a}{b} \,\middle|\, a \text{ and } b \text{ are integers and } b \neq 0\right\}$

Rational numbers can always be written as **terminating** or **repeating** decimals (p. 33). **Irrational numbers**, like $\sqrt{2}$ or π, can be thought of as nonterminating and nonrepeating decimals (p. 33). The set of **real numbers** consists of all rational and irrational numbers, taken together (p. 34). A natural number that has only itself and 1 as two different **factors**, like 2, 3, 5, 7, 11, 13, 17, 19, or 23, is said to be **prime** (p. 21). Natural numbers that have factors other than 1 and the number itself, like 4, 6, 8, and 9, are said to be **composite** (p. 21). The **prime factorization** of a composite number expresses that number as a product of prime numbers (p. 21).

In future chapters, the following properties and laws will be useful for solving equations (pp. 48, 55, 57, 60, 68):

Law of opposites:	$a + (-a) = 0$
Multiplicative property of 0:	$0 \cdot a = a \cdot 0 = 0$
Property of -1:	$-1 \cdot a = -a$
Opposite of a sum:	$-(a + b) = -a + (-b)$
Division involving 0:	$\frac{0}{a} = 0$; $\frac{a}{0}$ is undefined

$$\frac{-a}{b} = \frac{a}{-b} = -\frac{a}{b}, \qquad \frac{-a}{-b} = \frac{a}{b}$$

In geometric applications throughout the text, the following area formulas are used regularly (pp. 3, 4, 10):

Area of a rectangle:	$A = lw$
Area of a triangle:	$A = \frac{1}{2}bh$
Area of a parallelogram:	$A = bh$

The **terms** of a expression, like 4, $5x^2$, $-7y$, $2x$, and $3x^2$ in $4 + 5x^2 - 7y + 2x + 3x^2$, are separated by addition (p. 16). **Like terms** are either constants or have the same variable factors raised to the same power (p. 67).

When more than one operation appears in an algebraic expression or calculation, the following convention is used (p. 65).

Rules for Order of Operations

1. Calculate within the innermost grouping symbols, ( ), [ ], { }, | |, and above or below fraction bars.
2. Simplify all exponential expressions.
3. Perform all multiplication and division, working from left to right.
4. Perform all addition and subtraction, working from left to right.

1 Review Exercises

Concept Reinforcement In each of Exercises 1–10, classify the statement as either true or false.

1. $4x - 5y$ and $12 - 7a$ are both algebraic expressions containing two terms. [1.2]

2. $3t + 1 = 7$ and $8 - 2 = 9$ are both equations. [1.1]

3. The fact that $2 + x$ is equivalent to $x + 2$ is an illustration of the associative law for addition. [1.2]

4. The statement $4(a + 3) = 4 \cdot a + 4 \cdot 3$ illustrates the distributive law. [1.2]

1 Chapter Test

1. Evaluate $\frac{2x}{y}$ for $x = 10$ and $y = 5$.

2. Write an algebraic expression: Nine less than some number.

3. Find the area of a triangle when the height h is 30 ft and the base b is 16 ft.

4. Use the commutative law of addition to write an expression equivalent to $3p + q$.

5. Use the associative law of multiplication to write an expression equivalent to $x \cdot (4 \cdot y)$.

6. Determine whether 7 is a solution of $65 - x = 69$.

7. Translate to an equation. Do not solve.

   On a hot summer day, Green River Electric met a demand of 2518 megawatts. This is only 282 megawatts less than its maximum production capability. What is the maximum capability of production?

Multiply.

8. $7(5 - x)$

9. $-5(y - 2)$

Factor.

10. $11 - 44x$

11. $7x + 21 + 14y$

12. Find the prime factorization of 300.

13. Simplify: $\frac{10}{35}$.

Write a true sentence using either < or >.

14. $-4 \;\square\; 0$

15. $-3 \;\square\; -8$

Find the absolute value.

16. $\left|\frac{9}{4}\right|$

17. $|-2.7|$

18. Find the opposite of $\frac{2}{3}$.

19. Find the reciprocal of $-\frac{4}{7}$.

20. Find $-x$ when x is -8.

21. Write an inequality with the same meaning as $x \leq -2$.

Perform the indicated operations and, if possible, simplify.

22. $3.1 - (-4.7)$

23. $-8 + 4 + (-7) + 3$

24. $3.2 - 5.7$

25. $\frac{1}{8} - \left(-\frac{3}{4}\right)$

26. $4 \cdot (-12)$

27. $-\frac{1}{2} \cdot \left(-\frac{3}{8}\right)$

28. $-54 \div 9$

29. $-\frac{3}{5} \div \left(-\frac{4}{5}\right)$

30. $4.864 \div (-0.5)$

31. $-2(16) - |2(-8) - 5^3|$

32. $9 + 7 - 4 - (-3)$

33. $256 \div (-16) \div 4$

34. $2^3 - 10[4 - (-2 + 18)3]$

35. Combine like terms: $18y + 30a - 9a + 4y$.

36. Simplify: $(-2x)^4$.

Remove parentheses and simplify.

37. $4x - (3x - 7)$

38. $4(2a - 3b) + a - 7$

39. $4\{3[5(y - 3) + 9] + 2(y + 8)\}$

SYNTHESIS

40. Evaluate $\frac{5y - x}{2}$ when $x = 20$ and y is 4 less than half of x.

41. Insert one pair of parentheses to make the following a true statement:

    $9 - 3 - 4 + 5 = 15.$

Simplify.

42. $|-27 - 3(4)| - |-36| + |-12|$

43. $a - \{3a - [4a - (2a - 4a)]\}$

44. Classify the following as either true or false:

    $a|b - c| = |ab| - |ac|.$

2 Equations, Inequalities, and Problem Solving

AN APPLICATION

Local light rail service in Denver, Colorado, costs $1.15 per trip (one way). A student monthly pass costs $21 (*Source*: rtd-denver.com). Gail is a student at Community College of Denver. Express as an inequality the number of trips per month that Gail should make if the pass is to save her money.

This problem appears as Exercise 23 in Section 2.7.

Lee Cryer
TRANSPORTATION PLANNER
Denver, Colorado

As a transportation planner, I use math to forecast the number of passengers we can anticipate and then take that information to determine how many buses, train cars, and park-n-ride spaces we need to serve our customers. I also use math to determine capital and operating costs and the revenues needed to pay those costs.

Solving equations and inequalities is a recurring theme in much of mathematics. In this chapter, we will study some of the principles used to solve equations and inequalities. We will then use equations and inequalities to solve applied problems.

2.1 Solving Equations

Equations and Solutions • The Addition Principle • The Multiplication Principle • Selecting the Correct Approach

Solving equations is essential for problem solving in algebra. In this section, we study two of the most important principles used for this task.

Equations and Solutions

We have already seen that an equation is a number sentence stating that the expressions on either side of the equals sign represent the same number. Some equations, like $3 + 2 = 5$ or $2x + 6 = 2(x + 3)$, are *always* true and some, like $3 + 2 = 6$ or $x + 2 = x + 3$, are *never* true. In this text, we will concentrate on equations like $x + 6 = 13$ or $7x = 141$ that are *sometimes* true, depending on the replacement value for the variable.

Solution of an Equation

Any replacement for the variable that makes an equation true is called a *solution* of the equation. To *solve* an equation means to find all of its solutions.

To determine whether a number is a solution, we substitute that number for the variable throughout the equation. If the values on both sides of the equals sign are the same, then the number that was substituted is a solution.

EXAMPLE 1 Determine whether 7 is a solution of $x + 6 = 13$.

Solution We have

$x + 6 = 13$		Writing the equation
$7 + 6 \mid 13$		Substituting 7 for x
$13 \stackrel{?}{=} 13$	TRUE	$13 = 13$ is a true statement.

Since the left-hand and the right-hand sides are the same, 7 is a solution.

Caution! Note that in Example 1, the solution is 7, not 13.

EXAMPLE 2 Determine whether 19 is a solution of $7x = 141$.

Solution We have

$7x = 141$		Writing the equation
$7(19) \mid 141$		Substituting 19 for x
$133 \stackrel{?}{=} 141$	FALSE	The statement $133 = 141$ is false.

Since the left-hand and the right-hand sides differ, 19 is not a solution.

The Addition Principle

Consider the equation

$$x = 7.$$

We can easily see that the solution of this equation is 7. Replacing x with 7, we get

$$7 = 7, \quad \text{which is true.}$$

Now consider the equation

$$x + 6 = 13.$$

In Example 1, we found that the solution of $x + 6 = 13$ is also 7. Although the solution of $x = 7$ may seem more obvious, because $x + 6 = 13$ and $x = 7$ have identical solutions, the equations are said to be **equivalent**.

Student Notes

Be sure to remember that equivalent equations are *equations*, whereas equivalent expressions are *expressions* like $5a - 10$ or $5(a - 2)$.

Equivalent Equations

Equations with the same solutions are called *equivalent equations.*

There are principles that enable us to begin with one equation and end up with an equivalent equation, like $x = 7$, for which the solution is obvious. One such principle concerns addition. The equation $a = b$ says that a and b stand for the same number. Suppose this is true, and some number c is added to a. We get the same result if we add c to b, because a and b are the same number.

The Addition Principle

For any real numbers a, b, and c,

$$a = b \quad \text{is equivalent to} \quad a + c = b + c.$$

To visualize the addition principle, consider a balance similar to one a jeweler might use. When the two sides of a balance hold equal weight, the balance is level. If weight is then added or removed, equally, on both sides, the balance will remain level.

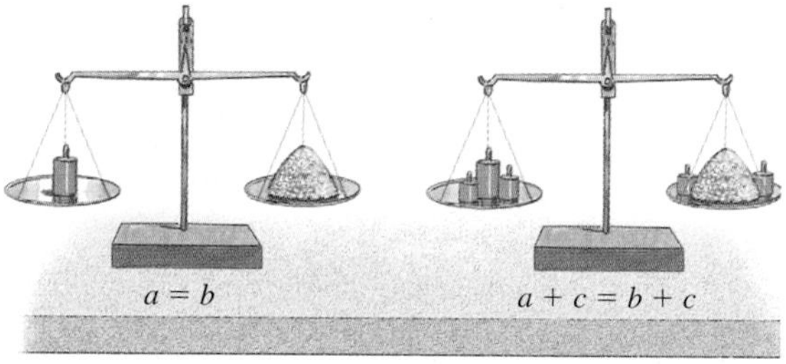

When using the addition principle, we often say that we "add the same number to both sides of an equation." We can also "subtract the same number from both sides," since subtraction can be regarded as the addition of an opposite.

EXAMPLE 3 Solve: $x + 5 = -7$.

Solution We can add any number we like to both sides. Since -5 is the opposite, or additive inverse, of 5, we add -5 to each side:

$x + 5 = -7$

$x + 5 - 5 = -7 - 5$ Using the addition principle: adding -5 to both sides or subtracting 5 from both sides

$x + 0 = -12$ Simplifying; $x + 5 - 5 = x + 5 + (-5) = x + 0$

$x = -12.$ Using the identity property of 0

It is obvious that the solution of $x = -12$ is the number -12. To check the answer in the original equation, we substitute.

Check:

$x + 5$	$= -7$
$-12 + 5$	-7

$-7 \stackrel{?}{=} -7$ TRUE $\quad -7 = -7$ is true.

The solution of the original equation is -12.

In Example 3, note that because we added the *opposite*, or *additive inverse*, of 5, the left side of the equation simplified to x plus the *additive identity*, 0, or simply x. These steps effectively replaced the 5 on the left with a 0. When solving $x + a = b$ for x, we simply add $-a$ to (or subtract a from) both sides.

EXAMPLE 4 Solve: $-6.5 = y - 8.4$.

Solution The variable is on the right side this time. We can isolate y by adding 8.4 to each side:

$-6.5 = y - 8.4$	$y - 8.4$ can be regarded as $y + (-8.4)$.
$-6.5 + 8.4 = y - 8.4 + 8.4$	Using the addition principle: Adding 8.4 to both sides "eliminates" -8.4 on the right side.
$1.9 = y.$	$y - 8.4 + 8.4 = y + (-8.4) + 8.4 = y + 0 = y$

Check:

$$\begin{array}{c|c} -6.5 & y - 8.4 \\ \hline -6.5 & 1.9 - 8.4 \\ -6.5 & \stackrel{?}{=} -6.5 \end{array}$$

TRUE $-6.5 = -6.5$ is true.

The solution is 1.9.

Note that the equations $a = b$ and $b = a$ have the same meaning. Thus, $-6.5 = y - 8.4$ could have been rewritten as $y - 8.4 = -6.5$.

The Multiplication Principle

A second principle for solving equations concerns multiplying. Suppose a and b are equal. If a and b are multiplied by some number c, then ac and bc will also be equal.

The Multiplication Principle

For any real numbers a, b, and c, with $c \neq 0$,

$a = b$ is equivalent to $a \cdot c = b \cdot c$.

EXAMPLE 5 Solve: $\frac{5}{4}x = 10$.

Solution We can multiply both sides by any nonzero number we like. Since $\frac{4}{5}$ is the reciprocal of $\frac{5}{4}$, we multiply each side by $\frac{4}{5}$:

$\frac{5}{4}x = 10$	
$\frac{4}{5} \cdot \frac{5}{4}x = \frac{4}{5} \cdot 10$	Using the multiplication principle: Multiplying both sides by $\frac{4}{5}$ "eliminates" the $\frac{5}{4}$ on the left.
$1 \cdot x = 8$	Simplifying
$x = 8.$	Using the identity property of 1

Check:

$$\begin{array}{c|c} \frac{5}{4}x & 10 \\ \hline \frac{5}{4} \cdot 8 & 10 \\ \frac{40}{4} & \\ 10 & \stackrel{?}{=} 10 \end{array}$$

Think of 8 as $\frac{8}{1}$.

TRUE $10 = 10$ is true.

The solution is 8.

In Example 5, to get x alone, we multiplied by the *reciprocal,* or *multiplicative inverse* of $\frac{5}{4}$. We then simplified the left-hand side to x times the *multiplicative identity,* 1, or simply x. These steps effectively replaced the $\frac{5}{4}$ on the left with 1.

Because division is the same as multiplying by a reciprocal, the multiplication principle also tells us that we can "divide both sides by the same nonzero number." That is,

$$\text{if } a = b, \text{ then } \quad \frac{1}{c} \cdot a = \frac{1}{c} \cdot b \quad \text{and} \quad \frac{a}{c} = \frac{b}{c} \quad (\text{provided } c \neq 0).$$

In a product like $3x$, the multiplier 3 is called the **coefficient**. *When the coefficient of the variable is an integer or a decimal, it is usually easiest to solve an equation by dividing on both sides. When the coefficient is in fraction notation, it is usually easier to multiply by the reciprocal.*

EXAMPLE 6 Solve: **(a)** $-4x = 92$; **(b)** $-x = 9$; **(c)** $\dfrac{2y}{9} = \dfrac{8}{3}$.

Solution

a) In $-4x = 92$, the coefficient of x is an integer, so we *divide* on both sides:

$\dfrac{-4x}{-4} = \dfrac{92}{-4}$ Using the multiplication principle: Dividing both sides by -4 is the same as multiplying by $-\frac{1}{4}$.

$1 \cdot x = -23$ Simplifying

$x = -23.$ Using the identity property of 1

Check:

$-4x = 92$	
$-4(-23)$	92

$92 \stackrel{?}{=} 92$ TRUE $\quad 92 = 92$ is true.

The solution is -23.

b) To solve an equation like $-x = 9$, remember that when an expression is multiplied or divided by -1, its sign is changed. Here we multiply both sides by -1 to change the sign of $-x$:

$-x = 9$

$(-1)(-x) = (-1)9$ Multiplying both sides by -1 (Dividing by -1 would also work). Note that the reciprocal of -1 is -1.

$x = -9.$ Note that $(-1)(-x)$ is the same as $(-1)(-1)x$.

Check:

$-x = 9$	
$-(-9)$	9

$9 \stackrel{?}{=} 9$ TRUE $\quad 9 = 9$ is true.

The solution is -9.

c) To solve an equation like $\frac{2y}{9} = \frac{8}{3}$, we rewrite the left-hand side as $\frac{2}{9} \cdot y$ and then use the multiplication principle, multiplying by the reciprocal of $\frac{2}{9}$:

$$\frac{2y}{9} = \frac{8}{3}$$

$$\frac{2}{9} \cdot y = \frac{8}{3} \qquad \text{Rewriting } \frac{2y}{9} \text{ as } \frac{2}{9} \cdot y$$

$$\frac{9}{2} \cdot \frac{2}{9} \cdot y = \frac{9}{2} \cdot \frac{8}{3} \qquad \text{Multiplying both sides by } \frac{9}{2}$$

$$1y = \frac{3 \cdot \cancel{3} \cdot \cancel{2} \cdot 4}{\cancel{2} \cdot \cancel{3}} \qquad \text{Removing a factor equal to 1: } \frac{3 \cdot 2}{2 \cdot 3} = 1$$

$$y = 12.$$

Check:

$$\begin{array}{c|c} \frac{2y}{9} & \frac{8}{3} \\ \hline \frac{2 \cdot 12}{9} & \frac{8}{3} \\ \frac{24}{9} & \\ \frac{8}{3} & \stackrel{?}{=} \frac{8}{3} \end{array} \quad \text{TRUE} \qquad \frac{8}{3} = \frac{8}{3} \text{ is true.}$$

The solution is 12.

Selecting the Correct Approach

It is important that you be able to determine which principle should be used to solve a particular equation.

EXAMPLE 7 Solve: **(a)** $-\frac{2}{3} + x = \frac{5}{2}$; **(b)** $12.6 = 3t$.

Solution

a) To undo addition of $-\frac{2}{3}$, we subtract $-\frac{2}{3}$ or add $\frac{2}{3}$ to both sides:

$$-\tfrac{2}{3} + x = \tfrac{5}{2}$$

$$-\tfrac{2}{3} + x + \tfrac{2}{3} = \tfrac{5}{2} + \tfrac{2}{3} \qquad \text{Using the addition principle}$$

$$x = \tfrac{5}{2} + \tfrac{2}{3}$$

$$= \tfrac{5}{2} \cdot \tfrac{3}{3} + \tfrac{2}{3} \cdot \tfrac{2}{2} \qquad \text{Finding a common denominator}$$

$$= \tfrac{15}{6} + \tfrac{4}{6}$$

$$= \tfrac{19}{6}.$$

Check:

$$\begin{array}{c|c} -\frac{2}{3} + x & \frac{5}{2} \\ \hline -\frac{2}{3} + \frac{19}{6} & \frac{5}{2} \\ -\frac{4}{6} + \frac{19}{6} & \\ \frac{15}{6} & \\ \frac{5 \cdot \cancel{3}}{2 \cdot \cancel{3}} & \\ \frac{5}{2} & \stackrel{?}{=} \frac{5}{2} \end{array}$$

$-\frac{2}{3} \cdot \frac{2}{2} = -\frac{4}{6}$

Removing a factor equal to 1: $\frac{3}{3} = 1$

TRUE $\frac{5}{2} = \frac{5}{2}$ is true.

The solution is $\frac{19}{6}$.

b) To undo multiplication by 3, we either divide both sides by 3 or multiply both sides by $\frac{1}{3}$:

$$12.6 = 3t$$

$$\frac{12.6}{3} = \frac{3t}{3} \quad \text{Using the multiplication principle}$$

$$4.2 = 1t$$

$$4.2 = t \quad \text{Simplifying}$$

Check:

$12.6 = 3t$		
12.6	$3(4.2)$	
$12.6 \stackrel{?}{=} 12.6$	TRUE	$12.6 = 12.6$ is true.

The solution is 4.2.

Study Skills

Seeking Help?

Using some or all of these resources can make studying easier and more enjoyable.

A variety of resources are available to help you learn math.

- **Textbook supplements.** Are you aware of all the supplements that exist for this textbook? See the preface for a description of each supplement: the *Student's Solutions Manual*, a complete set of lessons in video or CD form, tutorial exercises on CD, and complete online courses in MathXL and MyMathLab.
- **Your college or university.** Your own college or university probably has resources to enhance your math learning.
  1. There may be a learning lab or tutoring center for drop-in tutoring.
  2. There may be study skills workshops or group tutoring sessions tailored for the specific course you are taking.
  3. Often, there is a bulletin board or network where you can locate the names of experienced private tutors.
  4. You might be able to find classmates interested in forming a study group.
- **Your instructor.** Although it may seem obvious, you should consider an often overlooked resource: your instructor. Find out your instructor's office hours and make it a point to visit when you need additional help. Many instructors welcome student e-mail. If you are hesitant to visit your instructor, e-mail may prove quite useful.

2.1 Exercise Set

FOR EXTRA HELP

Student's Solutions Manual | Digital Video Tutor CD 1 Videotape 3 | AW Math Tutor Center | MathXL Tutorials on CD | MathXL | MyMathLab

Concept Reinforcement *For each of Exercises 1–6, match the statement with the most appropriate choice from the column on the right.*

1. ____ A replacement that makes an equation true
2. ____ The equations $x + 3 = 7$ and $6x = 24$
3. ____ The role of 9 in $9ab$
4. ____ The expressions $3(x - 2)$ and $3x - 6$
5. ____ The principle used to solve $\frac{2}{3} \cdot x = -4$
6. ____ The principle used to solve $\frac{2}{3} + x = -4$

a) Coefficient
b) Equivalent expressions
c) Equivalent equations
d) The multiplication principle
e) The addition principle
f) Solution

Solve using the addition principle. Don't forget to check!

7. $x + 6 = 23$ **8.** $x + 5 = 8$

9. $y + 7 = -4$ **10.** $t + 6 = 43$

11. $t + 9 = -12$ **12.** $y + 7 = -3$

13. $-6 = y + 25$ **14.** $-5 = x + 8$

15. $x - 8 = 5$ **16.** $x - 9 = 6$

17. $12 = -7 + y$ **18.** $15 = -8 + z$

19. $-5 + t = -9$ **20.** $-6 + y = -21$

21. $r + \frac{1}{3} = \frac{8}{3}$ **22.** $t + \frac{3}{8} = \frac{5}{8}$

23. $x + \frac{3}{5} = -\frac{7}{10}$ **24.** $x + \frac{2}{3} = -\frac{5}{6}$

25. $x - \frac{5}{6} = \frac{7}{8}$ **26.** $y - \frac{3}{4} = \frac{5}{6}$

27. $-\frac{1}{5} + z = -\frac{1}{4}$ **28.** $-\frac{1}{8} + y = -\frac{3}{4}$

29. $m + 3.9 = 5.4$ **30.** $y + 5.3 = 8.7$

31. $-9.7 = -4.7 + y$ **32.** $-7.8 = 2.8 + x$

Solve using the multiplication principle. Don't forget to check!

33. $5x = 70$ **34.** $3x = 39$

35. $9t = 36$ **36.** $6x = 72$

37. $84 = 7x$ **38.** $56 = 7t$

39. $-x = 23$ **40.** $100 = -x$

Aha! **41.** $-t = -8$ **42.** $-68 = -r$

43. $7x = -49$ **44.** $9x = -36$

45. $-1.3a = -10.4$ **46.** $-3.4t = -20.4$

47. $\frac{y}{-8} = 11$ **48.** $\frac{a}{4} = 13$

49. $\frac{4}{5}x = 16$ **50.** $\frac{3}{4}x = 27$

51. $\frac{-x}{6} = 9$ **52.** $\frac{-t}{5} = 9$

53. $\frac{1}{9} = \frac{z}{5}$ **54.** $\frac{2}{7} = \frac{x}{3}$

Aha! **55.** $-\frac{3}{5}r = -\frac{3}{5}$ **56.** $-\frac{2}{5}y = -\frac{4}{15}$

57. $\frac{-3r}{2} = -\frac{27}{4}$ **58.** $\frac{5x}{7} = -\frac{10}{14}$

Solve. The icon ▦ *indicates an exercise designed to give practice using a calculator.*

59. $4.5 + t = -3.1$

60. $\frac{3}{4}x = 18$

61. $-8.2x = 20.5$

62. $t - 7.4 = -12.9$

63. $x - 4 = -19$

64. $y - 6 = -14$

65. $3 + t = 21$

66. $9 + t = 3$

67. $-12x = 72$

68. $-15x = 105$

69. $48 = -\frac{3}{8}y$

70. $14 = t + 27$

71. $a - \frac{1}{6} = -\frac{2}{3}$

72. $-\frac{x}{7} = \frac{2}{9}$

73. $-24 = \frac{8x}{5}$

74. $\frac{1}{5} + y = -\frac{3}{10}$

75. $-\frac{4}{3}t = -16$

76. $\frac{17}{35} = -x$

▦ **77.** $-483.297 = -794.053 + t$

▦ **78.** $-0.2344x = 2028.732$

79. When solving an equation, how do you determine what number to add, subtract, multiply, or divide by on both sides of that equation?

80. What is the difference between equivalent expressions and equivalent equations?

SKILL MAINTENANCE

Simplify. [1.8]

81. $9 - 2 \cdot 5^2 + 7$

82. $10 \div 2 \cdot 3^2 - 4$

83. $16 \div (2 - 3 \cdot 2) + 5$

84. $12 - 5 \cdot 2^3 + 4 \cdot 3$

SYNTHESIS

85. To solve $-3.5 = 14t$, Anita adds 3.5 to both sides. Will this form an equivalent equation? Will it help solve the equation? Explain.

86. Explain why it is not necessary to state a subtraction principle: For any real numbers a, b, and c, $a = b$ is equivalent to $a - c = b - c$.

Some equations, like $3 = 7$ or $x + 2 = x + 5$, have no solution and are called ***contradictions****. Other equations, like $7 = 7$ or $2x = 2x$, are true for all numbers and are called* ***identities****. Solve each of the following and if an identity or contradiction is found, state this.*

87. $2x = x + x$

88. $x + 5 + x = 2x$

89. $5x = 0$

90. $4x - x = 2x + x$

91. $x + 8 = 3 + x + 7$

92. $3x = 0$

Aha! **93.** $2|x| = -14$

94. $|3x| = 6$

Solve for x. Assume $a, c, m \neq 0$.

95. $mx = 9.4m$

96. $x - 4 + a = a$

97. $cx + 5c = 7c$

98. $c \cdot \frac{21}{a} = \frac{7cx}{2a}$

99. $7 + |x| = 20$

100. $ax - 3a = 5a$

101. If $t - 3590 = 1820$, find $t + 3590$.

102. If $n + 268 = 124$, find $n - 268$.

▦ **103.** Lydia makes a calculation and gets an answer of 22.5. On the last step, she multiplies by 0.3 when she should have divided by 0.3. What should the correct answer be?

104. Are the equations $x = 5$ and $x^2 = 25$ equivalent? Why or why not?

2.2 Using the Principles Together

Applying Both Principles • Combining Like Terms • Clearing Fractions and Decimals

CONNECTING THE CONCEPTS

We have stated that most of algebra involves either simplifying expressions (by writing equivalent expressions) or solving equations (by writing equivalent equations). In Section 2.1, we used the addition and multiplication principles to produce equivalent equations, like $x = 5$, from which the solution—in this case, 5—is obvious. Here in Section 2.2, we will find that more complicated equations can be solved by using both principles together and by using the commutative, associative, and distributive laws to write equivalent expressions.

An important strategy for solving new problems is to find a way to make a new problem look like a problem that we already know how to solve. This is precisely the approach taken in this section. You will find that the last steps of the examples in this section are nearly identical to the steps used for solving the examples of Section 2.1. What is new in this section appears in the early steps of each example.

Applying Both Principles

The addition and multiplication principles, along with the laws discussed in Chapter 1, are our tools for solving equations. In this section, we will find that the sequence and manner in which these tools are used is especially important.

EXAMPLE 1 Solve: $5 + 3x = 17$.

Solution Were we to evaluate $5 + 3x$, the rules for the order of operations direct us to *first* multiply by 3 and *then* add 5. Because of this, we can isolate $3x$ and then x by reversing these operations: We first subtract 5 from both sides and then divide both sides by 3. Our goal is an equivalent equation of the form $x = a$.

	$5 + 3x = 17$	
	$5 + 3x - 5 = 17 - 5$	Using the addition principle: subtracting 5 from both sides (adding -5)
	$5 + (-5) + 3x = 12$	Using a commutative law. Try to perform this step mentally.
First isolate the x-term.	$3x = 12$	Simplifying
	$\frac{3x}{3} = \frac{12}{3}$	Using the multiplication principle: dividing both sides by 3 (multiplying by $\frac{1}{3}$)
Then isolate x.	$x = 4$.	Simplifying

Check:

$$\begin{array}{c|c} 5 + 3x & 17 \\ \hline 5 + 3 \cdot 4 & 17 \\ 5 + 12 & \\ 17 & \stackrel{?}{=} 17 \end{array}$$ TRUE

We use the rules for order of operations: Find the product, $3 \cdot 4$, and then add.

The solution is 4.

EXAMPLE 2 Solve: $\frac{4}{3}x - 7 = 1$.

Solution In $\frac{4}{3}x - 7$, we multiply first and then subtract. To reverse these steps, we first add 7 and then either divide by $\frac{4}{3}$ or multiply by $\frac{3}{4}$.

$$\frac{4}{3}x - 7 = 1$$

$$\frac{4}{3}x - 7 + 7 = 1 + 7 \quad \text{Adding 7 to both sides}$$

$$\frac{4}{3}x = 8$$

$$\frac{3}{4} \cdot \frac{4}{3}x = \frac{3}{4} \cdot 8 \quad \text{Multiplying both sides by } \frac{3}{4}$$

$$\left.\begin{aligned} 1 \cdot x &= \frac{3 \cdot \cancel{4} \cdot 2}{\cancel{4}} \\ x &= 6 \end{aligned}\right\} \quad \text{Simplifying}$$

Check:

$$\begin{array}{c|c} \frac{4}{3}x - 7 & 1 \\ \hline \frac{4}{3} \cdot 6 - 7 & 1 \\ 8 - 7 & \\ 1 & \stackrel{?}{=} 1 \end{array}$$ TRUE

The solution is 6.

Study Skills

Use the Answer Section Carefully

When using the answers listed at the back of this book, try not to "work backward" from the answer. If you frequently require two or more attempts to answer an exercise correctly, you probably need to work more carefully and/or reread the section preceding the exercise set. Remember that on quizzes and tests you have only one attempt per problem and no answer section to check.

EXAMPLE 3 Solve: $45 - t = 13$.

Solution We have

$$45 - t = 13$$

$$45 - t - 45 = 13 - 45 \quad \text{Subtracting 45 from both sides}$$

$$\left.\begin{aligned} 45 + (-t) + (-45) &= 13 - 45 \\ 45 + (-45) + (-t) &= 13 - 45 \end{aligned}\right\} \quad \text{Try to do these steps mentally.}$$

$$-t = -32 \quad \text{Try to go directly to this step.}$$

$$(-1)(-t) = (-1)(-32) \quad \text{Multiplying both sides by } -1 \text{ (Dividing by } -1 \text{ would also work.)}$$

$$t = 32.$$

Check:

$$\begin{array}{r|l} 45 - t & = 13 \\ \hline 45 - 32 & 13 \\ 13 & \stackrel{?}{=} 13 \quad \text{TRUE} \end{array}$$

The solution is 32.

As our skills improve, certain steps can be streamlined.

EXAMPLE 4 Solve: $16.3 - 7.2y = -8.18$.

Solution We have

$$\begin{aligned} 16.3 - 7.2y &= -8.18 \\ 16.3 - 7.2y - 16.3 &= -8.18 - 16.3 && \text{Subtracting 16.3 from both sides} \\ -7.2y &= -24.48 && \text{Simplifying} \\ \frac{-7.2y}{-7.2} &= \frac{-24.48}{-7.2} && \text{Dividing both sides by } -7.2 \\ y &= 3.4. && \text{Simplifying} \end{aligned}$$

Check:

$$\begin{array}{r|l} 16.3 - 7.2y & = -8.18 \\ \hline 16.3 - 7.2(3.4) & -8.18 \\ 16.3 - 24.48 & \\ -8.18 & \stackrel{?}{=} -8.18 \quad \text{TRUE} \end{array}$$

The solution is 3.4.

Combining Like Terms

If like terms appear on the same side of an equation, we combine them and then solve. Should like terms appear on both sides of an equation, we can use the addition principle to rewrite all like terms on one side.

EXAMPLE 5 Solve.

a) $3x + 4x = -14$

b) $2x - 4 = -3x + 1$

c) $6x + 5 - 7x = 10 - 4x + 7$

d) $2 - 5(x + 5) = 3(x - 2) - 1$

Solution

a)

$$\begin{aligned} 3x + 4x &= -14 \\ 7x &= -14 && \text{Combining like terms} \\ \frac{7x}{7} &= \frac{-14}{7} && \text{Dividing both sides by 7} \\ x &= -2 && \text{Simplifying} \end{aligned}$$

The check is left to the student. The solution is -2.

technology connection

Most graphing calculators have a TABLE feature that enables the calculator to evaluate a variable expression for different choices of x. For example, to evaluate $6x + 5 - 7x$ for $x = 0, 1, 2, \ldots$, we first use (Y=) to enter $6x + 5 - 7x$ as y_1. We then use (2ND) (TBLSET) to specify which x-values will be used. Using TblStart $= 0$, ΔTbl $= 1$, and selecting AUTO twice, we can generate a table in which the value of $6x + 5 - 7x$ is listed for values of x starting at 0 and increasing by ones.

X	Y1	
0	5	
1	4	
2	3	
3	2	
4	1	
5	0	
6	−1	

X = 0

1. Create the above table on your graphing calculator. Scroll up and down to extend the table.
2. Enter $10 - 4x + 7$ as y_2. Your table should now have three columns.
3. For what x-value is y_1 the same as y_2? Compare this with the solution of Example 5(c). Is this a reliable way to solve equations? Why or why not?

b) To solve $2x - 4 = -3x + 1$, we must first write only variable terms on one side and only constant terms on the other. This can be done by adding 4 to both sides, to get all constant terms on the right, and $3x$ to both sides, to get all variable terms on the left. We can add 4 first, or $3x$ first, or do both in one step.

> Isolate variable terms on one side and constant terms on the other side.

$$\begin{aligned}
2x - 4 &= -3x + 1 \\
2x + 3x - 4 &= -3x + 3x + 1 && \text{Adding } 3x \text{ to both sides} \\
5x - 4 &= 1 && \text{Simplifying} \\
5x - 4 + 4 &= 1 + 4 && \text{Adding 4 to both sides} \\
5x &= 5 && \text{Combining like terms} \\
\frac{5x}{5} &= \frac{5}{5} && \text{Dividing both sides by 5} \\
x &= 1
\end{aligned}$$

Check:

$$\begin{array}{r|l}
\multicolumn{2}{c}{2x - 4 = -3x + 1} \\ \hline
2 \cdot 1 - 4 & -3 \cdot 1 + 1 \\
2 - 4 & -3 + 1 \\
\multicolumn{2}{c}{-2 \stackrel{?}{=} -2}
\end{array} \qquad \text{TRUE}$$

The solution is 1.

c) $6x + 5 - 7x = 10 - 4x + 7$

$$\begin{aligned}
-x + 5 &= 17 - 4x && \text{Combining like terms within each side} \\
-x + 5 + 4x &= 17 - 4x + 4x && \text{Adding } 4x \text{ to both sides} \\
5 + 3x &= 17 && \text{Simplifying. This is identical to Example 1.} \\
3x &= 12 && \text{Subtracting 5 from both sides} \\
\frac{3x}{3} &= \frac{12}{3} && \text{Dividing both sides by 3} \\
x &= 4
\end{aligned}$$

Check:

$$\begin{array}{r|l}
\multicolumn{2}{c}{6x + 5 - 7x = 10 - 4x + 7} \\ \hline
6 \cdot 4 + 5 - 7 \cdot 4 & 10 - 4 \cdot 4 + 7 \\
24 + 5 - 28 & 10 - 16 + 7 \\
\multicolumn{2}{c}{1 \stackrel{?}{=} 1}
\end{array} \qquad \text{TRUE}$$

The solution is 4.

d) $2 - 5(x + 5) = 3(x - 2) - 1$

$$\begin{aligned}
2 - 5x - 25 &= 3x - 6 - 1 && \text{Using the distributive law. This is now similar to part (c) above.} \\
-5x - 23 &= 3x - 7 && \text{Combining like terms on each side} \\
-5x - 23 + 7 &= 3x && \\
-23 + 7 &= 3x + 5x && \text{Adding 7 and } 5x \text{ to both sides. This isolates the } x\text{-terms on one side and the constant terms on the other.} \\
-16 &= 8x && \text{Simplifying} \\
\frac{-16}{8} &= \frac{8x}{8} && \text{Dividing both sides by 8} \\
-2 &= x
\end{aligned}$$

The student can confirm that -2 checks and is the solution.

Clearing Fractions and Decimals

Equations are generally easier to solve when they do not contain fractions or decimals. The multiplication principle can be used to "clear" fractions or decimals, as shown here.

Clearing Fractions	Clearing Decimals
$\frac{1}{2}x + 5 = \frac{3}{4}$	$2.3x + 7 = 5.4$
$4\left(\frac{1}{2}x + 5\right) = 4 \cdot \frac{3}{4}$	$10(2.3x + 7) = 10 \cdot 5.4$
$2x + 20 = 3$	$23x + 70 = 54$

In each case, the resulting equation is equivalent to the original equation, but easier to solve.

The easiest way to clear an equation of fractions is to multiply *both sides* of the equation by the smallest, or *least*, common denominator.

EXAMPLE 6 Solve: **(a)** $\frac{2}{3}x - \frac{1}{6} = 2x$; **(b)** $\frac{2}{5}(3x + 2) = 8$.

Solution

a) We multiply both sides by 6, the least common denominator:

$$6\left(\frac{2}{3}x - \frac{1}{6}\right) = 6 \cdot 2x \qquad \text{Multiplying both sides by 6}$$

$$6 \cdot \frac{2}{3}x - 6 \cdot \frac{1}{6} = 6 \cdot 2x$$

Caution! Be sure the distributive law is used to multiply *all* the terms by 6.

$$4x - 1 = 12x$$
Simplifying. Note that the fractions are cleared: $6 \cdot \frac{2}{3} = 4$, $6 \cdot \frac{1}{6} = 1$, and $6 \cdot 2 = 12$.

$$-1 = 8x \qquad \text{Subtracting } 4x \text{ from both sides}$$

$$\frac{-1}{8} = \frac{8x}{8} \qquad \text{Dividing both sides by 8}$$

$$-\frac{1}{8} = x$$

The student can confirm that $-\frac{1}{8}$ checks and is the solution.

b) To solve $\frac{2}{5}(3x + 2) = 8$, we can multiply both sides by $\frac{5}{2}$ (or divide by $\frac{2}{5}$) to "undo" the multiplication by $\frac{2}{5}$ on the left side.

$$\frac{5}{2} \cdot \frac{2}{5}(3x + 2) = \frac{5}{2} \cdot 8 \qquad \text{Multiplying both sides by } \frac{5}{2}$$

$$3x + 2 = 20 \qquad \text{Simplifying; } \frac{5}{2} \cdot \frac{2}{5} = 1 \text{ and } \frac{5}{2} \cdot \frac{8}{1} = 20$$

$$3x = 18 \qquad \text{Subtracting 2 from both sides}$$

$$x = 6 \qquad \text{Dividing both sides by 3}$$

The student can confirm that 6 checks and is the solution.

To clear an equation of decimals, we count the greatest number of decimal places in any one number. If the greatest number of decimal places is 1, we multiply both sides by 10; if it is 2, we multiply by 100; and so on. This procedure is the same as multiplying by the least common denominator after converting the decimals to fractions.

EXAMPLE 7 Solve: $16.3 - 7.2y = -8.18$.

Solution The greatest number of decimal places in any one number is *two*. Multiplying by 100 will clear all decimals.

$100(16.3 - 7.2y) = 100(-8.18)$	Multiplying both sides by 100
$100(16.3) - 100(7.2y) = 100(-8.18)$	Using the distributive law
$1630 - 720y = -818$	Simplifying
$-720y = -818 - 1630$	Subtracting 1630 from both sides
$-720y = -2448$	Combining like terms
$y = \dfrac{-2448}{-720}$	Dividing both sides by -720
$y = 3.4$	

In Example 4, the same solution was found without clearing decimals. Finding the same answer in two ways is a good check. The solution is 3.4.

Student Notes

Compare the steps of Examples 4 and 7. Note that although the two approaches differ, they yield the same solution. Whenever you can use two approaches to solve a problem, try to do so, both as a check and as a valuable learning experience.

An Equation-Solving Procedure

1. Use the multiplication principle to clear any fractions or decimals. (This is optional, but can ease computations. See Examples 6 and 7.)
2. If necessary, use the distributive law to remove parentheses. Then combine like terms on each side. (See Example 5.)
3. Use the addition principle, as needed, to isolate all variable terms on one side. Then combine like terms. (See Examples 1–7.)
4. Multiply or divide to solve for the variable, using the multiplication principle. (See Examples 1–7.)
5. Check all possible solutions in the original equation. (See Examples 1–5.)

2.2 Exercise Set

FOR EXTRA HELP

Student's Solutions Manual | Digital Video Tutor CD 1 Videotape 3 | AW Math Tutor Center | MathXL Tutorials on CD | MathXL | MyMathLab

Concept Reinforcement *In each of Exercises 1–6, match the equation with an equivalent equation from the column on the right that could be the next step in finding a solution.*

1. ____ $3x - 1 = 7$ **a)** $6x - 6 = 2$
2. ____ $4x + 5x = 12$ **b)** $4x + 2x = 3$
3. ____ $6(x - 1) = 2$ **c)** $3x = 7 + 1$
4. ____ $7x = 9$ **d)** $8x + 2x = 6 + 5$
5. ____ $4x = 3 - 2x$ **e)** $9x = 12$
6. ____ $8x - 5 = 6 - 2x$ **f)** $x = \frac{9}{7}$

Solve and check.

7. $2x + 9 = 25$
8. $3x + 6 = 30$
9. $6z + 4 = 46$
10. $6z + 3 = 57$
11. $7t - 8 = 27$
12. $6x - 3 = 15$
13. $3x - 9 = 33$
14. $5x - 9 = 41$
15. $8z + 2 = -54$
16. $4x + 3 = -21$
17. $-91 = 9t + 8$
18. $-39 = 1 + 8x$
19. $12 - 4x = 108$
20. $9 - 4x = 37$
21. $-6z - 18 = -132$
22. $-7x - 24 = -129$
23. $4x + 5x = 10$
24. $13 = 5x + 7x$
25. $32 - 7x = 11$
26. $27 - 6x = 99$
27. $\frac{3}{5}t - 1 = 8$
28. $\frac{2}{3}t - 1 = 5$
29. $4 + \frac{7}{2}x = -10$
30. $6 + \frac{5}{4}x = -4$
31. $-\frac{3a}{4} - 5 = 2$
32. $-\frac{7a}{8} - 2 = 1$
33. $-5z - 6z = -44$
34. $-3z + 8z = 45$
35. $4x - 6 = 6x$
36. $9y - 35 = 4y$
37. $5y - 2 = 28 - y$
38. $6x - 5 = 7 + 2x$
39. $7(2a - 1) = 21$
40. $5(2t - 2) = 30$

Aha! **41.** $8 = 8(x + 1)$
42. $9 = 3(5x - 2)$
43. $2(3 + 4m) - 6 = 48$
44. $3(5 + 3m) - 8 = 88$
45. $7r - (2r + 8) = 32$
46. $6b - (3b + 8) = 16$
47. $6x + 3 = 2x + 3$
48. $5y + 3 = 2y + 15$
49. $5 - 2x = 3x - 7x + 25$
50. $10 - 3x = 2x - 8x + 40$
51. $7 + 3x - 6 = 3x + 5 - x$
52. $5 + 4x - 7 = 4x - 2 - x$
53. $4y - 4 + y + 24 = 6y + 20 - 4y$
54. $5y - 10 + y = 7y + 18 - 5y$
55. $13 - 3(2x - 1) = 4$
56. $5(d + 4) = 7(d - 2)$
57. $7(5x - 2) = 6(6x - 1)$
58. $5(t + 3) + 9 = 3(t - 2) + 6$
59. $19 - (2x + 3) = 2(x + 3) + x$
60. $13 - (2c + 2) = 2(c + 2) + 3c$

Clear fractions or decimals, solve, and check.

61. $\frac{5}{4}x + \frac{1}{4}x = 2x + \frac{1}{2} + \frac{3}{4}x$
62. $\frac{7}{8}x - \frac{1}{4} + \frac{3}{4}x = \frac{1}{16} + x$
63. $\frac{2}{3} + \frac{1}{4}t = 6$
64. $-\frac{1}{2} + x = -\frac{5}{6} - \frac{1}{3}$
65. $\frac{2}{3} + 4t = 6t - \frac{2}{15}$
66. $\frac{1}{2} + 4m = 3m - \frac{5}{2}$
67. $\frac{1}{3}x + \frac{2}{5} = \frac{4}{15} + \frac{3}{5}x - \frac{2}{3}$
68. $1 - \frac{2}{3}y = \frac{9}{5} - \frac{1}{5}y + \frac{3}{5}$
69. $2.1x + 45.2 = 3.2 - 8.4x$

70. $0.91 - 0.2z = 1.23 - 0.6z$

71. $0.76 + 0.21t = 0.96t - 0.49$

72. $1.7t + 8 - 1.62t = 0.4t - 0.32 + 8$

73. $\frac{2}{5}x - \frac{3}{2}x = \frac{3}{4}x + 2$

74. $\frac{5}{16}y + \frac{3}{8}y = 2 + \frac{1}{4}y$

75. $\frac{1}{3}(2x - 1) = 7$

76. $\frac{4}{3}(5x + 1) = 8$

77. $\frac{3}{4}(3t - 6) = 9$

78. $\frac{3}{2}(2x + 5) = -\frac{15}{2}$

79. $\frac{1}{6}\left(\frac{3}{4}x - 2\right) = -\frac{1}{5}$

80. $\frac{2}{3}\left(\frac{7}{8} - 4x\right) - \frac{5}{8} = \frac{3}{8}$

81. $0.7(3x + 6) = 1.1 - (x + 2)$

82. $0.9(2x + 8) = 20 - (x + 5)$

83. $a + (a - 3) = (a + 2) - (a + 1)$

84. $0.8 - 4(b - 1) = 0.2 + 3(4 - b)$

85. When an equation contains decimals, is it essential to clear the equation of decimals? Why or why not?

86. Why must the rules for the order of operations be understood before solving the equations in this section?

SKILL MAINTENANCE

Evaluate. [1.8]

87. $3 - 5a$, for $a = 2$

88. $12 \div 4 \cdot t$, for $t = 5$

89. $7x - 2x$, for $x = -3$

90. $t(8 - 3t)$, for $t = -2$

SYNTHESIS

91. What procedure would you follow to solve an equation like $0.23x + \frac{17}{3} = -0.8 + \frac{3}{4}x$? Could your procedure be streamlined? If so, how?

92. Dave is determined to solve the equation $3x + 4 = -11$ by first using the multiplication principle to "eliminate" the 3. How should he proceed and why?

Solve. If an equation is an identity or a contradiction (see p. 88), state this.

93. $8.43x - 2.5(3.2 - 0.7x) = -3.455x + 9.04$

94. $0.008 + 9.62x - 42.8 = 0.944x + 0.0083 - x$

95. $-2[3(x - 2) + 4] = 4(5 - x) - 2x$

96. $0 = y - (-14) - (-3y)$

97. $3(x + 4) = 3(4 + x)$

98. $5(x - 7) = 3(x - 2) + 2x$

99. $2x(x + 5) - 3(x^2 + 2x - 1) = 9 - 5x - x^2$

100. $x(x - 4) = 3x(x + 1) - 2(x^2 + x - 5)$

101. $9 - 3x = 2(5 - 2x) - (1 - 5x)$

102. $2(7 - x) - 20 = 7x - 3(2 + 3x)$

Aha! **103.** $[7 - 2(8 \div (-2))]x = 0$

104. $\frac{x}{14} - \frac{5x + 2}{49} = \frac{3x - 4}{7}$

105. $\frac{5x + 3}{4} + \frac{25}{12} = \frac{5 + 2x}{3}$

COLLABORATIVE CORNER

Step-by-Step Solutions

Focus: Solving linear equations

Time: 20 minutes

Group size: 3

In general, there is more than one correct sequence of steps for solving an equation. This makes it important that you write your steps clearly and logically so that others can follow your approach.

ACTIVITY

1. Each group member should select a different one of the following equations and, on a fresh sheet of paper, perform the first step of the solution.

$$4 - 3(x - 3) = 7x + 6(2 - x)$$
$$5 - 7[x - 2(x - 6)] = 3x + 4(2x - 7) + 9$$
$$4x - 7[2 + 3(x - 5) + x] = 4 - 9(-3x - 19)$$

2. Pass the papers around so that the second and third steps of each solution are performed by the other two group members. Before writing, make sure that the previous step is correct. If a mistake is discovered, return the problem to the person who made the mistake for repairs. Continue passing the problems around until all equations have been solved.
3. Each group should reach a consensus on what the three solutions are and then compare their answers to those of other groups.

2.3 Formulas

Evaluating Formulas • Solving for a Letter

Many applications of mathematics involve relationships among two or more quantities. An equation that represents such a relationship will use two or more letters and is known as a **formula**. Although most of the letters in this book represent variables, some—like c in $E = mc^2$ or π in $C = \pi d$—represent constants.

Evaluating Formulas

EXAMPLE 1 Outdoor concerts. The formula $d = 344t$ can be used to determine how far d, in meters, sound travels through room-temperature air in one second. In 2003,

technology connection

Sometimes we may wish to recall and modify a calculation. For example, suppose that after calculating $30 \cdot 1800$ we wish to find $30 \cdot 1870$. Pressing 2ND ENTRY gives the following.

```
30 * 1800
                54000
30 * 1800█
```

Moving the cursor left, we can change 1800 to 1870 and press ENTER.

```
30 * 1800
                54000
30 * 1870
                56100
```

1. Verify the work above and then use 2ND ENTRY to find $39 \cdot 1870$.

the Dave Matthews Band performed in New York City's Central Park. Fans near the back of the crowd experienced a 0.9-sec time lag between the time each word was pronounced on stage (as shown on large video monitors) and the time the sound reached their ears. How far were these fans from the stage?

Solution We substitute 0.9 for t in $d = 344t$ and calculate d:

$$d = 344(0.9) = 309.6.$$

The fans were about 309.6 m from the stage.

Solving for a Letter

In the Northeast, the formula $B = 30a$ is used to determine the minimum furnace output B, in British thermal units (Btu's), for a well-insulated home with a square feet of flooring. Suppose that a contractor has an extra furnace and wants to determine the size of the largest (well-insulated) house in which it can be used. The contractor can substitute the amount of the furnace's output in Btu's—say, 63,000—for B, and then solve for a:

$63{,}000 = 30a$ Replacing B with 63,000

$2100 = a.$ Dividing both sides by 30

The home should have no more than 2100 ft^2 of flooring.

Were these calculations to be performed for a variety of furnaces, the contractor would find it easier to first solve $B = 30a$ for a, and *then* substitute values for B. This can be done in much the same way that we solved equations in Sections 2.1 and 2.2.

EXAMPLE 2 Solve for a: $B = 30a$.

Solution We have

$B = 30a$ We want this letter alone.

$\dfrac{B}{30} = a.$ Dividing both sides by 30

The equation $a = B/30$ gives a quick, easy way to determine the floor area of the largest (well-insulated) house that a furnace supplying B Btu's could heat.

To see how solving a formula is just like solving an equation, compare the following. In (A), we solve as usual; in (B), we show steps but do not simplify; and in (C), we *cannot* simplify since *a*, *b*, and *c* are unknown.

A. $5x + 2 = 12$

$$5x = 12 - 2$$
$$5x = 10$$
$$x = \frac{10}{5} = 2$$

B. $5x + 2 = 12$

$$5x = 12 - 2$$
$$x = \frac{12 - 2}{5}$$

C. $ax + b = c$

$$ax = c - b$$
$$x = \frac{c - b}{a}$$

EXAMPLE 3 Circumference of a circle. The formula $C = 2\pi r$ gives the *circumference C* of a circle with radius *r*. Solve for *r*.

Solution The **circumference** is the distance around a circle.

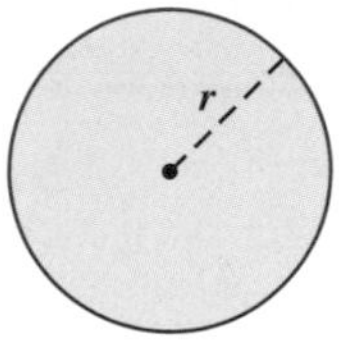

Given a radius *r*, we can use this equation to find a circle's circumference *C*.

$$C = 2\pi r \qquad \text{We want this letter alone.}$$

$$\frac{C}{2\pi} = \frac{2\pi r}{2\pi} \qquad \text{Dividing both sides by } 2\pi$$

$$\frac{C}{2\pi} = r$$

Given a circle's circumference *C*, we can use this equation to find the radius *r*.

EXAMPLE 4 Nutrition. The number of calories *K* needed each day by a moderately active woman who weighs *w* pounds, is *h* inches tall, and is *a* years old, can be estimated using the formula

$$K = 917 + 6(w + h - a).*$$

Solve for *w*.

Solution We reverse the order in which the operations occur on the right side:

We want *w* alone.

$$K = 917 + 6(w + h - a)$$

$$K - 917 = 6(w + h - a) \qquad \text{Subtracting 917 from both sides}$$

$$\frac{K - 917}{6} = w + h - a \qquad \text{Dividing both sides by 6}$$

$$\frac{K - 917}{6} + a - h = w. \qquad \text{Adding } a \text{ and subtracting } h \text{ on both sides}$$

This formula can be used to estimate a woman's weight, if we know her age, height, and caloric needs.

*Based on information from M. Parker (ed.), *She Does Math*! (Washington D.C.: Mathematical Association of America, 1995), p. 96.

The above steps are similar to those used in Section 2.2 to solve equations. We use the addition and multiplication principles just as before. An important difference that we will see in the next example is that we will sometimes need to factor.

To Solve a Formula for a Given Letter

1. If the letter for which you are solving appears in a fraction, use the multiplication principle to clear fractions.
2. Isolate the term(s), with the letter you are solving for on one side of the equation.
3. If two or more terms contain the letter you are solving for, factor the letter out.
4. Multiply or divide to solve for the letter in question.

EXAMPLE 5 Solve for x: $y = ax + bx - 4$.

Solution We solve as follows:

$y = ax + bx - 4$ We want this letter alone.

$y + 4 = ax + bx$ Adding 4 to both sides

$y + 4 = x(a + b)$ Factoring

$\dfrac{y + 4}{a + b} = x.$ Dividing both sides by $a + b$, or multiplying both sides by $1/(a + b)$

We can also write this as

$$x = \frac{y + 4}{a + b}.$$

Study Skills

How Did They Get That!?

The *Student's Solutions Manual* is an excellent resource if you need additional help with an exercise in the exercise sets. It contains step-by-step solutions to the odd-numbered exercises in each exercise set.

Caution! Had we performed the following steps in Example 5, we would *not* have solved for x:

$y = ax + bx - 4$

$y - ax + 4 = bx$ Subtracting ax and adding 4 to both sides

Two occurrences of x

$\dfrac{y - ax + 4}{b} = x.$ Dividing both sides by b

The mathematics of each step is correct, but since x occurs on both sides of the formula, *we have not solved the formula for x.* Remember that the letter being solved for should be alone on one side of the equation, with no occurrence of that letter on the other side!

2.3 Exercise Set

FOR EXTRA HELP

Student's Solutions Manual | Digital Video Tutor CD 1 Videotape 3 | AW Math Tutor Center | MathXL Tutorials on CD | MathXL | MyMathLab

1. *Distance from a storm.* The formula $M = \frac{1}{5}t$ can be used to determine how far M, in miles, you are from lightning when its thunder takes t seconds to reach your ears. If it takes 10 sec for the sound of thunder to reach you after you have seen the lightning, how far away is the storm?

2. *Electrical power.* The power rating P, in watts, of an electrical appliance is determined by
$$P = I \cdot V,$$
where I is the current, in amperes, and V is the voltage, measured in volts. If a kitchen requires 30 amps of current and the voltage in the house is 115 volts, what is the wattage of the kitchen?

3. *College enrollment.* At many colleges, the number of "full-time-equivalent" students f is given by
$$f = \frac{n}{15},$$
where n is the total number of credits for which students have enrolled in a given semester. Determine the number of full-time-equivalent students on a campus in which students registered for a total of 21,345 credits.

4. *Wavelength of a musical note.* The wavelength w, in meters per cycle, of a musical note is given by
$$w = \frac{r}{f},$$
where r is the speed of the sound, in meters per second, and f is the frequency, in cycles per second. The speed of sound in air is 344 m/sec. What is the wavelength of a note whose frequency in air is 24 cycles per second?

5. *Furnace output.* Contractors in the Northeast use the formula $B = 30a$ to determine the minimum furnace output B, in British thermal units (Btu's), for a well-insulated house with a square feet of flooring. Determine the minimum furnace output for an 1800-ft^2 house that is well insulated.
Source: U.S. Department of Energy

6. *Calorie density.* The calorie density D, in calories per ounce, of a food that contains c calories and weighs w ounces is given by
$$D = \frac{c}{w}.*$$
Eight ounces of fat-free milk contains 84 calories. Find the calorie density of fat-free milk.

7. *Absorption of ibuprofen.* When 400 mg of the painkiller ibuprofen is swallowed, the number of milligrams n in the bloodstream t hours later (for $0 \le t \le 6$) is estimated by
$$n = 0.5t^4 + 3.45t^3 - 96.65t^2 + 347.7t.$$
How many milligrams of ibuprofen remain in the blood 1 hr after 400 mg has been swallowed?

8. *Size of a league schedule.* When all n teams in a league play every other team twice, a total of N games are played, where
$$N = n^2 - n.$$
If a soccer league has 7 teams and all teams play each other twice, how many games are played?

Solve each formula for the indicated letter.

9. $A = bh$, for b
(Area of parallelogram with base b and height h)

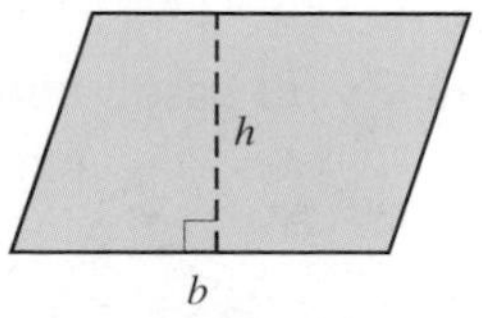

*Source: *Nutrition Action Healthletter*, March 2000, p. 9. Center for Science in the Public Interest, Suite 300; 1875 Connecticut Ave NW, Washington, D.C. 20008.

10. $A = bh$, for h

11. $d = rt$, for r
(A distance formula, where d is distance, r is speed, and t is time)

12. $d = rt$, for t

13. $I = Prt$, for P
(Simple-interest formula, where I is interest, P is principal, r is interest rate, and t is time)

14. $I = Prt$, for t

15. $H = 65 - m$, for m
(To determine the number of heating degree days H for a day with m degrees Fahrenheit as the average temperature)

16. $d = h - 64$, for h
(To determine how many inches d above average an h-inch-tall woman is)

17. $P = 2l + 2w$, for l
(Perimeter of a rectangle of length l and width w)

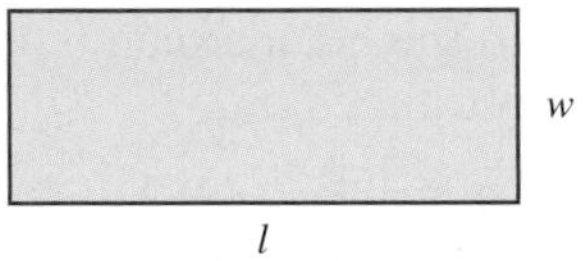

18. $P = 2l + 2w$, for w

19. $A = \pi r^2$, for π
(Area of a circle with radius r)

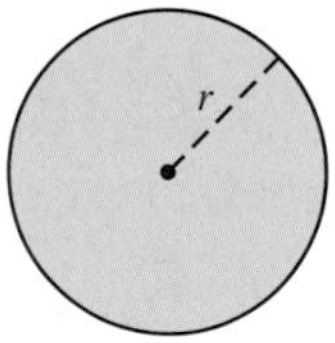

20. $A = \pi r^2$, for r^2

21. $A = \frac{1}{2}bh$, for h
(Area of a triangle with base b and height h)

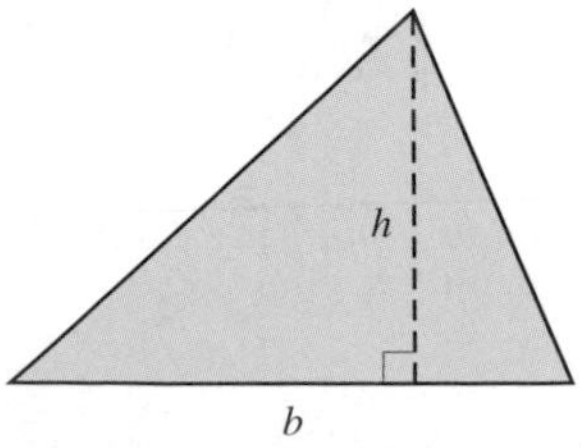

22. $A = \frac{1}{2}bh$, for b

23. $E = mc^2$, for m
(A relativity formula from physics)

24. $E = mc^2$, for c^2

25. $Q = \dfrac{c + d}{2}$, for d

26. $Q = \dfrac{p - q}{2}$, for p

27. $A = \dfrac{a + b + c}{3}$, for b

28. $A = \dfrac{a + b + c}{3}$, for c

29. $M = \dfrac{A}{s}$, for A
(To compute the Mach number M for speed A and speed of sound s)

30. $P = \dfrac{ab}{c}$, for b

31. $F = \dfrac{9}{5}C + 32$, for C
(To convert the Celsius temperature C to the Fahrenheit temperature F)

32. $M = \dfrac{3}{7}n + 29$, for n

33. $A = at + bt$, for t

34. $S = rx + sx$, for x

35. *Area of a trapezoid.* The formula

$$A = \tfrac{1}{2}ah + \tfrac{1}{2}bh$$

can be used to find the area A of a trapezoid with bases a and b and height h. Solve for h. (*Hint*: First clear fractions.)

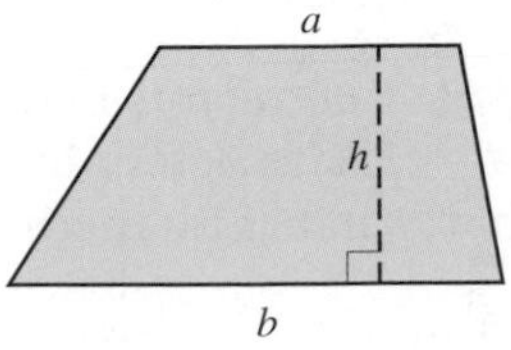

36. *Compounding interest.* The formula

$$A = P + Prt$$

is used to find the amount A in an account when simple interest is added to an investment of P dollars (see Exercise 13). Solve for P.

37. *Chess rating.* The formula

$$R = r + \frac{400(W - L)}{N}$$

is used to establish a chess player's rating R after that player has played N games, won W of them, and lost L of them. Here r is the average rating of the opponents. Solve for L.
Source: The U.S. Chess Federation

38. *Angle measure.* The angle measure S, of a sector of a circle, is given by

$$S = \frac{360A}{\pi r^2},$$

where r is the radius, A is the area of the sector, and S is in degrees. Solve for r^2.

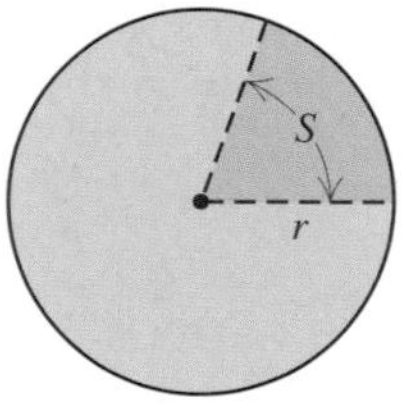

39. Naomi has a formula that allows her to convert Celsius temperatures to Fahrenheit temperatures. She needs a formula for converting Fahrenheit temperatures to Celsius temperatures. What advice can you give her?

40. Under what circumstances would it be useful to solve $d = rt$ for r? (See Exercise 11.)

SKILL MAINTENANCE

Multiply. [1.7]

Aha! 41. $0.79(38.4)0$

42. $(0.085)(108)$

Simplify. [1.8]

43. $20 \div (-4) \cdot 2 - 3$

44. $5|8 - (2 - 7)|$

SYNTHESIS

45. The equations

$$P = 2l + 2w \quad \text{and} \quad w = \frac{P}{2} - l$$

are equivalent formulas involving the perimeter P, length l, and width w of a rectangle. Devise a problem for which the second of the two formulas would be more useful.

46. While solving $2A = ah + bh$ for h, Lea writes $\frac{2A - ah}{b} = h$. What is her mistake?

47. The number of calories K needed each day by a moderately active man who weighs w kilograms, is h centimeters tall, and is a years old, can be determined by

$$K = 19.18w + 7h - 9.52a + 92.4.^*$$

If Janos is moderately active, weighs 82 kg, is 185 cm tall, and needs to consume 2627 calories a day, how old is he?

48. *Altitude and temperature.* Air temperature drops about 1° Celsius (C) for each 100-m rise above ground level, up to 12 km. If the ground level temperature is t°C, find a formula for the temperature T at an elevation of h meters.
Source: *A Sourcebook of School Mathematics*, Mathematical Association of America, 1980

49. *Surface area of a cube.* The surface area A of a cube with side s is given by

$$A = 6s^2.$$

If a cube's surface area is 54 in^2, find the volume of the cube.

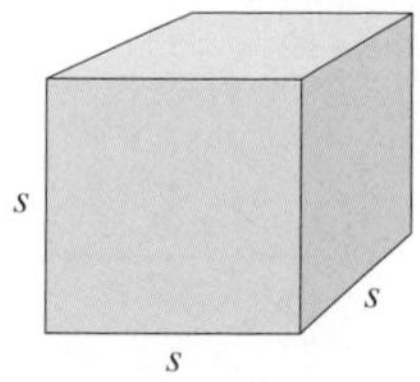

*Based on information from M. Parker (ed.), *She Does Math!* (Washington DC: Mathematical Association of America, 1995), p. 96.

50. *Weight of a fish.* An ancient fisherman's formula for estimating the weight of a fish is

$$w = \frac{lg^2}{800},$$

where w is the weight, in pounds, l is the length, in inches, and g is the girth (distance around the midsection), in inches. Estimate the girth of a 700-lb yellow tuna that is 8 ft long.

51. *Dosage size.* Clark's rule for determining the size of a particular child's medicine dosage c is

$$c = \frac{w}{a} \cdot d,$$

where w is the child's weight, in pounds, and d is the usual adult dosage for an adult weighing a pounds. Solve for a.
Source: Olsen, June Looby, et al., *Medical Dosage Calculations.* Redwood City, CA: Addison-Wesley, 1995

Solve each formula for the given letter.

52. $\frac{y}{z} \div \frac{z}{t} = 1$, for y

53. $ac = bc + d$, for c

54. $qt = r(s + t)$, for t

55. $3a = c - a(b + d)$, for a

56. *Furnace output.* The formula

$$B = 50a$$

is used in New England to estimate the minimum furnace output B, in Btu's, for an old, poorly insulated house with a square feet of flooring. Find an equation for determining the number of Btu's saved by insulating an old house. (*Hint*: See Exercise 5.)

57. Revise the formula in Example 4 so that a woman's weight in kilograms (2.2046 lb = 1 kg) and her height in centimeters (0.3937 in. = 1 cm) are used.

58. Revise the formula in Exercise 47 so that a man's weight in pounds (2.2046 lb = 1 kg) and his height in inches (0.3937 in. = 1 cm) are used.

2.4 Applications with Percent

Converting Between Percent Notation and Decimal Notation • Solving Percent Problems

Percent problems arise so frequently in everyday life that most often we are not even aware of them. In this section, we will solve some real-world percent problems. Before doing so, however, we need to review a few basics.

Study Skills

Pace Yourself

Most instructors agree that it is better for a student to study for one hour four days in a week, than to study once a week for four hours. Of course, the total weekly study time will vary from student to student. It is common to expect an average of two hours of homework for each hour of class time.

Converting Between Percent Notation and Decimal Notation

Nutritionists recommend that no more than 30% of the calories in a person's diet come from fat. This means that of every 100 calories consumed, no more than 30 should come from fat. Thus, 30% is a ratio of 30 to 100.

The percent symbol % means "per hundred." We can regard the percent symbol as part of a name for a number. For example,

$$30\% \quad \text{is defined to mean} \quad \frac{30}{100}, \quad \text{or} \quad 30 \times \frac{1}{100}, \quad \text{or} \quad 30 \times 0.01.$$

Percent Notation

$$n\% \quad \text{means} \quad \frac{n}{100}, \quad \text{or} \quad n \times \frac{1}{100}, \quad \text{or} \quad n \times 0.01.$$

EXAMPLE 1 Convert to decimal notation: **(a)** 78%; **(b)** 1.3%.

Solution

a) $78\% = 78 \times 0.01$ Replacing % with $\times 0.01$
$= 0.78$

b) $1.3\% = 1.3 \times 0.01$ Replacing % with $\times 0.01$
$= 0.013$

As shown above, multiplication by 0.01 simply moves the decimal point two places to the left.

To convert from percent notation to decimal notation, move the decimal point two places to the left and drop the percent symbol.

EXAMPLE 2 Convert the percent notation in the following sentence to decimal notation: 60% of the pollution from a typical car trip is emitted in the first few minutes (*Source*: Chittenden County Transportation Authority).

Solution

$60\% = 60.0\%$ 0.60.0 $60\% = 0.60$, or simply 0.6

Move the decimal point two places to the left.

The procedure used in Examples 1 and 2 can be reversed:

$$\begin{aligned} 0.38 &= 38 \times 0.01 \\ &= 38\%. \qquad \text{Replacing } \times 0.01 \text{ with } \% \end{aligned}$$

To convert from decimal notation to percent notation, move the decimal point two places to the right and write a percent symbol.

EXAMPLE 3 Convert to percent notation: **(a)** 1.27; **(b)** $\frac{1}{4}$; **(c)** 0.3.

Solution

a) We first move the decimal point two places to the right: 1.27.
and then write a % symbol: 127% — This is the same as multiplying 1.27 by 100 and writing %.

b) Note that $\frac{1}{4} = 0.25$. We move the decimal point two places to the right: 0.25.
and then write a % symbol: 25% — Multiplying by 100 and writing %

c) We first move the decimal point two places to the right (recall that $0.3 = 0.30$): 0.30.
and then write a % symbol: 30% — Multiplying by 100 and writing %

Solving Percent Problems

In solving percent problems, we first *translate* the problem to an equation. Then we *solve* the equation using the techniques discussed in Sections 2.1–2.3. The key words in the translation are as follows.

Key Words in Percent Translations

"**Of**" translates to " · " or " × ".

"**Is**" or "**Was**" translates to " = ".

"**What**" translates to a variable.

% translates to "$\times\frac{1}{100}$" or "×0.01".

EXAMPLE 4 What is 11% of 49?

Solution

Translate: What is 11% of 49?

$$a = 0.11 \cdot 49 \qquad \text{"of" means multiply; } 11\% = 0.11$$

$$a = 5.39$$

Thus, 5.39 is 11% of 49. The answer is 5.39.

Student Notes

A way of checking answers is by estimating as follows:

$$\begin{aligned} 11\% \times 49 &\approx 10\% \times 50 \\ &= 0.10 \times 50 = 5. \end{aligned}$$

Since 5 is close to 5.39, our answer is reasonable.

EXAMPLE 5 3 is 16 percent of what?

Solution

Translate: 3 is $\underbrace{\text{16 percent}}$ of what?

$$3 = 0.16 \cdot y$$

$$\frac{3}{0.16} = y \qquad \text{Dividing both sides by 0.16}$$

$$18.75 = y$$

Thus, 3 is 16 percent of 18.75. The answer is 18.75.

EXAMPLE 6 What percent of \$50 is \$34?

Solution

Translate: $\underbrace{\text{What percent}}$ of \$50 is \$34?

$$n \cdot 50 = 34$$

$$n = \frac{34}{50} \qquad \text{Dividing both sides by 50}$$

$$n = 0.68 = 68\% \qquad \text{Converting to percent notation}$$

Thus, 34 is 68% of 50. The answer is 68%.

Examples 4–6 represent the three basic types of percent problems.

EXAMPLE 7 Coronary heart disease. In 2003, there were 285 million people in the United States. About 2.5% of them had heart disease (*Source*: American Heart Association). How many had heart disease?

Student Notes

Always look for connections between examples. Here you should look for similarities between Examples 4 and 7 as well as between Examples 5 and 8 and between Examples 6 and 9.

Solution To solve the problem, we first reword and then translate. We let a = the number of people in the United States with heart disease.

Rewording: What is 2.5% of 285?

Translating: $a = 0.025 \times 285$

The letter is by itself. To solve the equation, we need only multiply:

$$a = 0.025 \times 285 = 7.125.$$

Thus, 7.125 million is 2.5% of 285 million, so in 2003, about 7.125 million people in the United States had heart disease.

EXAMPLE 8 Two-year college enrollments. In 2003, about 5.6 million students were enrolled in two-year institutions. This number was 38% of all enrollments in higher education. How many students in all were enrolled in higher education?

Solution Before translating the problem to mathematics, we reword and let S represent the total number of students, in millions, enrolled in higher education.

Rewording:	5.6	is	38%	of	S.
	↓	↓	↓	↓	↓
Translate:	5.6	$=$	0.38	$\cdot$	S

$$\frac{5.6}{0.38} = S$$

$$14.7 \approx S$$ The symbol $\approx$ means *is approximately equal to.*

There were about 14.7 million students enrolled in higher education in 2003.

EXAMPLE 9 Automobile prices. Recently, Harken Motors reduced the price of a 2003 Ford Focus from the manufacturer's suggested retail price (MSRP) of $17,500 to $15,925.

a) What percent of the MSRP does the sale price represent?

b) What is the percent of discount?

Solution

a) We reword and translate, using n for the unknown percent.

Rewording:	What percent	of	17,500	is	15,925?
	↓	↓	↓	↓	↓
Translating:	n	$\cdot$	17,500	$=$	15,925

$$n = \frac{15{,}925}{17{,}500}$$ Dividing both sides by 17,500

$$n = 0.91 = 91\%$$ Converting to percent notation

The sale price is 91% of the MSRP.

b) Since the original price of $17,500 represents 100% of the MSRP, the sale price represents a discount of $(100 - 91)\%$, or 9%.

2.4 Exercise Set

FOR EXTRA HELP

Student's Solutions Manual | Digital Video Tutor CD 1 Videotape 3 | AW Math Tutor Center | MathXL Tutorials on CD | MathXL | MyMathLab

Concept Reinforcement *In each of Exercises 1–10, match the question with the most appropriate translation from the column on the right. Some choices are used more than once.*

1. ____ What percent of 57 is 23?
2. ____ What percent of 23 is 57?
3. ____ 23 is 57% of what number?
4. ____ 57 is 23% of what number?
5. ____ 57 is what percent of 23?
6. ____ 23 is what percent of 57?
7. ____ What is 23% of 57?
8. ____ What is 57% of 23?
9. ____ 23% of what number is 57?
10. ____ 57% of what number is 23?

a) $a = (0.57)23$
b) $57 = 0.23y$
c) $n \cdot 23 = 57$
d) $n \cdot 57 = 23$
e) $23 = 0.57y$
f) $a = (0.23)57$

Convert the percent notation in each sentence to decimal notation.

11. *Pluto.* The planet Pluto is 30% ice.
Source: www.childrensmuseum.org/cosmicquest/fieldguide/pluto.html

12. *Pluto.* The planet Pluto is 70% rock.
Source: www.childrensmuseum.org/cosmicquest/fieldguide/pluto.html

13. *Dehydration.* A 2% drop in water content of the body can affect one's ability to study mathematics.
Source: High Performance Nutrition

14. *Left-handed golfers.* Of those who golf, 7% are left-handed.
Source: National Association of Left-Handed Golfers

15. *Wealth in the aged.* Those 60 and older own 77% of the nation's financial assets.

16. *Wealth in the aged.* Those 60 and older make up 66% of the nation's stockholders.

17. *Women in the workforce.* Women comprise 9% of all engineers.

18. *Women in the workforce.* Women comprise 30% of all chemists.

Convert to decimal notation.

19. 62.58%
20. 39.81%
21. 0.7%
22. 0.3%
23. 125%
24. 150%

Convert the decimal notation in each sentence to percent notation.

25. *NASCAR fans.* Of those who are fans of NASCAR racing, 0.64 of them have attended college or beyond.
Source: NASCAR, Goodyear

26. *NASCAR fans.* Of those who are fans of NASCAR racing, 0.41 of them earn more than $50,000 per year.
Source: NASCAR, Goodyear

27. *Foreign student enrollment.* Of all the foreign students studying in the United States, 0.106 are from China.
Source: Institute of International Education

28. *Heart attacks.* Of those suffering heart attacks, 0.67 will survive.
Source: American Heart Association

29. *Women in the workforce.* Women comprise 0.42 of all college faculty.

30. *Women in the workforce.* Women comprise 0.19 of all architects.

31. *Water in watermelon.* Watermelon is 0.9 water.

32. *Tax savings.* The tax cut enacted in 2003 will save 0.88 of all U.S. taxpayers less than $100.
Source: Citizens for Tax Justice

Convert to percent notation.

33. 0.0049
34. 0.0008
35. 1.08
36. 1.05
37. 2.3
38. 2.9
39. $\frac{4}{5}$
40. $\frac{3}{4}$
41. $\frac{8}{25}$
42. $\frac{3}{8}$

Solve.

43. What percent of 68 is 17?
44. What percent of 150 is 39?
45. What percent of 125 is 30?
46. What percent of 300 is 57?
47. 14 is 30% of what number?
48. 54 is 24% of what number?
49. 0.3 is 12% of what number?
50. 7 is 175% of what number?
51. What number is 35% of 240?
52. What number is 1% of one million?
53. What percent of 60 is 75?
Aha! **54.** What percent of 70 is 70?
55. What is 2% of 40?
56. What is 40% of 2?
Aha! **57.** 25 is what percent of 50?
58. 8 is 2% of what number?

Costs of owning a dog. The American Pet Products Manufacturers Association estimates that the total cost of owning a dog for its lifetime is $6600. The following circle graph shows the relative costs of raising a dog from birth to death.

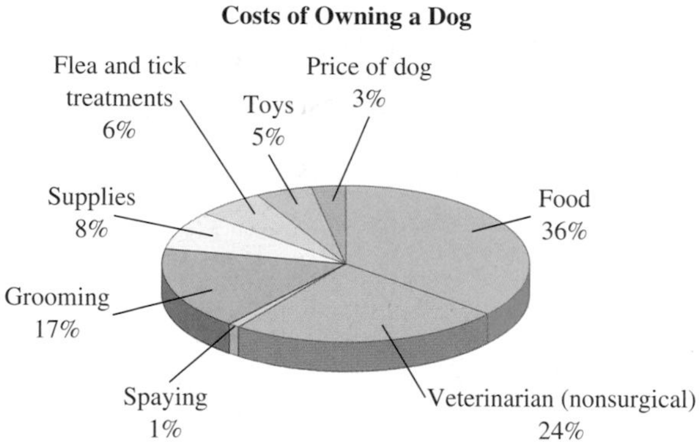

Source: The American Pet Products Manufacturers Association

In each of Exercises 59–64, determine the cost of owning a dog for its lifetime.

59. Price of dog
60. Food
61. Veterinarian
62. Grooming
63. Supplies
64. Flea and tick treatments

65. *College graduation.* To obtain his bachelor's degree in nursing, Frank must complete 125 credit hours of instruction. If he has completed 60% of his requirement, how many credits did Frank complete?

66. *College graduation.* To obtain her bachelor's degree in journalism, Beth must complete 125 credit hours of instruction. If 20% of Beth's credit hours remain to be completed, how many credits does she still need to take?

67. *Batting average.* At one point in a recent season, Ichiro Suzuki of the Seattle Mariners had 194 hits. His batting average was 0.310, or 31%. That is, of the total number of at-bats, 31% were hits. How many at-bats did he have?
Source: Major League Baseball

68. *Pass completions.* At one point in a recent season, Peyton Manning of the Indianapolis Colts had completed 357 passes. This was 62.5% of his attempts. How many attempts did he make?
Source: National Football League

69. *Tipping.* Leon left a $4 tip for a meal that cost $25.

a) What percent of the cost of the meal was the tip?

b) What was the total cost of the meal including the tip?

70. *Tipping.* Selena left a $12.76 tip for a meal that cost $58.

a) What percent of the cost of the meal was the tip?

b) What was the total cost of the meal including the tip?

71. *Auto sales.* In 2002, 8.3 million cars were sold in the United States. Of these, 6.0 million were manufactured in the United States. What percent were manufactured within the United States? outside the United States?
Source: *The World Almanac and Book of Facts*, 2004

72. *Auto sales.* Of the 2.3 million foreign cars sold in the United States in 2002, about 1.0 million were manufactured in Japan. What percent of foreign cars were manufactured in Japan? outside Japan?
Source: *Autodata*

73. *Student loans.* To finance her community college education, Sarah takes out a Stafford loan for $3500. After a year, Sarah decides to pay off the interest, which is 8% of $3500. How much will she pay?

74. *Student loans.* Paul takes out a subsidized federal Stafford loan for $2400. After a year, Paul decides to pay off the interest, which is 7% of $2400. How much will he pay?

75. *Infant health.* In a study of 300 pregnant women with "good-to-excellent" diets, 95% had babies in good or excellent health. How many women in this group had babies in good or excellent health?

76. *Infant health.* In a study of 300 pregnant women with "poor" diets, 8% had babies in good or excellent health. How many women in this group had babies in good or excellent health?

77. *Cost of self-employment.* Because of additional taxes and fewer benefits, it has been estimated that a self-employed person must earn 20% more than a non–self-employed person performing the same task(s). If Joy earns $15 an hour working for Village Copy, how much would she need to earn on her own for a comparable income?

78. Refer to Exercise 77. Ray earns $12 an hour working for Round Edge stairbuilders. How much would Ray need to earn on his own for a comparable income?

79. *Triathletes.* The number of USA Triathlon Members grew from 16,000 in 1993 to 40,000 in 2002. Calculate the percentage by which the number increased.
Source: USA Triathlon

80. *Fastest human.* In 2002, Tim Montgomery of the United States set a world record by sprinting 100 m in 9.78 sec. This broke the record of 9.79 sec established in 1999 by Maurice Green, also of the United States. Calculate the percentage by which the record decreased.
Source: www.runnersworld.com

81. A bill at Officeland totaled $37.80. How much did the merchandise cost if the sales tax is 5%?

82. Doreen's checkbook shows that she wrote a check for $987 for building materials. What was the price of the materials if the sales tax is 5%?

83. *Deducting sales tax.* A tax-exempt school group received a bill of $157.41 for educational software. The bill incorrectly included sales tax of 6%. How much should the school group pay?

84. *Deducting sales tax.* A tax-exempt charity received a bill of $145.90 for a sump pump. The bill incorrectly included sales tax of 5%. How much does the charity owe?

85. *Body fat.* One author of this text exercises regularly at a local YMCA that recently offered a body-fat percentage test to its members. The device used measures the passage of a very low voltage of electricity through the body. The author's body-fat percentage was found to be 16.5% and he weighs 191 lb. What part, in pounds, of his body weight is fat?

86. *Areas of Alaska and Arizona.* The area of Arizona is 19% of the area of Alaska. The area of Alaska is 586,400 mi^2. What is the area of Arizona?

87. *Junk mail.* The U.S. Postal Service reports that of the junk mail that is sent out, 78% is actually opened and read. A business sends out 9500 advertising brochures. How many of them can the business expect to be opened and read?

88. *Kissing and colds.* In a medical study, it was determined that if 800 people kiss someone else who has a cold, only 56 will actually catch the cold. What percent is this?

89. *Calorie content.* Pepperidge Farm Light Style 7 Grain Bread® has 140 calories in a 3-slice serving. This is 15% less than the number of calories in a serving of regular bread. How many calories are in a serving of regular bread?

90. *Fat content.* Peek Freans Shortbread Reduced Fat Cookies® contain 35 calories of fat in each serving. This is 40% less than the fat content in the leading imported shortbread cookie. How many calories of fat are in a serving of the leading shortbread cookie?

91. Campus Bookbuyers pays $30 for a book and sells it for $60. Is this a 100% markup or a 50% markup? Explain.

92. If Julian leaves a $12 tip for a $90 dinner, is he being generous, stingy, or neither? Explain.

SKILL MAINTENANCE

Translate to an algebraic expression. [1.1]

93. 5 more than some number

94. 4 less than Tino's weight

95. The product of 8 and twice a

96. 1 more than the product of two numbers

SYNTHESIS

97. Does the following advertisement provide a convincing argument that summertime is when most burglaries occur? Why or why not?

98. Erin is returning a tent that she bought during a 25%-off storewide sale that has ended. She is offered store credit for 125% of what she paid (not to be used on sale items). Is this fair to Erin? Why or why not?

99. The community of Bardville has 1332 left-handed females. If 48% of the community is female and 15% of all females are left-handed, how many people are in the community?

100. It has been determined that at the age of 15, a boy has reached 96.1% of his final adult height. Jaraan is 6 ft 4 in. at the age of 15. What will his final adult height be?

101. It has been determined that at the age of 10, a girl has reached 84.4% of her final adult height. Dana is 4 ft 8 in. at the age of 10. What will her final adult height be?

102. *U.S. birth rate.* Between 2001 and 2002, the U.S. birth rate dropped from 14.1 to 13.9 babies per 1000 women. Calculate the percentage by which the birth rate dropped and use that percentage to estimate birth rates for the United States in 2003 and 2004.
Source: www.socialsecurity.org

103. *Photography.* A 6-in. by 8-in. photo is framed using a mat meant for a 5 in. by 7 in. photo. What percentage of the photo will be hidden by the mat?

104. Would it be better to receive a 5% raise and then, a year later, an 8% raise or the other way around? Why?

Aha!

105. Herb is in the 30% tax bracket. This means that 30¢ of each dollar earned goes to taxes. Which would cost him the least: contributing $50 that is tax-deductible or contributing $40 that is not tax-deductible? Explain.

COLLABORATIVE CORNER

Sales and Discounts

Focus: Applications and models using percent

Time: 15 minutes

Group size: 3

Materials: Calculators are optional.

Often a store will reduce the price of an item by a fixed percentage. When the sale ends, the items are returned to their original prices. Suppose a department store reduces all sporting goods 20%, all clothing 25%, and all electronics 10%.

ACTIVITY

1. Each group member should select one of the following items: a \$50 basketball, an \$80 jacket, or a \$200 portable sound system. Fill in the first three columns of the first three rows of the chart below.
2. Apply the appropriate discount and determine the sale price of your item. Fill in the fourth column of the chart.
3. Next, find a multiplier that can be used to convert the sale price back to the original price and fill in the remaining column of the chart. Does this multiplier depend on the price of the item?
4. Working as a group, compare the results of part (3) for all three items. Then develop a formula for a multiplier that will restore a sale price to its original price, p, after a discount r has been applied. Complete the fourth row of the table and check that your formula will duplicate the results of part (3).
5. Use the formula from part (4) to find the multiplier that a store would use to return an item to its original price after a "30% off" sale expires. Fill in the last line on the chart.
6. Inspect the last column of your chart. How can these multipliers be used to determine the percentage by which a sale price is increased when a sale ends?

Original Price, p	**Discount, r**	**$1 - r$**	**Sale Price**	**Multiplier to convert back to p**
p	r	$1 - r$		
	0.30			

2.5 Problem Solving

Five Steps for Problem Solving • Applying the Five Steps

Probably the most important use of algebra is as a tool for problem solving. In this section, we develop a problem-solving approach that is used throughout the remainder of the text.

Five Steps for Problem Solving

In Section 2.4, we solved several real-world problems. To solve them, we first *familiarized* ourselves with percent notation. We then *translated* each problem into an equation, *solved* the equation, *checked* the solution, and *stated* the answer.

Five Steps for Problem Solving in Algebra

1. *Familiarize* yourself with the problem.
2. *Translate* to mathematical language. (This often means writing an equation.)
3. *Carry out* some mathematical manipulation. (This often means *solving* an equation.)
4. *Check* your possible answer in the original problem.
5. *State* the answer clearly, using a complete English sentence.

Of the five steps, the most important is probably the first one: becoming familiar with the problem. Here are some hints for familiarization.

To Become Familiar with a Problem

1. Read the problem carefully. Try to visualize the problem.
2. Reread the problem, perhaps aloud. Make sure you understand all important words.
3. List the information given and the question(s) to be answered. Choose a variable (or variables) to represent the unknown and specify what the variable represents. For example, let L = length in centimeters, d = distance in miles, and so on.
4. Look for similarities between the problem and other problems you have already solved.
5. Find more information. Look up a formula in a book, at a library, or online. Consult a reference librarian or an expert in the field.
6. Make a table that uses all the information you have available. Look for patterns that may help in the translation.
7. Make a drawing and label it with known and unknown information, using specific units if given.
8. Think of a possible answer and check the guess. Note the manner in which the guess is checked.

Applying the Five Steps

EXAMPLE 1 Hiking. In 1948, Earl Shaffer became the first person to hike all 2100 miles of the Appalachian trail—from Springer Mountain, Georgia, to Mt. Katahdin, Maine. Shaffer repeated the feat 50 years later, and at age 79 became the oldest person to hike the entire trail. When Shaffer stood atop Big Walker Mountain, Virginia, he was three times as far from the northern end of the trail as from the southern end. At that point, how far was he from each end of the trail?

Earl Shaffer 1918–2002

Solution

1. **Familiarize.** It may be helpful to make a drawing.

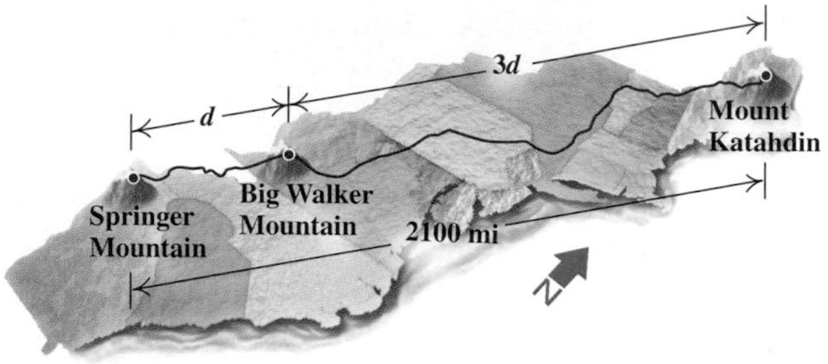

To gain some familiarity, let's suppose that Shaffer stood 600 mi from Springer Mountain. Three times 600 mi is 1800 mi. Since 600 mi + 1800 mi = 2400 mi and 2400 mi > 2100 mi, we see that our guess is too large. Rather than guess again, we let

d = the distance, in miles, to the southern end

and

$3d$ = the distance, in miles, to the northern end.

(We could also let x = the distance to the northern end and $\frac{1}{3}x$ = the distance to the southern end.)

2. **Translate.** From the drawing, we see that the lengths of the two parts of the trail must add up to 2100 mi. This leads to our translation.

Rewording:	Distance to southern end	plus	distance to northern end	is	2100 mi
	↓	↓	↓	↓	↓
Translating:	d	$+$	$3d$	$=$	2100

3. **Carry out.** We solve the equation:

$$d + 3d = 2100$$
$$4d = 2100 \quad \text{Combining like terms}$$
$$d = 525. \quad \text{Dividing both sides by 4}$$

4. **Check.** As predicted in the *Familiarize* step, d is less than 600 mi. If d = 525 mi, then $3d$ = 1575 mi. Since 525 mi + 1575 mi = 2100 mi, we have a check.

5. **State.** Atop Big Walker Mountain, Shaffer stood 525 mi from Springer Mountain and 1575 mi from Mount Katahdin.

Before we solve the next problem, we need to learn some additional terminology regarding integers.

The following are examples of **consecutive integers:** 16, 17, 18, 19, 20; and −31, −30, −29, −28. Note that consecutive integers can be represented in the form $x, x + 1, x + 2$, and so on.

The following are examples of **consecutive even integers:** 16, 18, 20, 22, 24; and −52, −50, −48, −46. Note that consecutive even integers can be represented in the form x, $x + 2$, $x + 4$, and so on.

The following are examples of **consecutive odd integers:** 21, 23, 25, 27, 29; and −71, −69, −67, −65. Note that consecutive odd integers can be represented in the form x, $x + 2$, $x + 4$, and so on.

EXAMPLE 2 Interstate mile markers. U.S. interstate highways post numbered markers at every mile to indicate location in case of an emergency (*Source*: Federal Highway Administration, Ed Rotalewski). The sum of two consecutive mile markers on I-70 in Kansas is 559. Find the numbers on the markers.

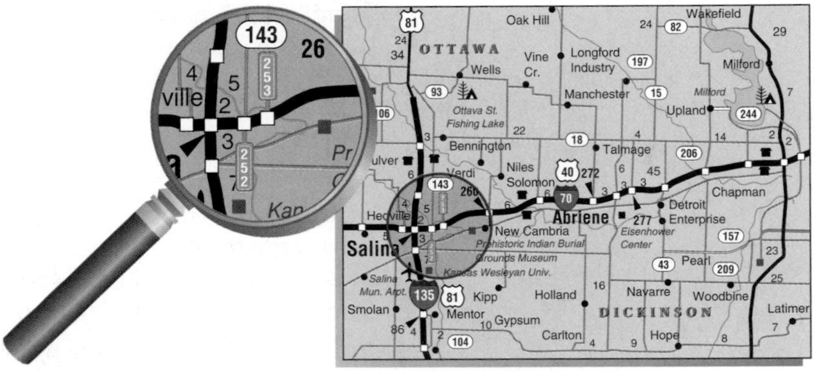

Study Skills

Set Reasonable Expectations

Do not be surprised if your success rate drops some as you work through the exercises in this section. *This is normal.* Your success rate will increase as you gain experience with these types of problems and use some of the study skills already listed.

Solution

1. **Familiarize.** The numbers on the mile markers are consecutive positive integers. Thus if we let $x =$ the smaller number, then $x + 1 =$ the larger number.

   To become familiar with the problem, we can make a table, as shown at left. First, we guess a value for x; then we find $x + 1$. Finally, we add the two numbers and check the sum.

x	$x + 1$	Sum of x and $x + 1$
114	115	229
252	253	505
302	303	605

   From the table, we see that the first marker will be between 252 and 302. We could continue guessing and solve the problem this way, but let's work on developing our algebra skills.

2. **Translate.** We reword the problem and translate as follows.

Rewording: First integer plus second integer is 559.

Translating: $x + (x + 1) = 559$

3. **Carry out.** We solve the equation:

$$x + (x + 1) = 559$$

$$2x + 1 = 559 \quad \text{Using an associative law and combining like terms}$$

$$2x = 558 \quad \text{Subtracting 1 from both sides}$$

$$x = 279. \quad \text{Dividing both sides by 2}$$

If x is 279, then $x + 1$ is 280.

4. **Check.** Our possible answers are 279 and 280. These are consecutive positive integers and $279 + 280 = 559$, so the answers check.
5. **State.** The mile markers are 279 and 280.

EXAMPLE 3 IKON copiers. IKON Office Solutions rents a Canon IR330 copier for \$225 per month plus 1.2¢ per copy. A law firm needs to lease a copy machine for use during a special case that they anticipate will take 3 months. If they allot a budget of \$1100, how many copies can they make?

Source: IKON Office Solutions, Nathan DuMond, Sales Manager

Solution

1. **Familiarize.** Suppose that the law firm makes 20,000 copies. Then the cost is monthly charges plus copy charges, or

3(\$225)	plus	cost per copy	times	number of copies
↓	↓	↓	↓	↓
\$675	+	\$0.012	·	20,000,

which is \$915. Our guess of 20,000 is too small, but we have familiarized ourselves with the way in which a calculation is made. Note that we convert 1.2¢ to \$0.012 so that all information is in the same unit, dollars. We let $c =$ the number of copies that can be made for \$1100.

Student Notes

For most students, the most challenging step is step 2, "Translate." The table on p. 4 (Section 1.1) can be helpful in this regard.

2. **Translate.** We reword the problem and translate as follows.

Rewording:	Monthly cost	plus	copying charges	is	\$1100.
	↓	↓	↓	↓	↓
Translating:	3(\$225)	+	(\$0.012)c	=	\$1100

3. **Carry out.** We solve the equation:

$$3(225) + 0.012c = 1100$$
$$675 + 0.012c = 1100$$
$$0.012c = 425 \quad \text{Subtracting 675 from both sides}$$
$$c = \frac{425}{0.012} \quad \text{Dividing both sides by 0.012}$$
$$c \approx 35{,}417. \quad \text{Rounding to the nearest one}$$

4. **Check.** We check in the original problem. The cost for 35,417 pages is $35{,}417(\$0.012) = \$425.004$. The rental for 3 months is $3(\$225) = \$675$. The total cost is then $\$425.004 + \$675 \approx \$1100$, which is the \$1100 that was allotted. Our answer exceeds 20,000, as we expected from the *Familiarize* step.
5. **State.** The law firm can make 35,417 copies on the copy rental allotment of \$1100.

EXAMPLE 4 Perimeter of NBA court. The perimeter of an NBA basketball court is 288 ft. The length is 44 ft longer than the width. (*Source*: National Basketball Association) Find the dimensions of the court.

Solution

1. **Familiarize.** Recall that the perimeter of a rectangle is twice the length plus twice the width. Suppose the court were 30 ft wide. The length would then be $30 + 44$, or 74 ft, and the perimeter would be $2 \cdot 30$ ft $+ 2 \cdot 74$ ft, or 208 ft. This shows that in order for the perimeter to be 288 ft, the width must exceed 30 ft. Instead of guessing again, we let $w =$ the width of the court, in feet. Since the court is "44 ft longer than it is wide," we let $w + 44 =$ the length of the court, in feet.

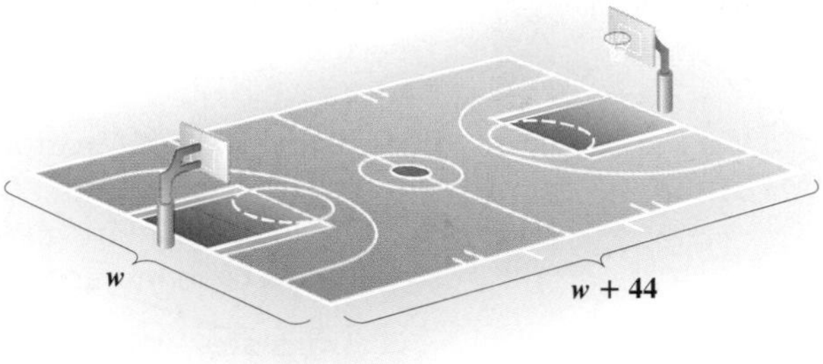

2. **Translate.** To translate, we use $w + 44$ as the length and 288 as the perimeter. To double the length, $w + 44$, parentheses are essential.

Rewording: Twice the length plus twice the width is 288 ft.

Translating: $2(w + 44) \quad + \quad 2w \quad = \quad 288$

3. **Carry out.** We solve the equation:

$$2(w + 44) + 2w = 288$$
$$2w + 88 + 2w = 288 \qquad \text{Using the distributive law}$$
$$4w + 88 = 288 \qquad \text{Combining like terms}$$
$$4w = 200$$
$$w = 50.$$

The dimensions appear to be $w = 50$ ft, and $l = w + 44 = 94$ ft.

4. **Check.** If the width is 50 ft and the length is 94 ft, then the court is 44 ft longer than it is wide. The perimeter is $2(50 \text{ ft}) + 2(94 \text{ ft}) = 100 \text{ ft} + 188 \text{ ft}$, or 288 ft, as specified. We have a check.

5. **State.** An NBA court is 50 ft wide and 94 ft long.

Caution! Always be sure to answer the original problem completely. For instance, in Example 1 we needed to find *two* numbers: the distances from *each* end of the trail to the hiker. Similarly, in Example 4 we needed to find two dimensions, not just the width. Be sure to label each answer with the proper unit.

EXAMPLE 5 Selling a home. The McCanns are planning to sell their home. If they want to be left with \$117,500 after paying 6% of the selling price to a realtor as a commission, for how much must they sell the house?

Solution

1. **Familiarize.** Suppose the McCanns sell the house for \$120,000. A 6% commission can be determined by finding 6% of \$120,000:

$$6\% \text{ of } \$120{,}000 = 0.06(\$120{,}000) = \$7200.$$

Subtracting this commission from \$120,000 would leave the McCanns with

$$\$120{,}000 - \$7200 = \$112{,}800.$$

This shows that in order for the McCanns to clear \$117,500, the house must sell for more than \$120,000. To determine what the sale price must be, we could check more guesses. Instead, we let $x =$ the selling price, in dollars. With a 6% commission, the realtor would receive $0.06x$.

2. **Translate.** We reword the problem and translate as follows.

Rewording:	Selling price	less	commission	is	amount remaining.
	↓	↓	↓	↓	↓
Translating:	x	$-$	$0.06x$	$=$	117,500

3. **Carry out.** We solve the equation:

$$x - 0.06x = 117{,}500$$
$$1x - 0.06x = 117{,}500$$
$$0.94x = 117{,}500$$
Combining like terms. Had we noted that after the commission has been paid, 94% remains, we could have begun with this equation.
$$x = \frac{117{,}500}{0.94}$$
Dividing both sides by 0.94
$$x = 125{,}000.$$

4. **Check.** To check, we first find 6% of \$125,000:

$$6\% \text{ of } \$125{,}000 = 0.06(\$125{,}000) = \$7500.$$ This is the commission.

Next, we subtract the commission to find the remaining amount:

$$\$125{,}000 - \$7500 = \$117{,}500.$$

Since, after the commission, the McCanns are left with \$117,500, our answer checks. Note that the \$125,000 sale price is greater than \$120,000, as predicted in the *Familiarize* step.

5. **State.** To be left with \$117,500, the McCanns must sell the house for \$125,000.

EXAMPLE 6 Cross section of a roof. In a triangular gable end of a roof, the angle of the peak is twice as large as the angle on the back side of the house. The measure of the angle on the front side is 20° greater than the angle on the back side. How large are the angles?

Solution

1. **Familiarize.** We make a drawing. In this case, the measure of the back angle is x, the measure of the front angle is $x + 20$, and the measure of the peak angle is $2x$.

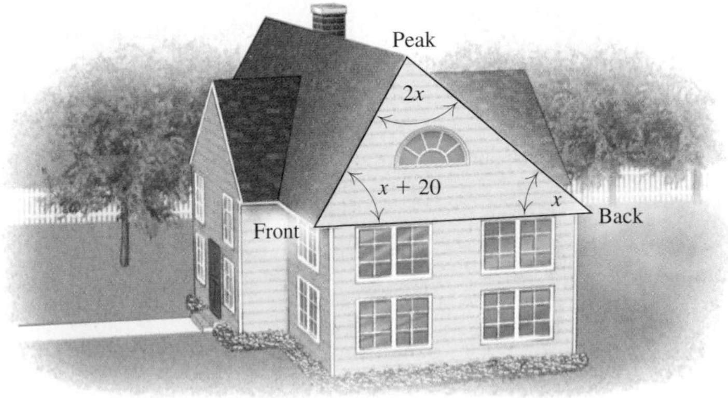

2. **Translate.** To translate, we need to recall that the sum of the measures of the angles in a triangle is 180°.

Rewording:	Measure of back angle	+	measure of front angle	+	measure of peak angle	is	180°
	↓	↓	↓	↓	↓	↓	↓
Translating:	x	$+$	$(x + 20)$	$+$	$2x$	$=$	180

3. **Carry out.** We solve:

$$\begin{aligned} x + (x + 20) + 2x &= 180 \\ 4x + 20 &= 180 \\ 4x &= 160 \\ x &= 40. \end{aligned}$$

The measures for the angles appear to be:

Back angle: $x = 40°$,
Front angle: $x + 20 = 40 + 20 = 60°$,
Peak angle: $2x = 2(40) = 80°$.

4. **Check.** Consider 40°, 60°, and 80°. The measure of the front angle is 20° greater than the measure of the back angle, the measure of the peak angle is twice the measure of the back angle, and the sum is 180°. These numbers check.

5. **State.** The measures of the angles are 40°, 60°, and 80°.

We close this section with some tips to aid you in problem solving.

Problem-Solving Tips

1. The more problems you solve, the more your skills will improve.
2. Look for patterns when solving problems. Each time you study an example in a text, you may observe a pattern for problems found later in the exercise sets or in other practical situations.
3. When translating in mathematics, consider the dimensions of the variables and constants in the equation. The variables that represent length should all be in the same unit, those that represent money should all be in dollars or all in cents, and so on.
4. Make sure that units appear in the answer whenever appropriate and that you completely answer the original problem.

2.5 Exercise Set

FOR EXTRA HELP

Student's Solutions Manual | Digital Video Tutor CD 2 Videotape 4 | AW Math Tutor Center | MathXL Tutorials on CD | MathXL | MyMathLab

Solve. Even though you might find the answer quickly in some other way, practice using the five-step problem-solving process.

1. Two fewer than ten times a number is 78. What is the number?

2. Three less than twice a number is 19. What is the number?

3. Five times the sum of 3 and some number is 70. What is the number?

4. Twice the sum of 4 and some number is 34. What is the number?

5. *Price of sneakers.* Amy paid \$72.25 for a pair of New Balance 765 running shoes during a 15%-off sale. What was the regular price?

6. *Price of a CD player.* Doug paid \$72 for a shockproof portable CD player during a 20%-off sale. What was the regular price?

7. *Price of a calculator.* Evelyn paid \$89.25, including 5% tax, for her graphing calculator. How much did the calculator itself cost?

8. *Price of a printer.* Jake paid \$100.70, including 6% tax, for a color printer. How much did the printer itself cost?

9. *Running.* In 1997, Yiannis Kouros of Australia set the record for the greatest distance run in 24 hr by running 188 mi. After 8 hr, he was approximately twice as far from the finish line as he was from the start. How far had he run?
Source: *Guinness World Records 2004 Edition*

10. *Sled-dog racing.* The Iditarod sled-dog race extends for 1049 mi from Anchorage to Nome. If a musher is twice as far from Anchorage as from Nome, how many miles has the musher traveled?

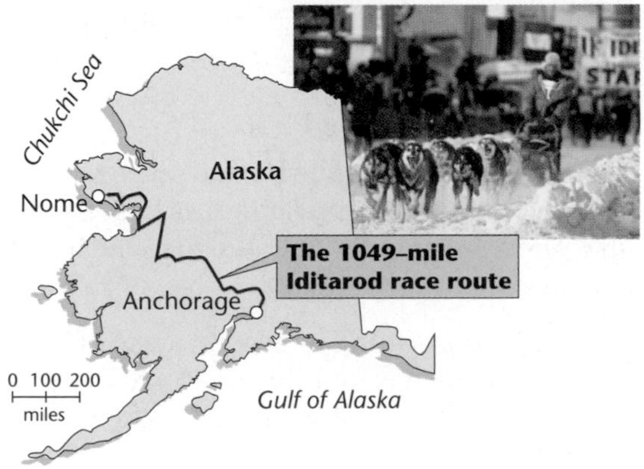

11. *Car racing.* In April 2004, Dan Wheldon won the Indy Japan 300 with a time of 1:49:48.2611 for the 300-mi race. At one point, Wheldon was 80 mi closer to the finish than the start. How far had Wheldon traveled at that point?

12. *Car racing.* In August 2004, Jeff Gordon won his fourth Brickyard 400 with a time of 3:29:56 for the 400-mi race. At one point, Gordon was 70 mi closer to the finish than the start. How far had Gordon traveled at that point?

13. *Apartment numbers.* The apartments in Joan's apartment house are consecutively numbered on each floor. The sum of her number and her next-door neighbor's number is 2409. What are the two numbers?

14. *Apartment numbers.* The apartments in Vincent's apartment house are numbered consecutively on each floor. The sum of his number and his next-door neighbor's number is 1419. What are the two numbers?

15. *Street addresses.* The houses on the south side of Elm Street are consecutive even numbers. Wanda and Larry are next-door neighbors and the sum of their house numbers is 794. Find their house numbers.

16. *Street addresses.* The houses on the west side of Lincoln Avenue are consecutive odd numbers. Sam and Colleen are next-door neighbors and the sum of their house numbers is 572. Find their house numbers.

17. The sum of three consecutive page numbers is 60. Find the numbers.

18. The sum of three consecutive page numbers is 99. Find the numbers.

19. *Oldest bride.* The world's oldest bride was 19 yr older than her groom. Together, their ages totaled 185 yr. How old were the bride and the groom?
Source: *Guinness World Records 2004 Edition*

20. *Oldest marrying couple.* As half of the world's oldest marrying couple, the woman was 2 yr younger than the man. Together, their ages totaled 190 yr. How old were the man and the woman?
Source: *Guinness World Records 2004 Edition*

21. *Home remodeling.* In a recent year, Americans spent a total of \$35 billion to remodel bathrooms and kitchens. Twice as much was spent on kitchens as bathrooms. How much was spent on each?

22. *Women's clothing.* Recently a total of \$12.8 billion was spent on women's blouses and dresses. Of that total, \$0.2 billion more was spent on blouses than on dresses. How much was spent on each type of clothing?

23. *Page numbers.* The sum of the page numbers on the facing pages of a book is 281. What are the page numbers?

24. *Perimeter of a triangle.* The perimeter of a triangle is 195 mm. If the lengths of the sides are consecutive odd integers, find the length of each side.

25. *Hancock Building dimensions.* The top of the John Hancock Building in Chicago is a rectangle whose length is 60 ft more than the width. The perimeter is 520 ft. Find the width and the length of the rectangle. Find the area of the rectangle.

26. *Dimensions of a state.* The perimeter of the state of Wyoming is 1280 mi. The width is 90 mi less than the length. Find the width and the length.

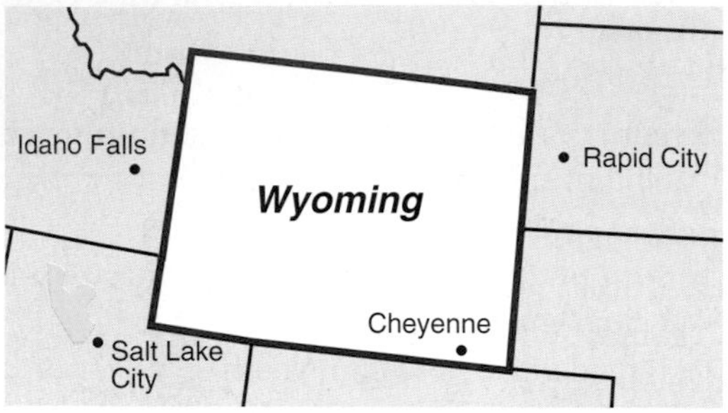

27. *Perimeter of a high school basketball court.* The perimeter of a standard high school basketball court is 268 ft. The length is 34 ft longer than the width. Find the dimensions of the court.
Source: Indiana High School Athletic Association

28. A rectangular community garden is to be enclosed with 92 m of fencing. In order to allow for compost storage, the garden must be 4 m longer than it is wide. Determine the dimensions of the garden.

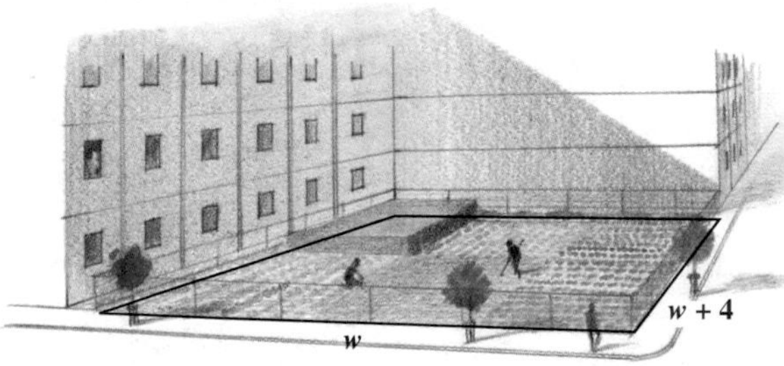

29. *Two-by-four.* The perimeter of a cross section of a "two-by-four" piece of lumber is $10\frac{1}{2}$ in. The length is twice the width. Find the actual dimensions of the cross section of a two-by-four.

30. *Standard billboard sign.* A standard rectangular highway billboard sign has a perimeter of 124 ft. The length is 6 ft more than three times the width. Find the dimensions of the sign.

31. *Angles of a triangle.* The second angle of an architect's triangle is three times as large as the first. The third angle is 30° more than the first. Find the measure of each angle.

32. *Angles of a triangle.* The second angle of a triangular garden is four times as large as the first. The third angle is 45° less than the sum of the other two angles. Find the measure of each angle.

33. *Angles of a triangle.* The second angle of a triangular building lot is three times as large as the first. The third angle is 10° more than the sum of the other two angles. Find the measure of the third angle.

34. *Angles of a triangle.* The second angle of a triangular kite is four times as large as the first. The third angle is 5° more than the sum of the other two angles. Find the measure of the second angle.

35. *Rocket sections.* A rocket is divided into three sections: the payload and navigation section in the top, the fuel section in the middle, and the rocket engine section in the bottom. The top section is one-sixth the length of the bottom section. The middle section is one-half the length of the bottom section. The total length is 240 ft. Find the length of each section.

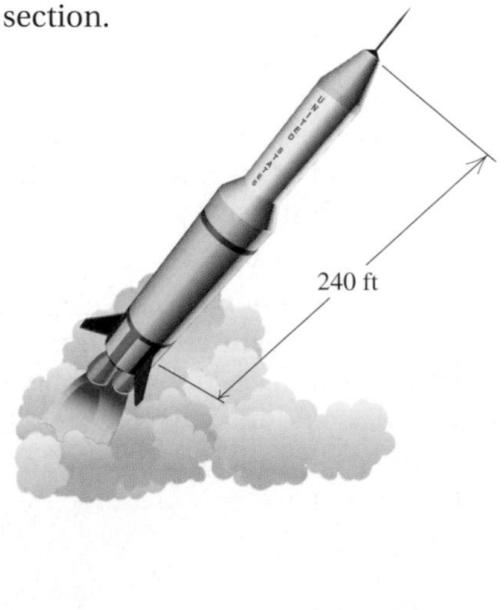

36. *Gourmet sandwiches.* Jenny, Demi, and Sarah buy an 18-in. long gourmet sandwich and take it back to their apartment. Since they have different appetites, Jenny cuts the sandwich so that Demi gets half of what Jenny gets and Sarah gets three-fourths of what Jenny gets. Find the length of each person's sandwich.

37. *Taxi rates.* In Chicago, a taxi ride costs \$1.90 plus \$1.60 for each mile traveled. Debbie and Alex have budgeted \$18 for a taxi ride (excluding tip). How far can they travel on their \$18 budget?

38. *Taxi fares.* In New York City, taxis charge \$2.50 plus \$2.00 per mile for off-peak fares. How far can Ralph travel for \$17.50 (assuming an off-peak fare)?
Source: *Burlington Free Press*, 3/31/04

39. *Truck rentals.* Truck-Rite Rentals rents trucks at a daily rate of \$49.95 plus 39¢ per mile. Concert Productions has budgeted \$100 for renting a truck to haul equipment to an upcoming concert. How far can they travel in one day and stay within their budget?

40. *Truck rentals.* Fine Line Trucks rents an 18-ft truck for \$42 plus 35¢ per mile. Judy needs a truck for one day to deliver a shipment of plants. How far can she drive and stay within a budget of \$70?

41. *Complementary angles.* The sum of the measures of two *complementary* angles is 90°. If one angle measures 15° more than twice the measure of its complement, find the measure of each angle.

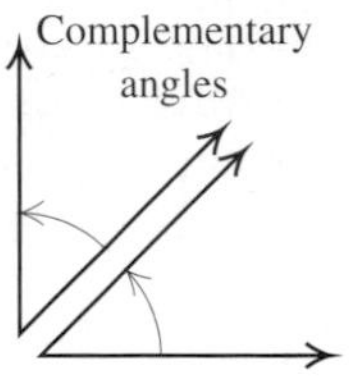

42. *Supplementary angles.* The sum of the measures of two *supplementary* angles is 180°. If one angle measures 45° less than twice the measure of its supplement, find the measure of each angle.

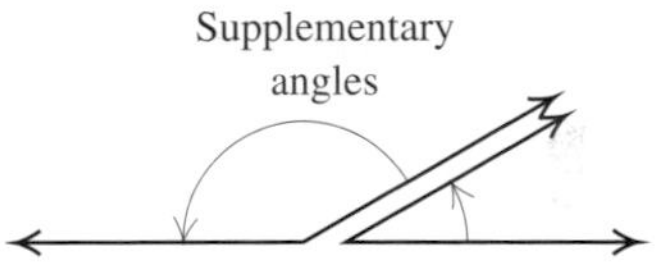

43. *Copier paper.* The perimeter of standard-size copier paper is 99 cm. The width is 6.3 cm less than the length. Find the length and the width.

44. *Stock prices.* Sarah's investment in Jet Blue stock grew 28% to \$448. How much did she invest?

45. *Savings interest.* Sharon invested money in a savings account at a rate of 6% simple interest. After 1 yr, she has \$6996 in the account. How much did Sharon originally invest?

46. *Credit cards.* The balance in Will's Mastercard® account grew 2%, to \$870, in one month. What was his balance at the beginning of the month?

47. *Scrabble®.* The highest one-game score for a Scrabble player occurred in the same game in which the record margin of victory, 796 points, was established. The winning and losing scores totaled 1302 points. What was the winning score?
Source: *Guinness World Records 2004 Edition*

48. *IKON copiers.* The law firm in Example 3 decides to raise its budget to \$1400 for the 3-month period. How many copies can they make for \$1400?

49. *Cricket chirps and temperature.* The equation $T = \frac{1}{4}N + 40$ can be used to determine the temperature T, in degrees Fahrenheit, given the number of times N a cricket chirps per minute. Determine the number of chirps per minute for a temperature of 80°F.

50. *Race time.* The equation $R = -0.028t + 20.8$ can be used to predict the world record in the 200-m dash, where R is the record in seconds and t is the number of years since 1920. In what year will the record be 18.0 sec?

51. Sean claims he can solve most of the problems in this section by guessing. Is there anything wrong with this approach? Why or why not?

52. When solving Exercise 19, Beth used a to represent the bride's age and Ben used a to represent the groom's age. Is one of these approaches preferable to the other? Why or why not?

SKILL MAINTENANCE

Write a true sentence using either $<$ *or* $>$. [1.4]

53. $-9 \;\square\; 5$

54. $1 \;\square\; 3$

55. $-4 \;\square\; 7$

56. $-9 \;\square\; -12$

SYNTHESIS

57. Write a problem for a classmate to solve. Devise it so that the problem can be translated to the equation $x + (x + 2) + (x + 4) = 375$.

58. Write a problem for a classmate to solve. Devise it so that the solution is "Audrey can drive the rental truck for 50 mi without exceeding her budget."

59. *Discounted dinners.* Kate's "Dining Card" entitles her to \$10 off the price of a meal after a 15% tip has been added to the cost of the meal. If, after the discount, the bill is \$32.55, how much did the meal originally cost?

60. *Test scores.* Pam scored 78 on a test that had 4 fill-ins worth 7 points each and 24 multiple-choice questions worth 3 points each. She had one fill-in wrong. How many multiple-choice questions did Pam get right?

61. *Gettysburg Address.* Abraham Lincoln's 1863 Gettysburg Address refers to the year 1776 as "four *score* and seven years ago." Determine what a score is.

62. One number is 25% of another. The larger number is 12 more than the smaller. What are the numbers?

63. A storekeeper goes to the bank to get \$10 worth of change. She requests twice as many quarters as half dollars, twice as many dimes as quarters, three times as many nickels as dimes, and no pennies or dollars. How many of each coin did the storekeeper get?

64. *Perimeter of a rectangle.* The width of a rectangle is three fourths of the length. The perimeter of the rectangle becomes 50 cm when the length and the width are each increased by 2 cm. Find the length and the width.

65. *Sharing fruit.* Apples are collected in a basket for six people. One third, one fourth, one eighth, and one fifth of the apples are given to four people, respectively. The fifth person gets ten apples, and one apple remains for the sixth person. Find the original number of apples in the basket.

66. *Discounts.* In exchange for opening a new credit account, Filene's Department Stores® subtracts 10% from all purchases made the day the account is established. Julio is opening an account and has a coupon for which he receives 10% off the first day's reduced price of a camera. If Julio's final price is \$77.75, what was the price of the camera before the two discounts?

67. *Winning percentage.* In a basketball league, the Falcons won 15 of their first 20 games. In order to win 60% of the total number of games, how many more games will they have to play, assuming they win only half of the remaining games?

68. *Music-club purchases.* During a recent sale, BMG Music Service® charged \$8.49 for the first CD ordered and \$3.99 for all others. For shipping and handling, BMG charged \$2.47 for the first CD, \$2.28 for the second CD, and \$1.99 for all others. The total cost of a shipment (excluding tax) was \$65.07. How many CD's were in the shipment?

69. *Test scores.* Ella has an average score of 82 on three tests. Her average score on the first two tests is 85. What was the score on the third test?

70. *Taxi fares.* In New York City, a taxi ride costs \$2.50 plus 40¢ per $\frac{1}{5}$ mile and 20¢ per minute stopped in traffic. Due to traffic, Glenda's taxi took 20 min to complete what is usually a 10-min drive. If she is charged \$16.50 for the ride, how far did Glenda travel?

71. A school purchases a piano and must choose between paying \$2000 at the time of purchase or \$2150 at the end of one year. Which option should the school select and why?

Aha! **72.** Annette claims the following problem has no solution: "The sum of the page numbers on facing pages is 191. Find the page numbers." Is she correct? Why or why not?

73. The perimeter of a rectangle is 101.74 cm. If the length is 4.25 cm longer than the width, find the dimensions of the rectangle.

74. The second side of a triangle is 3.25 cm longer than the first side. The third side is 4.35 cm longer than the second side. If the perimeter of the triangle is 26.87 cm, find the length of each side.

2.6 Solving Inequalities

Solutions of Inequalities • Graphs of Inequalities • Solving Inequalities Using the Addition Principle • Solving Inequalities Using the Multiplication Principle • Using the Principles Together

Many real-world situations translate to *inequalities*. For example, a student might need to register for *at least* 12 credits; an elevator might be designed to hold *at most* 2000 pounds; a tax credit might be allowable for families with incomes of *less than* \$25,000; and so on. Before solving applications of this type, we must adapt our equation-solving principles to the solving of inequalities.

Solutions of Inequalities

Recall from Section 1.4 that an inequality is a number sentence containing $>$ (is greater than), $<$ (is less than), $\geq$ (is greater than or equal to), or $\leq$ (is less than or equal to). Inequalities like

$$-7 > x, \qquad t < 5, \qquad 5x - 2 \geq 9, \qquad \text{and} \qquad -3y + 8 \leq -7$$

are true for some replacements of the variable and false for others.

EXAMPLE 1 Determine whether the given number is a solution of $x < 2$: **(a)** -3; **(b)** 2.

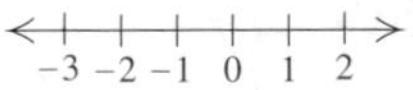

Solution

a) Since $-3 < 2$ is true, -3 is a solution.

b) Since $2 < 2$ is false, 2 is not a solution.

EXAMPLE 2 Determine whether the given number is a solution of $y \geq 6$: **(a)** 6; **(b)** -4.

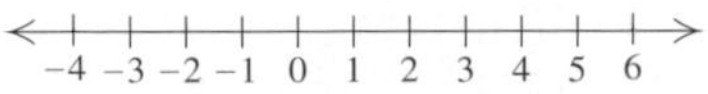

Solution

a) Since $6 \geq 6$ is true, 6 is a solution.

b) Since $-4 \geq 6$ is false, -4 is not a solution.

Graphs of Inequalities

Because the solutions of inequalities like $x < 2$ are too numerous to list, it is helpful to make a drawing that represents all the solutions. The **graph** of an inequality is such a drawing. Graphs of inequalities in one variable can be drawn on a number line by shading all points that are solutions. Open dots are used to indicate endpoints that are *not* solutions and closed dots indicate endpoints that *are* solutions.

EXAMPLE 3 Graph each inequality: **(a)** $x < 2$; **(b)** $y \geq -3$; **(c)** $-2 < x \leq 3$.

Solution

a) The solutions of $x < 2$ are those numbers less than 2. They are shown on the graph by shading all points to the left of 2. The open dot at 2 and the shading to its left indicate that 2 is *not* part of the graph, but numbers like 1.2 and 1.99 are.

b) The solutions of $y \geq -3$ are shown on the number line by shading the point for -3 and all points to the right of -3. The closed dot at -3 indicates that -3 *is* part of the graph.

Student Notes

Note that $-2 < x < 3$ means $-2 < x$ *and* $x < 3$. Because of this, statements like $2 < x < 1$ make no sense — no number is both greater than 2 and less than 1.

c) The inequality $-2 < x \leq 3$ is read "-2 is less than x *and* x is less than or equal to 3," or "x is greater than -2 *and* less than or equal to 3." To be a solution of $-2 < x \leq 3$, a number must be a solution of both $-2 < x$ *and* $x \leq 3$. The number 1 is a solution, as are -0.5, 1.9, and 3. The open dot indicates that -2 is *not* a solution, whereas the closed dot indicates that 3 *is* a solution. The other solutions are shaded.

Solving Inequalities Using the Addition Principle

Consider a balance similar to one that appears in Section 2.1. When one side of the balance holds more weight than the other, the balance tips in that direction. If equal amounts of weight are then added to or subtracted from both sides of the balance, the balance remains tipped in the same direction.

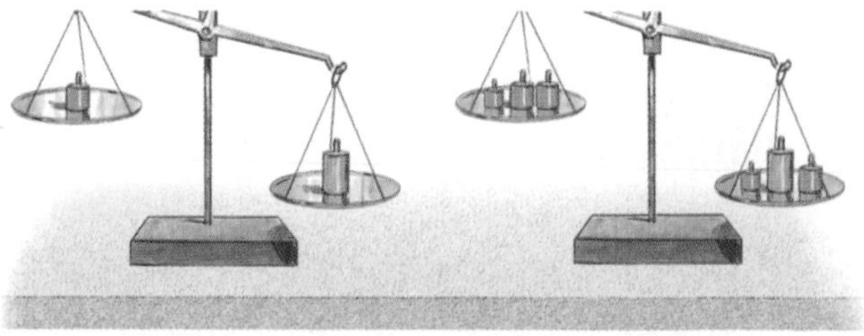

The balance illustrates the idea that when a number, such as 2, is added to (or subtracted from) both sides of a true inequality, such as $3 < 7$, we get another true inequality:

$$3 + 2 < 7 + 2, \quad \text{or} \quad 5 < 9.$$

Similarly, if we add -4 to both sides of $x + 4 < 10$, we get an *equivalent* inequality:

$$x + 4 + (-4) < 10 + (-4), \quad \text{or} \quad x < 6.$$

We say that $x + 4 < 10$ and $x < 6$ are **equivalent**, which means that both inequalities have the same solution set.

The Addition Principle for Inequalities

For any real numbers a, b, and c:

$a < b$ is equivalent to $a + c < b + c$;
$a \le b$ is equivalent to $a + c \le b + c$;
$a > b$ is equivalent to $a + c > b + c$;
$a \ge b$ is equivalent to $a + c \ge b + c$.

As with equations, our goal is to isolate the variable on one side.

EXAMPLE 4 Solve $x + 2 > 8$ and then graph the solution.

Solution We use the addition principle, subtracting 2 from both sides:

$$x + 2 - 2 > 8 - 2 \qquad \text{Subtracting 2 from, or adding } -2 \text{ to, both sides}$$

$$x > 6.$$

From the inequality $x > 6$, we can determine the solutions easily. Any number greater than 6 makes $x > 6$ true and is a solution of that inequality as well as the inequality $x + 2 > 8$. The graph is as follows:

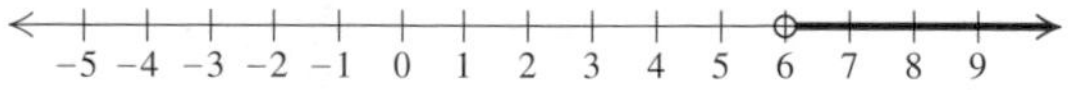

Because most inequalities have an infinite number of solutions, we cannot possibly check them all. A partial check can be made using one of the possible solutions. For this example, we can substitute any number greater than 6—say, 6.1—into the original inequality:

$x + 2 > 8$	
$6.1 + 2$	8

$8.1 \overset{?}{>} 8$ TRUE $\quad$ $8.1 > 8$ is a true statement.

Since $8.1 > 8$ is true, 6.1 is a solution. Any number greater than 6 is a solution.

Study Skills

Sleep Well

Being well rested, alert, and focused is very important when studying math. Often, problems that may seem confusing to a sleepy person are easily understood after a good night's sleep. Using your time efficiently is always important, so you should be aware that an alert, wide-awake student can often accomplish more in 10 minutes than a sleepy student can accomplish in 30 minutes.

Although the inequality $x > 6$ is easy to solve (we merely replace x with numbers greater than 6), it is worth noting that $x > 6$ is an *inequality*, not a *solution*. In fact, the solutions of $x > 6$ are numbers. To describe the set of all solutions, we will use **set-builder notation** to write the *solution set* of Example 4 as

$$\{x \mid x > 6\}.$$

This notation is read

"The set of all x such that x is greater than 6."

Thus a number is in $\{x \mid x > 6\}$ if that number is greater than 6. From now on, solutions of inequalities will be written using set-builder notation.

EXAMPLE 5 Solve $3x - 1 \leq 2x - 5$ and then graph the solution.

Solution We have

$$3x - 1 \leq 2x - 5$$

$$3x - 1 + 1 \leq 2x - 5 + 1 \qquad \text{Adding 1 to both sides}$$

$$3x \leq 2x - 4 \qquad \text{Simplifying}$$

$$3x - 2x \leq 2x - 4 - 2x \qquad \text{Subtracting } 2x \text{ from both sides}$$

$$x \leq -4. \qquad \text{Simplifying}$$

The graph is as follows:

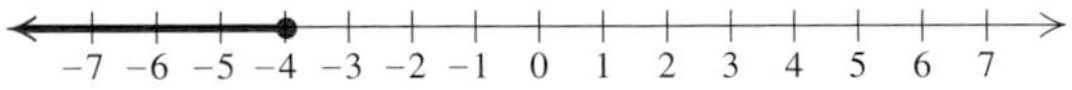

The student should check that any number less than or equal to -4 is a solution. The solution set is $\{x \mid x \leq -4\}$.

technology connection

As a partial check of Example 5, we can let $y_1 = 3x - 1$ and $y_2 = 2x - 5$. By scrolling up or down, you can note that for $x \leq -4$, we have $y_1 \leq y_2$.

X	Y1	Y2
−5	−16	−15
−4	−13	−13
−3	−10	−11
−2	−7	−9
−1	−4	−7
0	−1	−5
1	2	−3

X = −5

Solving Inequalities Using the Multiplication Principle

There is a multiplication principle for inequalities similar to that for equations, but it must be modified when multiplying both sides by a negative number. Consider the true inequality

$$3 < 7.$$

If we multiply both sides by a *positive* number, say 2, we get another true inequality:

$$3 \cdot 2 < 7 \cdot 2, \quad \text{or} \quad 6 < 14. \qquad \text{TRUE}$$

If we multiply both sides by a negative number, say -2, we get a *false* inequality:

$$3 \cdot (-2) < 7 \cdot (-2), \quad \text{or} \quad -6 < -14. \qquad \text{FALSE}$$

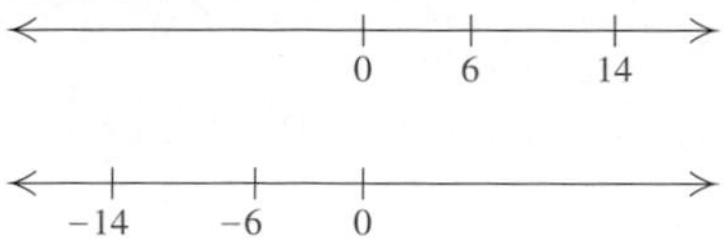

The fact that $6 < 14$ is true, but $-6 < -14$ is false, stems from the fact that the negative numbers, in a sense, *mirror* the positive numbers. Whereas 14 is to the *right* of 6, the number -14 is to the *left* of -6. Thus if we reverse the inequality symbol in $-6 < -14$, we get a true inequality:

$-6 > -14.$ TRUE

The Multiplication Principle for Inequalities

For any real numbers a and b, and for any *positive* number c:

$a < b$ is equivalent to $ac < bc$, and
$a > b$ is equivalent to $ac > bc$.

For any real numbers a and b, and for any *negative* number c:

$a < b$ is equivalent to $ac > bc$, and
$a > b$ is equivalent to $ac < bc$.

Similar statements hold for $\leq$ and $\geq$.

Caution! When multiplying or dividing both sides of an inequality by a negative number, don't forget to reverse the inequality symbol!

EXAMPLE 6 Solve and graph each inequality: **(a)** $\frac{1}{4}x < 7$; **(b)** $-2y < 18$.

Solution

a) $\frac{1}{4}x < 7$ Multiplying both sides by 4, the reciprocal of $\frac{1}{4}$

$4 \cdot \frac{1}{4}x < 4 \cdot 7$

The symbol stays the same, since 4 is positive.

$x < 28$ Simplifying

The solution set is $\{x | x < 28\}$. The graph is as shown at left.

b) $-2y < 18$

$\frac{-2y}{-2} > \frac{18}{-2}$ Multiplying both sides by $-\frac{1}{2}$, or dividing both sides by -2

At this step, we reverse the inequality, because $-\frac{1}{2}$ is negative.

$y > -9$ Simplifying

As a partial check, we substitute a number greater than -9, say -8, into the original inequality:

$-2y < 18$	
$-2(-8)$	18
$16 \overset{?}{<} 18$	TRUE

$16 < 18$ is a true statement.

The solution set is $\{y | y > -9\}$. The graph is as shown at left.

Using the Principles Together

We use the addition and multiplication principles together to solve inequalities much as we did when solving equations.

EXAMPLE 7 Solve: **(a)** $6 - 5y > 7$; **(b)** $2x - 9 \leq 7x + 1$.

Solution

a)

$6 - 5y > 7$	
$-6 + 6 - 5y > -6 + 7$	Adding -6 to both sides
$-5y > 1$	Simplifying
$-\frac{1}{5} \cdot (-5y) < -\frac{1}{5} \cdot 1$	Multiplying both sides by $-\frac{1}{5}$, or dividing both sides by -5
↑	Remember to reverse the inequality symbol!
$y < -\frac{1}{5}$	Simplifying

As a check, we substitute a number smaller than $-\frac{1}{5}$, say -1, into the original inequality:

$6 - 5y > 7$	
$6 - 5(-1)$	7
$6 - (-5)$	

$11 \overset{?}{>} 7$ TRUE $11 > 7$ is a true statement.

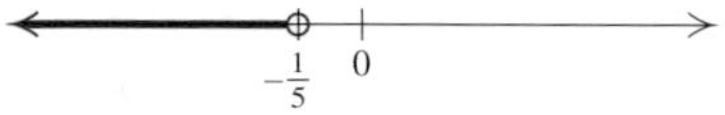

The solution set is $\{y \mid y < -\frac{1}{5}\}$. We show the graph in the margin for reference.

b)

$2x - 9 \leq 7x + 1$	
$2x - 9 - 1 \leq 7x + 1 - 1$	Subtracting 1 from both sides
$2x - 10 \leq 7x$	Simplifying
$2x - 10 - 2x \leq 7x - 2x$	Subtracting $2x$ from both sides
$-10 \leq 5x$	Simplifying
$\frac{-10}{5} \leq \frac{5x}{5}$	Dividing both sides by 5
$-2 \leq x$	Simplifying

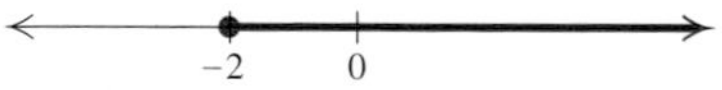

The solution set is $\{x \mid -2 \leq x\}$, or $\{x \mid x \geq -2\}$.

All of the equation-solving techniques used in Sections 2.1 and 2.2 can be used with inequalities provided we remember to reverse the inequality symbol when multiplying or dividing both sides by a negative number.

EXAMPLE 8 Solve: **(a)** $16.3 - 7.2p \leq -8.18$; **(b)** $3(x - 9) - 1 < 2 - 5(x + 6)$.

Solution

a) The greatest number of decimal places in any one number is *two*. Multiplying both sides by 100 will clear decimals. Then we proceed as before.

$16.3 - 7.2p \leq -8.18$	
$100(16.3 - 7.2p) \leq 100(-8.18)$	Multiplying both sides by 100
$100(16.3) - 100(7.2p) \leq 100(-8.18)$	Using the distributive law
$1630 - 720p \leq -818$	Simplifying
$-720p \leq -818 - 1630$	Subtracting 1630 from both sides
$-720p \leq -2448$	Simplifying
$p \geq \dfrac{-2448}{-720}$	Dividing both sides by -720
↑	Remember to reverse the symbol!
$p \geq 3.4$	

The solution set is $\{p \mid p \geq 3.4\}$.

b) $3(x - 9) - 1 < 2 - 5(x + 6)$

$3x - 27 - 1 < 2 - 5x - 30$	Using the distributive law to remove parentheses
$3x - 28 < -5x - 28$	Simplifying
$3x - 28 + 28 < -5x - 28 + 28$	Adding 28 to both sides
$3x < -5x$	
$3x + 5x < -5x + 5x$	Adding $5x$ to both sides
$8x < 0$	
$x < 0$	Dividing both sides by 8

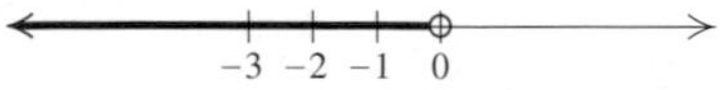

The solution set is $\{x \mid x < 0\}$.

2.6 Exercise Set

FOR EXTRA HELP

Student's Solutions Manual | Digital Video Tutor CD 2 Videotape 4 | AW Math Tutor Center | MathXL Tutorials on CD | MathXL | MyMathLab

Concept Reinforcement *Insert the symbol $<, >, \leq$, or $\geq$ to make each pair of inequalities equivalent.*

1. $-5x \leq 30$; x ■ -6

2. $-7t \geq 56$; t ■ -8

3. $-2t > -14$; t ■ 7

4. $-3x < -15$; x ■ 5

Concept Reinforcement *Classify each pair of inequalities as "equivalent" or "not equivalent."*

5. $x < -2$; $-2 > x$

6. $t > -1$; $-1 < t$

7. $-4x - 1 \leq 15$;
$-4x \leq 16$

8. $-2t + 3 \geq 11$;
$-2t \geq 14$

Determine whether each number is a solution of the given inequality.

9. $x > -2$
a) 5 **b)** 0 **c)** -1.9
d) -7.3 **e)** 1.6

10. $y < 5$
a) 0 **b)** 5 **c)** 4.99
d) -13 **e)** $7\frac{1}{4}$

11. $x \geq 6$
a) -6 **b)** 0 **c)** 6
d) 6.01 **e)** $-3\frac{1}{2}$

12. $x \leq 10$
a) 4 **b)** -10 **c)** 0
d) 10.2 **e)** -4.7

Graph on a number line.

13. $y < 2$
14. $x \leq 7$
15. $y > 4$
16. $t > -2$
17. $0 \leq t$
18. $1 \leq m$
19. $-5 \leq x < 2$
20. $-3 < x \leq 5$
21. $-5 \leq x \leq 0$
22. $0 < x < 3$

Describe each graph using set-builder notation.

23. 

24. 

25. 

26. 

27. 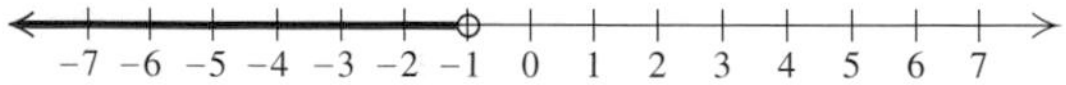

28. 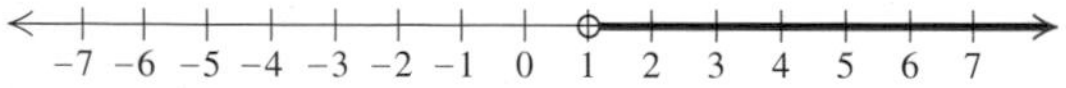

29. 

30. 

Solve using the addition principle. Graph and write set-builder notation for each answer.

31. $y + 6 > 9$
32. $y + 2 > 9$
33. $x + 9 \leq -12$
34. $x + 8 \leq -10$
35. $x - 3 < 14$
36. $x - 3 < 7$
37. $y - 10 > -16$
38. $y - 7 > -12$
39. $2x \leq x + 9$
40. $3x \leq 2x + 7$
41. $y + \frac{1}{3} \leq \frac{5}{6}$
42. $x + \frac{1}{4} \leq \frac{1}{2}$
43. $t - \frac{1}{8} > \frac{1}{2}$
44. $y - \frac{1}{3} > \frac{1}{4}$
45. $-9x + 17 > 17 - 8x$
46. $-8n + 12 > 12 - 7n$
Aha! **47.** $-23 < -t$
48. $19 < -x$

Solve using the multiplication principle. Graph and write set-builder notation for each answer.

49. $5x < 35$
50. $8x \geq 32$
51. $-7x < 13$
52. $8y < 17$
53. $-24 > 8t$
54. $-16x < -64$
55. $7y \geq -2$
56. $5x > -3$
57. $-2y \leq \frac{1}{5}$
58. $-2x \geq \frac{1}{5}$
59. $-\frac{8}{5} > -2x$
60. $-\frac{5}{8} < -10y$

Solve using the addition and multiplication principles.

61. $7 + 3x < 34$
62. $5 + 4y < 37$
63. $6 + 5y \geq 26$
64. $7 + 8x \geq 71$
65. $4t - 5 \leq 23$
66. $13x - 7 < -7$
67. $16 < 4 - 3y$
68. $22 < 6 - 8x$
69. $39 > 3 - 9x$
70. $5 > 5 - 7y$
71. $5 - 6y > 25$
72. $8 - 2y > 14$
73. $-3 < 8x + 7 - 7x$
74. $-5 < 9x + 8 - 8x$
75. $6 - 4y > 4 - 3y$
76. $7 - 8y > 5 - 7y$
77. $7 - 9y \leq 4 - 8y$
78. $6 - 13y \leq 4 - 12y$
79. $33 - 12x < 4x + 97$
80. $27 - 11x > 14x - 18$
81. $2.1x + 43.2 > 1.2 - 8.4x$
82. $0.96y - 0.79 \leq 0.21y + 0.46$
83. $0.7n - 15 + n \geq 2n - 8 - 0.4n$
84. $1.7t + 8 - 1.62t < 0.4t - 0.32 + 8$
85. $\frac{x}{3} - 4 \leq 1$
86. $\frac{2}{3} - \frac{x}{5} < \frac{4}{15}$
87. $3 < 5 - \frac{t}{7}$

88. $2 > 9 - \frac{x}{5}$

89. $4(2y - 3) < 36$

90. $3(2y - 3) > 21$

91. $3(t - 2) \geq 9(t + 2)$

92. $8(2t + 1) > 4(7t + 7)$

93. $3(r - 6) + 2 < 4(r + 2) - 21$

94. $5(t + 3) + 9 > 3(t - 2) + 6$

95. $\frac{2}{3}(2x - 1) \geq 10$

96. $\frac{4}{5}(3x + 4) \leq 20$

97. $\frac{3}{4}\left(3x - \frac{1}{2}\right) - \frac{2}{3} < \frac{1}{3}$

98. $\frac{2}{3}\left(\frac{7}{8} - 4x\right) - \frac{5}{8} < \frac{3}{8}$

99. Are the inequalities $x > -3$ and $x \geq -2$ equivalent? Why or why not?

100. Are the inequalities $t < -7$ and $t \leq -8$ equivalent? Why or why not?

SKILL MAINTENANCE

Translate to an algebraic expression. [1.1]

101. The sum of 3 and some number

102. Twice the sum of two numbers

103. Three less than twice a number

104. Five more than twice a number

SYNTHESIS

105. Explain how it is possible for the graph of an inequality to consist of just one number. (*Hint*: See Example 3c.)

106. Explain in your own words why it is necessary to reverse the inequality symbol when multiplying both sides of an inequality by a negative number.

Solve.

Aha! **107.** $x < x + 1$

108. $6[4 - 2(6 + 3t)] > 5[3(7 - t) - 4(8 + 2t)] - 20$

109. $27 - 4[2(4x - 3) + 7] \geq 2[4 - 2(3 - x)] - 3$

Solve for x.

110. $-(x + 5) \geq 4a - 5$

111. $\frac{1}{2}(2x + 2b) > \frac{1}{3}(21 + 3b)$

112. $y < ax + b$ (Assume $a > 0$.)

113. $y < ax + b$ (Assume $a < 0$.)

114. Graph the solutions of $|x| < 3$ on a number line.

Aha! **115.** Determine the solution set of $|x| > -3$.

116. Determine the solution set of $|x| < 0$.

2.7 Solving Applications with Inequalities

Translating to Inequalities • Solving Problems

The five steps for problem solving can be used for problems involving inequalities.

Translating to Inequalities

Before solving problems that involve inequalities, we list some important phrases to look for. Sample translations are listed as well.

Study Skills

Avoiding Temptation

Be kind to yourself when studying—in a supportive way. For example, sit in a comfortable chair in a well-lit location, but stay away from a coffee shop where friends may stop by. Once you begin studying, let the answering machine answer the phone, shut off any cell phones, and do not check e-mail.

Important Words	Sample Sentence	Translation
is at least	Bill is at least 21 years old.	$b \geq 21$
is at most	At most 5 students dropped the course.	$n \leq 5$
cannot exceed	To qualify, earnings cannot exceed $12,000.	$r \leq 12{,}000$
must exceed	The speed must exceed 15 mph.	$s > 15$
is less than	Tucker's weight is less than 50 lb.	$w < 50$
is more than	Boston is more than 200 miles away.	$d > 200$
is between	The film was between 90 and 100 minutes long.	$90 < t < 100$
no more than	Bing weighs no more than 90 lb.	$w \leq 90$
no less than	Valerie scored no less than 8.3.	$s \geq 8.3$

The following phrases deserve special attention.

Translating "at least" and "at most"

The quantity x is at least some amount q: $x \geq q$.
(If x is *at least* q, it cannot be less than q.)

The quantity x is at most some amount q: $x \leq q$.
(If x is *at most* q, it cannot be more than q.)

Solving Problems

EXAMPLE 1

Catering costs. To cater a party, Curtis' Barbeque charges a $50 setup fee plus $15 per person. The cost of Hotel Pharmacy's end-of-season softball party cannot exceed $450. How many people can attend the party?

Solution

1. **Familiarize.** Suppose that 20 people were to attend the party. The cost would then be $\$50 + \$15 \cdot 20$, or $350. This shows that more than 20 people could attend without exceeding $450. Instead of making another guess, we let $n =$ the number of people in attendance.
2. **Translate.** The cost of the party will be $50 for the setup fee plus $15 times the number of people attending. We can reword as follows:

Rewording:	The setup fee	plus	the cost of the meals	cannot exceed	$450.
	↓	↓	↓	↓	↓
Translating:	50	$+$	$15 \cdot n$	$\leq$	450

3. **Carry out.** We solve for n:

$$50 + 15n \leq 450$$
$$15n \leq 400 \quad \text{Subtracting 50 from both sides}$$
$$n \leq \frac{400}{15} \quad \text{Dividing both sides by 15}$$
$$n \leq 26\frac{2}{3}. \quad \text{Simplifying}$$

4. **Check.** Although the solution set of the inequality is all numbers less than or equal to $26\frac{2}{3}$, since n represents the number of people in attendance, we round *down* to 26. If 26 people attend, the cost will be $\$50 + \$15 \cdot 26$, or \$440, and if 27 attend, the cost will exceed \$450.

5. **State.** At most 26 people can attend the party.

> *Caution!* Solutions of problems should always be checked using the original wording of the problem. In some cases, answers might need to be whole numbers or integers or rounded off in a particular direction.

Some applications with inequalities involve *averages* or *means*. You are already familiar with the concept of averages from grades in courses that you have taken.

> *Average, or Mean*
>
> To find the **average** or **mean** of a set of numbers, add the numbers and then divide by the number of addends.

EXAMPLE 2 Nutrition. The U.S. Department of Health and Human Services and the Department of Agriculture recommend that for a typical 2000-calorie daily diet, no more than 65 g of fat be consumed. In the first three days of a four-day vacation, Phil consumed 70 g, 62 g, and 80 g of fat. Determine (in terms of an inequality) how many grams of fat Phil can consume on the fourth day if he is to average no more than 65 g of fat per day.

Solution

1. **Familiarize.** Suppose Phil consumed 64 g of fat on the fourth day. His daily average for the vacation would then be

$$\frac{70\text{ g} + 62\text{ g} + 80\text{ g} + 64\text{ g}}{4} = 69\text{ g}. \quad \text{There are 4 addends, so we divide by 4.}$$

This shows that Phil cannot consume 64 g of fat on the fourth day, if he is to average no more than 65 g of fat per day. Let's have x represent the number of grams of fat that Phil consumes on the fourth day.

2. **Translate.** We reword the problem and translate as follows:

Rewording:	The average consumption of fat	should be no more than	65 g.
Translating:	$\dfrac{70 + 62 + 80 + x}{4}$	$\leq$	65

3. **Carry out.** Because of the fraction, it is convenient to use the multiplication principle first:

$$\frac{70 + 62 + 80 + x}{4} \leq 65$$

$$4\left(\frac{70 + 62 + 80 + x}{4}\right) \leq 4 \cdot 65 \qquad \text{Multiplying both sides by 4}$$

$$70 + 62 + 80 + x \leq 260$$

$$212 + x \leq 260 \qquad \text{Simplifying}$$

$$x \leq 48. \qquad \text{Subtracting 212 from both sides}$$

4. **Check.** As a partial check, we show that Phil can consume 48 g of fat on the fourth day and not exceed a 65-g average for the four days:

$$\frac{70 + 62 + 80 + 48}{4} = \frac{260}{4} = 65. \qquad \text{Note that 65 does not, itself, exceed 65.}$$

5. **State.** Phil's average fat intake for the vacation will not exceed 65 g per day if he consumes no more than 48 g of fat on the fourth day.

2.7 Exercise Set

FOR EXTRA HELP

Student's Solutions Manual | Digital Video Tutor CD 2 Videotape 4 | AW Math Tutor Center | MathXL Tutorials on CD | MathXL | MyMathLab

Concept Reinforcement In each of Exercises 1–8, match the sentence with one of the following:
$a < b$; $a \leq b$; $b < a$; $b \leq a$.

1. a is at least b.

2. a exceeds b.

3. a is at most b.

4. a is exceeded by b.

5. b is no more than a.

6. b is no less than a.

7. b is less than a.

8. b is more than a.

Translate to an inequality.

9. A number is at least 8.

10. A number is greater than or equal to 4.

11. The temperature is at most -3°C.

12. The average credit-card holder is more than $4000 in debt.

13. The price of Pat's PT Cruiser exceeded $21,900.

14. The time of the test was between 45 and 55 min.

15. Normandale Community College is no more than 15 mi away.

16. Tania's weight is less than 110 lb.

17. That number is greater than -2.

18. The costs of production of that CD-ROM cannot exceed $12,500.

19. Between 400,000 and 1,200,000 people attended the Million Man March.

20. The cost of gasoline was at most $2 per gallon.

Use an inequality and the five-step process to solve each problem.

21. *Furnace repairs.* RJ's Plumbing and Heating charges $25 plus $30 per hour for emergency service. Gary remembers being billed over $100 for an emergency call. How long was RJ's there?

22. *College tuition.* Karen's financial aid stipulates that her tuition not exceed $1000. If her local community college charges a $35 registration fee plus $375 per course, what is the greatest number of courses for which Karen can register?

23. *Mass transit.* Local light rail service in Denver, Colorado, costs $1.15 per trip (one way). A student monthly pass costs $21. Gail is a student at Community College of Denver. Express as an inequality the number of trips per month that Gail should make if the pass is to save her money.
Source: rtd-denver.com

24. *Grade average.* Nadia is taking a literature course in which four tests are given. To get a B, a student must average at least 80 on the four tests. Nadia scored 82, 76, and 78 on the first three tests. What scores on the last test will earn her at least a B?

25. *Quiz average.* Rod's quiz grades are 73, 75, 89, and 91. What scores on a fifth quiz will make his average quiz grade at least 85?

26. *Nutrition.* Following the guidelines of the Food and Drug Administration, Dale tries to eat at least 5 servings of fruits or vegetables each day. For the first six days of one week, she had 4, 6, 7, 4, 6, and 4 servings. How many servings of fruits or vegetables should Dale eat on Saturday, in order to average at least 5 servings per day for the week?

27. *College course load.* To remain on financial aid, Millie needs to complete an average of at least 7 credits per quarter each year. In the first three quarters of 2004, Millie completed 5, 7, and 8 credits. How many credits of course work must Millie complete in the fourth quarter if she is to remain on financial aid?

28. *Music lessons.* Band members at Colchester Middle School are expected to average at least 20 min of practice time per day. One week Monroe practiced 15 min, 28 min, 30 min, 0 min, 15 min, and 25 min. How long must he practice on the seventh day if he is to meet expectations?

29. *Electrician visits.* Dot's Electric made 17 customer calls last week and 22 calls this week. How many calls must be made next week in order to maintain an average of at least 20 for the three-week period?

30. *Perimeter of a rectangle.* The width of a rectangle is fixed at 8 ft. What lengths will make the perimeter at least 200 ft? at most 200 ft?

31. *Perimeter of a triangle.* One side of a triangle is 2 cm shorter than the base. The other side is 3 cm longer than the base. What lengths of the base will allow the perimeter to be greater than 19 cm?

32. *Perimeter of a pool.* The perimeter of a rectangular swimming pool is not to exceed 70 ft. The length is to be twice the width. What widths will meet these conditions?

33. *Well drilling.* All Seasons Well Drilling offers two plans. Under the "pay-as-you-go" plan, they charge \$500 plus \$8 a foot for a well of any depth. Under their "guaranteed-water" plan, they charge a flat fee of \$4000 for a well that is guaranteed to provide adequate water for a household. For what depths would it save a customer money to use the pay-as-you-go plan?

34. *Cost of road service.* Rick's Automotive charges \$50 plus \$15 for each (15-min) unit of time when making a road call. Twin City Repair charges \$70 plus \$10 for each unit of time. Under what circumstances would it be more economical for a motorist to call Rick's?

35. *Insurance-covered repairs.* Most insurance companies will replace a vehicle if an estimated repair exceeds 80% of the "blue-book" value of the vehicle. Michelle's insurance company paid \$8500 for repairs to her Subaru after an accident. What can be concluded about the blue-book value of the car?

36. *Insurance-covered repairs.* Following an accident, Jeff's Ford pickup was replaced by his insurance company because the damage was so extensive. Before the damage, the blue-book value of the truck was \$21,000. How much would it have cost to repair the truck? (See Exercise 35.)

37. *Sizes of envelopes.* Rhetoric Advertising is a direct-mail company. It determines that for a particular campaign, it can use any envelope with a fixed width of $3\frac{1}{2}$ in. and an area of at least $17\frac{1}{2}$ in^2. Determine (in terms of an inequality) those lengths that will satisfy the company constraints.

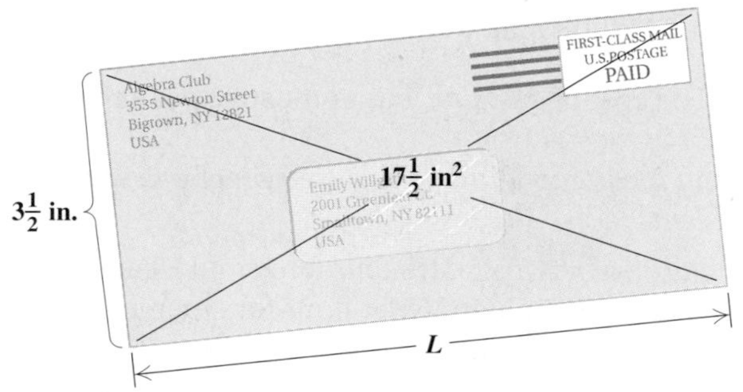

38. *Sizes of packages.* An overnight delivery service accepts packages of up to 165 in. in length and girth combined. (Girth is the distance around the package.) A package has a fixed girth of 53 in. Determine (in terms of an inequality) those lengths for which a package is acceptable.

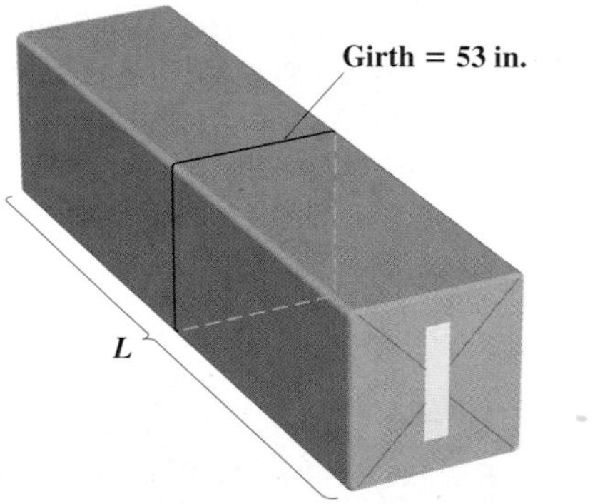

39. *Body temperature.* A person is considered to be feverish when his or her temperature is higher than 98.6°F. The formula $F = \frac{9}{5}C + 32$ can be used to convert Celsius temperatures C to Fahrenheit temperatures F. For which Celsius temperatures is a person considered feverish?

40. *Gold temperatures.* Gold stays solid at Fahrenheit temperatures below 1945.4°. Determine (in terms of an inequality) those Celsius temperatures for which gold stays solid. Use the formula given in Exercise 39.

41. *Area of a triangular flag.* As part of an outdoor education course, Wanda needs to make a bright-colored triangular flag with an area of at least 3 ft^2. What heights can the triangle be if the base is $1\frac{1}{2}$ ft?

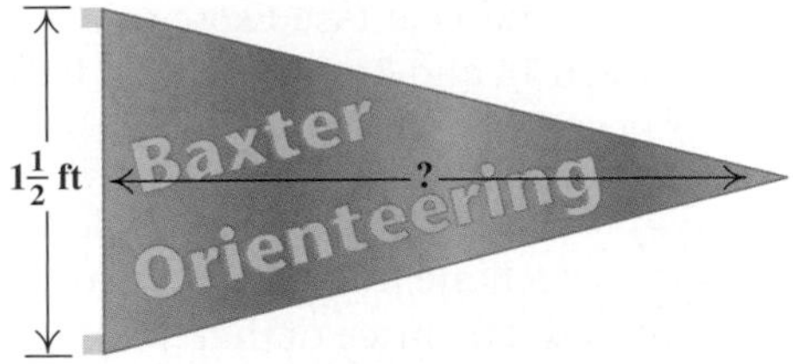

42. *Area of a triangular sign.* Zoning laws in Harrington prohibit displaying signs with areas exceeding 12 ft^2. If Flo's Marina is ordering a triangular sign with an 8-ft base, how tall can the sign be?

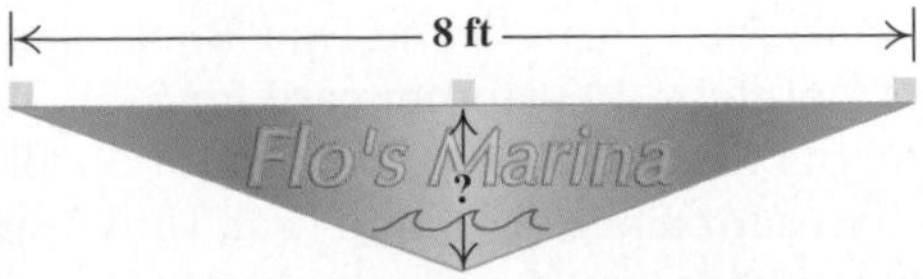

43. *Fat content in foods.* Reduced Fat Skippy® peanut butter contains 12 g of fat per serving. In order for a food to be labeled "reduced fat," it must have at least 25% less fat than the regular item. What can you conclude about the number of grams of fat in a serving of the regular Skippy peanut butter?
Source: Best Foods

44. *Fat content in foods.* Reduced Fat Chips Ahoy!® cookies contain 5 g of fat per serving. What can you conclude about the number of grams of fat in regular Chips Ahoy! cookies (see Exercise 43)?
Source: Nabisco Brands, Inc.

45. *Weight gain.* In the last weeks before the yearly Topsfield Weigh In, heavyweight pumpkins gain about 26 lb per day. Charlotte's heaviest pumpkin weighs 532 lb on September 5. For what dates will its weight exceed 818 lb?

46. *Pond depth.* On July 1, Garrett's Pond was 25 ft deep. Since that date, the water level has dropped $\frac{2}{3}$ ft per week. For what dates will the water level not exceed 21 ft?

47. *Blueprints.* To make copies of blueprints, Vantage Reprographics charges a \$6 setup fee plus \$4 per copy. Myra can spend no more than \$65 for the copying. What numbers of copies will allow her to stay within budget?

48. *Banquet costs.* The women's volleyball team can spend at most \$450 for its awards banquet at a local restaurant. If the restaurant charges a \$40 setup fee plus \$16 per person, at most how many can attend?

49. *World records in the mile run.* The formula

$$R = -0.0065t + 4.3222$$

can be used to predict the world record, in minutes, for the 1-mi run t years after 1900. Determine (in terms of an inequality) those years for which the world record will be less than 3.7 min.
Source: Based on information from Norris McWhirter, *Book of Historical Records.* New York: Sterling, 2000.

50. *Women's records in the women's 1500-m run.* The formula

$$R = -0.0223t + 4.4078$$

can be used to predict the world record, in minutes, for the 1500-m run t years after 1930. Determine (in terms of an inequality) those years for which the world record will be less than 3.5 min.

51. *Toll charges.* The equation $y = 0.03x + 0.21$ can be used to determine the approximate cost y, in dollars, of driving x miles on the Indiana toll road. For what mileages x will the cost be at most \$6?

52. *Price of a movie ticket.* The average price of a movie ticket can be estimated by the equation $P = 0.227Y - 448.71$, where Y is the year and P is the average price, in dollars. The price is lower than what might be expected due to senior-citizen discounts, children's prices, and special volume discounts. For what years will the average price of a movie ticket be at least \$7? (Include the year in which the \$7 ticket first occurs.)

53. If f represents Fran's age and t represents Todd's age, write a sentence that would translate to $t + 3 < f$.

54. Explain how the meanings of "Five more than a number" and "Five is more than a number" differ.

SKILL MAINTENANCE

Simplify. [1.8]

55. $\dfrac{9 - 5}{6 - 4}$

56. $\dfrac{8 - 5}{12 - 6}$

57. $\dfrac{8 - (-2)}{1 - 4}$

58. $\dfrac{7 - 9}{4 - (-6)}$

SYNTHESIS

59. Write a problem for a classmate to solve. Devise the problem so the answer is "At most 18 passengers can go on the boat." Design the problem so that at least one number in the solution must be rounded down.

60. Write a problem for a classmate to solve. Devise the problem so the answer is "The Rothmans can drive 90 mi without exceeding their truck rental budget."

61. *Ski wax.* Green ski wax works best between 5° and 15° Fahrenheit. Determine those Celsius temperatures for which green ski wax works best. (See Exercise 39.)

62. *Parking fees.* Mack's Parking Garage charges \$4.00 for the first hour and \$2.50 for each additional hour. For how long has a car been parked when the charge exceeds \$16.50?

Aha! **63.** The area of a square can be no more than 64 cm^2. What lengths of a side will allow this?

Aha! **64.** The sum of two consecutive odd integers is less than 100. What is the largest pair of such integers?

65. *Nutritional standards.* In order for a food to be labeled "lowfat," it must have fewer than 3 g of fat per serving. Reduced fat Tortilla Pops® contain 60% less fat than regular nacho cheese tortilla chips, but still cannot be labeled lowfat. What can you conclude about the fat content of a serving of nacho cheese tortilla chips?

66. *Parking fees.* When asked how much the parking charge is for a certain car (see Exercise 62), Mack replies "between 14 and 24 dollars." For how long has the car been parked?

67. *Frequent buyer bonus.* Alice's Books allows customers to select one free book for every 10 books purchased. The price of that book cannot exceed the average cost of the 10 books. Neoma has bought 9 books that average \$12 per book. How much should her tenth book cost if she wants to select a \$15 book for free?

68. *Grading.* After 9 quizzes, Blythe's average is 84. Is it possible for Blythe to improve her average by two points with the next quiz? Why or why not?

69. *Discount card.* Arnold and Diaz Booksellers offers a preferred-customer card for \$25. The card entitles a customer to a 10% discount on all purchases for a period of one year. Under what circumstances would an individual save money by purchasing a card?

2 Study Summary

Equations like $3x - 1 = 10$, $3x = 11$, and $x = \frac{11}{3}$, which share the same solution, are said to be **equivalent equations** (p. 81). **The addition principle** and **the multiplication principle** are the methods most frequently used for producing equivalent equations that lead to a solution (pp. 81, 83).

Addition principle (for equations):

For any real numbers *a*, *b*, and *c*,

$$a = b \quad \text{is equivalent to} \quad a + c = b + c.$$

Multiplication principle (for equations):

For any real numbers *a*, *b*, and *c*, with $c \neq 0$,

$$a = b \quad \text{is equivalent to} \quad a \cdot c = b \cdot c.$$

When we are solving equations like $5t - 3 = 14$, the addition principle is generally used first. When the **coefficient** of the variable is a fraction or a decimal, as in $\frac{2}{3}x - 5 = 8$ or $7 + 0.2r = 3$, the multiplication principle is often used first to **clear fractions** or **decimals** (pp. 93–94). The same principles and strategies are used when **solving formulas** for a specified letter (p. 98).

Inequalities, like $2x + 5 > -1$ and $9 \leq -7t + 3$, are solved in much the same manner as equations, using **the addition** and **multiplication principles for inequalities** (pp. 129, 131). When using the multiplication principle for inequalities, it is important to remember to reverse the direction of the inequality symbol whenever both sides are multiplied or divided by a negative number.

Addition principle (for inequalities):

For any real numbers *a*, *b*, and *c*,

$$a < b \quad \text{is equivalent to} \quad a + c < b + c;$$
$$a > b \quad \text{is equivalent to} \quad a + c > b + c.$$

Multiplication principle (for inequalities):

For any real numbers *a* and *b* and any *positive* number *c*,

$$a < b \quad \text{is equivalent to} \quad ac < bc;$$
$$a > b \quad \text{is equivalent to} \quad ac > bc.$$

For any real numbers *a* and *b* and any *negative* number *c*,

$$a < b \quad \text{is equivalent to} \quad ac > bc;$$
$$a > b \quad \text{is equivalent to} \quad ac < bc.$$

Similar statements hold for $\leq$ and $\geq$.

Because the solution of an inequality usually consists of too many numbers to list, **set-builder notation** and **graphs** are used to represent the **solution set** (p. 130).

Many real-world problems translate to equations or inequalities, and some involve **percent notation** (p. 105). Such problems can be solved using five steps (p. 115):

Five Steps for Problem Solving in Algebra

1. *Familiarize* yourself with the problem.
2. *Translate* to mathematical language. (This often means writing an equation.)
3. *Carry out* some mathematical manipulation. (This often means *solving* an equation.)
4. *Check* your possible answer in the original problem.
5. *State* the answer clearly.

2 Review Exercises

Concept Reinforcement *Classify each of the following as either true or false.*

1. $5x - 4 = 2x$ and $3x = 4$ are equivalent equations. [2.1]
2. $5 - 2t < 9$ and $t > 6$ are equivalent inequalities. [2.6]
3. Some equations have no solution. [2.1]
4. Consecutive odd integers are 2 units apart. [2.5]
5. For any number a, $a \leq a$. [2.6]
6. The addition principle is always used before the multiplication principle. [2.2]
7. A 10% discount results in a sale price that is 90% of the original price. [2.4]
8. Often it is impossible to list all solutions of an inequality number by number. [2.6]

Solve.

9. $x + 9 = -16$ [2.1]
10. $-8x = -56$ [2.1]
11. $-\frac{x}{5} = 13$ [2.1]
12. $n - 7 = -6$ [2.1]
13. $12x = -60$ [2.1]
14. $x - 0.1 = 1.01$ [2.1]
15. $-\frac{2}{3} + x = -\frac{1}{6}$ [2.1]
16. $\frac{4}{5}y = -\frac{3}{16}$ [2.1]
17. $5z + 3 = 41$ [2.2]
18. $5 - x = 13$ [2.2]
19. $5t + 9 = 3t - 1$ [2.2]
20. $7x - 6 = 25x$ [2.2]
21. $\frac{1}{4}x - \frac{5}{8} = \frac{3}{8}$ [2.2]
22. $14y = 23y - 17 - 10$ [2.2]
23. $0.22y - 0.6 = 0.12y + 3 - 0.8y$ [2.2]
24. $\frac{1}{4}x - \frac{1}{8}x = 3 - \frac{1}{16}x$ [2.2]
25. $3(x + 5) = 36$ [2.2]
26. $4(5x - 7) = -56$ [2.2]
27. $8(x - 2) = 5(x + 4)$ [2.2]
28. $-5x + 3(x + 8) = 16$ [2.2]

Solve each formula for the given letter. [2.3]

29. $C = \pi d$, for d
30. $V = \frac{1}{3}Bh$, for B
31. $A = \frac{a + b}{2}$, for b
32. Find decimal notation: 0.9%. [2.4]
33. Find percent notation: $\frac{11}{25}$. [2.4]
34. What percent of 60 is 42? [2.4]
35. 42 is 30% of what number? [2.4]

Determine whether each number is a solution of $x \leq 4$. [2.6]

36. -3 **37.** 7 **38.** 4

Graph on a number line. [2.6]

39. $5x - 6 < 2x + 3$ **40.** $-2 < x \leq 5$

41. $t > 0$

Solve. Write the answers in set-builder notation. [2.6]

42. $t + \frac{2}{3} \geq \frac{1}{6}$ **43.** $9x \geq 63$

44. $2 + 6y > 20$ **45.** $7 - 3y \geq 27 + 2y$

46. $3x + 5 < 2x - 6$ **47.** $-4y < 28$

48. $3 - 4x < 27$ **49.** $4 - 8x < 13 + 3x$

50. $13 \leq -\frac{2}{3}t + 5$ **51.** $7 \leq 1 - \frac{3}{4}x$

Solve.

52. A can of powdered infant formula makes 120 oz of formula. How many 6-oz bottles of formula will the can make? [2.5]

53. A 32-ft beam is cut into two pieces. One piece is 2 ft longer than the other. How long are the pieces? [2.5]

54. About 55% of all charitable contributions are made to religious organizations. In 1999, \$69.3 billion was given to religious organizations. How much was given to charities in general? [2.4]
Source: *Statistical Abstract of the United States*, 2002

55. The sum of two consecutive odd integers is 116. Find the integers. [2.5]

56. The perimeter of a rectangle is 56 cm. The width is 6 cm less than the length. Find the width and the length. [2.5]

57. After a 25% reduction, a picnic table is on sale for \$120. What was the regular price? [2.4]

58. In 2002, the average male with a bachelor's degree or above earned about \$78,000. This was 66% more than the average woman with a comparable background. How much did the average woman with a comparable background earn? [2.4]
Source: *The New York Times Almanac* 2003

59. The measure of the second angle of a triangle is 50° more than that of the first. The measure of the third angle is 10° less than twice the first. Find the measures of the angles. [2.5]

60. Lisa has budgeted an average of \$95 a month for entertainment. For the first five months of the year, she has spent \$98, \$89, \$110, \$85, and \$83. How much can Lisa spend in the sixth month without exceeding her average budget? [2.7]

61. The length of a rectangular frame is 43 cm. For what widths would the perimeter be greater than 120 cm? [2.7]

62. How does the multiplication principle for equations differ from the multiplication principle for inequalities? [2.1], [2.6]

SYNTHESIS

63. Explain how checking the solutions of an equation differs from checking the solutions of an inequality. [2.1], [2.6]

64. Children (aged 2–17) with access to computers, video games, and television spend an average of 33 hr 36 min per week viewing a screen of some type. This represents 31% more time than that spent by children who view only television. How much time each week does the average child spend in front of a television if he or she lives in a home without a computer or video games? [2.4]
Source: Stanger, J. D., and N. Gridina, *Media in the Home* 1999; the fourth annual survey of parents and children. Philadelphia: Annenberg Public Policy Center, University of Pennsylvania, 1999.

65. The combined length of the Nile and Amazon Rivers is 13,113 km. If the Amazon were 233 km longer, it would be as long as the Nile. Find the length of each river. [2.5]
Source: *The New York Times Almanac* 2003

66. Consumer experts advise us never to pay the sticker price for a car. A rule of thumb is to pay the sticker price minus 20% of the sticker price, plus \$200. A car is purchased for \$15,080 using the rule. What was the sticker price? [2.4], [2.5]

Solve.

67. $2|n| + 4 = 50$ [1.4], [2.2]

68. $|3n| = 60$ [1.4], [2.1]

69. $y = 2a - ab + 3$, for a [2.3]

2 Chapter Test

Solve.

1. $t + 7 = 16$

2. $t - 3 = 12$

3. $6x = -18$

4. $-\frac{4}{7}x = -28$

5. $3t + 7 = 2t - 5$

6. $\frac{1}{2}x - \frac{3}{5} = \frac{2}{5}$

7. $8 - y = 16$

8. $-\frac{2}{5} + x = -\frac{3}{4}$

9. $4(x + 2) = 36$

10. $9 - 3x = 6(x + 4)$

11. $\frac{5}{6}(3x + 1) = 20$

Solve. Write the answers in set-builder notation.

12. $x + 6 > 1$

13. $14x + 9 > 13x - 4$

14. $\frac{1}{3}x < \frac{7}{8}$

15. $-2y \geq 26$

16. $4y \leq -32$

17. $-5x \geq \frac{1}{4}$

18. $4 - 6x > 40$

19. $5 - 9x \geq 19 + 5x$

Solve each formula for the given letter.

20. $A = 2\pi rh$, for r

21. $w = \frac{P + l}{2}$, for l

22. Find decimal notation: 230%.

23. Find percent notation: 0.054.

24. What number is 32% of 50?

25. What percent of 75 is 33?

Graph on a number line.

26. $y < 4$

27. $-2 \leq x \leq 2$

Solve.

28. The perimeter of a rectangular calculator is 36 cm. The length is 4 cm greater than the width. Find the width and the length.

29. Kari is taking a 240-mi bicycle trip through Vermont. She has three times as many miles to go as she has already ridden. How many miles has she biked so far?

30. The perimeter of a triangle is 249 mm. If the sides are consecutive odd integers, find the length of each side.

31. By lowering the temperature of their electric hot-water heater from 140°F to 120°F, the Kellys' average electric bill dropped by 7% to \$60.45. What was their electric bill before they lowered the temperature of their hot water?

32. *Van rentals.* Atlas rents a cargo van at a daily rate of \$44.95 plus \$0.39 per mile. A business has budgeted \$250 for a one-day van rental. What mileages will allow the business to stay within budget? (Round to the nearest tenth of a mile.)

SYNTHESIS

Solve.

33. $c = \frac{2cd}{a - d}$, for d

34. $3|w| - 8 = 37$

35. A concert promoter had a certain number of tickets to give away. Five people got the tickets. The first got one third of the tickets, the second got one fourth of the tickets, and the third got one fifth of the tickets. The fourth person got eight tickets, and there were five tickets left for the fifth person. Find the total number of tickets given away.

3 Introduction to Graphing

AN APPLICATION

The plans for a skateboard "Fun Box" call for a ramp with a rise of 61 cm over a run of 167.6 cm (*Source*: www.heckler.com). Find the slope or grade of the ramp.

This problem appears as Exercise 83 in Section 3.5.

David M. Wood
CUSTOM SKATE-PARK DEVELOPER
Burlington, Vermont

I use geometry primarily when designing a skate park. Since all skate ramps are designed on an 8-ft radius, I use measurements that are multiples of 8. I make use of the concept of slope as well to design a bank ramp.

We now begin our study of graphing. First we will examine graphs as they commonly appear in newspapers or magazines and develop some terminology. Following that, we will graph certain equations and study the connection between rate and slope. We will also learn how graphs can be used as a problem-solving tool in many applications.

Our work in this chapter centers on solving equations that contain two variables.

3.1 Reading Graphs, Plotting Points, and Scaling Graphs

Problem Solving with Bar, Circle, and Line Graphs • Points and Ordered Pairs • Numbering the Axes Appropriately

Today's print and electronic media make almost constant use of graphs. This can be attributed to the widespread availability of graphing software and the large quantity of information that a graph can display. In this section, we consider problem solving with bar graphs, line graphs, and circle graphs. Then we examine graphs that use a coordinate system.

Problem Solving with Bar, Circle, and Line Graphs

A *bar graph* is a convenient way of showing comparisons. In every bar graph, certain categories, such as body weight in the example below, are paired with certain numbers.

EXAMPLE 1 Driving under the influence. A blood-alcohol level of 0.08% or higher makes driving illegal in the United States. This bar graph shows how many drinks a person of a certain weight would need to consume in 1 hr to achieve a blood-alcohol level of 0.08% (*Source*: Adapted from soberup.com and vsa.vassar.edu/~source/drugs/alcohol.html). Note that a 12-oz beer, a 5-oz glass of wine, or a cocktail containing $1\frac{1}{2}$ oz of distilled liquor all count as one drink.

Study Skills

To Err Is Human

It is no coincidence that the students who experience the greatest success in this course work in pencil. We all make mistakes and by using pencil and eraser we are more willing to admit to ourselves that something needs to be rewritten. Please work with a pencil and eraser if you aren't doing so already.

a) Approximately how many drinks would a 200-lb person have consumed if he or she had a blood-alcohol level of 0.08%?

b) What can be concluded about the weight of someone who can consume 3 drinks in an hour without reaching a blood-alcohol level of 0.08%?

Solution

a) We go to the top of the bar that is above the body weight 200 lb. Then we move horizontally from the top of the bar to the vertical scale listing numbers of drinks. It appears that approximately 4 drinks will give a 200-lb person a blood-alcohol level of 0.08%.

b) By moving up the vertical scale to the number 3, and then moving horizontally, we see that the first bar to reach a height of 3 corresponds to a weight of 140 lb. Thus an individual should weigh over 140 lb if he or she wishes to consume 3 drinks in an hour without exceeding a blood-alcohol level of 0.08%.

Circle graphs, or *pie charts,* are often used to show what percent of the whole each particular item in a group represents.

EXAMPLE 2 Color preference. The circle graph below shows the favorite colors of Americans and the percentage that prefers each color (*Source*: Vitaly Komar and Alex Melamid: The Most Wanted Paintings on the Web). Because of rounding, the total is slightly less than 100%. There are approximately 292 million Americans, and three quarters of them live in cities. Assuming that color preference is unaffected by geographical location, how many urban Americans choose red as their favorite color?

What is Your Favorite Color?

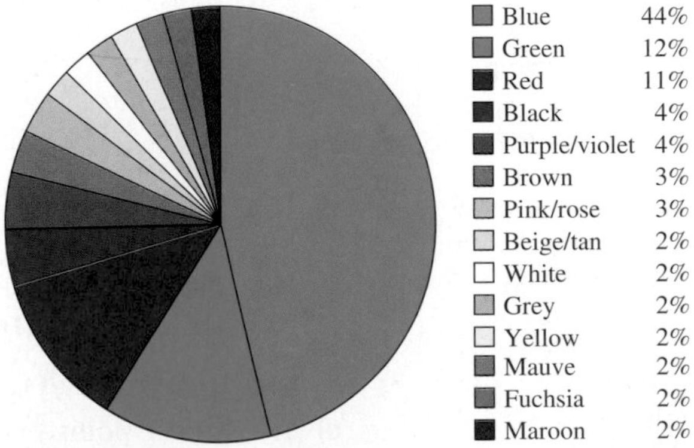

Solution

1. **Familiarize.** The problem involves percents, so if we were unsure of how to solve percent problems, we might review Section 2.4. We are told that three quarters of all Americans live in cities. Since there are about 292 million Americans, this amounts to

$$\frac{3}{4} \cdot 292, \quad \text{or 219 million urban Americans.}$$

The chart indicates that 11% of the U.S. population prefers red. We let $r =$ the number of urban Americans who select red as their favorite color. We assume that the color preferences of urban Americans are typical of all Americans.

2. **Translate.** We reword and translate the problem as follows:

Rewording:	What	is	11%	of	219 million?
	↓	↓	↓	↓	↓
Translating:	r	$=$	11%	$\cdot$	219,000,000

3. **Carry out.** We solve the equation:

$$r = 0.11 \cdot 219{,}000{,}000 = 24{,}090{,}000.$$

4. **Check.** The check is left to the student.

5. **State.** About 24,090,000 urban Americans choose red as their favorite color.

EXAMPLE 3 Exercise and pulse rate. The following line graph shows the relationship between a person's resting pulse rate and months of regular exercise.* Note that the symbol ≀ is used to indicate that counting on the vertical axis begins at 50.

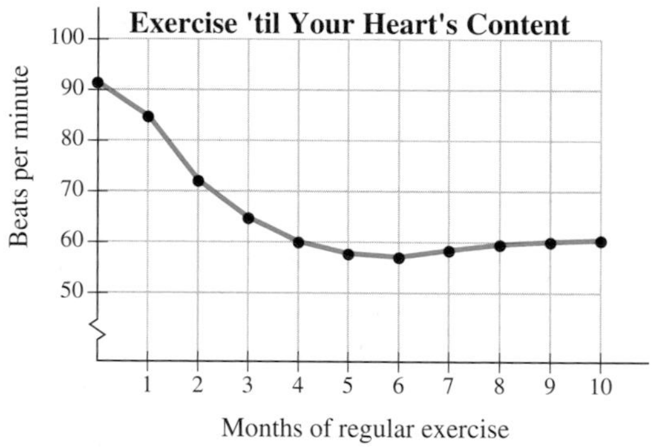

a) How many months of regular exercise are required to lower the pulse rate as much as possible?

b) How many months of regular exercise are needed to achieve a pulse rate of 65 beats per minute?

Solution

a) The lowest point on the graph occurs above the number 6. Thus, after 6 months of regular exercise, the pulse rate is lowered as much as possible.

b) To determine how many months of exercise are needed to lower a person's resting pulse rate to 65, we locate 65 midway between 60 and 70 on the vertical axis. From that location, we move right until the line is reached.

technology connection

The portion of the coordinate plane shown by a graphing calculator is called a **viewing window**. We indicate the **dimensions** of the window by setting a minimum x-value, a maximum x-value, a minimum y-value, and a maximum y-value. The **scale** by which we count must also be chosen. Window settings are often abbreviated in the form [L, R, B, T], with the letters representing **L**eft, **R**ight, **B**ottom, and **T**op endpoints. The window $[-10, 10, -10, 10]$ is called the **standard viewing window**. On most graphing calculators, a standard viewing window can be set up using an option in the ZOOM menu.

(*continued*)

*Data from *Body Clock* by Dr. Martin Hughes (New York: Facts on File, Inc.), p. 60.

At that point, we move down to the horizontal scale and read the number of months required, as shown.

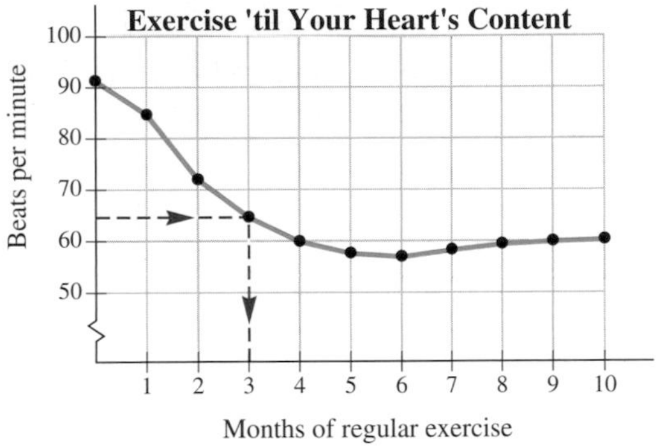

The pulse rate is 65 beats per minute after 3 months of regular exercise.

Points and Ordered Pairs

The line graph in Example 3 contains a collection of points. Each point pairs up a number of months of exercise with a pulse rate. To create such a graph, we **graph**, or **plot**, pairs of numbers on a plane. This is done using two perpendicular number lines called **axes** (pronounced "ak-sēz"; singular, **axis**). The point at which the axes cross is called the **origin**. Arrows on the axes indicate the positive directions.

Consider the pair (3, 4). The numbers in such a pair are called **coordinates.** The **first coordinate** in this case is 3 and the **second coordinate** is 4. To plot (3, 4), we start at the origin, move horizontally to the 3, move up vertically 4 units, and then make a "dot." Thus, (3, 4) is located above 3 on the first axis and to the right of 4 on the second axis.

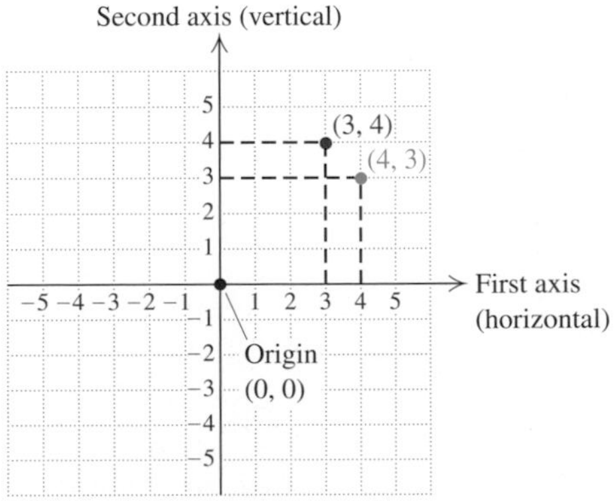

The point (4, 3) is also plotted in the figure above. Note that (3, 4) and (4, 3) are different points. For this reason, coordinate pairs are called **ordered pairs**—the order in which the numbers appear is important.

To set up a [−100, 100, −5, 5] window, we press WINDOW and use the following settings. A scale of 10 for the x-axis is large enough for the marks on the x-axis to be distinct.

```
WINDOW
  Xmin=-100
  Xmax=100
  Xscl=10
  Ymin=-5
  Ymax=5
  Yscl=1
  Xres=1
```

When GRAPH is pressed, a graph extending from −100 to 100 along the x-axis (counted by 10's) and from −5 to 5 along the y-axis appears. When the arrow keys are pressed, a cursor can be moved, its coordinates appearing at the bottom of the window.

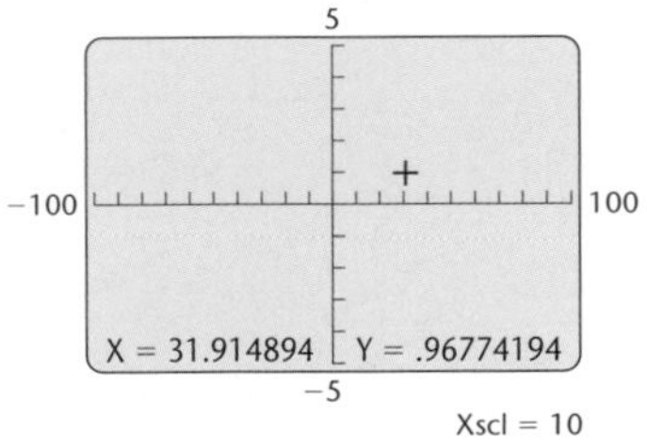

Set up the following viewing windows, choosing an appropriate scale for each axis. Then move the cursor and practice reading coordinates.

1. [−10, 10, −10, 10]
2. [−5, 5, 0, 100]
3. [−1, 1, −0.1, 0.1]

EXAMPLE 4 Plot the point $(-3, 4)$.

Solution The first number, -3, is negative. Starting at the origin, we move 3 units in the negative horizontal direction (3 units to the left). The second number, 4, is positive, so we move 4 units in the positive vertical direction (up). The point $(-3, 4)$ is above -3 on the first axis and to the left of 4 on the second axis.

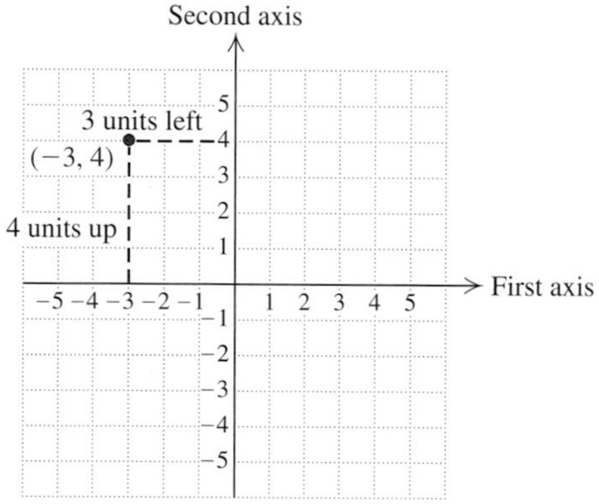

To find the coordinates of a point, we see how far to the right or left of the origin the point is and how far above or below the origin it is. Note that the coordinates of the origin itself are $(0, 0)$.

EXAMPLE 5 Find the coordinates of points A, B, C, D, E, F, and G.

Student Notes

It is important that you remember that the first coordinate of an ordered pair is always represented on the horizontal axis. It is better to go slowly and plot points correctly than to go quickly and require more than one attempt.

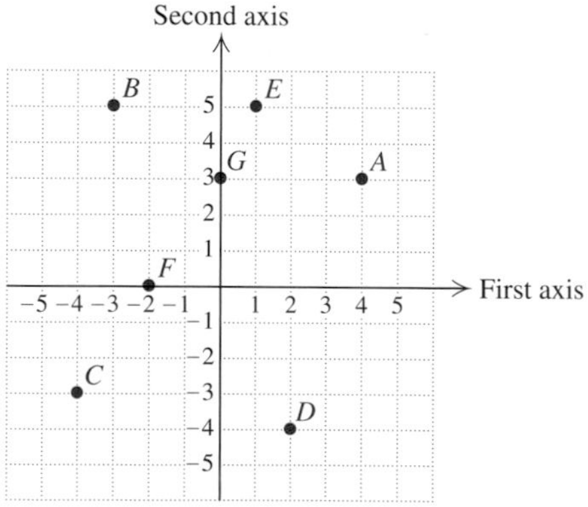

Solution Point A is 4 units to the right of the origin and 3 units above the origin. Its coordinates are $(4, 3)$. The coordinates of the other points are as follows:

B: $(-3, 5)$; C: $(-4, -3)$; D: $(2, -4)$;
E: $(1, 5)$; F: $(-2, 0)$; G: $(0, 3)$.

Numbering the Axes Appropriately

Often it is necessary to graph a range of x-values and/or y-values that is too large to be displayed if each square of the grid is one unit wide and one unit high. For example, if we wish to plot the points $(-34, 450)$, $(48, 95)$, and $(10, -200)$ using a grid that is 10 squares wide and 10 squares high, we must make sure that x-values range, at least, from -34 to 48 and y-values extend, at least, from -200 to 450.

EXAMPLE 6 Use a grid 10 squares wide and 10 squares high to plot $(-34, 450)$, $(48, 95)$, and $(10, -200)$.

Solution Since x-values vary from a low of -34 to a high of 48, the 10 horizontal squares must span $48 - (-34)$, or 82 units. Because 82 is not a multiple of 10, we round *up* to the next multiple of 10, which is 90. Dividing 90 by 10, we note that if each square is 9 units wide (has a *scale* of 9), we could count backward from 0 four squares and forward six squares to include x-values from -36 to 54. However, since it is more convenient to count by 10's, we will instead count backward to -40 and forward to 60.

This is how we will arrange the x-axis.

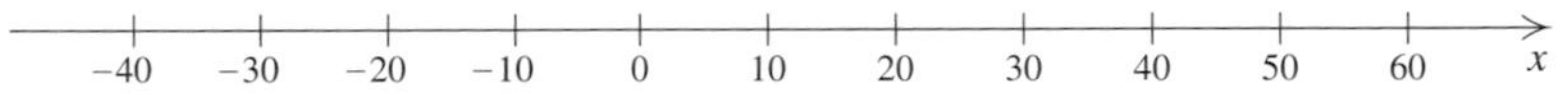

There is more than one correct way to cover the values from -34 to 48 using 10 increments. For instance, we could have counted from -60 to 90, using a scale of 15. In general, we try to use the smallest range and scale that will cover the given coordinates. Scales that are multiples of 2, 5, or 10 are especially convenient. It is essential that the numbering always starts from the origin.

This is how we will arrange the y-axis.

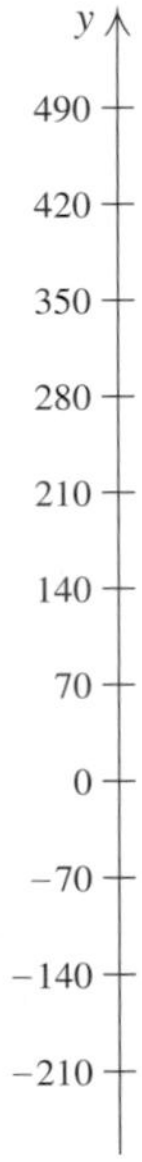

Since we must be able to show y-values from -200 to 450, the 10 vertical squares must span $450 - (-200)$, or 650 units. For convenience, we round 650 *up* to 700 and then divide by 10: $700 \div 10 = 70$. Using 70 as the scale, we count *down* from 0 until we pass -200 and *up* from 0 until we pass 450, as shown at left.

Next, we combine our work with the x-values and the y-values to draw a graph in which the x-axis extends from -40 to 60 with a scale of 10 and the y-axis extends from -210 to 490 with a scale of 70. To correctly locate the axes on the grid, the two 0's must coincide where the axes cross. Finally, once the graph has been numbered, we plot the points as shown below.

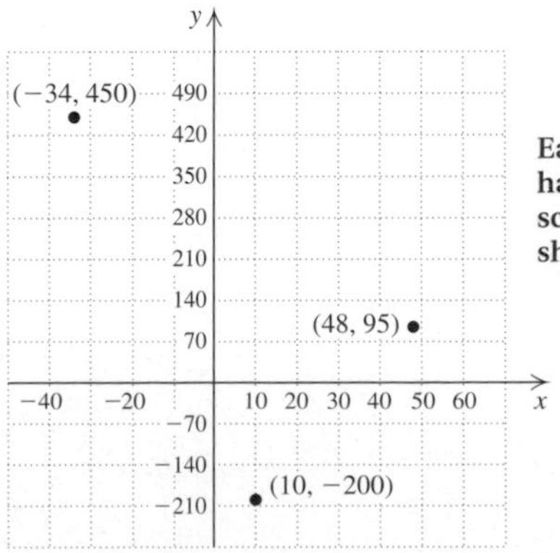

Each axis can have its own scale, as shown here.

The horizontal and vertical axes divide the plane into four regions, or **quadrants**, as indicated by Roman numerals in the following figure. In region I (the *first quadrant*), both coordinates of any point are positive. In region II (the *second quadrant*), the first coordinate is negative and the second is positive. In region III (the *third quadrant*), both coordinates are negative. In region IV (the *fourth quadrant*), the first coordinate is positive and the second is negative.

Note that the point $(-4, 5)$ is in the second quadrant and the point $(5, -5)$ is in the fourth quadrant. The points $(3, 0)$ and $(0, 1)$ are on the axes and are not considered to be in any quadrant.

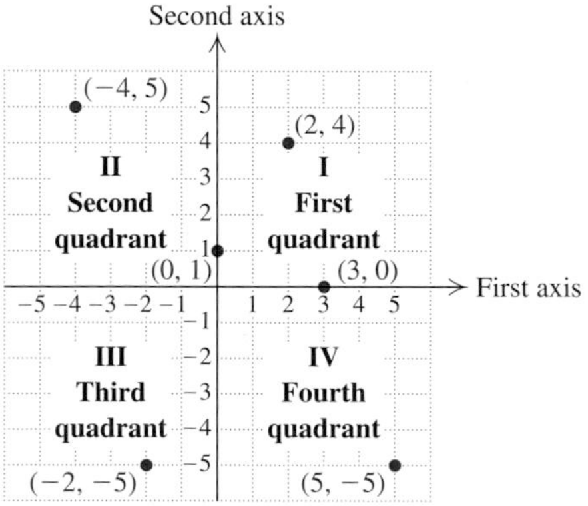

3.1 Exercise Set

FOR EXTRA HELP

Student's Solutions Manual | Digital Video Tutor CD 2 Videotape 5 | AW Math Tutor Center | MathXL Tutorials on CD | MathXL | MyMathLab

Concept Reinforcement In each of Exercises 1–4, match the set of coordinates with the graph from the column on the right that would be the best for plotting the points.

1. ____ $(-9, 3), (-2, -1), (1, 5)$
2. ____ $(-2, -1), (1, 5), (7, 3)$
3. ____ $(-2, -9), (2, 1), (4, -6)$
4. ____ $(-2, -1), (-9, 3), (-4, -6)$

a)

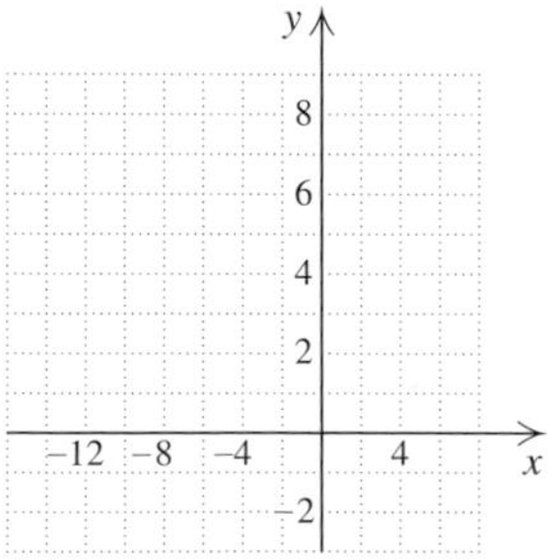

b)

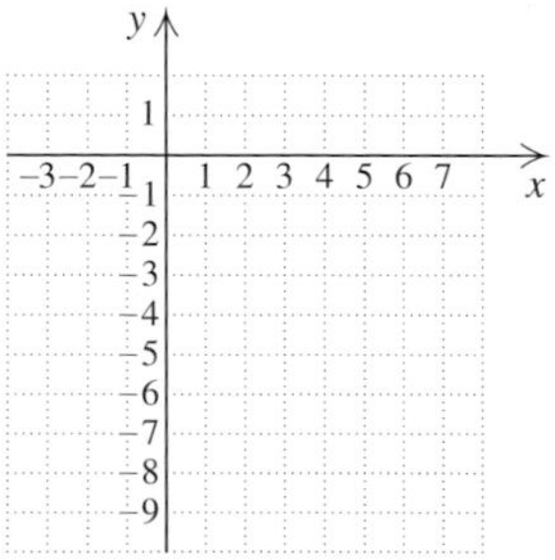

c)

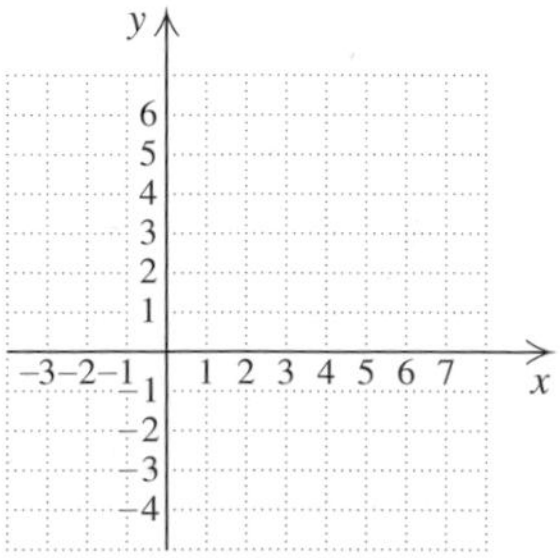

d)

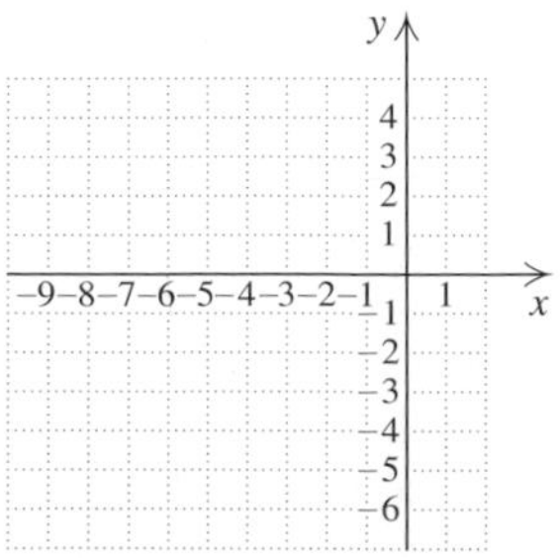

Blood alcohol level. Use the bar graph in Example 1 to answer Exercises 5–8.

5. Approximately how many drinks would a 100-lb person have consumed in 1 hr to reach a blood-alcohol level of 0.08%?

6. Approximately how many drinks would a 160-lb person have consumed in 1 hr to reach a blood-alcohol level of 0.08%?

7. What can you conclude about the weight of someone who has consumed 4 drinks in 1 hr without reaching a blood-alcohol level of 0.08%?

8. What can you conclude about the weight of someone who has consumed 5 drinks in 1 hr without reaching a blood-alcohol level of 0.08%?

Favorite color. Use the information in Example 2 to answer Exercises 9–12. Assume that color preference is unaffected by geographical location or age.

9. About one third of all Americans live in the South. How many Southerners choose brown as their favorite color?

10. About 50% of all Americans are at least 35 years old. How many Americans who are 35 or older choose purple/violet as their favorite color?

11. About one eighth of all Americans are senior citizens. How many senior citizens choose black as their favorite color?

12. About one fourth of all Americans are minors (under 18 years old). How many minors choose yellow as their favorite color?

Sorting solid waste. Use the following pie chart to answer Exercises 13–16.

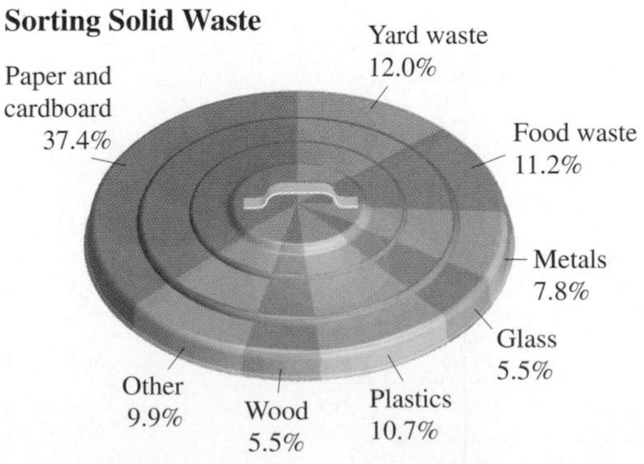

Source: *Statistical Abstract of the United States*, 2002, based on data from 2000

13. In 2000, Americans generated 231.9 million tons of waste. How much of the waste was plastic?

14. In 2000, the average American generated 4.5 lb of waste per day. How much of that was paper and cardboard?

15. Americans are recycling about 22.7% of all glass that is in the waste stream. How much glass did Americans recycle in 2000? (See Exercise 13.)

16. Americans are recycling about 5.3% of all plastic waste. How much plastic did the average American recycle per day in 2000? (Use the information in Exercise 14.)

Cell-phone Internet access. The graph below shows estimates of the number of cell phones with access to the Internet.

Source: Forrester Research

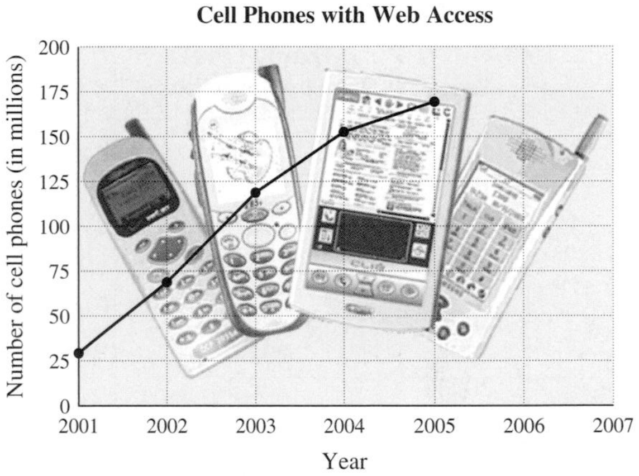

17. Approximately how many cell phones had Internet access in 2003?

18. Approximately how many cell phones had Internet access in 2002?

19. In what year did approximately 150 million cell phones have Internet access?

20. In what year did approximately 29 million cell phones have Internet access?

Plot each group of points.

21. $(1, 2), (-2, 3), (4, -1), (-5, -3), (4, 0), (0, -2)$

22. $(-2, -4), (4, -3), (5, 4), (-1, 0), (-4, 4), (0, 5)$

23. $(4, 4), (-2, 4), (5, -3), (-5, -5), (0, 4), (0, -4), (3, 0), (-4, 0)$

24. $(2, 5), (-1, 3), (3, -2), (-2, -4), (0, 4), (0, -5), (5, 0), (-5, 0)$

25. *Cell phones.* Listed below are estimates of the number of cell phones with or without access to the Internet. Make a line graph of the data.

Year	Number of Cell Phones (in millions)
2001	119.8
2002	135.3
2003	150.2
2004	163.8
2005	176.9

Source: Forrester Research

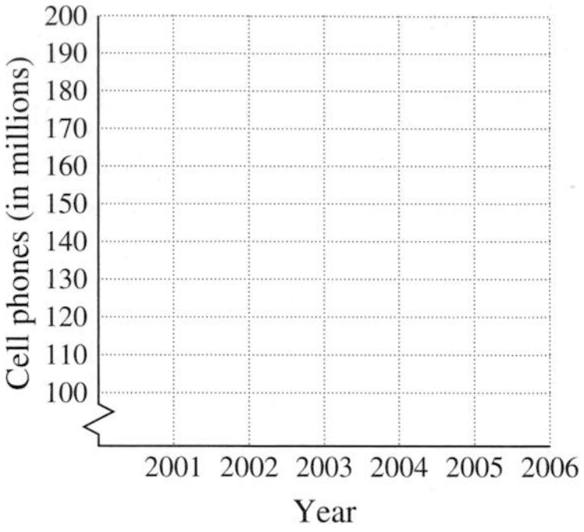

26. *Ozone layer.* Make a line graph of the data, listing years on the horizontal scale.

Year	Ozone Level (in Dobson Units)
1996	290
1997	293
1998	294
1999	293
2000	292.1
2001	290.4
2002	292.6
2003	287.9
2004	284.3

Source: johnstonsarchive.net

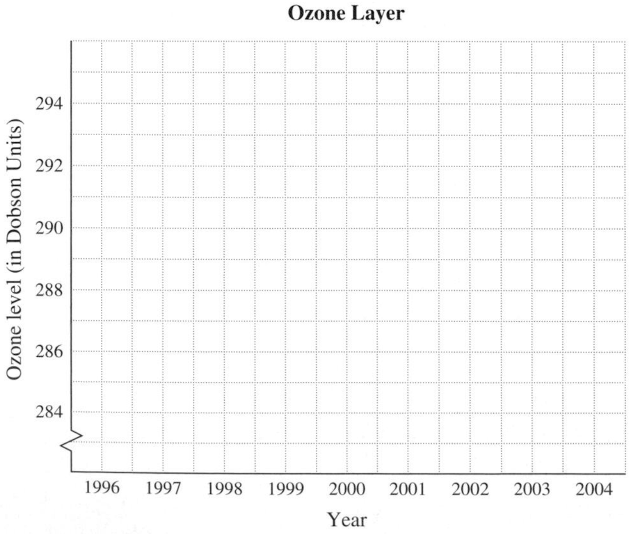

In Exercises 27–30, find the coordinates of points A, B, C, D, and E.

27.

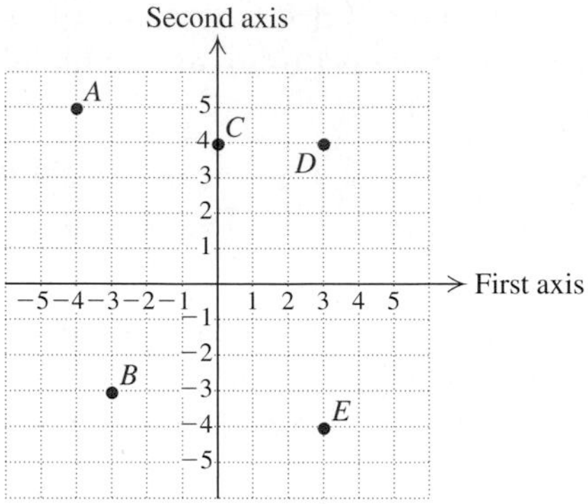

28.

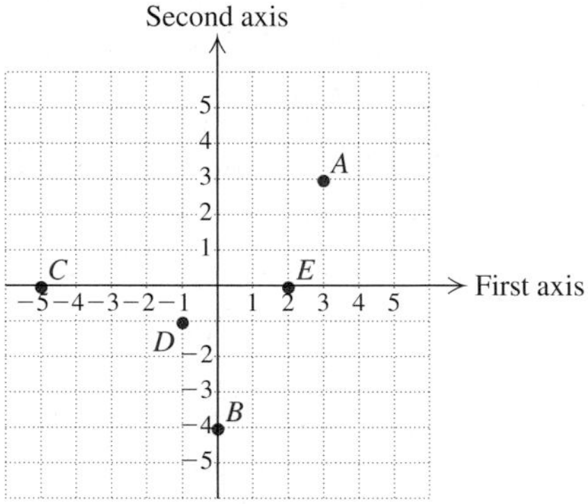

29.

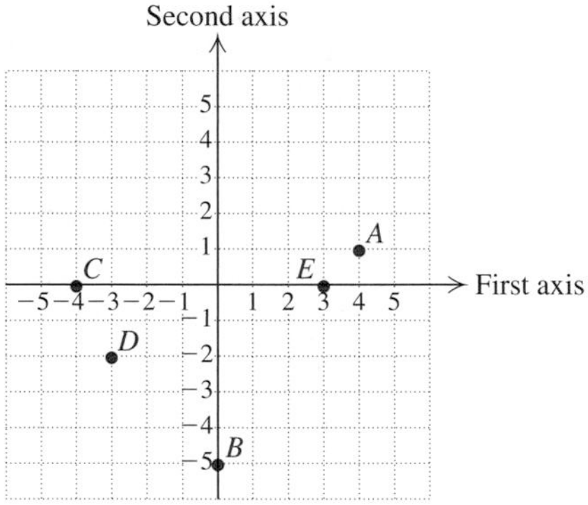

30.

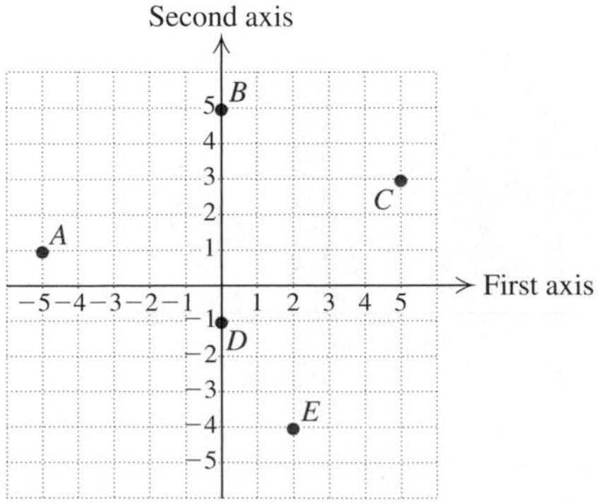

In Exercises 31–40, use a grid 10 squares wide and 10 squares high to plot the given coordinates. Choose your scale carefully. Scales may vary.

31. $(-75, 5), (-18, -2), (9, -4)$

32. $(-13, 3), (48, -1), (62, -4)$

33. $(-1, 83), (-5, -14), (5, 37)$

34. $(2, -79), (4, -25), (-4, 12)$

35. $(-10, -4), (-16, 7), (3, 15)$

36. $(5, -16), (-7, -4), (12, 3)$

37. $(-100, -5), (350, 20), (800, 37)$

38. $(750, -8), (-150, 17), (400, 32)$

39. $(-83, 491), (-124, -95), (54, -238)$

40. $(738, -89), (-49, -6), (-165, 53)$

In which quadrant is each point located?

41. $(7, -2)$ **42.** $(-1, -4)$ **43.** $(-4, -3)$

44. $(1, -5)$ **45.** $(2, 1)$ **46.** $(-4, 6)$

47. $(-4.9, 8.3)$ **48.** $(7.5, 2.9)$

49. In which quadrants are the first coordinates positive?

50. In which quadrants are the second coordinates negative?

51. In which quadrants do both coordinates have the same sign?

52. In which quadrants do the first and second coordinates have opposite signs?

53. The following graph was included in a mailing sent by Agway® to their oil customers in 2000. What information is missing from the graph and why is the graph misleading?

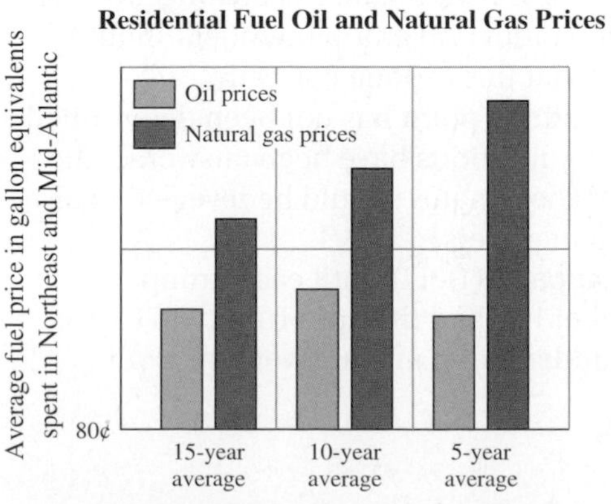

Source: Energy Research Center, Inc. *3/1/99–2/29/00

54. What do all of the points on the vertical axis of a graph have in common?

SKILL MAINTENANCE

Simplify. [1.8]

55. $4 \cdot 3 - 6 \cdot 5$

56. $5(-2) + 3(-7)$

57. $-\frac{1}{2}(-6) + 3$

58. $-\frac{2}{3}(-12) - 7$

Solve for y. [2.3]

59. $3x - 2y = 6$

60. $7x - 4y = 14$

SYNTHESIS

61. Describe what the result would be if the first and second coordinates of every point in the following graph of an arrow were interchanged.

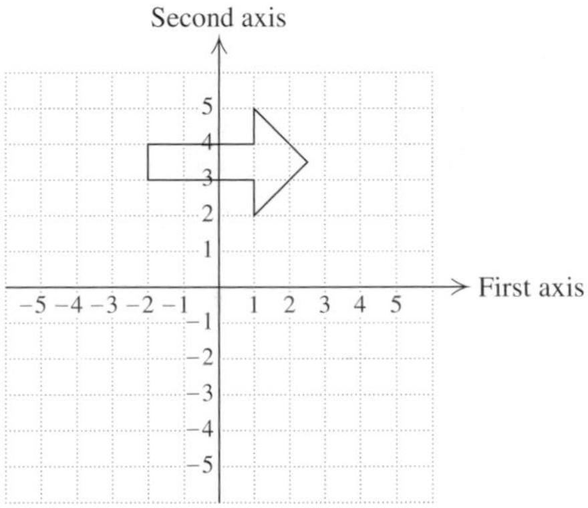

62. What advantage(s) does the use of a line graph have over that of a bar graph?

63. In which quadrant(s) could a point be located if its coordinates are opposites of each other?

64. In which quadrant(s) could a point be located if its coordinates are reciprocals of each other?

65. The points $(-1, 1)$, $(4, 1)$, and $(4, -5)$ are three vertices of a rectangle. Find the coordinates of the fourth vertex.

66. The pairs $(-2, -3)$, $(-1, 2)$, and $(4, -3)$ can serve as three (of four) vertices for three different parallelograms. Find the fourth vertex of each parallelogram.

67. Graph eight points such that the sum of the coordinates in each pair is 7. Answers may vary.

68. Find the perimeter of a rectangle if three of its vertices are $(5, -2)$, $(-3, -2)$, and $(-3, 3)$.

69. Find the area of a triangle whose vertices have coordinates $(0, 9)$, $(0, -4)$, and $(5, -4)$.

Coordinates on the globe. Coordinates can also be used to describe the location on a sphere: 0° latitude is the equator and 0° longitude is a line from the North Pole to the South Pole through France and Algeria. In the figure shown here, hurricane Clara is at a point about 260 mi northwest of Bermuda near latitude 36.0° *North, longitude* 69.0° *West.*

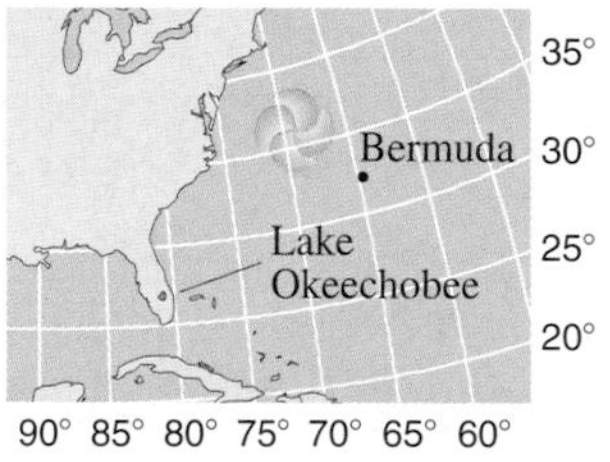

70. Approximate the latitude and the longitude of Bermuda.

71. Approximate the latitude and the longitude of Lake Okeechobee.

72. In the *Star Trek* science-fiction series, a three-dimensional coordinate system is used to locate objects in space. If the center of a planet is used as the origin, how many "quadrants" will exist? Why? If possible, sketch a three-dimensional coordinate system and label each "quadrant."

73. The graph accompanying Example 3 flattens out. Why do you think this occurs?

COLLABORATIVE CORNER

You Sank My Battleship!

Focus: Graphing points
Time: 15–25 minutes
Group size: 3–5
Materials: Graph paper

In the game Battleship®, a player places a miniature ship on a grid that only that player can see. An opponent guesses at coordinates that might "hit" the "hidden" ship. The following activity is similar to this game.

ACTIVITY

1. Using only integers from -10 to 10 (inclusive), one group member should secretly record the coordinates of a point on a slip of paper. (This point is the hidden "battleship.")
2. The other group members can then ask up to 10 "yes/no" questions in an effort to determine the coordinates of the secret point. Be sure to phrase each question mathematically (for example, "Is the x-coordinate negative?")
3. The group member who selected the point should answer each question. On the basis of the answer given, another group member should cross out the points no longer under consideration. All group members should check that this is done correctly.
4. If the hidden point has not been determined after 10 questions have been answered, the secret coordinates should be revealed to all group members.
5. Repeat parts (1)–(4) until each group member has had the opportunity to select the hidden point and answer questions.

3.2 Graphing Linear Equations

Solutions of Equations • Graphing Linear Equations • Applications

We have seen how bar, line, and circle graphs can represent information. Now we begin to learn how graphs can be used to represent solutions of equations.

Solutions of Equations

When an equation contains two variables, solutions must be ordered pairs in which each number in the pair replaces a letter in the equation. Unless stated otherwise, the first number in each pair replaces the variable that occurs first alphabetically.

Study Skills

Talk Through Your Troubles

If you are finding it difficult to master a particular topic or concept, talk about it with a classmate. Verbalizing your questions about the material might help clarify it for you. If your classmate is also finding the material difficult, it is possible that the majority of the students in your class are confused and you can ask your instructor to explain the concept again.

EXAMPLE 1 Determine whether each of the following pairs is a solution of $4b - 3a = 22$: **(a)** (2, 7); **(b)** (1, 6).

Solution

a) We substitute 2 for a and 7 for b (alphabetical order of variables):

$$\begin{array}{r|l} 4b - 3a & = 22 \\ \hline 4 \cdot 7 - 3 \cdot 2 & 22 \\ 28 - 6 & \\ 22 & \stackrel{?}{=} 22 \quad \text{TRUE} \end{array}$$

Since $22 = 22$ is *true*, the pair (2, 7) *is* a solution.

b) In this case, we replace a with 1 and b with 6:

$$\begin{array}{r|l} 4b - 3a & = 22 \\ \hline 4 \cdot 6 - 3 \cdot 1 & 22 \\ 24 - 3 & \\ 21 & \stackrel{?}{=} 22 \quad \text{FALSE} \end{array}$$

Since $21 = 22$ is *false*, the pair (1, 6) is *not* a solution.

EXAMPLE 2 Show that the pairs (3, 7), (0, 1), and $(-3, -5)$ are solutions of $y = 2x + 1$. Then graph the three points to determine another pair that is a solution.

Solution To show that a pair is a solution, we substitute, replacing x with the first coordinate and y with the second coordinate of each pair:

$$\begin{array}{l|l} y & = 2x + 1 \\ \hline 7 & 2 \cdot 3 + 1 \\ & 6 + 1 \\ 7 & \stackrel{?}{=} 7 \quad \text{TRUE} \end{array} \qquad \begin{array}{l|l} y & = 2x + 1 \\ \hline 1 & 2 \cdot 0 + 1 \\ & 0 + 1 \\ 1 & \stackrel{?}{=} 1 \quad \text{TRUE} \end{array} \qquad \begin{array}{l|l} y & = 2x + 1 \\ \hline -5 & 2(-3) + 1 \\ & -6 + 1 \\ -5 & \stackrel{?}{=} -5 \quad \text{TRUE} \end{array}$$

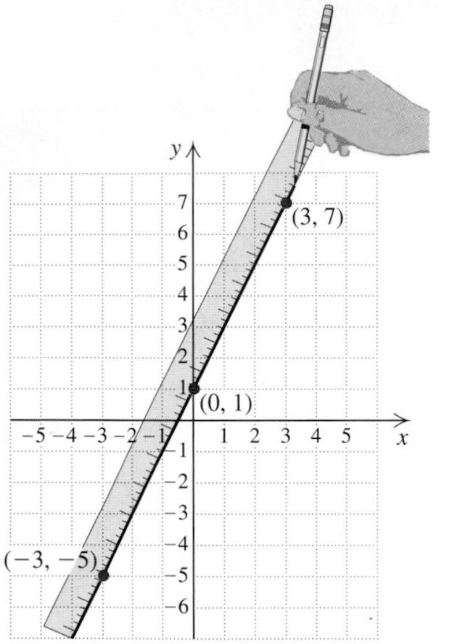

In each of the three cases, the substitution results in a true equation. Thus the pairs (3, 7), (0, 1), and (−3, −5) are all solutions. We graph them at left, labeling the "first" axis x and the "second" axis y. Note that the three points appear to "line up." Will other points that line up with these points also represent solutions of $y = 2x + 1$? To find out, we use a ruler and draw a line passing through (−3, −5), (0, 1), and (3, 7).

The line appears to pass through (2, 5). Let's check if this pair is a solution of $y = 2x + 1$:

$$\begin{array}{c|l} y & = 2x + 1 \\ \hline 5 & 2 \cdot 2 + 1 \\ & 4 + 1 \\ \end{array}$$

$$5 \stackrel{?}{=} 5 \qquad \text{TRUE}$$

We see that (2, 5) *is* a solution. You should perform a similar check for at least one other point that appears to be on the line.

Example 2 leads us to suspect that *any* point on the line passing through (3, 7), (0, 1), and (−3, −5) represents a solution of $y = 2x + 1$. In fact, every solution of $y = 2x + 1$ is represented by a point on this line and every point on this line represents a solution. The line is called the **graph** of the equation.

Graphing Linear Equations

Equations like $y = 2x + 1$ or $4b - 3a = 22$ are said to be **linear** because the graph of each equation is a line. In general, any equation that can be written in the form $y = mx + b$ or $Ax + By = C$ (where m, b, A, B, and C are constants and A and B are not both 0) is linear.

To *graph* an equation is to make a drawing that represents its solutions. Linear equations can be graphed as follows.

To Graph a Linear Equation

1. Select a value for one coordinate and calculate the corresponding value of the other coordinate. Form an ordered pair. This pair is one solution of the equation.
2. Repeat step (1) to find a second ordered pair. A third ordered pair can be used as a check.
3. Plot the ordered pairs and draw a straight line passing through the points. The line represents all solutions of the equation.

EXAMPLE 3 Graph: $y = -3x + 1$.

Solution We select a convenient value for x, compute y, and form an ordered pair. Then we repeat the process for other choices of x.

If $x = 2$, then $y = -3 \cdot 2 + 1 = -5$, and $(2, -5)$ is a solution.
If $x = 0$, then $y = -3 \cdot 0 + 1 = 1$, and $(0, 1)$ is a solution.
If $x = -1$, then $y = -3(-1) + 1 = 4$, and $(-1, 4)$ is a solution.

Results are often listed in a table, as shown below. The points corresponding to each pair are then plotted.

$y = -3x + 1$

x	y	(x, y)
2	−5	(2, −5)
0	1	(0, 1)
−1	4	(−1, 4)

(1) Choose x.
(2) Compute y.
(3) Form the pair (x, y).
(4) Plot the points.

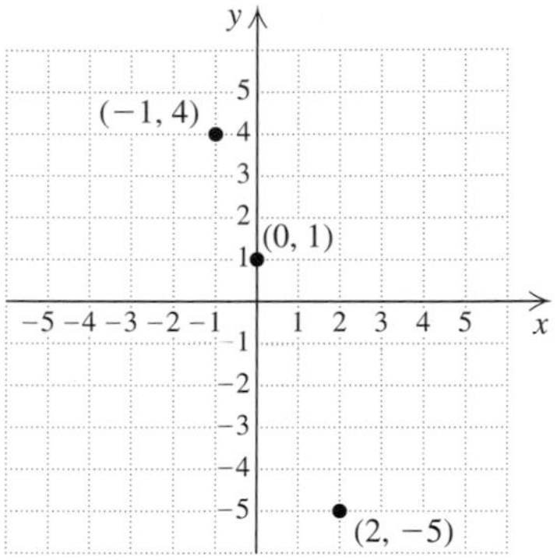

Note that all three points line up. If they didn't, we would know that we had made a mistake, because the equation is linear. When only two points are plotted, an error is more difficult to detect.

Finally, we use a ruler or other straightedge to draw a line. Every point on the line represents a solution of $y = -3x + 1$.

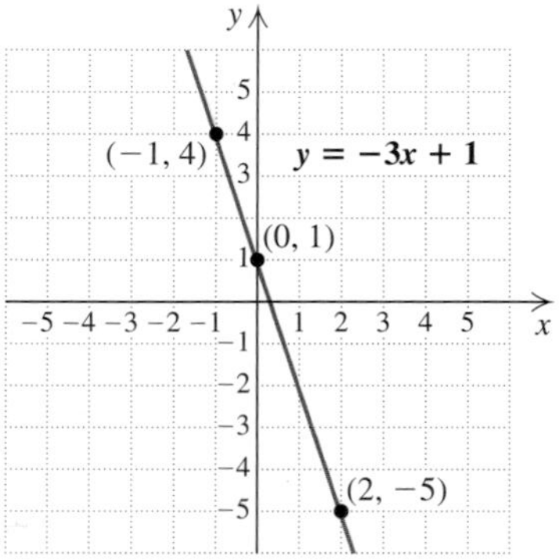

EXAMPLE 4 Graph: $y = 2x - 3$.

Solution We select some convenient x-values and compute y-values.

If $x = 0$, then $y = 2 \cdot 0 - 3 = -3$, and $(0, -3)$ is a solution.
If $x = 1$, then $y = 2 \cdot 1 - 3 = -1$, and $(1, -1)$ is a solution.
If $x = 4$, then $y = 2 \cdot 4 - 3 = 5$, and $(4, 5)$ is a solution.

$y = 2x - 3$

x	y	(x, y)
0	−3	(0, −3)
1	−1	(1, −1)
4	5	(4, 5)

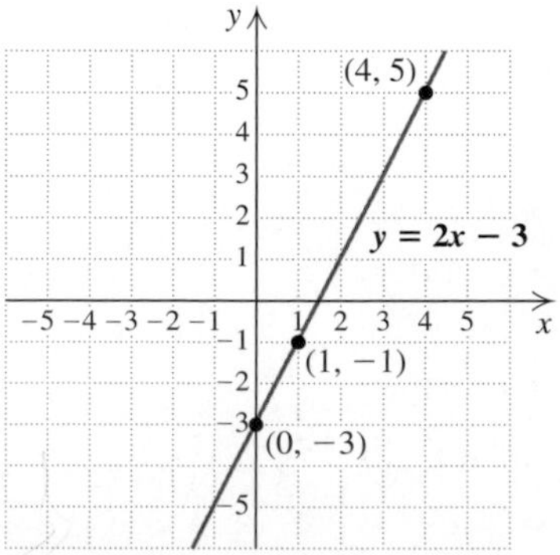

EXAMPLE 5 Graph: $4x + 2y = 12$.

Solution To form ordered pairs, we can replace either variable with a number and then calculate the other coordinate:

$$\begin{aligned} \text{If } y = 0, \text{ we have } \quad 4x + 2 \cdot 0 &= 12 \\ 4x &= 12 \\ x &= 3, \end{aligned}$$

so (3, 0) is a solution.

$$\begin{aligned} \text{If } x = 0, \text{ we have } \quad 4 \cdot 0 + 2y &= 12 \\ 2y &= 12 \\ y &= 6, \end{aligned}$$

so (0, 6) is a solution.

$$\begin{aligned} \text{If } y = 2, \text{ we have } \quad 4x + 2 \cdot 2 &= 12 \\ 4x + 4 &= 12 \\ 4x &= 8 \\ x &= 2, \end{aligned}$$

so (2, 2) is a solution.

$4x + 2y = 12$

x	y	(x, y)
3	0	(3, 0)
0	6	(0, 6)
2	2	(2, 2)

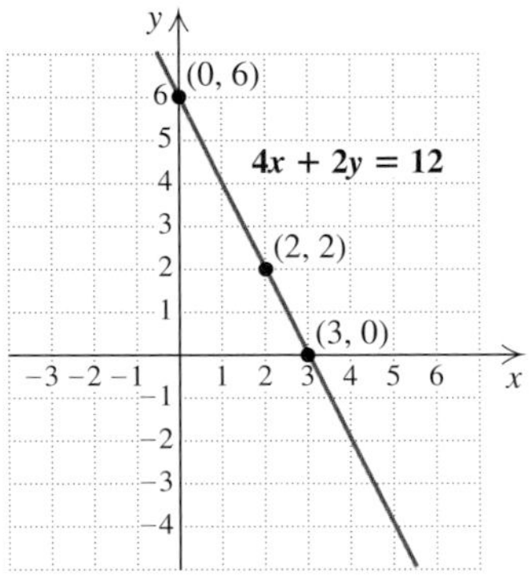

Note that in Examples 3 and 4 the variable y is isolated on one side of the equation. This generally simplifies calculations, so it is important to be able to solve for y before graphing.

EXAMPLE 6 Graph $3y = 2x$ by first solving for y.

Solution To isolate y, we divide both sides by 3, or multiply both sides by $\frac{1}{3}$:

$$3y = 2x$$

$$\frac{1}{3} \cdot 3y = \frac{1}{3} \cdot 2x \qquad \text{Using the multiplication principle to multiply both sides by } \frac{1}{3}$$

$$\left.\begin{aligned} 1y &= \frac{2}{3} \cdot x \\ y &= \frac{2}{3}x. \end{aligned}\right\} \qquad \text{Simplifying}$$

Because all the equations above are equivalent, we can use $y = \frac{2}{3}x$ to draw the graph of $3y = 2x$.

To graph $y = \frac{2}{3}x$, we can select x-values that are multiples of 3. This will allow us to avoid fractions when the corresponding y-values are computed.

$$\left.\begin{aligned} &\text{If } x = 3, && \text{then } y = \tfrac{2}{3} \cdot 3 = 2. \\ &\text{If } x = -3, && \text{then } y = \tfrac{2}{3}(-3) = -2. \\ &\text{If } x = 6, && \text{then } y = \tfrac{2}{3} \cdot 6 = 4. \end{aligned}\right\} \quad \text{Note that when multiples of 3 are substituted for } x\text{, the } y\text{-coordinates are not fractions.}$$

The following table lists these solutions. Next, we plot the points and see that they form a line. Finally, we draw and label the line.

$$3y = 2x, \text{ or } y = \frac{2}{3}x$$

x	y	(x, y)
3	2	(3, 2)
−3	−2	(−3, −2)
6	4	(6, 4)

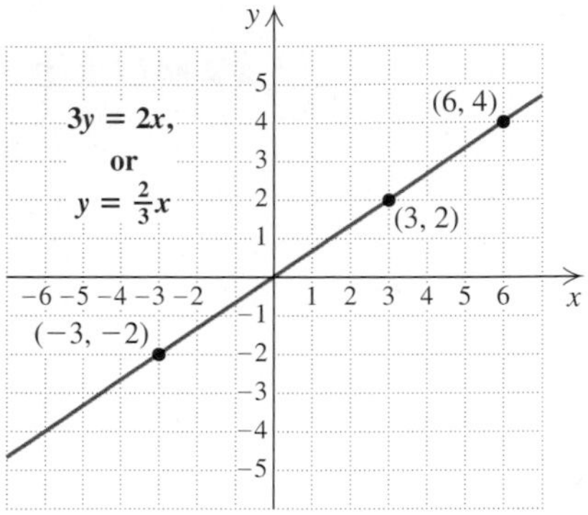

EXAMPLE 7 Graph $x + 5y = -10$ by first solving for y.

Solution We have

$$\begin{aligned} x + 5y &= -10 \\ 5y &= -x - 10 && \text{Adding } -x \text{ to both sides} \\ y &= \tfrac{1}{5}(-x - 10) && \text{Multiplying both sides by } \tfrac{1}{5} \\ y &= -\tfrac{1}{5}x - 2. && \text{Using the distributive law} \end{aligned}$$

> *Caution!* It is very important to multiply *both* $-x$ and -10 by $\frac{1}{5}$.

Student Notes

If you are troubled by calculations involving fractions, please review the manner in which fractions are added and subtracted. If necessary, ask your instructor for additional practice in this area.

Thus, $x + 5y = -10$ is equivalent to $y = -\frac{1}{5}x - 2$. If we choose x-values that are multiples of 5, we can avoid fractions when calculating the corresponding y-values.

If $x = 5$, then $y = -\frac{1}{5} \cdot 5 - 2 = -1 - 2 = -3$.
If $x = 0$, then $y = -\frac{1}{5} \cdot 0 - 2 = 0 - 2 = -2$.
If $x = -5$, then $y = -\frac{1}{5}(-5) - 2 = 1 - 2 = -1$.

$$x + 5y = -10, \text{ or } y = -\frac{1}{5}x - 2$$

x	y	(x, y)
5	−3	(5, −3)
0	−2	(0, −2)
−5	−1	(−5, −1)

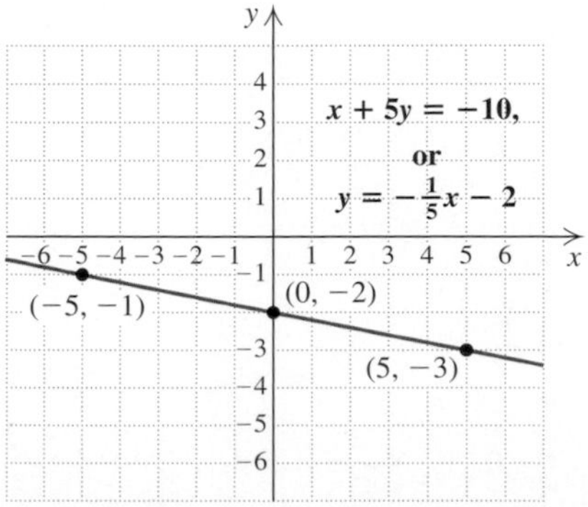

Applications

Linear equations appear in many real-life situations.

EXAMPLE 8 FedEx mailing costs. The cost c, in dollars, of shipping a FedEx Priority Overnight package weighing 1 lb or more a distance of 1001 to 1400 mi is given by

$$c = 2.8w + 21.05,$$

where w is the package's weight in pounds (*Source*: Federal Express Corporation). Graph the equation and then use the graph to estimate the cost of shipping a $6\frac{1}{2}$-lb package.

Solution We graph $c = 2.8w + 21.05$ by selecting values for w and then calculating the associated value c. In selecting values for w, note that, according to the problem, we must have $w \geq 1$.

If $w = 1$, then $c = 2.8(1) + 21.05 = \$23.85$.
If $w = 4$, then $c = 2.8(4) + 21.05 = \$32.25$.
If $w = 7$, then $c = 2.8(7) + 21.05 = \$40.65$.

w	c
1	23.85
4	32.25
7	40.65

Because we are *selecting* values for w and *calculating* values for c, we represent w on the horizontal axis and c on the vertical axis. Counting by 2's horizontally and by 5's vertically will allow us to plot all three pairs, as shown on the left below.

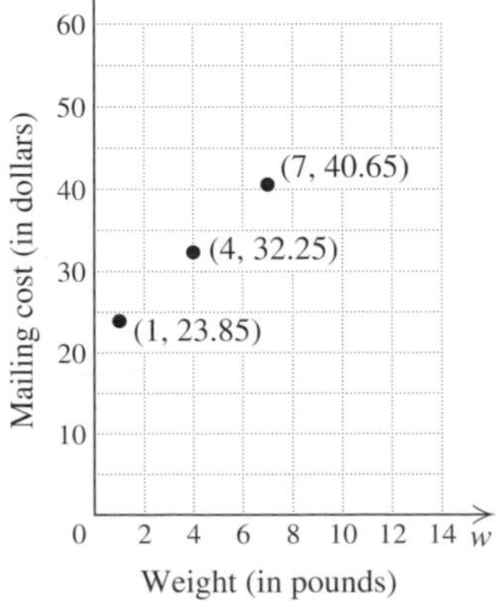

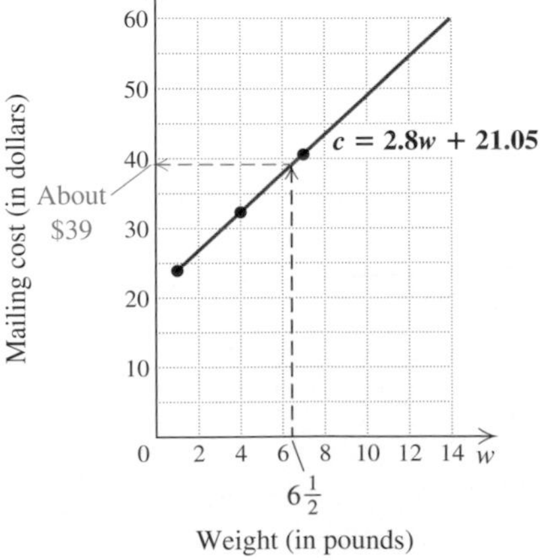

Since the three points line up, our calculations are probably correct. We draw a line, beginning at (1, 23.85). To estimate the cost of shipping a $6\frac{1}{2}$-lb package, we locate the point on the line that is above $6\frac{1}{2}$ and then find the value on the c-axis that corresponds to that point, as shown on the right above. The cost of shipping a $6\frac{1}{2}$-lb package is about \$39.

> ***Caution!*** When the coordinates of a point are read from a graph, as in Example 8, values should not be considered exact.

Many equations in two variables have graphs that are not straight lines. Three such graphs are shown below. As before, each graph represents the solutions of the given equation. Graphing calculators are especially helpful when drawing these *nonlinear* graphs. Nonlinear graphs are studied in Chapter 9 and in more advanced courses.

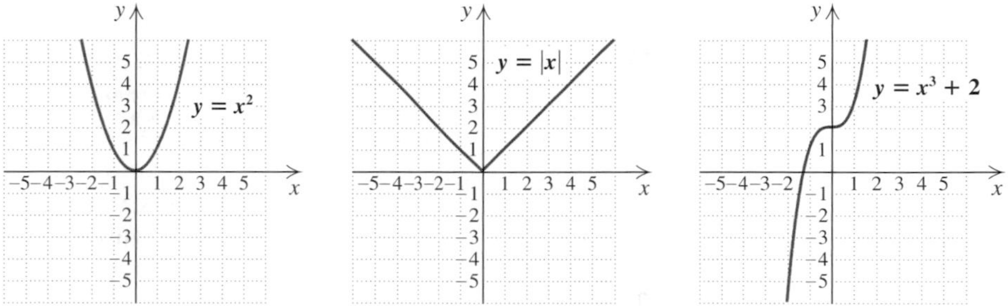

technology connection

Most graphing calculators require that y be alone on one side before the equation is entered. For example, to graph $5y + 4x = 13$, we would first solve for y. The student can check that solving for y yields the equation $y = -\frac{4}{5}x + \frac{13}{5}$.

We enter $-\frac{4}{5}x + \frac{13}{5}$ as Y1 and press GRAPH. The standard viewing window $[-10, 10, -10, 10]$ results in the graph shown here.

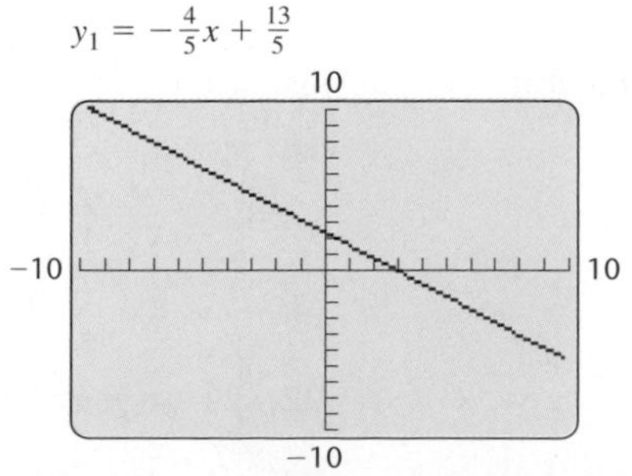

Using a graphing calculator, graph each of the following. Select the "standard" $[-10, 10, -10, 10]$ window.

1. $y = -5x + 6.5$

2. $y = 3x + 4.5$

3. $7y - 4x = 22$

4. $5y + 11x = -20$

5. $2y - x^2 = 0$

6. $y + x^2 = 8$

3.2 Exercise Set

FOR EXTRA HELP

Student's Solutions Manual | Digital Video Tutor CD 2 Videotape 5 | AW Math Tutor Center | MathXL Tutorials on CD | MathXL | MyMathLab

Determine whether each equation has the given ordered pair as a solution.

1. $y = 5x + 1$; $(0, 2)$

2. $y = 2x + 3$; $(0, 3)$

3. $3y + 2x = 12$; $(4, 2)$

4. $5x - 3y = 15$; $(0, 5)$

5. $4a - 3b = 11$; $(2, -1)$

6. $3q - 2p = -8$; $(1, -2)$

In Exercises 7–14, an equation and two ordered pairs are given. Show that each pair is a solution of the equation. Then graph the two pairs to determine another solution. Answers may vary.

7. $y = x + 3$; $(-1, 2), (4, 7)$

8. $y = x - 2$; $(3, 1), (-2, -4)$

9. $y = \frac{1}{2}x + 3$; $(4, 5), (-2, 2)$

10. $y = \frac{1}{2}x - 1$; $(6, 2), (0, -1)$

11. $y + 3x = 7$; $(2, 1), (4, -5)$

12. $2y + x = 5$; $(-1, 3), (7, -1)$

13. $4x - 2y = 10$; $(0, -5), (4, 3)$

14. $6x - 3y = 3$; $(1, 1), (-1, -3)$

Graph each equation.

15. $y = x + 1$

16. $y = x - 1$

17. $y = -x$

18. $y = x$

19. $y = \frac{1}{3}x$

20. $y = \frac{1}{2}x$

21. $y = x + 3$

22. $y = x + 2$

23. $y = 2x + 2$

24. $y = 3x - 2$

25. $y = \frac{1}{3}x - 4$

26. $y = \frac{1}{2}x + 1$

27. $x + y = 4$

28. $x + y = -5$

29. $y = \frac{5}{2}x + 3$

30. $y = \frac{5}{3}x - 2$

31. $x + 2y = -6$

32. $x + 2y = 8$

33. $y = -\frac{2}{3}x + 4$

34. $y = \frac{3}{2}x + 1$

35. $8x - 4y = 12$

36. $6x - 3y = 9$

37. $6y + 2x = 8$

38. $8y + 2x = -4$

Solve by graphing. Label all axes, and show where each solution is located on the graph.

39. *Health insurance.* The number of full-time workers in the United States without health insurance continues to grow. This number, n, can be approximated by

$$n = 0.9t + 19,$$

where n is in millions and t is the number of years since 2001. Graph the equation and use the graph to estimate the number of uninsured full-time workers in 2010.

Source: *The New York Times*, 9/30/03

40. *Value of a color copier.* The value of Dupliographic's color copier is given by

$$v = -0.68t + 3.4,$$

where v is the value, in thousands of dollars, t years from the date of purchase. Graph the equation and use the graph to estimate the value of the copier after $2\frac{1}{2}$ yr.

41. *Increasing life expectancy.* A smoker is 15 times more likely to die from lung cancer than a nonsmoker. An ex-smoker who stopped smoking t years ago is w times more likely to die from lung cancer than a nonsmoker, where

$$w = 15 - t.$$

Graph the equation and use the graph to estimate how much more likely it is for Sandy to die from lung cancer than Polly, if Polly never smoked and Sandy quit $2\frac{1}{2}$ years ago.

Source: Data from *Body Clock* by Dr. Martin Hughes, p. 60. New York: Facts on File, Inc.

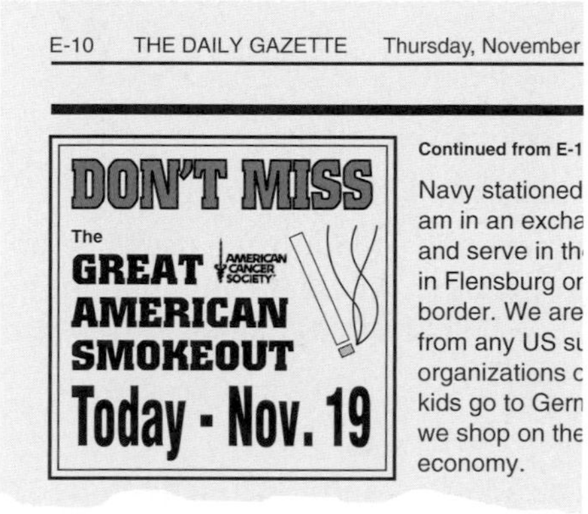

42. *Price of printing.* The price p, in cents, of a photocopied and bound lab manual is given by $p = \frac{7}{2}n + 20$, where n is the number of pages in the manual. Graph the equation and use the graph to estimate the cost of a 25-page manual.

43. *Value of computer software.* The value v of a shopkeeper's inventory software program, in hundreds of dollars, is given by $v = -\frac{3}{4}t + 6$, where t is the number of years since the shopkeeper first bought the program. Graph the equation and use the graph to estimate what the program is worth 4 yr after it was first purchased.

44. *Bottled water.* The number of gallons of bottled water w consumed by an average American in one year is given by $w = 1.1t + 7.3$, where t is the number of years since 1990. Graph the equation and use the graph to predict the number of gallons consumed per person in 2008.

Source: Beverage Marketing Corporation

45. *Cost of college.* The cost T, in hundreds of dollars, of tuition and fees at many community colleges can be approximated by $T = \frac{3}{4}c + 1$, where c is the number of credits for which a student registers. Graph the equation and use the graph to estimate the cost of tuition and fees when a student registers for 4 three-credit courses.

46. *Cost of college.* The cost C, in thousands of dollars, of a year at a private four-year college (all expenses) can be approximated by $C = \frac{6}{5}t + 21$, where t is the number of years since 1995. Graph the equation and use the graph to estimate the cost of a year at a private four-year college in 2009.

Source: Based on information in *Statistical Abstract of the United States*, 2002

47. *Record temperature drop.* On January 22, 1943, the temperature T, in degrees Fahrenheit, in Spearfish, South Dakota, could be approximated by $T = -2m + 54$, where m is the number of minutes since 9:00 A.M. that morning. Graph the equation and use the graph to estimate the temperature at 9:15 A.M.

Source: Based on information from the National Oceanic Atmospheric Administration

48. *Coffee consumption.* The number of gallons of coffee n consumed each year by the average U.S. consumer can be approximated by $n = \frac{6}{5}d + 20$, where d is the number of years since 1995. Graph the equation and use the graph to estimate what the average coffee consumption was in 2004.

Source: Based on information in *Statistical Abstract of the United States*, 2002

49. The equations $3x + 4y = 8$ and $y = -\frac{3}{4}x + 2$ are equivalent. Which equation would be easier to graph and why?

50. Suppose that a linear equation is graphed by plotting three points and that the three points line up with each other. Does this *guarantee* that the equation is being correctly graphed? Why or why not?

SKILL MAINTENANCE

Solve and check. [2.2]

51. $5x + 3 \cdot 0 = 12$

52. $2x - 5 \cdot 0 = 9$

53. $7 \cdot 0 - 4y = 10$

Solve. [2.3]

54. $pq + p = w$, for p

55. $Ax + By = C$, for y

56. $A = \dfrac{T + Q}{2}$, for Q

SYNTHESIS

57. Janice consistently makes the mistake of plotting the x-coordinate of an ordered pair using the y-axis, and the y-coordinate using the x-axis. How will Janice's incorrect graph compare with the appropriate graph?

58. Explain how the graph in Example 8 can be used to determine when the cost of a shipment will reach $50.

59. *Bicycling.* Long Beach Island in New Jersey is a long, narrow, flat island. For exercise, Lauren routinely bikes to the northern tip of the island and back. Because of the steady wind, she uses one gear going north and another for her return. Lauren's bike has 14 gears and the sum of the two gears used on her ride is always 18. Write and graph an equation that represents the different pairings of gears that Lauren uses. Note that there are no fractional gears on a bicycle.

In Exercises 60–63, try to find an equation for the graph shown.

60.

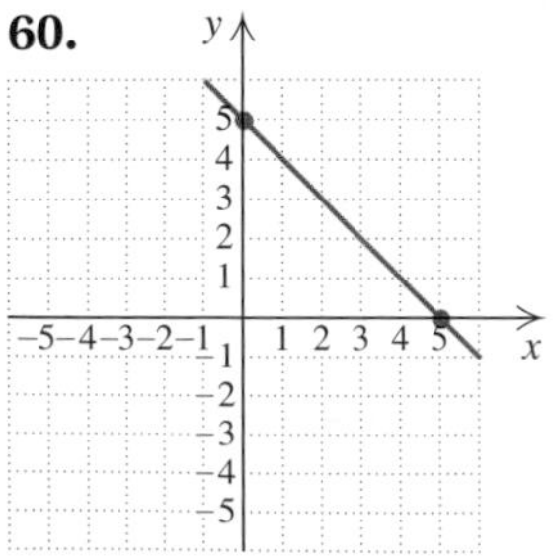

61.

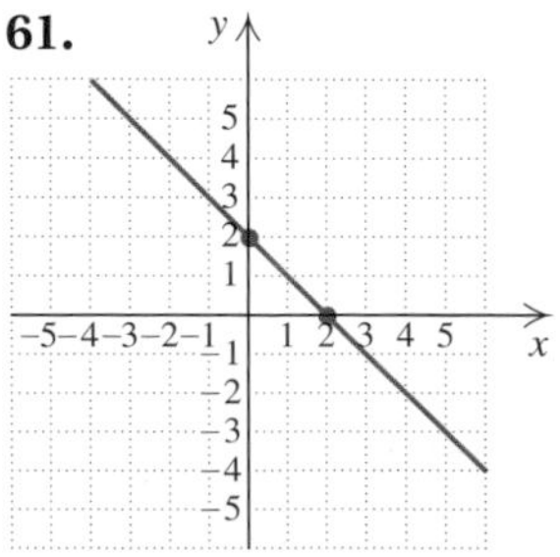

62.

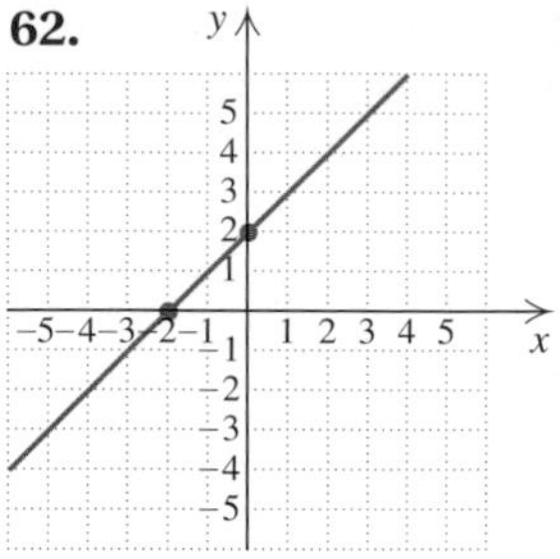

63.

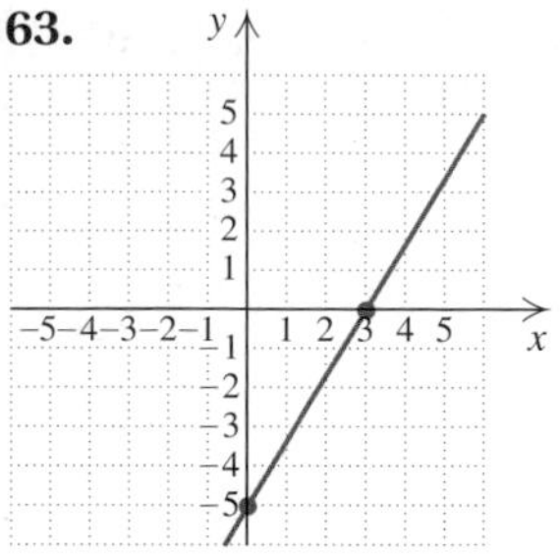

64. Translate to an equation:

d dimes and n nickels total $1.75.

Then graph the equation and use the graph to determine three different combinations of dimes and nickels that total $1.75 (see also Exercise 77).

65. Translate to an equation:

d $25 dinners and l $5 lunches total $225.

Then graph the equation and use the graph to determine three different combinations of lunches and dinners that total $225 (see also Exercise 77).

Use the suggested x-values $-3, -2, -1, 0, 1, 2,$ *and* 3 *to graph each equation.*

66. $y = |x|$

Aha! **67.** $y = -|x|$

Aha! **68.** $y = |x| - 2$

69. $y = -|x| + 2$

70. $y = |x| + 3$

For Exercises 71–76, use a graphing calculator to graph the equation. Use a $[-10, 10, -10, 10]$ *window.*

71. $y = -2.8x + 3.5$

72. $y = 4.5x + 2.1$

73. $y = 2.8x - 3.5$

74. $y = -4.5x - 2.1$

75. $y = x^2 + 4x + 1$

76. $y = -x^2 + 4x - 7$

77. Study the graph of Exercise 64 or 65. Does *every* point on the graph represent a solution of the associated problem? Why or why not?

3.3 Graphing and Intercepts

Intercepts • Using Intercepts to Graph • Graphing Horizontal or Vertical Lines

Unless a line is horizontal or vertical, it will cross both axes. Knowing where the axes are crossed gives us another way of graphing linear equations.

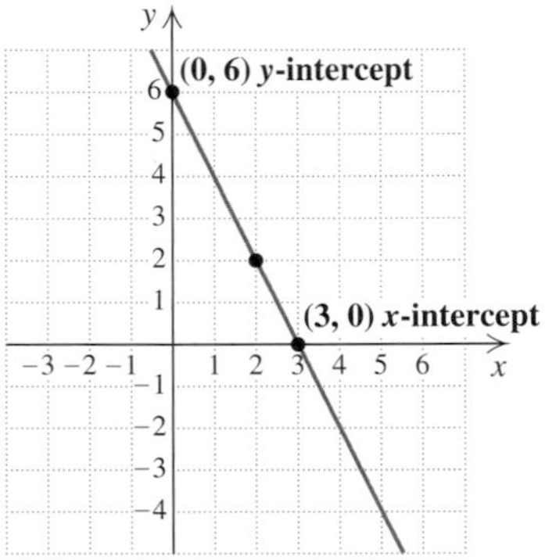

Intercepts

In Example 5 of Section 3.2, we graphed $4x + 2y = 12$ by plotting the points (3, 0), (0, 6), and (2, 2) and then drawing the line.

The point at which a graph crosses the y-axis is called the ***y*-intercept**. In the figure at left, the y-intercept is (0, 6). The x-coordinate of a y-intercept is always 0.

The point at which a graph crosses the x-axis is called the ***x*-intercept**. In the figure at left, the x-intercept is (3, 0). The y-coordinate of an x-intercept is always 0.

It is possible for the graph of a curve to have more than one y-intercept or more than one x-intercept.

EXAMPLE 1 For the graph shown below, **(a)** give the coordinates of any x-intercepts and **(b)** give the coordinates of any y-intercepts.

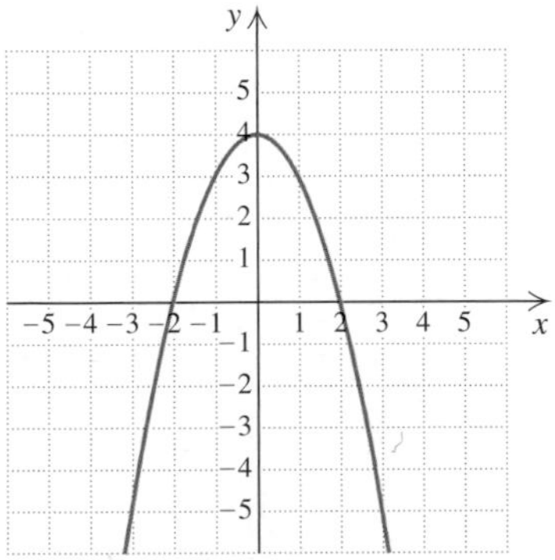

Solution

a) The x-intercepts are the points at which the graph crosses the x-axis. For the graph shown, the x-intercepts are $(-2, 0)$ and $(2, 0)$.

b) The y-intercept is the point at which the graph crosses the y-axis. For the graph shown, the y-intercept is (0, 4).

Study Skills

Create Your Own Glossary

Understanding the meaning of mathematical terminology is essential for success in any math course. To assist with this, try writing your own glossary of important words toward the back of your notebook. Often, just the act of writing out a word's definition can help you remember what the word means.

Using Intercepts to Graph

It is important to know how to locate a graph's intercepts from the equation being graphed.

> *To Find Intercepts*
>
> To find the y-intercept(s) of an equation's graph, replace x with 0 and solve for y.
>
> To find the x-intercept(s) of an equation's graph, replace y with 0 and solve for x.

EXAMPLE 2 Find the y-intercept and the x-intercept of the graph of $2x + 4y = 20$.

Solution To find the y-intercept, we let $x = 0$ and solve for y:

$$2 \cdot 0 + 4y = 20 \qquad \text{Replacing } x \text{ with } 0$$
$$4y = 20$$
$$y = 5.$$

Thus the y-intercept is $(0, 5)$.

To find the x-intercept, we let $y = 0$ and solve for x:

$$2x + 4 \cdot 0 = 20 \qquad \text{Replacing } y \text{ with } 0$$
$$2x = 20$$
$$x = 10.$$

Thus the x-intercept is $(10, 0)$.

Since two points are sufficient to graph a line, intercepts can be used to graph linear equations.

EXAMPLE 3 Graph $2x + 4y = 20$ using intercepts.

Solution In Example 2, we showed that the y-intercept is $(0, 5)$ and the x-intercept is $(10, 0)$. Before drawing a line, we plot a third point as a check. We substitute any convenient value for x and solve for y.

If we let $x = 5$, then

$$2 \cdot 5 + 4y = 20 \qquad \text{Substituting 5 for } x$$
$$10 + 4y = 20$$
$$4y = 10 \qquad \text{Subtracting 10 from both sides}$$
$$y = \tfrac{10}{4}, \text{ or } 2\tfrac{1}{2}. \qquad \text{Solving for } y$$

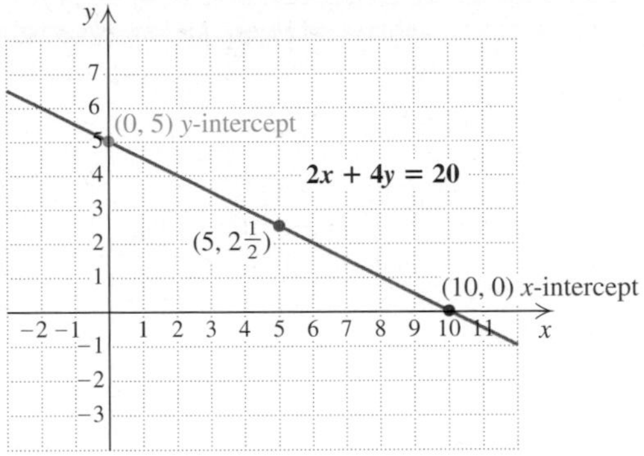

The point $\left(5, 2\frac{1}{2}\right)$ appears to line up with the intercepts, so our work is probably correct. To finish, we draw and label the line.

Note that when we solved for the y-intercept, we replaced x with 0 and simplified $2x + 4y = 20$ to $4y = 20$. Thus, to find the y-intercept, we can momentarily ignore the x-term and solve the remaining equation.

In a similar manner, when we solved for the x-intercept, we simplified $2x + 4y = 20$ to $2x = 20$. Thus, to find the x-intercept, we can momentarily ignore the y-term and then solve this remaining equation.

EXAMPLE 4 Graph $3x - 2y = 60$ using intercepts.

Solution To find the y-intercept, we let $x = 0$. This amounts to temporarily ignoring the x-term and then solving:

$$-2y = 60 \qquad \text{For } x = 0, \text{ we have } 3 \cdot 0 - 2y, \text{ or simply } -2y.$$
$$y = -30.$$

The y-intercept is $(0, -30)$.

To find the x-intercept, we let $y = 0$. This amounts to temporarily disregarding the y-term and then solving:

$$3x = 60 \qquad \text{For } y = 0, \text{ we have } 3x - 2 \cdot 0, \text{ or simply } 3x.$$
$$x = 20.$$

The x-intercept is $(20, 0)$.

To find a third point, we replace x with 4 and solve for y:

$$3 \cdot 4 - 2y = 60 \qquad \text{Numbers other than 4 can be used for } x.$$
$$12 - 2y = 60$$
$$-2y = 48$$
$$y = -24. \qquad \text{This means that } (4, -24) \text{ is on the graph.}$$

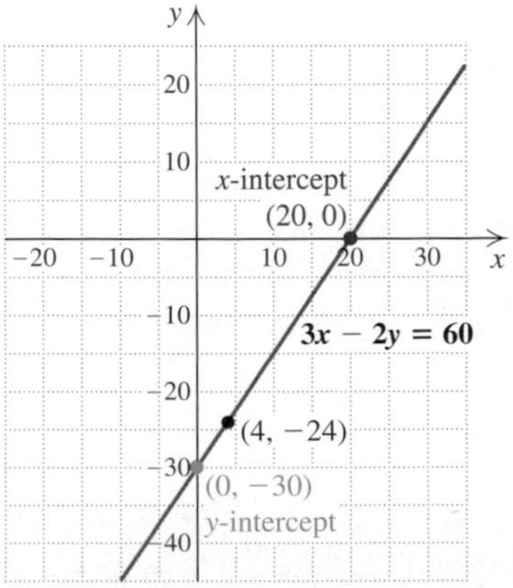

In order for us to graph all three points, the y-axis of our graph must go down to at least -30 and the x-axis must go up to at least 20. Using a scale of 5 units per square allows us to display both intercepts and $(4, -24)$, as well as the origin.

The point $(4, -24)$ appears to line up with the intercepts, so we draw and label the line, as shown at left.

---

technology connection

When an equation has been entered into a graphing calculator, we may not be able to see both intercepts. For example, if $y = -0.8x + 17$ is graphed in the $[-10, 10, -10, 10]$ window, neither intercept is visible.

$y_1 = -0.8x + 17$

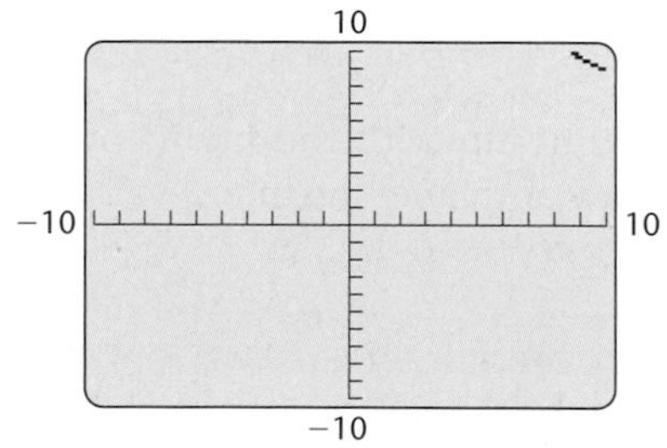

To better view the intercepts, we can change the window dimensions or we can zoom out. The ZOOM

$y_1 = -0.8x + 17$

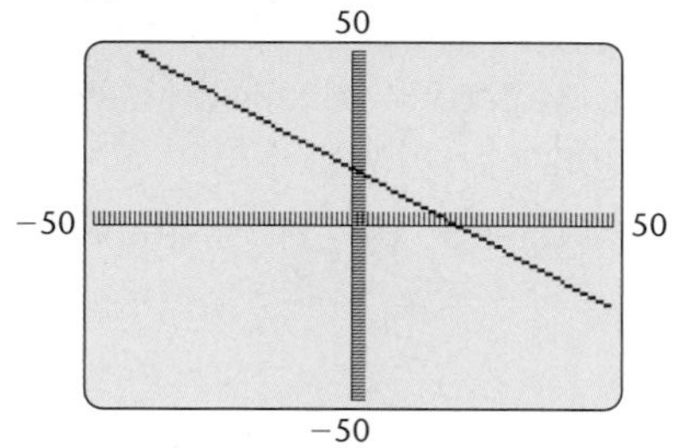

feature allows us to reduce or magnify a graph or a portion of a graph. Before zooming, the ZOOM *factors* must be set in the memory of the ZOOM key. If we zoom out with factors set at 5, both intercepts are visible but the axes are heavily drawn, as shown in the preceding figure.

This suggests that the *scales* of the axes should be changed. To do this, we use the WINDOW menu and set Xscl to 5 and Yscl to 5. The resulting graph has tick marks 5 units apart and clearly shows both intercepts. Other choices for Xscl and Yscl can also be made.

$y_1 = -0.8x + 17$

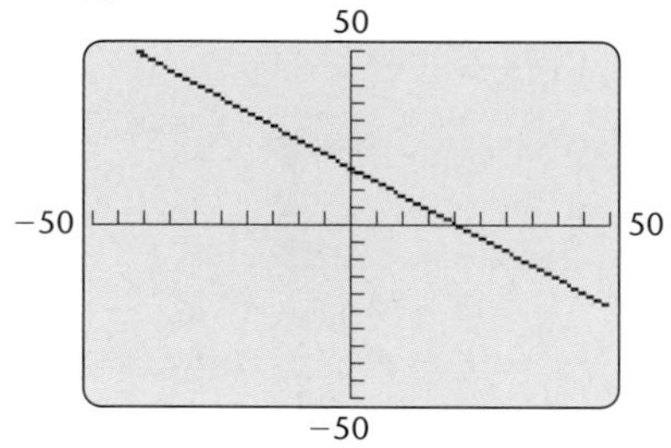

$\text{Xscl} = 5, \ \text{Yscl} = 5$

Graph each equation so that both intercepts can be easily viewed. Zoom or adjust the window settings so that tick marks can be clearly seen on both axes.

1. $y = -0.72x - 15$

2. $y - 2.13x = 27$

3. $5x + 6y = 84$

4. $2x - 7y = 150$

5. $19x - 17y = 200$

6. $6x + 5y = 159$

Graphing Horizontal or Vertical Lines

The equations graphed in Examples 3 and 4 are both in the form $Ax + By = C$. We have already stated that any equation in the form $Ax + By = C$ is linear, provided A and B are not both zero. What if A or B (but not both) is zero? We will find that when A is zero, there is no x-term and the graph is a horizontal line. We will also find that when B is zero, there is no y-term and the graph is a vertical line.

EXAMPLE 5 Graph: $y = 3$.

Solution We can regard the equation $y = 3$ as $0 \cdot x + y = 3$. No matter what number we choose for x, we find that y must be 3 if the equation is to be solved. Consider the following table.

Student Notes

Many students draw horizontal lines when they should be drawing vertical lines and vice versa. To keep this straight, locate the correct number on the axis whose label is given and then draw a line perpendicular to that axis. Thus, to graph $x = 2$, we locate 2 on the x-axis and then draw a line perpendicular to that axis at that point. Note that the graph of $x = 2$ on a plane is a line, whereas the graph of $x = 2$ on a number line is a point.

$y = 3$

Choose any number for x. →

x	y	(x, y)
-2	3	$(-2, 3)$
0	3	$(0, 3)$
4	3	$(4, 3)$

y must be 3.

All pairs will have 3 as the y-coordinate.

When we plot the ordered pairs $(-2, 3)$, $(0, 3)$, and $(4, 3)$ and connect the points, we obtain a horizontal line. Any ordered pair of the form $(x, 3)$ is a solution, so the line is parallel to the x-axis with y-intercept $(0, 3)$.

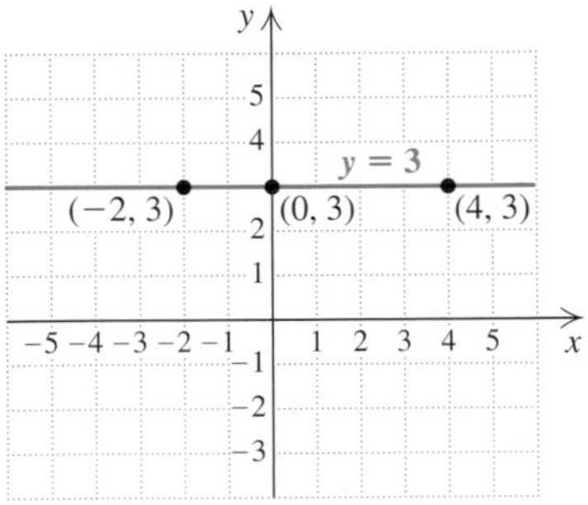

EXAMPLE 6 Graph: $x = -4$.

Solution We can regard the equation $x = -4$ as $x + 0 \cdot y = -4$. We make up a table with all -4's in the x-column.

$x = -4$

x must be -4. →

x	y	(x, y)
-4	-5	$(-4, -5)$
-4	1	$(-4, 1)$
-4	3	$(-4, 3)$

Any number can be used for y.

All pairs will have -4 as the x-coordinate.

When we plot the ordered pairs $(-4, -5)$, $(-4, 1)$, and $(-4, 3)$ and connect them, we obtain a vertical line. Any ordered pair of the form $(-4, y)$ is a solution. The line is parallel to the y-axis with x-intercept $(-4, 0)$.

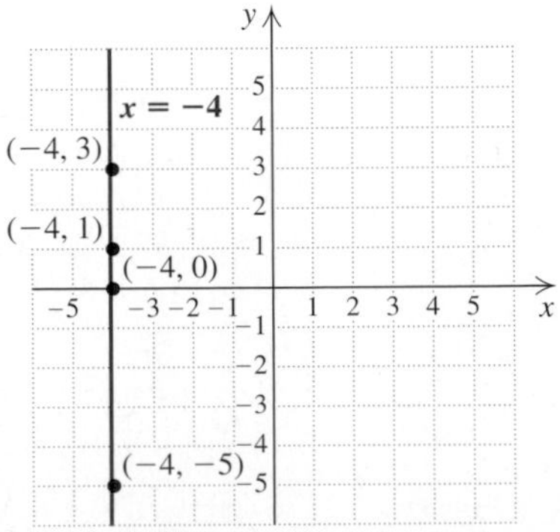

Linear Equations in One Variable

The graph of $y = b$ is a horizontal line, with y-intercept $(0, b)$.

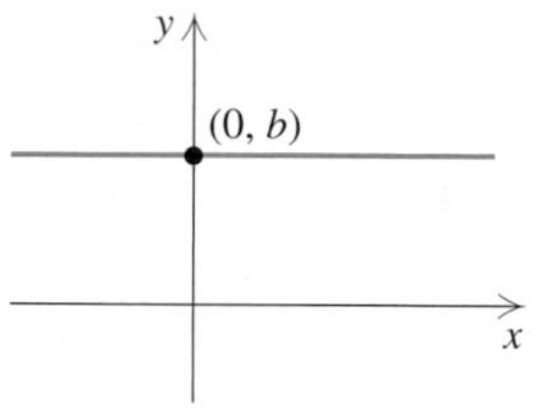

The graph of $x = a$ is a vertical line, with x-intercept $(a, 0)$.

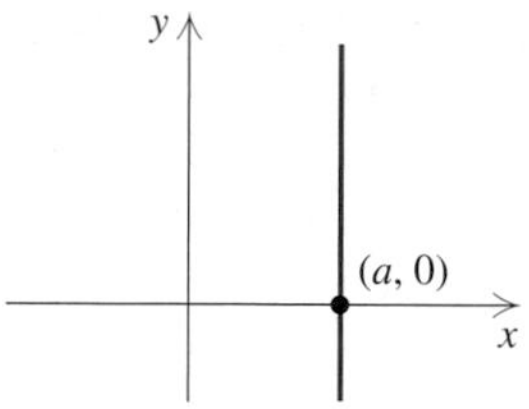

EXAMPLE 7 Write an equation for each graph.

a)

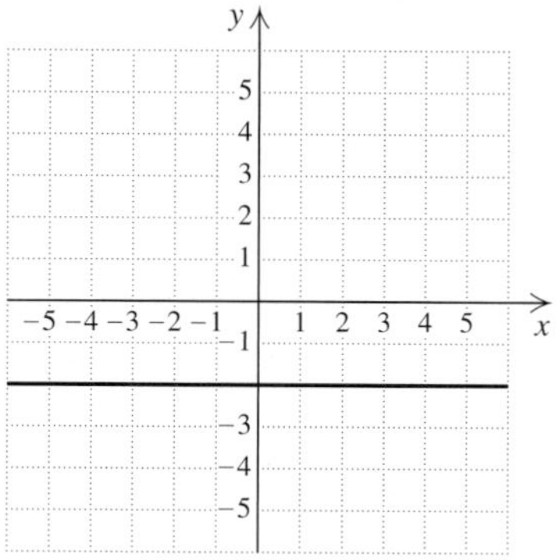

b)

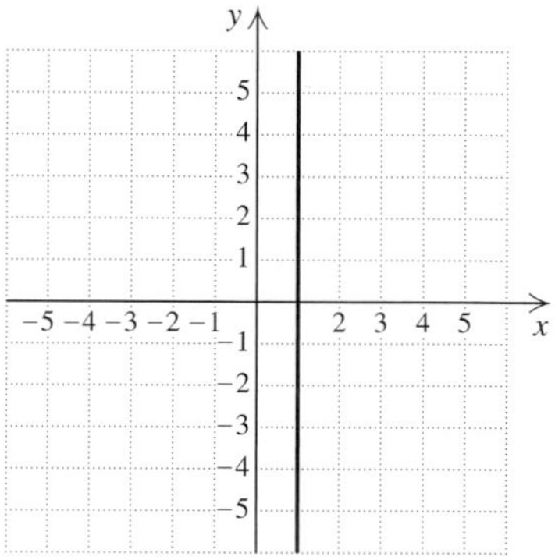

Solution

a) Note that every point on the horizontal line passing through $(0, -2)$ has -2 as the y-coordinate. Thus the equation of the line is $y = -2$.

b) Note that every point on the vertical line passing through $(1, 0)$ has 1 as the x-coordinate. Thus the equation of the line is $x = 1$.

3.3 Exercise Set

FOR EXTRA HELP

Student's Solutions Manual | Digital Video Tutor CD 2 Videotape 5 | AW Math Tutor Center | MathXL Tutorials on CD | MathXL | MyMathLab

Concept Reinforcement *In each of Exercises 1–6, match the phrase with the most appropriate choice from the column on the right.*

1. ____ A vertical line — **a)** $2x + 5y = 100$
2. ____ A horizontal line — **b)** $(3, -2)$
3. ____ A y-intercept — **c)** $(1, 0)$
4. ____ An x-intercept — **d)** $(0, 2)$
5. ____ A third point as a check — **e)** $y = 3$
6. ____ Use a scale of 10 units per square. — **f)** $x = -4$

For Exercises 7–12, list **(a)** *the coordinates of the y-intercept and* **(b)** *the coordinates of all x-intercepts.*

7.

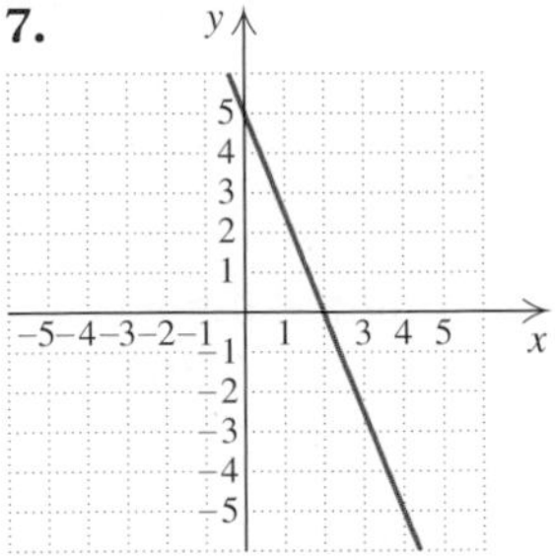

8.

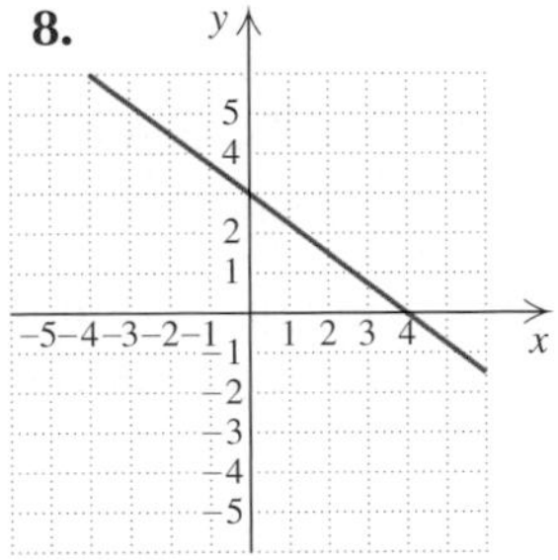

9.

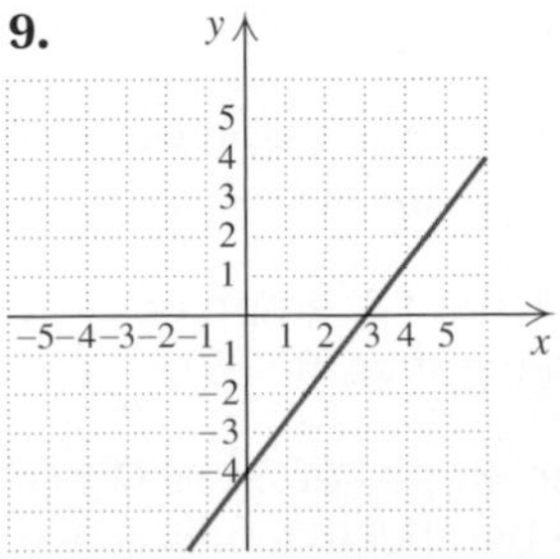

10.

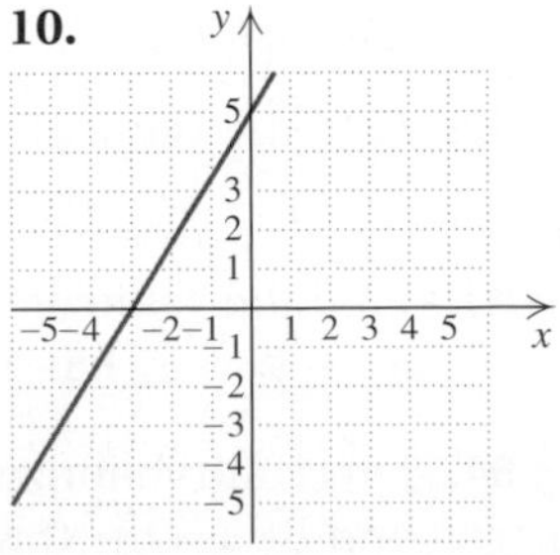

11.

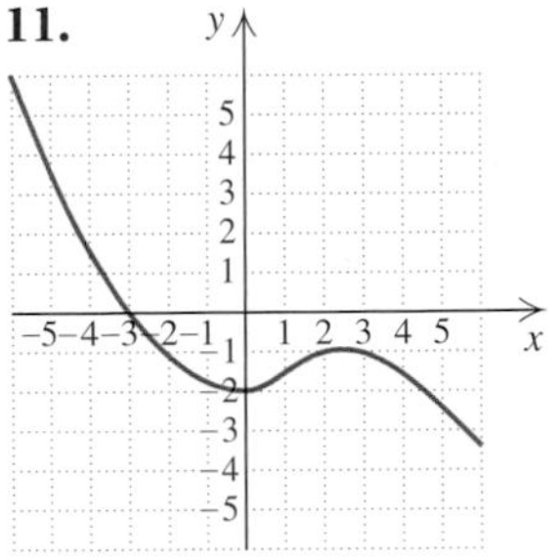

12.

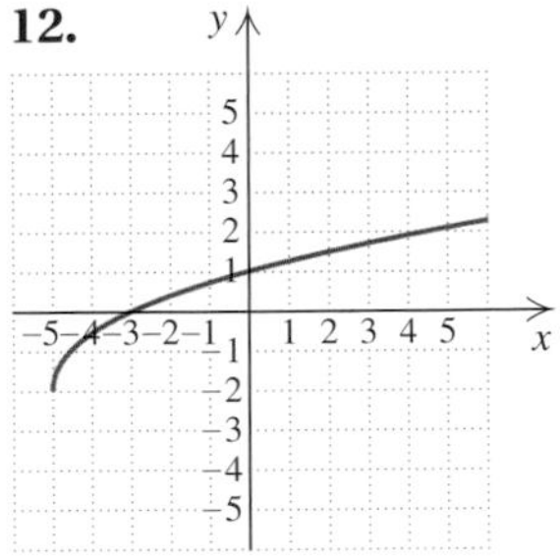

For Exercises 13–22, list **(a)** *the coordinates of any y-intercept and* **(b)** *the coordinates of any x-intercept. Do not graph.*

13. $5x + 3y = 15$

14. $5x + 2y = 20$

15. $7x - 2y = 28$

16. $4x - 3y = 24$

17. $-4x + 3y = 150$

18. $-2x + 3y = 80$

Aha! **19.** $y = 9$

20. $x = 8$

21. $x = -7$

22. $y = -1$

Find the intercepts. Then graph.

23. $3x + 2y = 12$

24. $x + 2y = 6$

25. $x + 3y = 6$

26. $6x + 9y = 36$

27. $-x + 2y = 8$

28. $-x + 3y = 9$

29. $3x + y = 9$

30. $2x - y = 8$

31. $y = 2x - 6$

32. $y = -3x + 6$

33. $3x - 9 = 3y$

34. $5x - 10 = 5y$

35. $2x - 3y = 6$

36. $2x - 5y = 10$

37. $4x + 5y = 20$

38. $6x + 2y = 12$

39. $3x + 2y = 8$

40. $x - 1 = y$

41. $2x + 4y = 6$

42. $5x - 6y = 18$

43. $5x + 3y = 180$

44. $10x + 7y = 210$

45. $y = -30 + 3x$

46. $y = -40 + 5x$

47. $-4x = 20y + 80$

48. $60 = 20x - 3y$

49. $y - 3x = 0$

50. $x + 2y = 0$

Graph.

51. $y = 5$

52. $y = 2$

53. $x = 4$

54. $x = 6$

55. $y = -2$

56. $y = -4$

57. $x = -1$

58. $x = -6$

59. $x = 18$

60. $x = -20$

61. $y = 0$

62. $y = \frac{3}{2}$

63. $x = -\frac{5}{2}$

64. $x = 0$

65. $-5y = -300$

66. $12x = -480$

67. $35 + 7y = 0$

68. $-3x - 24 = 0$

Write an equation for each graph.

69.

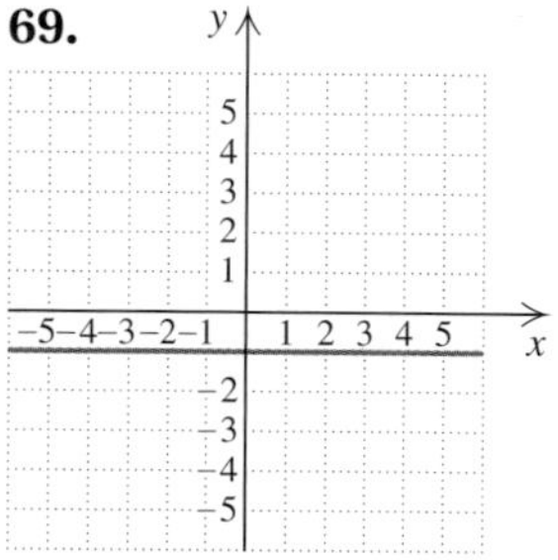

70.

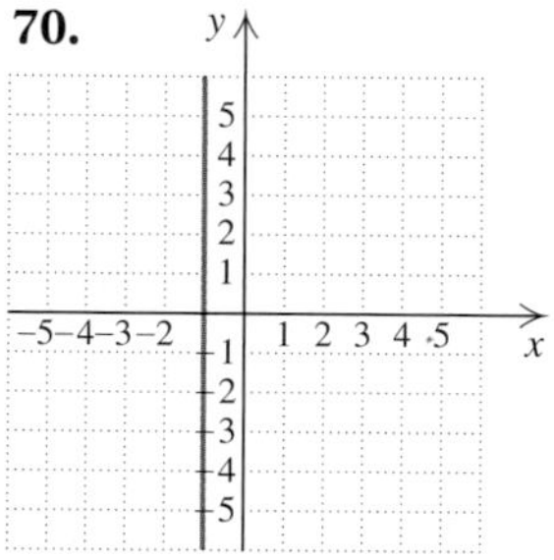

71.

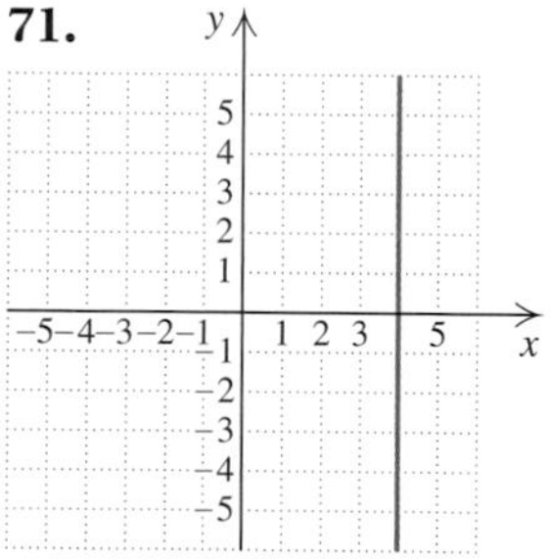

72.

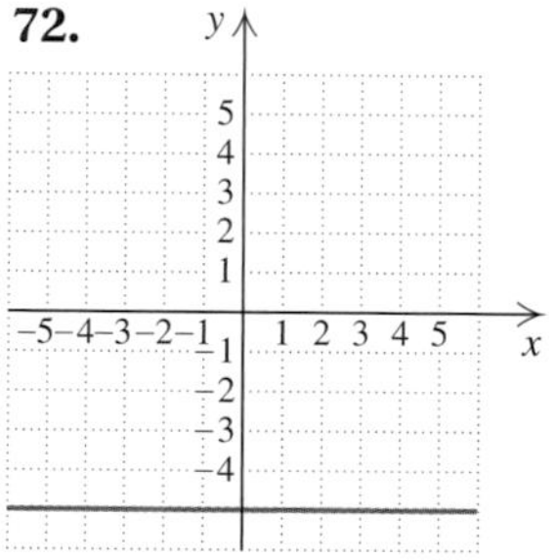

73.

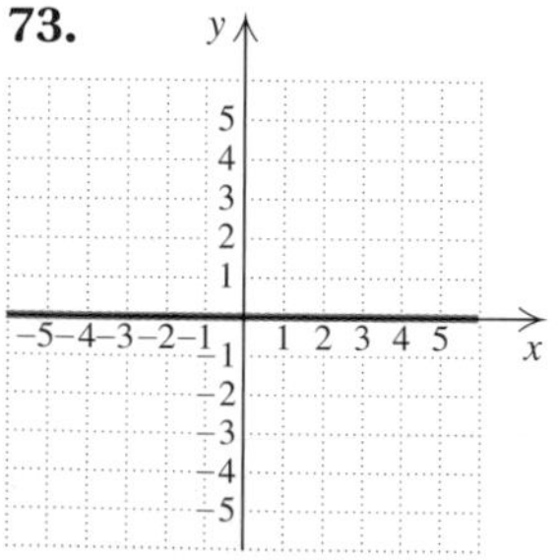

74.

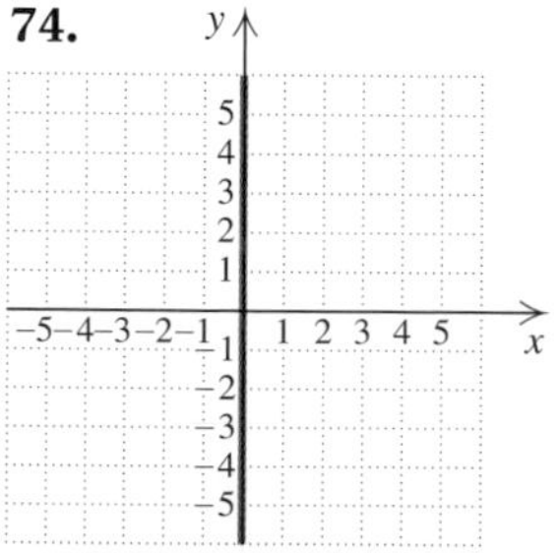

75. Explain in your own words why the graph of $y = 8$ is a horizontal line.

76. Explain in your own words why the graph of $x = -4$ is a vertical line.

SKILL MAINTENANCE

Translate to an algebraic expression. [1.1]

77. 7 less than d

78. 5 more than w

79. The sum of 2 and a number

80. The product of 3 and a number

81. Twice the sum of two numbers

82. Half of the sum of two numbers

SYNTHESIS

83. Describe what the graph of $x + y = C$ will look like for any choice of C.

84. If the graph of a linear equation has one point that is both the x- and the y-intercepts, what is that point? Why?

85. Write an equation for the x-axis.

86. Write an equation of the line parallel to the x-axis and passing through $(3, 5)$.

87. Write an equation of the line parallel to the y-axis and passing through $(-2, 7)$.

88. Find the coordinates of the point of intersection of the graphs of $y = x$ and $y = 6$.

89. Find the coordinates of the point of intersection of the graphs of the equations $x = -3$ and $y = x$.

90. Write an equation of the line shown in Exercise 7.

91. Write an equation of the line shown in Exercise 10.

92. Find the value of C such that the graph of $3x + C = 5y$ has an x-intercept of $(-4, 0)$.

93. Find the value of C such that the graph of $4x = C - 3y$ has a y-intercept of $(0, -8)$.

94. For A and B nonzero, the graphs of $Ax + D = C$ and $By + D = C$ will be parallel to an axis. Explain why.

In Exercises 95–100, find the intercepts of each equation algebraically. Then adjust the window and scale so that the intercepts can be checked graphically with no further window adjustments.

95. $3x + 2y = 50$

96. $2x - 7y = 80$

97. $y = 0.2x - 9$

98. $y = 1.3x - 15$

99. $25x - 20y = 1$

100. $50x + 25y = 1$

3.4 Rates

Rates of Change • Visualizing Rates

Rates of Change

Because graphs make use of two axes, they allow us to visualize how two quantities change with respect to each other. A number accompanied by units is used to represent this type of change and is referred to as a *rate*.

Study Skills

Find a Study Buddy

It is not always a simple matter to find a study partner. Friendships can become strained and tension can develop if one of the study partners feels that he or she is working too much or too little. Try to find a partner with whom you feel compatible and don't take it personally if your first partner is not a good match. With some effort you will be able to locate a suitable partner. Often tutor centers or learning labs are good places to look for one.

Rate

A *rate* is a ratio that indicates how two quantities change with respect to each other.

Rates occur often in everyday life:

A town that grows by 3400 residents over a period of 2 yr has a *growth rate* of $\frac{3400}{2}$, or 1700, residents per year.

A person running 150 m in 20 sec is moving at a *rate* of $\frac{150}{20}$, or 7.5, m/sec (meters per second).

A class of 25 students pays a total of \$93.75 to visit a museum. The *rate* is $\frac{\$93.75}{25}$, or \$3.75, per student.

Caution! To calculate a rate, it is important to keep track of the units being used.

EXAMPLE 1 On January 3, Nell rented a Ford Focus with a full tank of gas and 9312 mi on the odometer. On January 7, she returned the car with 9630 mi on the odometer.* If the rental agency charged Nell $108 for the rental and needed 12 gal of gas to fill up the gas tank, find the following rates:

a) The car's rate of gas consumption, in miles per gallon

b) The average cost of the rental, in dollars per day

c) The car's rate of travel, in miles per day

Solution

a) The rate of gas consumption, in miles per gallon, is found by dividing the number of miles traveled by the number of gallons used for that amount of driving:

$$\text{Rate, in miles per gallon} = \frac{9630 \text{ mi} - 9312 \text{ mi}}{12 \text{ gal}}$$ The word "per" indicates division.

$$= \frac{318 \text{ mi}}{12 \text{ gal}}$$

$$= 26.5 \text{ mi/gal}$$ Dividing

$$= 26.5 \text{ miles per gallon.}$$

b) The average cost of the rental, in dollars per day, is found by dividing the cost of the rental by the number of days:

$$\text{Rate, in dollars per day} = \frac{108 \text{ dollars}}{4 \text{ days}}$$ From January 3 to January 7 is $7 - 3 = 4$ days.

$$= 27 \text{ dollars/day}$$

$$= \$27 \text{ per day.}$$

c) The car's rate of travel, in miles per day, is found by dividing the number of miles traveled by the number of days:

$$\text{Rate, in miles per day} = \frac{318 \text{ mi}}{4 \text{ days}}$$ $9630 \text{ mi} - 9312 \text{ mi} = 318 \text{ mi}$; From January 3 to January 7 is $7 - 3 = 4$ days.

$$= 79.5 \text{ mi/day}$$

$$= 79.5 \text{ mi per day.}$$

Many problems involve a rate of travel, or *speed*. The **speed** of an object is found by dividing the distance traveled by the time required to travel that distance.

*For all rental problems, assume that the pickup time was later in the day than the return time so that no late fees were applied.

EXAMPLE 2 Transportation. An Atlantic City Express bus makes regular trips between Paramus and Atlantic City, New Jersey. At 6:00 P.M., the bus is at mileage marker 40 on the Garden State Parkway, and at 8:00 P.M. it is at marker 170. Find the average speed of the bus.

Solution Speed is the distance traveled divided by the time spent traveling:

$$\text{Bus speed} = \frac{\text{Distance traveled}}{\text{Time spent traveling}}$$

$$= \frac{\text{Change in mileage}}{\text{Change in time}}$$

$$= \frac{130\text{ mi}}{2\text{ hr}}$$ 170 mi − 40 mi = 130 mi; 8:00 P.M. − 6:00 P.M. = 2 hr

$$= 65\frac{\text{mi}}{\text{hr}}$$

$= 65$ miles per hour. This *average* speed does not indicate by how much the bus speed may vary along the route.

Visualizing Rates

Graphs allow us to visualize a rate of change. As a rule, the quantity listed in the numerator appears on the vertical axis and the quantity listed in the denominator appears on the horizontal axis.

EXAMPLE 3 Phone lines. Between 1992 and 2002, the number of U.S. telephone lines (land and cellular combined) increased at a rate of approximately 17.5 million lines per year.* In 1992, there were about 155 million U.S. telephone lines. Draw a graph to represent this information.

Solution To label the axes, note that the rate is given in millions of telephone lines per year. Thus we list *Number of telephone lines, in millions,* on the vertical axis and *Year* on the horizontal axis.

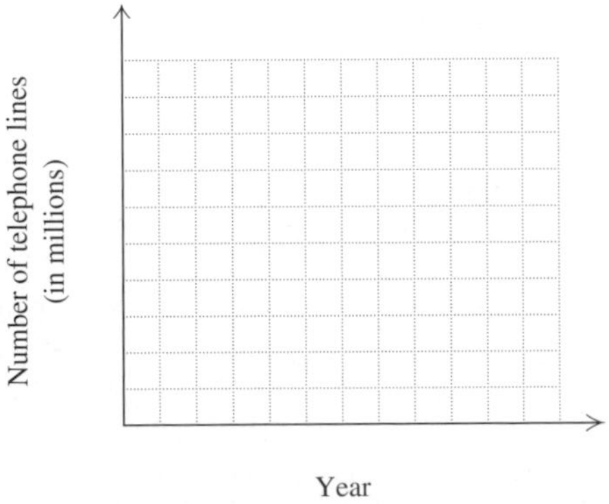

17.5 million per year is 17.5 million/yr; millions of customers is the vertical axis; year is the horizontal axis.

*Based on information from the Federal Communications Commission and the Cellular Telecommunications and Internet Associations

Next, we select a scale for each axis that allows us to plot the given information. If we count by increments of 40 million on the vertical axis, we can easily reach 155 million and beyond—allowing for growth. On the horizontal axis, we list years, making certain that both 1992 and 2002 are included (see the figure on the left below).

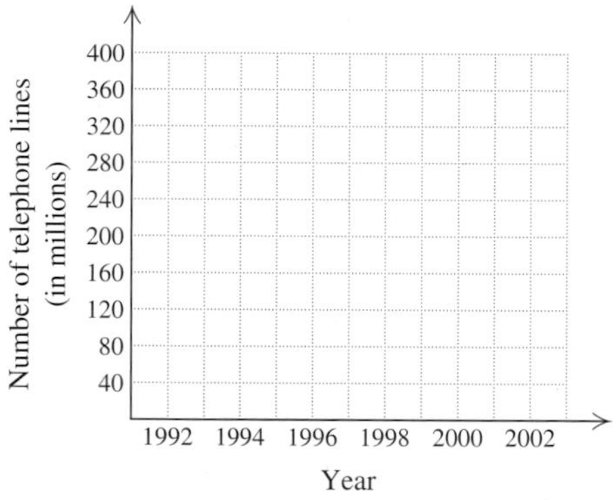

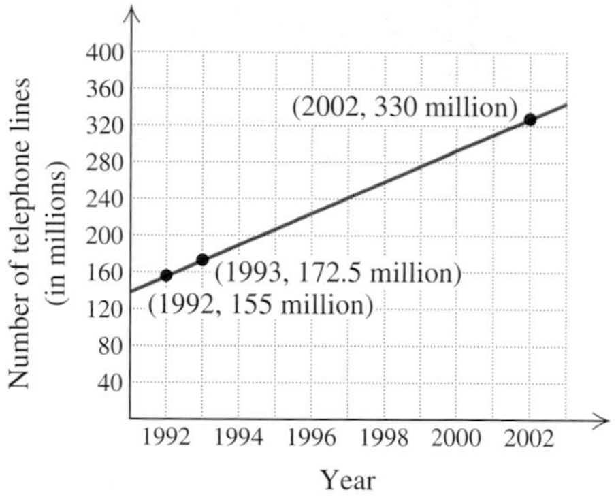

To display the given information, we plot the end point that corresponds to (1992, 155 million). Then, to display the rate of growth, we move from that point to a second point that represents 17.5 million more telephone lines one year later. The coordinates of this point are $(1992 + 1, 155 + 17.5 \text{ million})$, or (1993, 172.5 million). To find the coordinates of the year 2002, note that 2002 is 10 years after 1992. Assuming a constant growth rate for those years, we calculate and plot $(1992 + 10, 155 + 10 \cdot 17.5 \text{ million})$, or (2002, 330 million). Finally, we draw a line through the three points.

EXAMPLE 4 Haircutting. Sylvia's World of Hair has a graph displaying data from a recent day of work.

a) What rate can be determined from the graph?

b) What is that rate?

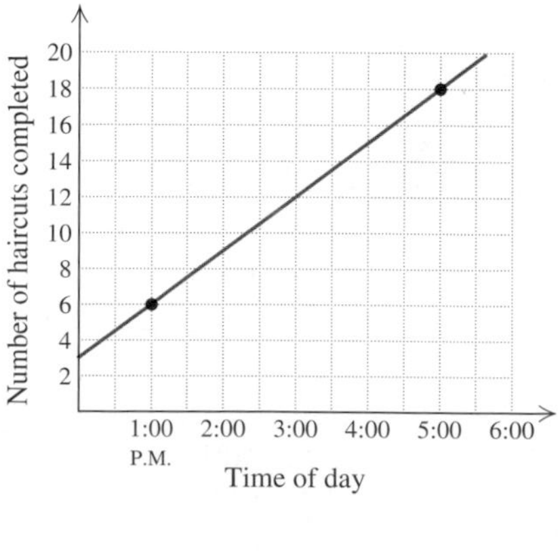

Solution

a) Because the vertical axis shows the number of haircuts completed and the horizontal axis lists the time in hour-long increments, we can find the rate *Number of haircuts per hour.*

b) The points (1:00, 6 haircuts) and (5:00, 18 haircuts) are both on the graph. This tells us that in the 4 hr between 1:00 and 5:00, there were $18 - 6 = 12$ haircuts completed. Thus the rate is

$$\frac{18 \text{ haircuts} - 6 \text{ haircuts}}{5{:}00 - 1{:}00} = \frac{12 \text{ haircuts}}{4 \text{ hours}}$$
$$= 3 \text{ haircuts per hour.}$$

3.4 Exercise Set

FOR EXTRA HELP

Student's Solutions Manual | Digital Video Tutor CD 2 Videotape 5 | AW Math Tutor Center | MathXL Tutorials on CD | MathXL | MyMathLab

Solve. For Exercises 1–8, round answers to the nearest cent. For Exercises 1 and 2, assume that the pickup time was later in the day than the return time so that no late fees were applied.

1. *Van rentals.* Late on June 5, Deb rented a Dodge Caravan with a full tank of gas and 13,741 mi on the odometer. On June 8, she returned the van with 14,014 mi on the odometer. The rental agency charged Deb $118 for the rental and needed 13 gal of gas to fill up the tank.

a) Find the van's rate of gas consumption, in miles per gallon.
b) Find the average cost of the rental, in dollars per day.
c) Find the rate of travel, in miles per day.
d) Find the rental rate, in cents per mile.

2. *Car rentals.* On February 10, Oscar rented a Chevy Blazer with a full tank of gas and 13,091 mi on the odometer. On February 12, he returned the vehicle with 13,322 mi on the odometer. The rental agency charged $92 for the rental and needed 14 gal of gas to fill the tank.

a) Find the Blazer's rate of gas consumption, in miles per gallon.
b) Find the average cost of the rental, in dollars per day.
c) Find the rate of travel, in miles per day.
d) Find the rental rate, in cents per mile.

3. *Bicycle rentals.* At 2:00, Perry rented a mountain bike from The Slick Rock Cyclery. He returned the bike at 5:00, after cycling 18 mi. Perry paid $12 for the rental.

a) Find Perry's average speed, in miles per hour.
b) Find the rental rate, in dollars per hour.
c) Find the rental rate, in dollars per mile.

4. *Bicycle rentals.* At 9:00, Jodi rented a mountain bike from The Bike Rack. She returned the bicycle at 11:00, after cycling 14 mi. Jodi paid $15 for the rental.

a) Find Jodi's average speed, in miles per hour.
b) Find the rental rate, in dollars per hour.
c) Find the rental rate, in dollars per mile.

5. *Temporary help.* A typist from Jobsite Services, Inc., reports to AKA International for work at 9:00 A.M. and leaves at 5:00 P.M. after having typed from the end of page 12 to the end of page 48 of a prospectus. AKA International pays \$128 for the typist's services.

a) Find the rate of pay, in dollars per hour.
b) Find the average typing rate, in number of pages per hour.
c) Find the rate of pay, in dollars per page.

6. *Temporary help.* A typist for Kelly Services reports to 3E's Properties for work at 10:00 A.M. and leaves at 6:00 P.M. after having typed from the end of page 8 to the end of page 50 of a proposal. 3E's pays \$120 for the typist's services.

a) Find the rate of pay, in dollars per hour.
b) Find the average typing rate, in number of pages per hour.
c) Find the rate of pay, in dollars per page.

7. *Two-year-college tuition.* The average tuition at a public two-year college was \$1327 in 1999 and approximately \$1359 in 2001. Find the rate at which tuition was increasing.
Source: *Statistical Abstract of the United States*, 2002

8. *Four-year-college tuition.* The average tuition at a public four-year college was \$3640 in 1999 and approximately \$3983 in 2001. Find the rate at which tuition was increasing.
Source: *Statistical Abstract of the United States*, 2002

9. *Elevators.* At 2:38, Serge entered an elevator on the 34th floor of the Regency Hotel. At 2:40, he stepped off at the 5th floor.

a) Find the elevator's average rate of travel, in number of floors per minute.
b) Find the elevator's average rate of travel, in seconds per floor.

10. *Snow removal.* By 1:00 P.M., Erin had already shoveled 2 driveways, and by 6:00 P.M., the number was up to 7.

a) Find Erin's shoveling rate, in number of driveways per hour.
b) Find Erin's shoveling rate, in hours per driveway.

11. *Mountaineering.* As part of an ill-fated expedition to climb Mt. Everest in 1996, author Jon Krakauer departed "The Balcony," elevation 27,600 ft, at 7:00 A.M. and reached the summit, elevation 29,028 ft, at 1:25 P.M.
Source: Krakauer, Jon, *Into Thin Air, the Illustrated Edition*. New York: Random House, 1998

a) Find Krakauer's average rate of ascent, in feet per minute.
b) Find Krakauer's average rate of ascent, in minutes per foot.

12. *Mountaineering.* The fastest ascent of Mt. Everest was accomplished by Lakpa Gelu Sherpa of Nepal in 2003. Lakpa Gelu Sherpa climbed from base camp, elevation 17,552 ft, to the summit, elevation 29,028 ft, in 10 hr 57 min.
Source: *Guinness Book of World Records* 2004 Edition

a) Find Lakpa Gelu Sherpa's rate of ascent, in feet per minute.
b) Find Lakpa Gelu Sherpa's rate of ascent, in minutes per foot.

In Exercises 13–22, draw a linear graph to represent the given information. Be sure to label and number the axes appropriately (see Example 3).

13. *Healthcare costs.* In 2003, the average copayment for a prescription drug on an insurance company's preferred list was \$19, and the figure was rising at a rate of \$2 per year.
Source: *Daily Reporter*, Greenfield IN, 9/9/03

14. *Healthcare costs.* In 2003, the average cost for health insurance for a family was about \$9000, and the figure was rising at a rate of about \$875 per year.
Source: *Daily Reporter*, Greenfield IN, 9/9/03

15. *Law enforcement.* In 2000, there were approximately 26 million crimes reported in the United States, and the figure was dropping at a rate of about 1.2 million per year.
Source: Based on data from the Bureau of Justice Statistics

16. *Fire fighting.* In 2000, there were approximately 1.7 million fires in the United States, and the figure was dropping at a rate of about 0.1 million per year.
Source: Based on data from the *Statistical Abstract of the United States*, 2002

17. *Train travel.* At 3:00 P.M., the Boston–Washington Metroliner had traveled 230 mi and was cruising at a rate of 90 miles per hour.

18. *Plane travel.* At 4:00 P.M., the Seattle–Los Angeles shuttle had traveled 400 mi and was cruising at a rate of 300 miles per hour.

19. *Wages.* By 2:00 P.M., Diane had earned \$50. She continued earning money at a rate of \$15 per hour.

20. *Wages.* By 3:00 P.M., Arnie had earned \$70. He continued earning money at a rate of \$12 per hour.

21. *Telephone bills.* Roberta's phone bill was already \$7.50 when she made a call for which she was charged at a rate of \$0.10 per minute.

22. *Telephone bills.* At 3:00 P.M., Larry's phone bill was \$6.50 and increasing at a rate of 7¢ per minute.

In Exercises 23–32, use the graph provided to calculate a rate of change in which the units of the horizontal axis are used in the denominator.

23. *Hairdresser.* Eve's Custom Cuts has a graph displaying data from a recent day of work. At what rate does Eve work?

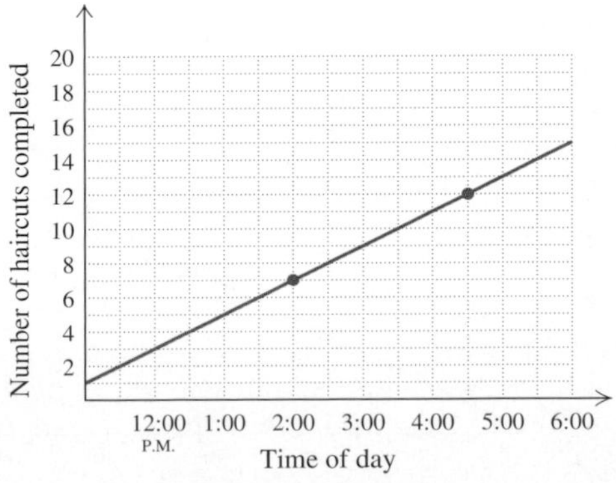

24. *Manicures.* The following graph shows data from a recent day's work at the O'Hara School of Cosmetology. At what rate do they work?

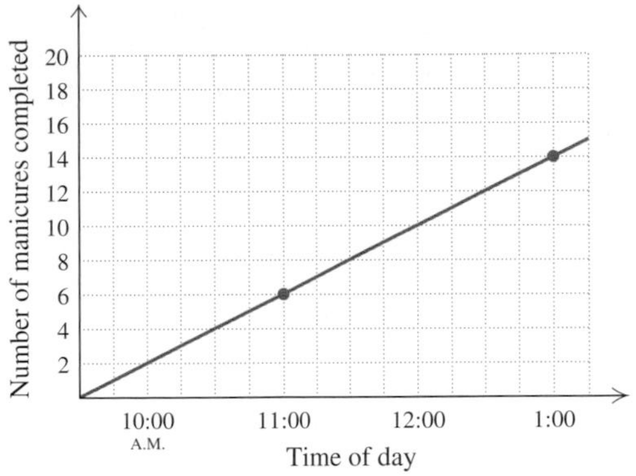

25. *Train travel.* The following graph shows data from a recent train ride from Chicago to St. Louis. At what rate did the train travel?

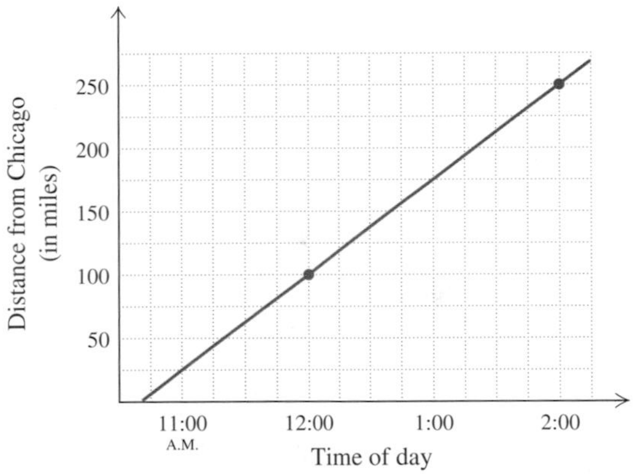

26. *Train travel.* The following graph shows data from a recent train ride from Denver to Kansas City. At what rate did the train travel?

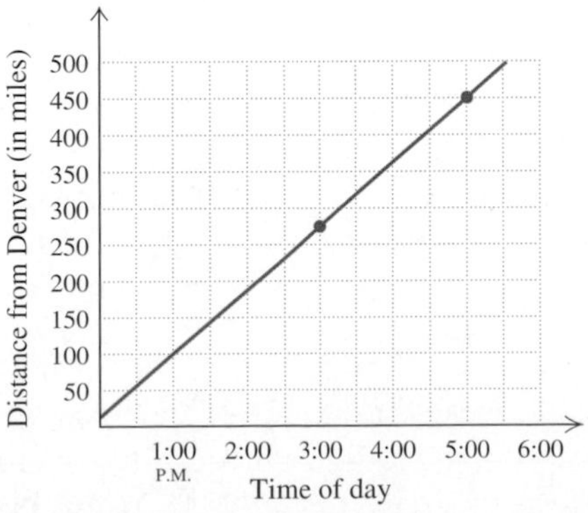

27. *Cost of a telephone call.* The following graph shows data from a recent MCI phone call between San Francisco, CA, and Pittsburgh, PA. At what rate was the customer being billed?

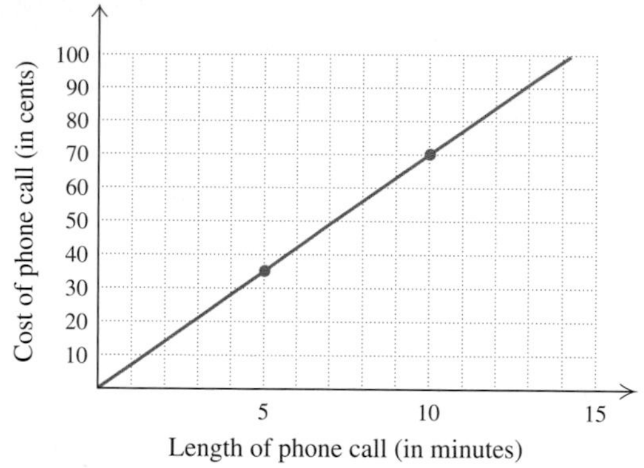

28. *Cost of a telephone call.* The following graph shows data from a recent AT&T phone call between Burlington, VT, and Austin, TX. At what rate was the customer being billed?

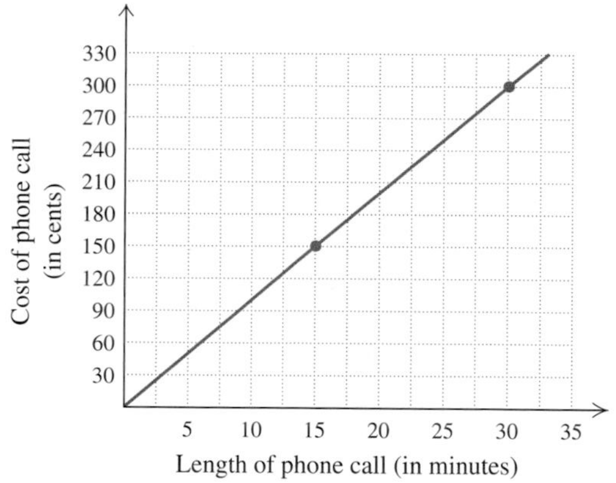

29. *Depreciation of an office machine.* Data regarding the value of a particular color copier is represented in the following graph. At what rate is the value changing?

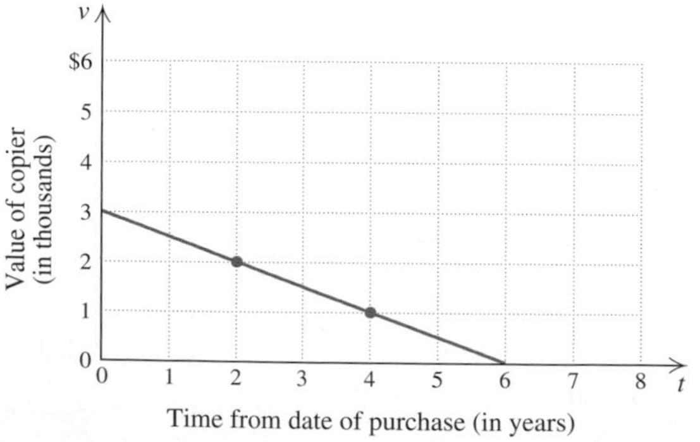

30. *NASA spending.* Spending on the National Aeronautics and Space Administration (NASA) during the late 1990s is represented in the following graph. At what rate was the amount spent on NASA changing?

Source: Based on information in the *Statistical Abstract of the United States*, 1999, 2002

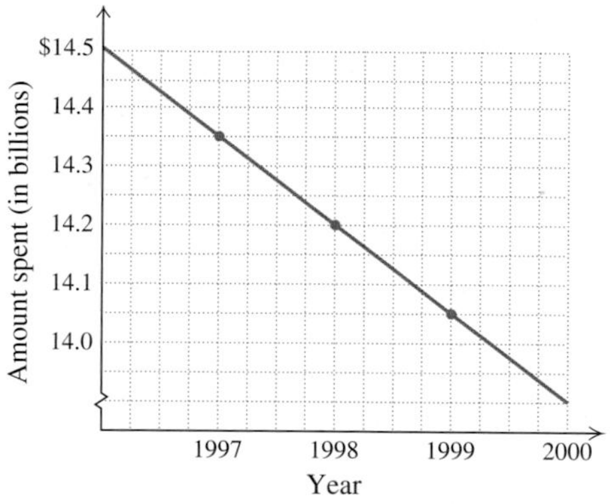

31. *Gas mileage.* The following graph shows data for a Honda Odyssey driven on interstate highways. At what rate was the vehicle consuming gas?

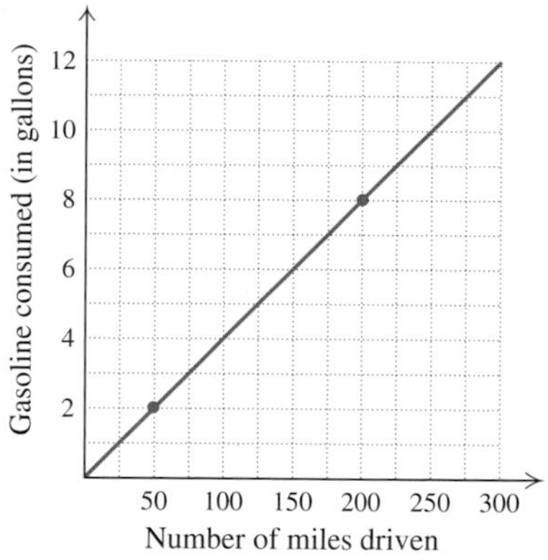

32. *Gas mileage.* The following graph shows data for a Ford Explorer driven on city streets. At what rate was the vehicle consuming gas?

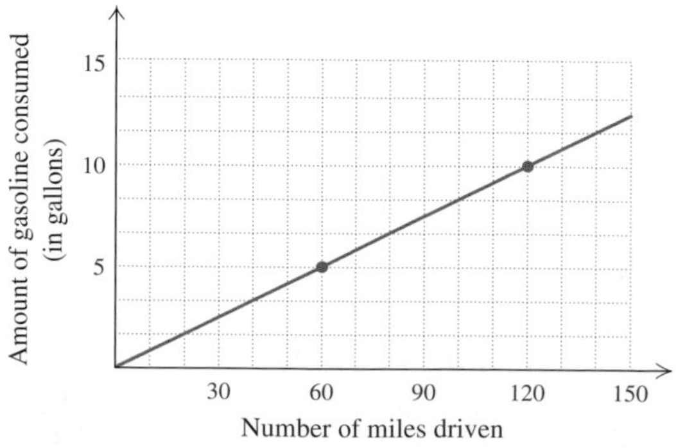

In each of Exercises 33–38, match the description with the most appropriate graph from the choices below. Scales are intentionally omitted. Assume that of the three sports listed, swimming is the slowest and biking is the fastest.

33. ____ Robin trains for triathlons by running, biking, and then swimming every Saturday.

34. ____ Gene trains for triathlons by biking, running, and then swimming every Sunday.

35. ____ Shirley trains for triathlons by swimming, biking, and then running every Sunday.

36. ____ Evan trains for triathlons by swimming, running, and then biking every Saturday.

37. ____ Angie trains for triathlons by biking, swimming, and then running every Sunday.

38. ____ Mick trains for triathlons by running, swimming, and then biking every Saturday.

a)
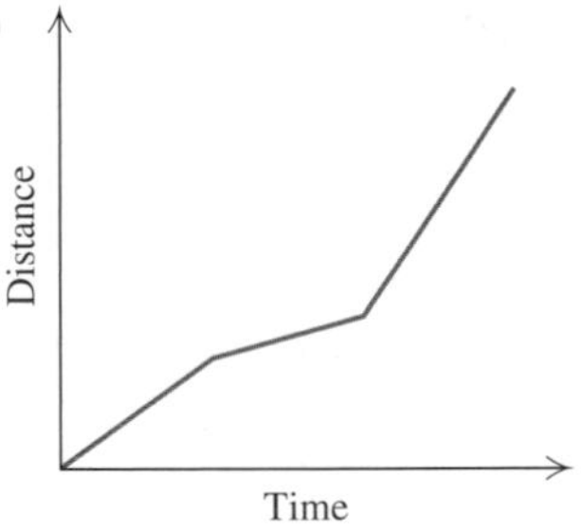

b)
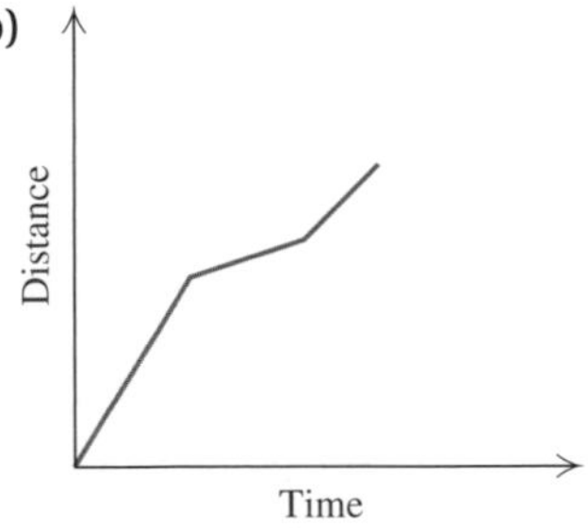

c)
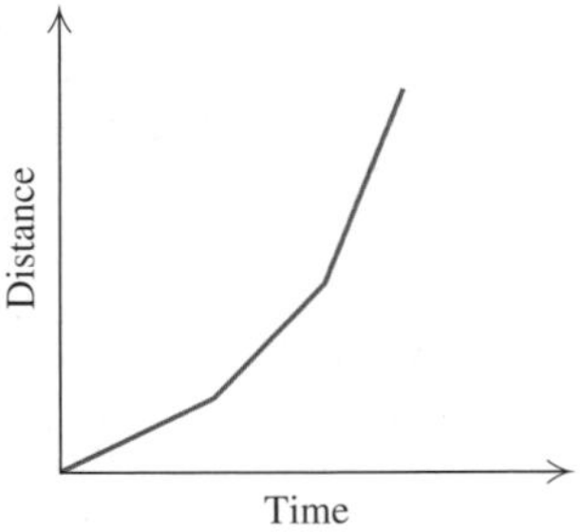

d)
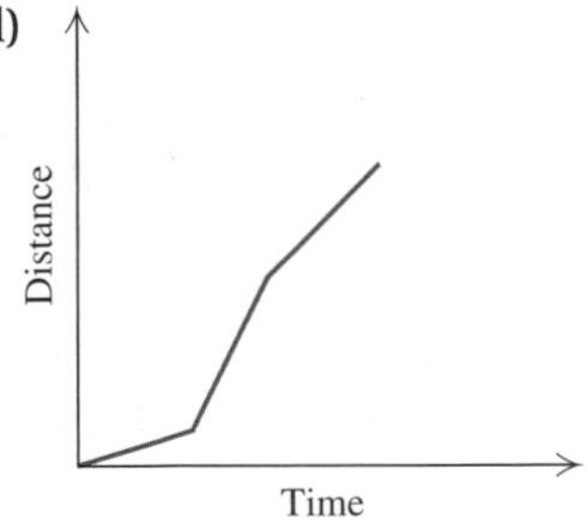

e)
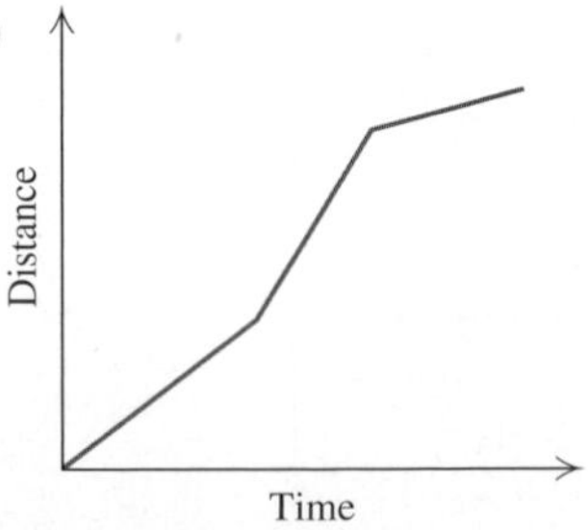

f)
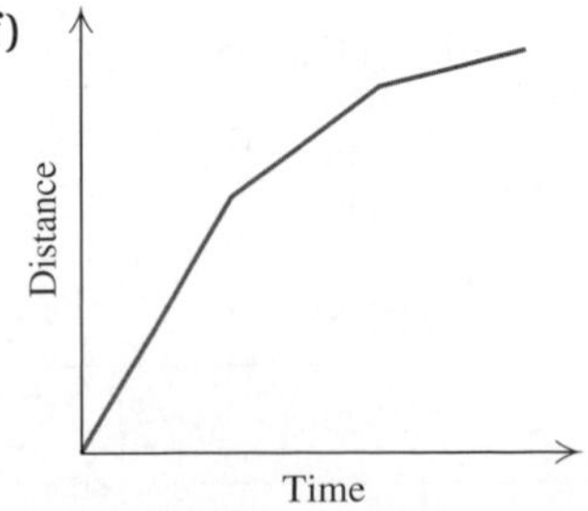

39. What does a negative rate of travel indicate? Explain.

40. Explain how to convert from kilometers per hour to meters per second.

SKILL MAINTENANCE

41. $-2 - (-7)$ [1.6]

42. $-9 - (-3)$ [1.6]

43. $\dfrac{5 - (-4)}{-2 - 7}$ [1.8]

44. $\dfrac{8 - (-4)}{2 - 11}$ [1.8]

45. $\dfrac{-4 - 8}{7 - (-2)}$ [1.8]

46. $\dfrac{-5 - 3}{6 - (-4)}$ [1.8]

SYNTHESIS

47. Write an exercise similar to Exercises 23–32 for a classmate to solve. Design the problem so that the solution is "The plane was traveling at a rate of 300 miles per hour."

48. Write an exercise similar to Exercises 1–12 for a classmate to solve. Design the problem so that the solution is "The motorcycle's rate of gas consumption was 65 miles per gallon."

49. *Aviation.* A Boeing 737 climbs from sea level to a cruising altitude of 31,500 ft at a rate of 6300 ft/min. After cruising for 3 min, the jet is forced to land, descending at a rate of 3500 ft/min. Represent the flight with a graph in which altitude is measured on the vertical axis and time on the horizontal axis.

50. *Wages with commissions.* Each salesperson at Mike's Bikes is paid \$140 a week plus 13% of all sales up to \$2000, and then 20% on any sales in excess of \$2000. Draw a graph in which sales are measured on the horizontal axis and wages on the vertical axis. Then use the graph to estimate the wages paid when a salesperson sells \$2700 in merchandise in one week.

51. *Taxi fares.* The driver of a New York City Yellow Cab recently charged \$2 plus 50¢ for each fifth of a mile traveled. Draw a graph that could be used to determine the cost of a fare.

52. *Gas mileage.* Suppose that a Honda motorcycle goes twice as far as a Honda Odyssey on the same amount of gas (see Exercise 31). Draw a graph that reflects this information.

53. *Navigation.* In 3 sec, Penny walks 24 ft, to the bow (front) of a tugboat. The boat is cruising at a rate of 5 feet per second. What is Penny's rate of travel with respect to land?

54. *Aviation.* Tim's F-16 jet is moving forward at a deck speed of 95 mph aboard an aircraft carrier that is traveling 39 mph in the same direction. How fast is the jet traveling, in minutes per mile, with respect to the sea?

55. *Running.* Annette ran from the 4-km mark to the 7-km mark of a 10-km race in 15.5 min. At this rate, how long would it take Annette to run a 5-mi race?

56. *Running.* Jerod ran from the 2-mi marker to the finish line of a 5-mi race in 25 min. At this rate, how long would it take Jerod to run a 10-km race?

57. At 3:00 P.M., Catanya and Chad had already made 46 candles. By 5:00 P.M., the total reached 100 candles. Assuming a constant production rate, at what time did they make their 82nd candle?

58. Marcy picks apples twice as fast as Ryan. By 4:30, Ryan had already picked 4 bushels of apples. Fifty minutes later, his total reached $5\frac{1}{2}$ bushels. Find Marcy's picking rate. Give your answer in number of bushels per hour.

COLLABORATIVE CORNER

Determining Depreciation Rates

Focus: Modeling, graphing, and rates
Time: 30 minutes
Group size: 3
Materials: Graph paper and straightedges

From the minute a new car is driven out of the dealership, it *depreciates*, or drops in value with the passing of time. The Kelley Blue Book Auto Market Report is a periodic listing of the trade-in values of used cars. The data below are taken from two such reports from 2003.

ACTIVITY

1. Each group member should select a different one of the cars listed in the table below as his or her own. Assuming that the values are dropping linearly, each student should draw a line representing the trade-in value of his or her car. Draw all three lines on the same graph. Let the horizontal axis represent the time, in months, since April 2003, and let the vertical axis represent the trade-in value of each car. Decide as a group how many months or dollars each square should represent. Make the drawings as neat as possible.
2. At what *rate* is each car depreciating and how are the different rates illustrated in the graph of part (1)?
3. If one of the three cars had to be sold in April 2004, which one would your group sell and why? Compare answers with other groups.

Car	Trade-in Value in April 2003	Trade-in Value in October 2003
2001 Chevrolet Camaro convertible V6	\$14,650	\$13,600
2001 Ford Mustang convertible V6	\$12,550	\$11,450
2001 Mitsubishi Eclipse convertible V6	\$15,250	\$13,800

3.5 Slope

Rate and Slope • Horizontal and Vertical Lines • Applications

Study Skills

Add Your Voice to the Author's

If you own your text, consider using it as a notebook. Since many instructors' work closely parallels the book, it is often useful to make notes on the appropriate page as he or she is lecturing.

In Section 3.4, we introduced *rate* as a method of measuring how two quantities change with respect to each other. In this section, we will discuss how rate can be related to the slope of a line.

Rate and Slope

Suppose that a car manufacturer operates two plants: one in Michigan and one in Pennsylvania. Knowing that the Michigan plant produces 3 cars every 2 hours and the Pennsylvania plant produces 5 cars every 4 hours, we can set up tables listing the number of cars produced after various amounts of time.

Michigan Plant	
Hours Elapsed	**Cars Produced**
0	0
2	3
4	6
6	9
8	12

Pennsylvania Plant	
Hours Elapsed	**Cars Produced**
0	0
4	5
8	10
12	15
16	20

By comparing the number of cars produced at each plant over a specified period of time, we can compare the two production rates. For example, the Michigan plant produces 3 cars every 2 hours, so its *rate* is $3 \div 2 = 1\frac{1}{2}$, or $\frac{3}{2}$ cars per hour. Since the Pennsylvania plant produces 5 cars every 4 hours, its rate is $5 \div 4 = 1\frac{1}{4}$, or $\frac{5}{4}$ cars per hour.

Let's now graph the pairs of numbers listed in the tables, using the horizontal axis for time and the vertical axis for the number of cars produced. Note that the rate in the Michigan plant is slightly greater so its graph is slightly steeper.

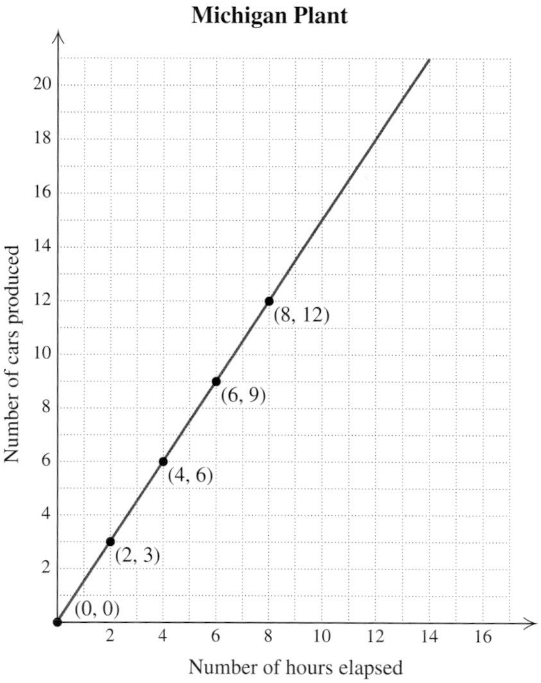

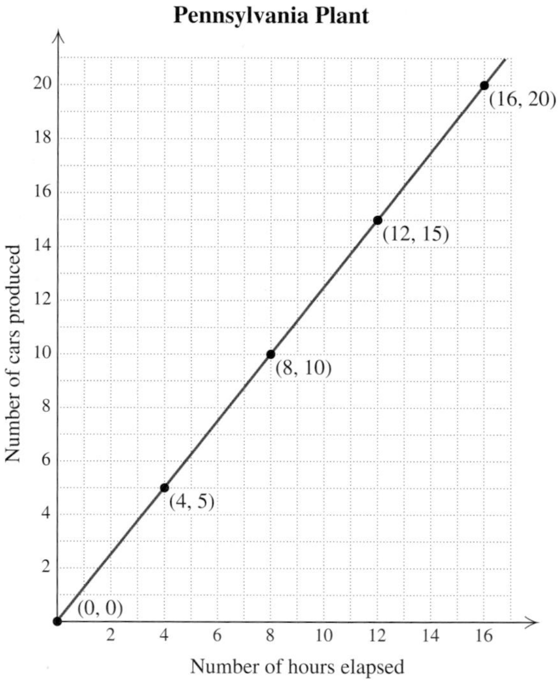

The rates $\frac{3}{2}$ and $\frac{5}{4}$ can also be found using the coordinates of any two points that are on the line. For example, we can use the points (6, 9) and (8, 12) to find the production rate for the Michigan plant. To do so, remember that these coordinates tell us that after 6 hr, 9 cars have been produced, and after 8 hr, 12 cars have been produced. In the 2 hr between the 6-hr and 8-hr points, $12 - 9$, or 3 cars were produced. Thus,

$$\begin{aligned}\text{Michigan production rate} &= \frac{\text{change in number of cars produced}}{\text{corresponding change in time}}\\ &= \frac{12 - 9 \text{ cars}}{8 - 6 \text{ hr}}\\ &= \frac{3 \text{ cars}}{2 \text{ hr}} = \frac{3}{2} \text{ cars per hour.}\end{aligned}$$

Because the line is straight, the same rate is found using *any* pair of points on the line. For example, using (0, 0) and (4, 6), we have

$$\text{Michigan production rate} = \frac{6 - 0 \text{ cars}}{4 - 0 \text{ hr}} = \frac{6 \text{ cars}}{4 \text{ hr}} = \frac{3}{2} \text{ cars per hour.}$$

Note that the rate is always the vertical change divided by the corresponding horizontal change.

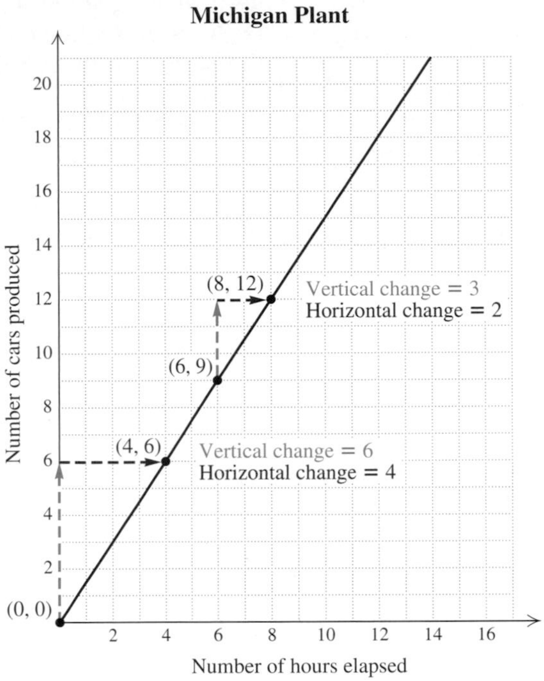

EXAMPLE 1 Use the graph of car production at the Pennsylvania plant to find the rate of production.

Solution We can use any two points on the line, such as (12, 15) and (16, 20):

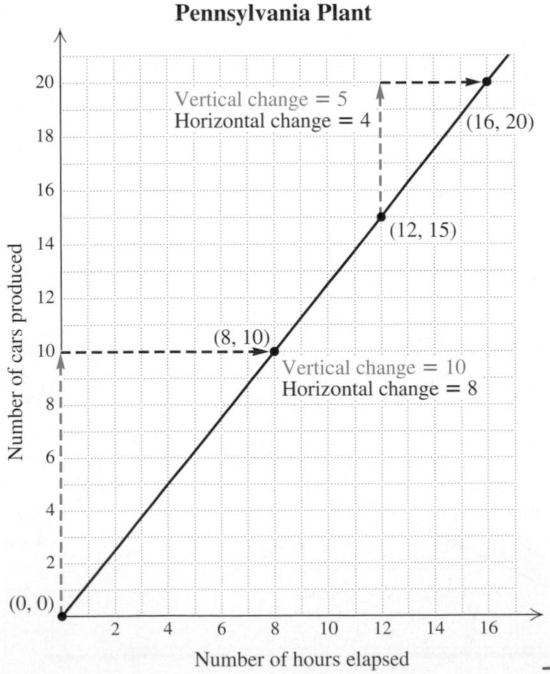

$$\begin{aligned}\text{Pennsylvania production rate} &= \frac{\text{change in number of cars produced}}{\text{corresponding change in time}}\\ &= \frac{20 - 15 \text{ cars}}{16 - 12 \text{ hr}}\\ &= \frac{5 \text{ cars}}{4 \text{ hr}}\\ &= \frac{5}{4} \text{ cars per hour.}\end{aligned}$$

As a check, we can use another pair of points, like (0, 0) and (8, 10):

$$\begin{aligned}\text{Pennsylvania production rate} &= \frac{10 - 0 \text{ cars}}{8 - 0 \text{ hr}}\\ &= \frac{10 \text{ cars}}{8 \text{ hr}}\\ &= \frac{5}{4} \text{ cars per hour.}\end{aligned}$$

When the axes of a graph are simply labeled x and y, it is still useful to know the ratio of vertical change to horizontal change. This ratio is a measure of a line's slant, or **slope**, and is the rate at which y is changing with respect to x.

Consider a line passing through (2, 3) and (6, 5), as shown below. We find the ratio of vertical change, or *rise*, to horizontal change, or *run*, as follows:

$$\text{Ratio of vertical change to horizontal change} = \frac{\text{change in } y}{\text{change in } x} = \frac{\text{rise}}{\text{run}}$$

$$= \frac{5-3}{6-2}$$

$$= \frac{2}{4}, \text{ or } \frac{1}{2}.$$

Note that these calculations can be performed without viewing a graph.

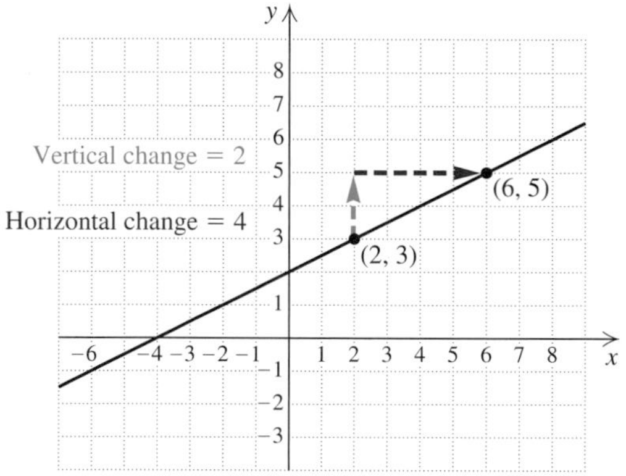

Thus the y-coordinates of points on this line increase at a rate of 2 units for every 4-unit increase in x, 1 unit for every 2-unit increase in x, or $\frac{1}{2}$ unit for every 1-unit increase in x. The slope of the line is $\frac{1}{2}$.

In the box below, the *subscripts* 1 and 2 are used to distinguish two arbitrary points, point 1 and point 2, from each other. The slightly lowered 1's and 2's are not exponents but are used to denote x-values (or y-values) that differ from each other.

Slope

The *slope* of the line containing points (x_1, y_1) and (x_2, y_2) is given by

$$m = \frac{\text{change in } y}{\text{change in } x} = \frac{\text{rise}}{\text{run}} = \frac{y_2 - y_1}{x_2 - x_1}.$$

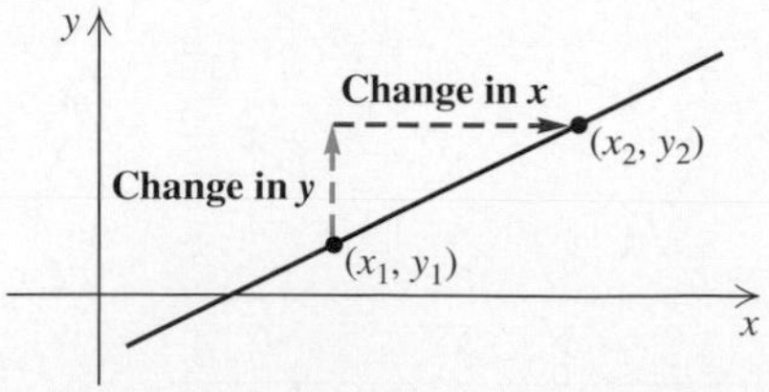

EXAMPLE 2 Graph the line containing the points $(-4, 3)$ and $(2, -6)$ and find the slope.

Solution The graph is shown below. From $(-4, 3)$ to $(2, -6)$, the change in y, or rise, is $-6 - 3$, or -9. The change in x, or run, is $2 - (-4)$, or 6. Thus,

$$\begin{aligned}\text{Slope} &= \frac{\text{change in } y}{\text{change in } x}\\ &= \frac{\text{rise}}{\text{run}}\\ &= \frac{-6-3}{2-(-4)}\\ &= \frac{-9}{6}\\ &= -\frac{9}{6}, \text{ or } -\frac{3}{2}.\end{aligned}$$

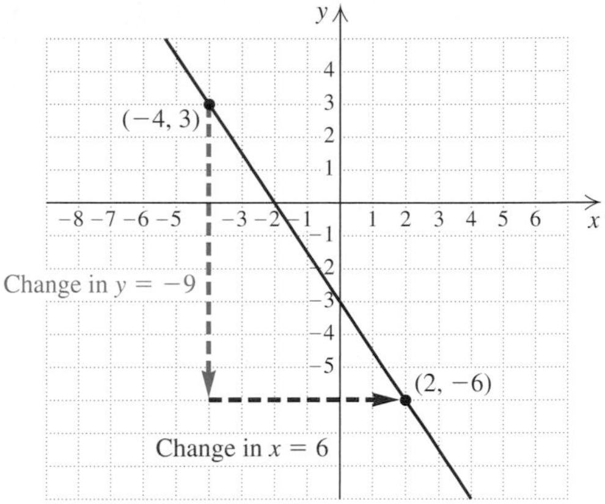

Student Notes

You may wonder which point should be regarded as (x_1, y_1) and which should be (x_2, y_2). To see that the math works out the same either way, perform both calculations on your own.

> *Caution!* When we use the formula
>
> $$m = \frac{y_2 - y_1}{x_2 - x_1},$$
>
> it makes no difference which point is considered (x_1, y_1). What matters is that we subtract the y-coordinates in the same order that we subtract the x-coordinates.
>
> To illustrate, we reverse *both* of the subtractions in Example 2. The slope is still $-\frac{3}{2}$:
>
> $$\text{Slope} = \frac{\text{change in } y}{\text{change in } x} = \frac{3-(-6)}{-4-2} = \frac{9}{-6} = -\frac{3}{2}.$$

As shown in the graphs below, a line with positive slope slants up from left to right, and a line with negative slope slants down from left to right. The larger the absolute value of the slope, the steeper the line.

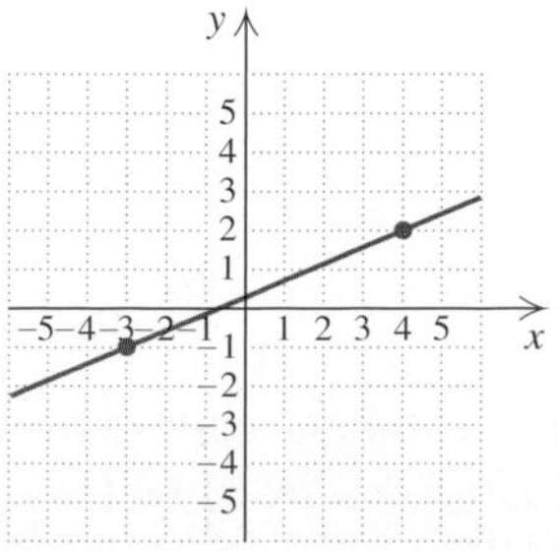

$m = \frac{3}{7}$

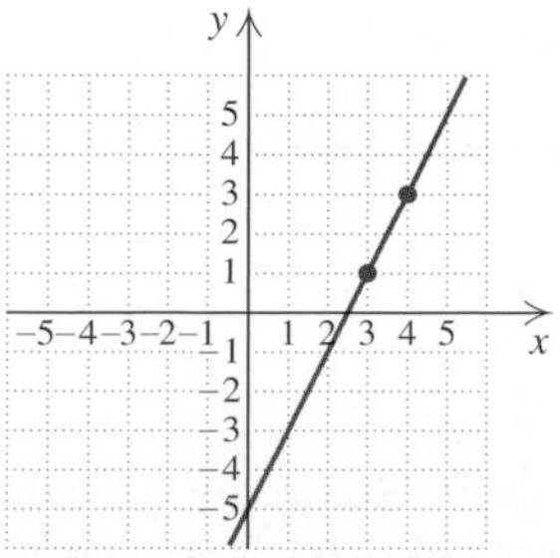

$m = 2$, or $\frac{2}{1}$

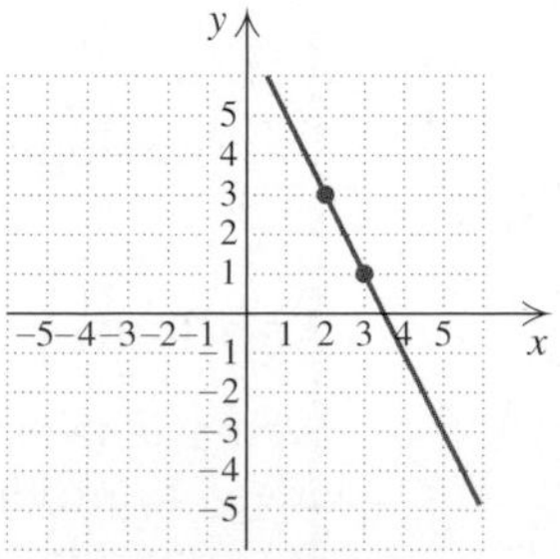

$m = -2$, or $\frac{-2}{1}$

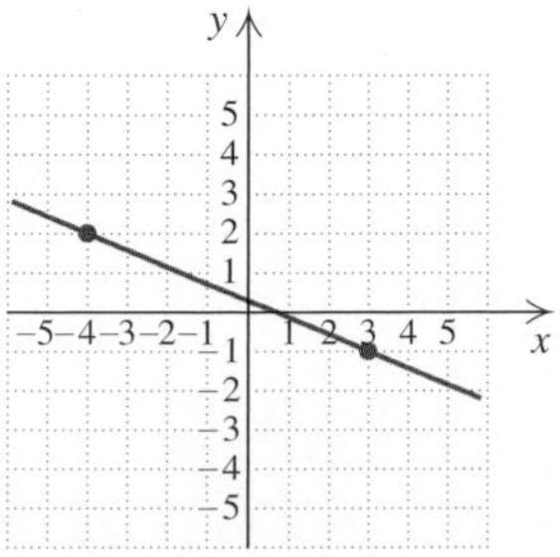

$m = -\frac{3}{7}$

Horizontal and Vertical Lines

What about the slope of a horizontal or a vertical line?

EXAMPLE 3 Find the slope of the line $y = 4$.

Solution Consider the points (2, 4) and (−3, 4), which are on the line. The change in y, or the rise, is $4 - 4$, or 0. The change in x, or the run, is $-3 - 2$, or −5. Thus,

$$m = \frac{4-4}{-3-2} = \frac{0}{-5} = 0.$$

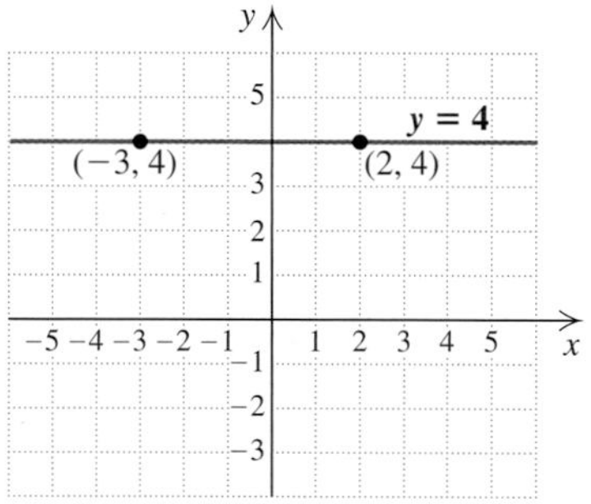

Any two points on a horizontal line have the same y-coordinate. Thus the change in y is 0, so the slope is 0.

A horizontal line has slope 0.

EXAMPLE 4 Find the slope of the line $x = -3$.

Solution Consider the points (−3, 4) and (−3, −2), which are on the line. The change in y, or the rise, is $-2 - 4$, or −6. The change in x, or the run, is $-3 - (-3)$, or 0. Thus,

$$m = \frac{-2-4}{-3-(-3)} = \frac{-6}{0}. \quad \text{(undefined)}$$

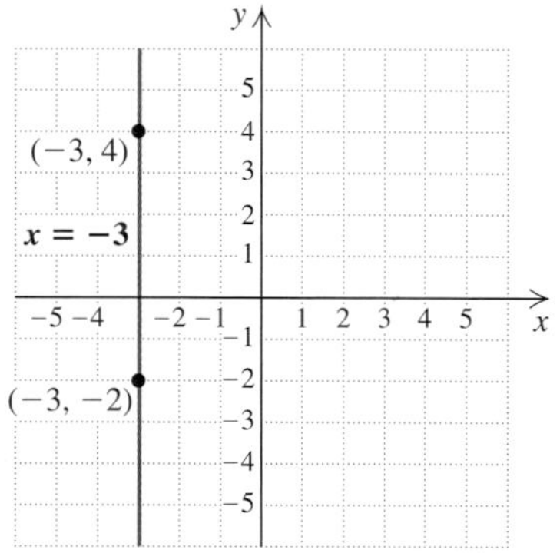

Since division by 0 is not defined, the slope of this line is not defined. The answer to a problem of this type is "The slope of this line is undefined."

The slope of a vertical line is undefined.

Applications

We have seen that slope has many real-world applications, ranging from car speed to production rate. Some applications use slope to measure steepness. For example, numbers like 2%, 3%, and 6% are often used to represent the **grade** of a road, a measure of a road's steepness. That is, a 3% grade means that for every horizontal distance of 100 ft, the road rises or drops 3 ft. The concept of grade also occurs in skiing or snowboarding, where a 7% grade is considered very tame, but a 70% grade is considered steep.

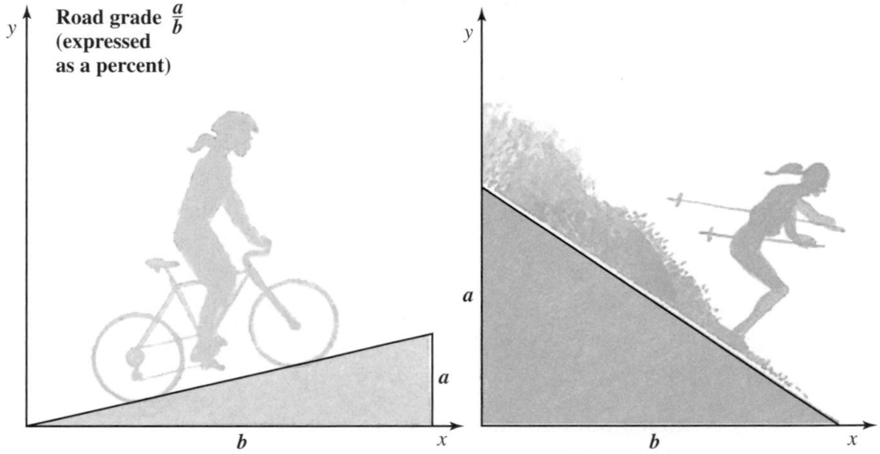

EXAMPLE 5 Skiing. Among the steepest skiable terrain in North America, the Headwall on Mount Washington, in New Hampshire, drops 720 ft over a horizontal distance of 900 ft. Find the grade of the Headwall.

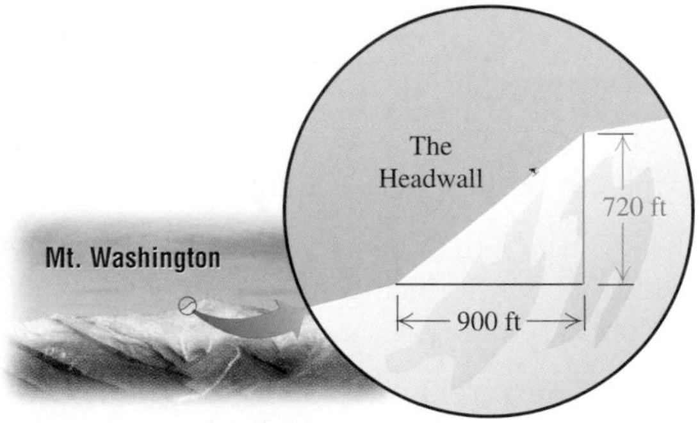

Solution The grade of the Headwall is its slope, expressed as a percent:

$$\left.\begin{aligned} m &= \frac{720}{900} \\ &= \frac{8}{10} \\ &= 80\%. \end{aligned}\right\}\quad \text{Grade is slope expressed as a percent.}$$

Carpenters use slope when designing stairs, ramps, or roof pitches. Another application occurs in the engineering of a dam—the force or strength of a river depends on how much the river drops over a specified distance.

3.5 Exercise Set

FOR EXTRA HELP

Student's Solutions Manual | Digital Video Tutor CD 2 Videotape 6 | AW Math Tutor Center | MathXL Tutorials on CD | MathXL | MyMathLab

Concept Reinforcement *State whether each of the following rates is positive, negative, or zero.*

1. The rate at which a teenager's height changes

2. The rate at which an elderly person's height changes

3. The rate at which a pond's water level changes during a drought

4. The rate at which a pond's water level changes during the rainy season

5. The rate at which the number of people in attendance at a basketball game changes in the moments before the opening tipoff

6. The rate at which the number of people in attendance at a basketball game changes in the moments after the final buzzer sounds

7. The rate at which a person's IQ changes during his or her sleep

8. The rate at which a gift shop's sales change as the holidays approach

9. The rate at which a bookstore's inventory changes during a liquidation sale

10. The rate at which a buoy's elevation changes while floating for an evening in a lake

11. Find the rate of change of the U.S. population.
Source: Based on information in the *Statistical Abstract of the United States*, 2002

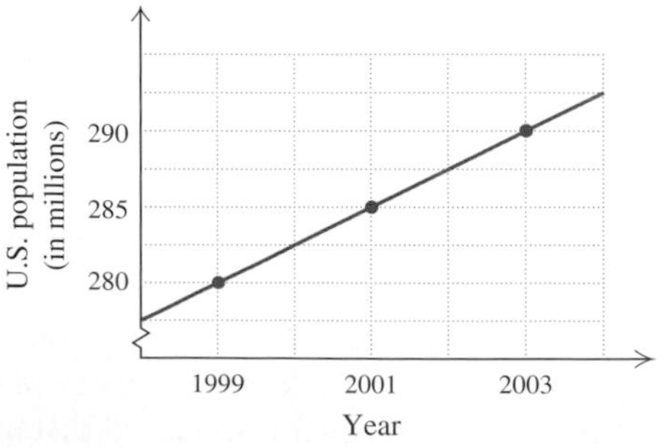

12. Find the rate at which a runner burns calories.

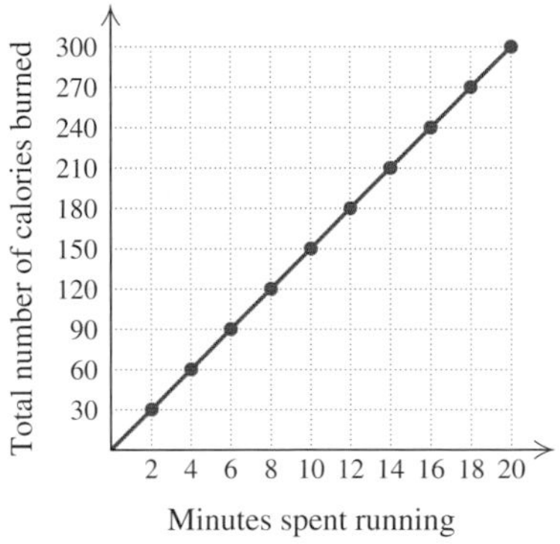

13. Find the rate of change in the percentage of high school students who admitted to cheating on an exam at least once in the past year.
Source: Based on information from Josephson Institute of Ethics, as reported in *The New York Times*, 10/4/03

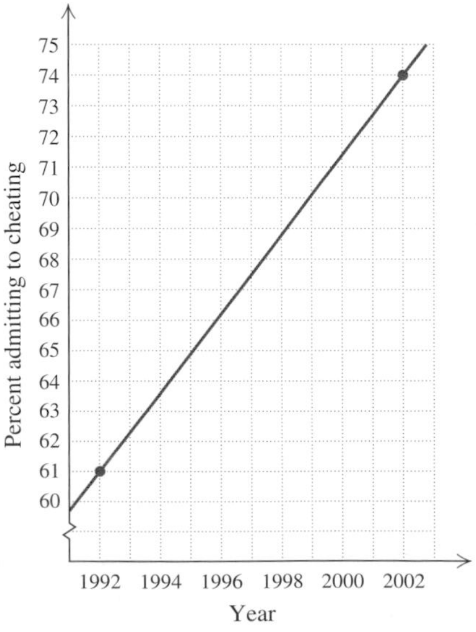

14. Find the rate of change in the percentage of college students who admitted to taking

material from the Internet and claiming it as their own.
Source: Based on information from Donald L. McCabe, as reported in *The New York Times*, 10/4/03

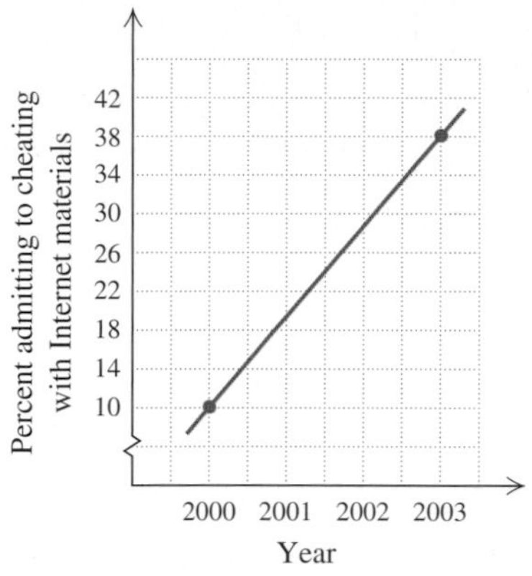

15. Find the rate of change in SAT math scores with respect to family income.
Source: Based on data from 1999 college-bound seniors in Massachusetts

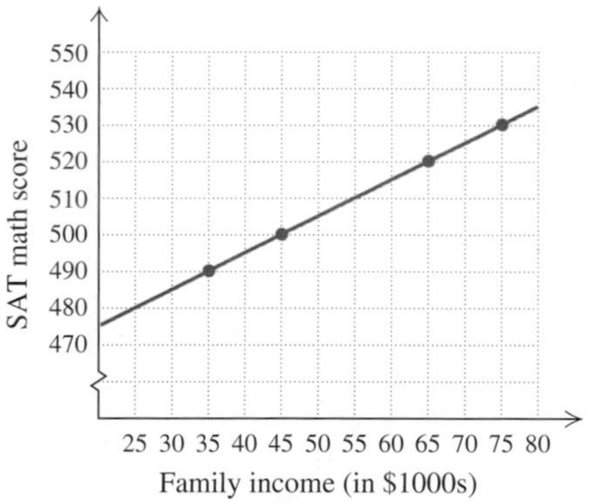

16. Find the rate of change in SAT verbal scores with respect to family income.
Source: Based on data from 1999 college-bound seniors in Massachusetts

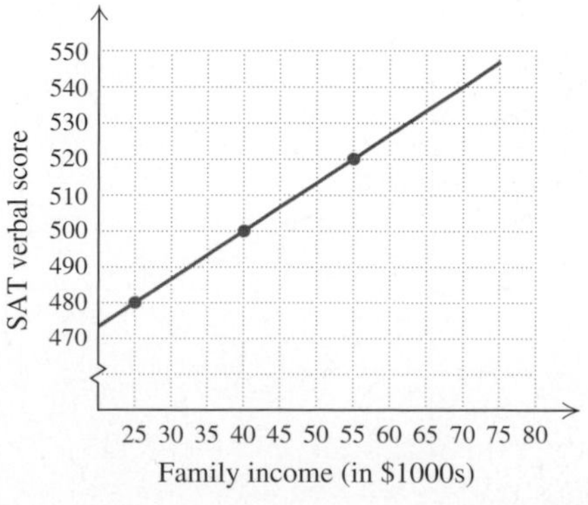

17. Find the rate of change in the temperature in Spearfish, Montana, on January 22, 1943, as shown below.
Source: National Oceanic Atmospheric Administration

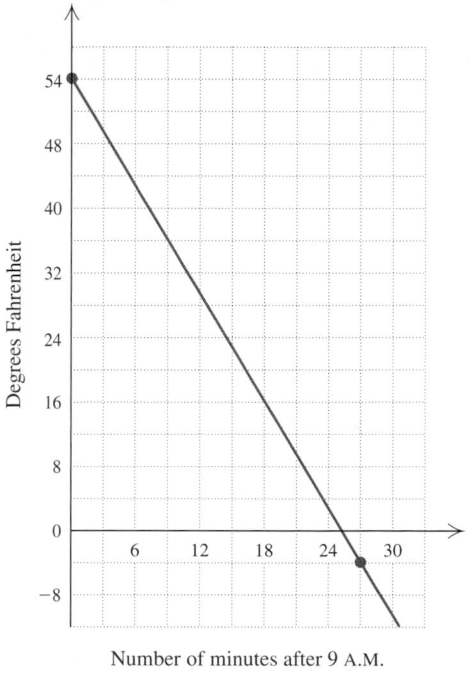

18. Find the rate of change in the number of crimes reported in the United States.
Source: Based on statistics from the U.S. Bureau of Justice

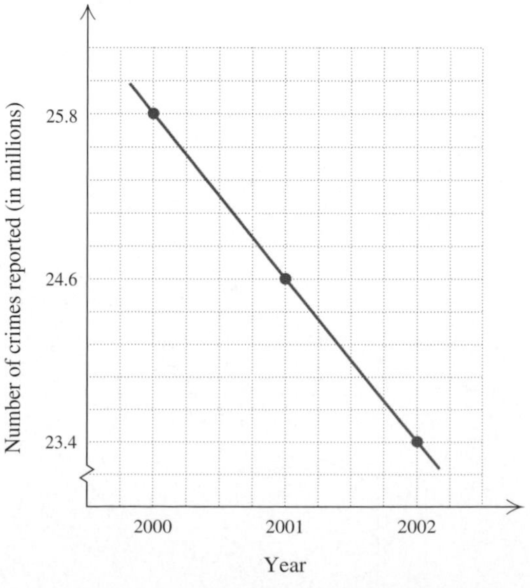

Find the slope, if it is defined, of each line. If the slope is undefined, state this.

19.

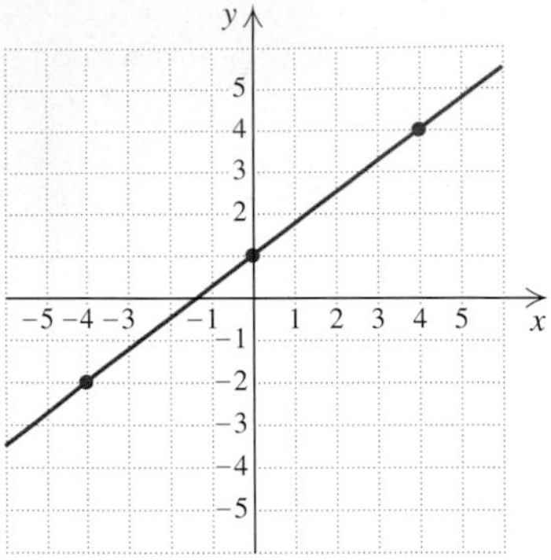

20.

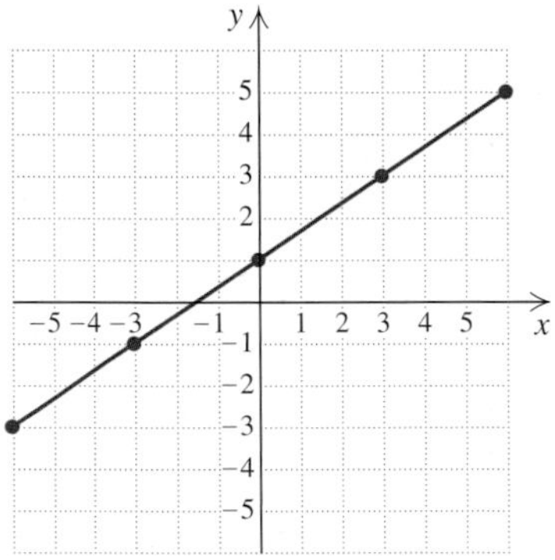

21.

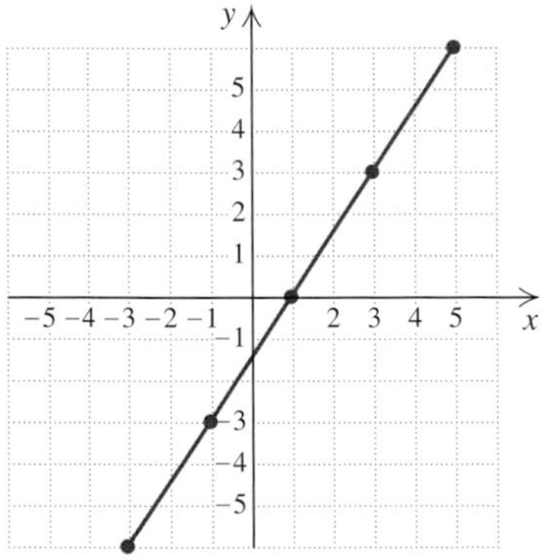

22.

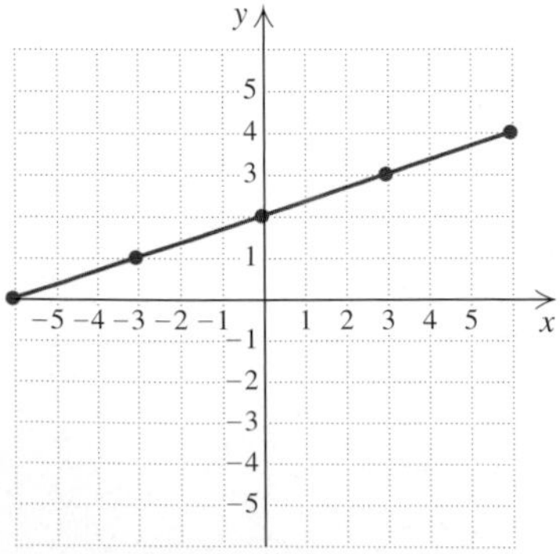

23.

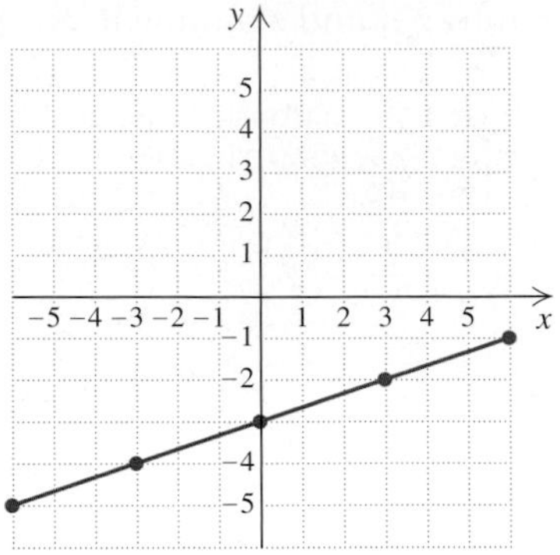

24.

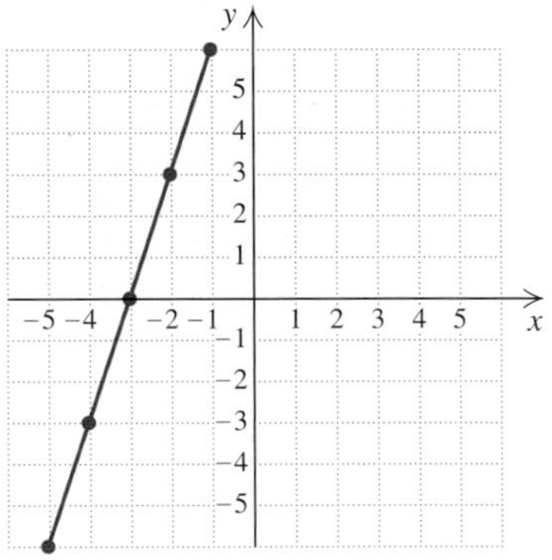

25.

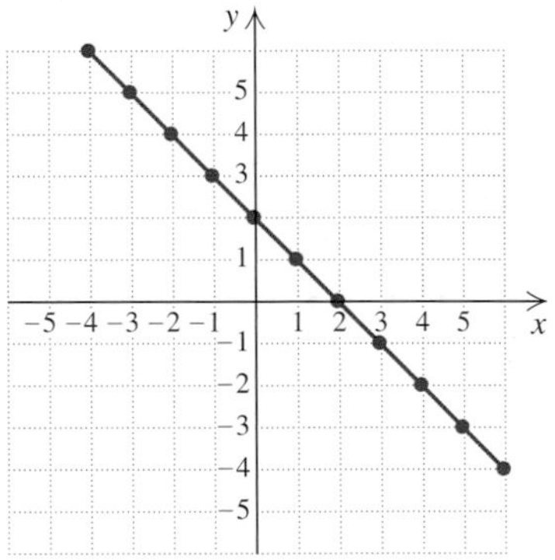

26.

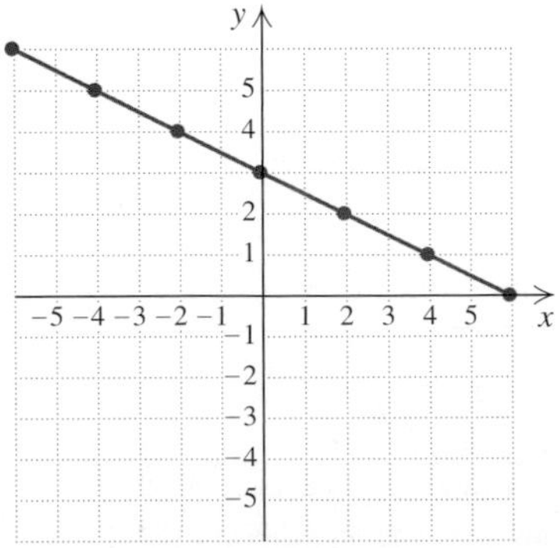

27.

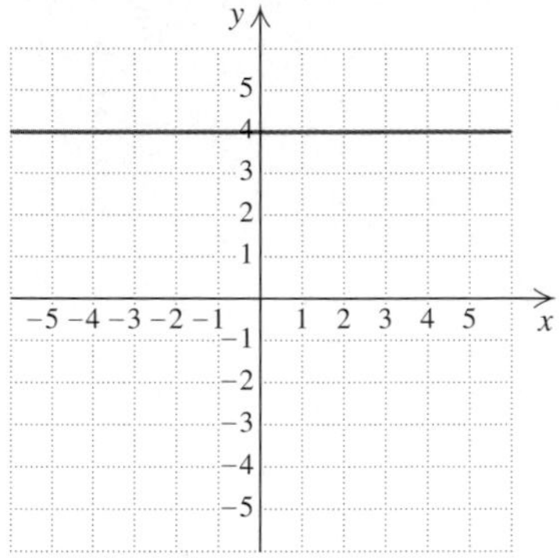

28.

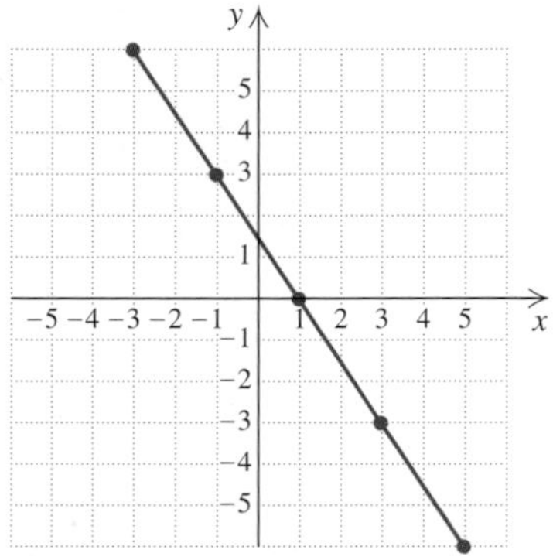

29.

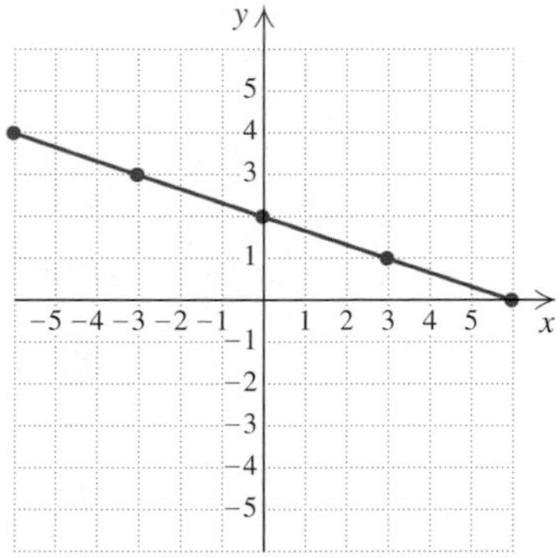

30.

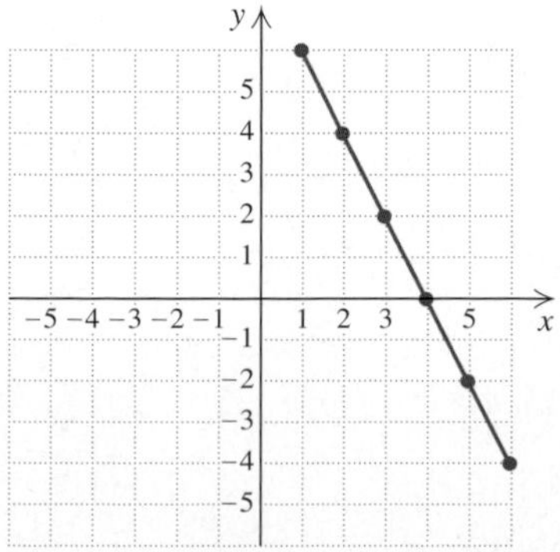

31.

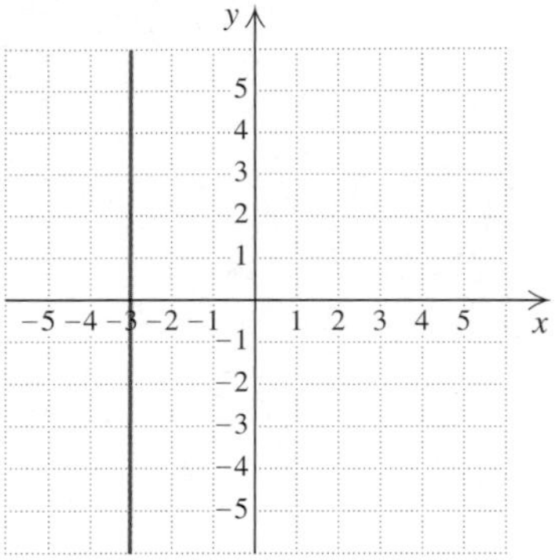

32.

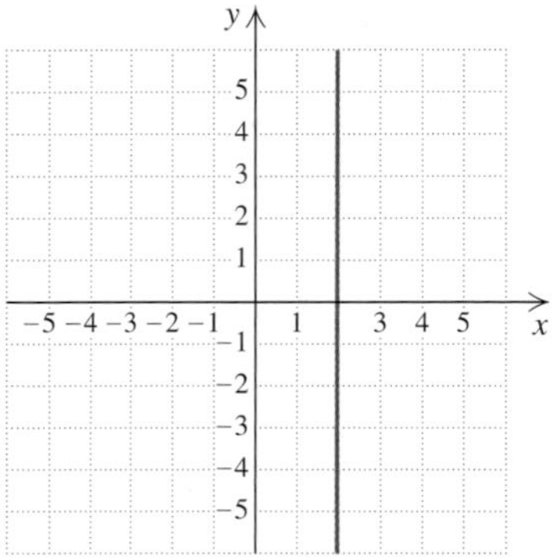

33.

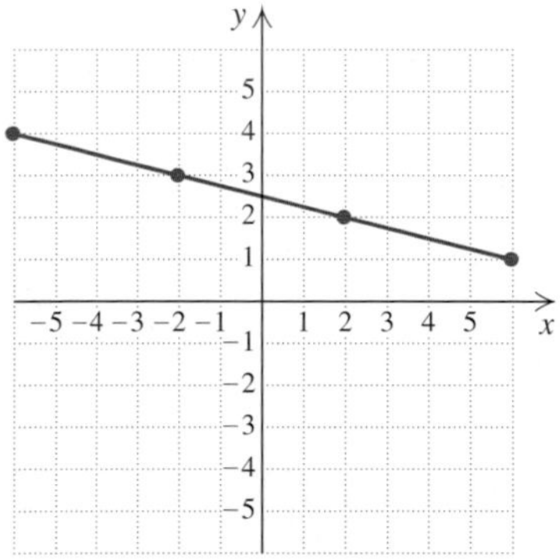

34.

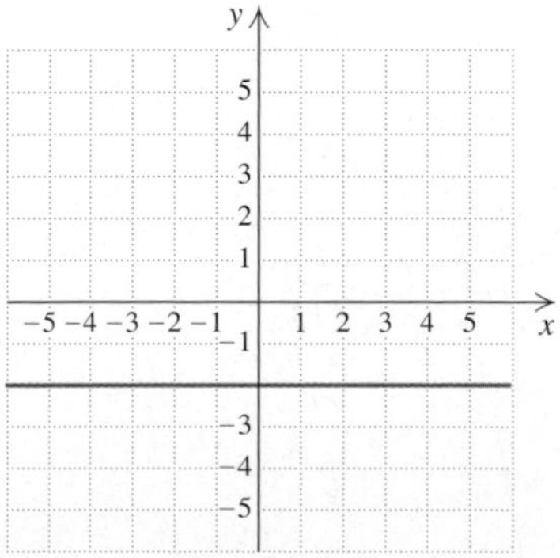

35.

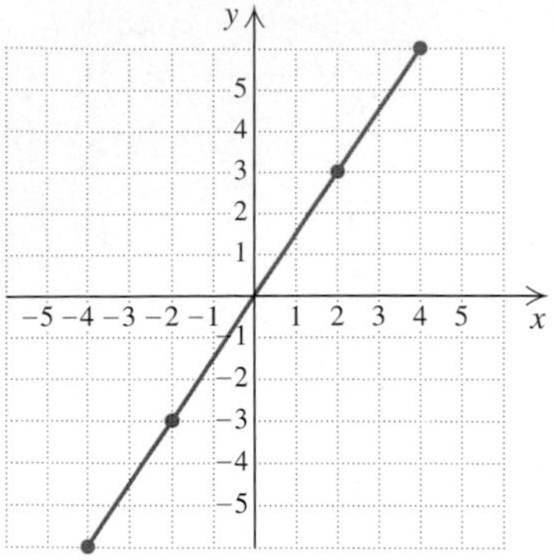

36.

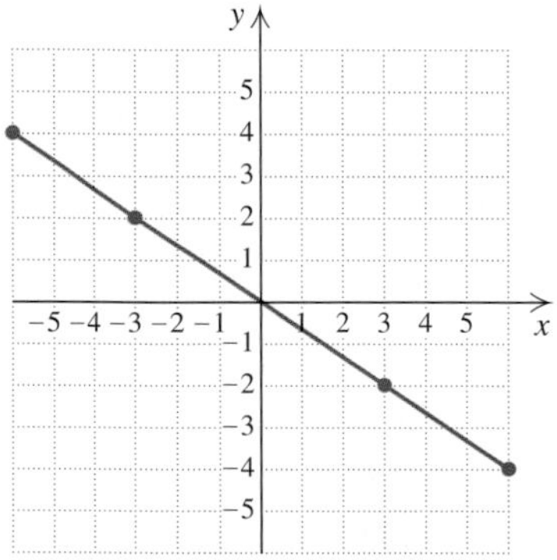

37.

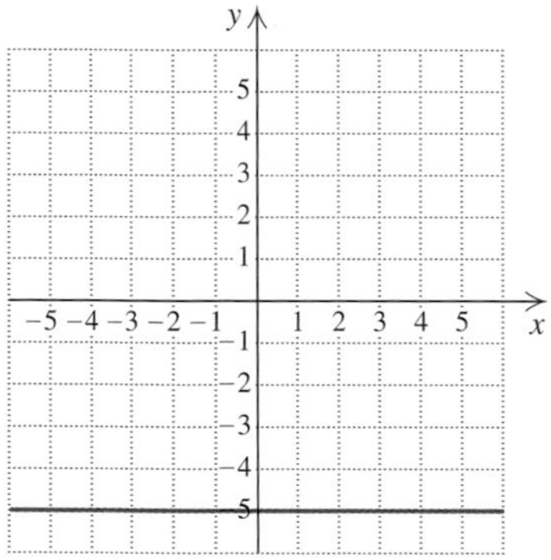

38.

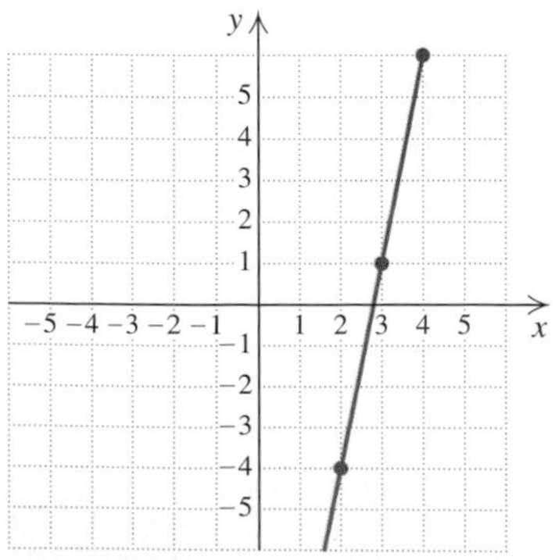

39.

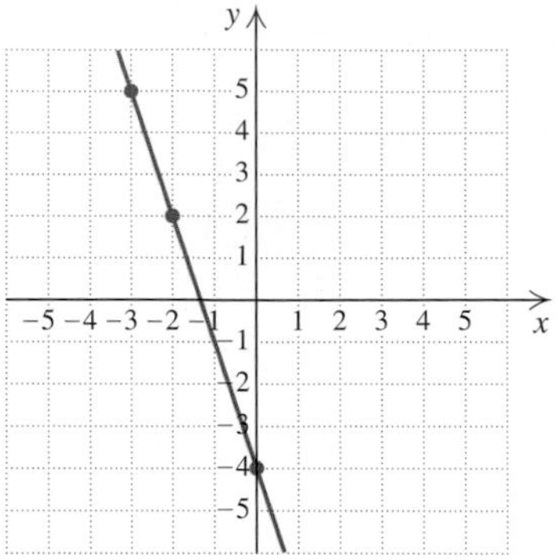

40.

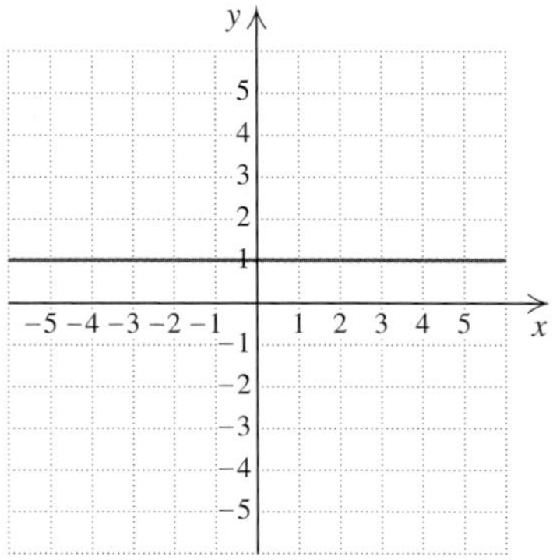

Find the slope of the line containing each given pair of points. If the slope is undefined, state this.

41. $(1, 2)$ and $(5, 8)$

42. $(2, 1)$ and $(6, 9)$

43. $(-2, 4)$ and $(3, 0)$

44. $(-4, 2)$ and $(2, -3)$

45. $(-4, 0)$ and $(5, 7)$

46. $(3, 0)$ and $(6, 2)$

47. $(0, 8)$ and $(-3, 10)$

48. $(0, 9)$ and $(-5, 0)$

49. $(-2, 3)$ and $(-6, 5)$

50. $(-2, 4)$ and $(6, -7)$

Aha! **51.** $\left(-2, \frac{1}{2}\right)$ and $\left(-5, \frac{1}{2}\right)$

52. $(-5, -1)$ and $(2, 3)$

53. $(3, 4)$ and $(9, -7)$

54. $(-10, 3)$ and $(-10, 4)$

55. $(6, -4)$ and $(6, 5)$

56. $(5, -2)$ and $(-4, -2)$

Find the slope of each line whose equation is given. If the slope is undefined, state this.

57. $x = -3$

58. $x = -4$

59. $y = 4$

60. $y = 17$

61. $x = 9$

62. $x = 6$

63. $y = -9$

64. $y = -4$

65. *Surveying.* Tucked between two ski areas, Vermont Route 108 rises 106 m over a horizontal distance of 1325 m. What is the grade of the road?

66. *Navigation.* Capital Rapids drops 54 ft vertically over a horizontal distance of 1080 ft. What is the slope of the rapids?

67. *Architecture.* To meet federal standards, a wheelchair ramp cannot rise more than 1 ft over a horizontal distance of 12 ft. Express this slope as a grade.

68. *Engineering.* At one point, Yellowstone's Beartooth Highway rises 315 ft over a horizontal distance of 4500 ft. Find the grade of the road.

69. *Carpentry.* Find the slope (or pitch) of the roof.

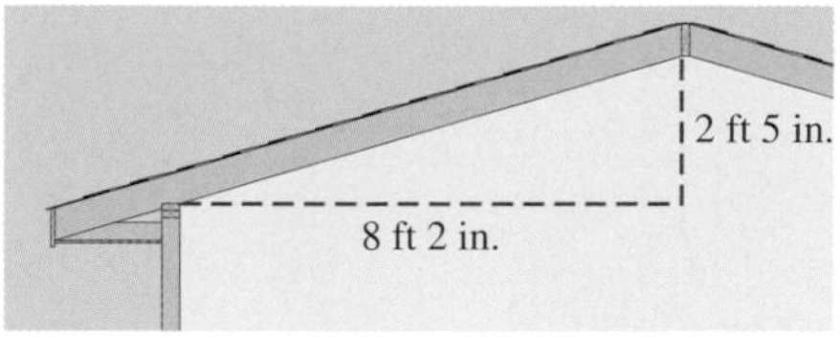

70. *Exercise.* Find the slope (or grade) of the treadmill.

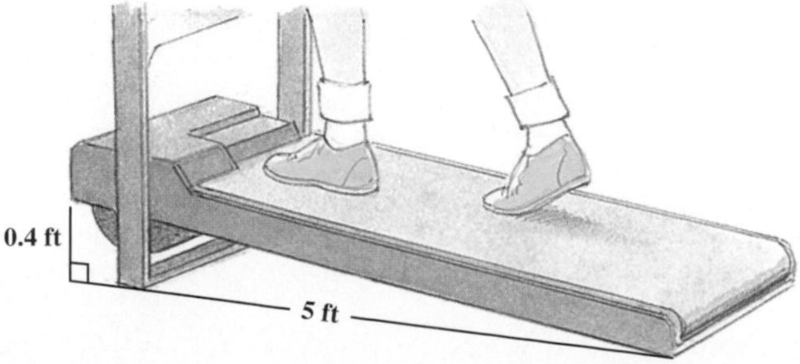

71. *Surveying.* From a base elevation of 9600 ft, Longs Peak, Colorado, rises to a summit elevation of 14,255 ft over a horizontal distance of 15,840 ft. Find the average grade of Longs Peak.

72. *Construction.* Public buildings regularly include steps with 7-in. risers and 11-in. treads. Find the grade of such a stairway.

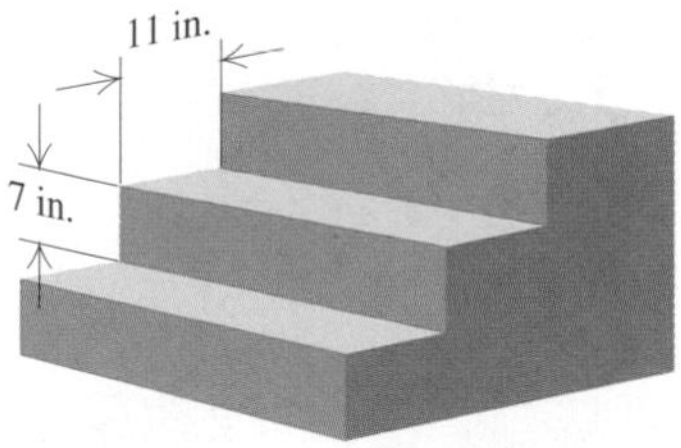

73. Explain why the order in which coordinates are subtracted to find slope does not matter so long as y-coordinates and x-coordinates are subtracted in the same order.

74. If one line has a slope of -3 and another has a slope of 2, which line is steeper? Why?

SKILL MAINTENANCE

Solve. [2.3]

75. $ax + by = c$, for y

76. $rx - mn = p$, for r

77. $ax - by = c$, for y

78. $rs + nt = q$, for t

Evaluate. [1.8]

79. $\frac{2}{3}x - 5$, for $x = 12$

80. $\frac{3}{5}x - 7$, for $x = 15$

SYNTHESIS

81. The points $(-4, -3)$, $(1, 4)$, $(4, 2)$, and $(-1, -5)$ are vertices of a quadrilateral. Use slopes to explain why the quadrilateral is a parallelogram.

82. Which is steeper and why: a ski slope that is 50° or one with a grade of 100%?

83. The plans below are for a skateboard "Fun Box". For the ramps labeled A, find the slope or grade.
Source: www.heckler.com

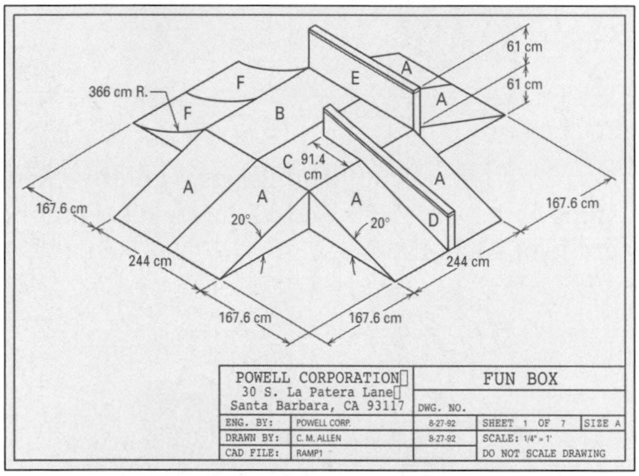

84. A line passes through $(4, -7)$ and never enters the first quadrant. What numbers could the line have for its slope?

85. A line passes through $(2, 5)$ and never enters the second quadrant. What numbers could the line have for its slope?

86. *Architecture.* Architects often use the equation $x + y = 18$ to determine the height y, in inches, of the riser of a step when the tread is x inches wide. Express the slope of stairs designed with this equation without using the variable y.

In Exercises 87 and 88, the slope of the line is $-\frac{2}{3}$, *but the numbering on one axis is missing. How many units should each tick mark on that unnumbered axis represent?*

87.

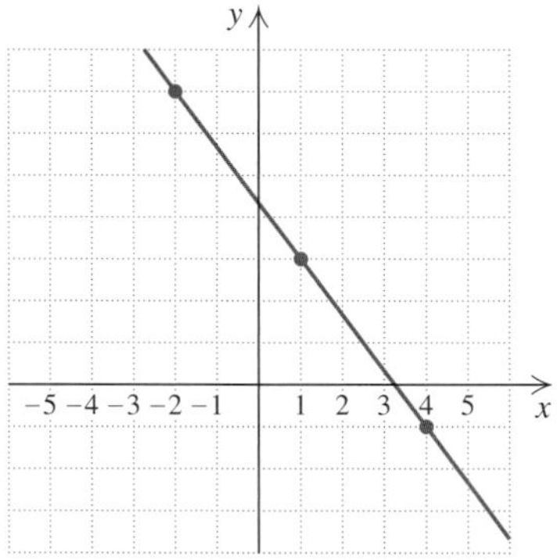

88.

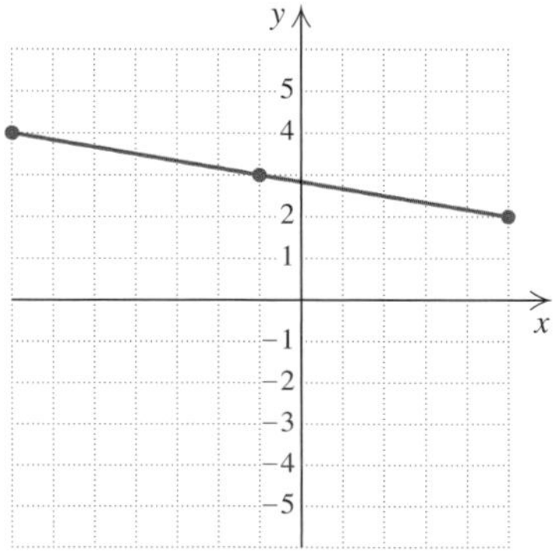

3.6 Slope–Intercept Form

Using the y-intercept and the Slope to Graph a Line • Equations in Slope–Intercept Form • Graphing and Slope–Intercept Form

CONNECTING THE CONCEPTS

In Chapters 1 and 2, we simplified expressions and solved equations. In Sections 3.1–3.3 of this chapter, we learned how a graph can be used to represent the solutions of an equation in two variables, like $y = 4 - x$ or $2x + 5y = 15$.

Graphs are used in many important applications. Sections 3.4 and 3.5 have shown us that the slope of a line can be used to represent the rate at which the quantity measured on the vertical axis changes with respect to the quantity measured on the horizontal axis.

In Section 3.6, we return to the task of graphing equations. This time, however, our understanding of rates and slope will provide us with the tools necessary to develop shortcuts that will streamline our work.

If we know the slope and the y-intercept of a line, it is possible to graph the line. In this section, we will discover that a line's slope and y-intercept can be determined directly from the line's equation, provided the equation is written in a certain form.

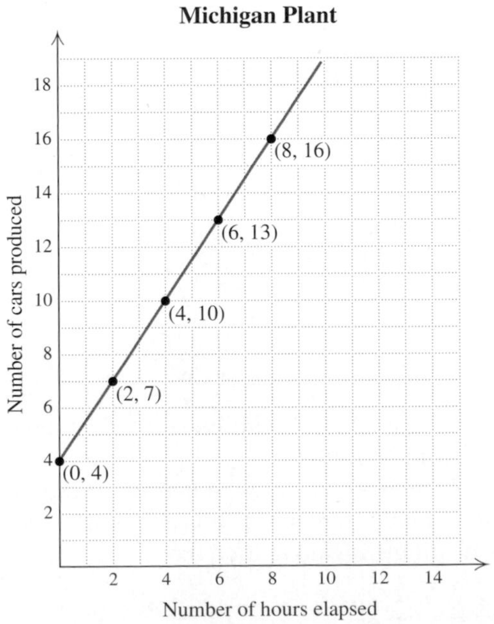

Using the y-intercept and the Slope to Graph a Line

Let's modify the car production situation that first appeared in Section 3.5. Suppose that as a new workshift begins, 4 cars have already been produced. At the Michigan plant, 3 cars were being produced every 2 hours, a rate of $\frac{3}{2}$ cars per hour. If this rate remains the same regardless of how many cars have already been produced, the table and graph shown here can be made.

Michigan Plant	
Hours Elapsed	**Cars Produced**
0	4
2	7
4	10
6	13
8	16

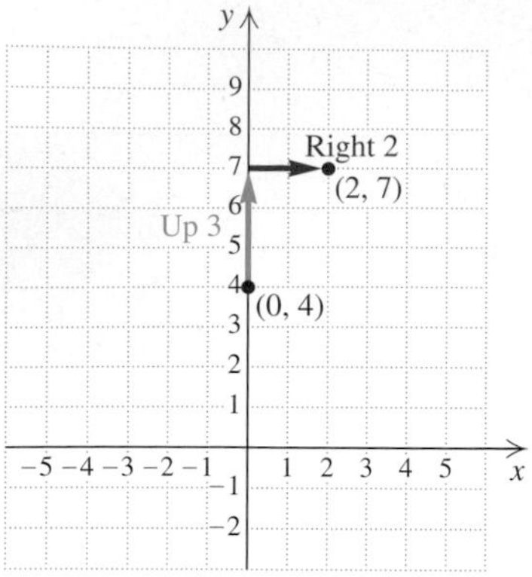

To confirm that the production rate is still $\frac{3}{2}$, we calculate the slope. Recall that

$$\text{Slope} = \frac{\text{change in } y}{\text{change in } x} = \frac{\text{rise}}{\text{run}} = \frac{y_2 - y_1}{x_2 - x_1},$$

where (x_1, y_1) and (x_2, y_2) are any two points on the graphed line. Here we select (0, 4) and (2, 7):

$$\text{Slope} = \frac{\text{change in } y}{\text{change in } x} = \frac{7 - 4}{2 - 0} = \frac{3}{2}.$$

Knowing that the slope is $\frac{3}{2}$, we could have drawn the graph by plotting (0, 4) and from there moving *up* 3 units and *to the right* 2 units. This would have located the point (2, 7). Using (0, 4) and (2, 7), we can then draw the line. This is the method used in the next example.

EXAMPLE 1 Draw a line that has slope $\frac{1}{4}$ and y-intercept (0, 2).

Solution We plot (0, 2) and from there move *up* 1 unit and *to the right* 4 units. This locates the point (4, 3). We plot (4, 3) and draw a line passing through (0, 2) and (4, 3), as shown on the right below.

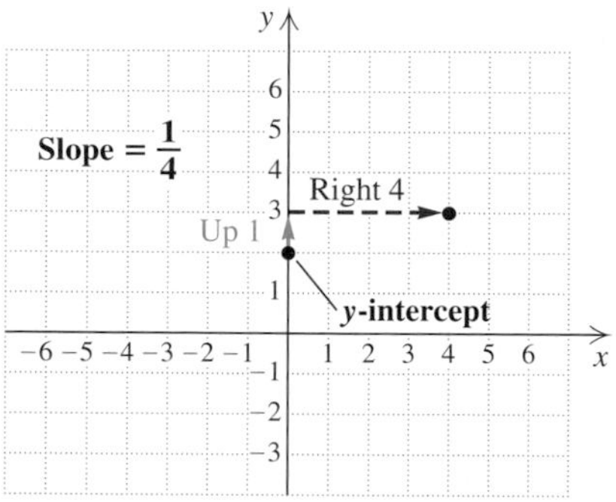

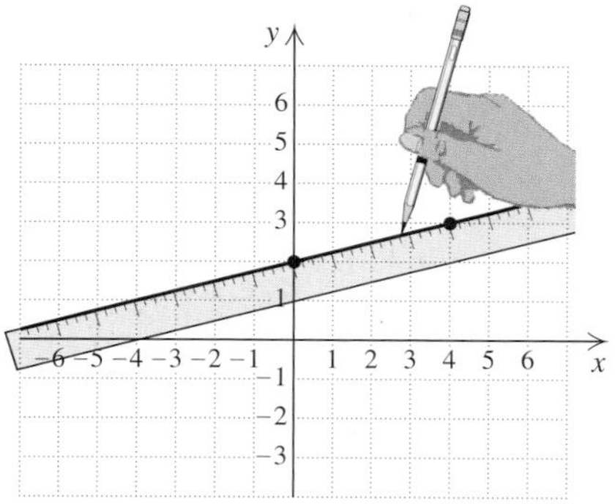

Study Skills

When One Just Isn't Enough

When an exercise gives you difficulty, it is usually wise to practice solving some other exercises that are very similar to the one that gave you trouble. Usually, if the troubling exercise is odd-numbered, the next (even-numbered) exercise is quite similar. Checking the Chapter Review and Test for similar problems is also a good idea.

Equations in Slope–Intercept Form

It is not difficult to find the slope and the y-intercept of a line from its equation. Recall from Section 3.3 that to find the y-intercept of an equation's graph, we replace x with 0 and solve the resulting equation for y. For example, to find the y-intercept of the graph of $y = 2x + 3$, we replace x with 0 and solve as follows:

$$y = 2x + 3$$
$$= 2 \cdot 0 + 3 = 0 + 3 = 3. \qquad \text{The } y\text{-intercept is } (0, 3).$$

The y-intercept of the graph of $y = 2x + 3$ is $(0, 3)$. It can be similarly shown that the graph of $y = mx + b$ has the y-intercept $(0, b)$.

To calculate the slope of the graph of $y = 2x + 3$, we need two ordered pairs that are solutions of the equation. The y-intercept (0, 3) is one pair; a second pair, (1, 5), can be found by substituting 1 for x. We then have

$$\text{Slope} = \frac{\text{change in } y}{\text{change in } x} = \frac{5 - 3}{1 - 0} = \frac{2}{1} = 2.$$

Note that the slope, 2, is also the x-coefficient in $y = 2x + 3$. It can be similarly shown that the graph of any equation of the form $y = mx + b$ has slope m (see Exercise 75).

The Slope–Intercept Equation

The equation $y = mx + b$ is called the *slope–intercept equation.* The equation represents a line of slope m with y-intercept $(0, b)$.

The equation of any nonvertical line can be written in this form.

EXAMPLE 2 Find the slope and the y-intercept of each line whose equation is given.

a) $y = \frac{4}{5}x - 8$

b) $2x + y = 5$

c) $3x - 4y = 7$

Solution

a) We rewrite $y = \frac{4}{5}x - 8$ as $y = \frac{4}{5}x + (-8)$. Now we simply read the slope and the y-intercept from the equation:

$$y = \frac{4}{5}x + (-8).$$

The slope is $\frac{4}{5}$. The y-intercept is $(0, -8)$.

b) We first solve for y to find an equivalent equation in the form $y = mx + b$:

$$2x + y = 5$$

$$y = -2x + 5. \qquad \text{Adding } -2x \text{ to both sides}$$

The slope is -2. The y-intercept is $(0, 5)$.

c) We rewrite the equation in the form $y = mx + b$:

$$3x - 4y = 7$$

$$-4y = -3x + 7 \qquad \text{Adding } -3x \text{ to both sides}$$

$$y = -\frac{1}{4}(-3x + 7) \qquad \text{Multiplying both sides by } -\frac{1}{4}$$

$$y = \frac{3}{4}x - \frac{7}{4}. \qquad \text{Using the distributive law}$$

The slope is $\frac{3}{4}$. The y-intercept is $\left(0, -\frac{7}{4}\right)$.

EXAMPLE 3 A line has slope $-\frac{12}{5}$ and y-intercept $(0, 11)$. Find an equation of the line.

Solution We use the slope–intercept equation, substituting $-\frac{12}{5}$ for m and 11 for b:

$$y = mx + b = -\frac{12}{5}x + 11.$$

The desired equation is $y = -\frac{12}{5}x + 11$.

EXAMPLE 4 Determine an equation for the graph shown at left (*Source*: Based on information from The Kaiser Family Foundation; Health Research and Education Trust, reported in *The Daily Reporter*, Greenfield IN, 9/9/03).

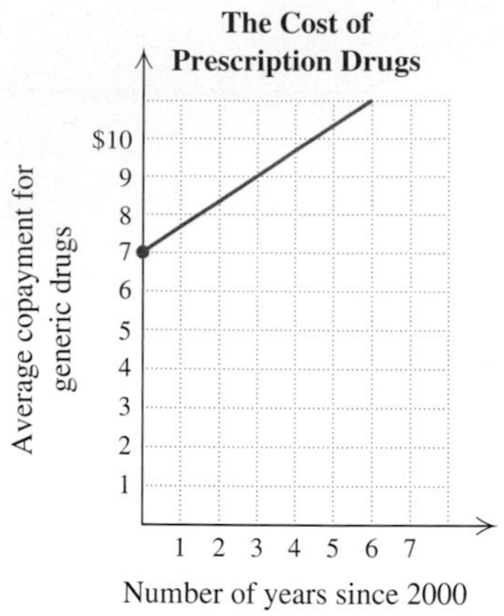

Solution To write an equation for a line, we can use slope–intercept form, provided the slope and the y-intercept are known. From the graph, we see that $(0, 7)$ is the y-intercept. Looking closely, we see that the line passes through $(3, 9)$. We can either count squares on the graph or use the formula to calculate the slope:

$$m = \frac{\text{change in } y}{\text{change in } x} = \frac{9 - 7}{3 - 0} = \frac{2}{3}.$$

The desired equation is

$$y = \frac{2}{3}x + 7, \qquad \text{Using } \tfrac{2}{3} \text{ for } m \text{ and 7 for } b$$

where y is the average cost, in dollars, of a copayment for generic drugs x years after 2000.

Graphing and Slope–Intercept Form

In Example 1, we drew a graph, knowing only the slope and the y-intercept. In Example 2, we determined the slope and the y-intercept of a line by examining its equation. We now combine the two procedures to develop a quick way to graph a linear equation.

EXAMPLE 5 Graph: **(a)** $y = \frac{3}{4}x + 5$; **(b)** $2x + 3y = 3$.

Solution

a) From the equation $y = \frac{3}{4}x + 5$, we see that the slope of the graph is $\frac{3}{4}$ and the y-intercept is $(0, 5)$. We plot $(0, 5)$ and then consider the slope, $\frac{3}{4}$. Starting at $(0, 5)$, we plot a second point by moving *up* 3 units (since the numerator is *positive* and corresponds to the change in y) and *to the right* 4 units (since the denominator is *positive* and corresponds to the change in x). We reach a new point, $(4, 8)$.

We can also rewrite the slope as $\frac{-3}{-4}$. We again start at the y-intercept, $(0, 5)$, but move *down* 3 units (since the numerator is *negative* and corresponds to the change in y) and *to the left* 4 units (since the denominator is *negative* and corresponds to the change in x). We reach another point, $(-4, 2)$. Once two or three points have been plotted, the line representing all solutions of $y = \frac{3}{4}x + 5$ can be drawn.

Student Notes

Graphing an equation in slope–intercept form can be done rather easily. First, identify and plot the y-intercept. Then identify the slope and use the slope to plot a second point. Finally, use a straightedge to draw a line passing through the two points.

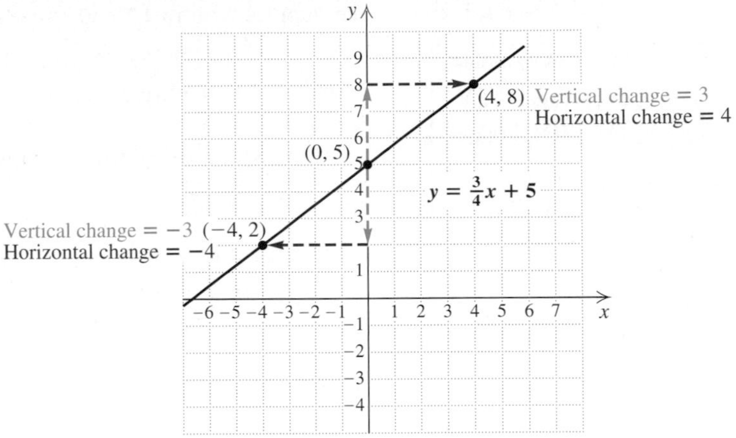

b) To graph $2x + 3y = 3$, we first rewrite it in slope–intercept form:

$2x + 3y = 3$	
$3y = -2x + 3$	Adding $-2x$ to both sides
$y = \frac{1}{3}(-2x + 3)$	Multiplying both sides by $\frac{1}{3}$
$y = -\frac{2}{3}x + 1.$	Using the distributive law

To graph $y = -\frac{2}{3}x + 1$, we first plot the y-intercept, $(0, 1)$. We can think of the slope as $\frac{-2}{3}$. Starting at $(0, 1)$ and using the slope, we find a second point by moving *down* 2 units (since the numerator is *negative*) and *to the right* 3 units (since the denominator is *positive*). We plot the new point, $(3, -1)$. In a similar manner, we can move from the point $(3, -1)$ to locate a third point, $(6, -3)$. The line can then be drawn.

Since $-\frac{2}{3} = \frac{2}{-3}$, an alternative approach is to again plot $(0, 1)$, but this time move *up* 2 units (since the numerator is *positive*) and *to the left* 3 units (since the denominator is *negative*). This leads to another point on the graph, $(-3, 3)$.

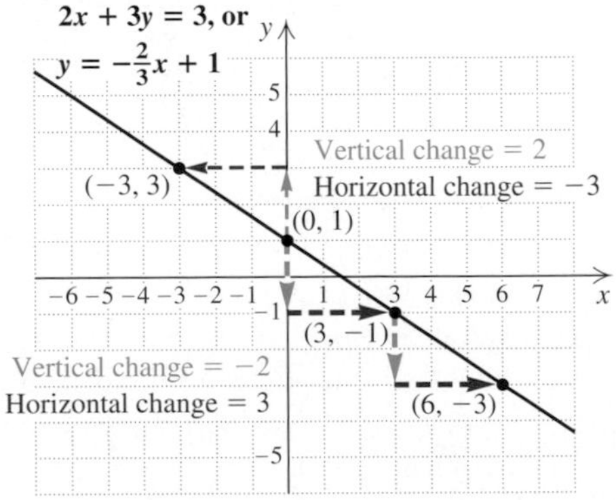

It is important to be able to use both $\frac{2}{-3}$ and $\frac{-2}{3}$ to draw the graph.

Slope–intercept form allows us to quickly determine the slope of a line by simply inspecting its equation. This can be especially helpful when attempting to decide whether two lines are parallel.

EXAMPLE 6 Determine whether the graphs of $y = -3x + 4$ and $6x + 2y = -10$ are parallel.

Solution Recall that *parallel* lines extend indefinitely without intersecting. Thus, when two lines have the same slope but different y-intercepts, they are parallel.

One of the two equations given,

$$y = -3x + 4,$$

represents a line with slope -3 and y-intercept $(0, 4)$. To find the slope of the other line, we need to rewrite

$$6x + 2y = -10$$

in slope–intercept form:

$$6x + 2y = -10$$
$$2y = -6x - 10 \qquad \text{Adding } -6x \text{ to both sides}$$
$$y = -3x - 5. \qquad \text{The slope is } -3 \text{ and the } y\text{-intercept is } (0, -5).$$

Since both lines have slope -3 but different y-intercepts, the graphs are parallel. There is no need for us to actually graph either equation.

---

technology connection

Using a standard $[-10, 10, -10, 10]$ window, graph the equations $y_1 = \frac{2}{3}x + 1$, $y_2 = \frac{3}{8}x + 1$, $y_3 = \frac{2}{3}x + 5$, and $y_4 = \frac{3}{8}x + 5$. If you can, use your graphing calculator in the MODE that graphs equations *simultaneously*. Once all lines have been drawn, try to decide which equation corresponds to each line. After matching equations with lines, you can check your matches by using TRACE and the up and down arrow keys to move from one line to the next. The number of the equation will appear in a corner of the screen.

1. Graph $y_1 = -\frac{3}{4}x - 2$, $y_2 = -\frac{1}{5}x - 2$, $y_3 = -\frac{3}{4}x - 5$, and $y_4 = -\frac{1}{5}x - 5$ using the SIMULTANEOUS mode. Then match each line with the corresponding equation. Check using TRACE.

3.6 Exercise Set

FOR EXTRA HELP

Student's Solutions Manual | Digital Video Tutor CD 2 Videotape 6 | AW Math Tutor Center | MathXL Tutorials on CD | MathXL | MyMathLab

Concept Reinforcement *In each of Exercises 1–6, match the phrase with the most appropriate choice from the column on the right.*

1. ____ The y-intercept of the graph of $y = 2x - 3$
2. ____ The y-intercept of the graph of $y = 3x - 2$
3. ____ The slope of the graph of $y = 3x - 2$
4. ____ The slope of the graph of $y = 2x - 3$
5. ____ The slope of the graph of $y = \frac{2}{3}x + 3$
6. ____ The y-intercept of the graph of $y = \frac{2}{3}x + \frac{3}{4}$

a) $(0, \frac{3}{4})$
b) 2
c) $(0, -3)$
d) $\frac{2}{3}$
e) $(0, -2)$
f) 3

Draw a line that has the given slope and y-intercept.

7. Slope $\frac{2}{5}$; y-intercept $(0, 1)$

8. Slope $\frac{3}{5}$; y-intercept $(0, -1)$

9. Slope $\frac{5}{3}$; y-intercept $(0, -2)$

10. Slope $\frac{5}{2}$; y-intercept $(0, 1)$

11. Slope $-\frac{3}{4}$; y-intercept $(0, 5)$

12. Slope $-\frac{4}{5}$; y-intercept $(0, 6)$

13. Slope 2; y-intercept $(0, -4)$

14. Slope -2; y-intercept $(0, -3)$

15. Slope -3; y-intercept $(0, 2)$

16. Slope 3; y-intercept $(0, 4)$

Find the slope and the y-intercept of each line whose equation is given.

17. $y = -\frac{2}{7}x + 5$

18. $y = -\frac{3}{8}x + 4$

19. $y = \frac{5}{8}x + 3$

20. $y = \frac{4}{5}x + 1$

21. $y = \frac{9}{5}x - 4$

22. $y = \frac{7}{4}x - 5$

23. $-3x + y = 7$

24. $-4x + y = 7$

25. $5x + 2y = 8$

26. $3x + 4y = 12$

Aha! **27.** $y = 4$

28. $y - 3 = 5$

29. $2x - 5y = -8$

30. $5x - 6y = 9$

Find the slope–intercept equation for the line with the indicated slope and y-intercept.

31. Slope 3; y-intercept $(0, 7)$

32. Slope -4; y-intercept $(0, -2)$

33. Slope $\frac{7}{8}$; y-intercept $(0, -1)$

34. Slope $\frac{5}{7}$; y-intercept $(0, 4)$

35. Slope $-\frac{5}{3}$; y-intercept $(0, -8)$

36. Slope $\frac{3}{4}$; y-intercept $(0, 23)$

Aha! **37.** Slope 0; y-intercept $(0, 3)$

38. Slope 7; y-intercept $(0, 0)$

Determine an equation for each graph shown.

39.

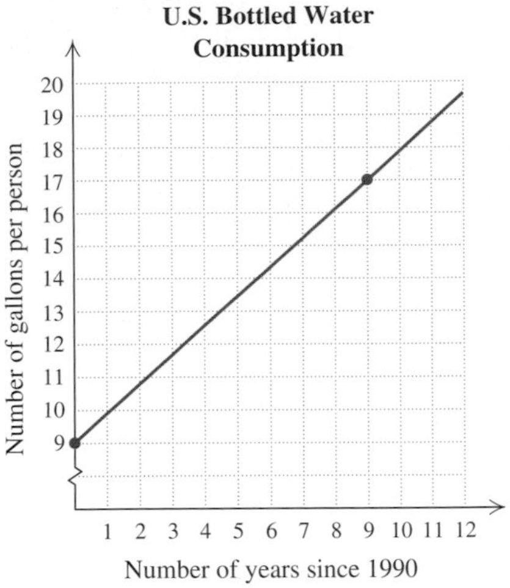

Based on information from the International Bottled Water Association 2002

40.

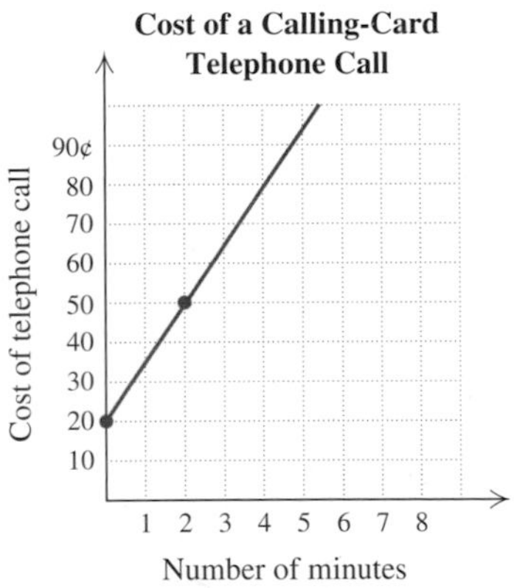

41.

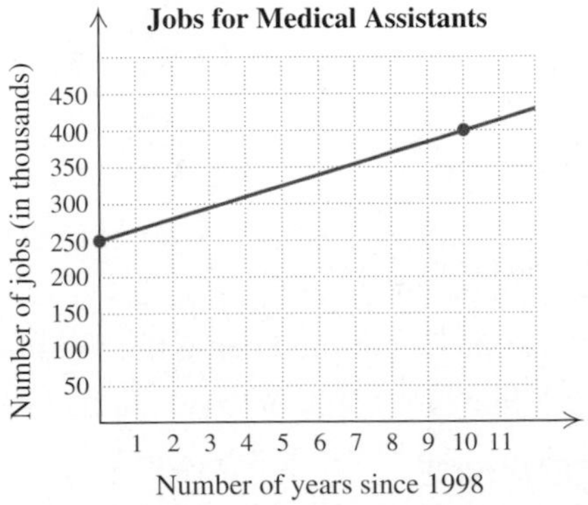

Estimates based on information from *Handbook of U.S. Labor*

42.

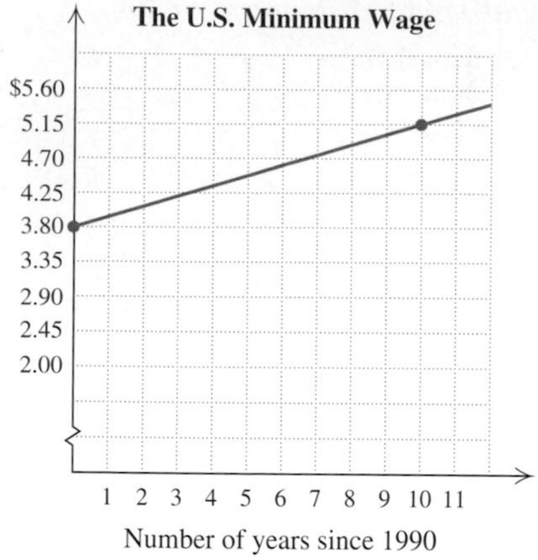

Based on information from United for a Fair Economy

Graph.

43. $y = \frac{3}{5}x + 2$

44. $y = -\frac{3}{5}x - 1$

45. $y = -\frac{3}{5}x + 1$

46. $y = \frac{3}{5}x - 2$

47. $y = \frac{5}{3}x + 3$

48. $y = \frac{5}{3}x - 2$

49. $y = -\frac{3}{2}x - 2$

50. $y = -\frac{4}{3}x + 3$

51. $2x + y = 1$

52. $3x + y = 2$

53. $3x + y = 0$

54. $2x + y = 0$

55. $2x + 3y = 9$

56. $4x + 5y = 15$

57. $x - 4y = 12$

58. $x + 5y = 20$

Determine whether each pair of equations represents parallel lines.

59. $y = \frac{2}{3}x + 7,$
$y = \frac{2}{3}x - 5$

60. $y = -\frac{5}{4}x + 1,$
$y = \frac{5}{4}x + 3$

61. $y = 2x - 5,$
$4x + 2y = 9$

62. $y = -3x + 1,$
$6x + 2y = 8$

63. $3x + 4y = 8,$
$7 - 12y = 9x$

64. $3x = 5y - 2,$
$10y = 4 - 6x$

65. Can a horizontal line be graphed using the method of Example 5? Why or why not?

66. Can a vertical line be graphed using the method of Example 5? Why or why not?

SKILL MAINTENANCE

Solve. [2.3]

67. $y - k = m(x - h)$, for y

68. $y - 9 = -2(x + 4)$, for y

Simplify. [1.6]

69. $-5 - (-7)$

70. $7 - (-9)$

71. $-3 - 6$

72. $-2 - 8$

SYNTHESIS

73. Explain how it is possible for an incorrect graph to be drawn, even after plotting three points that line up.

74. Which would you prefer, and why: graphing an equation of the form $y = mx + b$ or graphing an equation of the form $Ax + By = C$?

75. Show that the slope of the line given by $y = mx + b$ is m. (*Hint*: Substitute both 0 and 1 for x to find two pairs of coordinates. Then use the formula, Slope = change in y/change in x.)

76. Write an equation of the line with the same slope as the line given by $5x + 2y = 8$ and the same y-intercept as the line given by $3x - 7y = 10$.

77. Write an equation of the line parallel to the line given by $2x - 6y = 10$ and having the same y-intercept as the line given by $9x + 6y = 18$.

78. Write an equation of the line parallel to the line given by $3x - 2y = 8$ and having the same y-intercept as the line given by $2y + 3x = -4$.

79. Write an equation of the line parallel to the line given by $4x + 5y = 9$ and having the same y-intercept as the line given by $2x + 3y = 12$.

80. Write an equation of the line parallel to the line given by $2x + 7y = 10$ and having the same y-intercept as the line given by $3x - 5y = 4$.

81. Write an equation of the line parallel to the line given by $-4x + 8y = 5$ and having the same y-intercept as the line given by $4x - 3y = 0$.

Two lines are perpendicular if either the product of their slopes is -1, or one line is vertical and the other horizontal. For Exercises 82–87, determine whether each pair of equations represents perpendicular lines.

82. $3y = 5x - 3,$
$3x + 5y = 10$

83. $y + 3x = 10,$
$2x - 6y = 18$

84. $3x + 5y = 10,$
$15x + 9y = 18$

85. $10 - 4y = 7x,$
$7y + 21 = 4x$

86. $x = 5,$
$y = \frac{1}{2}$

87. $y = -2x,$
$x = \frac{1}{2}$

88. Write an equation of the line perpendicular to the line given by $3x - 5y = 8$ (see Exercises 82–87) and having the same y-intercept as the line given by $2x + 4y = 12$.

89. Write an equation of the line perpendicular to the line given by $2x + 3y = 7$ (see Exercises 82–87) and having the same y-intercept as the line given by $5x + 2y = 10$.

90. Write an equation of the line perpendicular to the line given by $3x - 2y = 9$ (see Exercises 82–87) and having the same y-intercept as the line given by $2x + 5y = 0$.

91. Write an equation of the line perpendicular to the line given by $2x + 5y = 6$ (see Exercises 82–87) that passes through (2, 6). (*Hint*: Draw a graph.)

92. *Aerobic exercise.* The formula $T = -\frac{3}{4}a + 165$ can be used to determine the *target heart rate,* in beats per minute, for a person, a years old, participating in aerobic exercise. Graph the equation and interpret the significance of its slope.

3.7 Point–Slope Form

Writing Equations in Point–Slope Form • Graphing and Point–Slope Form • Estimations and Predictions Using Two Points

There are many applications in which a slope—or a rate of change—and an ordered pair are known. When the ordered pair is the y-intercept, an equation in slope–intercept form can be easily produced. When the ordered pair represents a point other than the y-intercept, a different form, known as *point–slope form,* is more convenient.

Writing Equations in Point–Slope Form

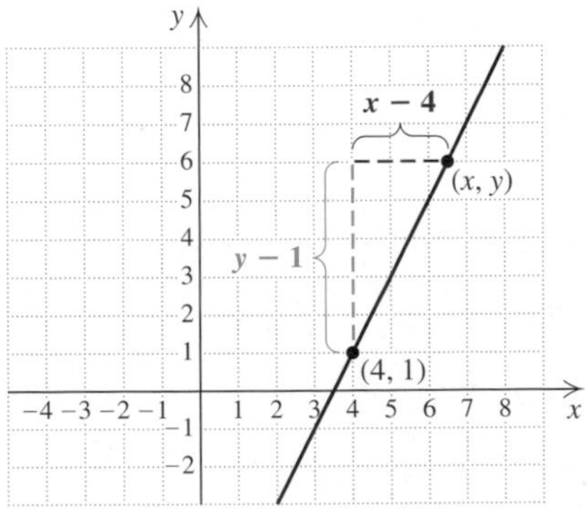

Consider a line with slope 2 passing through the point (4, 1), as shown in the figure. In order for a point (x, y) to be on the line, the coordinates x and y must be solutions of the slope equation

$$\frac{y - 1}{x - 4} = 2.$$

Take a moment to examine this equation. Pairs like (5, 3) and (3, −1) are solutions, since

$$\frac{3 - 1}{5 - 4} = 2 \quad \text{and} \quad \frac{-1 - 1}{3 - 4} = 2.$$

Note, however, that (4, 1) is not itself a solution of the equation:

$$\frac{1 - 1}{4 - 4} \neq 2.$$

To avoid this difficulty, we can use the multiplication principle:

$$(x-4)\cdot\frac{y-1}{x-4} = 2(x-4) \qquad \text{Multiplying both sides by } x-4$$

$$y-1 = 2(x-4). \qquad \text{Removing a factor equal to 1: } \frac{x-4}{x-4}=1$$

This is considered **point–slope form** for the line shown on the preceding page. A point–slope equation can be written any time a line's slope and a point on the line are known.

The Point–Slope Equation

The equation $y - y_1 = m(x - x_1)$ is called the *point–slope equation* for the line with slope m that contains the point (x_1, y_1).

Point–slope form is especially useful in more advanced mathematics courses, where problems similar to the following often arise.

EXAMPLE 1 Write a point–slope equation for the line with slope $\frac{1}{5}$ that contains the point (7, 2).

Solution We substitute $\frac{1}{5}$ for m, 7 for x_1, and 2 for y_1:

$$y - y_1 = m(x - x_1) \qquad \text{Using the point–slope equation}$$

$$y - 2 = \tfrac{1}{5}(x - 7) \qquad \text{Substituting}$$

EXAMPLE 2 Write a point–slope equation for the line with slope $-\frac{4}{3}$ that contains the point $(1, -6)$.

Solution We substitute $-\frac{4}{3}$ for m, 1 for x_1, and -6 for y_1:

$$y - y_1 = m(x - x_1) \qquad \text{Using the point–slope equation}$$

$$y - (-6) = -\tfrac{4}{3}(x - 1). \qquad \text{Substituting}$$

EXAMPLE 3 Write the slope–intercept equation for the line with slope 2 that contains the point (3, 1).

Solution There are two parts to this solution. First, we write an equation in point–slope form:

$$y - y_1 = m(x - x_1)$$

$$y - 1 = 2(x - 3). \qquad \text{Substituting}$$

Next, we find an equivalent equation of the form $y = mx + b$:

$$y - 1 = 2(x - 3)$$

$$y - 1 = 2x - 6 \qquad \text{Using the distributive law}$$

$$y = 2x - 5. \qquad \text{Adding 1 to both sides to get slope–intercept form}$$

Student Notes

There are several forms in which a line's equation can be written. For instance, as shown in Example 3, $y - 1 = 2(x - 3)$, $y - 1 = 2x - 6$, and $y = 2x - 5$ all are equations for the same line.

Graphing and Point–Slope Form

When we know a line's slope and a point that is on the line, we can draw the graph, much as we did in Section 3.6. For example, the information given in the statement of Example 3 is sufficient for drawing a graph.

EXAMPLE 4 Graph the line with slope 2 that passes through (3, 1).

Solution We plot (3, 1), move *up* 2 and *to the right* 1 (since $2 = \frac{2}{1}$), and draw the line.

Study Skills

Understand Your Mistakes

When you receive a graded quiz, test, or assignment back from your instructor, it is important to review and understand what your mistakes were. Too often students simply file away old papers without first making an effort to learn from their mistakes.

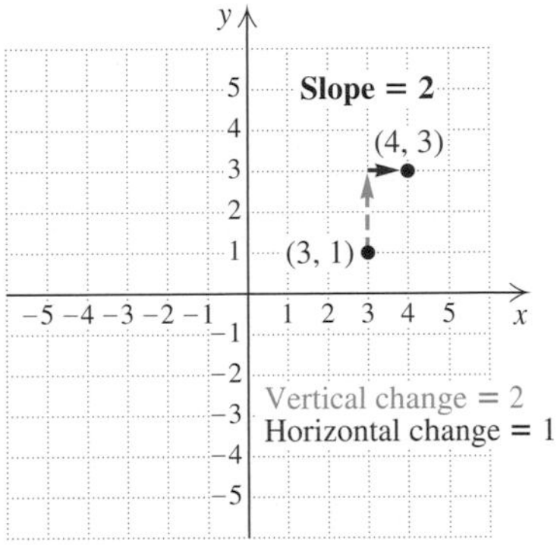

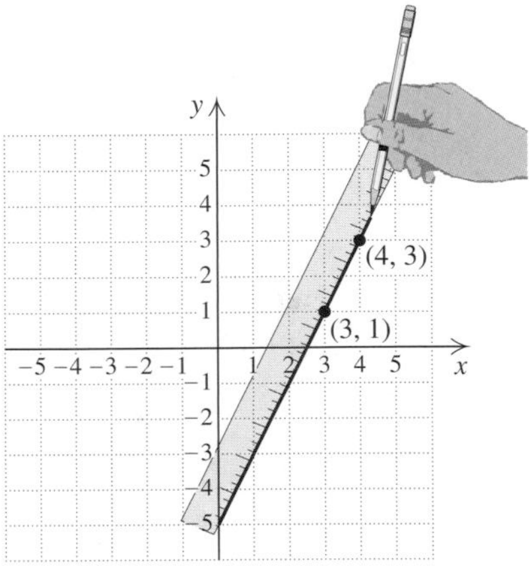

EXAMPLE 5 Graph: $y - 2 = 3(x - 4)$.

Solution Since $y - 2 = 3(x - 4)$ is in point–slope form, we know that the line has slope 3, or $\frac{3}{1}$, and passes through the point (4, 2). We plot (4, 2) and then find a second point by moving *up* 3 units and *to the right* 1 unit. The line can then be drawn, as shown below.

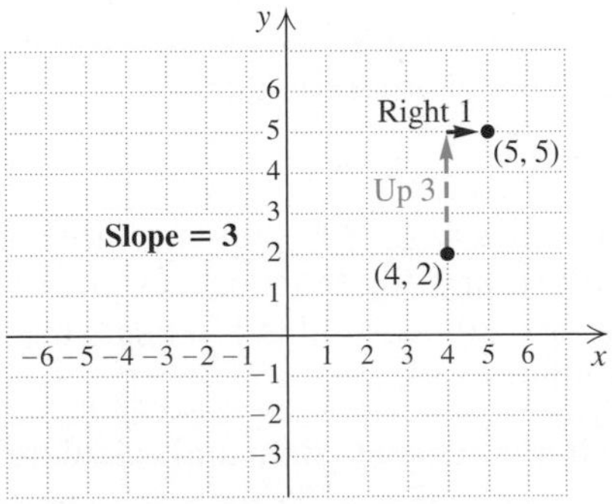

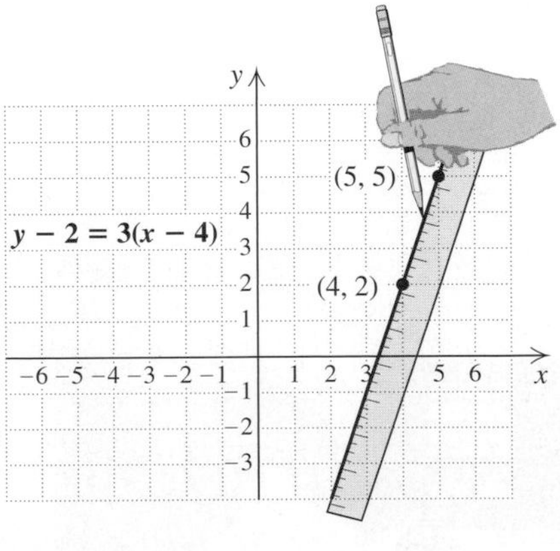

EXAMPLE 6 Graph: $y + 4 = -\frac{5}{2}(x + 3)$.

Solution Once we have written the equation in point–slope form, $y - y_1 = m(x - x_1)$, we can proceed much as we did in Example 5. To find an equivalent equation in point–slope form, we subtract opposites instead of adding:

$$y + 4 = -\tfrac{5}{2}(x + 3)$$

$$y - (-4) = -\tfrac{5}{2}(x - (-3)).$$ Subtracting a negative instead of adding a positive. This is now in point–slope form.

From this last equation, $y - (-4) = -\frac{5}{2}(x - (-3))$, we see that the line passes through $(-3, -4)$ and has slope $-\frac{5}{2}$, or $\frac{5}{-2}$.

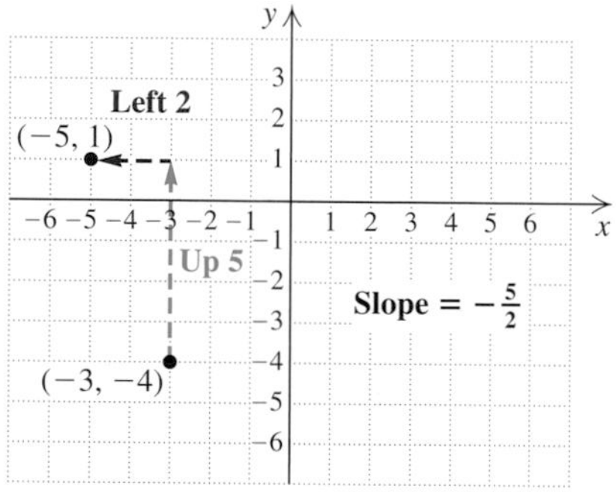

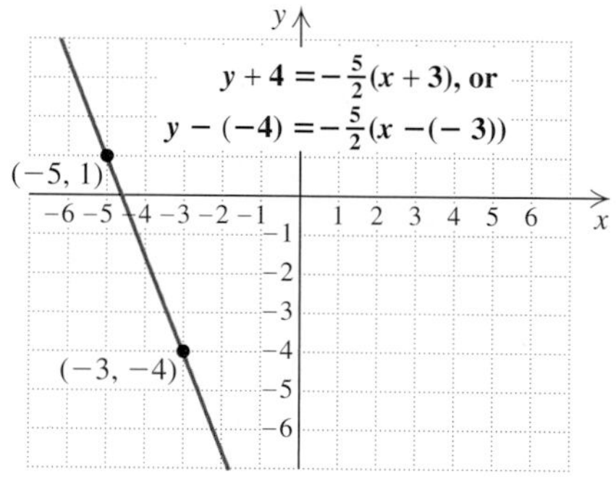

Estimations and Predictions Using Two Points

It is possible to use line graphs to estimate real-life quantities that are not already known. To do so, we calculate the coordinates of an unknown point by using two points with known coordinates. When the unknown point is located *between* the two points, this process is called **interpolation**.* Sometimes a graph passing through the known points is *extended* to predict future values. Making predictions in this manner is called **extrapolation**.* In statistics, methods exist for using a set of several points to interpolate or extrapolate values using curves other than lines.

EXAMPLE 7

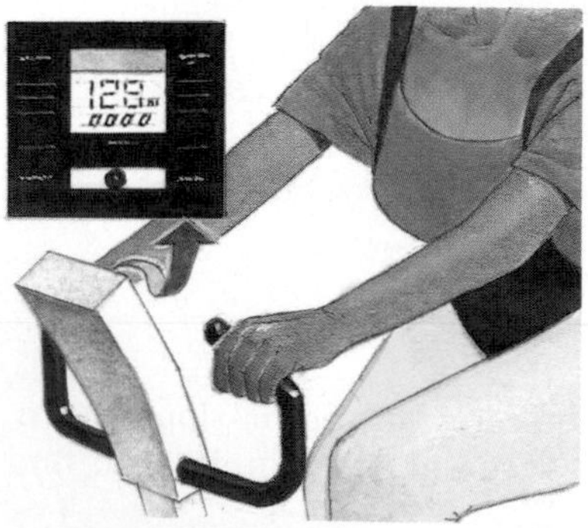

Aerobic exercise. A person's target heart rate is the number of beats per minute that bring the most aerobic benefit to his or her heart. The target heart rate for a 20-year-old is 150 beats per minute and for a 60-year-old, 120 beats per minute.

a) Graph the given data and calculate the target heart rate for a 36-year-old.

b) Calculate the target heart rate for a 75-year-old.

*Both interpolation and extrapolation can be performed using more than two known points and using curves other than lines.

Solution

a) We first draw a horizontal axis for "Age" and a vertical axis for "Target heart rate." Next, we number the axes, using a scale that will permit us to view both the given and the desired data. The given information allows us to then plot (20, 150) and (60, 120).

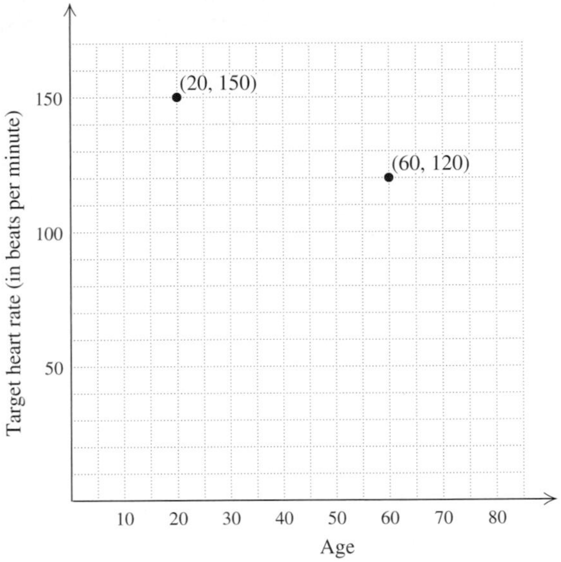

Next, we draw a line passing through both points. The slope of the line is given by

$$m = \frac{\text{change in } y}{\text{change in } x} = \frac{150 - 120 \text{ beats per minute}}{20 - 60 \text{ years}}$$

$$= \frac{30 \text{ beats per minute}}{-40 \text{ years}} = -\frac{3}{4} \text{beats per minute per year.}$$

The target heart rate drops at a rate of $\frac{3}{4}$ beat per minute for each year that we age. We can use either of the given points to write a point–slope equation for the line. Let's use (20, 150) and then use algebra to write an equivalent equation in slope–intercept form:

$$y - 150 = -\frac{3}{4}(x - 20) \qquad \text{This is a point–slope equation.}$$

$$y - 150 = -\frac{3}{4}x + 15 \qquad \text{Using the distributive law}$$

$$y = -\frac{3}{4}x + 165. \qquad \text{Adding 150 to both sides; this is slope–intercept form.}$$

To calculate the target heart rate for a 36-year-old, we substitute 36 for x in the slope–intercept equation:

$$y = -\frac{3}{4} \cdot 36 + 165 = -27 + 165 = 138.$$

As the graph confirms, the target heart rate for a 36-year-old is about 138 beats per minute.

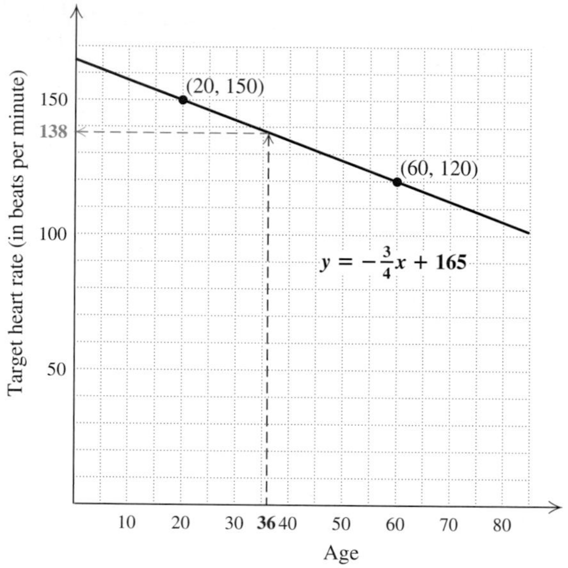

Because 36 is *between* the given values of 20 and 60, we are *interpolating* here.

b) To calculate the target heart rate for a 75-year-old, we again substitute for x in the slope–intercept equation:

$$y = -\frac{3}{4} \cdot 75 + 165 = -56.25 + 165 = 108.75 \approx 109.$$

As the graph confirms, the target heart rate for a 75-year-old is about 109 beats per minute.

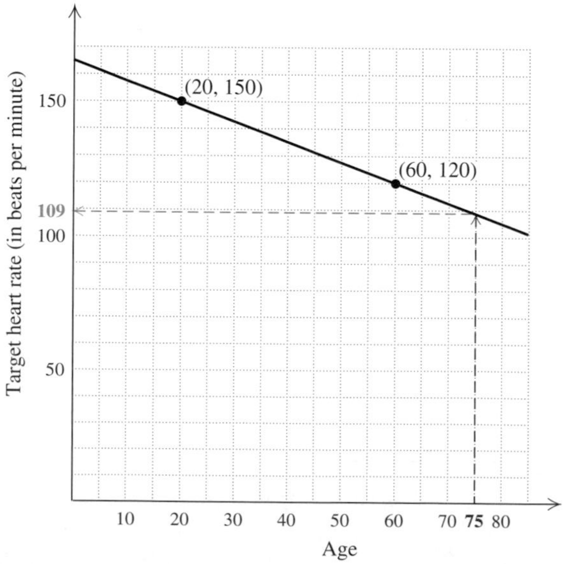

Because 75 is *beyond* the given values, we are *extrapolating* here.

3.7 Exercise Set

FOR EXTRA HELP

Student's Solutions Manual | Digital Video Tutor CD 2 Videotape 6 | AW Math Tutor Center | MathXL Tutorials on CD | MathXL | MyMathLab

Concept Reinforcement *In each of Exercises 1–8, match the given information about a line with the appropriate equation from the column on the right.*

1. ___ Slope 5; includes (2, 3)

2. ___ Slope −5; includes (2, 3)

3. ___ Slope −5; includes (−2, −3)

4. ___ Slope 5; includes (−2, −3)

5. ___ Slope 5; includes (3, 2)

6. ___ Slope −5; includes (3, 2)

7. ___ Slope −5; includes (−3, −2)

8. ___ Slope 5; includes (−3, −2)

a) $y + 3 = 5(x + 2)$

b) $y - 2 = 5(x - 3)$

c) $y + 2 = 5(x + 3)$

d) $y - 3 = -5(x - 2)$

e) $y + 3 = -5(x + 2)$

f) $y + 2 = -5(x + 3)$

g) $y - 3 = 5(x - 2)$

h) $y - 2 = -5(x - 3)$

In each of Exercises 9–12, match the graph with the appropriate equation from the column on the right.

9.

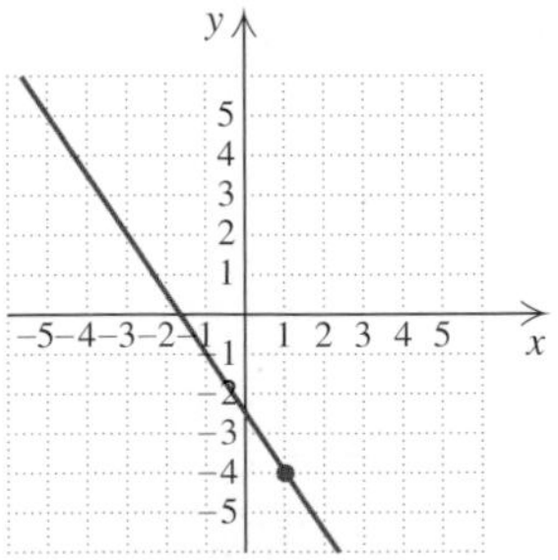

10.

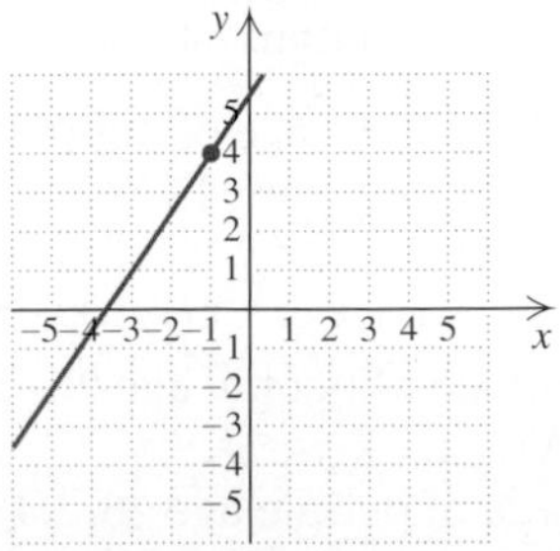

11.

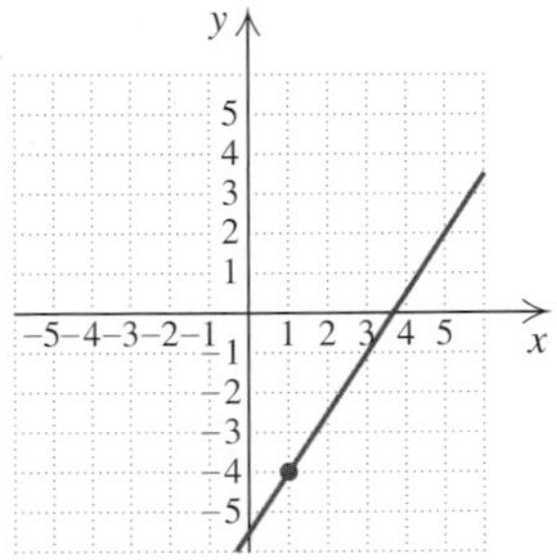

12.

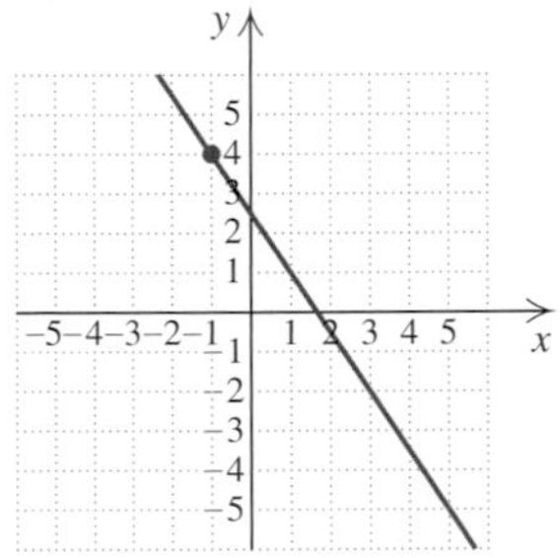

a) $y - 4 = -\frac{3}{2}(x + 1)$

b) $y - 4 = \frac{3}{2}(x + 1)$

c) $y + 4 = -\frac{3}{2}(x - 1)$

d) $y + 4 = \frac{3}{2}(x - 1)$

Write a point–slope equation for the line with the given slope that contains the given point.

13. $m = 5$; (6, 2)

14. $m = 4$; (3, 5)

15. $m = \frac{3}{5}$; (7, 3)

16. $m = \frac{2}{3}$; (4, 1)

17. $m = -4$; (3, 1)

18. $m = -5$; (6, 2)

19. $m = \frac{3}{2}$; (5, −4)

20. $m = \frac{4}{3}$; (7, −1)

21. $m = \frac{5}{4}$; (−2, 6)

22. $m = \frac{7}{2}$; (−3, 4)

23. $m = -2$; (−4, −1)

24. $m = -3$; (−2, −5)

25. $m = 1$; (−2, 8)

26. $m = -1$; (−3, 6)

Write the slope–intercept equation for the line with the given slope that contains the given point.

27. $m = 2$; (5, 7)

28. $m = 3$; (6, 2)

29. $m = \frac{7}{4}$; (4, −2)

30. $m = \frac{8}{3}$; (3, −4)

31. $m = -3$; (−1, 6)

32. $m = -2$; (−1, 3)

33. $m = -4$; (−2, −1)

34. $m = -5$; (−1, −4)

35. $m = \frac{2}{3}$; (6, 5)

36. $m = \frac{3}{2}$; (4, 7)

Aha! **37.** $m = -\frac{5}{6}$; (0, 4)

38. $m = -\frac{3}{4}$; (0, 5)

39. Graph the line with slope $\frac{4}{3}$ that passes through the point (1, 2).

40. Graph the line with slope $\frac{2}{5}$ that passes through the point (3, 4).

41. Graph the line with slope $-\frac{3}{4}$ that passes through the point (2, 5).

42. Graph the line with slope $-\frac{3}{2}$ that passes through the point (1, 4).

Graph.

43. $y - 2 = \frac{1}{2}(x - 1)$

44. $y - 5 = \frac{1}{3}(x - 2)$

45. $y - 1 = -\frac{1}{2}(x - 3)$

46. $y - 1 = -\frac{1}{4}(x - 3)$

47. $y + 2 = \frac{1}{2}(x - 3)$

48. $y - 1 = \frac{1}{3}(x + 5)$

49. $y + 4 = 3(x + 1)$

50. $y + 3 = 2(x + 1)$

51. $y - 4 = -2(x + 1)$

52. $y + 3 = -1(x - 4)$

53. $y + 3 = -(x + 2)$

54. $y + 4 = 3(x + 2)$

55. $y + 1 = -\frac{3}{5}(x + 2)$

56. $y + 2 = -\frac{2}{3}(x + 1)$

In Exercises 57–64, graph the given data and determine an equation for the related line (as in Example 7). Then use the equation to answer parts (a) and (b).

57. *Birth rate among teenagers.* The birth rate among teenagers, measured in births per 1000 females age 15–19, fell steadily from 62.1 in 1991 to 45.9 in 2001.

Source: National Center for Health Statistics; 2001 figure is preliminary.

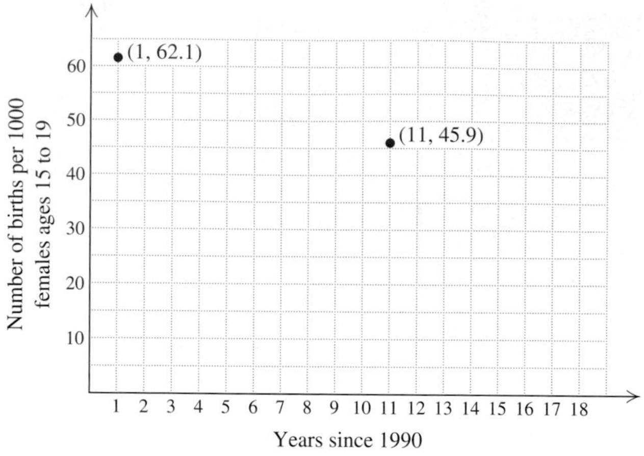

a) Calculate the birth rate among teenagers in 1999.

b) Predict the birth rate among teenagers in 2008.

58. *Food-stamp program participation.* Participation in the U.S. food-stamp program grew from approximately 17.1 million people in 2000 to approximately 19.1 million in 2002.

Source: U.S. Department of Agriculture

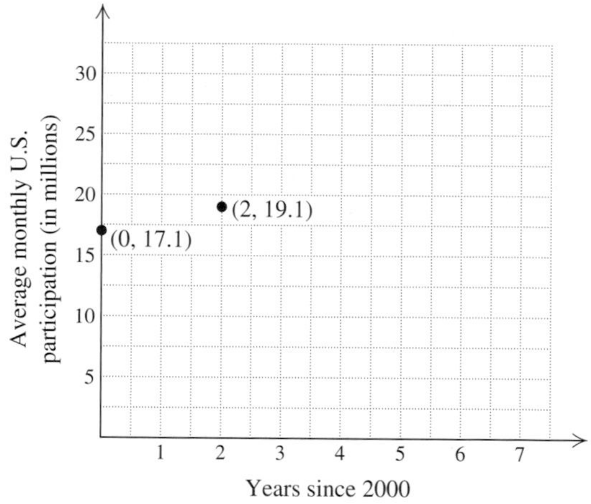

a) Calculate the number of participants in 2001.

b) Predict the number of participants in 2007.

59. *Cigarette smoking.* The percentage of people age 26–34 who smoke has dropped from 45.7% in 1985 to 32.5% in 1998.

Source: *The World Almanac and Book of Facts 2000*, 1999

a) Calculate the percentage of people age 26–34 who smoked in 1990.

b) Predict the percentage of people age 26–34 who will smoke in 2008.

60. *Cigarette smoking.* The percentage of people age 18–25 who smoke has changed from 47.4% in 1985 to 41.8% in 1998.
Source: *The World Almanac and Book of Facts 2000*, 1999

a) Calculate the percentage of people age 18–25 who smoked in 1990.
b) Predict the percentage of people age 18–25 who will smoke in 2008.

61. *College enrollment.* U.S. college enrollment has grown from approximately 60.3 million in 1990 to 68.3 million in 2000.
Source: *The World Almanac and Book of Facts 2000*, 1999

a) Calculate the U.S. college enrollment for 1996.
b) Predict the U.S. college enrollment for 2005.

62. *High school enrollment.* U.S. high school enrollment has changed from approximately 12.5 million in 1990 to 14.9 million in 2000.
Source: *The World Almanac and Book of Facts 2000*, 1999

a) Calculate the U.S. high school enrollment for 1996.
b) Predict the U.S. high school enrollment for 2005.

63. *Aging population.* The number of U.S. residents over the age of 65 was approximately 31 million in 1990 and 35.6 million in 2002.
Source: U.S. Bureau of the Census

Aha! **a)** Calculate the number of U.S. residents over the age of 65 in 1996.
b) Predict the number of U.S. residents over the age of 65 in 2010.

64. *Urban population.* The percentage of the U.S. population that resides in metropolitan areas increased from about 78% in 1980 to about 80% in 1996.

a) Calculate the percentage of the U.S. population residing in metropolitan areas in 1992.
b) Predict the percentage of the U.S. population residing in metropolitan areas in 2008.

Write the slope–intercept equation for the line containing the given pair of points.

65. $(1, 5)$ and $(4, 2)$

66. $(3, 7)$ and $(4, 8)$

67. $(-3, 1)$ and $(3, 5)$

68. $(-2, 3)$ and $(2, 5)$

69. $(5, 0)$ and $(0, -2)$

70. $(-2, 0)$ and $(0, 3)$

71. $(-2, -4)$ and $(2, -1)$

72. $(-3, 5)$ and $(-1, -3)$

73. Can equations for horizontal or vertical lines be written in point–slope form? Why or why not?

74. Describe a situation in which it is easier to graph the equation of a line in point–slope form than in slope–intercept form.

SKILL MAINTENANCE

Simplify. [1.8]

75. $(-5)^3$

76. $(-2)^6$

77. $3 \cdot 2^4 - 5 \cdot 2^3$

78. $5 \cdot 3^2 - 7 \cdot 3$

79. $(-2)^3(-3)^2$

80. $(5 - 7)^2(3 - 2 \cdot 2)$

SYNTHESIS

81. Describe a procedure that can be used to write the slope–intercept equation for any nonvertical line passing through two given points.

82. Any nonvertical line has many equations in point–slope form, but only one in slope–intercept form. Why is this?

Graph.

Aha! **83.** $y - 3 = 0(x - 52)$

84. $y + 4 = 0(x + 93)$

Write the slope–intercept equation for each line shown.

85.

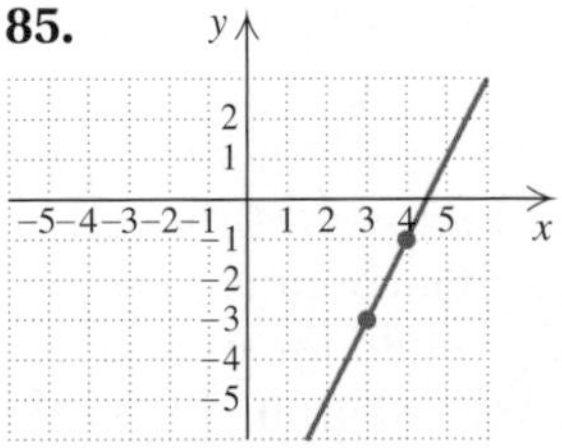

86.

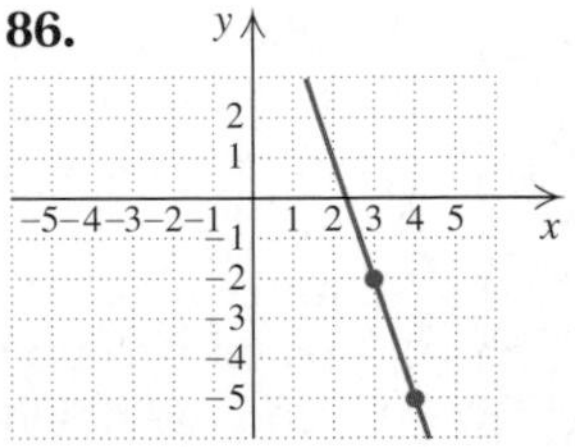

87.

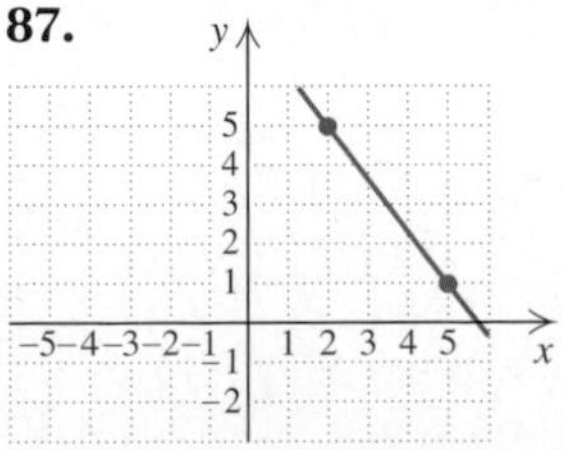

88.

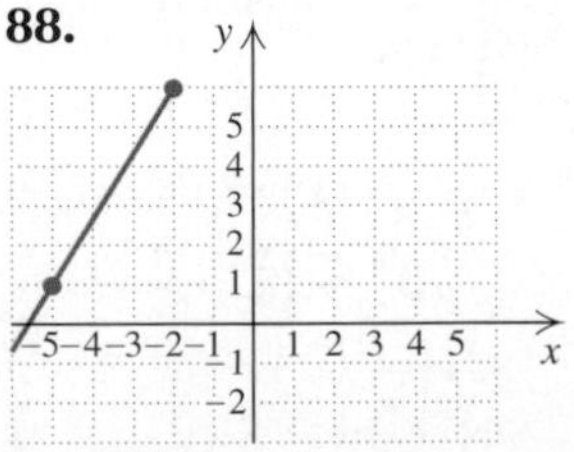

89. Write a point–slope equation of the line passing through $(-4, 7)$ that is parallel to the line given by $2x + 3y = 11$.

90. Write a point–slope equation of the line passing through $(3, -1)$ that is parallel to the line given by $4x - 5y = 9$.

Aha! **91.** Write an equation of the line parallel to the line given by $y = 3 - 4x$ that passes through $(0, 7)$.

92. Write the slope–intercept equation of the line that has the same y-intercept as the line $x - 3y = 6$ and contains the point $(5, -1)$.

93. Write the slope–intercept equation of the line that contains the point $(-1, 5)$ and is parallel to the line passing through $(2, 7)$ and $(-1, -3)$.

94. Write the slope–intercept equation of the line that has x-intercept $(-2, 0)$ and is parallel to $4x - 8y = 12$.

95. Why is slope–intercept form more useful than point–slope form when using a graphing calculator? How can point–slope form be modified so that it is more easily used with graphing calculators?

COLLABORATIVE CORNER

Follow the Bouncing Ball

Focus: Graphing and problem solving

Time: 25 minutes

Group size: 3

Materials: Each group will need a rubber ball, graph paper, and a tape measure.

Does a rubber ball always rebound a fixed percentage of the height from which it is dropped? The following activity attempts to answer this. Please be sure to read all steps before beginning.

ACTIVITY

1. One group member should hold a rubber ball 5 ft above the floor. A second group member should measure this height for accuracy. The ball should then be dropped and caught at the peak of its bounce. The second group member should measure this rebound height and the third group member should record the measurement.
2. Repeat part (1) two more times from the same height. Then find the average of the three rebound heights and use that number to form the ordered pair (original height, rebound height).
3. Repeat parts (1) and (2) four more times at heights of 4 ft, 3 ft, 2 ft, and 1 ft to find five ordered pairs. Graph the five pairs on graph paper and draw a straight line starting at (0, 0) that comes as close as possible to all six points.
4. Use the graph in part (3) to predict the rebound height for a ball dropped from a height of 7 ft. Then perform the drop and check your prediction.
5. Repeat part (4), dropping the ball from a "new" height of the group's choice.
6. Does it appear that a rubber ball will always rebound a fixed percentage of its original height? Why or why not?
7. Compare results from other class groups. What conclusions can you draw?

3 Study Summary

Information can be communicated quickly and effectively in a visual form through the use of graphs. **Bar graphs, circle graphs**, and **line graphs** are three of the most commonly used types of graphs (pp. 148–150)

When information is given as **ordered pairs**, like $(-3, 2)$ or $(5, 17)$, the pairs can be **plotted** or **graphed** using a **coordinate system** that uses two **axes**, which are most often labeled x and y. The axes intersect at the **origin**, $(0, 0)$ (p. 151).

When an equation contains two variables, any solution is an ordered pair. When all ordered pairs that are solutions of an equation are graphed, we say that we have **graphed the equation** (p. 160). Some equations are said to be **linear**, like $y = 2x - 7$ or $2x + 3y = 12$, because their graphs are lines (p. 160). Other equations have **nonlinear graphs** (p. 165). When a graph crosses the y-axis, the point at which the axis is crossed is called a ***y*-intercept.** Similarly, an ***x*-intercept** is any point at which a graph crosses the x-axis (p. 169).

A line's slant is measured as its **slope.** Slope measures the **rate** at which the quantity measured on the vertical axis changes with respect to the quantity measured on the horizontal axis (p. 190).

$$\text{Slope} = m = \frac{\text{change in } y}{\text{change in } x} = \frac{\text{rise}}{\text{run}} = \frac{y_2 - y_1}{x_2 - x_1}$$

An equation in **slope–intercept form**, $y = mx + b$, represents a line with slope m and y-intercept $(0, b)$ (p. 203). An equation in **point–slope form**, $y - y_1 = m(x - x_1)$, represents a line with slope m passing through (x_1, y_1) (p. 210).

3 Review Exercises

Classify each statement as either true or false.

1. Not every ordered pair lies in one of the four quadrants. [3.1]

2. The equation of a vertical line cannot be written in slope–intercept form. [3.6]

3. Equations for lines written in slope–intercept form appear in the form $Ax + By = C$. [3.6]

4. Every horizontal line has an x-intercept. [3.3]

5. A line's slope is a measure of rate. [3.5]

6. A positive rate of inflation means prices are rising. [3.4]

7. Any two points on a line can be used to determine the line's slope. [3.5]

8. Knowing a line's slope is enough to write the equation of the line. [3.6]

9. Parallel lines that are not vertical have the same slope. [3.6]

10. Knowing two points on a line is enough to write the equation of the line. [3.7]

The following circle graph shows a breakdown of the charities to which Americans donated in a recent year. Use the graph for Exercises 11 and 12.
Source: American Association of Fund-Raising Counsel Trust for Philanthropy Giving USA 2003

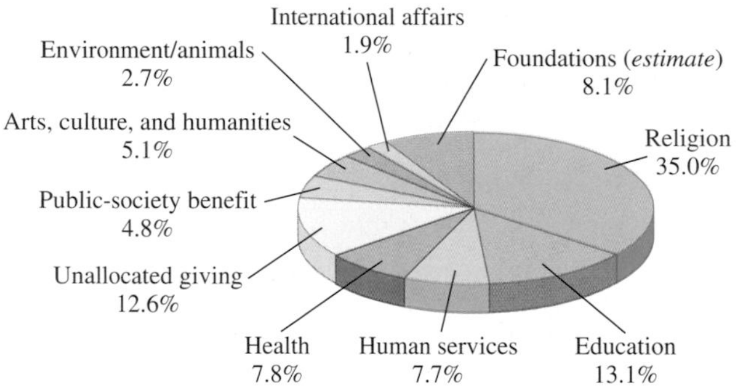

All figures are rounded. Total may not be 100%.

11. The citizens of Pittsford are typical of Americans in general with regard to charitable contributions. If the citizens donated a total of \$2 million to charities, how much was given to the environment/animals? [3.1]

12. About 5% of the Velez's income of \$70,000 goes to charity. If their giving habits are typical, approximate the amount that they contribute to human services. [3.1]

Plot each point. [3.1]

13. $(5, -1)$ **14.** $(2, 3)$ **15.** $(-4, 0)$

In which quadrant is each point located? [3.1]

16. $(2, -6)$ **17.** $(-16.5, -20.3)$

18. $(-3, 12)$

Find the coordinates of each point in the figure. [3.1]

19. A **20.** B **21.** C

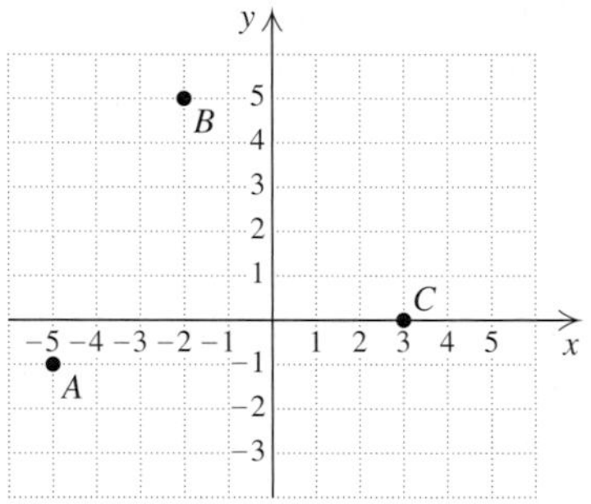

22. Use a grid 10 squares wide and 10 squares high to plot $(-65, -2)$, $(-10, 6)$, and $(25, 7)$. Choose the scale carefully. [3.1]

23. Determine whether the equation $y = 2x - 5$ has *each* ordered pair as a solution: **(a)** $(3, 1)$; **(b)** $(-3, 1)$. [3.2]

24. Show that the ordered pairs $(0, -3)$ and $(2, 1)$ are solutions of the equation $2x - y = 3$. Then use the graph of the two points to determine another solution. Answers may vary. [3.2]

Graph.

25. $y = x - 5$ [3.2]

26. $y = -\frac{1}{4}x$ [3.2]

27. $y = -x + 4$ [3.2]

28. $4x + y = 3$ [3.2]

29. $4x + 5 = 3$ [3.3]

30. $5x - 2y = 10$ [3.3]

31. *Meal service.* At 8:30 A.M., the Colchester Boy Scouts had served 47 people at their annual pancake breakfast. By 9:15, the total served had reached 67.

a) Find the Boy Scouts' serving rate, in number of meals per minute. [3.4]

b) Find the Boy Scouts' serving rate, in minutes per meal. [3.4]

32. *Gas mileage.* The following graph shows data for a Ford Explorer driven on city streets. At what rate was the vehicle consuming gas? [3.4]

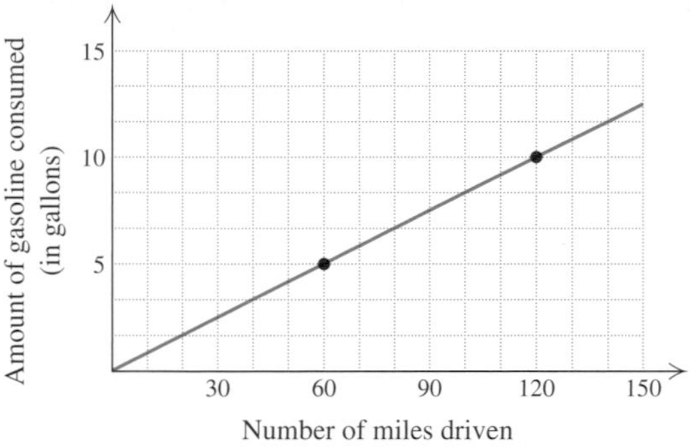

Find the slope of each line. [3.5]

33.

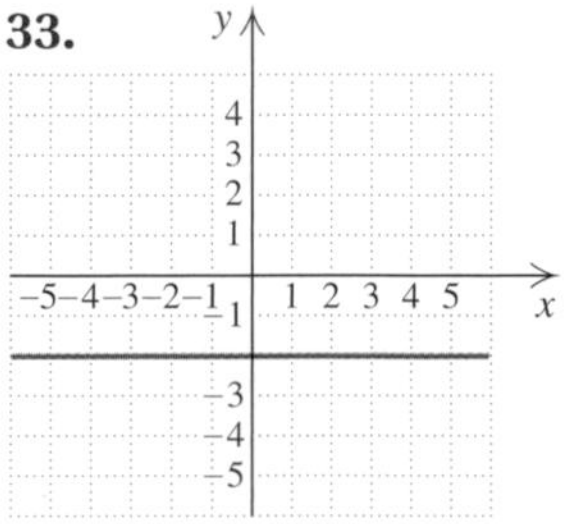

34.

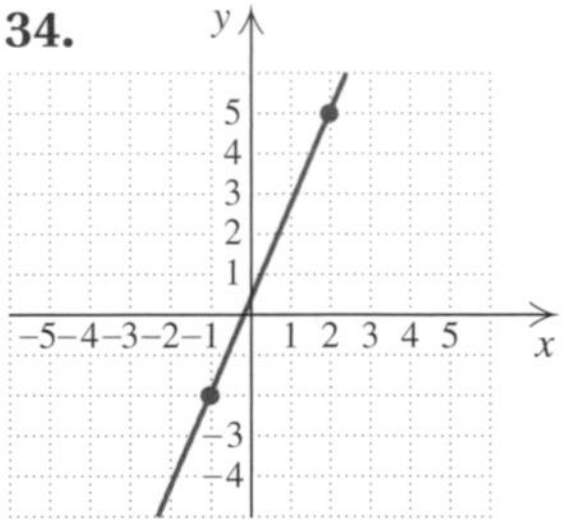

35.

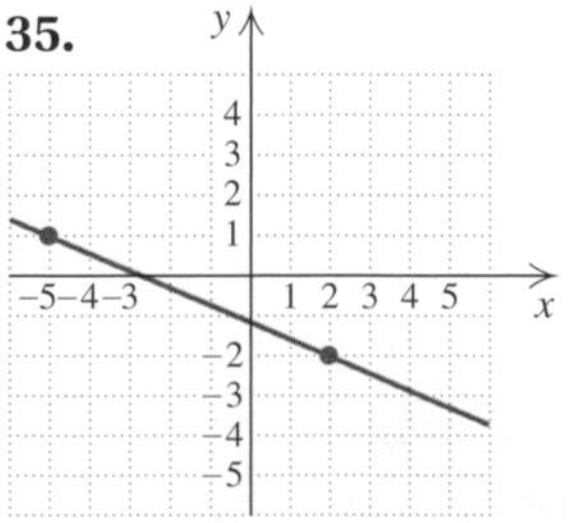

Find the slope of the line containing the given pair of points. [3.5]

36. $(6, 8)$ and $(-2, -4)$

37. $(5, 1)$ and $(-1, 1)$

38. $(-3, 0)$ and $(-3, 5)$

39. $(-8.3, 4.6)$ and $(-9.9, 1.4)$

40. Lombard Street in San Francisco, sometimes called the world's most crooked street, at one point drops 35 ft over a 125-ft horizontal distance. Find the grade. [3.5]

41. Find the x-intercept and the y-intercept of the line given by $3x + 2y = 18$. [3.3]

42. Find the slope and the y-intercept of the line given by $2x + 4y = 20$. [3.6]

43. Write the slope–intercept equation of the line with slope $-\frac{3}{4}$ and y-intercept $(0, 6)$. [3.6]

44. Write a point–slope equation for the line with slope $-\frac{1}{2}$ that contains the point $(3, 6)$. [3.7]

45. The average annual cost of health insurance for a single person rose from about \$2500 in 2000 to about \$3400 in 2003. Graph the data and determine an equation for the related line. Then **(a)** calculate the cost of health insurance for a single person in 2002 and **(b)** predict the cost of health insurance for a single person in 2008. [3.7]
Source: The Kaiser Family Foundation and the Health Research and Education Trust

46. Write the slope–intercept equation for the line with slope 4 that contains the point $(-3, -7)$. [3.7]

Graph.

47. $y = \frac{2}{3}x - 5$ [3.6]

48. $2x + y = 4$ [3.3]

49. $y = 6$ [3.3]

50. $x = -2$ [3.3]

51. $y + 2 = -\frac{1}{2}(x - 3)$ [3.7]

SYNTHESIS

52. Can two perpendicular lines share the same y-intercept? Why or why not? [3.3]

53. Explain why the first coordinate of the y-intercept is always 0. [3.3]

54. Find the value of m in $y = mx + 3$ such that $(-2, 5)$ is on the graph. [3.2]

55. Find the value of b in $y = -5x + b$ such that $(3, 4)$ is on the graph. [3.2]

56. Find the area and the perimeter of a rectangle for which $(-2, 2)$, $(7, 2)$, and $(7, -3)$ are three of the vertices. [3.1]

57. Find three solutions of $y = 4 - |x|$. [3.2]

3 Chapter Test

Use of tax dollars. The following pie chart shows how federal income tax dollars were spent in 2003.
Source: Based on information from www.taxfoundation.com

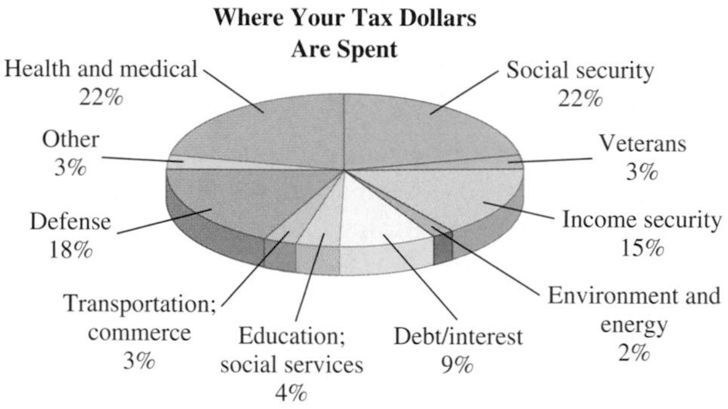

1. Debbie pays 15% of her taxable income of $34,200 in taxes. How much of her income will go to education and social services?

2. Larry pays 10% of his taxable income of $29,000 in taxes. How much of his income will go to social security?

In which quadrant is each point located?

3. $\left(-\frac{1}{2}, 7\right)$

4. $(-5, -6)$

Find the coordinates of each point in the figure.

5. A

6. B

7. C

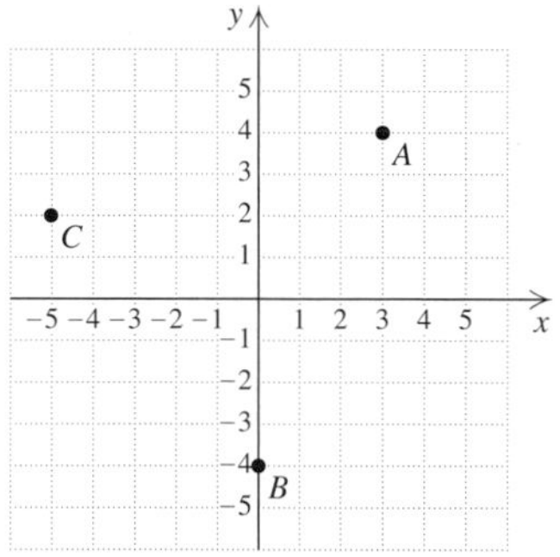

Graph.

8. $y = 2x - 1$

9. $2x - 4y = -8$

10. $y + 1 = 6$

11. $y = \frac{3}{4}x$

12. $y = 7$

13. $2x - y = 3$

14. $x = -1$

Find the x- and y-intercepts. Do not graph.

15. $5x - 3y = 30$

16. $x = 10 - 4y$

Find the slope of the line containing each pair of points.

17. $(4, -1)$ and $(6, 8)$

18. $(-3, -5)$ and $(9, 2)$

19. *Running.* Ted reached the 3-km mark of a race at 2:15 P.M. and the 6-km mark at 2:24 P.M. What is his running rate?

20. At one point Filbert Street, the steepest street in San Francisco, drops 63 ft over a horizontal distance of 200 ft. Find the road grade.

21. Find the slope and the y-intercept of the line given by $y - 3x = 7$.

Graph.

22. $y = \frac{1}{4}x - 2$

23. $y + 4 = -\frac{1}{2}(x - 3)$

24. Write a point–slope equation for the line of slope -3 that contains the point $(6, 8)$.

SYNTHESIS

25. Write an equation of the line that is parallel to the graph of $2x - 5y = 6$ and has the same y-intercept as the graph of $3x + y = 9$.

26. A diagonal of a square connects the points $(-3, -1)$ and $(2, 4)$. Find the area and the perimeter of the square.

27. List the coordinates of three other points that are on the same line as $(-2, 14)$ and $(17, -5)$. Answers may vary.

1–3 Cumulative Review

1. Evaluate $\frac{x}{2y}$ for $x = 70$ and $y = 5$. [1.1]

2. Multiply: $3(4x - 5y + 7)$. [1.2]

3. Factor: $15x - 9y + 3$. [1.2]

4. Find the prime factorization of 42. [1.3]

5. Find decimal notation: $\frac{9}{20}$. [1.4]

6. Find the absolute value: $|-4|$. [1.4]

7. Find the opposite of $-\frac{1}{4}$. [1.6]

8. Find the reciprocal of $-\frac{1}{4}$. [1.7]

9. Combine like terms: $2x - 5y + (-3x) + 4y$. [1.6]

10. Find decimal notation: 78.5%. [2.4]

Simplify.

11. $\frac{3}{5} - \frac{5}{12}$ [1.3]

12. $3.4 + (-0.8)$ [1.5]

13. $(-2)(-1.4)(2.6)$ [1.7]

14. $\frac{3}{8} \div \left(-\frac{9}{10}\right)$ [1.7]

15. $1 - [32 \div (4 + 2^2)]$ [1.8]

16. $-5 + 16 \div 2 \cdot 4$ [1.8]

17. $y - (3y + 7)$ [1.8]

18. $3(x - 1) - 2[x - (2x + 7)]$ [1.8]

Solve.

19. $2.6 = 3.8 + x$ [2.1]

20. $\frac{2}{7}x = -6$ [2.1]

21. $5x - 8 = 37$ [2.2]

22. $\frac{2}{3} = \frac{-m}{10}$ [2.1]

23. $5.4 - 1.9x = 0.8x$ [2.2]

24. $x - \frac{7}{8} = \frac{3}{4}$ [2.1]

25. $2(2 - 3x) = 3(5x + 7)$ [2.2]

26. $\frac{1}{4}x - \frac{2}{3} = \frac{3}{4} + \frac{1}{3}x$ [2.2]

27. $y + 5 - 3y = 5y - 9$ [2.2]

28. $x - 28 < 20 - 2x$ [2.6]

29. $2(x + 2) \geq 5(2x + 3)$ [2.6]

30. Solve $A = 2\pi rh + \pi r^2$ for h. [2.3]

31. In which quadrant is the point $(3, -1)$ located? [3.1]

32. Graph on a number line: $-1 < x \leq 2$. [2.6]

33. Use a grid 10 squares wide and 10 squares high to plot $(-150, -40)$, $(40, -7)$, and $(0, 6)$. Choose the scale carefully. [3.1]

Graph.

34. $x = 3$ [3.3]

35. $2x - 5y = 10$ [3.3]

36. $y = -2x + 1$ [3.2]

37. $y = \frac{2}{3}x$ [3.2]

38. $y = -\frac{3}{4}x + 2$ [3.6]

Find the coordinates of the x- and y-intercepts. Do not graph.

39. $2x - 7y = 21$ [3.3]

40. $y = 4x + 5$ [3.3]

Solve.

41. *Donating blood.* Each year 8 million Americans donate blood. This is 5% of those healthy enough to do so. How many Americans are eligible to donate blood? [2.4]
Source: *Indianapolis Star*, 10/6/96

42. *Blood types.* There were recently 117 million Americans with either O-positive or O-negative blood. Those with O-positive blood outnumbered those with O-negative blood by 85.8 million. How many Americans had O-negative blood? [2.5]

43. Tina paid $126 for a cordless drill, including a 5% sales tax. How much did the drill itself cost? [2.4]

44. A 143-m wire is cut into three pieces. The second is 3 m longer than the first. The third is four fifths as long as the first. How long is each piece? [2.5]

45. Tori's contract stipulates that she cannot work more than 40 hr per week. For the first 4 days of one week, she worked 7, 10, 9, and 6 hr. How many hours can she work the fifth day without violating her contract? [2.5]

46. *Fund raising.* The following graph shows data from a recent road race held to raise money for Amnesty International. At what rate was money raised? [3.4]

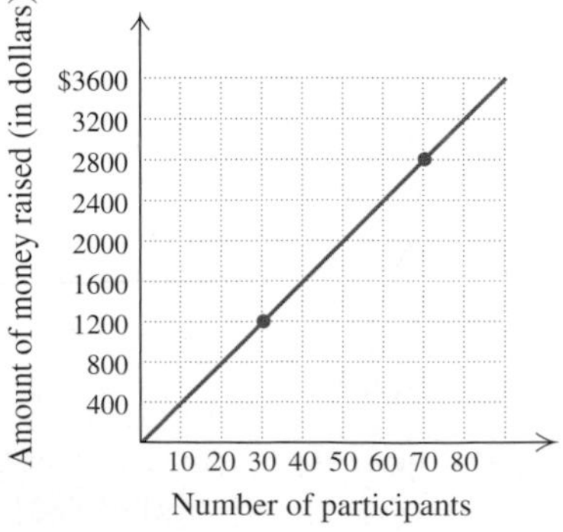

47. Find the slope of the line containing the points $(-4, 1)$ and $(2, -1)$. [3.5]

48. Write an equation of the line with slope $\frac{2}{7}$ and y-intercept $(0, -4)$. [3.6]

49. Find the slope and the y-intercept of the line given by $2x + 6y = 18$. [3.6]

50. Write a point–slope equation of the line with slope $-\frac{3}{8}$ that contains the point $(-6, 4)$. [3.7]

SYNTHESIS

51. *Yearly earnings.* Paula's salary at the end of a year is $26,780. This reflects a 4% salary increase in February and then a 3% cost-of-living adjustment in June. What was her salary at the beginning of the year? [2.4]

Solve. If no solution exists, state this.

52. $4|x| - 13 = 3$ [1.4], [2.2]

53. $4(x + 2) = 9(x - 2) + 16$ [2.2]

54. $2(x + 3) + 4 = 0$ [2.2]

55. $\frac{2 + 5x}{4} = \frac{11}{28} + \frac{8x + 3}{7}$ [2.2]

56. $5(7 + x) = (x + 6)5$ [2.2]

57. Solve $p = \frac{2}{m + Q}$ for Q. [2.3]

58. The points $(-3, 0)$, $(0, 7)$, $(3, 0)$, and $(0, -7)$ are vertices of a parallelogram. Find four equations of lines that intersect to form the parallelogram. [3.6]

4 Polynomials

AN APPLICATION

In computer science, 1 kilobyte (KB) is 1×2^{10}, or approximately 1000, bytes of memory. The TI-84 Plus Silver Edition graphing calculator has 1.5 megabytes (MB) of "FLASH ROM," where 1 MB = 1000 KB. How many bytes of FLASH ROM does this calculator have?

This problem appears as Exercise 121 in Section 4.1.

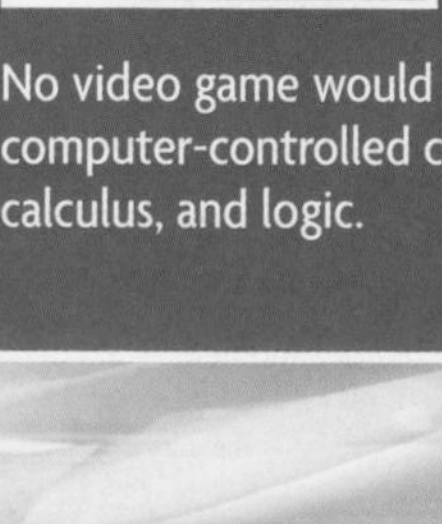

Damian Isla
AI PROGRAMMER
Seattle, Washington

No video game would ever be developed without math. My job is to simulate the thought processes of computer-controlled characters, and I do this using techniques from trigonometry, vector geometry, calculus, and logic.

Our work in Chapter 3 concentrated on using graphs to represent solutions of equations in two variables. Here in Chapter 4 we will focus on finding equivalent expressions, not on solving equations.

Algebraic expressions such as $16t^2$, $5a^2 - 3ab$, *and* $3x^2 - 7x + 5$ *are called polynomials. Polynomials occur frequently in applications and appear in most branches of mathematics. Thus learning to add, subtract, multiply, and divide polynomials is an important part of nearly every course in elementary algebra.*

4.1 Exponents and Their Properties

Multiplying Powers with Like Bases • Dividing Powers with Like Bases • Zero as an Exponent • Raising a Power to a Power • Raising a Product or a Quotient to a Power

In Section 4.2, we begin our study of polynomials. Before doing so, however, we must develop some rules for manipulating exponents.

Multiplying Powers with Like Bases

Recall from Section 1.8 that an expression like a^3 means $a \cdot a \cdot a$. We can use this fact to find the product of two expressions that have the same base:

$$a^3 \cdot a^2 = (a \cdot a \cdot a)(a \cdot a)$$ There are three factors in a^3 and two factors in a^2.

$$= a \cdot a \cdot a \cdot a \cdot a$$ Using an associative law

$$= a^5.$$

Note that the exponent in a^5 is the sum of the exponents in $a^3 \cdot a^2$. That is, $3 + 2 = 5$. Similarly,

$$b^4 \cdot b^3 = (b \cdot b \cdot b \cdot b)(b \cdot b \cdot b)$$

$$= b^7, \quad \text{where } 4 + 3 = 7.$$

Adding the exponents gives the correct result.

The Product Rule

For any number a and any positive integers m and n,

$$a^m \cdot a^n = a^{m+n}.$$

(To multiply powers with the same base, keep the base and add the exponents.)

EXAMPLE 1 Multiply and simplify each of the following. (Here "simplify" means express the product as one base to a power whenever possible.)

a) $x^2 \cdot x^9$

b) $5^3 \cdot 5^8 \cdot 5^1$

c) $(r + s)^7(r + s)^6$

d) $(a^3b^2)(a^3b^5)$

Study Skills

Helping Yourself by Helping Others

When you feel confident in your command of a topic, don't hesitate to help classmates experiencing trouble. Your understanding and retention of a concept will deepen when you explain it to someone else and your classmate will appreciate your help.

Solution

a) $x^2 \cdot x^9 = x^{2+9}$ Adding exponents: $a^m \cdot a^n = a^{m+n}$

$= x^{11}$

b) $5^3 \cdot 5^8 \cdot 5^1 = 5^{3+8+1}$ Adding exponents

$= 5^{12}$

Caution! $5^{12} \neq 5 \cdot 12.$

c) $(r + s)^7(r + s)^6 = (r + s)^{7+6}$ The base here is $r + s$.

$= (r + s)^{13}$

Caution! $(r + s)^{13} \neq r^{13} + s^{13}.$

d) $(a^3b^2)(a^3b^5) = a^3b^2a^3b^5$ Using an associative law

$= a^3a^3b^2b^5$ Using a commutative law

$= a^6b^7$ Adding exponents

Dividing Powers with Like Bases

Recall that any expression that is divided or multiplied by 1 is unchanged. This, together with the fact that anything (besides 0) divided by itself is 1, can lead to a rule for division:

$$\frac{a^5}{a^2} = \frac{a \cdot a \cdot a \cdot a \cdot a}{a \cdot a}$$

$$= \frac{a \cdot a \cdot a}{1} \cdot \frac{a \cdot a}{a \cdot a}$$

$$= \frac{a \cdot a \cdot a}{1} \cdot 1$$

$$= a \cdot a \cdot a = a^3.$$

Note that the exponent in a^3 is the difference of the exponents in a^5/a^2. Similarly,

$$\frac{x^4}{x^3} = \frac{x \cdot x \cdot x \cdot x}{x \cdot x \cdot x} = \frac{x}{1} \cdot \frac{x \cdot x \cdot x}{x \cdot x \cdot x} = \frac{x}{1} \cdot 1 = x^1, \quad \text{or } x.$$

Subtracting the exponents gives the correct result.

The Quotient Rule

For any nonzero number a and any positive integers m and n for which $m > n$,

$$\frac{a^m}{a^n} = a^{m-n}.$$

(To divide powers with the same base, subtract the exponent of the denominator from the exponent of the numerator.)

EXAMPLE 2 Divide and simplify. (Here "simplify" means express the quotient as one base to a power whenever possible.)

a) $\dfrac{x^8}{x^2}$ **b)** $\dfrac{7^9}{7^4}$ **c)** $\dfrac{(5a)^{12}}{(5a)^4}$ **d)** $\dfrac{4p^5q^7}{6p^2q}$

Solution

a) $\dfrac{x^8}{x^2} = x^{8-2}$ Subtracting exponents: $\dfrac{a^m}{a^n} = a^{m-n}$

$= x^6$

b) $\dfrac{7^9}{7^4} = 7^{9-4}$

$= 7^5$

Caution! When we are using the quotient rule, the base is unchanged:

$$\frac{7^9}{7^4} \neq 1^5, \quad \text{rather} \quad \frac{7^9}{7^4} = 7^5.$$

c) $\dfrac{(5a)^{12}}{(5a)^4} = (5a)^{12-4} = (5a)^8$ The base here is $5a$.

d) $\dfrac{4p^5q^7}{6p^2q} = \dfrac{4}{6} \cdot \dfrac{p^5}{p^2} \cdot \dfrac{q^7}{q^1}$ Note that the 4 and 6 are factors, not exponents!

$= \dfrac{2}{3} \cdot p^{5-2} \cdot q^{7-1} = \dfrac{2}{3}p^3q^6$ Using the quotient rule twice; simplifying

Zero as an Exponent

The quotient rule can be used to help determine what 0 should mean when it appears as an exponent. Consider a^4/a^4, where a is nonzero. Since the numerator and the denominator are the same,

$$\frac{a^4}{a^4} = 1.$$

On the other hand, using the quotient rule would give us

$$\frac{a^4}{a^4} = a^{4-4} = a^0.$$ Subtracting exponents

Since $a^0 = a^4/a^4 = 1$, this suggests that $a^0 = 1$ for any nonzero value of a.

The Exponent Zero

For any real number a, $a \neq 0$,

$$a^0 = 1.$$

(Any nonzero number raised to the 0 power is 1.)

Note that in the above box, 0^0 is not defined. For this text, we will assume that expressions like a^m do not represent 0^0.

EXAMPLE 3 Simplify: **(a)** 1948^0; **(b)** $(-9)^0$; **(c)** $(3x)^0$; **(d)** $(-1)9^0$; **(e)** -9^0.

Solution

a) $1948^0 = 1$ Any nonzero number raised to the 0 power is 1.

b) $(-9)^0 = 1$ Any nonzero number raised to the 0 power is 1. The base here is -9.

c) $(3x)^0 = 1$, for any $x \neq 0$. The parentheses indicate that the base is $3x$.

d) Recall that, unless there are calculations within parentheses, exponents are calculated before multiplication:

$$(-1)9^0 = (-1)1 = -1. \quad \text{The base here is 9.}$$

e) -9^0 is read "the opposite of 9^0" and is equivalent to $(-1)9^0$:

$$-9^0 = (-1)9^0 = (-1)1 = -1.$$

Note from parts (b), (d), and (e) that $-9^0 = (-1)9^0$ and $-9^0 \neq (-9)^0$.

Caution! $-9^0 \neq (-9)^0$, and, in general, $-a^n \neq (-a)^n$.

Raising a Power to a Power

Consider an expression like $(7^2)^4$:

$$\begin{aligned}(7^2)^4 &= (7^2)(7^2)(7^2)(7^2) && \text{There are four factors of } 7^2.\\ &= (7 \cdot 7)(7 \cdot 7)(7 \cdot 7)(7 \cdot 7) && \text{We could also use the product rule.}\\ &= 7 \cdot 7 \cdot 7 \cdot 7 \cdot 7 \cdot 7 \cdot 7 \cdot 7 && \text{Using an associative law}\\ &= 7^8.\end{aligned}$$

Note that the exponent in 7^8 is the product of the exponents in $(7^2)^4$. Similarly,

$$\begin{aligned}(y^5)^3 &= y^5 \cdot y^5 \cdot y^5 && \text{There are three factors of } y^5.\\ &= (y \cdot y \cdot y \cdot y \cdot y)(y \cdot y \cdot y \cdot y \cdot y)(y \cdot y \cdot y \cdot y \cdot y)\\ &= y^{15}.\end{aligned}$$

Once again, we get the same result if we multiply exponents:

$$(y^5)^3 = y^{5 \cdot 3} = y^{15}.$$

The Power Rule

For any number a and any whole numbers m and n,

$$(a^m)^n = a^{mn}.$$

(To raise a power to a power, multiply the exponents and leave the base unchanged.)

Remember that for this text we assume that 0^0 is not considered.

EXAMPLE 4 Simplify: **(a)** $(m^2)^5$; **(b)** $(3^5)^4$.

Solution

a) $(m^2)^5 = m^{2\cdot 5}$ Multiplying exponents: $(a^m)^n = a^{mn}$

$= m^{10}$

b) $(3^5)^4 = 3^{5\cdot 4}$

$= 3^{20}$

Student Notes

There are several rules for manipulating exponents in this section. One way to remember them all is to replace variables with small numbers and see what the results suggest. For example, multiplying $2^2 \cdot 2^3$ and examining the result is a fine way of reminding yourself that $a^m \cdot a^n = a^{m+n}$.

Raising a Product or a Quotient to a Power

When an expression inside parentheses is raised to a power, the inside expression is the base. Let's compare $2a^3$ and $(2a)^3$:

$2a^3 = 2 \cdot a \cdot a \cdot a$; The base is a.

$(2a)^3 = (2a)(2a)(2a)$ The base is $2a$.

$= (2 \cdot 2 \cdot 2)(a \cdot a \cdot a)$

$= 2^3a^3$

$= 8a^3.$

We see that $2a^3$ and $(2a)^3$ are *not* equivalent. Note too that $(2a)^3$ can be simplified by cubing each factor. This leads to the following rule for raising a product to a power.

Raising a Product to a Power

For any numbers a and b and any whole number n,

$$(ab)^n = a^nb^n.$$

(To raise a product to a power, raise each factor to that power.)

EXAMPLE 5 Simplify: **(a)** $(4a)^3$; **(b)** $(-5x^4)^2$; **(c)** $(a^7b)^2(a^3b^4)$.

Solution

a) $(4a)^3 = 4^3a^3 = 64a^3$ Raising each factor to the third power and simplifying

b) $(-5x^4)^2 = (-5)^2(x^4)^2$ Raising each factor to the second power. Parentheses are important here.

$= 25x^8$ Simplifying $(-5)^2$ and using the product rule

c) $(a^7b)^2(a^3b^4) = (a^7)^2b^2a^3b^4$ Raising a product to a power

$= a^{14}b^2a^3b^4$ Multiplying exponents

$= a^{17}b^6$ Adding exponents

Caution! The rule $(ab)^n = a^nb^n$ applies only to *products* raised to a power, not to sums or differences. For example, $(3 + 4)^2 \neq 3^2 + 4^2$ since $49 \neq 9 + 16$.

There is a similar rule for raising a quotient to a power.

Raising a Quotient to a Power

For any numbers a and b, $b \neq 0$, and any whole number n,

$$\left(\frac{a}{b}\right)^n = \frac{a^n}{b^n}.$$

(To raise a quotient to a power, raise the numerator to the power and divide by the denominator to the power.)

EXAMPLE 6 Simplify: **(a)** $\left(\frac{x}{5}\right)^2$; **(b)** $\left(\frac{5}{a^4}\right)^3$; **(c)** $\left(\frac{3a^4}{b^3}\right)^2$.

Solution

a) $\left(\frac{x}{5}\right)^2 = \frac{x^2}{5^2} = \frac{x^2}{25}$ Squaring the numerator and the denominator

b) $\left(\frac{5}{a^4}\right)^3 = \frac{5^3}{(a^4)^3}$ Raising a quotient to a power

$= \frac{125}{a^{4\cdot 3}} = \frac{125}{a^{12}}$ Using the power rule and simplifying

c) $\left(\frac{3a^4}{b^3}\right)^2 = \frac{(3a^4)^2}{(b^3)^2}$ Raising a quotient to a power

$= \frac{3^2(a^4)^2}{b^{3\cdot 2}} = \frac{9a^8}{b^6}$ Raising a product to a power and using the power rule

---

In the following summary of definitions and rules, we assume that no denominators are 0 and that 0^0 is not considered.

Definitions and Properties of Exponents

For any whole numbers m and n,

1 as an exponent:	$a^1 = a$
0 as an exponent:	$a^0 = 1$
The Product Rule:	$a^m \cdot a^n = a^{m+n}$
The Quotient Rule:	$\frac{a^m}{a^n} = a^{m-n}$
The Power Rule:	$(a^m)^n = a^{mn}$
Raising a product to a power:	$(ab)^n = a^n b^n$
Raising a quotient to a power:	$\left(\frac{a}{b}\right)^n = \frac{a^n}{b^n}$

4.1 Exercise Set

FOR EXTRA HELP

Student's Solutions Manual | Digital Video Tutor CD 2 Videotape 7 | AW Math Tutor Center | MathXL Tutorials on CD | MathXL | MyMathLab

Concept Reinforcement *In each of Exercises 1–8, complete the sentence using the most appropriate phrase from the column on the right.*

1. To raise a power to a power, ____

2. To raise a quotient to a power, ____

3. To raise a product to a power, ____

4. To divide powers with the same base, ____

5. Any nonzero number raised to the 0 power ____

6. To multiply powers with the same base, ____

7. To square a fraction, ____

8. To square a product, ____

a) keep the base and add the exponents.

b) multiply the exponents and leave the base unchanged.

c) square the numerator and square the denominator.

d) square each factor.

e) raise each factor to that power.

f) raise the numerator to the power and divide by the denominator to the power.

g) is one.

h) subtract the exponent of the denominator from the exponent of the numerator.

Simplify. Assume that no denominator is zero and that 0^0 is not considered.

9. $r^4 \cdot r^6$
10. $8^4 \cdot 8^3$
11. $9^5 \cdot 9^3$
12. $n^3 \cdot n^{20}$
13. $a^6 \cdot a$
14. $y^7 \cdot y^9$
15. $8^4 \cdot 8^7$
16. $t^0 \cdot t^{16}$
17. $(3y)^4(3y)^8$
18. $(2t)^8(2t)^{17}$
19. $(5t)(5t)^6$
20. $(8x)^0(8x)^1$
21. $(a^2b^7)(a^3b^2)$
22. $(m - 3)^4(m - 3)^5$
23. $(x + 1)^5(x + 1)^7$
24. $(a^8b^3)(a^4b)$
25. $r^3 \cdot r^7 \cdot r^0$
26. $s^4 \cdot s^5 \cdot s^2$
27. $(xy^4)(xy)^3$
28. $(a^3b)(ab)^4$
29. $\dfrac{7^5}{7^2}$
30. $\dfrac{4^7}{4^3}$
31. $\dfrac{x^{15}}{x^3}$
32. $\dfrac{a^{10}}{a^2}$
33. $\dfrac{t^5}{t}$
34. $\dfrac{x^7}{x}$
35. $\dfrac{(5a)^7}{(5a)^6}$
36. $\dfrac{(3m)^9}{(3m)^8}$

Aha! 37. $\dfrac{(x + y)^8}{(x + y)^8}$

38. $\dfrac{(a - b)^4}{(a - b)^3}$
39. $\dfrac{6m^5}{8m^2}$
40. $\dfrac{10n^7}{15n^3}$
41. $\dfrac{8a^9b^7}{2a^2b}$
42. $\dfrac{12r^{10}s^7}{4r^2s}$
43. $\dfrac{m^9n^8}{m^0n^4}$
44. $\dfrac{a^{10}b^{12}}{a^2b^0}$

Simplify.

45. x^0 when $x = 13$
46. y^0 when $y = 38$
47. $5x^0$ when $x = -4$
48. $7m^0$ when $m = 1.7$
49. $7^0 + 4^0$
50. $(8 + 5)^0$
51. $(-3)^1 - (-3)^0$
52. $(-4)^0 - (-4)^1$

Simplify. Assume that no denominator is zero and that 0^0 is not considered.

53. $(x^4)^7$
54. $(a^3)^8$
55. $(5^8)^2$
56. $(2^5)^3$
57. $(m^7)^5$
58. $(n^9)^2$
59. $(t^{20})^4$
60. $(t^3)^9$
61. $(7x)^2$
62. $(5a)^2$
63. $(-2a)^3$
64. $(-3x)^3$
65. $(4m^3)^2$
66. $(5n^4)^2$
67. $(a^2b)^7$
68. $(xy^4)^9$
69. $(x^3y)^2(x^2y^5)$
70. $(a^4b^6)(a^2b)^5$
71. $(2x^5)^3(3x^4)$
72. $(5x^3)^2(2x^7)$
73. $\left(\dfrac{a}{4}\right)^3$
74. $\left(\dfrac{3}{x}\right)^4$
75. $\left(\dfrac{7}{5a}\right)^2$
76. $\left(\dfrac{5x}{2}\right)^3$
77. $\left(\dfrac{a^4}{b^3}\right)^5$
78. $\left(\dfrac{x^5}{y^2}\right)^7$
79. $\left(\dfrac{y^3}{2}\right)^2$
80. $\left(\dfrac{a^5}{2}\right)^3$
81. $\left(\dfrac{x^2y}{z^3}\right)^4$
82. $\left(\dfrac{x^3}{y^2z}\right)^5$
83. $\left(\dfrac{a^3}{-2b^5}\right)^4$
84. $\left(\dfrac{x^5}{-3y^3}\right)^4$
85. $\left(\dfrac{5x^7y}{2z^4}\right)^3$
86. $\left(\dfrac{4a^2b}{3c^7}\right)^3$

Aha! 87. $\left(\dfrac{4x^3y^5}{3z^7}\right)^0$

88. $\left(\dfrac{5a^7}{2b^5c}\right)^0$
89. Explain in your own words why $-5^2 \neq (-5)^2$.
90. Under what circumstances should exponents be added?

SKILL MAINTENANCE

Factor. [1.2]

91. $3s - 3r + 3t$
92. $-7x + 7y - 7z$

Combine like terms. [1.6]

93. $9x + 2y - x - 2y$
94. $5a - 7b - 8a + b$

Use the commutative law of addition to write an equivalent expression. [1.2]

95. $3x + 2y$
96. $2xy + 5z$

SYNTHESIS

97. Under what conditions does a^n represent a negative number? Why?

98. Using the quotient rule, explain why 9^0 is 1.

99. Suppose that the width of a square is three times the width of a second square. How do the areas of the squares compare? Why?

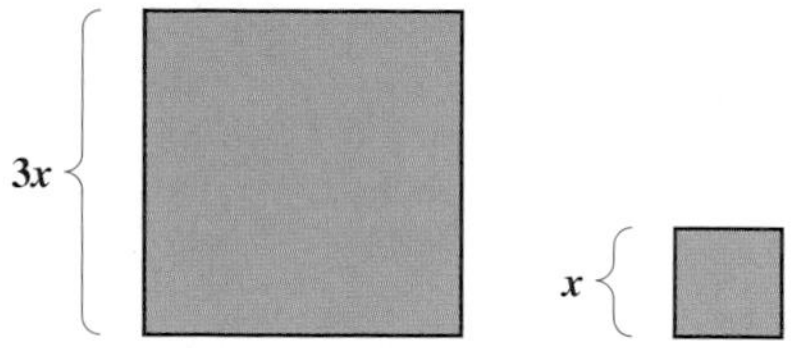

100. Suppose that the width of a cube is twice the width of a second cube. How do the volumes of the cubes compare? Why?

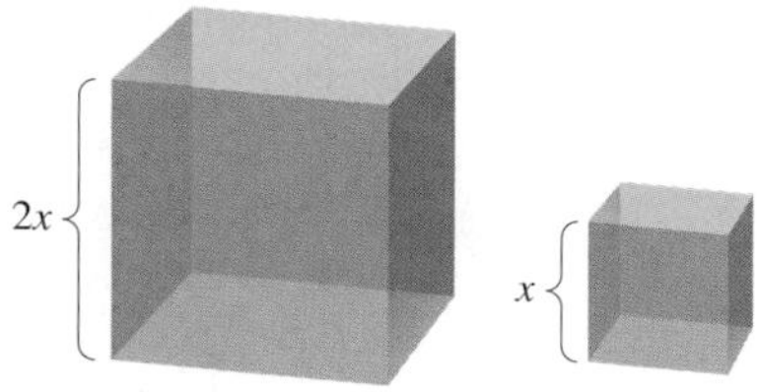

Find a value of the variable that shows that the two expressions are not *equivalent. Answers may vary.*

101. $(a + 5)^2;\ a^2 + 5^2$

102. $3x^2;\ (3x)^2$

103. $\dfrac{a + 7}{7};\ a$

104. $\dfrac{t^6}{t^2};\ t^3$

Simplify.

105. $a^{10k} \div a^{2k}$

106. $y^{4x} \cdot y^{2x}$

107. $\dfrac{\left(\frac{1}{2}\right)^3\left(\frac{2}{3}\right)^4}{\left(\frac{5}{6}\right)^3}$

108. $\dfrac{x^{5t}(x^t)^2}{(x^{3t})^2}$

109. Solve for x:

$$\frac{t^{26}}{t^x} = t^x.$$

Replace $\square$ *with* $>$, $<$, *or* $=$ *to write a true sentence.*

110. $3^5 \ \square\ 3^4$

111. $4^2 \ \square\ 4^3$

112. $4^3 \ \square\ 5^3$

113. $4^3 \ \square\ 3^4$

114. $9^7 \ \square\ 3^{13}$

115. $25^8 \ \square\ 125^5$

Use the fact that $10^3 \approx 2^{10}$ *to estimate each of the following powers of 2. Then compute the power of 2 with a calculator and find the difference between the exact value and the approximation.*

116. 2^{14}

117. 2^{22}

118. 2^{26}

119. 2^{31}

In computer science, 1 KB of memory refers to 1 kilobyte, or 1×10^3 *bytes, of memory. This is really an approximation of* 1×2^{10} *bytes (since computer memory uses powers of 2).*

120. The TI-84 Plus graphing calculator has 480 KB of "FLASH ROM." How many bytes is this?

121. The TI-84 Plus Silver Edition graphing calculator has 1.5 MB (megabytes) of FLASH ROM, where 1 MB is 1000 KB (see Exercise 120). How many bytes of FLASH ROM does this calculator have?

4.2 Polynomials

Terms • Types of Polynomials • Degree and Coefficients • Combining Like Terms • Evaluating Polynomials and Applications

We now examine an important algebraic expression known as a *polynomial*. Certain polynomials have appeared earlier in this text so you already have some experience working with them.

Terms

At this point, we have seen a variety of algebraic expressions like

$$3a^2b^4, \qquad 2l + 2w, \qquad \text{and} \qquad 5x^2 + x - 2.$$

Of these, $3a^2b^4$, $2l$, $2w$, $5x^2$, x, and -2 are examples of *terms*. A **term** (see p. 16) can be a number (like -2), a variable (like x), a product of numbers and/or variables (like $3a^2b^4$, $2l$, $2w$, or $5x^2$), or a quotient of numbers and/or variables (like $7/t$ or $(a^2b^3)/(4c)$).*

Types of Polynomials

A term that is a product of constants and/or variables is called a **monomial**.† All of the terms listed above, except for the quotients, are monomials. Other examples of monomials are

$$7, \qquad t, \qquad 23x^2y, \qquad \text{and} \qquad \tfrac{3}{7}a^5.$$

A **polynomial** is a monomial or a sum of monomials. The following are examples of polynomials:

$$4x + 7, \quad \tfrac{2}{3}t^2, \quad 6a + 7, \quad -5n^2 + m - 1, \quad 42r^5, \quad x, \quad \text{and} \quad 0.$$

The following algebraic expressions are *not* polynomials:

$$\textbf{(1)}\ \frac{x+3}{x-4}, \qquad \textbf{(2)}\ 5x^3 - 2x^2 + \frac{1}{x}, \qquad \textbf{(3)}\ \frac{1}{x^3 - 2}.$$

Expressions (1) and (3) are not polynomials because they represent quotients, not sums. Expression (2) is not a polynomial because $1/x$ is not a monomial.

When a polynomial is written as a sum of monomials, each monomial is called a *term of the polynomial*.

Study Skills

A Text Is Not Light Reading

Do not expect a math text to read like a magazine or novel. On one hand, most assigned readings in a math text consist of only a few pages. On the other hand, every sentence and word is important and should make sense. If they don't, seek help as soon as possible.

---

*Later in this text, expressions like $5x^{3/2}$ and $2a^{-7}b$ will be discussed. Such expressions are also considered terms.

†Note that a term, but not a monomial, can include division by a variable.

EXAMPLE 1 Identify the terms of the polynomial $3t^4 - 5t^6 - 4t + 2$.

Solution The terms are $3t^4$, $-5t^6$, $-4t$, and 2. We can see this by rewriting all subtractions as additions of opposites:

$$3t^4 - 5t^6 - 4t + 2 = 3t^4 + (-5t^6) + (-4t) + 2.$$

↑ ↑ ↑ ↑

These are the terms of the polynomial.

A polynomial that is composed of two terms is called a **binomial**, whereas those composed of three terms are called **trinomials**. Polynomials with four or more terms have no special name.

Monomials	Binomials	Trinomials	No Special Name
$4x^2$	$2x + 4$	$3t^3 + 4t + 7$	$4x^3 - 5x^2 + xy - 8$
9	$3a^5 + 6bc$	$6x^7 - 8z^2 + 4$	$z^5 + 2z^4 - z^3 + 7z + 3$
$-7a^{19}b^5$	$-9x^7 - 6$	$4x^2 - 6x - \frac{1}{2}$	$4x^6 - 3x^5 + x^4 - x^3 + 2x - 1$

Degree and Coefficients

The **degree of a term** of a polynomial is the number of variable factors in that term. Thus the degree of $7t^2$ is 2 because $7t^2$ has two variable factors: $7t^2 = 7 \cdot t \cdot t$. We will revisit the meaning of degree in Section 4.6 when polynomials in several variables are examined.

EXAMPLE 2 Determine the degree of each term: **(a)** $8x^4$; **(b)** $3x$; **(c)** 7.

Solution

a) The degree of $8x^4$ is 4. x^4 represents 4 variable factors: $x \cdot x \cdot x \cdot x$.

b) The degree of $3x$ is 1. There is 1 variable factor.

c) The degree of 7 is 0. There is no variable factor.

The part of a term that is a constant factor is the **coefficient** of that term. Thus the coefficient of $3x$ is 3, and the coefficient for the term 7 is simply 7.

EXAMPLE 3 Identify the coefficient of each term in the polynomial

$$4x^3 - 7x^2y + x - 8.$$

Solution

The coefficient of $4x^3$ is 4.

The coefficient of $-7x^2y$ is -7.

The coefficient of the third term is 1, since $x = 1x$.

The coefficient of -8 is simply -8.

The **leading term** of a polynomial is the term of highest degree. Its coefficient is called the **leading coefficient** and its degree is referred to as the **degree of the polynomial**. To see how this terminology is used, consider the polynomial

$$3x^2 - 8x^3 + 5x^4 + 7x - 6.$$

The *terms* are	$3x^2$,	$-8x^3$,	$5x^4$,	$7x$,	and	-6.
The *coefficients* are	3,	-8,	5,	7,	and	-6.
The *degree of each term* is	2,	3,	4,	1,	and	0.

The *leading term* is $5x^4$ and the *leading coefficient* is 5.

The *degree of the polynomial* is 4.

Combining Like Terms

Recall from Section 1.8 that *like,* or *similar, terms* are either constant terms or terms containing the same variable(s) raised to the same power(s). To simplify certain polynomials, we can often *combine,* or *collect,* like terms.

EXAMPLE 4 Identify the like terms in $4x^3 + 5x - 7x^2 + 2x^3 + x^2$.

Solution

Like terms: $4x^3$ and $2x^3$ — Same variable and exponent

Like terms: $-7x^2$ and x^2 — Same variable and exponent

EXAMPLE 5 Combine like terms.

a) $2x^3 - 6x^3$

b) $5x^2 + 7 + 2x^4 + 4x^2 - 11 - 2x^4$

c) $7a^3 - 5a^2 + 9a^3 + a^2$

d) $\frac{2}{3}x^4 - x^3 - \frac{1}{6}x^4 + \frac{2}{5}x^3 - \frac{3}{10}x^3$

Solution

a) $2x^3 - 6x^3 = (2 - 6)x^3$ — Using the distributive law

$= -4x^3$

b) $5x^2 + 7 + 2x^4 + 4x^2 - 11 - 2x^4 = 5x^2 + 4x^2 + 2x^4 - 2x^4 + 7 - 11$

$= (5 + 4)x^2 + (2 - 2)x^4 + (7 - 11)$
$= 9x^2 + 0x^4 + (-4)$ — These steps are often done mentally.

$= 9x^2 - 4$

c) $7a^3 - 5a^2 + 9a^3 + a^2 = 7a^3 - 5a^2 + 9a^3 + 1a^2$ — When a term appears without a coefficient, we can write in 1.

$= 16a^3 - 4a^2$

d) $\frac{2}{3}x^4 - x^3 - \frac{1}{6}x^4 + \frac{2}{5}x^3 - \frac{3}{10}x^3 = \left(\frac{2}{3} - \frac{1}{6}\right)x^4 + \left(-1 + \frac{2}{5} - \frac{3}{10}\right)x^3$

$= \left(\frac{4}{6} - \frac{1}{6}\right)x^4 + \left(-\frac{10}{10} + \frac{4}{10} - \frac{3}{10}\right)x^3$

$= \frac{3}{6}x^4 - \frac{9}{10}x^3$

$= \frac{1}{2}x^4 - \frac{9}{10}x^3$ — There are no similar terms, so we are done.

Student Notes

Remember that when we combine like terms, we are not solving equations, but are forming equivalent expressions.

Note in Example 5 that the solutions are written so that the term of highest degree appears first, followed by the term of next highest degree, and so on. This is known as **descending order** and is the form in which answers will normally appear.

Evaluating Polynomials and Applications

When each variable in a polynomial is replaced with a number, the polynomial then represents a number, or *value*, that can be calculated using the rules for order of operations.

EXAMPLE 6 Evaluate $-x^2 + 3x + 9$ for $x = -2$.

Solution For $x = -2$, we have

$$-x^2 + 3x + 9 = -(-2)^2 + 3(-2) + 9$$

The negative sign in front of x^2 remains.

$$= -(4) + 3(-2) + 9$$
$$= -4 + (-6) + 9$$
$$= -10 + 9 = -1.$$

EXAMPLE 7 Games in a sports league. In a sports league of n teams in which each team plays every other team twice, the total number of games to be played is given by the polynomial

$$n^2 - n.$$

A girls' soccer league has 10 teams. How many games are played if each team plays every other team twice?

Solution We evaluate the polynomial for $n = 10$:

$$n^2 - n = 10^2 - 10$$
$$= 100 - 10 = 90.$$

The league plays 90 games.

EXAMPLE 8 Daily accidents. The average number of accidents per day involving drivers of age r can be approximated by the polynomial

$$0.4r^2 - 40r + 1039.$$

Find the average number of accidents per day involving 20-year-old drivers.

Solution To find the average number of accidents involving 20-year-olds, we evaluate the polynomial for $r = 20$:

$$0.4r^2 - 40r + 1039 = 0.4(20)^2 - 40 \cdot 20 + 1039$$
$$= 0.4 \cdot 400 - 800 + 1039$$
$$= 160 - 800 + 1039$$
$$= 399.$$

There are, on average, approximately 399 accidents each day involving 20-year-old drivers.

Sometimes, a graph can be used to estimate the value of a polynomial visually.

EXAMPLE 9

Daily accidents. In the following graph, the polynomial from Example 8 has been graphed by evaluating it for several choices of x. Use the graph to estimate the average number of accidents per day involving 30-year-old drivers.

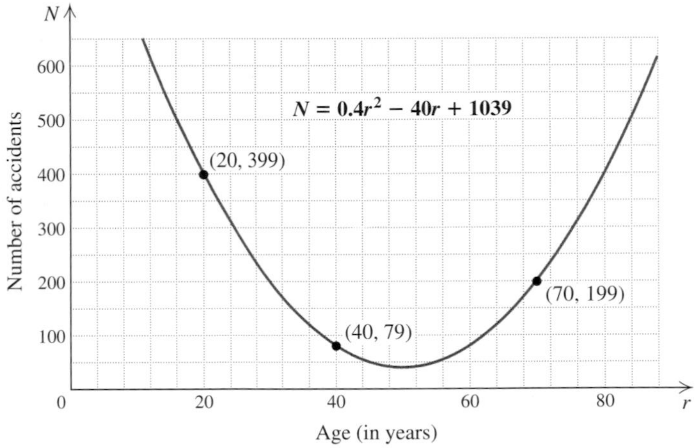

Solution To estimate the number of accidents involving 30-year-olds, we locate 30 on the horizontal axis. From there, we move vertically until we meet the curve at some point. From that point, we move horizontally to the N-axis.

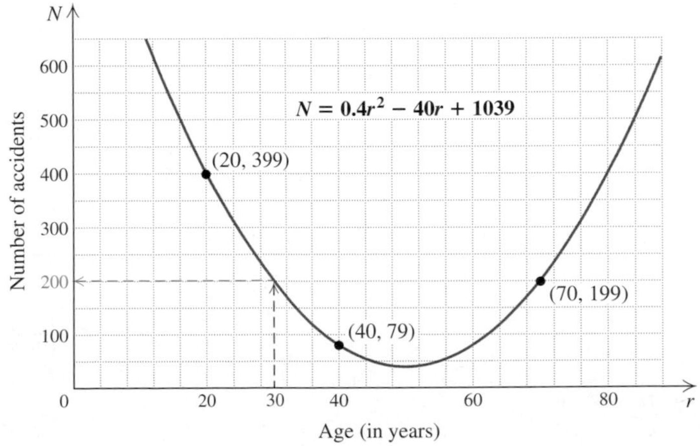

There are, on average, about 200 accidents each day involving 30-year-old drivers. (For $r = 30$, the value of $0.4r^2 - 40r + 1039$ is approximately 200.)

technology connection

One way to evaluate a polynomial is to use the TRACE key. For example, to evaluate $0.4r^2 - 40r + 1039$ in Example 9 for $r = 30$, we can enter the polynomial as $y = 0.4x^2 - 40x + 1039$. We then use TRACE and enter an x-value of 30. The value of the polynomial appears as y, and the cursor automatically appears at (30, 199). The Value option of the CALC menu works in a similar way.

1. Use TRACE or CALC Value to find the value of $0.4r^2 - 40r + 1039$ for $r = 60$.

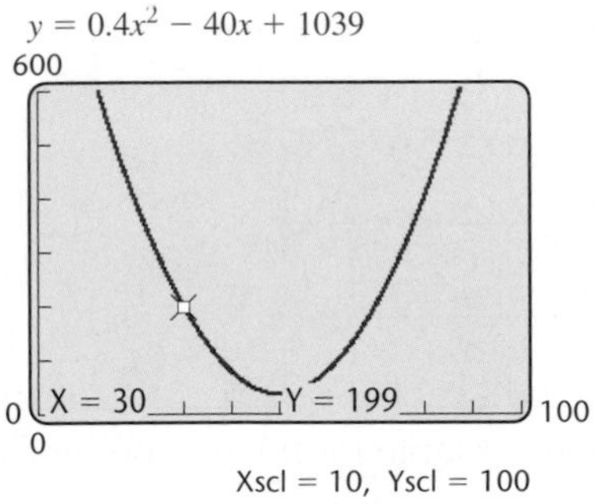

4.2 Exercise Set

FOR EXTRA HELP

Student's Solutions Manual | Digital Video Tutor CD 2 Videotape 7 | AW Math Tutor Center | MathXL Tutorials on CD | MathXL | MyMathLab

Concept Reinforcement *In each of Exercises 1–8, match the description with the most appropriate algebraic expression from the column on the right.*

1. ___ A polynomial with four terms
2. ___ A trinomial written in descending order
3. ___ A polynomial with degree 5
4. ___ A polynomial with 7 as its leading coefficient
5. ___ A binomial with degree 7
6. ___ An expression with two terms that is not a binomial
7. ___ An expression with three terms that is not a trinomial
8. ___ A monomial of degree 0

a) $8x^3 + \dfrac{2}{x^2}$

b) $5x^4 + 3x^3 - 4x + 7$

c) $\dfrac{3}{x} - 6x^2 + 9$

d) $8t - 4t^5$

e) 5

f) $6x^2 + 7x^4 - 2x^3$

g) $4t - 2t^7$

h) $3t^2 + 4t + 7$

Identify the terms of each polynomial.

9. $7x^4 + x^3 - 5x + 8$

10. $5a^3 + 4a^2 - a - 7$

11. $-t^4 + 7t^3 - 3t^2 + 6$

12. $n^5 - 4n^3 + 2n - 8$

Determine the coefficient and the degree of each term in each polynomial.

13. $4x^5 + 7x$

14. $9a^3 - 4a^2$

15. $9t^2 - 3t + 4$

16. $7x^4 + 5x - 3$

17. $7a^4 + 9a + a^3$

18. $6t^5 - 3t^2 - t$

19. $x^4 - x^3 + 4x - 3$

20. $3a^4 - a^3 + a - 9$

For each of the following polynomials, **(a)** *list the degree of each term;* **(b)** *determine the leading term and the leading coefficient; and* **(c)** *determine the degree of the polynomial.*

21. $5x - 9x^2 + 3x^6$

22. $2t + 3 + 4t^2$

23. $3a^2 - 7 + 2a^4$

24. $9x^4 + x^2 + x^7 + 4$

25. $8 + 6x^2 - 3x - x^5$

26. $9a - a^4 + 3 + 2a^3$

27. Complete the following table for the polynomial $7x^2 + 8x^5 - 4x^3 + 6 - \frac{1}{2}x^4$.

Term	Coefficient	Degree of the Term	Degree of the Polynomial
		5	
$-\frac{1}{2}x^4$			
	-4		
		2	
	6		

28. Complete the following table for the polynomial $-3x^4 + 6x^3 - 2x^2 + 8x + 7$.

Term	Coefficient	Degree of the Term	Degree of the Polynomial
	-3		
$6x^3$			
		2	
		1	
	7		

Classify each polynomial as a monomial, binomial, trinomial, or none of these.

29. $x^2 - 23x + 17$

30. $-9x^2$

31. $x^3 - 7x^2 + 2x - 4$

32. $t^3 + 4$

33. $8t^2 + 5t$

34. $4x^2 + 12x + 9$

35. 17

36. $2x^4 - 7x^3 + x^2 + x - 6$

Combine like terms. Write all answers in descending order.

37. $7x^2 + 3x + 4x^2$

38. $5a + 7a^2 + 3a$

39. $3a^4 - 2a + 2a + a^4$

40. $9b^5 + 3b^2 - 2b^5 - 3b^2$

41. $2x^2 - 6x + 3x + 4x^2$

42. $3x^4 - 7x + x^4 - 2x$

43. $9x^3 + 2x - 4x^3 + 5 - 3x$

44. $6x^2 + 2x^4 - 2x^2 - x^4 - 4x^2$

45. $10x^2 + 2x^3 - 3x^3 - 4x^2 - 6x^2 - x^4$

46. $8x^5 - x^4 + 2x^5 + 5x^4 - 4x^4 - x^6$

47. $\frac{1}{5}x^4 + 7 - 2x^2 + 3 - \frac{2}{15}x^4 + 2x^2$

48. $\frac{1}{6}x^3 + 3x^2 - \frac{1}{3}x^3 + 7 + x^2 - 10$

49. $5.9x^2 - 2.1x + 6 + 3.4x - 2.5x^2 - 0.5$

50. $7.4x^3 - 4.9x + 2.9 - 3.5x - 4.3 + 1.9x^3$

Evaluate each polynomial for $x = 3$ and for $x = -3$.

51. $-7x + 4$

52. $-5x + 7$

53. $2x^2 - 3x + 7$

54. $4x^2 - 6x + 9$

55. $-2x^3 - 3x^2 + 4x + 2$

56. $-3x^3 + 7x^2 - 4x - 8$

57. $\frac{1}{3}x^4 - 2x^3$

58. $2x^4 - \frac{1}{9}x^3$

59. $-x^4 - x^3 - x^2$

60. $-x^2 - 3x^3 - x^4$

Consumer debt. *The amount of debt, in trillions of dollars, held by U.S. consumers can be estimated by the polynomial*

$$0.15t + 1.42,$$

where t is the number of years since 2000.
Source: Based on information from the Federal Reserve

61. Estimate U.S. consumer debt in 2005.

62. Estimate U.S. consumer debt in 2008.

63. *Skydiving.* During the first 13 sec of a jump, the number of feet that a skydiver falls in t seconds is approximated by the polynomial

$$11.12t^2.$$

Approximately how far has a skydiver fallen 10 sec after jumping from a plane?

64. *Skydiving.* For jumps that exceed 13 sec, the polynomial $173t - 369$ can be used to approximate the distance, in feet, that a skydiver has fallen in t seconds. Approximately how far has a skydiver fallen 20 sec after jumping from a plane?

Circumference. *The circumference of a circle of radius r is given by the polynomial $2\pi r$, where π is an irrational number. For an approximation of π, use 3.14.*

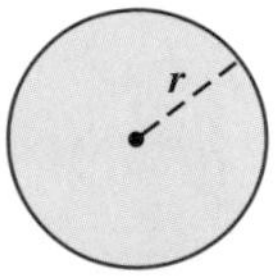

65. Find the circumference of a circle with radius 10 cm.

66. Find the circumference of a circle with radius 5 ft.

Area of a circle. *The area of a circle of radius r is given by the polynomial πr^2. Use 3.14 for π.*

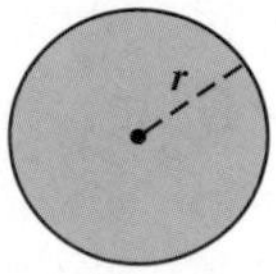

67. Find the area of a circle with radius 7 m.

68. Find the area of a circle with radius 6 ft.

Electricity use. *The consumption of electricity in the United States, in millions of gigawatt hours, t years after 2000, can be approximated by*

$$0.19t + 3.93.$$

Use the following graph for Exercises 69–72.
Source: Based on information from Cambridge Energy Research Associates

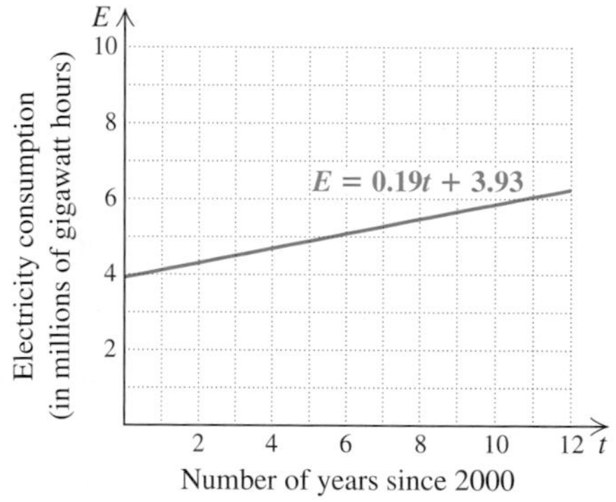

69. Estimate U.S. electricity consumption in 2006.

70. Estimate U.S. electricity consumption in 2008.

71. Estimate U.S. electricity consumption in 2003.

72. Estimate U.S. electricity consumption in 2005.

Memorizing words. *Participants in a psychology experiment were able to memorize an average of M words in t minutes, where* $M = -0.001t^3 + 0.1t^2$. *Use the following graph for Exercises 73–76.*

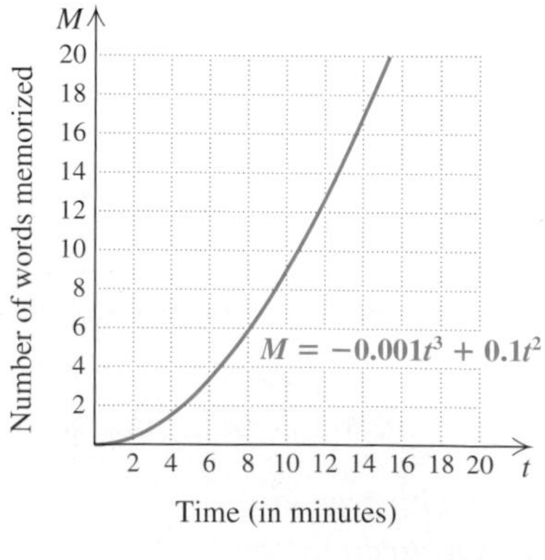

73. Estimate the number of words memorized after 10 min.

74. Estimate the number of words memorized after 14 min.

75. Find the approximate value of M for $t = 8$.

76. Find the approximate value of M for $t = 12$.

Hearing-impaired Americans. *The number, in millions, of hearing-impaired Americans of age x can be approximated by*

$$-0.00006x^3 + 0.006x^2 - 0.1x + 1.9.$$

Use the following graph for Exercises 77 and 78.
Source: Based on information from American Speech-Language Hearing Association

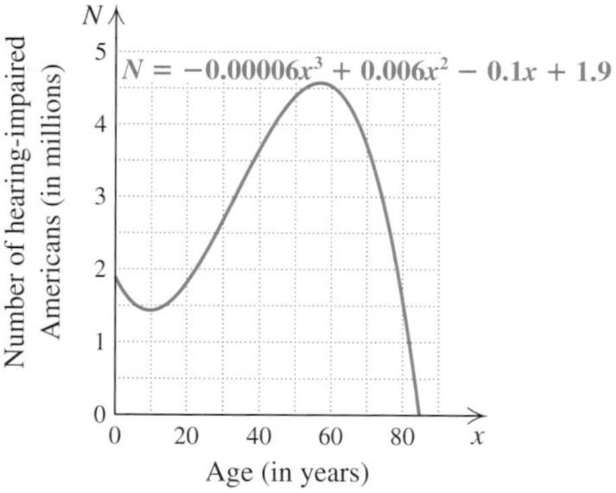

77. Approximate the number of hearing-impaired Americans of ages 20 and 50.

78. Approximate the number of hearing-impaired Americans of ages 30 and 60.

79. Explain how it is possible for a term to not be a monomial.

80. Is it possible to evaluate polynomials without understanding the rules for order of operations? Why or why not?

SKILL MAINTENANCE

Simplify.

81. $-19 + 24$ [1.5]

82. $5 - 14$ [1.6]

Factor. [1.2]

83. $5x + 15$

84. $7a - 21$

85. A family spent $2011 to drive a car one year, during which the car was driven 14,800 mi. The family spent $972 for insurance and $114 for registration and oil. The only other cost was for gasoline. How much did gasoline cost per mile? [3.4]

86. The sum of the page numbers on the facing pages of a book is 549. What are the page numbers? [2.5]

SYNTHESIS

87. Suppose that the coefficients of a polynomial are all integers and the polynomial is evaluated for some integer. Must the value of the polynomial then also be an integer? Why or why not?

88. Is it easier to evaluate a polynomial before or after like terms have been combined? Why?

89. Construct a polynomial in x (meaning that x is the variable) of degree 5 with four terms, with coefficients that are consecutive even integers. Write in descending order.

Revenue, cost, and profit. Gigabytes Electronics is selling a new type of computer monitor. Total revenue *is the total amount of money taken in and* total cost *is the total amount paid for producing the items. The firm estimates that for the monitor's first year, revenue from the sale of x monitors is*

$$250x - 0.5x^2 \text{ dollars,}$$

and the total cost is given by

$$4000 + 0.6x^2 \text{ dollars.}$$

Profit *is the difference between revenue and cost.*

90. Find the profit when 20 monitors are produced and sold.

91. Find the profit when 30 monitors are produced and sold.

Simplify.

92. $\frac{9}{2}x^8 + \frac{1}{9}x^2 + \frac{1}{2}x^9 + \frac{9}{2}x + \frac{9}{2}x^9 + \frac{8}{9}x^2 + \frac{1}{2}x - \frac{1}{2}x^8$

93. $(3x^2)^3 + 4x^2 \cdot 4x^4 - x^4(2x)^2 + ((2x)^2)^3 - 100x^2(x^2)^2$

94. A polynomial in x has degree 3. The coefficient of x^2 is 3 less than the coefficient of x^3. The coefficient of x is three times the coefficient of x^2. The remaining constant is 2 more than the coefficient of x^3. The sum of the coefficients is -4. Find the polynomial.

95. Use the graph for Exercises 77 and 78 to determine the ages at which 1.5 million Americans of that age are hearing-impaired.

96. *Path of the Olympic arrow.* The Olympic flame at the 1992 Summer Olympics was lit by a flaming arrow. As the arrow moved d meters horizontally from the archer, its height h, in meters, was approximated by the polynomial

$$-0.0064d^2 + 0.8d + 2.$$

Complete the table for the choices of d given. Then plot the points and draw a graph representing the path of the arrow.

d	$-0.0064d^2 + 0.8d + 2$
0	
30	
60	
90	
120	

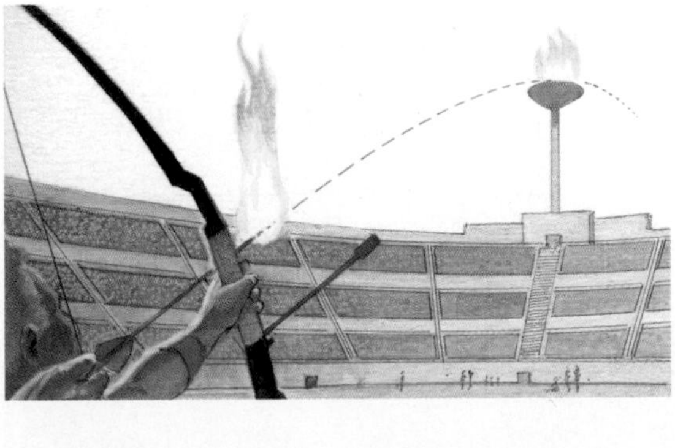

Semester averages. *Professor Kopecki calculates a student's average for her course using*

$$A = 0.3q + 0.4t + 0.2f + 0.1h,$$

with q, t, f, and h representing a student's quiz average, test average, final exam score, and homework average, respectively. In Exercises 97 and 98, find the given student's course average rounded to the nearest tenth.

97. Mary Lou: quizzes: 60, 85, 72, 91; final exam: 84; tests: 89, 93, 90; homework: 88

98. Nigel: quizzes: 95, 99, 72, 79; final exam: 91; tests: 68, 76, 92; homework: 86

In Exercises 99 and 100, complete the table for the given choices of t. Then plot the points and connect them with a smooth curve representing the graph of the polynomial.

99.

t	$-t^2 + 10t - 18$
3	
4	
5	
6	
7	

100.

t	$-t^2 + 6t - 4$
1	
2	
3	
4	
5	

4.3 Addition and Subtraction of Polynomials

Addition of Polynomials • Opposites of Polynomials • Subtraction of Polynomials • Problem Solving

Addition of Polynomials

To add two polynomials, we write a plus sign between them and combine like terms.

EXAMPLE 1 Add.

a) $(-5x^3 + 6x - 1) + (4x^3 + 3x^2 + 2)$

b) $\left(\frac{2}{3}x^4 + 3x^2 - 7x + \frac{1}{2}\right) + \left(-\frac{1}{3}x^4 + 5x^3 - 3x^2 + 3x - \frac{1}{2}\right)$

Solution

a) $(-5x^3 + 6x - 1) + (4x^3 + 3x^2 + 2)$

$= (-5 + 4)x^3 + 3x^2 + 6x + (-1 + 2)$ Combining like terms; using the distributive law

$= -x^3 + 3x^2 + 6x + 1$ Note that $-1x^3 = -x^3$.

b) $\left(\frac{2}{3}x^4 + 3x^2 - 7x + \frac{1}{2}\right) + \left(-\frac{1}{3}x^4 + 5x^3 - 3x^2 + 3x - \frac{1}{2}\right)$

$= \left(\frac{2}{3} - \frac{1}{3}\right)x^4 + 5x^3 + (3 - 3)x^2 + (-7 + 3)x + \left(\frac{1}{2} - \frac{1}{2}\right)$ Combining like terms

$= \frac{1}{3}x^4 + 5x^3 - 4x$

After some practice, polynomial addition is often performed mentally.

EXAMPLE 2 Add: $(2 - 3x + x^2) + (-5 + 7x - 3x^2 + x^3)$.

Solution We have

$$(2 - 3x + x^2) + (-5 + 7x - 3x^2 + x^3)$$
$$= (2 - 5) + (-3 + 7)x + (1 - 3)x^2 + x^3 \quad \text{You might do this step mentally.}$$
$$= -3 + 4x - 2x^2 + x^3. \quad \text{Then you would write only this.}$$

Study Skills

Aim for Mastery

In each exercise set, you may encounter one or more exercises that give you trouble. Do not ignore these problems, but instead work to master them. These are the problems (not the "easy" problems) that you will need to revisit as you progress through the course. Consider marking these exercises with a star so that you can easily locate them when studying or reviewing for a quiz or test.

The polynomials in the last example have the terms arranged according to degree, from least to greatest. Such an arrangement is called *ascending order.* As a rule, answers are written in ascending order when the polynomials in the original problem are given in ascending order. If the polynomials in the original problem are given in descending order, the answer is written in descending order.

We can also add polynomials by writing like terms in columns. Sometimes this makes like terms easier to see.

EXAMPLE 3 Add: $9x^5 - 2x^3 + 6x^2 + 3$ and $5x^4 - 7x^2 + 6$ and $3x^6 - 5x^5 + x^2 + 5$.

Solution We arrange the polynomials with like terms in columns.

$$\begin{array}{rrrrrrl}
 & 9x^5 & & -\ 2x^3 & +\ 6x^2 & +\ 3 & \\
 & & 5x^4 & & -\ 7x^2 & +\ 6 & \text{We leave spaces for missing terms.} \\
3x^6 & -\ 5x^5 & & & +\ 1x^2 & +\ 5 & \text{Writing } x^2 \text{ as } 1x^2 \\
\hline
3x^6 & +\ 4x^5 & +\ 5x^4 & -\ 2x^3 & & +\ 14 & \text{Adding}
\end{array}$$

The answer is $3x^6 + 4x^5 + 5x^4 - 2x^3 + 14$.

CONNECTING THE CONCEPTS

In many ways, polynomials are to algebra as numbers are to arithmetic. Like numbers, polynomials can be added, subtracted, multiplied, and divided. In Sections 4.3–4.7, we examine how these operations are performed. Thus we are again learning how to write equivalent expressions, not how to solve equations.

Note that equations like those in Examples 1–3 are written to show how one expression can be rewritten in an equivalent form. This is very different from solving an equation.

There is much to learn about manipulating polynomials. Not until Section 5.6 will we return to the task of solving equations.

Opposites of Polynomials

In Section 1.8, we used the property of -1 to show that the opposite of a sum is the sum of the opposites. This idea can be extended.

The Opposite of a Polynomial

To find an equivalent polynomial for the *opposite,* or *additive inverse,* of a polynomial, change the sign of every term. This is the same as multiplying the polynomial by -1.

EXAMPLE 4 Write the opposite of $4x^5 - 7x^3 - 8x + \frac{5}{6}$ in two different forms.

Solution

i) $-\left(4x^5 - 7x^3 - 8x + \frac{5}{6}\right)$ This is one representation of the opposite of $4x^5 - 7x^3 - 8x + \frac{5}{6}$.

ii) $-4x^5 + 7x^3 + 8x - \frac{5}{6}$ Changing the sign of every term

Thus, $-\left(4x^5 - 7x^3 - 8x + \frac{5}{6}\right)$ and $-4x^5 + 7x^3 + 8x - \frac{5}{6}$ are equivalent. Both expressions represent the opposite of $4x^5 - 7x^3 - 8x + \frac{5}{6}$.

EXAMPLE 5 Simplify: $-\left(-7x^4 - \frac{5}{9}x^3 + 8x^2 - x + 67\right)$.

Solution We have

$$-\left(-7x^4 - \frac{5}{9}x^3 + 8x^2 - x + 67\right) = 7x^4 + \frac{5}{9}x^3 - 8x^2 + x - 67.$$

The same result can be found by multiplying by -1:

$$\begin{aligned} &-\left(-7x^4 - \tfrac{5}{9}x^3 + 8x^2 - x + 67\right) \\ &\quad = -1(-7x^4) + (-1)\left(-\tfrac{5}{9}x^3\right) + (-1)(8x^2) + (-1)(-x) + (-1)67 \\ &\quad = 7x^4 + \tfrac{5}{9}x^3 - 8x^2 + x - 67. \end{aligned}$$

Subtraction of Polynomials

We can now subtract one polynomial from another by adding the opposite of the polynomial being subtracted.

EXAMPLE 6 Subtract: $(9x^5 + x^3 - 2x^2 + 4) - (-2x^5 + x^4 - 4x^3 - 3x^2)$.

Solution

$$(9x^5 + x^3 - 2x^2 + 4) - (-2x^5 + x^4 - 4x^3 - 3x^2)$$

$= 9x^5 + x^3 - 2x^2 + 4 + 2x^5 - x^4 + 4x^3 + 3x^2$ Adding the opposite

$= 11x^5 - x^4 + 5x^3 + x^2 + 4$ Combining like terms

EXAMPLE 7 Subtract: $(7x^5 + x^3 - 9x) - (3x^5 - 4x^3 + 5)$.

Solution

$$(7x^5 + x^3 - 9x) - (3x^5 - 4x^3 + 5)$$

$= 7x^5 + x^3 - 9x + (-3x^5) + 4x^3 - 5$ Adding the opposite

$= 7x^5 + x^3 - 9x - 3x^5 + 4x^3 - 5$ Try to go directly to this step.

$= 4x^5 + 5x^3 - 9x - 5$ Combining like terms

To subtract using columns, we first replace the coefficients in the polynomial being subtracted with their opposites. We then add as before.

EXAMPLE 8 Write in columns and subtract: $(5x^2 - 3x + 6) - (9x^2 - 5x - 3)$.

Solution

i) $\begin{array}{r} 5x^2 - 3x + 6 \\ \underline{-(9x^2 - 5x - 3)} \end{array}$ Writing similar terms in columns

ii) $\begin{array}{r} 5x^2 - 3x + 6 \\ \underline{-9x^2 + 5x + 3} \end{array}$ Changing signs and removing parentheses

iii) $\begin{array}{r} 5x^2 - 3x + 6 \\ \underline{-9x^2 + 5x + 3} \\ -4x^2 + 2x + 9 \end{array}$ Adding

---

If you can do so without error, you can arrange the polynomials in columns, mentally find the opposite of each term being subtracted, and write the answer. Lining up like terms is important and may require leaving some blanks.

EXAMPLE 9 Write in columns and subtract: $(x^3 + x^2 + 2x - 12) - (-2x^3 + x^2 - 3x)$.

Solution We have

$$\begin{array}{rrrrr} & x^3 + x^2 + 2x - 12 & \\ \underline{-(-2x^3 + x^2 - 3x \qquad)} & & \text{Leaving a blank space for the missing term} \\ 3x^3 \qquad + 5x - 12. & & \end{array}$$

Problem Solving

EXAMPLE 10 Find a polynomial for the sum of the areas of rectangles *A*, *B*, *C*, and *D*.

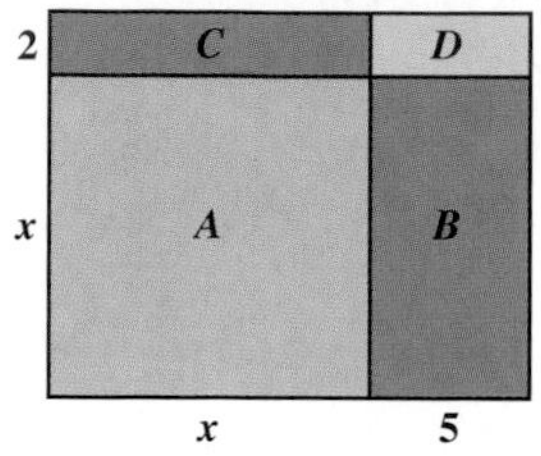

Solution

1. **Familiarize.** Recall that the area of a rectangle is the product of its length and width.
2. **Translate.** We translate the problem to mathematical language. The sum of the areas is a sum of products. We find each product and then add:

Area of *A*	plus	area of *B*	plus	area of *C*	plus	area of *D*
↓	↓	↓	↓	↓	↓	↓
$x \cdot x$	$+$	$5x$	$+$	$2x$	$+$	$2 \cdot 5.$

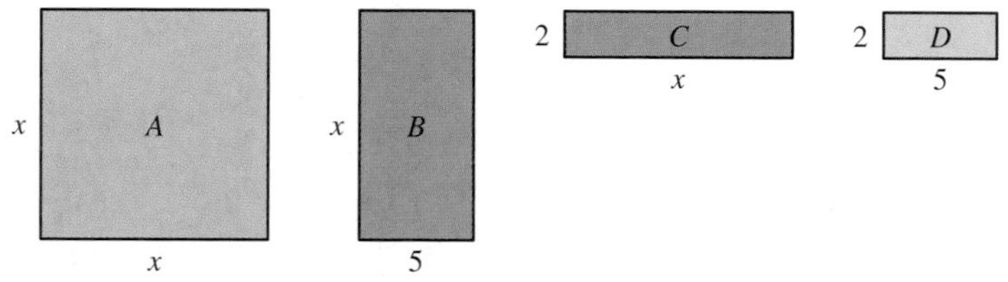

3. **Carry out.** We simplify $x \cdot x$ and $2 \cdot 5$ and combine like terms:

$$x^2 + 5x + 2x + 10 = x^2 + 7x + 10.$$

4. **Check.** A partial check is to replace x with a number, say 3. Then we evaluate $x^2 + 7x + 10$ and compare that result with an alternative calculation:

$$3^2 + 7 \cdot 3 + 10 = 9 + 21 + 10 = 40.$$

When we substitute 3 for x and calculate the total area by regarding the figure as one large rectangle, we should also get 40:

$$\text{Total area} = (x + 5)(x + 2) = (3 + 5)(3 + 2) = 8 \cdot 5 = 40.$$

Our check is only partial, since it is possible for an incorrect answer to equal 40 when evaluated for $x = 3$. This would be unlikely, especially if a second choice of x, say $x = 5$, also checks. We leave that check to the student.

5. **State.** A polynomial for the sum of the areas is $x^2 + 7x + 10$.

EXAMPLE 11 An 8-ft by 8-ft shed is placed on a square lawn x ft on a side. Find a polynomial for the remaining area.

Solution

1. **Familiarize.** We make a drawing of the situation as follows.

2. **Translate.** We reword the problem and translate as follows.

Rewording:	Area of lawn	−	area of shed	=	area left over
Translating:	x ft · x ft	−	8 ft · 8 ft	=	Area left over

3. **Carry out.** We carry out the multiplication:

$$x^2\ \text{ft}^2 - 64\ \text{ft}^2 = \text{Area left over.}$$

4. **Check.** As a partial check, note that the units in the answer are square feet (ft^2), a measure of area, as expected.

5. **State.** The remaining area in the yard is $(x^2 - 64)\ \text{ft}^2$.

technology connection

To check polynomial addition or subtraction, we can let y_1 = the expression before the addition or subtraction has been performed and y_2 = the simplified sum or difference. If the addition or subtraction is correct, y_1 will equal y_2 and $y_2 - y_1$ will be 0. We enter $y_2 - y_1$ as y_3, using the VARS key. Below is a check of Example 7 in which

$$y_1 = (7x^5 + x^3 - 9x) - (3x^5 - 4x^3 + 5),$$
$$y_2 = 4x^5 + 5x^3 - 9x - 5,$$

and

$$y_3 = y_2 - y_1.$$

We graph only y_3. If indeed y_1 and y_2 are equivalent, then y_3 should equal 0. This means its graph should coincide with the x-axis. The TRACE or TABLE features can confirm that y_3 is always 0, or we can select y_3 to be drawn bold at the Y= window.

$y_3 = y_2 - y_1$

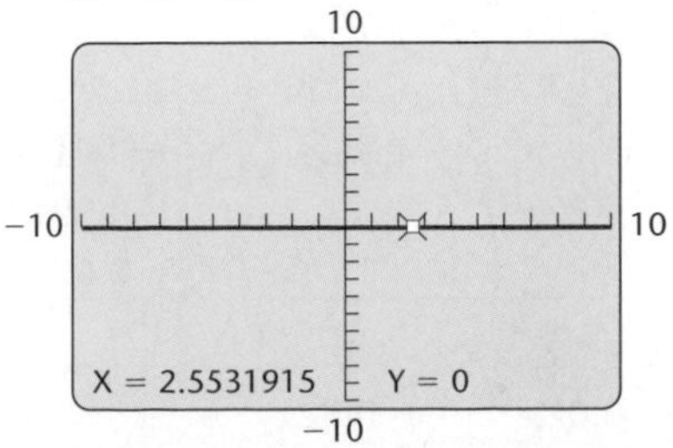

1. Use a graphing calculator to check Examples 1, 2, and 6.

4.3 Exercise Set

FOR EXTRA HELP

Student's Solutions Manual | Digital Video Tutor CD 2 Videotape 7 | AW Math Tutor Center | MathXL Tutorials on CD | MathXL | MyMathLab

Add.

1. $(3x + 2) + (-5x + 4)$

2. $(5x + 1) + (-9x + 4)$

3. $(-6x + 2) + (x^2 + x - 3)$

4. $(x^2 - 5x + 4) + (8x - 9)$

5. $(7t^2 - 3t + 6) + (2t^2 + 8t - 9)$

6. $(8a^2 + 4a - 7) + (6a^2 - 3a - 1)$

7. $(4m^3 - 4m^2 + m - 5) + (4m^3 + 7m^2 - 4m - 2)$

8. $(5n^3 - n^2 + 4n - 3) + (2n^3 - 4n^2 + 3n - 4)$

9. $(3 + 6a + 7a^2 + 8a^3) + (4 + 7a - a^2 + 6a^3)$

10. $(7 + 4t - 5t^2 + 6t^3) + (2 + t + 6t^2 - 4t^3)$

11. $(9x^8 - 7x^4 + 2x^2 + 5) + (8x^7 + 4x^4 - 2x)$

12. $(4x^5 - 6x^3 - 9x + 1) + (6x^3 + 9x^2 + 9x)$

13. $\left(\frac{1}{4}x^4 + \frac{2}{3}x^3 + \frac{5}{8}x^2 + 9\right) + \left(-\frac{3}{4}x^4 + \frac{3}{8}x^2 - 7\right)$

14. $\left(\frac{1}{3}x^9 + \frac{1}{5}x^5 - \frac{1}{2}x^2 + 7\right) + \left(-\frac{1}{5}x^9 + \frac{1}{4}x^4 - \frac{3}{5}x^5\right)$

15. $(5.3t^2 - 6.4t - 9.1) + (4.2t^3 - 1.8t^2 + 7.3)$

16. $(4.9a^3 + 3.2a^2 - 5.1a) + (2.1a^2 - 3.7a + 4.6)$

17.
$$\begin{array}{r} -3x^4 + 6x^2 + 2x - 4 \\ \underline{\quad - 3x^2 + 2x + 4} \end{array}$$

18.
$$\begin{array}{r} -4x^3 + 8x^2 + 3x - 2 \\ \underline{\quad - 4x^2 + 3x + 2} \end{array}$$

19.
$$\begin{array}{rrrrr} 0.15x^4 & + 0.10x^3 & - 0.9x^2 & & \\ & - 0.01x^3 & + 0.01x^2 & + x & \\ 1.25x^4 & & + 0.11x^2 & & + 0.01 \\ & 0.27x^3 & & & + 0.99 \\ \hline -0.35x^4 & & + 15x^2 & & - 0.03 \end{array}$$

20.
$$\begin{array}{rrrrr} 0.05x^4 & + 0.12x^3 & - 0.5x^2 & & \\ & - 0.02x^3 & + 0.02x^2 & + 2x & \\ 1.5x^4 & & + 0.01x^2 & & + 0.15 \\ & 0.25x^3 & & & + 0.85 \\ \hline -0.25x^4 & & + 10x^2 & & - 0.04 \end{array}$$

Write the opposite of each polynomial in two different forms, as in Example 4.

21. $-t^3 + 4t^2 - 9$

22. $-4x^3 - 5x^2 + 2x$

23. $12x^4 - 3x^3 + 3$

24. $5a^3 + 2a - 17$

Simplify.

25. $-(8x - 9)$

26. $-(-6x + 5)$

27. $-(3a^4 - 5a^2 + 9)$

28. $-(-6a^3 + 2a^2 - 7)$

29. $-(-4x^4 + 6x^2 + \frac{3}{4}x - 8)$

30. $-(-5x^4 + 4x^3 - x^2 + 0.9)$

Subtract.

31. $(7x + 4) - (-2x + 1)$

32. $(5x + 6) - (-2x + 4)$

33. $(-5t + 6) - (t^2 + 3t - 1)$

34. $(a^2 - 5a + 2) - (3a^2 + 2a - 4)$

35. $(6x^4 + 3x^3 - 1) - (4x^2 - 3x + 3)$

36. $(-4x^2 + 2x) - (3x^3 - 5x^2 + 3)$

37. $(1.2x^3 + 4.5x^2 - 3.8x) - (-3.4x^3 - 4.7x^2 + 23)$

38. $(0.5x^4 - 0.6x^2 + 0.7) - (2.3x^4 + 1.8x - 3.9)$

Aha! **39.** $(7x^3 - 2x^2 + 6) - (7x^3 - 2x^2 + 6)$

40. $(8x^5 + 3x^4 + x - 1) - (8x^5 + 3x^4 - 1)$

41. $(3 + 5a + 3a^2 - a^3) - (2 + 3a - 4a^2 + 2a^3)$

42. $(7 + t - 5t^2 + 2t^3) - (1 + 2t - 4t^2 + 5t^3)$

43. $\left(\frac{5}{8}x^3 - \frac{1}{4}x - \frac{1}{3}\right) - \left(-\frac{1}{8}x^3 + \frac{1}{4}x - \frac{1}{3}\right)$

44. $\left(\frac{1}{5}x^3 + 2x^2 - \frac{3}{10}\right) - \left(-\frac{2}{5}x^3 + 2x^2 + \frac{7}{1000}\right)$

45. $(0.07t^3 - 0.03t^2 + 0.01t) - (0.02t^3 + 0.04t^2 - 1)$

46. $(0.9a^3 + 0.2a - 5) - (0.7a^4 - 0.3a - 0.1)$

47. $\begin{array}{r} x^2 + 5x + 6 \\ \underline{-(x^2 + 2x + 1)} \end{array}$

48. $\begin{array}{r} x^3 + 3x^2 + 1 \\ \underline{-(x^3 + x^2 - 5)} \end{array}$

49. $\begin{array}{r} 5x^4 + 6x^3 - 9x^2 \\ \underline{-(-6x^4 - 6x^3 + x^2)} \end{array}$

50. $\begin{array}{r} 4x^4 - 2x^3 + 6x^2 \\ \underline{-(7x^4 + 6x^3 + 7x^2)} \end{array}$

51. Solve.

a) Find a polynomial for the sum of the areas of the rectangles shown in the figure.

b) Find the sum of the areas when $x = 5$ and $x = 7$.

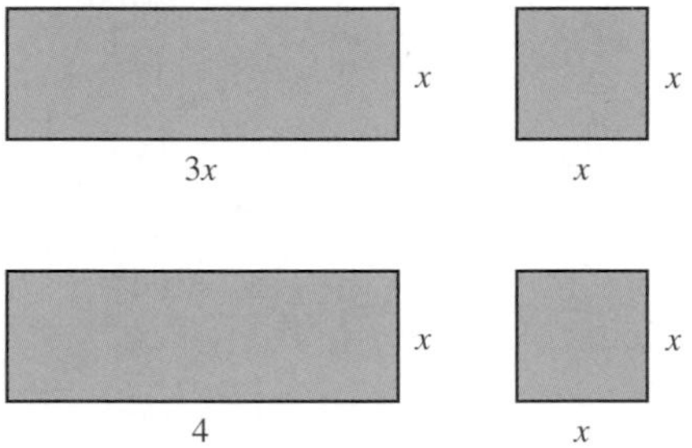

52. Solve.

a) Find a polynomial for the sum of the areas of the circles shown in the figure.

b) Find the sum of the areas when $r = 5$ and $r = 11.3$.

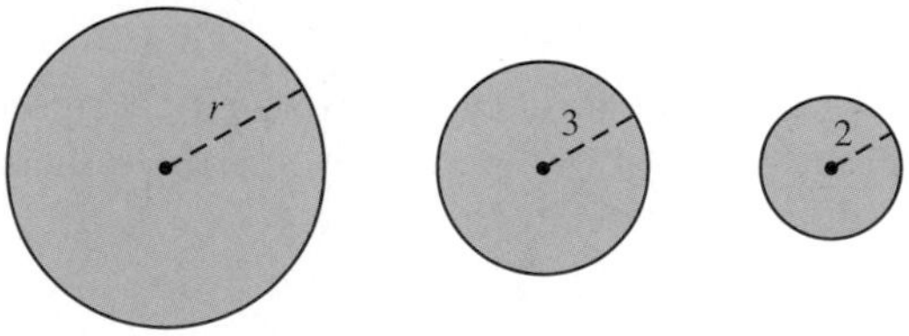

Find a polynomial for the perimeter of each figure in Exercises 53 and 54.

53.

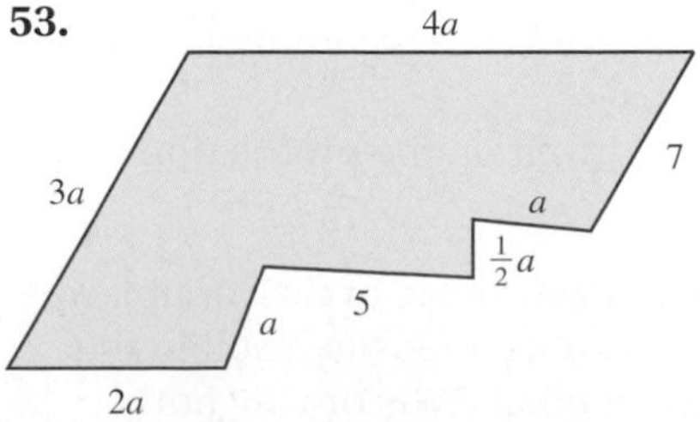

54.

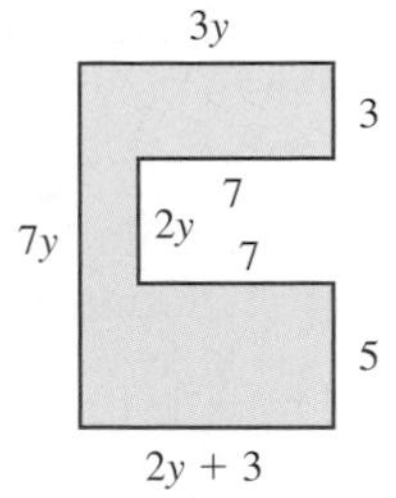

Find two algebraic expressions for the area of each figure. First, regard the figure as one large rectangle, and then regard the figure as a sum of four smaller rectangles.

55.

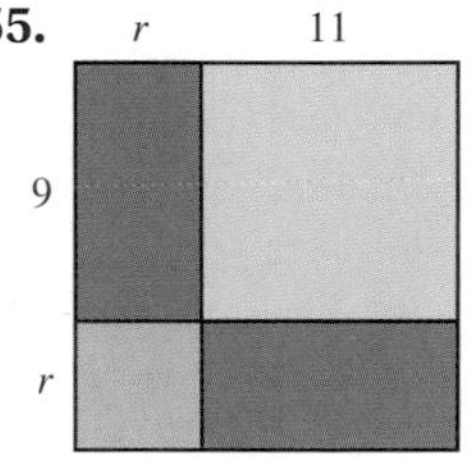

56.

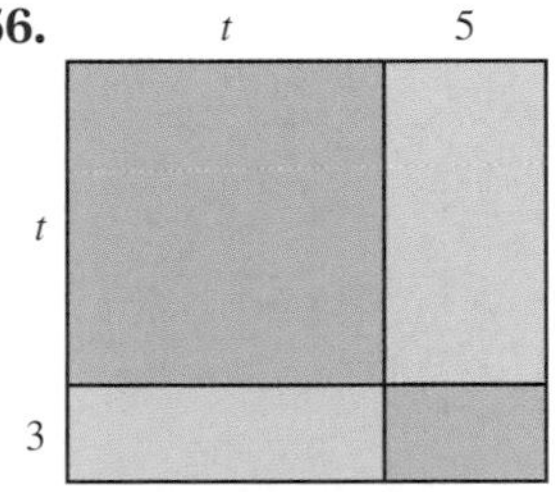

57.

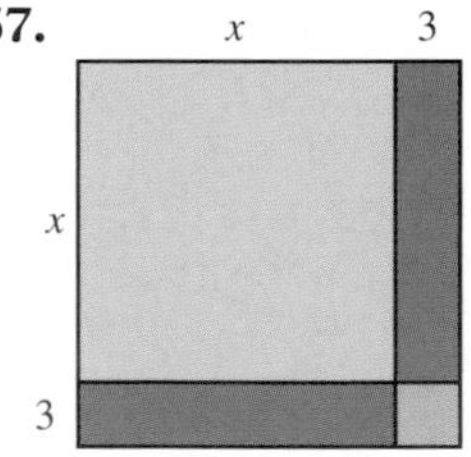

58.

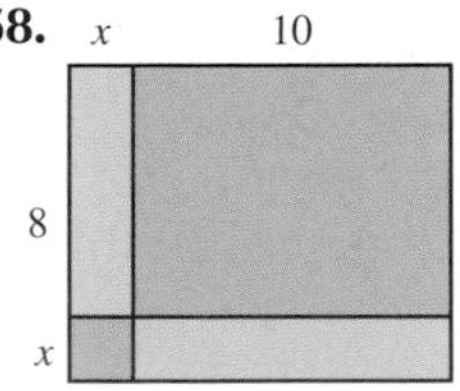

Find a polynomial for the shaded area of each figure.

59.

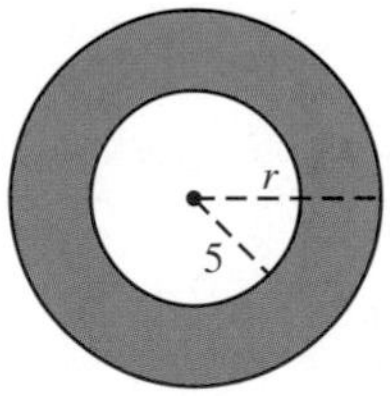

60.

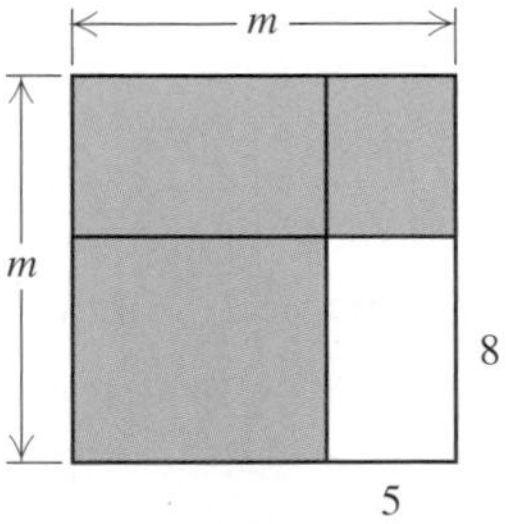

61.

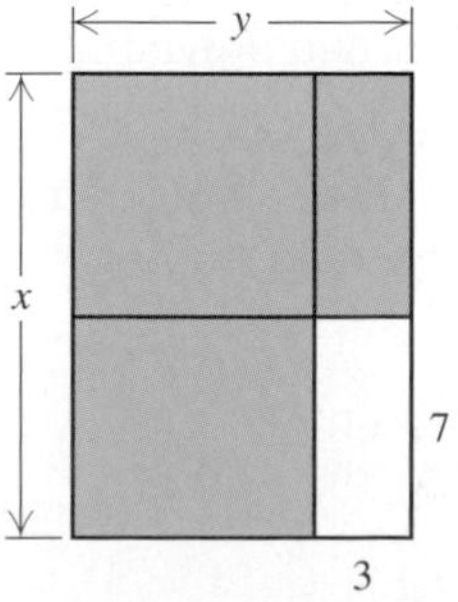

62.

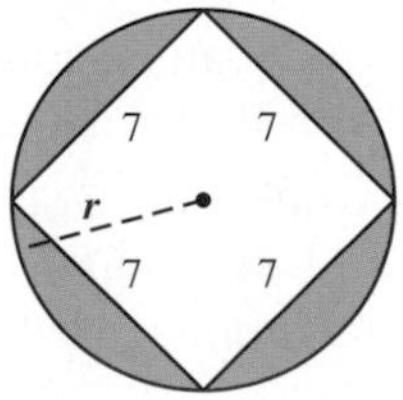

63. A 2-ft by 6-ft bath enclosure is installed in a new bathroom measuring x ft by x ft. Find a polynomial for the remaining floor area.

64. A 5-ft by 7-ft Jacuzzi™ is installed on an outdoor deck measuring y ft by y ft. Find a polynomial for the remaining area of the deck.

65. An 8-ft–wide round hot tub is installed in a patio measuring z ft by z ft. Find a polynomial for the remaining area of the patio.

66. A 10-ft–wide round water trampoline is floating in a pool measuring x ft by x ft. Find a polynomial for the remaining surface area of the pool.

67. A 12-m by 12-m mat includes a circle of diameter d meters for wrestling. Find a polynomial for the area of the mat outside the wrestling circle.

68. A 2-m by 3-m rug is spread inside a tepee that has a diameter of x meters. Find a polynomial for the area of the tepee's floor that is not covered.

69. What advice would you offer to a student who is successful at adding, but not subtracting, polynomials?

70. Is the sum of two trinomials always a trinomial? Why or why not?

SKILL MAINTENANCE

Simplify. [1.8]

71. $5(4 + 3) - 5 \cdot 4 - 5 \cdot 3$

72. $7(2 + 6) - 7 \cdot 2 - 7 \cdot 6$

73. $2(5t + 7) + 3t$

74. $3(4t - 5) + 2t$

Solve. [2.6]

75. $2(x + 3) > 5(x - 3) + 7$

76. $7(x - 8) \leq 4(x - 5)$

SYNTHESIS

77. What can be concluded about two polynomials whose sum is zero?

78. Which, if any, of the commutative, associative, and distributive laws are needed for adding polynomials? Why?

Simplify.

79. $(6t^2 - 7t) + (3t^2 - 4t + 5) - (9t - 6)$

80. $(3x^2 - 4x + 6) - (-2x^2 + 4) + (-5x - 3)$

81. $(-8y^2 - 4) - (3y + 6) - (2y^2 - y)$

82. $(-4 + x^2 + 2x^3) - (-6 - x + 3x^3) - (-x^2 - 5x^3)$

83. $(345.099x^3 - 6.178x) - (94.508x^3 - 8.99x)$

Find a polynomial for the surface area of the right rectangular solid.

84.

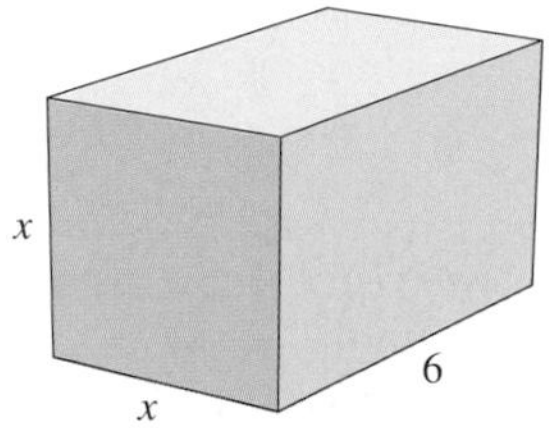

85.

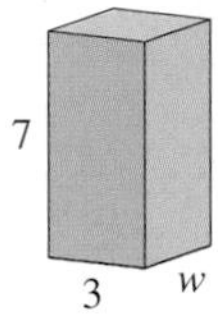

86.

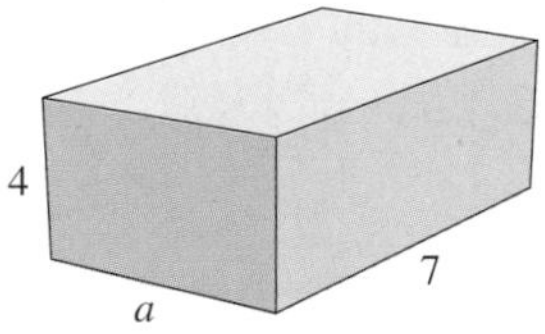

87.

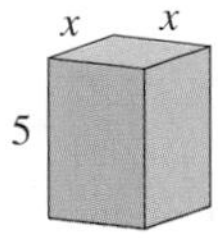

88. Find a polynomial for the total length of all edges in the figure appearing in Exercise 87.

89. Find a polynomial for the total length of all edges in the figure appearing in Exercise 84.

90. *Total profit.* Hadley Electronics is marketing a new kind of stereo. Total revenue is the total amount of money taken in. The firm determines that when it sells x stereos, its total revenue is given by

$$R = 280x - 0.4x^2.$$

Total cost is the total cost of producing x stereos. Hadley Electronics determines that the total cost of producing x stereos is given by

$$C = 5000 + 0.6x^2.$$

The total profit P is

$$(\text{Total Revenue}) - (\text{Total Cost}) = R - C.$$

a) Find a polynomial for total profit.
b) What is the total profit on the production and sale of 75 stereos?
c) What is the total profit on the production and sale of 100 stereos?

91. Does replacing each occurrence of the variable x in $4x^7 - 6x^3 + 2x$ with its opposite result in the opposite of the polynomial? Why or why not?

4.4 Multiplication of Polynomials

Multiplying Monomials • Multiplying a Monomial and a Polynomial • Multiplying Any Two Polynomials • Checking by Evaluating

We now multiply polynomials using techniques based largely on the distributive, associative, and commutative laws and the rules for exponents.

Multiplying Monomials

Consider $(3x)(4x)$. We multiply as follows:

$$(3x)(4x) = 3 \cdot x \cdot 4 \cdot x \qquad \text{Using an associative law}$$
$$= 3 \cdot 4 \cdot x \cdot x \qquad \text{Using a commutative law}$$
$$= (3 \cdot 4) \cdot x \cdot x \qquad \text{Using an associative law}$$
$$= 12x^2.$$

To Multiply Monomials

To find an equivalent expression for the product of two monomials, multiply the coefficients and then multiply the variables using the product rule for exponents.

EXAMPLE 1 Multiply: **(a)** $(5x)(6x)$; **(b)** $(3a)(-a)$; **(c)** $(-7x^5)(4x^3)$.

Solution

a) $(5x)(6x) = (5 \cdot 6)(x \cdot x)$ — Multiplying the coefficients; multiplying the variables

$= 30x^2$ — Simplifying

b) $(3a)(-a) = (3a)(-1a)$ — Writing $-a$ as $-1a$ can ease calculations.

$= (3)(-1)(a \cdot a)$ — Using an associative and a commutative law

$= -3a^2$

c) $(-7x^5)(4x^3) = (-7 \cdot 4)(x^5 \cdot x^3)$

$= -28x^{5+3}$
$= -28x^8$ } Using the product rule for exponents

Student Notes

Remember that when we compute $(3 \cdot 5)(2 \cdot 4)$, each factor is used only once, even if we change the order:

$$(3 \cdot 5)(2 \cdot 4) = (5 \cdot 2)(3 \cdot 4)$$
$$= 10 \cdot 12 = 120.$$

Some students mistakenly "reuse" a factor, as if the distributive law applied.

After some practice, you can try writing only the answer.

Multiplying a Monomial and a Polynomial

To find an equivalent expression for the product of a monomial, such as $5x$, and a polynomial, such as $2x^2 - 3x + 4$, we use the distributive law.

EXAMPLE 2 Multiply: **(a)** x and $x + 3$; **(b)** $5x(2x^2 - 3x + 4)$.

Solution

a) $x(x + 3) = x \cdot x + x \cdot 3$ Using the distributive law

$= x^2 + 3x$

b) $5x(2x^2 - 3x + 4) = (5x)(2x^2) - (5x)(3x) + (5x)(4)$ Using the distributive law

$= 10x^3 - 15x^2 + 20x$ Performing the three multiplications

The product in Example 2(a) can be visualized as the area of a rectangle with width x and length $x + 3$.

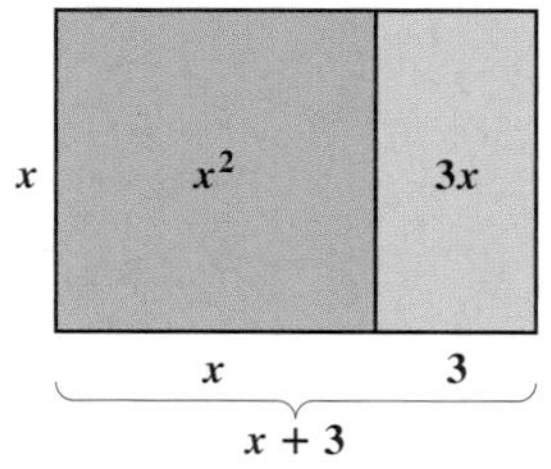

Note that the total area can be expressed as $x(x + 3)$ or, by adding the two smaller areas, $x^2 + 3x$.

The Product of a Monomial and a Polynomial

To multiply a monomial and a polynomial, multiply each term of the polynomial by the monomial.

Try to do this mentally, when possible. Remember that we multiply coefficients and, when the bases match, add exponents.

EXAMPLE 3 Multiply: $2x^2(x^3 - 7x^2 + 10x - 4)$.

Solution

Think: $2x^2 \cdot x^3 - 2x^2 \cdot 7x^2 + 2x^2 \cdot 10x - 2x^2 \cdot 4$

$2x^2(x^3 - 7x^2 + 10x - 4) = 2x^5 - 14x^4 + 20x^3 - 8x^2$

Multiplying Any Two Polynomials

Before considering the product of *any* two polynomials, let's look at products when both polynomials are binomials.

To find an equivalent expression for the product of two binomials, we again begin by using the distributive law. This time, however, it is a *binomial* rather than a monomial that is being distributed.

EXAMPLE 4 Multiply each of the following.

a) $x + 5$ and $x + 4$ **b)** $4x - 3$ and $x - 2$

Solution

a) $(x + 5)(x + 4) = (x + 5)\,x + (x + 5)\,4$ Using the distributive law

$= x(x + 5) + 4(x + 5)$ Using the commutative law for multiplication

$= x \cdot x + x \cdot 5 + 4 \cdot x + 4 \cdot 5$ Using the distributive law (twice)

$= x^2 + 5x + 4x + 20$ Multiplying the monomials

$= x^2 + 9x + 20$ Combining like terms

b) $(4x - 3)(x - 2) = (4x - 3)\,x - (4x - 3)\,2$ Using the distributive law

$= x(4x - 3) - 2(4x - 3)$ Using the commutative law for multiplication. This step is often omitted.

$= x \cdot 4x - x \cdot 3 - 2 \cdot 4x - 2(-3)$ Using the distributive law (twice)

$= 4x^2 - 3x - 8x + 6$ Multiplying the monomials

$= 4x^2 - 11x + 6$ Combining like terms

Study Skills

Take a Peek Ahead

Try to at least glance at the next section of material that will be covered in class. This will make it easier to concentrate on your instructor's lecture instead of trying to write everything down.

To visualize the product in Example 4(a), consider a rectangle of length $x + 5$ and width $x + 4$, as shown here.

The total area can be expressed as $(x + 5)(x + 4)$ or, by adding the four smaller areas, $x^2 + 5x + 4x + 20$.

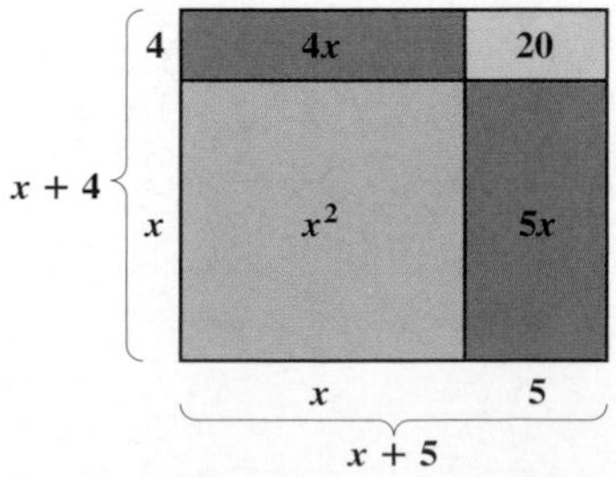

Let's consider the product of a binomial and a trinomial. Again we make repeated use of the distributive law.

EXAMPLE 5 Multiply: $(x^2 + 2x - 3)(x + 4)$.

Solution

$$
\begin{aligned}
&(x^2 + 2x - 3)\,(x + 4) \\
&\quad = (x^2 + 2x - 3)\,x + (x^2 + 2x - 3)\,4 && \text{Using the distributive law} \\
&\quad = x(x^2 + 2x - 3) + 4(x^2 + 2x - 3) && \text{Using the commutative law} \\
&\quad = x \cdot x^2 + x \cdot 2x - x \cdot 3 + 4 \cdot x^2 + 4 \cdot 2x - 4 \cdot 3 && \text{Using the distributive law (twice)} \\
&\quad = x^3 + 2x^2 - 3x + 4x^2 + 8x - 12 && \text{Multiplying the monomials} \\
&\quad = x^3 + 6x^2 + 5x - 12 && \text{Combining like terms}
\end{aligned}
$$

Perhaps you have discovered the following in the preceding examples.

The Product of Two Polynomials

To multiply two polynomials P and Q, select one of the polynomials, say P. Then multiply each term of P by every term of Q and combine like terms.

To use columns for long multiplication, multiply each term in the top row by every term in the bottom row. We write like terms in columns, and then add the results. Such multiplication is like multiplying with whole numbers:

321	300 + 20 + 1	
× 12	× 10 + 2	
642	600 + 40 + 2	Multiplying the top row by 2
321	3000 + 200 + 10	Multiplying the top row by 10
3852	3000 + 800 + 50 + 2	Adding

EXAMPLE 6 Multiply: $(4x^3 - 2x^2 + 3x)(x^2 + 2x)$.

Solution

$$
\begin{array}{r}
4x^3 - 2x^2 + 3x \\
x^2 + 2x \\
\hline
8x^4 - 4x^3 + 6x^2 \\
4x^5 - 2x^4 + 3x^3 \qquad\quad \\
\hline
4x^5 + 6x^4 - x^3 + 6x^2
\end{array}
$$

Note that each polynomial is written in descending order.

Multiplying the top row by $2x$

Multiplying the top row by x^2

Combining like terms

Line up like terms in columns.

If a term is missing, it helps to leave space for it so that like terms can be easily aligned.

EXAMPLE 7 Multiply: $(-2x^2 - 3)(5x^3 - 3x + 4)$.

Solution

$$\begin{array}{rrrrrl}
 & 5x^3 & & -3x & +4 & \\
 & & -2x^2 & & -3 & \text{Leaving space for missing terms} \\
\hline
 & -15x^3 & & +9x & -12 & \text{Multiplying by } -3 \\
-10x^5 & +6x^3 & -8x^2 & & & \text{Multiplying by } -2x^2 \\
\hline
-10x^5 & -9x^3 & -8x^2 & +9x & -12 & \text{Combining like terms}
\end{array}$$

With practice, some steps can be skipped. Sometimes we multiply horizontally, while still aligning like terms.

EXAMPLE 8 Multiply: $(2x^3 + 3x^2 - 4x + 6)(3x + 5)$.

Solution

$$\begin{aligned}
(2x^3 + 3x^2 - 4x + 6)(3x + 5) &= \overbrace{6x^4 + 9x^3 - 12x^2 + 18x}^{\text{Multiplying by } 3x} \\
&\quad + \underbrace{10x^3 + 15x^2 - 20x + 30}_{\text{Multiplying by } 5} \\
&= 6x^4 + 19x^3 + 3x^2 - 2x + 30
\end{aligned}$$

Checking by Evaluating

How can we be certain that our multiplication (or addition or subtraction) of polynomials is correct? One check is to simply review our calculations. A different type of check, used in Example 10 of Section 4.3, makes use of the fact that equivalent expressions have the same value when evaluated for the same replacement. Thus a quick, partial, check of Example 8 can be made by selecting a convenient replacement for x (say, 1) and comparing the values of the expressions $(2x^3 + 3x^2 - 4x + 6)(3x + 5)$ and $6x^4 + 19x^3 + 3x^2 - 2x + 30$:

$$\begin{aligned}
(2x^3 + 3x^2 - 4x + 6)(3x + 5) &= (2 \cdot 1^3 + 3 \cdot 1^2 - 4 \cdot 1 + 6)(3 \cdot 1 + 5) \\
&= (2 + 3 - 4 + 6)(3 + 5) \\
&= 7 \cdot 8 = 56;
\end{aligned}$$

$$\begin{aligned}
6x^4 + 19x^3 + 3x^2 - 2x + 30 &= 6 \cdot 1^4 + 19 \cdot 1^3 + 3 \cdot 1^2 - 2 \cdot 1 + 30 \\
&= 6 + 19 + 3 - 2 + 30 \\
&= 28 - 2 + 30 = 56.
\end{aligned}$$

Since the value of both expressions is 56, the multiplication in Example 8 is very likely correct.

It is possible, by chance, for two expressions that are not equivalent to share the same value when evaluated. For this reason, checking by evaluating is only a partial check. Consult your instructor for the checking approach that he or she prefers.

technology connection

Tables can also be used to check polynomial multiplication. To illustrate, we can check Example 8 by entering $y_1 = (2x^3 + 3x^2 - 4x + 6)(3x + 5)$ and $y_2 = 6x^4 + 19x^3 + 3x^2 - 2x + 30$.

When TABLE is then pressed, we are shown two columns of values—one for y_1 and one for y_2. If our multiplication was correct, the columns of values will match.

X	Y1	Y2
−3	36	36
−2	−10	−10
−1	22	22
0	30	30
1	56	56
2	286	286
3	1050	1050

X = −3

1. Form a table and scroll up and down to check Example 7.
2. Check Example 8 using the method discussed in Section 4.3: Let

$$y_1 = (2x^3 + 3x^2 - 4x + 6)(3x + 5),$$
$$y_2 = 6x^4 + 19x^3 + 3x^2 - 2x + 30,$$

and

$$y_3 = y_2 - y_1.$$

Then check that y_3 is always 0.

4.4 Exercise Set

FOR EXTRA HELP

Student's Solutions Manual | Digital Video Tutor CD 3 Videotape 7 | AW Math Tutor Center | MathXL Tutorials on CD | MathXL | MyMathLab

Concept Reinforcement *In each of Exercises 1–4, match the product with the correct result from the column on the right.*

1. ____ $4x^4 \cdot 2x^2$ **a)** $6x^8$

2. ____ $3x^2 \cdot 2x^4$ **b)** $8x^6$

3. ____ $4x^3 \cdot 2x^5$ **c)** $6x^6$

4. ____ $3x^5 \cdot 2x^3$ **d)** $8x^8$

Multiply.

5. $(4x^3)9$

6. $(5x^4)6$

7. $(-x^3)(x^4)$

8. $(-x^2)(-x)$

9. $(-x^6)(-x^2)$

10. $(-x^5)(x^3)$

11. $(8a^2)(3a^2)$

12. $(7t^5)(4t^3)$

13. $(0.3x^3)(-0.4x^6)$

14. $(-0.1x^6)(0.2x^4)$

15. $\left(-\frac{1}{4}x^4\right)\left(\frac{1}{5}x^8\right)$

16. $\left(-\frac{1}{5}x^3\right)\left(-\frac{1}{3}x\right)$

17. $(-5n^3)(-1)$

18. $19t^2 \cdot 0$

19. $(-4y^5)(6y^2)(-3y^3)$
20. $7x^2(-2x^3)(2x^6)$
21. $2x(4x - 6)$
22. $3x(-x + 5)$
23. $3x(x + 2)$
24. $4x(x + 1)$
25. $(a + 9)3a$
26. $(a - 7)4a$
27. $x^2(x^3 + 1)$
28. $-2x^3(x^2 - 1)$
29. $3x(2x^2 - 6x + 1)$
30. $-4x(2x^3 - 6x^2 - 5x + 1)$
31. $5t^2(3t + 6)$
32. $7t^2(2t + 1)$
33. $-6x^2(x^2 + x)$
34. $-4x^2(x^2 - x)$
35. $\frac{2}{3}a^4(6a^5 - 12a^3 - \frac{5}{8})$
36. $\frac{3}{4}t^5(8t^6 - 12t^4 + \frac{12}{7})$
37. $(x + 2)(x + 6)$
38. $(x + 5)(x + 2)$
39. $(x + 5)(x - 2)$
40. $(x + 6)(x - 2)$
41. $(a - 6)(a - 7)$
42. $(a - 4)(a - 8)$
43. $(x + 3)(x - 3)$
44. $(x + 6)(x - 6)$
45. $(5 - x)(5 - 2x)$
46. $(3 + x)(6 + 2x)$
47. $(t + \frac{3}{2})(t + \frac{4}{3})$
48. $(a - \frac{2}{5})(a + \frac{5}{2})$
49. $(\frac{1}{4}a + 2)(\frac{3}{4}a - 1)$
50. $(\frac{2}{5}t - 1)(\frac{3}{5}t + 1)$

Draw and label rectangles similar to those following Examples 2 and 4 to illustrate each product.

51. $x(x + 5)$
52. $x(x + 2)$
53. $(x + 1)(x + 2)$
54. $(x + 3)(x + 1)$
55. $(x + 5)(x + 3)$
56. $(x + 4)(x + 6)$

Multiply and check.

57. $(x^2 - x + 5)(x + 1)$
58. $(x^2 + x - 7)(x + 2)$
59. $(2a + 5)(a^2 - 3a + 2)$
60. $(3t + 4)(t^2 - 5t + 1)$
61. $(y^2 - 7)(2y^3 + y + 1)$
62. $(a^2 + 4)(5a^3 - 3a - 1)$
63. Aha! $(3x + 2)(5x + 4x + 7)$
64. $(4x - 5x - 3)(1 + 2x^2)$
65. $(x^2 - 3x + 2)(x^2 + x + 1)$
66. $(x^2 + 5x - 1)(x^2 - x + 3)$
67. $(2t^2 - 5t - 4)(3t^2 - t + \frac{1}{2})$
68. $(5t^2 - t + \frac{1}{2})(2t^2 + t - 4)$
69. $(x + 1)(x^3 + 7x^2 + 5x + 4)$
70. $(x + 2)(x^3 + 5x^2 + 9x + 3)$
71. Is it possible to understand polynomial multiplication without understanding the distributive law? Why or why not?
72. The polynomials

$$(a + b + c + d) \quad \text{and} \quad (r + s + m + p)$$

are multiplied. Without performing the multiplication, determine how many terms the product will contain. Provide a justification for your answer.

SKILL MAINTENANCE

Simplify. [1.8]

73. $5 - 3 \cdot 2 + 7$
74. $4 + 6 \cdot 5 - 3$
75. $(8 - 2)(8 + 2) + 2^2 - 8^2$
76. $(7 - 3)(7 + 3) + 3^2 - 7^2$

SYNTHESIS

77. Under what conditions will the product of two binomials be a trinomial?
78. How can the following figure be used to show that $(x + 3)^2 \neq x^2 + 9$?

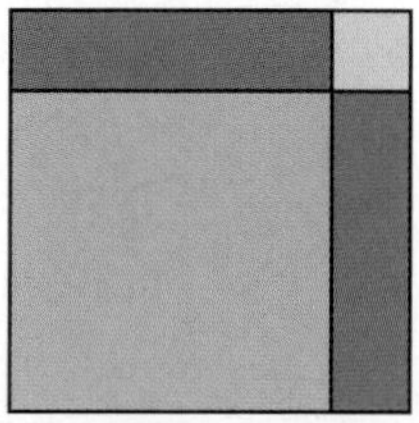

Find a polynomial for the shaded area of each figure.

79.

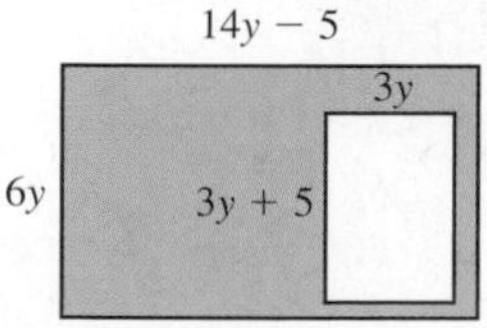

80.

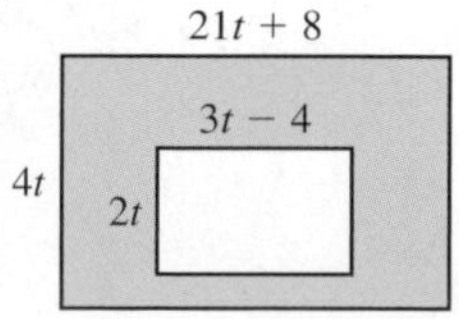

For each figure, determine what the missing number must be in order for the figure to have the given area.

81. Area is $x^2 + 7x + 10$

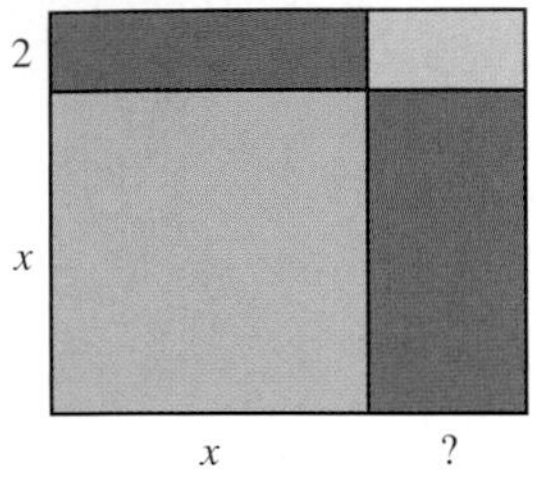

82. Area is $x^2 + 8x + 15$

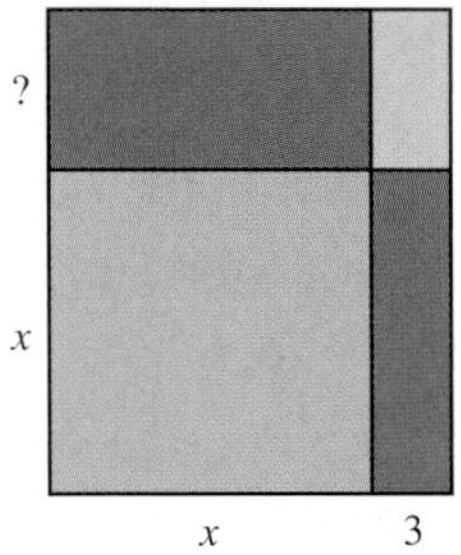

83. A box with a square bottom and no top is to be made from a 12-in.-square piece of cardboard. Squares with side x are cut out of the corners and the sides are folded up. Find the polynomials for the volume and the outside surface area of the box.

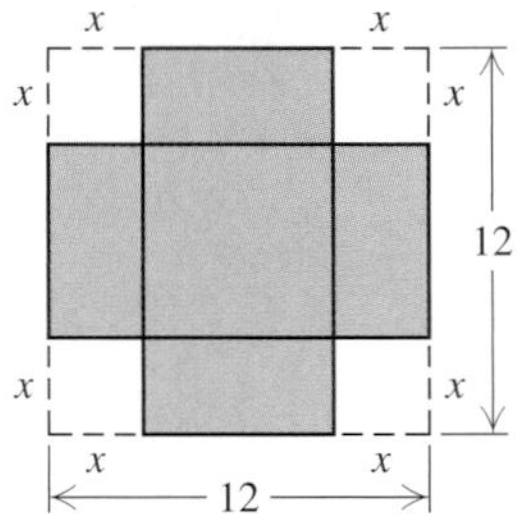

84. An open wooden box is a cube with side x cm. The box, including its bottom, is made of wood that is 1 cm thick. Find a polynomial for the interior volume of the cube.

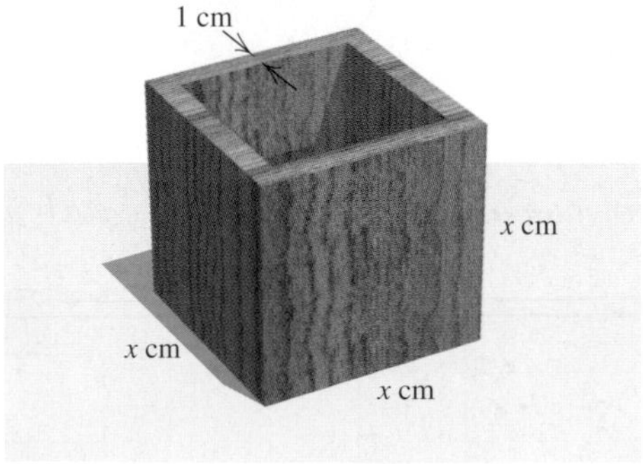

85. Find a polynomial for the volume of the solid shown below.

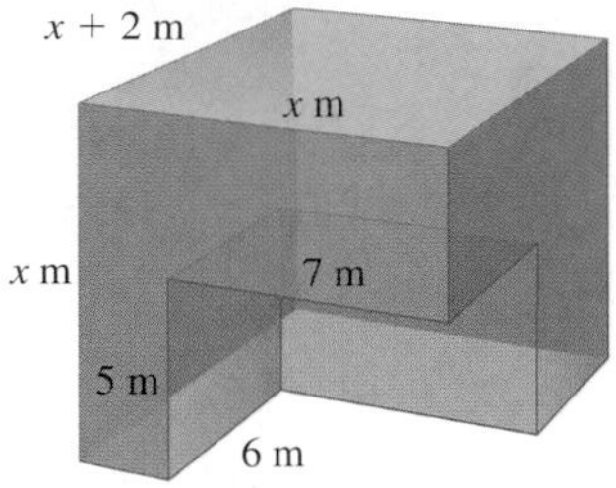

86. A side of a cube is $(x + 2)$ cm long. Find a polynomial for the volume of the cube.

87. A rectangular garden is twice as long as it is wide and is surrounded by a sidewalk that is 4 ft wide (see the figure below). The area of the sidewalk is 256 ft^2. Find the dimensions of the garden.

Compute and simplify.

88. $(x + 3)(x + 6) + (x + 3)(x + 6)$

Aha! **89.** $(x - 2)(x - 7) - (x - 7)(x - 2)$

90. $(x + 5)^2 - (x - 3)^2$

Aha! **91.** Extend the pattern and simplify

$$(x - a)(x - b)(x - c)(x - d) \cdots (x - z).$$

92. Use a graphing calculator to check your answers to Exercises 23, 45, and 57. Use graphs, tables, or both, as directed by your instructor.

COLLABORATIVE CORNER

Slick Tricks with Algebra

Focus: Polynomial multiplication
Time: 15 minutes
Group size: 2

Consider the following dialogue.

Jinny: Cal, let me do a number trick with you. Think of a number between 1 and 7. I'll have you perform some manipulations to this number, you'll tell me the result, and I'll tell you your number.

Cal: OK. I've thought of a number.

Jinny: Good. Write it down so I can't see it. Now double it, and then subtract x from the result.

Cal: Hey, this is algebra!

Jinny: I know. Now square your binomial. After you're through squaring, subtract x^2.

Cal: How did you know I had an x^2? I *thought* this was rigged!

Jinny: It is. Now divide each of the remaining terms by 4 and tell me either your constant term or your x-term. I'll tell you the other term and the number you chose.

Cal: OK. The constant term is 16.

Jinny: Then the other term is $-4x$ and the number you chose was 4.

Cal: You're right! How did you do it?

ACTIVITY

1. Each group member should follow Jinny's instructions. Then determine how Jinny determined Cal's number and the other term.
2. Suppose that, at the end, Cal told Jinny the x-term. How would Jinny have determined Cal's number and the other term?
3. Would Jinny's "trick" work with *any* real number? Why do you think she specified numbers between 1 and 7?

4.5 Special Products

Products of Two Binomials • Multiplying Sums and Differences of Two Terms • Squaring Binomials • Multiplications of Various Types

Certain products of two binomials occur so often that it is helpful to be able to compute them quickly. In this section, we develop methods for doing so.

Products of Two Binomials

In Section 4.4, we found the product $(x + 5)(x + 4)$ by using the distributive law a total of three times (see p. 255). Note that each term in $x + 5$ is multiplied by each term in $x + 4$. To shorten our work, we can go right to this step:

$$\begin{aligned}(x + 5)(x + 4) &= x \cdot x + x \cdot 4 + 5 \cdot x + 5 \cdot 4 \\ &= x^2 + 4x + 5x + 20 \\ &= x^2 + 9x + 20.\end{aligned}$$

Study Skills

Two Books Are Better Than One

Many students find it helpful to use a second book as a reference when studying. Perhaps you or a friend own a text from a previous math course that can serve as a resource. Often professors have older texts that they will happily give away. Library book sales and thrift shops can also be excellent sources for extra books. Saving your text when you finish a math course can provide you with an excellent aid for your next course.

Note that $x \cdot x$ is found by multiplying the *First* terms of each binomial, $x \cdot 4$ is found by multiplying the *Outer* terms of the two binomials, $5 \cdot x$ is the product of the *Inner* terms of the two binomials, and $5 \cdot 4$ is the product of the *Last* terms of each binomial:

First terms, Outer terms, Inner terms, Last terms

$$(x + 5)(x + 4) = \underbrace{x \cdot x}_{\text{First terms}} + \underbrace{4 \cdot x}_{\text{Outer terms}} + \underbrace{5 \cdot x}_{\text{Inner terms}} + \underbrace{5 \cdot 4}_{\text{Last terms}}.$$

To remember this shortcut for multiplying, we use the initials **FOIL**.

The FOIL Method

To multiply two binomials, $A + B$ and $C + D$, multiply the First terms AC, the Outer terms AD, the Inner terms BC, and then the Last terms BD. Then combine like terms, if possible.

$$(A + B)(C + D) = AC + AD + BC + BD$$

1. Multiply First terms: AC.
2. Multiply Outer terms: AD.
3. Multiply Inner terms: BC.
4. Multiply Last terms: BD.

↓

FOIL

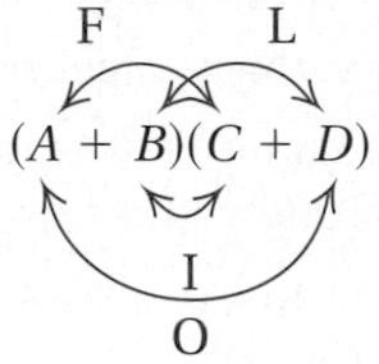

Because addition is commutative, the individual multiplications can be performed in any order. Both FLOI and FIOL yield the same result as FOIL, but FOIL is most easily remembered and most widely used.

EXAMPLE 1 Multiply: $(x + 8)(x^2 + 5)$.

Solution

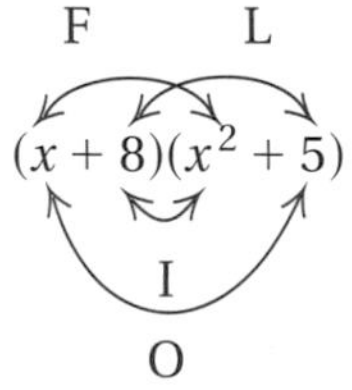

$$\begin{aligned} (x + 8)(x^2 + 5) &= \overset{F}{x^3} + \overset{O}{5x} + \overset{I}{8x^2} + \overset{L}{40} && \text{There are no like terms.} \\ &= x^3 + 8x^2 + 5x + 40 && \text{Writing in descending order} \end{aligned}$$

After multiplying, remember to combine any like terms.

EXAMPLE 2 Multiply.

a) $(x + 7)(x + 4)$ **b)** $(y + 3)(y - 2)$

c) $(4t^3 + 5t)(3t^2 - 2)$ **d)** $(3 - 4x)(7 - 5x^3)$

Solution

a) $(x + 7)(x + 4) = x^2 + 4x + 7x + 28$ Using FOIL
$= x^2 + 11x + 28$ Combining like terms

b) $(y + 3)(y - 2) = y^2 - 2y + 3y - 6$
$= y^2 + y - 6$

c) $(4t^3 + 5t)(3t^2 - 2) = 12t^5 - 8t^3 + 15t^3 - 10t$ Remember to add exponents when multiplying terms with the same base.
$= 12t^5 + 7t^3 - 10t$

d) $(3 - 4x)(7 - 5x^3) = 21 - 15x^3 - 28x + 20x^4$
$= 21 - 28x - 15x^3 + 20x^4$ In general, if the original binomials are written in *ascending* order, the answer is also written that way.

Multiplying Sums and Differences of Two Terms

Consider the product of the sum and difference of the same two terms, such as

$$(x + 5)(x - 5).$$

Since this is the product of two binomials, we can use FOIL. In doing so, we find that the "outer" and "inner" products are opposites:

a) $(x + 5)(x - 5) = x^2 - 5x + 5x - 25$
$= x^2 - 25;$

b) $(3a - 2)(3a + 2) = 9a^2 + 6a - 6a - 4$
$= 9a^2 - 4;$

c) $\left(x^3 + \frac{2}{7}\right)\left(x^3 - \frac{2}{7}\right) = x^6 - \frac{2}{7}x^3 + \frac{2}{7}x^3 - \frac{4}{49}$
$= x^6 - \frac{4}{49}.$

The "outer" and "inner" terms "drop out." Their sum is zero.

Because opposites always add to zero, for products like $(x + 5)(x - 5)$ we can use a shortcut that is faster than FOIL.

The Product of a Sum and Difference

The product of the sum and difference of the same two terms is the square of the first term minus the square of the second term:

$$(A + B)(A - B) = \underbrace{A^2 - B^2}.$$

This is called a *difference of squares*.

EXAMPLE 3 Multiply.

a) $(x + 4)(x - 4)$

b) $(5 + 2w)(5 - 2w)$

c) $(3a^4 - 5)(3a^4 + 5)$

Solution

$$(A + B)(A - B) = A^2 - B^2$$

$$\downarrow \quad \downarrow \downarrow \quad \downarrow \quad \downarrow \quad \downarrow$$

a) $(x + 4)(x - 4) = x^2 - 4^2$ Saying the words can help: "The square of the first term, x^2, minus the square of the second, 4^2"

$= x^2 - 16$ Simplifying

b) $(5 + 2w)(5 - 2w) = 5^2 - (2w)^2$

$= 25 - 4w^2$ Squaring both 5 and $2w$

c) $(3a^4 - 5)(3a^4 + 5) = (3a^4)^2 - 5^2$

$= 9a^8 - 25$ Using the rules for exponents. Remember to multiply exponents when raising a power to a power.

Squaring Binomials

Consider the square of a binomial, such as $(x + 3)^2$. This can be expressed as $(x + 3)(x + 3)$. Since this is the product of two binomials, we can use FOIL. But again, this product occurs so often that a faster method has been developed. Look for a pattern in the following:

a) $(x + 3)^2 = (x + 3)(x + 3)$

$= x^2 + 3x + 3x + 9$

$= x^2 + 6x + 9;$

b) $(5 - 3p)^2 = (5 - 3p)(5 - 3p)$

$= 25 - 15p - 15p + 9p^2$

$= 25 - 30p + 9p^2;$

c) $(a^3 - 7)^2 = (a^3 - 7)(a^3 - 7)$

$= a^6 - 7a^3 - 7a^3 + 49$

$= a^6 - 14a^3 + 49.$

Perhaps you noticed that in each product the "outer" and "inner" products are identical. The other two terms, the "first" and "last" products, are squares.

The Square of a Binomial

The square of a binomial is the square of the first term, plus twice the product of the two terms, plus the square of the last term:

$$\left.\begin{array}{l}(A + B)^2 = A^2 + 2AB + B^2;\\ (A - B)^2 = A^2 - 2AB + B^2.\end{array}\right\}$$ These are called *perfect-square trinomials.**

EXAMPLE 4 Multiply: **(a)** $(x + 7)^2$; **(b)** $(t - 5)^2$; **(c)** $(3a + 0.4)^2$; **(d)** $(5x - 3x^4)^2$.

Solution

$$(A + B)^2 = A^2 + 2 \cdot A \cdot B + B^2$$

$$\downarrow \quad \downarrow \qquad \downarrow \quad \downarrow \quad \downarrow \quad \downarrow \quad \downarrow$$

a) $(x + 7)^2 = x^2 + 2 \cdot x \cdot 7 + 7^2$ Saying the words can help: "The square of the first term, x^2, plus twice the product of the terms, $2 \cdot 7x$, plus the square of the second term, 7^2"

$= x^2 + 14x + 49$

b) $(t - 5)^2 = t^2 - 2 \cdot t \cdot 5 + 5^2$

$= t^2 - 10t + 25$

c) $(3a + 0.4)^2 = (3a)^2 + 2 \cdot 3a \cdot 0.4 + 0.4^2$

$= 9a^2 + 2.4a + 0.16$

d) $(5x - 3x^4)^2 = (5x)^2 - 2 \cdot 5x \cdot 3x^4 + (3x^4)^2$

$= 25x^2 - 30x^5 + 9x^8$ Using the rules for exponents

Caution! Although the square of a product is the product of the squares, the square of a sum is *not* the sum of the squares. That is, $(AB)^2 = A^2B^2$, but

The term $2AB$ is missing.

$$(A + B)^2 \neq A^2 + B^2.$$

To confirm this inequality, note that

$$(7 + 5)^2 = 12^2 = 144,$$

whereas

$$7^2 + 5^2 = 49 + 25 = 74, \quad \text{and} \quad 74 \neq 144.$$

---

*In some books, these are called *trinomial squares.*

Geometrically, $(A + B)^2$ can be viewed as the area of a square with sides of length $A + B$:

$$(A + B)(A + B) = (A + B)^2.$$

This is equal to the sum of the areas of the four smaller regions:

$$A^2 + AB + AB + B^2 = A^2 + 2AB + B^2.$$

Thus,

$$(A + B)^2 = A^2 + 2AB + B^2.$$

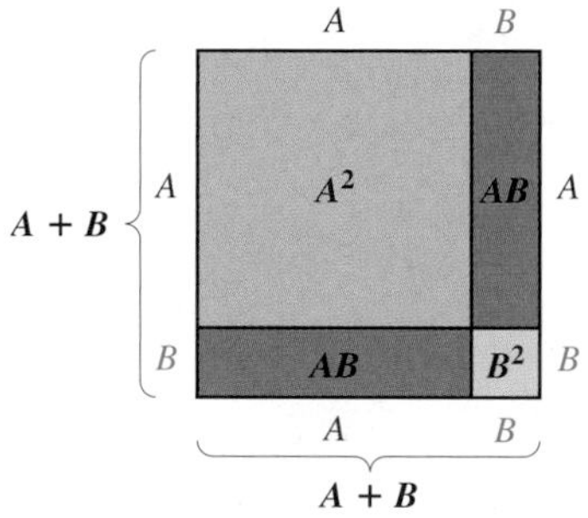

Multiplications of Various Types

Recognizing patterns often helps when new problems are encountered. To simplify a new multiplication problem, always examine what type of product it is so that the best method for finding that product can be used. To do this, ask yourself questions similar to the following.

Multiplying Two Polynomials

1. Is the multiplication the product of a monomial and a polynomial? If so, multiply each term of the polynomial by the monomial.
2. Is the multiplication the product of two binomials? If so:
   a) Is it the product of the sum and difference of the *same* two terms? If so, use the pattern
   $$(A + B)(A - B) = A^2 - B^2.$$
   b) Is the product the square of a binomial? If so, use the pattern
   $$(A + B)(A + B) = (A + B)^2 = A^2 + 2AB + B^2,$$
   or
   $$(A - B)(A - B) = (A - B)^2 = A^2 - 2AB + B^2.$$
   c) If neither (a) nor (b) applies, use FOIL.
3. Is the multiplication the product of two polynomials other than those above? If so, multiply each term of one by every term of the other. Use columns if you wish.

EXAMPLE 5 Multiply.

a) $(x + 3)(x - 3)$
b) $(t + 7)(t - 5)$
c) $(x + 7)(x + 7)$
d) $2x^3(9x^2 + x - 7)$
e) $(p + 3)(p^2 + 2p - 1)$
f) $\left(3x + \frac{1}{4}\right)^2$

Solution

a) $(x + 3)(x - 3) = x^2 - 9$ This is the product of the sum and difference of the same two terms.

b) $(t + 7)(t - 5) = t^2 - 5t + 7t - 35$ Using FOIL
$= t^2 + 2t - 35$

c) $(x + 7)(x + 7) = x^2 + 14x + 49$ This is the square of a binomial, $(x + 7)^2$.

d) $2x^3(9x^2 + x - 7) = 18x^5 + 2x^4 - 14x^3$ Multiplying each term of the trinomial by the monomial

e)

$$\begin{array}{r l}
p^2 + 2p - 1 & \text{Using columns to multiply a binomial and a trinomial} \\
p + 3 & \\
\hline
3p^2 + 6p - 3 & \text{Multiplying by 3} \\
p^3 + 2p^2 - p & \text{Multiplying by } p \\
\hline
p^3 + 5p^2 + 5p - 3 &
\end{array}$$

f) $\left(3x + \frac{1}{4}\right)^2 = 9x^2 + 2(3x)\left(\frac{1}{4}\right) + \frac{1}{16}$ Squaring a binomial
$= 9x^2 + \frac{3}{2}x + \frac{1}{16}$

4.5 Exercise Set

FOR EXTRA HELP

Student's Solutions Manual | Digital Video Tutor CD 3 Videotape 8 | AW Math Tutor Center | MathXL Tutorials on CD | MathXL | MyMathLab

Concept Reinforcement *Identify each statement as either true or false.*

1. FOIL is simply a memory device for finding the product of two binomials.
2. Once FOIL is used, it is always possible to combine like terms.
3. The square of a binomial cannot be found using FOIL.
4. The square of $A + B$ is not the sum of the squares of A and B.

Multiply.

5. $(x + 3)(x^2 + 5)$
6. $(x^2 - 3)(x - 1)$
7. $(x^3 + 6)(x + 2)$
8. $(x^4 + 2)(x + 12)$
9. $(y + 2)(y - 3)$
10. $(a + 2)(a + 2)$
11. $(3x + 2)(3x + 5)$
12. $(4x + 1)(2x + 7)$
13. $(5x - 4)(x + 2)$
14. $(t - 9)(t + 9)$
15. $(1 + 3t)(2 - 3t)$
16. $(7 - a)(2 + 3a)$
17. $(2x - 5)(x - 4)$
18. $(2x - 1)(3x + 1)$

19. $\left(p - \frac{1}{4}\right)\left(p + \frac{1}{4}\right)$ **20.** $\left(q + \frac{3}{4}\right)\left(q + \frac{3}{4}\right)$

21. $(x - 0.1)(x + 0.1)$ **22.** $(x + 0.3)(x - 0.4)$

23. $(-2x + 1)(x + 6)$ **24.** $(-x + 4)(2x - 5)$

25. $(a + 9)(a + 9)$ **26.** $(2y + 7)(2y + 7)$

27. $(1 + 3t)(1 - 5t)$ **28.** $(1 + 2t)(1 - 3t^2)$

29. $(x^2 + 3)(x^3 - 1)$ **30.** $(x^4 - 3)(2x + 1)$

31. $(3x^2 - 2)(x^4 - 2)$ **32.** $(x^{10} + 3)(x^{10} - 3)$

33. $(2t^3 + 5)(2t^3 + 3)$ **34.** $(5t^2 + 1)(2t^2 + 3)$

35. $(8x^3 + 5)(x^2 + 2)$ **36.** $(4 - 2x)(5 - 2x^2)$

37. $(4x^2 + 3)(x - 3)$ **38.** $(7x - 2)(2x - 7)$

Multiply. Try to recognize what type of product each multiplication is before multiplying.

39. $(x + 7)(x - 7)$ **40.** $(x + 1)(x - 1)$

41. $(2x + 1)(2x - 1)$ **42.** $(x^2 + 1)(x^2 - 1)$

43. $(5m - 2)(5m + 2)$ **44.** $(3x^4 + 2)(3x^4 - 2)$

45. $(3x^4 - 1)(3x^4 + 1)$ **46.** $(t^2 - 0.2)(t^2 + 0.2)$

47. $(x^4 + 7)(x^4 - 7)$ **48.** $(t^3 + 4)(t^3 - 4)$

49. $\left(t - \frac{3}{4}\right)\left(t + \frac{3}{4}\right)$ **50.** $\left(m - \frac{2}{3}\right)\left(m + \frac{2}{3}\right)$

51. $(x + 2)^2$ **52.** $(2x - 1)^2$

53. $(7x^3 + 1)^2$ **54.** $(4x^3 + 1)^2$

55. $\left(a - \frac{2}{5}\right)^2$ **56.** $\left(t - \frac{1}{5}\right)^2$

57. $(t^3 + 5)^2$ **58.** $(a^4 + 3)^2$

59. $(2 - 3x^4)^2$ **60.** $(5 - 2t^3)^2$

61. $(5 + 6t^2)^2$ **62.** $(3p^2 - p)^2$

63. $(7x - 0.3)^2$ **64.** $(4a - 0.6)^2$

65. $5a^3(2a^2 - 1)$ **66.** $9x^3(2x^2 - 5)$

67. $(a - 3)(a^2 + 2a - 4)$ **68.** $(x^2 - 5)(x^2 + x - 1)$

69. $(3 - 2x^3)^2$ **70.** $(x - 4x^3)^2$

71. $5x(x^2 + 6x - 2)$ **72.** $6x(-x^5 + 6x^2 + 9)$

73. $(-t^3 + 1)^2$ **74.** $(-x^2 + 1)^2$

75. $3t^2(5t^3 - t^2 + t)$ **76.** $-5x^3(x^2 + 8x - 9)$

77. $(6x^4 - 3)^2$ **78.** $(8a^3 + 5)^2$

79. $(3x + 2)(4x^2 + 5)$ **80.** $(2x^2 - 7)(3x^2 + 9)$

81. $(5 - 6x^4)^2$ **82.** $(3 - 4t^5)^2$

83. $(a + 1)(a^2 - a + 1)$ **84.** $(x - 5)(x^2 + 5x + 25)$

Find the total area of all shaded rectangles.

85.

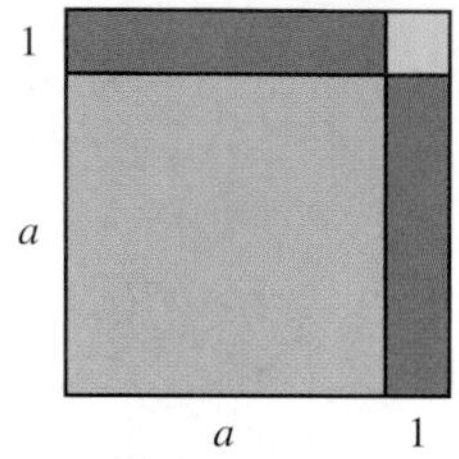

86.

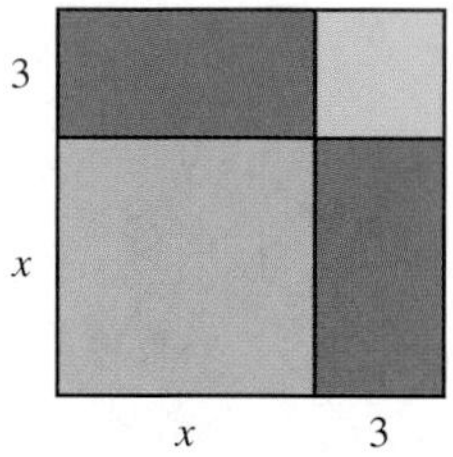

87.

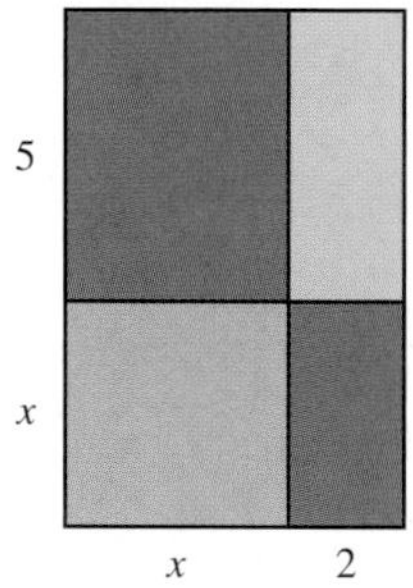

88.

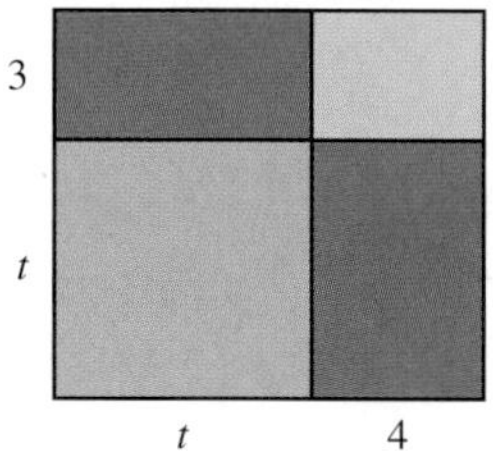

89.

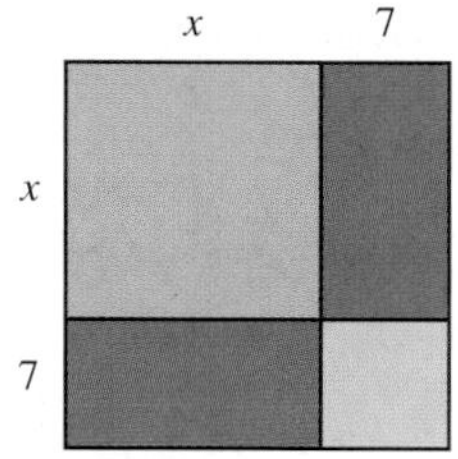

90.

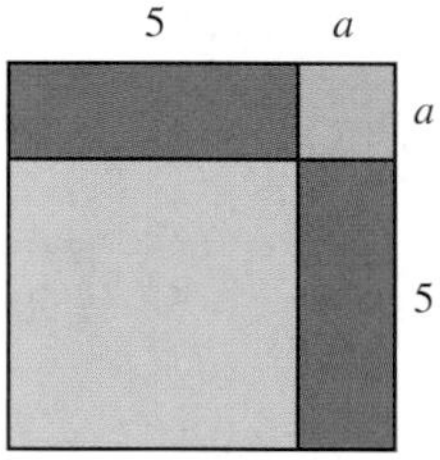

91.

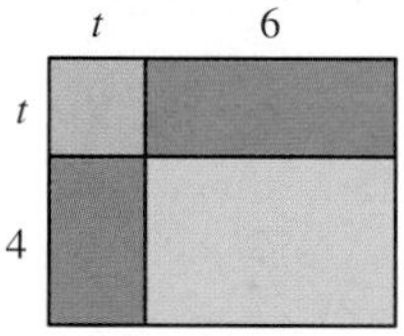

92.

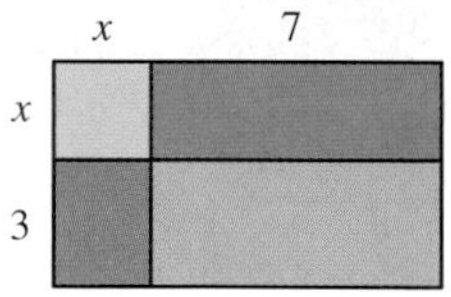

93.

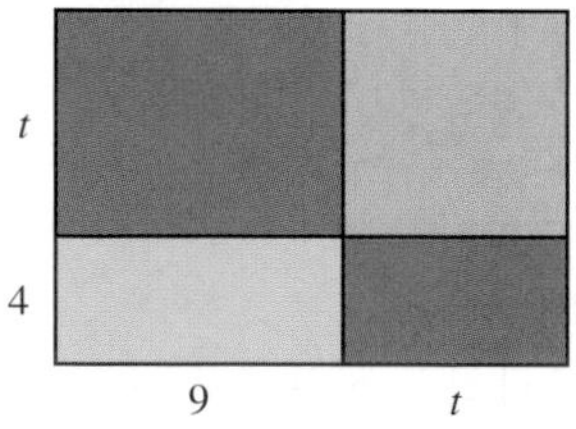

94.

95.

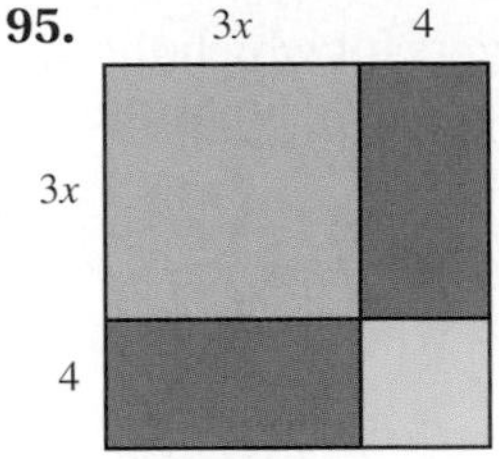

96.

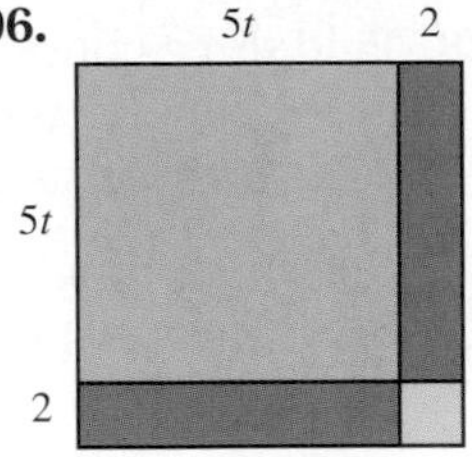

Draw and label rectangles similar to those in Exercises 85–96 to illustrate each of the following.

97. $(x + 5)^2$

98. $(x + 8)^2$

99. $(t + 9)^2$

100. $(a + 12)^2$

101. $(3 + x)^2$

102. $(7 + t)^2$

103. Patti feels that since she can find the product of any two binomials using FOIL, she needn't study the other special products. What advice would you give her?

104. Under what conditions is the product of two binomials a binomial?

SKILL MAINTENANCE

105. *Energy use.* In an apartment, lamps, an air conditioner, and a television set are all operating at the same time. The lamps take 10 times as many watts as the television set, and the air conditioner takes 40 times as many watts as the television set. The total wattage used in the apartment is 2550 watts. How many watts are used by each appliance? [2.5]

106. In what quadrant is the point $(-3, 4)$ located? [3.1]

Solve. [2.3]

107. $5xy = 8$, for y

108. $3ab = c$, for a

109. $ax - b = c$, for x

110. $st + r = u$, for t

SYNTHESIS

111. Beth claims that by writing $19 \cdot 21$ as $(20 - 1)(20 + 1)$, she can find the product mentally. How is this possible?

112. The product $(A + B)^2$ can be regarded as the sum of the areas of four regions (as shown following Example 4). How might one visually represent $(A + B)^3$? Why?

Multiply.

Aha! **113.** $(4x^2 + 9)(2x + 3)(2x - 3)$

114. $(9a^2 + 1)(3a - 1)(3a + 1)$

Aha! **115.** $(3t - 2)^2(3t + 2)^2$

116. $(5a + 1)^2(5a - 1)^2$

117. $(t^3 - 1)^4(t^3 + 1)^4$

118. $(32.41x + 5.37)^2$

Calculate as the difference of squares.

119. 18×22 [*Hint*: $(20 - 2)(20 + 2)$.]

120. 93×107

Solve.

121. $(x + 2)(x - 5) = (x + 1)(x - 3)$

122. $(2x + 5)(x - 4) = (x + 5)(2x - 4)$

Find a polynomial for the total shaded area in each figure.

123.

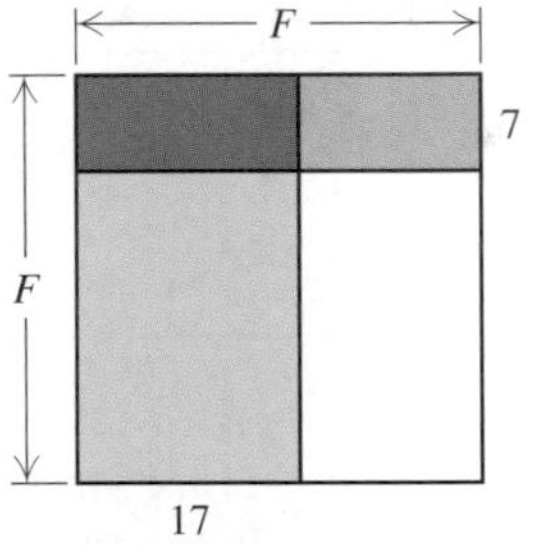

124.

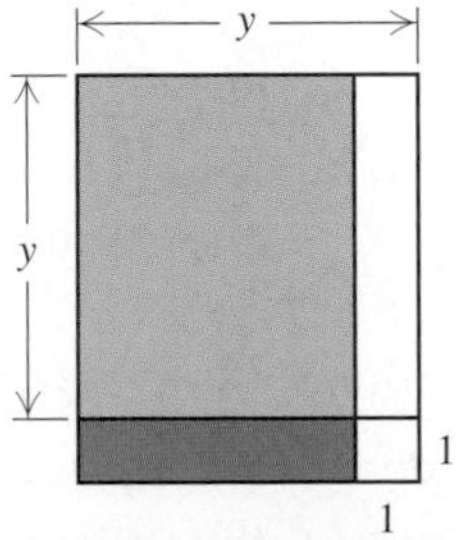

125.

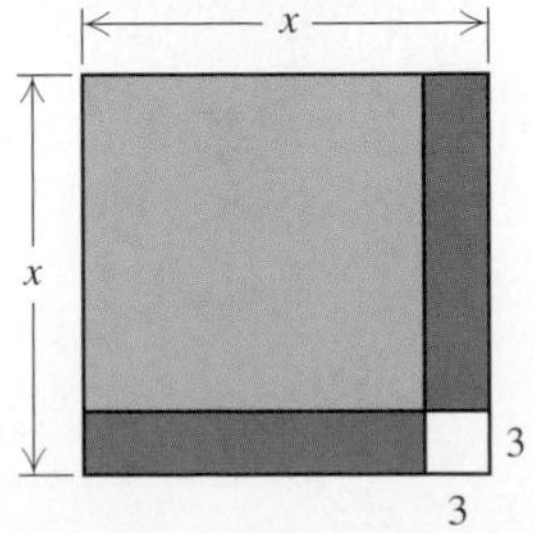

126. Find $(y - 2)^2$ by subtracting the white areas from y^2.

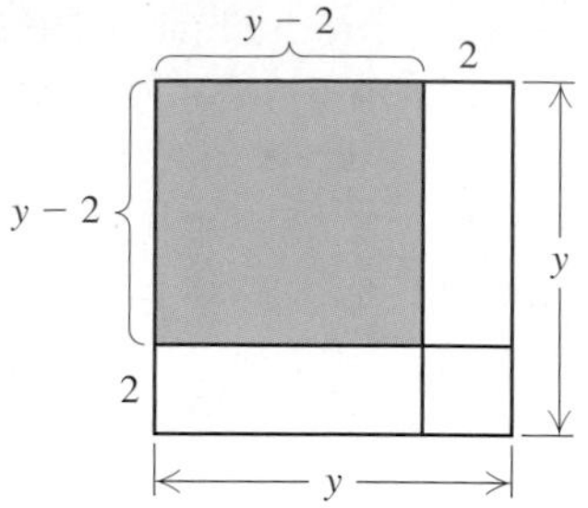

127. Find $(10 - 2x)^2$ by subtracting the white areas from 10^2.

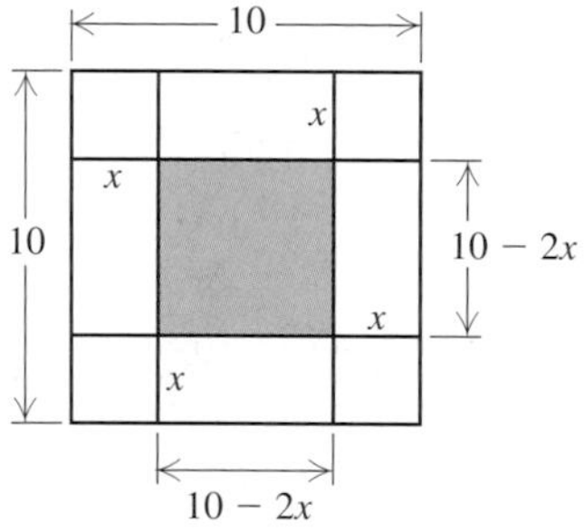

128. Find three consecutive integers for which the sum of the squares is 65 more than three times the square of the smallest integer.

129. Use a graphing calculator and the method developed on p. 258 to check your answers to Exercises 21, 47, and 83.

4.6 Polynomials in Several Variables

Evaluating Polynomials • Like Terms and Degree • Addition and Subtraction • Multiplication

Thus far, the polynomials that we have studied have had only one variable. Polynomials such as

$$5x + x^2y - 3y + 7, \qquad 9ab^2c - 2a^3b^2 + 8a^2b^3, \quad \text{and} \quad 4m^2 - 9n^2$$

contain two or more variables. In this section, we will add, subtract, multiply, and evaluate such **polynomials in several variables**.

Evaluating Polynomials

To evaluate a polynomial in two or more variables, we substitute numbers for the variables. Then we compute, using the rules for order of operations.

EXAMPLE 1 Evaluate the polynomial $4 + 3x + xy^2 + 8x^3y^3$ for $x = -2$ and $y = 5$.

Solution We substitute -2 for x and 5 for y:

$$4 + 3x + xy^2 + 8x^3y^3 = 4 + 3(-2) + (-2) \cdot 5^2 + 8(-2)^3 \cdot 5^3$$
$$= 4 - 6 - 50 - 8000 = -8052.$$

EXAMPLE 2 Surface area of a right circular cylinder. The surface area of a right circular cylinder is given by the polynomial

$$2\pi rh + 2\pi r^2,$$

where h is the height and r is the radius of the base. A 12-oz can has a height of 4.7 in. and a radius of 1.2 in. Approximate its surface area.

Solution We evaluate the polynomial for $h = 4.7$ in. and $r = 1.2$ in. If 3.14 is used to approximate π, we have

$$\begin{aligned} 2\pi rh + 2\pi r^2 &\approx 2(3.14)(1.2 \text{ in.})(4.7 \text{ in.}) + 2(3.14)(1.2 \text{ in.})^2 \\ &\approx 2(3.14)(1.2 \text{ in.})(4.7 \text{ in.}) + 2(3.14)(1.44 \text{ in}^2) \\ &\approx 35.4192 \text{ in}^2 + 9.0432 \text{ in}^2 \approx 44.4624 \text{ in}^2. \end{aligned}$$

If the π key of a calculator is used, we have

$$\begin{aligned} 2\pi rh + 2\pi r^2 &\approx 2(3.141592654)(1.2 \text{ in.})(4.7 \text{ in.}) + 2(3.141592654)(1.2 \text{ in.})^2 \\ &\approx 44.48495197 \text{ in}^2. \end{aligned}$$

Note that the unit in the answer (square inches) is a unit of area. The surface area is about 44.5 in^2 (square inches).

Like Terms and Degree

Recall that the degree of a monomial is the number of variable factors in the term. For example, the degree of $5x^2$ is 2 because there are two variable factors in $5 \cdot x \cdot x$. Similarly, the degree of $5a^2b^4$ is 6 because there are 6 variable factors in $5 \cdot a \cdot a \cdot b \cdot b \cdot b \cdot b$. Note that 6 can be found by adding the exponents 2 and 4.

As we learned in Section 4.2, the degree of a polynomial is the degree of the term of highest degree.

EXAMPLE 3 Identify the coefficient and the degree of each term and the degree of the polynomial

$$9x^2y^3 - 14xy^2z^3 + xy + 4y + 5x^2 + 7.$$

Solution

Term	Coefficient	Degree	Degree of the Polynomial
$9x^2y^3$	9	5	
$-14xy^2z^3$	-14	6	6
xy	1	2	
$4y$	4	1	
$5x^2$	5	2	
7	7	0	

Study Skills

Use Your Voice

Don't be hesitant to ask questions in class at appropriate times. Most instructors welcome questions and encourage students to ask them. Other students in your class probably have the same questions you do.

Note in Example 3 that although both xy and $5x^2$ have degree 2, they are *not* like terms. *Like*, or *similar, terms* either have exactly the same variables with exactly the same exponents or are constants. For example,

$$8a^4b^7 \text{ and } 5b^7a^4 \text{ are like terms}$$

and

$$-17 \text{ and } 3 \text{ are like terms,}$$

but

$$-2x^2y \text{ and } 9xy^2 \text{ are } not \text{ like terms.}$$

As always, combining like terms is based on the distributive law.

EXAMPLE 4 Combine like terms.

a) $9x^2y + 3xy^2 - 5x^2y - xy^2$

b) $7ab - 5ab^2 + 3ab^2 + 6a^3 + 9ab - 11a^3 + b - 1$

Solution

a) $9x^2y + 3xy^2 - 5x^2y - xy^2 = (9 - 5)x^2y + (3 - 1)xy^2$

$= 4x^2y + 2xy^2$ Try to go directly to this step.

b) $7ab - 5ab^2 + 3ab^2 + 6a^3 + 9ab - 11a^3 + b - 1$

$= -5a^3 - 2ab^2 + 16ab + b - 1$ We choose to write descending powers of a. Other, equivalent, forms can also be used.

Addition and Subtraction

The procedure used for adding polynomials in one variable is used to add polynomials in several variables.

EXAMPLE 5 Add.

a) $(-5x^3 + 3y - 5y^2) + (8x^3 + 4x^2 + 7y^2)$

b) $(5ab^2 - 4a^2b + 5a^3 + 2) + (3ab^2 - 2a^2b + 3a^3b - 5)$

Solution

a) $(-5x^3 + 3y - 5y^2) + (8x^3 + 4x^2 + 7y^2)$

$= (-5 + 8)x^3 + 4x^2 + 3y + (-5 + 7)y^2$ Try to do this step mentally.

$= 3x^3 + 4x^2 + 3y + 2y^2$

b) $(5ab^2 - 4a^2b + 5a^3 + 2) + (3ab^2 - 2a^2b + 3a^3b - 5)$

$= 8ab^2 - 6a^2b + 5a^3 + 3a^3b - 3$

Student Notes

Always read the problem carefully. The difference between

$(-5x^3 + 3y - 5y^2) + (8x^3 + 4x^2 + 7y^2)$

and

$(-5x^3 + 3y - 5y^2)(8x^3 + 4x^2 + 7y^2)$

is enormous. To avoid wasting time working on an incorrectly copied exercise, be sure to double-check that you have written the correct problem in your notebook.

When subtracting a polynomial, remember to find the opposite of each term in that polynomial and then add.

EXAMPLE 6 Subtract: $(4x^2y + x^3y^2 + 3x^2y^3 + 6y) - (4x^2y - 6x^3y^2 + x^2y^2 - 5y)$.

Solution

$$\begin{aligned}
&(4x^2y + x^3y^2 + 3x^2y^3 + 6y) - (4x^2y - 6x^3y^2 + x^2y^2 - 5y)\\
&\quad = 4x^2y + x^3y^2 + 3x^2y^3 + 6y - 4x^2y + 6x^3y^2 - x^2y^2 + 5y\\
&\quad = 7x^3y^2 + 3x^2y^3 - x^2y^2 + 11y \qquad \text{Combining like terms}
\end{aligned}$$

Multiplication

To multiply polynomials in several variables, multiply each term of one polynomial by every term of the other, just as we did in Sections 4.4 and 4.5.

EXAMPLE 7 Multiply: $(3x^2y - 2xy + 3y)(xy + 2y)$.

Solution

$$\begin{array}{rrrrl}
 & 3x^2y & -\ 2xy & +\ 3y & \\
 & & xy & +\ 2y & \\
\hline
 & 6x^2y^2 & -\ 4xy^2 & +\ 6y^2 & \quad\text{Multiplying by } 2y\\
3x^3y^2 - 2x^2y^2 & +\ 3xy^2 & & & \quad\text{Multiplying by } xy\\
\hline
3x^3y^2 + 4x^2y^2 & -\ xy^2 & +\ 6y^2 & & \quad\text{Adding}
\end{array}$$

The special products discussed in Section 4.5 can speed up our work.

EXAMPLE 8 Multiply.

a) $(p + 5q)(2p - 3q)$

b) $(3x + 2y)^2$

c) $(a^3 - 7a^2b)^2$

d) $(3x^2y + 2y)(3x^2y - 2y)$

e) $(-2x^3y^2 + 5t)(2x^3y^2 + 5t)$

f) $(2x + 3 - 2y)(2x + 3 + 2y)$

Solution

a)
$$\begin{aligned}
&\qquad\qquad\qquad\quad \text{F} \qquad \text{O} \qquad\quad \text{I} \qquad\quad \text{L}\\
(p + 5q)(2p - 3q) &= 2p^2 - 3pq + 10pq - 15q^2\\
&= 2p^2 + 7pq - 15q^2 \qquad \text{Combining like terms}
\end{aligned}$$

$$(A + B)^2 = A^2 + 2 \cdot A \cdot B + B^2$$

b)
$$\begin{aligned}
(3x + 2y)^2 &= (3x)^2 + 2(3x)(2y) + (2y)^2\\
&= 9x^2 + 12xy + 4y^2
\end{aligned}$$
Remembering the pattern for squaring a binomial speeds our work.

$$(A - B)^2 = A^2 - 2 \cdot A \cdot B + B^2$$

c)
$$\begin{aligned}
(a^3 - 7a^2b)^2 &= (a^3)^2 - 2(a^3)(7a^2b) + (7a^2b)^2 \qquad \text{Squaring a binomial}\\
&= a^6 - 14a^5b + 49a^4b^2 \qquad \text{Using the rules for exponents}
\end{aligned}$$

technology connection

One way to evaluate the polynomial in Example 1 for $x = -2$ and $y = 5$ is to store -2 to X and 5 to Y and enter the polynomial.

```
-2→X
                    -2
5→Y
                     5
4+3X+XY2+8X^3Y^3
                 -8052
▮
```

Evaluate.

1. $3x^2 - 2y^2 + 4xy + x$, for $x = -6$ and $y = 2.3$
2. $a^2b^2 - 8c^2 + 4abc + 9a$, for $a = 11$, $b = 15$, and $c = -7$

$$(\ A\ +\ B\ )(\ A\ -\ B\ ) = \ A^2 \ - \ B^2$$

d) $(3x^2y + 2y)(3x^2y - 2y) = (3x^2y)^2 - (2y)^2$ Remembering the pattern for multiplying the sum and difference of two terms speeds our work.

$= 9x^4y^2 - 4y^2$ Using the rules for exponents

e) $(-2x^3y^2 + 5t)(2x^3y^2 + 5t) = (5t - 2x^3y^2)(5t + 2x^3y^2)$ Using the commutative law for addition twice

$= (5t)^2 - (2x^3y^2)^2$ Multiplying the sum and the difference of the same two terms

$= 25t^2 - 4x^6y^4$

$$(\ A\ -\ B\ )(\ A\ +\ B\ ) = \ A^2 \ - \ B^2$$

f) $(\ 2x + 3\ - 2y)(\ 2x + 3\ + 2y) = (\ 2x + 3\ )^2 - (2y)^2$ Multiplying a sum and a difference

$= 4x^2 + 12x + 9 - 4y^2$ Squaring a binomial

In Example 8, we recognized patterns that might elude some students, particularly in parts (e) and (f). In part (e), we *can* use FOIL, and in part (f), we *can* use long multiplication, but doing so is much slower. By carefully inspecting a problem before "jumping in," we can save ourselves considerable work. At least one instructor refers to this as "working smart" instead of "working hard."*

*Thanks to Pauline Kirkpatrick of Wharton County Junior College for this language.

4.6 Exercise Set

FOR EXTRA HELP

Student's Solutions Manual | Digital Video Tutor CD 3 Videotape 8 | AW Math Tutor Center | MathXL Tutorials on CD | MathXL | MyMathLab

Concept Reinforcement *Each of the expressions in Exercises 1–8 can be regarded as either* **(a)** *the square of a binomial,* **(b)** *the product of the sum and difference of the same two terms, or* **(c)** *neither* (a) *nor* (b). *Select the appropriate choice for each expression.*

1. $(2x - 7y)^2$

2. $(4x - 9y)(4x + 9y)$

3. $(5a + 6b)(-6b + 5a)$

4. $(7a - 2b)(7a - 2b)$

5. $(r - 3s)(5r + 3s)$

6. $(2x - 7y)(7y - 2x)$

7. $(4x - 9y)(4x - 9y)$

8. $(2r - 3t)^2$

Evaluate each polynomial for $x = 5$ and $y = -2$.

9. $x^2 - 3y^2 + 2xy$

10. $x^2 + 5y^2 - 4xy$

Evaluate each polynomial for $x = 2$, $y = -3$, and $z = -4$.

11. $xyz^2 - z$

12. $xy - xz + yz$

Lung capacity. *The polynomial*

$$0.041h - 0.018A - 2.69$$

can be used to estimate the lung capacity, in liters, of a female with height h, in centimeters, and age A, in years.

13. Find the lung capacity of a 50-year-old woman who is 160 cm tall.

14. Find the lung capacity of a 20-year-old woman who is 165 cm tall.

15. *Male caloric needs.* The number of calories needed each day by a moderately active man who weighs w kilograms, is h centimeters tall, and is a years old can be estimated by the polynomial

$$19.18w + 7h - 9.52a + 92.4.$$

One of the authors of this text is moderately active, weighs 87 kg, is 185 cm tall, and is 59 yr old. What are his daily caloric needs?

Source: Parker, M., *She Does Math.* Mathematical Association of America

16. *Female caloric needs.* The number of calories needed each day by a moderately active woman who weighs w pounds, is h inches tall, and is a years old can be estimated by the polynomial

$$917 + 6w + 6h - 6a.$$

Christine is moderately active, weighs 125 lb, is 64 in. tall, and is 27 yr old. What are her daily caloric needs?

Source: Parker, M., *She Does Math.* Mathematical Association of America

Surface area of a silo. *A silo is a structure that is shaped like a right circular cylinder with a half sphere on top. The surface area of a silo of height h and radius r (including the area of the base) is given by the polynomial* $2\pi rh + \pi r^2$.

17. A $1\frac{1}{2}$-oz bottle of roll-on deodorant has a height of 4 in. and a radius of $\frac{3}{4}$ in. Find the surface area of the bottle if the bottle is shaped like a silo. Use 3.14 for π.

18. A container of tennis balls is silo-shaped, with a height of $7\frac{1}{2}$ in. and a radius of $1\frac{1}{4}$ in. Find the surface area of the container. Use 3.14 for π.

Altitude of a launched object. *The altitude of an object, in meters, is given by the polynomial*

$$h + vt - 4.9t^2,$$

where h is the height, in meters, at which the launch occurs, v is the initial upward speed (or velocity), in meters per second, and t is the number of seconds for which the object is airborne.

19. A bocce ball is thrown upward with an initial speed of 18 m/sec by a person atop the Leaning Tower of Pisa, which is 50 m above the ground. How high will the ball be 2 sec after it is thrown?

20. A golf ball is launched upward with an initial speed of 30 m/sec by a golfer atop the Washington Monument, which is 160 m above the ground. How high above the ground will the ball be after 3 sec?

Identify the coefficient and the degree of each term of each polynomial. Then find the degree of each polynomial.

21. $x^3y - 2xy + 3x^2 - 5$

22. $xy^2 - y^2 + 9x^2y + 7$

23. $17x^2y^3 - 3x^3yz - 7$

24. $6 - xy + 8x^2y^2 - y^5$

Combine like terms.

25. $7a + b - 4a - 3b$

26. $8r + s - 5r - 4s$

27. $3x^2y - 2xy^2 + x^2 + 5x$

28. $m^3 + 2m^2n - 3m^2 + 3mn^2$

29. $2u^2v - 3uv^2 + 6u^2v - 2uv^2 + 7u^2$

30. $3x^2 + 6xy + 3y^2 - 5x^2 - 10xy$

31. $5a^2c - 2ab^2 + a^2b - 3ab^2 + a^2c - 2ab^2$

32. $3s^2t + r^2t - 4st^2 - s^2t + 3st^2 - 7r^2t$

Add or subtract, as indicated.

33. $(4x^2 - xy + y^2) + (-x^2 - 3xy + 2y^2)$

34. $(2r^3 + 3rs - 5s^2) - (5r^3 + rs + 4s^2)$

35. $(3a^4 - 5ab + 6ab^2) - (9a^4 + 3ab - ab^2)$

36. $(2r^2t - 5rt + rt^2) - (7r^2t + rt - 5rt^2)$

Aha! 37. $(5r^2 - 4rt + t^2) + (-6r^2 - 5rt - t^2) + (-5r^2 + 4rt - t^2)$

38. $(2x^2 - 3xy + y^2) + (-4x^2 - 6xy - y^2) + (4x^2 + 6xy + y^2)$

39. $(x^3 - y^3) - (-2x^3 + x^2y - xy^2 + 2y^3)$

40. $(a^3 + b^3) - (-5a^3 + 2a^2b - ab^2 + 3b^3)$

41. $(2y^4x^2 - 5y^3x) + (5y^4x^2 - y^3x) + (3y^4x^2 - 2y^3x)$

42. $(5a^2b + 7ab) + (9a^2b - 5ab) + (a^2b - 6ab)$

43. Subtract $7x + 3y$ from the sum of $4x + 5y$ and $-5x + 6y$.

44. Subtract $5a + 2b$ from the sum of $2a + b$ and $3a - 4b$.

Multiply.

45. $(3z - u)(2z + 3u)$

46. $(5x + y)(2x - 3y)$

47. $(xy + 7)(xy - 4)$

48. $(ab + 3)(ab - 5)$

49. $(2a - b)(2a + b)$

50. $(a - 3b)(a + 3b)$

51. $(5rt - 2)(3rt + 1)$

52. $(3xy - 1)(4xy + 2)$

53. $(m^3n + 8)(m^3n - 6)$

54. $(3 - c^2d^2)(4 + c^2d^2)$

55. $(6x - 2y)(5x - 3y)$

56. $(7a - 6b)(5a + 4b)$

57. $(pq + 0.1)(-pq + 0.1)$

58. $(rt + 0.2)(-rt + 0.2)$

59. $(x + h)^2$

60. $(r + t)^2$

61. $(4a + 5b)^2$

62. $(3x + 2y)^2$

63. $(c^2 - d)(c^2 + d)$

64. $(p^3 - 5q)(p^3 + 5q)$

65. $(ab + cd^2)(ab - cd^2)$

66. $(xy + pq)(xy - pq)$

Aha! 67. $(a + b - c)(a + b + c)$

68. $(x + y + z)(x + y - z)$

69. $[a + b + c][a - (b + c)]$

70. $(a + b + c)(a - b - c)$

Find the total area of each shaded area.

71.

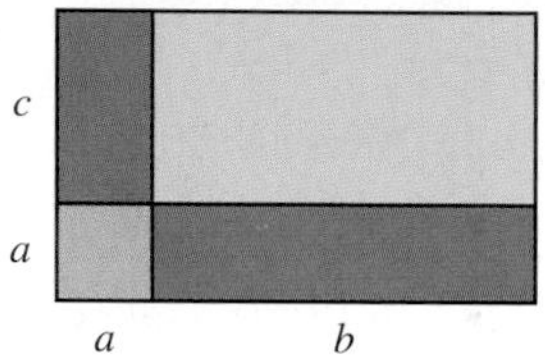

72.

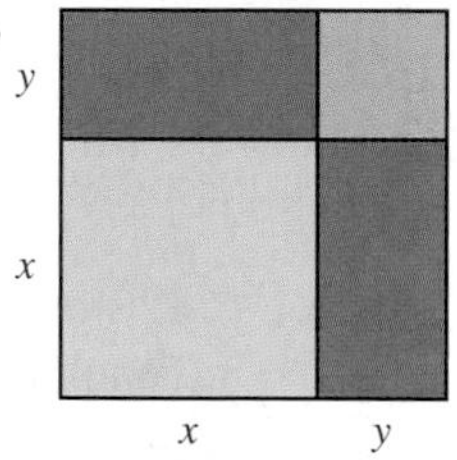

73.

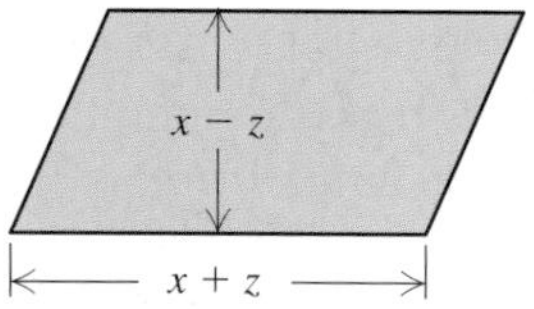

74.

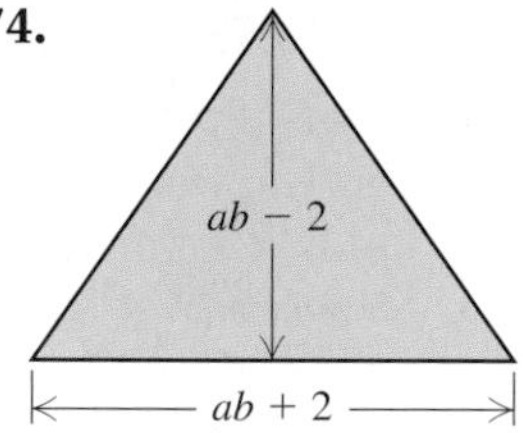

75.

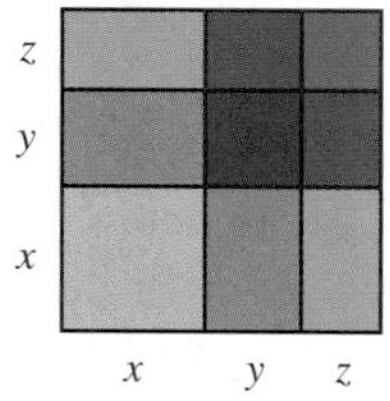

76.

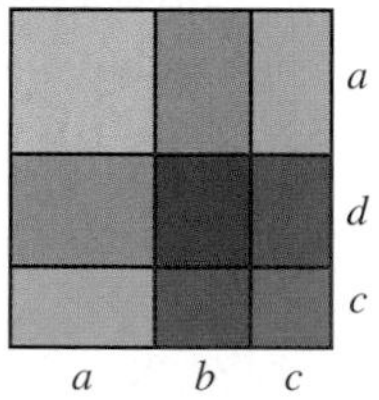

77.

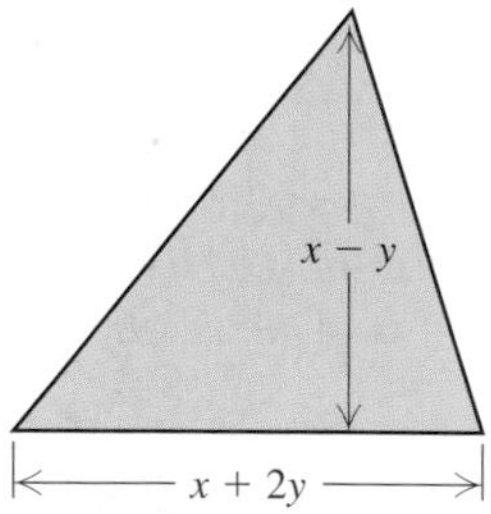

78.

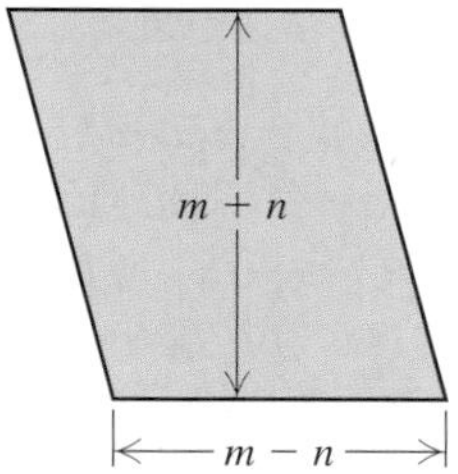

Draw and label rectangles similar to those in Exercises 71, 72, 75, and 76 to illustrate each product.

79. $(r + s)(u + v)$

80. $(m + r)(n + v)$

81. $(a + b + c)(a + d + f)$

82. $(r + s + t)^2$

83. Is it possible for a polynomial in 4 variables to have a degree less than 4? Why or why not?

84. A fourth-degree monomial is multiplied by a third-degree monomial. What is the degree of the product? Explain your reasoning.

SKILL MAINTENANCE

Simplify. [1.8]

85. $5 + \dfrac{7 + 4 + 2 \cdot 5}{3}$

86. $9 - \dfrac{2 + 6 \cdot 3 + 4}{6}$

87. $(4 + 3 \cdot 5 + 8) \div 3 \cdot 3$

88. $(5 + 2 \cdot 7 + 5) \div 2 \cdot 3$

89. $[3 \cdot 5 - 4 \cdot 2 + 7(-3)] \div (-2)$

90. $(7 - 3 \cdot 9 - 2 \cdot 5) \div (-6)$

SYNTHESIS

91. Explain how it is possible for the sum of two trinomials in several variables to be a binomial in one variable.

92. Explain how it is possible for the sum of two trinomials in several variables to be a trinomial in one variable.

Find a polynomial for the shaded area. (Leave results in terms of π where appropriate.)

93.

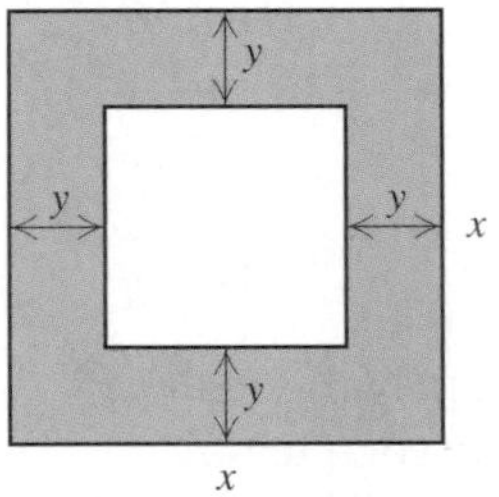

94.

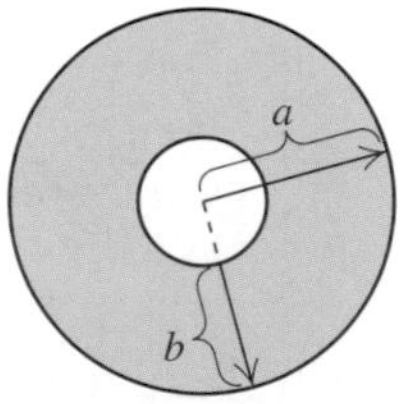

95.

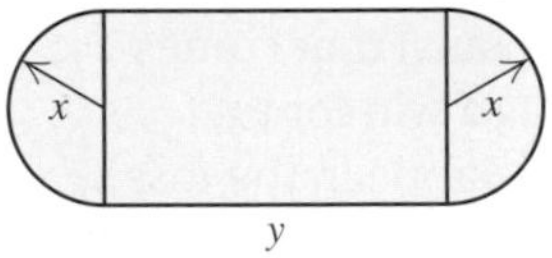

96.

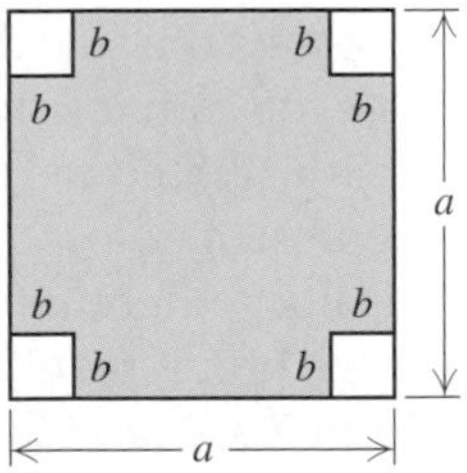

97. Find a polynomial for the total volume of the figure shown.

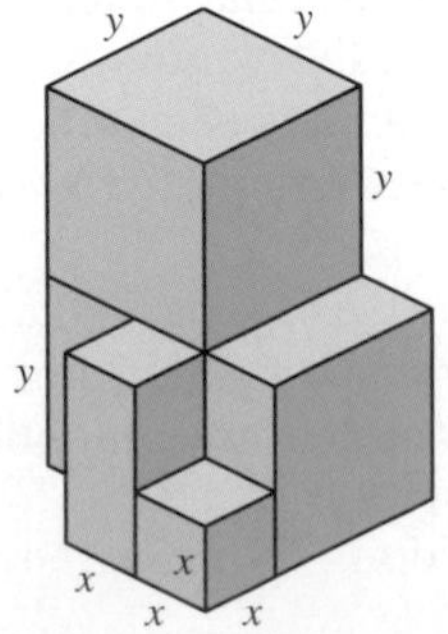

98. Find the shaded area in this figure using each of the approaches given below. Then check that both answers match.

a) Find the shaded area by subtracting the area of the unshaded square from the total area of the figure.

b) Find the shaded area by adding the areas of the three shaded rectangles.

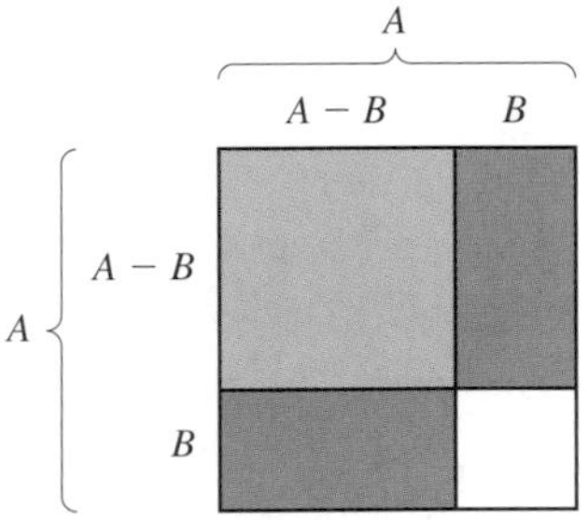

Find a polynomial for the surface area of each solid object shown. (Leave results in terms of π.)

99.

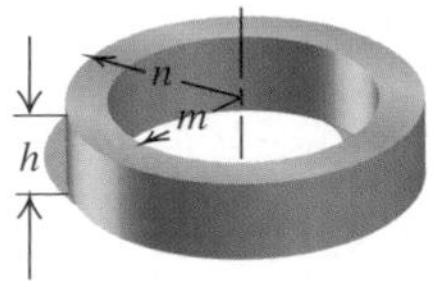

100.

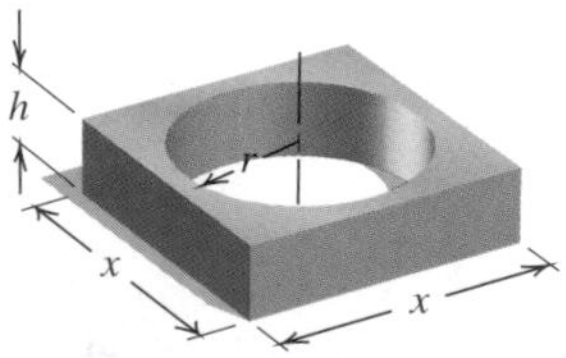

101. The observatory at Danville University is shaped like a silo that is 40 ft high and 30 ft wide (see Exercise 17). The Heavenly Bodies Astronomy Club is to paint the exterior of the observatory using paint that covers 250 ft^2 per gallon. How many gallons should they purchase? Explain your reasoning.

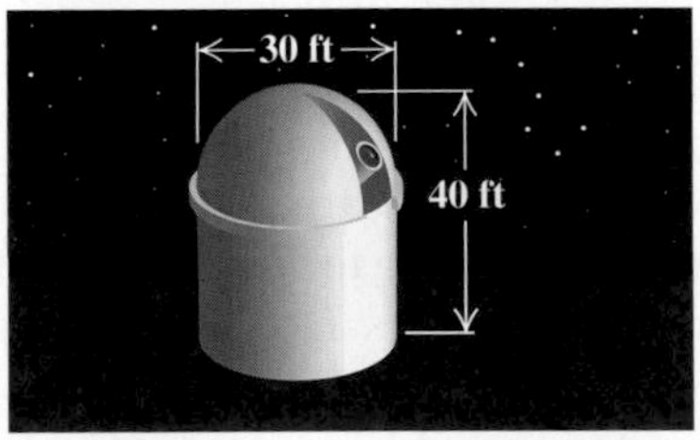

102. Multiply: $(x + a)(x - b)(x - a)(x + b)$.

103. *Interest compounded annually.* An amount of money P that is invested at the yearly interest rate r grows to the amount $P(1 + r)^t$ after t years. Find a polynomial that can be used to determine the amount to which P will grow after 2 yr.

104. *Yearly depreciation.* An investment P that drops in value at the yearly rate r drops in value to

$$P(1 - r)^t$$

after t years. Find a polynomial that can be used to determine the value to which P has dropped after 2 yr.

105. Suppose that \$10,400 is invested at 8.5% compounded annually. How much is in the account at the end of 5 yr? (See Exercise 103.)

106. A \$90,000 investment in computer hardware is depreciating at a yearly rate of 12.5%. How much is the investment worth after 4 yr? (See Exercise 104.)

COLLABORATIVE CORNER

Finding the Magic Number

Focus: Evaluating polynomials in several variables

Time: 15–25 minutes

Group size: 3

Materials: A coin for each person

When a team nears the end of its schedule in first place, fans begin to discuss the team's "magic number." A team's magic number is the combined number of wins by that team and losses by the second-place team that guarantee the leading team a first-place finish. For example, if the Cubs' magic number is 3 over the Reds, any combination of Cubs wins and Reds losses that totals 3 will guarantee a first-place finish for the Cubs, regardless of how subsequent games are decided. A team's magic number is computed using the polynomial

$$G - P - L + 1,$$

where G is the length of the season, in games, P is the number of games that the leading team has played, and L is the total number of games that the second-place team has lost minus the total number of games that the leading team has lost.

ACTIVITY

1. The standings below are from a fictitious baseball league. Together, the group should calculate the Jaguars' magic number with respect to the Catamounts as well as the Jaguars' magic number with respect to the Wildcats. (Assume that the schedule is 162 games long.)

	W	L
Jaguars	92	64
Catamounts	90	66
Wildcats	89	66

2. Each group member should play the role of one of the teams. To simulate each team's remaining games, coin tosses will be performed. If a group member correctly predicts the side (heads or tails) that comes up, the coin toss represents a win for that team. Should the other side appear, the toss represents a loss. Assume that these games are against other (unlisted) teams in the league. Each group member should perform three coin tosses and then update the standings.
3. Recalculate the two magic numbers, using the updated standings from part (2).
4. Slowly—one coin toss at a time—play out the remainder of the season. Record all wins and losses, update the standings, and recalculate the magic numbers each time all three group members have completed a round of coin tosses.
5. Examine the work in part (4) and explain why a magic number of 0 indicates that a team has been eliminated from contention.

4.7 Division of Polynomials

Dividing by a Monomial • Dividing by a Binomial

In this section, we study division of polynomials. We will find that polynomial division is similar to division in arithmetic.

Dividing by a Monomial

We first consider division by a monomial. When dividing a monomial by a monomial, we use the quotient rule of Section 4.1 to subtract exponents when bases are the same. For example,

$$\frac{15x^{10}}{3x^4} = 5x^{10-4}$$
$$= 5x^6$$

> *Caution!* The coefficients are divided but the exponents are subtracted.

and

$$\frac{42a^2b^5}{-3ab^2} = \frac{42}{-3}a^{2-1}b^{5-2} \qquad \text{Recall that } a^m/a^n = a^{m-n}.$$
$$= -14ab^3.$$

To divide a polynomial by a monomial, we note that since

$$\frac{A}{C} + \frac{B}{C} = \frac{A+B}{C},$$

it follows that

$$\frac{A+B}{C} = \frac{A}{C} + \frac{B}{C}. \qquad \text{Switching the left and right sides of the equation}$$

This is actually how we perform divisions like $86 \div 2$. Although we might simply write

$$\frac{86}{2} = 43,$$

we are really saying

$$\frac{80+6}{2} = \frac{80}{2} + \frac{6}{2} = 40 + 3.$$

Similarly, to divide a polynomial by a monomial, we divide each term by the monomial:

$$\frac{80x^5 + 6x^7}{2x^3} = \frac{80x^5}{2x^3} + \frac{6x^7}{2x^3}$$
$$= \frac{80}{2}x^{5-3} + \frac{6}{2}x^{7-3} \qquad \text{Dividing coefficients and subtracting exponents}$$
$$= 40x^2 + 3x^4.$$

Study Skills

Anticipate the Future

It is never too soon to begin reviewing for an exam. Take a few minutes each week to review important problems, formulas, and properties. There is also at least one Connecting the Concepts in each chapter. Spend time reviewing the information in this special feature as a way of keeping the "big picture" in focus.

EXAMPLE 1 Divide $x^4 + 15x^3 - 6x^2$ by $3x$.

Solution We have

$$\frac{x^4 + 15x^3 - 6x^2}{3x} = \frac{x^4}{3x} + \frac{15x^3}{3x} - \frac{6x^2}{3x}$$

$$= \frac{1}{3}x^{4-1} + \frac{15}{3}x^{3-1} - \frac{6}{3}x^{2-1}$$ Dividing coefficients and subtracting exponents

$$= \frac{1}{3}x^3 + 5x^2 - 2x.$$ This is the quotient.

To check, we multiply our answer by $3x$, using the distributive law:

$$3x\left(\frac{1}{3}x^3 + 5x^2 - 2x\right) = 3x \cdot \frac{1}{3}x^3 + 3x \cdot 5x^2 - 3x \cdot 2x$$
$$= x^4 + 15x^3 - 6x^2.$$

This is the polynomial that was being divided, so our answer, $\frac{1}{3}x^3 + 5x^2 - 2x$, checks.

EXAMPLE 2 Divide and check: $(10a^5b^4 - 2a^3b^2 + 6a^2b) \div (-2a^2b)$.

Solution We have

$$\frac{10a^5b^4 - 2a^3b^2 + 6a^2b}{-2a^2b} = \frac{10a^5b^4}{-2a^2b} - \frac{2a^3b^2}{-2a^2b} + \frac{6a^2b}{-2a^2b}$$

$$= -\frac{10}{2}a^{5-2}b^{4-1} - \left(-\frac{2}{2}\right)a^{3-2}b^{2-1} + \left(-\frac{6}{2}\right)$$

Dividing coefficients and subtracting exponents

$$= -5a^3b^3 + ab - 3.$$

Check: $-2a^2b(-5a^3b^3 + ab - 3)$

$$= -2a^2b(-5a^3b^3) + (-2a^2b)(ab) + (-2a^2b)(-3)$$
$$= 10a^5b^4 - 2a^3b^2 + 6a^2b$$

Our answer, $-5a^3b^3 + ab - 3$, checks.

Dividing by a Binomial

For divisors with more than one term, we use long division, much as we do in arithmetic. Polynomials are written in descending order and any missing terms in the dividend are written in, using 0 for the coefficients.

EXAMPLE 3 Divide $x^2 + 5x + 6$ by $x + 3$.

Solution We have

$$\begin{array}{r} x \\ x+3\,\overline{)\,x^2 + 5x + 6} \\ \underline{-(x^2 + 3x)} \\ 2x \end{array}$$

x ← Divide the first term, x^2, by the first term in the divisor: $x^2/x = x$. Ignore the term 3 for the moment.

$-(x^2 + 3x)$ ← Multiply $x + 3$ by x, using the distributive law

$2x$ ← Subtract by changing signs and adding: $x^2 + 5x - (x^2 + 3x) = 2x$.

Student Notes

Long division of polynomials offers many opportunities to make errors. Rather than have one small mistake throw off all your work, we recommend that you double-check each step of your work as you move forward.

Now we "bring down" the next term—in this case, 6. To divide the remainder, $2x + 6$, by $x + 3$, we focus on $2x$ and x.

$$\begin{array}{r} x + 2 \\ x+3\,\overline{)\,x^2 + 5x + 6} \\ \underline{-(x^2 + 3x)} \\ 2x + 6 \\ \underline{-(2x + 6)} \\ 0 \end{array}$$

$2x + 6$: Divide $2x$ by x: $2x/x = 2$.

$-(2x + 6)$ ← Multiply 2 by the divisor, $x + 3$, using the distributive law

0 ← Subtract: $(2x + 6) - (2x + 6) = 0$.

The quotient is $x + 2$. The notation R 0 indicates a remainder of 0, although a remainder of 0 is generally not listed in an answer.

Check: To check, we multiply the quotient by the divisor and add any remainder to see if we get the dividend:

$$\underbrace{(x + 3)}_{\text{Divisor}}\ \underbrace{(x + 2)}_{\text{Quotient}} + \underbrace{0}_{\text{Remainder}} = \underbrace{x^2 + 5x + 6}_{\text{Dividend}}.$$

Our answer, $x + 2$, checks.

EXAMPLE 4 Divide: $(2x^2 + 5x - 1) \div (2x - 1)$.

Solution We have

$$\begin{array}{r} x \\ 2x-1\,\overline{)\,2x^2 + 5x - 1} \\ \underline{-(2x^2 - x)} \\ 6x \end{array}$$

x ← Divide the first term by the first term: $2x^2/(2x) = x$.

$-(2x^2 - x)$ ← Multiply $2x - 1$ by x.

$6x$ ← Subtract by changing signs and adding: $2x^2 + 5x - (2x^2 - x) = 6x$.

Now, we bring down the -1 and divide $6x - 1$ by $2x - 1$.

$$\begin{array}{r} x + 3 \\ 2x-1\,\overline{)\,2x^2 + 5x - 1} \\ \underline{-(2x^2 - x)} \\ 6x - 1 \\ \underline{-(6x - 3)} \\ 2 \end{array}$$

$6x - 1$: Divide $6x$ by $2x$: $6x/(2x) = 3$.

$-(6x - 3)$ ← Multiply 3 by the divisor, $2x - 1$.

2 ← Note that $-1 - (-3) = -1 + 3 = 2$.

The answer is $x + 3$ with R 2.

Another way to write $x + 3$ R 2 is as

$$\underbrace{x + 3}_{\text{Quotient}} + \frac{\overset{\text{Remainder}}{2}}{\underbrace{2x - 1}_{\text{Divisor}}}.$$

Quotient $x + 3 + \dfrac{2}{2x - 1}$. ← Remainder, Divisor

(This is the way answers will be given at the back of the book.)

Check: To check, we multiply the divisor by the quotient and add the remainder:

$$\begin{aligned}(2x - 1)(x + 3) + 2 &= 2x^2 + 5x - 3 + 2\\ &= 2x^2 + 5x - 1. \qquad \text{Our answer checks.}\end{aligned}$$

Our division procedure ends when the degree of the remainder is less than that of the divisor. Check that this was indeed the case in Example 4.

EXAMPLE 5 Divide each of the following.

a) $(x^3 + 1) \div (x + 1)$ **b)** $(x^4 - 3x^2 + 4x - 3) \div (x^2 - 5)$

Solution

a)

$$\begin{array}{rll}
 & x^2 - x + 1 & \\
x + 1 \,\big) & x^3 + 0x^2 + 0x + 1 & \leftarrow \text{Writing in the missing terms}\\
 & -(x^3 + x^2) & \\
 & -x^2 + 0x & \leftarrow \text{Subtracting } x^3 + x^2 \text{ from } x^3 + 0x^2 \text{ and bringing down the } 0x\\
 & -(-x^2 - x) & \\
 & x + 1 & \leftarrow \text{Subtracting } -x^2 - x \text{ from } -x^2 + 0x \text{ and bringing down the } 1\\
 & -(x + 1) & \\
 & 0 &
\end{array}$$

The answer is $x^2 - x + 1$.

Check: $\begin{aligned}(x + 1)(x^2 - x + 1) &= x^3 - x^2 + x + x^2 - x + 1\\ &= x^3 + 1.\end{aligned}$

b)

$$\begin{array}{rll}
 & x^2 + 2 & \\
x^2 - 5 \,\big) & x^4 + 0x^3 - 3x^2 + 4x - 3 & \text{Writing in the missing term}\\
 & -(x^4 - 5x^2) & \\
 & 2x^2 + 4x - 3 & \text{Subtracting } x^4 - 5x^2 \text{ from } x^4 - 3x^2 \text{ and bringing down } 4x - 3\\
 & -(2x^2 - 10) & \\
 & 4x + 7 & \leftarrow \text{Subtracting } 2x^2 - 10 \text{ from } 2x^2 + 4x - 3
\end{array}$$

Since the remainder, $4x + 7$, is of lower degree than the divisor, the division process stops. The answer is

$$x^2 + 2 + \frac{4x + 7}{x^2 - 5}.$$

Check: $\begin{aligned}(x^2 - 5)(x^2 + 2) + 4x + 7 &= x^4 + 2x^2 - 5x^2 - 10 + 4x + 7\\ &= x^4 - 3x^2 + 4x - 3.\end{aligned}$

4.7 Exercise Set

FOR EXTRA HELP

Student's Solutions Manual | Digital Video Tutor CD 3 Videotape 8 | AW Math Tutor Center | MathXL Tutorials on CD | MathXL | MyMathLab

Divide and check.

1. $\dfrac{32x^5 - 24x}{8}$

2. $\dfrac{12a^4 - 3a^2}{6}$

3. $\dfrac{u - 2u^2 + u^7}{u}$

4. $\dfrac{50x^5 - 7x^4 + x^2}{x}$

5. $(18t^3 - 24t^2 + 6t) \div (3t)$

6. $(20t^3 - 15t^2 + 30t) \div (5t)$

7. $(25x^6 - 20x^4 - 5x^2) \div (-5x^2)$

8. $(16x^6 + 32x^5 - 8x^2) \div (-8x^2)$

9. $(24t^5 - 40t^4 + 6t^3) \div (4t^3)$

10. $(18t^6 - 27t^5 - 3t^3) \div (9t^3)$

11. $\dfrac{8x^2 - 10x + 1}{2}$

12. $\dfrac{9x^2 + 3x - 2}{3}$

13. $\dfrac{4x^7 + 6x^5 + 4x^2}{4x^3}$

14. $\dfrac{10x^6 + 15x^3 + 5x^2}{5x^2}$

15. $\dfrac{9r^2s^2 + 3r^2s - 6rs^2}{-3rs}$

16. $\dfrac{4x^4y - 8x^6y^2 + 12x^8y^6}{4x^4y}$

17. $(x^2 + 4x - 12) \div (x - 2)$

18. $(x^2 - 6x + 8) \div (x - 4)$

19. $(t^2 - 10t - 20) \div (t - 5)$

20. $(t^2 + 8t - 15) \div (t + 4)$

21. $(2x^2 + 11x - 5) \div (x + 6)$

22. $(3x^2 - 2x - 13) \div (x - 2)$

23. $\dfrac{a^3 + 8}{a + 2}$

24. $\dfrac{t^3 + 27}{t + 3}$

25. $\dfrac{t^2 - 13}{t - 4}$

26. $\dfrac{a^2 - 21}{a - 5}$

27. $(3x^2 + 11x - 4) \div (3x - 1)$

28. $(10x^2 + 13x - 3) \div (5x - 1)$

29. $(6a^2 + 17a + 8) \div (2a + 5)$

30. $(10a^2 + 19a + 9) \div (2a + 3)$

31. $\dfrac{2t^3 - 9t^2 + 11t - 3}{2t - 3}$

32. $\dfrac{8t^3 - 22t^2 - 5t + 12}{4t + 3}$

33. $(t^3 - t^2 + t - 1) \div (t + 1)$

34. $(x^3 - x^2 + x - 1) \div (x - 1)$

35. $(t^4 - 2t^2 + 4t - 5) \div (t^2 - 3)$

36. $(t^4 + 4t^2 + 3t - 6) \div (t^2 + 5)$

37. $(4x^4 - 4x^2 - x - 3) \div (2x^2 - 3)$

38. $(6x^4 - 3x^2 + x - 4) \div (2x^2 + 1)$

39. How is the distributive law used when dividing a polynomial by a binomial?

40. On an assignment, Emmy Lou *incorrectly* writes

$$\frac{12x^3 - 6x}{3x} = 4x^2 - 6x.$$

What mistake do you think she is making and how might you convince her that a mistake has been made?

SKILL MAINTENANCE

Simplify.

41. $-4 + (-13)$ [1.5]

42. $-8 + (-15)$ [1.5]

43. $-9 - (-7)$ [1.6]

44. $-2 - (-7)$ [1.6]

45. The perimeter of a rectangular community garden is 640 ft. The length is 15 ft greater than the width. Find the length of the rectangle. [2.5]

46. Solve: $3(2x - 1) = 7x - 5$. [2.2]

47. Graph: $3x - 2y = 12$. [3.2]

48. Plot the points $(4, -1)$, $(0, 5)$, $(-2, 3)$, and $(-3, 0)$. [3.1]

SYNTHESIS

49. Explain how to form trinomials for which division by $x - 5$ results in a remainder of 3.

50. Explain how the quotient of two binomials can have more than two terms.

Divide.

51. $(10x^{9k} - 32x^{6k} + 28x^{3k}) \div (2x^{3k})$

52. $(45a^{8k} + 30a^{6k} - 60a^{4k}) \div (3a^{2k})$

53. $(6t^{3h} + 13t^{2h} - 4t^{h} - 15) \div (2t^{h} + 3)$

54. $(x^4 + a^2) \div (x + a)$

55. $(5a^3 + 8a^2 - 23a - 1) \div (5a^2 - 7a - 2)$

56. $(15y^3 - 30y + 7 - 19y^2) \div (3y^2 - 2 - 5y)$

57. Divide the sum of $4x^5 - 14x^3 - x^2 + 3$ and $2x^5 + 3x^4 + x^3 - 3x^2 + 5x$ by $3x^3 - 2x - 1$.

58. Divide $5x^7 - 3x^4 + 2x^2 - 10x + 2$ by the sum of $(x - 3)^2$ and $5x - 8$.

If the remainder is 0 when one polynomial is divided by another, the divisor is a factor *of the dividend. Find the value(s) of c for which $x - 1$ is a factor of each polynomial.*

59. $x^2 - 4x + c$

60. $2x^2 - 3cx - 8$

61. $c^2x^2 + 2cx + 1$

4.8 Negative Exponents and Scientific Notation

Negative Integers as Exponents • Scientific Notation • Multiplying and Dividing Using Scientific Notation

We now attach a meaning to negative exponents. Once we understand both positive and negative exponents, we can study a method of writing numbers known as *scientific notation.*

Negative Integers as Exponents

Let's define negative exponents so that the rules that apply to whole-number exponents will hold for all integer exponents. To do so, consider a^{-5} and the rule for adding exponents:

$$
\begin{aligned}
a^{-5} &= a^{-5} \cdot 1 && \text{Using the identity property of 1} \\
&= \frac{a^{-5}}{1} \cdot \frac{a^5}{a^5} && \text{Writing 1 as } \frac{a^5}{a^5} \text{ and } a^{-5} \text{ as } \frac{a^{-5}}{1} \\
&= \frac{a^{-5+5}}{a^5} && \text{Adding exponents} \\
&= \frac{1}{a^5}. && -5 + 5 = 0 \text{ and } a^0 = 1
\end{aligned}
$$

This leads to our definition of negative exponents.

Negative Exponents

For any real number a that is nonzero and any integer n,

$$a^{-n} = \frac{1}{a^n}.$$

(The numbers a^{-n} and a^n are reciprocals of each other.)

EXAMPLE 1 Express using positive exponents and, if possible, simplify.

a) m^{-3} **b)** 4^{-2} **c)** $(-3)^{-2}$ **d)** ab^{-1}

Solution

a) $m^{-3} = \frac{1}{m^3}$ — m^{-3} is the reciprocal of m^3.

b) $4^{-2} = \frac{1}{4^2} = \frac{1}{16}$ — 4^{-2} is the reciprocal of 4^2. Note that $4^{-2} \neq 4(-2)$.

c) $(-3)^{-2} = \frac{1}{(-3)^2} = \frac{1}{(-3)(-3)} = \frac{1}{9}$ — $(-3)^{-2}$ is the reciprocal of $(-3)^2$. Note that $(-3)^{-2} \neq -\frac{1}{3^2}$.

d) $ab^{-1} = a\left(\frac{1}{b^1}\right) = a\left(\frac{1}{b}\right) = \frac{a}{b}$ — b^{-1} is the reciprocal of b^1.

Study Skills

If You Must Miss a Class

Occasionally you may be forced to miss an upcoming class. It is usually best to alert your instructor to this situation as soon as possible. He or she may permit you to make up a missed quiz or test *if you provide enough advance notice.* Make an effort to find out what assignment will be given in your absence and try your best to learn the material on your own beforehand so that you can ask questions in advance of your absence. Sometimes it is possible to attend another section of the course for the one class that you must miss.

Caution! A negative exponent does not, in itself, indicate that an expression is negative. As shown in Example 1,

$$4^{-2} \neq 4(-2) \quad \text{and} \quad (-3)^{-2} \neq -\frac{1}{3^2}.$$

The following is another way to illustrate why negative exponents are defined as they are.

On this side, we divide by 5 at each step. ↓		On this side, the exponents decrease by 1. ↓
	$125 = 5^3$	
	$25 = 5^2$	
	$5 = 5^1$	
	$1 = 5^0$	
	$\frac{1}{5} = 5^?$	
	$\frac{1}{25} = 5^?$	

To continue the pattern, it follows that

$$\frac{1}{5} = \frac{1}{5^1} = 5^{-1}, \quad \frac{1}{25} = \frac{1}{5^2} = 5^{-2}, \quad \text{and, in general,} \quad \frac{1}{a^n} = a^{-n}.$$

EXAMPLE 2 Express $\frac{1}{x^7}$ using negative exponents.

Solution We know that $\frac{1}{a^n} = a^{-n}$. Thus,

$$\frac{1}{x^7} = x^{-7}.$$

The rules for powers still hold when exponents are negative.

EXAMPLE 3 Simplify. Do not use negative exponents in the answer.

a) $t^5 \cdot t^{-2}$ **b)** $(y^{-5})^{-7}$ **c)** $(5x^2y^{-3})^4$

d) $\frac{x^{-4}}{x^{-5}}$ **e)** $\frac{1}{t^{-5}}$ **f)** $\frac{s^{-3}}{t^{-5}}$

Solution

a) $t^5 \cdot t^{-2} = t^{5+(-2)} = t^3$ Adding exponents

b) $(y^{-5})^{-7} = y^{(-5)(-7)}$ Multiplying exponents
$= y^{35}$

c) $(5x^2y^{-3})^4 = 5^4(x^2)^4(y^{-3})^4$ Raising each factor to the fourth power
$= 625x^8y^{-12} = \frac{625x^8}{y^{12}}$

d) $\frac{x^{-4}}{x^{-5}} = x^{-4-(-5)} = x^1 = x$ We subtract exponents even if the exponent in the denominator is negative.

e) Since $\frac{1}{a^n} = a^{-n}$, we have $\frac{1}{t^{-5}} = t^{-(-5)} = t^5$.

f) $\frac{s^{-3}}{t^{-5}} = s^{-3} \cdot \frac{1}{t^{-5}}$
$= \frac{1}{s^3} \cdot t^5 = \frac{t^5}{s^3}$ Using the result from part (e) above

The result from Example 3(f) can be generalized.

Factors and Negative Exponents

For any nonzero real numbers a and b and any integers m and n,

$$\frac{a^{-n}}{b^{-m}} = \frac{b^m}{a^n}.$$

(A factor can be moved to the other side of the fraction bar if the sign of the exponent is changed.)

EXAMPLE 4 Simplify: $\dfrac{-15x^{-7}}{5y^2z^{-4}}$.

Solution We can move the factors x^{-7} and z^{-4} to the other side of the fraction bar if we change the sign of each exponent:

$$\frac{-15x^{-7}}{5y^2z^{-4}} = \frac{-3z^4}{y^2x^7}, \quad \text{or} \quad \frac{-3z^4}{x^7y^2}.$$

When possible, be sure to simplify the constant factors: $-15/5 = -3$.

Another way to change the sign of the exponent is to take the reciprocal of the base. To understand why this is true, note that

$$\left(\frac{s}{t}\right)^{-5} = \frac{s^{-5}}{t^{-5}} = \frac{t^5}{s^5} = \left(\frac{t}{s}\right)^5.$$

This often provides the easiest way to simplify an expression containing a negative exponent.

Reciprocals and Negative Exponents

For any nonzero real numbers a and b and any integer n,

$$\left(\frac{a}{b}\right)^{-n} = \left(\frac{b}{a}\right)^n.$$

(Any base to a power is equal to the reciprocal of the base raised to the opposite power.)

EXAMPLE 5 Simplify: $\left(\dfrac{x^4}{2y}\right)^{-3}$.

Solution

$$\left(\frac{x^4}{2y}\right)^{-3} = \left(\frac{2y}{x^4}\right)^3$$ Taking the reciprocal of the base and changing the sign of the exponent

$$= \frac{(2y)^3}{(x^4)^3}$$ Raising a quotient to a power by raising both the numerator and denominator to the power

$$= \frac{2^3y^3}{x^{12}}$$ Raising a product to a power; using the power rule in the denominator

$$= \frac{8y^3}{x^{12}}$$ Cubing 2

Definitions and Properties of Exponents

The following summary assumes that no denominators are 0 and that 0^0 is not considered. For any integers m and n,

1 as an exponent:	$a^1 = a$
0 as an exponent:	$a^0 = 1$
Negative exponents:	$a^{-n} = \frac{1}{a^n}$,
	$\frac{a^{-n}}{b^{-m}} = \frac{b^m}{a^n}$,
	$\left(\frac{a}{b}\right)^{-n} = \left(\frac{b}{a}\right)^n$
The Product Rule:	$a^m \cdot a^n = a^{m+n}$
The Quotient Rule:	$\frac{a^m}{a^n} = a^{m-n}$
The Power Rule:	$(a^m)^n = a^{mn}$
Raising a product to a power:	$(ab)^n = a^n b^n$
Raising a quotient to a power:	$\left(\frac{a}{b}\right)^n = \frac{a^n}{b^n}$

Scientific Notation

When we are working with the very large or very small numbers that frequently occur in science, **scientific notation** provides a useful way of writing numbers. The following are examples of scientific notation.

The mass of the earth:

$$6.0 \times 10^{24} \text{ kilograms (kg)} = 6{,}000{,}000{,}000{,}000{,}000{,}000{,}000{,}000 \text{ kg}$$

The mass of a hydrogen atom:

$$1.7 \times 10^{-24} \text{ g} = 0.0000000000000000000000017 \text{ g}$$

Scientific Notation

Scientific notation for a number is an expression of the type

$$N \times 10^m,$$

where N is at least 1 but less than 10 (that is, $1 \le N < 10$), N is expressed in decimal notation, and m is an integer.

Converting from scientific to decimal notation involves multiplying by a power of 10. Consider the following.

Scientific Notation	*Multiplication*	*Decimal Notation*
4.52×10^2	4.52×100	452.
4.52×10^1	4.52×10	45.2
4.52×10^0	4.52×1	4.52
4.52×10^{-1}	4.52×0.1	0.452
4.52×10^{-2}	4.52×0.01	0.0452

Note that when m, the power of 10, is positive, the decimal point moves right m places in decimal notation. When m is negative, the decimal point moves left $|m|$ places. We generally try to perform this multiplication mentally.

EXAMPLE 6 Convert to decimal notation: **(a)** 7.893×10^5; **(b)** 4.7×10^{-8}.

Solution

a) Since the exponent is positive, the decimal point moves to the right:

7.89300. (5 places) $\quad 7.893 \times 10^5 = 789{,}300 \quad$ The decimal point moves 5 places to the right.

b) Since the exponent is negative, the decimal point moves to the left:

0.00000004.7 (8 places) $\quad 4.7 \times 10^{-8} = 0.000000047 \quad$ The decimal point moves 8 places to the left.

To convert from decimal to scientific notation, this procedure is reversed.

EXAMPLE 7 Write in scientific notation: **(a)** 83,000; **(b)** 0.0327.

Solution

a) We need to find m such that $83{,}000 = 8.3 \times 10^m$. To change 8.3 to 83,000 requires moving the decimal point 4 places to the right. This can be accomplished by multiplying by 10^4. Thus,

$83{,}000 = 8.3 \times 10^4. \quad$ This is scientific notation.

b) We need to find m such that $0.0327 = 3.27 \times 10^m$. To change 3.27 to 0.0327 requires moving the decimal point 2 places to the left. This can be accomplished by multiplying by 10^{-2}. Thus,

$0.0327 = 3.27 \times 10^{-2}. \quad$ This is scientific notation.

Conversions to and from scientific notation are often made mentally. Remember that positive exponents are used when representing large numbers and negative exponents are used when representing numbers between 0 and 1.

Multiplying and Dividing Using Scientific Notation

Products and quotients of numbers written in scientific notation are found using the rules for exponents.

EXAMPLE 8 Simplify.

a) $(1.8 \times 10^9) \cdot (2.3 \times 10^{-4})$

b) $(3.41 \times 10^5) \div (1.1 \times 10^{-3})$

Solution

a) $(1.8 \times 10^9) \cdot (2.3 \times 10^{-4})$

$= 1.8 \times 2.3 \times 10^9 \times 10^{-4}$ Using the associative and commutative laws

$= 4.14 \times 10^{9+(-4)}$ Adding exponents

$= 4.14 \times 10^5$

b) $(3.41 \times 10^5) \div (1.1 \times 10^{-3})$

$$= \frac{3.41 \times 10^5}{1.1 \times 10^{-3}}$$

$$= \frac{3.41}{1.1} \times \frac{10^5}{10^{-3}}$$

$= 3.1 \times 10^{5-(-3)}$ Subtracting exponents

$= 3.1 \times 10^8$

When a problem is stated using scientific notation, we normally use scientific notation for the answer. This often requires an additional conversion.

EXAMPLE 9 Simplify.

a) $(3.1 \times 10^5) \cdot (4.5 \times 10^{-3})$

b) $(7.2 \times 10^{-7}) \div (8.0 \times 10^6)$

Solution

a) We have

$$(3.1 \times 10^5) \cdot (4.5 \times 10^{-3}) = 3.1 \times 4.5 \times 10^5 \times 10^{-3} = 13.95 \times 10^2.$$

Our answer is not yet in scientific notation because 13.95 is not between 1 and 10. We convert to scientific notation as follows:

$13.95 \times 10^2 = 1.395 \times 10^1 \times 10^2$ Substituting 1.395×10^1 for 13.95

$= 1.395 \times 10^3.$ Adding exponents

b) $(7.2 \times 10^{-7}) \div (8.0 \times 10^6) = \dfrac{7.2 \times 10^{-7}}{8.0 \times 10^6} = \dfrac{7.2}{8.0} \times \dfrac{10^{-7}}{10^6}$

$= 0.9 \times 10^{-13}$

$= 9.0 \times 10^{-1} \times 10^{-13}$ Substituting 9.0×10^{-1} for 0.9

$= 9.0 \times 10^{-14}$ Adding exponents

technology connection

A key labeled (10^x), (^), or (EE) is used to enter scientific notation into a calculator. Sometimes this is a secondary function, meaning that another key—often labeled SHIFT or (2ND) —must be pressed first.

To check Example 8(a), we press

1.8 (EE) 9 (×) 2.3 (EE) ((−)) 4.

When we then press (=) or (ENTER), the result 4.14E5 appears. This represents 4.14×10^5. On many calculators, the MODE Sci must be selected in order to display scientific notation.

```
1.8E9*2.3E-4
                4.14E5
```

On some calculators, this appears as

```
4.14 05
```

or

```
4.14e+05
```

Calculate each of the following.

1. $(3.8 \times 10^9) \cdot (4.5 \times 10^7)$

2. $(2.9 \times 10^{-8}) \div (5.4 \times 10^6)$

3. $(9.2 \times 10^7) \div (2.5 \times 10^{-9})$

4.8 Exercise Set

FOR EXTRA HELP

Student's Solutions Manual | Digital Video Tutor CD 3 Videotape 8 | AW Math Tutor Center | MathXL Tutorials on CD | MathXL | MyMathLab

Express using positive exponents. Then, if possible, simplify.

1. 7^{-2} **2.** 2^{-4} **3.** 10^{-4}

4. 5^{-3} **5.** $(-2)^{-6}$ **6.** $(-3)^{-4}$

7. x^{-8} **8.** t^{-5} **9.** xy^{-2}

10. $a^{-3}b$ **11.** $r^{-5}t$ **12.** xy^{-9}

13. $\frac{1}{t^{-8}}$ **14.** $\frac{1}{z^{-9}}$ **15.** $\frac{1}{h^{-8}}$

16. $\frac{1}{a^{-12}}$ **17.** 7^{-1} **18.** 3^{-1}

19. $\left(\frac{3}{5}\right)^{-2}$ **20.** $\left(\frac{3}{4}\right)^{-2}$ **21.** $\left(\frac{a}{2}\right)^{-3}$

22. $\left(\frac{x}{2}\right)^{-4}$ **23.** $\left(\frac{s}{t}\right)^{-7}$ **24.** $\left(\frac{r}{v}\right)^{-5}$

Express using negative exponents.

25. $\frac{1}{6^2}$ **26.** $\frac{1}{5^2}$ **27.** $\frac{1}{t^6}$

28. $\frac{1}{y^2}$ **29.** $\frac{1}{a^4}$ **30.** $\frac{1}{t^5}$

31. $\frac{1}{p^7}$ **32.** $\frac{1}{m^{12}}$ **33.** $\frac{1}{5}$

34. $\frac{1}{8}$ **35.** $\frac{1}{t}$ **36.** $\frac{1}{m}$

Simplify. Do not use negative exponents in the answer.

37. $2^{-5} \cdot 2^8$ **38.** $5^{-8} \cdot 5^{10}$ **39.** $x^{-2} \cdot x^{-7}$

40. $x^{-2} \cdot x^{-9}$ **41.** $t^{-3} \cdot t$ **42.** $y^{-5} \cdot y$

43. $(a^{-2})^9$ **44.** $(x^{-5})^6$ **45.** $(t^{-3})^{-6}$

46. $(a^{-4})^{-7}$ **47.** $(t^4)^{-3}$ **48.** $(t^5)^{-2}$

49. $(x^{-2})^{-4}$ **50.** $(t^{-6})^{-5}$ **51.** $(ab)^{-3}$

52. $(xy)^{-6}$ **53.** $(mn)^{-7}$ **54.** $(ab)^{-9}$

55. $(3x^{-4})^2$ **56.** $(2a^{-5})^3$ **57.** $(5r^{-4}t^3)^2$

58. $(4x^5y^{-6})^3$ **59.** $\frac{t^7}{t^{-3}}$ **60.** $\frac{x^7}{x^{-2}}$

61. $\frac{y^{-7}}{y^{-3}}$ **62.** $\frac{z^{-6}}{z^{-2}}$ **63.** $\frac{12y^{-4}}{4y^{-9}}$

64. $\frac{8a^{-6}}{2a^{-10}}$ **65.** $\frac{2x^6}{x}$ **66.** $\frac{3x}{x^{-1}}$

67. $\frac{15a^{-7}}{10b^{-9}}$ **68.** $\frac{12x^{-6}}{8y^{-10}}$ Aha! **69.** $\frac{t^{-7}}{t^{-7}}$

70. $\frac{a^{-5}}{b^{-7}}$ **71.** $\frac{3x^{-5}}{y^{-6}z^{-2}}$ **72.** $\frac{4a^{-6}}{b^{-5}c^{-7}}$

73. $\frac{3t^4}{s^{-2}u^{-4}}$ **74.** $\frac{5x^{-8}}{y^{-3}z^2}$ **75.** $(x^4y^5)^{-3}$

76. $(t^5x^3)^{-4}$ **77.** $(x^{-6}y^{-2})^{-4}$ **78.** $(x^{-2}y^{-7})^{-5}$

79. $(a^{-5}b^7c^{-2})(a^{-3}b^{-2}c^6)$

80. $(x^3y^{-4}z^{-5})(x^{-4}y^{-2}z^9)$

81. $\left(\frac{a^4}{3}\right)^{-2}$ **82.** $\left(\frac{y^2}{2}\right)^{-2}$ **83.** $\left(\frac{m^{-1}}{n^{-4}}\right)^3$

84. $\left(\frac{x^2y}{z^{-5}}\right)^3$ **85.** $\left(\frac{2a^2}{3b^4}\right)^{-3}$ **86.** $\left(\frac{a^2b}{cd^3}\right)^{-5}$

Aha! **87.** $\left(\frac{5x^{-2}}{3y^{-2}z}\right)^0$ **88.** $\left(\frac{4a^3b^{-2}}{5c^{-3}}\right)^1$

Convert to decimal notation.

89. 7.12×10^4 **90.** 8.92×10^2

91. 8.92×10^{-3} **92.** 7.26×10^{-4}

93. 9.04×10^8 **94.** 1.35×10^7

95. 2.764×10^{-10} **96.** 9.043×10^{-3}

97. 4.209×10^7 **98.** 5.029×10^8

Convert to scientific notation.

99. 490,000 **100.** 71,500

101. 0.00583 **102.** 0.0814

103. 78,000,000,000 **104.** 3,700,000,000,000

105. 0.000000527 **106.** 0.00000000648

107. 0.000000018 **108.** 0.00000000002

109. 1,094,000,000,000,000

110. 1,030,200,000,000,000,000

Multiply or divide, and write scientific notation for the result.

111. $(4 \times 10^7)(2 \times 10^5)$

112. $(1.9 \times 10^8)(3.4 \times 10^{-3})$

113. $(3.8 \times 10^9)(6.5 \times 10^{-2})$

114. $(7.1 \times 10^{-7})(8.6 \times 10^{-5})$

115. $(8.7 \times 10^{-12})(4.5 \times 10^{-5})$

116. $(4.7 \times 10^5)(6.2 \times 10^{-12})$

117. $\frac{8.5 \times 10^8}{3.4 \times 10^{-5}}$

118. $\frac{5.6 \times 10^{-2}}{2.5 \times 10^5}$

119. $(3.0 \times 10^6) \div (6.0 \times 10^9)$

120. $(1.5 \times 10^{-3}) \div (1.6 \times 10^{-6})$

121. $\frac{7.5 \times 10^{-9}}{2.5 \times 10^{12}}$

122. $\frac{4.0 \times 10^{-3}}{8.0 \times 10^{20}}$

123. Without performing actual computations, explain why 3^{-29} is smaller than 2^{-29}.

124. What is it about scientific notation that makes it so useful?

SKILL MAINTENANCE

Simplify. [1.8]

125. $(3 - 8)(9 - 12)$

126. $(2 - 9)^2$

127. $7 \cdot 2 + 8^2$

128. $5 \cdot 6 - 3 \cdot 2 \cdot 4$

129. Plot the points $(-3, 2)$, $(4, -1)$, $(5, 3)$, and $(-5, -2)$. [3.1]

130. Solve $cx + bt = r$ for t. [2.3]

SYNTHESIS

131. Explain what requirements must be met in order for x^{-n} to represent a negative integer.

132. Explain why scientific notation cannot be used without an understanding of the rules for exponents.

133. Write the reciprocal of 1.25×10^{-6} in scientific notation.

134. Write the reciprocal of 2.5×10^9 in scientific notation.

135. Write $8^{-3} \cdot 32 \div 16^2$ as a power of 2.

136. Write $81^3 \cdot 27 \div 9^2$ as a power of 3.

Simplify each of the following. Use a calculator only where indicated.

137. $\dfrac{125^{-4}(25^2)^4}{125}$

138. $(13^{-12})^2 \cdot 13^{25}$

139. $\dfrac{4.2 \times 10^8[(2.5 \times 10^{-5}) \div (5.0 \times 10^{-9})]}{3.0 \times 10^{-12}}$

140. $\dfrac{27^{-2}(81^2)^3}{9^8}$

141. $\dfrac{7.4 \times 10^{29}}{(5.4 \times 10^{-6})(2.8 \times 10^8)}$

142. $\dfrac{5.8 \times 10^{17}}{(4.0 \times 10^{-13})(2.3 \times 10^4)}$

143. $\dfrac{(7.8 \times 10^7)(8.4 \times 10^{23})}{2.1 \times 10^{-12}}$

144. $\dfrac{(2.5 \times 10^{-8})(6.1 \times 10^{-11})}{1.28 \times 10^{-3}}$

145. Determine whether each of the following is true for all pairs of integers m and n and all positive numbers x and y.

a) $x^m \cdot y^n = (xy)^{mn}$
b) $x^m \cdot y^m = (xy)^{2m}$
c) $(x - y)^m = x^m - y^m$

Write scientific notation for each answer.

146. *Household income.* In 2001, there were about 109.3 million households in the United States. The average income of these households (before taxes) was about \$79,463. Find the total income generated by these households.
Source: *Statistical Abstract of the United States* 2002

147. *Computers.* A gigabyte is a measure of a computer's storage capacity. One gigabyte holds about one billion bytes of information. If a firm's computer network contains 2500 gigabytes of memory, how many bytes are in the network?

148. *River discharge.* The average discharge at the mouth of the Amazon River is 4,200,000 cubic feet per second. How much water is discharged from the Amazon River in 1 yr?

149. *Biology.* A strand of DNA (deoxyribonucleic acid) is about 1.5 m long and 1.3×10^{-10} cm wide. How many times longer is DNA than it is wide?
Source: Human Genome Project Information

150. *Water contamination.* In the United States, 200 million gal of used motor oil is improperly disposed of each year. One gallon of used oil can contaminate one million gallons of drinking water. How many gallons of drinking water can 200 million gallons of oil contaminate?
Source: *The Macmillan Visual Almanac*

4 Study Summary

Terms were first introduced in Chapter 1 and include expressions like

$$\frac{9}{x^2}, \quad 5a^3, \quad \text{and} \quad -7x^4y^5 \text{ (p. 235).}$$

Of the terms listed, $5a^3$ and $-7x^4y^5$ do not involve division by a variable expression and are examples of **monomials** (p. 235). A **binomial** is the sum or difference of two monomials, such as

$$3x + 5, \quad 2a^4 - 7a^3, \quad \text{or} \quad -x^2y + 6z,$$

and a **trinomial** is formed by adding and/or subtracting three monomials (p. 236). Examples of trinomials include

$$a^2 + 3a - 7, \quad 5x^3 - 4x^2 + 9x, \quad \text{and} \quad 2r^2t + 7rt - r^3.$$

Monomials, binomials, and trinomials are types of **polynomials** (p. 235).

The **degree of a term** in a polynomial is the number of variable factors in the term (p. 236). The **coefficient** of a term is the constant factor in that term (p. 236):

Degree is 2 — Degree is 3 — Degree is 6

$$5x^2, \quad -abc, \quad -2r^4t^2.$$

Coefficient is 5 — Coefficient is -1 — Coefficient is -2

The **leading term of a polynomial** is the term with the highest degree. The **leading coefficient** of a polynomial is the same as the coefficient of the polynomial's leading term, and the **degree of a polynomial** is the degree of the leading term (p. 237). To illustrate, note that

$$5x^2 - abc - 2r^4t^2$$

has degree 6, a leading coefficient of -2, and $-2r^4t^2$ as its leading term. Because this trinomial makes use of more than one variable, it is an example of a **polynomial in several variables** (p. 270).

A polynomial in one variable is written in **descending order** (p. 238) if the degrees of the terms decrease from left to right. Thus,

$2x^5 + 7x^3 - 5x + 9$ is written in descending order,

whereas

$2 + 4a + 3a^2 - 2a^5$ is written in **ascending order** (p. 245).

Polynomials can be added (p. 244) by combining **like terms** (p. 244). To subtract a polynomial (p. 246), we first find its **opposite** (p. 246) and then add. Multiplication (p. 253) is performed by multiplying every term in one polynomial by each term in the other polynomial and, if possible, then combining like terms. Division (p. 279) is performed much like long division of numbers.

Addition: $(3x^2 + 5x - 9) + (4x^2 - 7x) = (3 + 4)x^2 + (5 + (-7))x - 9$
$= 7x^2 - 2x - 9$

Subtraction: $(8t^3 + 2t^2 + 3) - (5t^3 + t - 6) = 8t^3 + 2t^2 + 3 + (-5t^3) - t + 6$
$= (8 - 5)t^3 + 2t^2 - t + (3 + 6)$
$= 3t^3 + 2t^2 - t + 9$

Multiplication: $(x + 4)(x^2 + 3x - 2) = x(x^2 + 3x - 2) + 4(x^2 + 3x - 2)$
$= x \cdot x^2 + x \cdot 3x + x(-2) + 4 \cdot x^2 + 4 \cdot 3x + 4(-2)$
$= x^3 + 3x^2 - 2x + 4x^2 + 12x - 8$
$= x^3 + 7x^2 + 10x - 8$

Division: $(4x^2 + 8x + 7) \div (2x + 3) = 2x + 1 + \frac{4}{2x + 3}$

$$\begin{array}{r} 2x + 1 \\ 2x + 3 \overline{)4x^2 + 8x + 7} \\ -(4x^2 + 6x) \\ \hline 2x + 7 \\ -(2x + 3) \\ \hline 4 \end{array}$$

Important definitions and properties of exponents are listed on p. 288 in Section 4.8.

4 Review Exercises

Concept Reinforcement *Classify each statement as either true or false.*

1. When two polynomials that are written in descending order are added, the result is generally written in ascending order. [4.3]
2. The product of the sum and difference of the same two terms is a difference of squares. [4.5]
3. When a binomial is squared, the result is a perfect-square trinomial. [4.5]
4. FOIL can be used whenever two polynomials are being multiplied. [4.5]
5. The degree of a polynomial can exceed the value of the polynomial's leading coefficient. [4.2]
6. Scientific notation is used only for extremely large numbers. [4.8]
7. FOIL can be used with polynomials in several variables. [4.6]
8. A positive number raised to a negative exponent can never represent a negative number. [4.8]

Simplify. [4.1]

9. $y^7 \cdot y^3 \cdot y$

10. $(3x)^5 \cdot (3x)^9$

11. $t^6 \cdot t^0$

12. $\dfrac{4^5}{4^2}$

13. $\dfrac{(a+b)^4}{(a+b)^4}$

14. $\left(\dfrac{3t^4}{2s^3}\right)^2$

15. $(-2xy^2)^3$

16. $(2x^3)(-3x)^2$

17. $(a^2b)(ab)^5$

Identify the terms of each polynomial. [4.2]

18. $3x^2 + 6x + \frac{1}{2}$

19. $-4y^5 + 7y^2 - 3y - 2$

List the coefficients of the terms in each polynomial. [4.2]

20. $9x^2 - x + 7$

21. $4x^3 + 6x^2 - 5x + \frac{5}{3}$

For each polynomial, **(a)** *list the degree of each term;* **(b)** *determine the leading term and the leading coefficient; and* **(c)** *determine the degree of the polynomial.* [4.2]

22. $4t^2 + 6 + 15t^5$

23. $-2x^5 + 7 - 3x^2 + x$

Classify each polynomial as a monomial, a binomial, a trinomial, or none of these. [4.2]

24. $4x^3 - 1$

25. $4 - 9t^3 - 7t^4 + 10t^2$

26. $7y^2$

Combine like terms and write in descending order. [4.2]

27. $3x - x^2 + 4x$

28. $\frac{3}{4}x^3 + 4x^2 - x^3 + 7$

29. $-2x^4 + 16 + 2x^4 + 9 - 3x^5$

30. $3x^2 - 2x + 3 - 5x^2 - 1 - x$

31. $-x + \frac{1}{2} + 14x^4 - 7x^2 - 1 - 4x^4$

Evaluate each polynomial for $x = -1$. [4.2]

32. $9x - 6$

33. $x^2 - 3x + 6$

Add or subtract. [4.3]

34. $(8x^4 - x^3 + x - 4) + (x^5 + 7x^3 - 3x - 5)$

35. $(3x^4 - 5x^3 + 3x^2) + (4x^5 + 4x^3) + (-5x^5 - 5x^2)$

36. $(5x^2 - 4x + 1) - (3x^2 + 7)$

37. $(3x^5 - 4x^4 + 2x^2 + 3) - (2x^5 - 4x^4 + 3x^3 + 4x^2 - 5)$

38.
$$\begin{array}{rrrrr} -\frac{3}{4}x^4 & +\frac{1}{2}x^3 & & & +\frac{7}{8} \\ & -\frac{1}{4}x^3 & -x^2 & -\frac{7}{4}x & \\ +\frac{3}{2}x^4 & & +\frac{2}{3}x^2 & & -\frac{1}{2} \\ \hline \end{array}$$

39.
$$\begin{array}{l} \quad 2x^5 \qquad\quad - x^3 \qquad\qquad + x + 3 \\ -(3x^5 - x^4 + 4x^3 + 2x^2 - x + 3) \\ \hline \end{array}$$

40. The length of a rectangle is 3 m greater than its width.

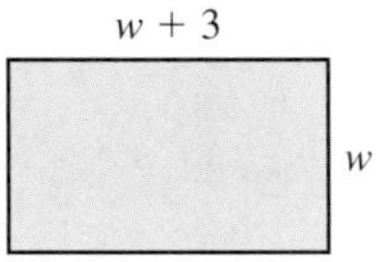

a) Find a polynomial for the perimeter. [4.3]
b) Find a polynomial for the area. [4.4]

Multiply.

41. $3x(-4x^2)$ [4.4]

42. $(7x + 1)^2$ [4.5]

43. $(a - 7)(a + 4)$ [4.5]

44. $(m + 5)(m - 5)$ [4.5]

45. $(4x^2 - 5x + 1)(3x - 2)$ [4.4]

46. $(x - 8)^2$ [4.5]

47. $3t^2(5t^3 - 2t^2 + 4t)$ [4.4]

48. $(a - 9)(a + 9)$ [4.5]

49. $(x - 0.8)(x - 0.5)$ [4.5]

50. $(x^4 - 2x + 3)(x^3 + x - 1)$ [4.4]

51. $(3x - 5)^2$ [4.5]

52. $(2t^2 + 3)(t^2 - 7)$ [4.5]

53. $\left(a - \frac{1}{2}\right)\left(a + \frac{2}{3}\right)$ [4.5]

54. $(-7 + 3x)(7 + 3x)$ [4.5]

55. Evaluate $2 - 5xy + y^2 - 4xy^3 + x^6$ for $x = -1$ and $y = 2$. [4.6]

Identify the coefficient and the degree of each term of each polynomial. Then find the degree of each polynomial. [4.6]

56. $x^5y - 7xy + 9x^2 - 8$

57. $x^2y^5z^9 - y^{40} + x^{13}z^{10}$

Combine like terms. [4.6]

58. $y + w - 2y + 8w - 5$

59. $6m^3 + 3m^2n + 4mn^2 + m^2n - 5mn^2$

Add or subtract. [4.6]

60. $(5x^2 - 7xy + y^2) + (-6x^2 - 3xy - y^2)$

61. $(6x^3y^2 - 4x^2y - 6x) - (-5x^3y^2 + 4x^2y + 6x^2 - 6)$

Multiply. [4.6]

62. $(2x + 5y)(x - 3y)$

63. $\left(3a^4 - \frac{1}{3}b^3\right)^2$

64. Find a polynomial for the shaded area. [4.6]

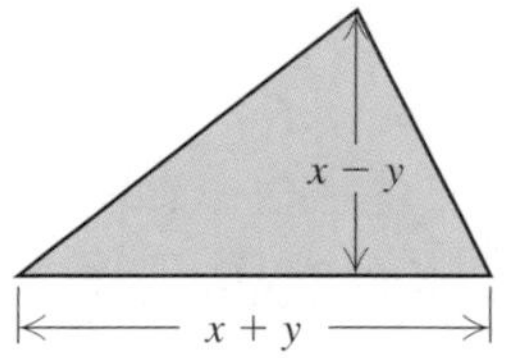

Divide. [4.7]

65. $(10x^3 - x^2 + 8x) \div (2x)$

66. $(6x^3 - 5x^2 - 13x + 13) \div (2x + 3)$

67. $\dfrac{t^4 + t^3 + 2t^2 - t - 3}{t + 1}$

68. Express using a positive exponent: m^{-4}. [4.8]

69. Express using a negative exponent: $\dfrac{1}{a^9}$. [4.8]

Simplify. [4.8]

70. $7^2 \cdot 7^{-4}$

71. $\dfrac{6a^{-5}b}{3a^8b^8}$

72. $(x^3)^{-4}$

73. $(2x^{-3}y)^{-2}$

74. $\left(\dfrac{2x}{y}\right)^{-3}$

75. Convert to decimal notation: 8.3×10^6. [4.8]

76. Convert to scientific notation: 0.0000328. [4.8]

Multiply or divide and write scientific notation for the result. [4.8]

77. $(3.8 \times 10^4)(5.5 \times 10^{-1})$

78. $\dfrac{1.28 \times 10^{-8}}{2.5 \times 10^{-4}}$

79. *Blood donors.* Every 4–6 weeks, one of the authors of this text donates 1.14×10^6 cubic millimeters (two pints) of whole blood, from which platelets are removed and the blood returned to the body. In one cubic millimeter of blood, there are about 2×10^5 platelets. Approximate the number of platelets in a typical donation by this author. [4.8]

SYNTHESIS

80. Explain why $5x^3$ and $(5x)^3$ are not equivalent expressions. [4.1]

81. A binomial is squared and the result, written in descending form, is $x^2 - 6x + 9$. Is it possible to determine what binomial was squared? Why or why not? [4.5]

82. How many terms are there in each of the following? [4.2], [4.5]

a) $(x - a)(x - b) + (x - a)(x - b)$

b) $(x + a)(x - b) + (x - a)(x + b)$

83. Simplify:

$$(-3x^5 \cdot 3x^3 - x^6(2x)^2 + (3x^4)^2 + (2x^2)^4 - 20x^2(x^3)^2)^2.$$ [4.1], [4.2]

84. A polynomial has degree 4. The x^2-term is missing. The coefficient of x^4 is 2 times the coefficient of x^3. The coefficient of x is 3 less than the coefficient of x^4. The remaining coefficient is 7 less than the coefficient of x. The sum of the coefficients is 15. Find the polynomial. [4.2]

Aha! **85.** Multiply: $[(x - 5) - 4x^3][(x - 5) + 4x^3]$. [4.5]

86. Solve: $(x - 7)(x + 10) = (x - 4)(x - 6)$. [2.2], [4.5]

4 Chapter Test

Simplify.

1. $a^4 \cdot a \cdot a^5$
2. $\frac{4^5}{4^2}$
3. $\frac{(2x)^5}{(2x)^5}$
4. $(x^3)^2$
5. $(-3y^2)^3$
6. $\left(\frac{5}{4a^3}\right)^2$
7. $(3x^2)(-2x^5)^3$
8. $(a^3b^2)(ab)^3$
9. Classify $4x^2y - 7y^3$ as a monomial, a binomial, a trinomial, or none of these.
10. Identify the coefficient of each term of the polynomial:
$\frac{1}{3}x^5 - x + 7.$
11. Determine the degree of each term, the leading term and the leading coefficient, and the degree of the polynomial:
$2t^3 - t + 7t^5 + 4.$
12. Evaluate $x^2 + 5x - 1$ for $x = -2$.

Combine like terms and write in descending order.

13. $4a^2 - 6 + a^2$
14. $y^2 - 3y - y + \frac{3}{4}y^2$
15. $3 - x^2 + 2x^3 + 5x^2 - 6x - 2x + x^5$

Add or subtract.

16. $(3x^5 + 5x^3 - 5x^2 - 3) + (x^5 + x^4 - 3x^2 + 2x - 4)$
17. $\left(x^4 + \frac{2}{3}x + 5\right) + \left(4x^4 + 5x^2 + \frac{1}{3}x\right)$
18. $(2x^4 + x^3 - 8x^2 - 6x - 3) - (6x^4 - 8x^2 + 2x)$
19. $(x^3 - 0.4x^2 - 12) - (x^5 - 0.3x^3 + 0.4x^2 - 9)$

Multiply.

20. $-2x^2(3x^2 - 3x - 5)$
21. $\left(x - \frac{1}{3}\right)^2$
22. $(5t - 7)(5t + 7)$
23. $(3b + 5)(b - 3)$
24. $(x^6 - 4)(x^8 + 4)$
25. $(8 - y)(6 + 5y)$
26. $(2x + 1)(3x^2 - 5x - 3)$
27. $(8a + 3)^2$
28. Evaluate $2x^2y - 3y^2$ for $x = -3$ and $y = 2$.
29. Combine like terms:
$2x^3y - y^3 + xy^3 + 8 - 6x^3y - x^2y^2 + 11.$
30. Subtract:
$(8a^2b^2 - ab + b^3) - (-6ab^2 - 7ab - ab^3 + 5b^3).$
31. Multiply: $(3x^5 - y)(3x^5 + y)$.

Divide.

32. $(12x^4 + 9x^3 - 15x^2) \div (3x^2)$
33. $(6x^3 - 8x^2 - 14x + 13) \div (3x + 2)$
34. Express using a positive exponent: 5^{-3}.
35. Express using a negative exponent: $\frac{1}{y^8}$.

Simplify.

36. $t^{-4} \cdot t^{-2}$
37. $\frac{x^3y^2}{x^8y^{-3}}$
38. $(2a^3b^{-1})^{-4}$
39. $\left(\frac{ab}{c}\right)^{-3}$
40. Convert to scientific notation: 3,900,000,000.
41. Convert to decimal notation: 5×10^{-8}.

Multiply or divide and write scientific notation for the result.

42. $\frac{5.6 \times 10^6}{3.2 \times 10^{-11}}$
43. $(2.4 \times 10^5)(5.4 \times 10^{16})$

SYNTHESIS

44. The height of a box is 1 less than its length, and the length is 2 more than its width. Express the volume in terms of the length.
45. Solve: $x^2 + (x - 7)(x + 4) = 2(x - 6)^2$.
46. A CD-ROM can hold about 600 million pieces of information. How many sound files, each needing 40,000 pieces of information, can a 20-pack of CD-ROMs hold? Write scientific notation for the answer.

5 Polynomials and Factoring

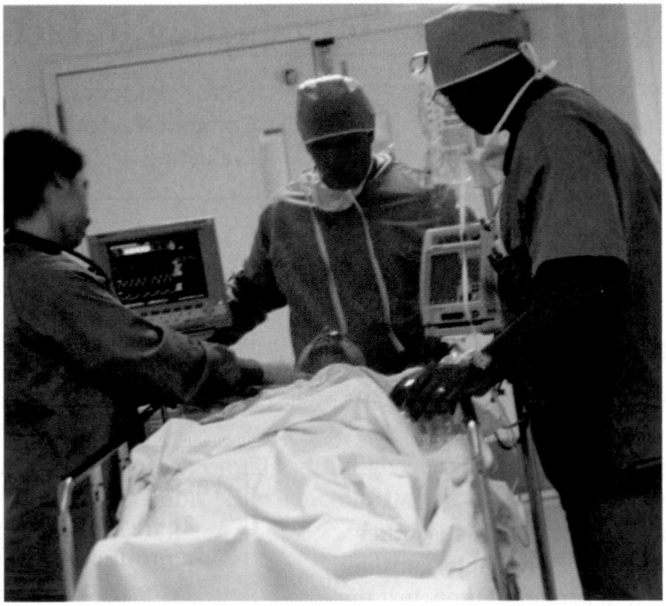

AN APPLICATION

For certain people suffering an extreme allergic reaction, the drug epinephrine (adrenaline) is sometimes prescribed. The number of micrograms N of epinephrine in an adult's bloodstream t minutes after 250 micrograms have been injected can be approximated by $N = -10t^2 + 100t$. How long after an injection will there be about 210 micrograms of epinephrine in the bloodstream?

This problem appears as Example 4 in Section 5.7.

Mary Novinger
EMT
Lima, New York

As an EMT, I use math quite often. In many situations, time is crucial, and quick and accurate calculations of vital signs are essential. I also use math to measure volume and to evaluate burn victims.

Although factoring by grouping can be useful, some polynomials, like $x^3 + x^2 + 2x - 2$, cannot be factored this way. Factoring polynomials of this type is beyond the scope of this text.

Checking by Evaluating

We have seen that one way to check a factorization is to multiply. A second type of check, discussed toward the end of Section 4.4, uses the fact that equivalent expressions have the same value when evaluated for the same replacement. Thus a quick, partial check of Example 7(a) can be made by using a convenient replacement for x (say, 1) and evaluating both $2x^3 + 8x^2 + x + 4$ and $(x + 4)(2x^2 + 1)$:

$$2 \cdot 1^3 + 8 \cdot 1^2 + 1 + 4 = 2 + 8 + 1 + 4$$
$$= 15;$$
$$(1 + 4)(2 \cdot 1^2 + 1) = 5 \cdot 3$$
$$= 15.$$

Since the value of both expressions is the same, the factorization is probably correct.

Keep in mind the possibility that two expressions that are not equivalent may share the same value when evaluated at a certain value. Because of this, unless several values are used (at least one more than the degree of the polynomial, it turns out), evaluating offers only a partial check. Consult with your instructor before making extensive use of this type of check.

technology connection

A partial check of a factorization can be performed using a table or a graph. To check Example 7(a), we let

$y_1 = 2x^3 + 8x^2 + x + 4$ and $y_2 = (x + 4)(2x^2 + 1)$.

Then we set up a table in AUTO mode (see p. 92). If the factorization is correct, the values of y_1 and y_2 will be the same regardless of the table settings used.

ΔTBL = 1

X	Y1	Y2
0	4	4
1	15	15
2	54	54
3	133	133
4	264	264
5	459	459
6	730	730
X = 0		

We can also graph $y_1 = 2x^3 + 8x^2 + x + 4$ and $y_2 = (x + 4)(2x^2 + 1)$. If the graphs appear to coincide, the factorization is probably correct. The TRACE feature can be used to confirm this.

$y_1 = 2x^3 + 8x^2 + x + 4$,
$y_2 = (x + 4)(2x^2 + 1)$

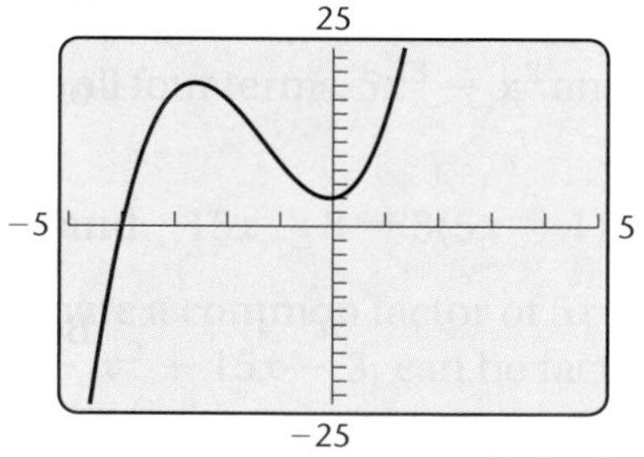

Yscl = 2

Use a table or a graph to determine whether each factorization is correct.

1. $x^2 - 7x - 8 = (x - 8)(x + 1)$
2. $4x^2 - 5x - 6 = (4x + 3)(x - 2)$
3. $5x^2 + 17x - 12 = (5x + 3)(x - 4)$
4. $10x^2 + 37x + 7 = (5x - 1)(2x + 7)$
5. $12x^2 - 17x - 5 = (6x + 1)(2x - 5)$
6. $12x^2 - 17x - 5 = (4x + 1)(3x - 5)$
7. $x^2 - 4 = (x - 2)(x - 2)$
8. $x^2 - 4 = (x + 2)(x - 2)$

5.1 Exercise Set

FOR EXTRA HELP

Student's Solutions Manual | Digital Video Tutor CD 3 Videotape 9 | AW Math Tutor Center | MathXL Tutorials on CD | MathXL | MyMathLab

Concept Reinforcement *In each of Exercises 1–8, match the phrase with the most appropriate choice from the column on the right.*

1. ____ A factorization of $35a^2b$ — **a)** $3a(1 + 2a)$

2. ____ A factor of $35a^2b$ — **b)** $x + 2$

3. ____ A common factor of $5x + 10$ and $4x + 8$ — **c)** $3x^2(3x^2 - 1)$

4. ____ A factorization of $3x^4 - 9x^2$ — **d)** $1 + 2a$

5. ____ A factorization of $9x^4 - 3x^2$ — **e)** $3x^2(x^2 - 3)$

6. ____ A common factor of $2x + 10$ and $4x + 8$ — **f)** $5a^2$

7. ____ A factor of $3a + 6a^2$ — **g)** 2

8. ____ A factorization of $3a + 6a^2$ — **h)** $7a \cdot 5ab$

Find three factorizations for each monomial. Answers may vary.

9. $10x^3$ **10.** $6x^3$ **11.** $-15a^4$

12. $-8t^5$ **13.** $26x^5$ **14.** $25x^4$

Factor. Remember to use the largest common factor and to check by multiplying.

15. $7x - 14$ **16.** $5x - 15$

17. $3t^2 + t$ **18.** $2t^2 + t$

19. $-4a^2 - 8a$ **20.** $-6a^2 - 9a$

21. $x^3 + 6x^2$ **22.** $4x^4 + x^2$

23. $8x^4 - 24x^2$ **24.** $5x^5 + 10x^3$

25. $2x^2 + 2x - 8$ **26.** $6x^2 + 3x - 15$

27. $-7a^6 + 10a^4 - 14a^2$ **28.** $-10t^5 + 15t^4 + 9t^3$

29. $6x^8 + 12x^6 - 24x^4 + 30x^2$

30. $10x^4 - 30x^3 - 50x - 20$

31. $x^5y^5 + x^4y^3 + x^3y^3 - x^2y^2$

32. $x^9y^6 - x^7y^5 + x^4y^4 + x^3y^3$

33. $-5a^3b^4 + 10a^2b^3 - 15a^3b^2$

34. $-21r^5t^4 - 14r^4t^6 + 21r^3t^6$

Factor.

35. $y(y - 2) + 7(y - 2)$ **36.** $b(b + 5) + 3(b + 5)$

37. $x^2(x + 3) - 7(x + 3)$ **38.** $3z^2(2z + 9) + (2z + 9)$

39. $y^2(y + 8) + (y + 8)$ **40.** $x^2(x - 7) - 3(x - 7)$

Factor by grouping, if possible, and check.

41. $x^3 + 3x^2 + 4x + 12$ **42.** $6z^3 + 3z^2 + 4z + 2$

43. $5a^3 + 15a^2 + 2a + 6$ **44.** $3a^3 + 2a^2 + 6a + 4$

45. $9x^3 - 12x^2 + 3x - 4$ **46.** $10x^3 - 25x^2 + 2x - 5$

47. $4t^3 - 20t^2 + 3t - 15$ **48.** $6a^3 - 8a^2 + 9a - 12$

49. $7x^3 + 2x^2 - 14x - 4$ **50.** $5x^3 + 4x^2 - 10x - 8$

51. $6a^3 - 7a^2 + 6a - 7$ **52.** $7t^3 - 5t^2 + 7t - 5$

53. $x^3 + 8x^2 - 3x - 24$ **54.** $x^3 - x^2 - 2x + 5$

55. $2x^3 + 12x^2 - 5x - 30$ **56.** $w^3 - 7w^2 + 4w - 28$

57. $p^3 + p^2 - 3p + 10$ **58.** $x^3 + 7x^2 - 2x - 14$

59. $y^3 + 8y^2 - 2y - 16$ **60.** $3x^3 + 18x^2 - 5x - 25$

61. $2x^3 - 8x^2 - 9x + 36$ **62.** $20g^3 - 4g^2 - 25g + 5$

63. In answering a factoring problem, Taylor says the largest common factor is $-5x^2$ and Natasha says the largest common factor is $5x^2$. Can they both be correct? Why or why not?

64. Write a two-sentence paragraph in which the word "factor" is used at least once as a noun and once as a verb.

SKILL MAINTENANCE

Simplify. [4.4]

65. $(x + 3)(x + 5)$ **66.** $(x + 2)(x + 7)$

67. $(a - 7)(a + 3)$ **68.** $(a + 5)(a - 8)$

69. $(2x + 5)(3x - 4)$ **70.** $(3t + 2)(4t - 7)$

71. $(3t - 5)^2$ **72.** $(2t - 9)^2$

SYNTHESIS

73. Marlene recognizes that evaluating provides only a partial check of her factoring. Because of this, she often performs a second check with a different replacement value. Is this a good idea? Why or why not?

74. Josh says that for Exercises 15–62 there is no need to print answers at the back of the book. Is he correct in saying this? Why or why not?

Factor, if possible.

75. $4x^5 + 6x^2 + 6x^3 + 9$

76. $x^6 + x^2 + x^4 + 1$

77. $x^{12} + x^7 + x^5 + 1$

78. $x^3 + x^2 - 2x + 2$

Aha! **79.** $5x^5 - 5x^4 + x^3 - x^2 + 3x - 3$

Aha! **80.** $ax^2 + 2ax + 3a + x^2 + 2x + 3$

81. Write a trinomial of degree 7 for which $8x^2y^3$ is the largest common factor. Answers may vary.

5.2 Factoring Trinomials of the Type $x^2 + bx + c$

Constant Term Positive • Constant Term Negative • Prime Polynomials

We now learn how to factor trinomials like

$$x^2 + 5x + 4 \quad \text{or} \quad x^2 + 3x - 10,$$

for which no common factor exists and the leading coefficient is 1. As preparation for the factoring that follows, compare the following multiplications:

$$\begin{aligned}
& \qquad\qquad\qquad\quad \text{F} \quad\ \text{O} \quad\ \text{I} \quad\ \text{L} \\
(x + 2)(x + 5) &= x^2 + 5x + 2x + 2 \cdot 5 \\
&= x^2 + 7x + 10; \\
(x - 2)(x - 5) &= x^2 - 5x - 2x + (-2)(-5) \\
&= x^2 - 7x + 10; \\
(x + 3)(x - 7) &= x^2 - 7x + 3x + 3(-7) \\
&= x^2 - 4x - 21; \\
(x - 3)(x + 7) &= x^2 + 7x - 3x + (-3)7 \\
&= x^2 + 4x - 21.
\end{aligned}$$

Note that for all four products:

- The product of the two binomials is a trinomial.
- The coefficient of x in the trinomial is the sum of the constant terms in the binomials.
- The constant term in the trinomial is the product of the constant terms in the binomials.

These observations lead to a method for factoring certain trinomials. The first type we consider has a positive constant term, just as in the first two multiplications above.

Study Skills

Leave a Trail

Students sometimes make the mistake of viewing their supporting work as "scrap" work. Most instructors regard your reasoning as more important than your final answer. Try to organize your supporting work so that your instructor (and you as well) can follow your steps.

Constant Term Positive

To factor a polynomial like $x^2 + 7x + 10$, we think of FOIL in reverse. The x^2 resulted from x times x, which suggests that the first term of each binomial factor is x. Next, we look for numbers p and q such that

$$x^2 + 7x + 10 = (x + p)(x + q).$$

To get the middle term and the last term of the trinomial, we need two numbers, p and q, whose product is 10 and whose sum is 7. Those numbers are 2 and 5. Thus the factorization is

$$(x + 2)(x + 5). \qquad \textit{Check: } (x + 2)(x + 5) = x^2 + 5x + 2x + 10$$
$$= x^2 + 7x + 10$$

EXAMPLE 1 Factor: $x^2 + 5x + 6$.

Solution Think of FOIL in reverse. The first term of each factor is x:

$$(x + \quad)(x + \quad).$$

To complete the factorization, we need a constant term for each binomial. The constants must have a product of 6 and a sum of 5. We list some pairs of numbers that multiply to 6.

Pairs of Factors of 6	Sums of Factors
1, 6	7
2, 3	5 ←
−1, −6	−7
−2, −3	−5

The numbers we seek are 2 and 3.

Since

$$2 \cdot 3 = 6 \quad \text{and} \quad 2 + 3 = 5,$$

the factorization of $x^2 + 5x + 6$ is $(x + 2)(x + 3)$. To check, we simply multiply the two binomials.

Check: $(x + 2)(x + 3) = x^2 + 3x + 2x + 6$
$= x^2 + 5x + 6.$

The product is the original polynomial.

Note that since 5 and 6 are both positive, when factoring $x^2 + 5x + 6$ we need not consider negative factors of 6. Note too that changing the signs of the factors changes only the sign of the sum (see the table above).

A GEOMETRIC APPROACH TO EXAMPLE 1

In Section 4.4, we saw that the product of two binomials can be regarded as the sum of the areas of four rectangles (see p. 255). Thus we can regard the factoring of $x^2 + 5x + 6$ as a search for p and q so that the sum of areas A, B, C, and D is $x^2 + 5x + 6$.

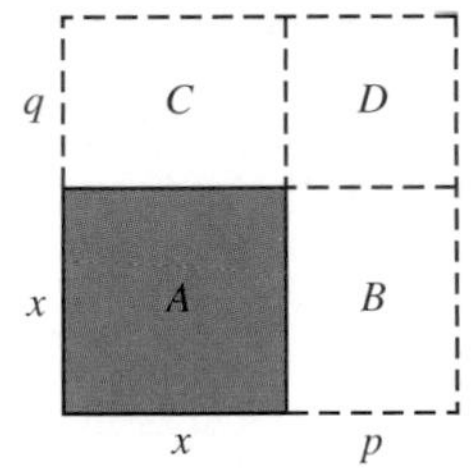

Note that area D is simply the product of p and q. Since p and q are constants, area D is a constant. In order for area D to be 6, p and q must be either 1 and 6 or 2 and 3. We illustrate both below.

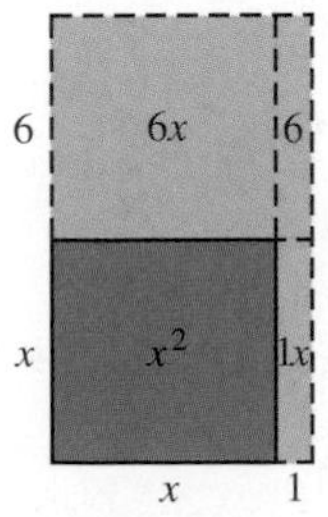

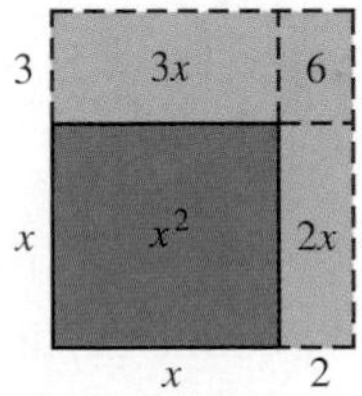

When p and q are 1 and 6, the total area is $x^2 + 7x + 6$, but when p and q are 2 and 3, as shown on the right, the total area is $x^2 + 5x + 6$, as desired. Thus the factorization of $x^2 + 5x + 6$ is $(x + 2)(x + 3)$.

At the beginning of this section, we considered the multiplication $(x - 2)(x - 5)$. For this product, the resulting trinomial, $x^2 - 7x + 10$, has a positive constant term but a negative coefficient of x. This is because the *product* of two negative numbers is always positive, whereas the *sum* of two negative numbers is always negative.

> *To Factor $x^2 + bx + c$ When c Is Positive*
>
> When the constant term of a trinomial is positive, look for two numbers with the same sign. The sign is that of the middle term:
>
> $$x^2 - 7x + 10 = (x - 2)(x - 5);$$
>
> $$x^2 + 7x + 10 = (x + 2)(x + 5).$$

EXAMPLE 2 Factor: $y^2 - 8y + 12$.

Solution Since the constant term is positive and the coefficient of the middle term is negative, we look for a factorization of 12 in which both factors are negative. Their sum must be -8.

Pairs of Factors of 12	Sums of Factors
$-1, -12$	-13
$-2, -6$	-8 ← We need a sum of -8. The numbers we need are -2 and -6.
$-3, -4$	-7

The factorization of $y^2 - 8y + 12$ is $(y - 2)(y - 6)$. The check is left to the student.

Constant Term Negative

As we saw in two of the multiplications earlier in this section, the product of two binomials can have a negative constant term:

$$(x + 3)(x - 7) = x^2 - 4x - 21$$

and

$$(x - 3)(x + 7) = x^2 + 4x - 21.$$

It is important to note that when the signs of the constants in the binomials are reversed, only the sign of the middle term of the trinomial changes.

EXAMPLE 3 Factor: $x^2 - 8x - 20$.

Solution The constant term, -20, must be expressed as the product of a negative number and a positive number. Since the sum of these two numbers must be negative (specifically, -8), the negative number must have the greater absolute value.

Pairs of Factors of -20	Sums of Factors
1, -20	-19
2, -10	-8
4, -5	-1
5, -4	1
10, -2	8
20, -1	19

-8 ← The numbers we need are 2 and -10.

Because these sums (1, 8, 19) are all positive, for this problem all of the corresponding pairs can be disregarded. Note that in all three pairs, the positive number has the greater absolute value.

The numbers that we are looking for are 2 and -10.

Check: $(x + 2)(x - 10) = x^2 - 10x + 2x - 20$

$= x^2 - 8x - 20.$

The factorization of $x^2 - 8x - 20$ is $(x + 2)(x - 10)$.

To Factor $x^2 + bx + c$ When c Is Negative

When the constant term of a trinomial is negative, look for two numbers whose product is negative. One must be positive and the other negative:

$$x^2 - 4x - 21 = (x + 3)(x - 7);$$

$$x^2 + 4x - 21 = (x - 3)(x + 7).$$

Select the two numbers so that the number with the larger absolute value has the same sign as b, the coefficient of the middle term.

EXAMPLE 4 Factor: $t^2 - 24 + 5t$.

Solution It helps to first write the trinomial in descending order: $t^2 + 5t - 24$. The factorization of the constant term, -24, must have one factor positive and one factor negative. The sum must be 5, so the positive factor must have the larger absolute value. Thus we consider only pairs of factors in which the positive factor has the larger absolute value.

Pairs of Factors of -24	Sums of Factors
$-1, 24$	23
$-2, 12$	10
$-3, 8$	5 ← The numbers we need are -3 and 8.
$-4, 6$	2

The factorization is $(t - 3)(t + 8)$. The check is left to the student.

Polynomials in two or more variables, such as $a^2 + 4ab - 21b^2$, are factored in a similar manner.

EXAMPLE 5 Factor: $a^2 + 4ab - 21b^2$.

Solution It may help to write the trinomial in the equivalent form

$$a^2 + 4ba - 21b^2.$$

We now regard $-21b^2$ as the "constant" term and $4b$ as the "coefficient" of a. Then we try to express $-21b^2$ as a product of two factors whose sum is $4b$. Those factors are $-3b$ and $7b$.

Check: $(a - 3b)(a + 7b) = a^2 + 7ab - 3ba - 21b^2$
$= a^2 + 4ab - 21b^2.$

The factorization is $(a - 3b)(a + 7b)$.

Prime Polynomials

EXAMPLE 6 Factor: $x^2 - x + 5$.

Solution Since 5 has very few factors, we can easily check all possibilities.

Pairs of Factors of 5	Sums of Factors
$5, 1$	6
$-5, -1$	-6

Since there are no factors whose sum is -1, the polynomial is *not* factorable into binomials.

In this text, a polynomial like $x^2 - x + 5$ that cannot be factored further is said to be **prime**. In more advanced courses, polynomials like $x^2 - x + 5$ can be factored and are not considered prime.

Often factoring requires two or more steps. Remember, when told to factor, we should *factor completely.* This means that the final factorization should contain only prime polynomials.

EXAMPLE 7 Factor: $-2x^3 + 20x^2 - 50x$.

Student Notes

Whenever a new set of parentheses is created while factoring, check the expression inside the parentheses to see if it can be factored further.

Solution *Always* look first for a common factor. Since the leading coefficient is negative, we begin by factoring out $-2x$:

$$-2x^3 + 20x^2 - 50x = -2x(x^2 - 10x + 25).$$

Now consider $x^2 - 10x + 25$. Since the constant term is positive and the coefficient of the middle term is negative, we look for a factorization of 25 in which both factors are negative. Their sum must be -10.

Pairs of Factors of 25	Sums of Factors
$-25, -1$	-26
$-5, -5$	-10 ← The numbers we need are -5 and -5.

The factorization of $x^2 - 10x + 25$ is $(x - 5)(x - 5)$, or $(x - 5)^2$.

> *Caution!* When factoring involves more than one step, be careful to write out the *entire* factorization.

Check: $-2x(x - 5)(x - 5) = -2x[x^2 - 10x + 25]$ Multiplying binomials

$= -2x^3 + 20x^2 - 50x.$ Using the distributive law

The factorization of $-2x^3 + 20x^2 - 50x$ is $-2x(x - 5)(x - 5)$, or $-2x(x - 5)^2$.

Once any common factors have been factored out, the following summary can be used to factor $x^2 + bx + c$.

To Factor $x^2 + bx + c$

1. Find a pair of factors that have c as their product and b as their sum.
   a) If c is positive, its factors will have the same sign as b.
   b) If c is negative, one factor will be positive and the other will be negative. Select the factors such that the factor with the larger absolute value has the same sign as b.
2. Check by multiplying.

5.2 Exercise Set

FOR EXTRA HELP

Student's Solutions Manual | Digital Video Tutor CD 3 Videotape 9 | AW Math Tutor Center | MathXL Tutorials on CD | MathXL | MyMathLab

Concept Reinforcement *For Exercises 1–6, assume that a polynomial of the form $x^2 + bx + c$ can be factored as $(x + p)(x + q)$. Complete each sentence by replacing each blank with either "positive" or "negative."*

1. If b is positive and c is positive, then p will be __________ and q will be __________.

2. If b is negative and c is positive, then p will be __________ and q will be __________.

3. If p is negative and q is negative, then b must be __________ and c must be __________.

4. If p is positive and q is positive, then b must be __________ and c must be __________.

5. If b, c, and p are all negative, then q must be __________.

6. If b and c are negative and p is positive, then q must be __________.

Factor completely. Remember that you can check by multiplying. If a polynomial is prime, state this.

7. $x^2 + 7x + 6$
8. $x^2 + 6x + 5$
9. $x^2 + 7x + 12$
10. $x^2 + 7x + 10$
11. $x^2 - 6x + 9$
12. $y^2 + 11y + 28$
13. $x^2 + 9x + 14$
14. $a^2 - 11a + 30$
15. $b^2 - 5b + 4$
16. $x^2 + 5x + 4$
17. $a^2 + 4a - 12$
18. $z^2 - 8z + 7$
19. $d^2 - 7d + 10$
20. $x^2 - 8x + 15$
21. $x^2 - 2x - 15$
22. $y^2 - 11y + 10$
23. $x^2 + 2x - 15$
24. $x^2 + x - 42$
25. $3y^2 - 9y - 84$
26. $2x^2 - 14x - 36$
27. $-x^3 + x^2 + 42x$
28. $-x^3 + 6x^2 + 16x$
29. $7x - 60 + x^2$
30. $4y - 45 + y^2$
31. $x^2 - 72 + 6x$
32. $-2x - 99 + x^2$
33. $-5b^2 - 25b + 120$
34. $-c^4 - c^3 + 56c^2$
35. $x^5 - x^4 - 2x^3$
36. $2a^2 - 4a - 70$
37. $x^2 + 2x + 3$
38. $x^2 + x + 1$
39. $50 + 15t + t^2$
40. $27 + 12y + y^2$
41. $x^2 + 20x + 99$
42. $x^2 + 20x + 100$
43. $2x^3 - 40x^2 + 192x$
44. $3x^3 - 63x^2 - 300x$
45. $-4x^2 - 40x - 100$
46. $-2x^2 + 42x + 144$
47. $y^2 - 21y + 108$
48. $x^2 - 25x + 144$
49. $-a^6 - 9a^5 + 90a^4$
50. $-a^4 - a^3 + 132a^2$
51. $t^2 + \frac{2}{3}t + \frac{1}{9}$
52. $x^2 - \frac{2}{5}x + \frac{1}{25}$
53. $11 + w^2 - 4w$
54. $6 - p^2 - 2p$
55. $p^2 + 3pq - 10q^2$
56. $a^2 - 2ab - 3b^2$
57. $m^2 + 5mn + 5n^2$
58. $x^2 - 11xy + 24y^2$
59. $s^2 - 2st - 15t^2$
60. $b^2 + 8bc - 20c^2$
61. $6a^{10} - 30a^9 - 84a^8$
62. $7x^9 - 28x^8 - 35x^7$

63. Without multiplying $(x - 17)(x - 18)$, explain why it cannot possibly be a factorization of $x^2 + 35x + 306$.

64. Marge factors $x^3 - 8x^2 + 15x$ as $(x^2 - 5x)(x - 3)$. Is she wrong? Why or why not? What advice would you offer?

SKILL MAINTENANCE

Solve. [2.2]

65. $3x - 8 = 0$
66. $2x + 7 = 0$

Multiply. [4.4]

67. $(x + 6)(3x + 4)$
68. $(7w + 6)^2$

69. In a recent year, 29,090 people were arrested for counterfeiting. This figure was down 1.2% from the year before. How many people were arrested the year before? [2.4]

70. The first angle of a triangle is four times as large as the second. The measure of the third angle is 30° greater than that of the second. How large are the angles? [2.5]

SYNTHESIS

71. When searching for a factorization, why do we list pairs of numbers with the correct *product* instead of pairs of numbers with the correct *sum*?

72. What is the advantage of writing out the prime factorization of c when factoring $x^2 + bx + c$ with a large value of c?

73. Find all integers b for which $a^2 + ba - 50$ can be factored.

74. Find all integers m for which $y^2 + my + 50$ can be factored.

Factor completely.

75. $y^2 - 0.2y - 0.08$

76. $x^2 + \frac{1}{2}x - \frac{3}{16}$

77. $-\frac{1}{3}a^3 + \frac{1}{3}a^2 + 2a$

78. $-a^7 + \frac{25}{7}a^5 + \frac{30}{7}a^6$

79. $x^{2m} + 11x^m + 28$

80. $-t^{2n} + 7t^n - 10$

ha! **81.** $(a + 1)x^2 + (a + 1)3x + (a + 1)2$

82. $ax^2 - 5x^2 + 8ax - 40x - (a - 5)9$
(*Hint*: See Exercise 81.)

83. Find the volume of a cube if its surface area is $6x^2 + 36x + 54$ square meters.

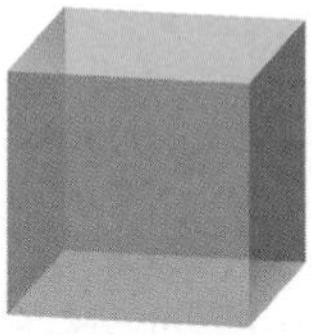

Find a polynomial in factored form for the shaded area in each figure. (Use π in your answers.)

84.

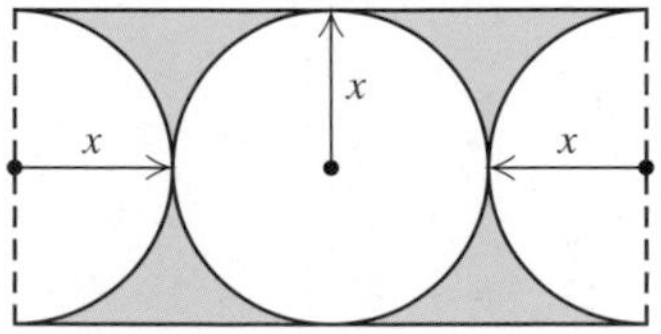

85.

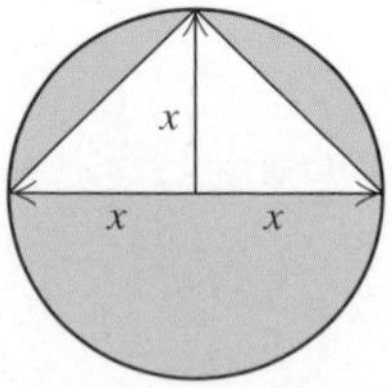

86.

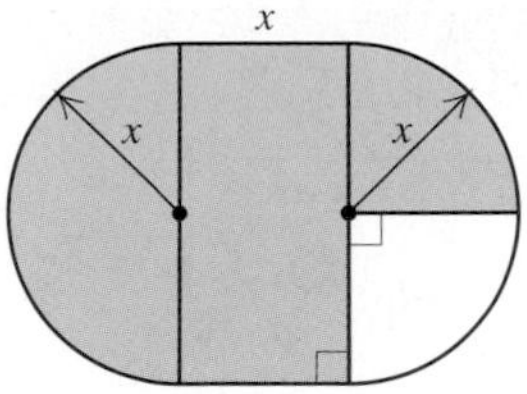

87.

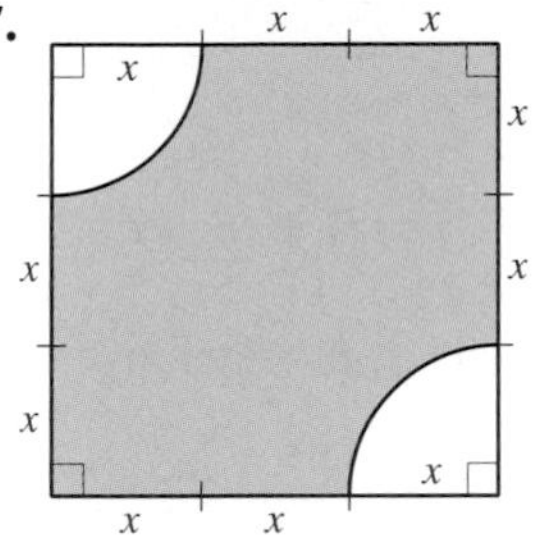

88.

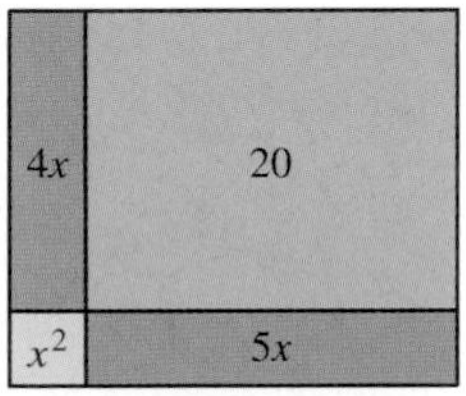

89.

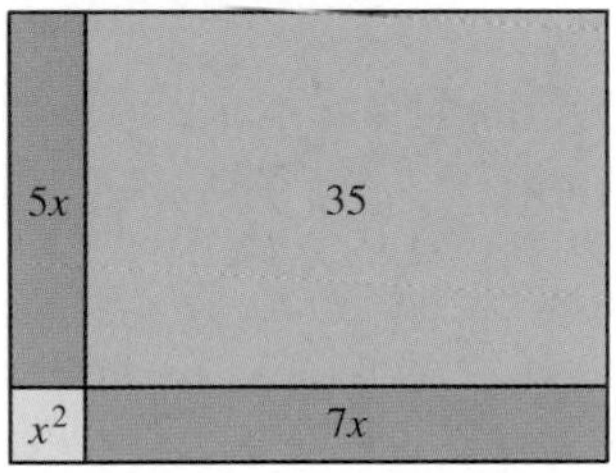

90. A census taker asks a woman, "How many children do you have?"

"Three," she answers.

"What are their ages?"

She responds, "The product of their ages is 36. The sum of their ages is the house number next door."

The math-savvy census taker walks next door, reads the house number, appears puzzled, and returns to the woman, asking, "Is there something you forgot to tell me?"

"Oh yes," says the woman. "I'm sorry. The oldest child is at the park."

The census taker records the three ages, thanks the woman for her time, and leaves.

How old is each child? Explain how you reached this conclusion. (*Hint*: Consider factorizations.)

Source: Adapted from Anita Harnadek, *Classroom Quickies*. Pacific Grove, CA: Critical Thinking Press and Software

COLLABORATIVE CORNER

Visualizing Factoring

Focus: Visualizing factoring

Time: 20–30 minutes

Group size: 3

Materials: Graph paper and scissors

The product $(x + 2)(x + 3)$ can be regarded as the area of a rectangle with width $x + 2$ and length $x + 3$. Similarly, factoring a polynomial like $x^2 + 5x + 6$ can be thought of as determining the length and the width of a rectangle that has area $x^2 + 5x + 6$. This is the approach used below.

ACTIVITY

1. a) To factor $x^2 + 11x + 10$ geometrically, the group needs to cut out shapes like those below to represent x^2, $11x$, and 10. This can be done by either tracing the figures below or by selecting a value for x, say 4, and using the squares on the graph paper to cut out the following:

x^2: Using the value selected for x, cut out a square that is x units on each side.

$11x$: Using the value selected for x, cut out a rectangle that is 1 unit wide and x units long. Repeat this to form 11 such strips.

10: Cut out two rectangles with whole-number dimensions and an area of 10. One should be 2 units by 5 units and the other 1 unit by 10 units.

b) The group, working together, should then attempt to use one of the two rectangles with area 10, along with all of the other shapes, to piece together one large rectangle. Only one of the rectangles with area 10 will work.

c) From the large rectangle formed in part (b), use the length and the width to determine the factorization of $x^2 + 11x + 10$. Where do the dimensions of the rectangle representing 10 appear in the factorization?

2. Repeat step (1) above, but this time use the other rectangle with area 10, and use only 7 of the 11 strips, along with the x^2-shape. Piece together the shapes to form one large rectangle. What factorization do the dimensions of this rectangle suggest?

3. Cut out rectangles with area 12 and use the above approach to factor $x^2 + 8x + 12$. What dimensions should be used for the rectangle with area 12?

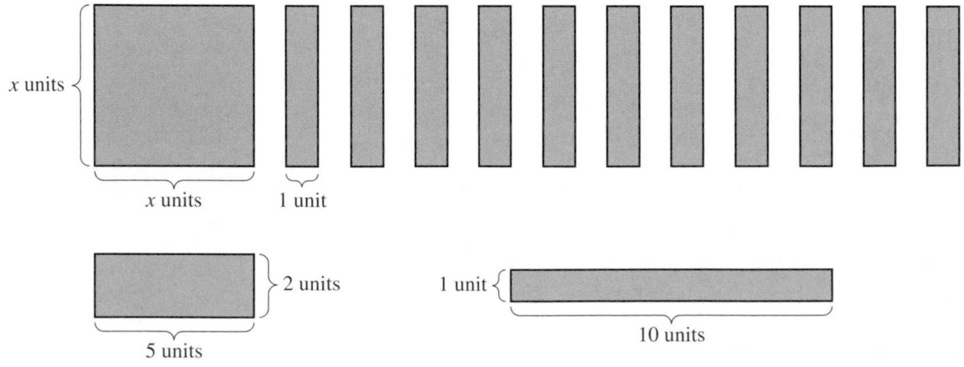

5.3 Factoring Trinomials of the Type $ax^2 + bx + c$

Factoring with FOIL • The Grouping Method

In Section 5.2, we learned a FOIL-based method for factoring trinomials of the type $x^2 + bx + c$. Now we learn to factor trinomials in which the leading, or x^2, coefficient is not 1. First we will use another FOIL-based method and then we will use an alternative method that involves factoring by grouping. Use the method that you prefer or the one recommended by your instructor.

Factoring with FOIL

Before factoring trinomials of the type $ax^2 + bx + c$, consider the following:

$$\begin{aligned} & \qquad\ \ \text{F} \qquad \text{O} \qquad \text{I} \qquad \text{L} \\ (2x + 5)(3x + 4) &= 6x^2 + 8x + 15x + 20 \\ &= 6x^2 + \quad 23x \quad + 20. \end{aligned}$$

To factor $6x^2 + 23x + 20$, we reverse the multiplication above and look for two binomials whose product is this trinomial. The product of the First terms must be $6x^2$. The product of the Outer terms plus the product of the Inner terms must be $23x$. The product of the Last terms must be 20. This leads us to

$(2x + 5)(3x + 4)$. This factorization is verified above.

How can such a factorization be found without first seeing the corresponding multiplication? Our first approach relies on trial and error and FOIL.

To Factor $ax^2 + bx + c$ Using FOIL

1. Factor out the largest common factor, if one exists.
2. Find two First terms whose product is ax^2:
   $$(\square x + \quad)(\square x + \quad) = ax^2 + bx + c.$$
   FOIL
3. Find two Last terms whose product is c:
   $$(\quad x + \square)(\quad x + \square) = ax^2 + bx + c.$$
   FOIL
4. Repeat steps (2) and (3) until a combination is found for which the sum of the Outer and Inner products is bx:
   $$(\square x + \square)(\square x + \square) = ax^2 + bx + c.$$
   I, O — FOIL

   Always check by multiplying. If no correct combination exists, state that the polynomial is prime.

Study Skills

Math Web Sites

If for some reason you feel uneasy about asking an instructor or tutor for help, and have already considered the Addison-Wesley Math Tutor Center (see the Preface and p. 8), you may benefit from visiting the Web sites www.hotmath.com, www.mathforum.org/dr.math, www.sosmath.com, and www.webmath.com. These sites are not specifically for adult learners, but can be very helpful nonetheless.

Source: *The Burlington Free Press*, 4/30/02, p. 8 B

EXAMPLE 1 Factor: $3x^2 - 10x - 8$.

Solution

1. First, check for a common factor. In this case, there is none (other than 1 or -1).
2. Find two **F**irst terms whose product is $3x^2$.
   The only possibilities for the **F**irst terms are $3x$ and x:

   $(3x + \quad)(x + \quad)$.
3. Find two **L**ast terms whose product is -8.
   Possible factorizations of -8 are

   $(-8) \cdot 1$, $\quad 8 \cdot (-1)$, $\quad (-2) \cdot 4$, and $\quad 2 \cdot (-4)$.

   Important!: Since the First terms are not identical, we must also consider the above factors in reverse order:

   $1 \cdot (-8)$, $\quad (-1) \cdot 8$, $\quad 4 \cdot (-2)$, and $\quad (-4) \cdot 2$.
4. Knowing that all **F**irst and **L**ast products will check, inspect the **O**uter and **I**nner products resulting from steps (2) and (3). Look for the combination in which the sum of the products is the middle term, $-10x$. This may take several tries. Of course, our search normally ends as soon as the correct combination is found. If none exists, we state that the polynomial is prime.

Trial	*Product*	
$(3x - 8)(x + 1)$	$3x^2 + 3x - 8x - 8$	
	$= 3x^2 - 5x - 8$	Wrong middle term
$(3x + 8)(x - 1)$	$3x^2 - 3x + 8x - 8$	
	$= 3x^2 + 5x - 8$	Wrong middle term
$(3x - 2)(x + 4)$	$3x^2 + 12x - 2x - 8$	
	$= 3x^2 + 10x - 8$	Wrong middle term
$(3x + 2)(x - 4)$	$3x^2 - 12x + 2x - 8$	
	$= 3x^2 - 10x - 8$	Correct middle term!
$(3x + 1)(x - 8)$	$3x^2 - 24x + x - 8$	
	$= 3x^2 - 23x - 8$	Wrong middle term
$(3x - 1)(x + 8)$	$3x^2 + 24x - x - 8$	
	$= 3x^2 + 23x - 8$	Wrong middle term
$(3x + 4)(x - 2)$	$3x^2 - 6x + 4x - 8$	
	$= 3x^2 - 2x - 8$	Wrong middle term
$(3x - 4)(x + 2)$	$3x^2 + 6x - 4x - 8$	
	$= 3x^2 + 2x - 8$	Wrong middle term

The correct factorization is $(3x + 2)(x - 4)$.

Two observations can be made from Example 1. First, we listed all possible trials even though we usually stop after finding the correct factorization. We did this to show that **each trial differs only in the middle term of the product**. Second, note that as in Section 5.2, **only the sign of the middle term changes when the signs in the binomials are reversed**.

EXAMPLE 2 Factor: $10x^2 + 37x + 7$.

A GEOMETRIC APPROACH TO EXAMPLE 2

The factoring of $10x^2 + 37x + 7$ can be regarded as a search for r and s so that the sum of areas A, B, C, and D is $10x^2 + 37x + 7$.

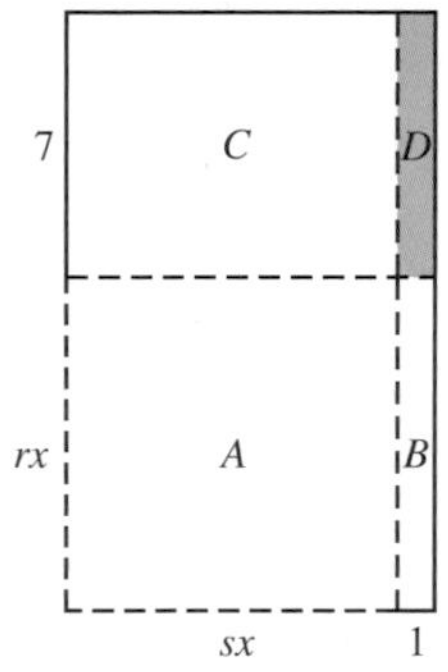

Because A must be $10x^2$, the product rs must be 10. Only when r is 2 and s is 5 will the sum of areas B and C be $37x$ (see below).

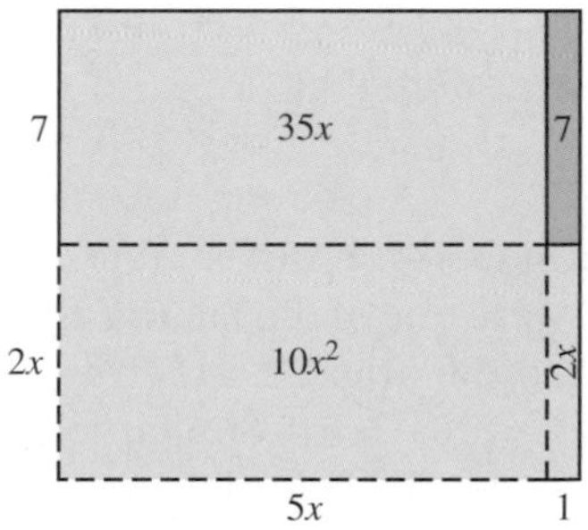

Solution

1. There is no factor (other than 1 or -1) common to all three terms.
2. Because $10x^2$ factors as $10x \cdot x$ or $5x \cdot 2x$, we have two possibilities:

   $$(10x + \quad)(x + \quad) \quad \text{or} \quad (5x + \quad)(2x + \quad).$$

3. There are two pairs of factors of 7 and each can be listed two ways:

   $1, 7 \qquad -1, -7$

   and

   $7, 1 \qquad -7, -1.$

4. From steps (2) and (3), we see that there are 8 possibilities for factorizations. Look for **O**uter and **I**nner products for which the sum is the middle term. Because all coefficients in $10x^2 + 37x + 7$ are positive, we need consider only positive factors of 7.

Trial	*Product*	
$(10x + 1)(x + 7)$	$10x^2 + 70x + 1x + 7$	
	$= 10x^2 + 71x + 7$	Wrong middle term
$(10x + 7)(x + 1)$	$10x^2 + 10x + 7x + 7$	
	$= 10x^2 + 17x + 7$	Wrong middle term
$(5x + 7)(2x + 1)$	$10x^2 + 5x + 14x + 7$	
	$= 10x^2 + 19x + 7$	Wrong middle term
$(5x + 1)(2x + 7)$	$10x^2 + 35x + 2x + 7$	
	$= 10x^2 + 37x + 7$	Correct middle term!

The correct factorization is $(5x + 1)(2x + 7)$.

EXAMPLE 3 Factor: $24x^3 - 76x^2 + 40x$.

Solution

1. First, we factor out the largest common factor, $4x$:

   $$4x(6x^2 - 19x + 10).$$

2. Next, we factor $6x^2 - 19x + 10$. Since $6x^2$ can be factored as $3x \cdot 2x$ or $6x \cdot x$, we have two possibilities:

   $$(3x + \quad)(2x + \quad) \quad \text{or} \quad (6x + \quad)(x + \quad).$$

3. There are four pairs of factors of 10 and each can be listed two ways:

   $10, 1 \qquad -10, -1 \qquad 5, 2 \qquad -5, -2$

   and

   $1, 10 \qquad -1, -10 \qquad 2, 5 \qquad -2, -5.$

4. The two possibilities from step (2) and the eight possibilities from step (3) give $2 \cdot 8$, or 16 possibilities for factorizations. We look for **O**uter and **I**nner products resulting from steps (2) and (3) for which the sum is the middle term, $-19x$. Since the sign of the middle term is negative, but the sign of the last term, 10, is positive, the two factors of 10 must both be negative. This means only four pairings from step (3) need be considered. We first try these factors with $(3x + \quad)(2x + \quad)$. If none gives the correct factorization of $6x^2 - 19x + 10$, then we will consider $(6x + \quad)(x + \quad)$.

Trial	*Product*	
$(3x - 10)(2x - 1)$	$6x^2 - 3x - 20x + 10$	
	$= 6x^2 - 23x + 10$	Wrong middle term
$(3x - 1)(2x - 10)$	$6x^2 - 30x - 2x + 10$	
	$= 6x^2 - 32x + 10$	Wrong middle term
$(3x - 5)(2x - 2)$	$6x^2 - 6x - 10x + 10$	
	$= 6x^2 - 16x + 10$	Wrong middle term
$(3x - 2)(2x - 5)$	$6x^2 - 15x - 4x + 10$	
	$= 6x^2 - 19x + 10$	Correct middle term!

Since we have a correct factorization, we need not consider

$$(6x + \quad)(x + \quad).$$

Look again at the possibility $(3x - 5)(2x - 2)$. Without multiplying, we can reject such a possibility. To see why, note that

$$(3x - 5)(2x - 2) = (3x - 5)2(x - 1).$$

The expression $2x - 2$ has a common factor, 2. But we removed the *largest* common factor in step (1). If $2x - 2$ were one of the factors, then 2 would be *another* common factor in addition to the original, $4x$. Thus, $(2x - 2)$ cannot be part of the factorization of $6x^2 - 19x + 10$. Similar reasoning can be used to reject $(3x - 1)(2x - 10)$ as a possible factorization.

Once the largest common factor is factored out, none of the remaining factors can have a common factor.

The factorization of $6x^2 - 19x + 10$ is $(3x - 2)(2x - 5)$, but do not forget the common factor! The factorization of $24x^3 - 76x^2 + 40x$ is

$$4x(3x - 2)(2x - 5).$$

Student Notes

Keep your work organized so that you can see what you have already considered. For example, when factoring $6x^2 - 23x + 10$, we can list all possibilities and cross out those in which a common factor appears:

$(3x - 10)(2x - 1)$,
~~$(3x - 1)(2x - 10)$~~,
~~$(3x - 5)(2x - 2)$~~,
$(3x - 2)(2x - 5)$,
~~$(6x - 10)(x - 1)$~~,
$(6x - 1)(x - 10)$,
$(6x - 5)(x - 2)$,
~~$(6x - 2)(x - 5)$~~.

By being organized and not erasing, we can see that there are only four possible factorizations.

Tips for Factoring $ax^2 + bx + c$

To factor $ax^2 + bx + c \; (a > 0)$:

- Always factor out the largest common factor, if one exists.
- Once the largest common factor has been factored out of the original trinomial, no binomial factor can contain a common factor (other than 1 or -1).

(*continued*)

- If c is positive, then the signs in both binomial factors must match the sign of b.
- Reversing the signs in the binomials reverses the sign of the middle term of their product.
- Organize your work so that you can keep track of which possibilities you have checked.
- Remember to include the largest common factor—if there is one—in the final factorization.
- Always check by multiplying.

EXAMPLE 4 Factor: $10x + 8 - 3x^2$.

Solution An important problem-solving strategy is to find a way to make new problems look like problems we already know how to solve. The factoring tips above apply only to trinomials of the form $ax^2 + bx + c$, with $a > 0$. This leads us to rewrite $10x + 8 - 3x^2$ in descending order:

$$10x + 8 - 3x^2 = -3x^2 + 10x + 8.$$ Using the commutative law to write descending order

Although $-3x^2 + 10x + 8$ looks similar to the trinomials we have factored, the tips above require a positive leading coefficient. This can be found by factoring out -1:

$$-3x^2 + 10x + 8 = -1(3x^2 - 10x - 8)$$ Factoring out -1 changes the signs of the coefficients.

$$= -1(3x + 2)(x - 4).$$ Using the result from Example 1

The factorization of $10x + 8 - 3x^2$ is $-1(3x + 2)(x - 4)$.

EXAMPLE 5 Factor: $6p^2 - 13pq - 28q^2$.

Solution Since no common factor exists, we examine the first term, $6p^2$. There are two possibilities:

$$(2p + \quad)(3p + \quad) \quad \text{or} \quad (6p + \quad)(p + \quad).$$

The last term, $-28q^2$, has the following pairs of factors:

$$28q, -q \qquad 14q, -2q \qquad 7q, -4q,$$

and

$$-28q, \; q \qquad -14q, \; 2q \qquad -7q, \; 4q,$$

as well as each of the pairings reversed.

Some trials, like $(2p + 28q)(3p - q)$ and $(2p + 14q)(3p - 2q)$, cannot be correct because both $(2p + 28q)$ and $(2p + 14q)$ contain a common factor, 2. We try $(2p + 7q)(3p - 4q)$:

$$\begin{aligned}(2p + 7q)(3p - 4q) &= 6p^2 - 8pq + 21pq - 28q^2\\ &= 6p^2 + 13pq - 28q^2.\end{aligned}$$

Our trial is incorrect, but only because of the sign of the middle term. To correctly factor $6p^2 - 13pq - 28q^2$, we simply change the signs in the binomials:

$$\begin{aligned}(2p - 7q)(3p + 4q) &= 6p^2 + 8pq - 21pq - 28q^2\\ &= 6p^2 - 13pq - 28q^2.\end{aligned}$$

The correct factorization is $(2p - 7q)(3p + 4q)$.

The Grouping Method

Another method of factoring trinomials of the type $ax^2 + bx + c$ is known as the *grouping method.* The grouping method relies on rewriting $ax^2 + bx + c$ in the form $ax^2 + px + qx + c$ and then factoring by grouping. To develop this method, consider the following*:

$$\begin{aligned}(2x + 5)(3x + 4) &= 2x \cdot 3x + 2x \cdot 4 + 5 \cdot 3x + 5 \cdot 4 \qquad \text{Using FOIL}\\ &= 2 \cdot 3 \cdot x^2 + 2 \cdot 4x + 5 \cdot 3x + 5 \cdot 4\\ &= \underbrace{2 \cdot 3}_{a} \cdot x^2 + (\underbrace{2 \cdot 4 + 5 \cdot 3}_{b})x + \underbrace{5 \cdot 4}_{c}\\ &= 6x^2 + 23x + 20.\end{aligned}$$

Note that reversing these steps shows that $6x^2 + 23x + 20$ can be rewritten as $6x^2 + 8x + 15x + 20$ and then factored by grouping. Note that the numbers that add to b (in this case, $2 \cdot 4$ and $5 \cdot 3$), also multiply to ac (in this case, $2 \cdot 3 \cdot 5 \cdot 4$).

To Factor $ax^2 + bx + c$, Using the Grouping Method

1. Factor out the largest common factor, if one exists.
2. Multiply the leading coefficient a and the constant c.
3. Find a pair of factors of ac whose sum is b.
4. Rewrite the middle term, bx, as a sum or difference using the factors found in step (3).
5. Factor by grouping.
6. Include any common factor from step (1) and check by multiplying.

*This discussion was inspired by a lecture given by Irene Doo at Austin Community College.

EXAMPLE 6 Factor: $3x^2 - 10x - 8$.

Solution

1. First, we note that there is no common factor (other than 1 or -1).
2. We multiply the leading coefficient, 3, and the constant, -8:

$$3(-8) = -24.$$

3. We next look for a factorization of -24 in which the sum of the factors is the coefficient of the middle term, -10.

Pairs of Factors of -24	Sums of Factors
$1, -24$	-23
$-1, 24$	23
$2, -12$	-10 ← $2 + (-12) = -10$
$-2, 12$	10
$3, -8$	-5
$-3, 8$	5
$4, -6$	-2
$-4, 6$	2

We normally stop listing pairs of factors once we have found the one we are after.

4. Next, we express the middle term as a sum or difference using the factors found in step (3):

$$-10x = 2x - 12x.$$

5. We now factor by grouping as follows:

$3x^2 - 10x - 8 = 3x^2 + 2x - 12x - 8$ — Substituting $2x - 12x$ for $-10x$. We could also use $-12x + 2x$.

$= x(3x + 2) - 4(3x + 2)$ — Factoring by grouping; see Section 5.1

$= (3x + 2)(x - 4).$ — Factoring out the common factor, $3x + 2$

6. *Check:* $(3x + 2)(x - 4) = 3x^2 - 12x + 2x - 8 = 3x^2 - 10x - 8$.

The factorization of $3x^2 - 10x - 8$ is $(3x + 2)(x - 4)$.

EXAMPLE 7 Factor: $8x^3 + 22x^2 - 6x$.

Solution

1. We factor out the largest common factor, $2x$:

$$8x^3 + 22x^2 - 6x = 2x(4x^2 + 11x - 3).$$

2. To factor $4x^2 + 11x - 3$ by grouping, we multiply the leading coefficient, 4, and the constant term, -3:

$$4(-3) = -12.$$

3. We next look for factors of -12 that add to 11.

Pairs of Factors of -12	Sums of Factors
$1, -12$	-11
$-1, \ 12$	11 ← Since $-1 + 12 = 11$, there is no need to list other pairs of factors.
.	.
.	.
.	.

4. We then rewrite the $11x$ in $4x^2 + 11x - 3$ using

$$11x = -1x + 12x, \quad \text{or} \quad 11x = 12x - 1x.$$

5. Next, we factor by grouping:

$$4x^2 + 11x - 3 = 4x^2 - 1x + 12x - 3$$ Rewriting the middle term; $12x - 1x$ could also be used.

$$= x(4x - 1) + 3(4x - 1)$$ Factoring by grouping. Note the common factor, $4x - 1$.

$$= (4x - 1)(x + 3).$$ Factoring out the common factor

6. The factorization of $4x^2 + 11x - 3$ is $(4x - 1)(x + 3)$. But don't forget the common factor, $2x$. The factorization of the original trinomial is

$$2x(4x - 1)(x + 3).$$

5.3 Exercise Set

FOR EXTRA HELP

Student's Solutions Manual | Digital Video Tutor CD 3 Videotape 9 | AW Math Tutor Center | MathXL Tutorials on CD | MathXL | MyMathLab

Concept Reinforcement *In each of Exercises 1–4, match the polynomial with the correct factorization from the column on the right.*

1. ____ $12x^2 + 16x - 3$ **a)** $(7x - 1)(2x + 3)$
2. ____ $14x^2 + 19x - 3$ **b)** $(6x + 1)(2x - 3)$
3. ____ $14x^2 - 19x - 3$ **c)** $(6x - 1)(2x + 3)$
4. ____ $12x^2 - 16x - 3$ **d)** $(7x + 1)(2x - 3)$

Factor completely. If a polynomial is prime, state this.

5. $2x^2 + 7x - 4$

6. $3x^2 + x - 4$

7. $3t^2 + 4t - 15$

8. $5t^2 + t - 18$

9. $6x^2 - 23x + 7$

10. $6x^2 - 13x + 6$

11. $7x^2 + 15x + 2$

12. $6x^2 + 8x + 2$

13. $9a^2 - 6a - 8$

14. $4a^2 - 4a - 15$

15. $6x^2 - 10x - 4$

16. $15x^2 - 19x - 10$

17. $12t^2 - 6t - 6$

18. $18t^2 + 36t - 32$

19. $6 + 19x + 15x^2$

20. $-20 + 31x - 12x^2$

21. $-35x^2 - 34x - 8$

22. $28x^2 + 38x - 6$

23. $4 + 6t^2 - 13t$

24. $9 + 8t^2 - 18t$

25. $25x^2 + 40x + 16$

26. $49t^2 + 42t + 9$

27. $16a^2 + 78a + 27$

28. $24x^2 + 47x - 2$

29. $18t^2 + 24t - 10$

30. $35x^2 - 57x - 44$

31. $-2x^2 + 15 + x$

32. $2t^2 - 19 - 6t$

33. $-6x^2 - 33x - 15$

34. $-12x^2 - 28x + 24$

35. $20x^2 - 25x + 5$

36. $30x^2 - 24x - 54$

37. $12x^2 + 68x - 24$

38. $6x^2 + 21x + 15$

39. $4x + 1 + 3x^2$

40. $-9 + 18x^2 + 21x$

Factor. Use factoring by grouping even though it would seem reasonable to first combine like terms.

41. $y^2 + 4y - 2y - 8$

42. $x^2 + 5x - 2x - 10$

43. $8t^2 - 6t - 28t + 21$

44. $35t^2 - 40t + 21t - 24$

45. $6x^2 + 4x + 9x + 6$

46. $3x^2 - 2x + 3x - 2$

47. $2t^2 + 6t - t - 3$

48. $5t^2 + 10t - t - 2$

49. $3a^2 - 12a - a + 4$

50. $2a^2 - 10a - a + 5$

Factor completely. If a polynomial is prime, state this.

51. $9t^2 + 14t + 5$

52. $16t^2 + 23t + 7$

53. $-16x^2 - 32x - 7$

54. $-9x^2 - 18x - 5$

55. $10a^2 + 25a - 15$

56. $10x^2 + 30x - 70$

57. $18x^3 + 21x^2 - 9x$

58. $6x^3 - 4x^2 - 10x$

59. $89x + 64 + 25x^2$

60. $47 - 42y + 9y^2$

61. $168x^3 + 45x^2 + 3x$

62. $144x^5 - 168x^4 + 48x^3$

63. $-14t^4 + 19t^3 + 3t^2$

64. $-70a^4 + 68a^3 - 16a^2$

65. $3x + 45x^2 - 18$

66. $2x + 24x^2 - 40$

67. $2a^2 + 5ab + 2b^2$

68. $3p^2 - 16pq - 12q^2$

69. $8s^2 + 18st + 9t^2$

70. $10s^2 + 4st - 6t^2$

71. $18x^2 - 6xy - 24y^2$

72. $-30a^2 - 87ab - 30b^2$

73. $-24a^2 + 34ab - 12b^2$

74. $15a^2 - 5ab - 20b^2$

75. $35x^2 + 34x^3 + 8x^4$

76. $19x^3 - 3x^2 + 14x^4$

77. $18a^7 + 8a^6 + 9a^8$

78. $40a^8 + 16a^7 + 25a^9$

79. Asked to factor $2x^2 - 18x + 36$, Amy *incorrectly* answers

$$\begin{aligned} 2x^2 - 18x + 36 &= 2(x^2 + 9x + 18) \\ &= 2(x + 3)(x + 6). \end{aligned}$$

If this were a 10-point quiz question, how many points would you take off? Why?

80. Asked to factor $4x^2 + 28x + 48$, Herb *incorrectly* answers

$$\begin{aligned} 4x^2 + 28x + 48 &= (2x + 6)(2x + 8) \\ &= 2(x + 3)(x + 4). \end{aligned}$$

If this were a 10-point quiz question, how many points would you take off? Why?

SKILL MAINTENANCE

81. The earth is a sphere (or ball) that is about 40,000 km in circumference. Find the radius of the earth, in kilometers and in miles. Use 3.14 for π. (*Hint*: 1 km $\approx$ 0.62 mi.) [2.5]

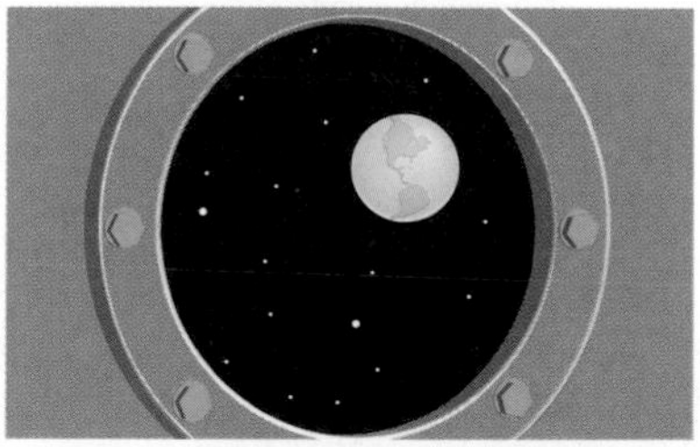

82. The second angle of a triangle is 10° less than twice the first. The third angle is 15° more than four times the first. Find the measure of the second angle. [2.5]

Multiply. [4.5]

83. $(3x + 1)^2$

84. $(5x - 2)^2$

85. $(4t - 5)^2$

86. $(7a + 1)^2$

87. $(5x - 2)(5x + 2)$

88. $(2x - 3)(2x + 3)$

89. $(2t + 7)(2t - 7)$

90. $(4a + 7)(4a - 7)$

SYNTHESIS

91. Which one of the seven tips listed after Example 3 do you find most helpful? Which one do you find least helpful? Explain how you made these determinations.

92. For the trinomial $ax^2 + bx + c$, suppose that a is the product of three different prime factors and c is the product of another two prime factors. How many possible factorizations (like those in Example 1) exist? Explain how you determined your answer.

Factor. If a polynomial is prime, state this.

93. $18x^2y^2 - 3xy - 10$

94. $8x^2y^3 + 10xy^2 + 2y$

95. $9a^2b^3 + 25ab^2 + 16$

96. $-9t^{10} - 12t^5 - 4$

97. $16t^{10} - 8t^5 + 1$

98. $9a^2b^2 - 15ab - 2$

99. $-20x^{2n} - 16x^n - 3$

100. $-15x^{2m} + 26x^m - 8$

101. $a^{2n+1} - 2a^{n+1} + a$

102. $3a^{6n} - 2a^{3n} - 1$

103. $3(a + 1)^{n+1}(a + 3)^2 - 5(a + 1)^n(a + 3)^3$

104. $7(t - 3)^{2n} + 5(t - 3)^n - 2$

5.4 Factoring Perfect-Square Trinomials and Differences of Squares

Recognizing Perfect-Square Trinomials • Factoring Perfect-Square Trinomials • Recognizing Differences of Squares • Factoring Differences of Squares • Factoring Completely

In Section 4.5, we studied some shortcuts for finding the products of certain binomials. Reversing these procedures provides shortcuts for factoring certain polynomials.

Recognizing Perfect-Square Trinomials

Some trinomials are squares of binomials. For example, $x^2 + 10x + 25$ is the square of the binomial $x + 5$. To see this, we can calculate $(x + 5)^2$. It is $x^2 + 2 \cdot x \cdot 5 + 5^2$, or $x^2 + 10x + 25$. A trinomial that is the square of a binomial is called a **perfect-square trinomial**.

In Section 4.5, we considered squaring binomials as a special-product rule:

$$(A + B)^2 = A^2 + 2AB + B^2;$$
$$(A - B)^2 = A^2 - 2AB + B^2.$$

Reading the right sides first, we see that these equations can be used to factor perfect-square trinomials. Note that in order for a trinomial to be the square of a binomial, it must have the following:

1. Two terms, A^2 and B^2, must be squares, such as

   $4, \quad x^2, \quad 81m^2, \quad 16t^2.$

2. Neither A^2 nor B^2 is being subtracted.
3. The remaining term is either $2 \cdot A \cdot B$ or $-2 \cdot A \cdot B$, where A and B are the square roots of A^2 and B^2.

EXAMPLE 1 Determine whether each of the following is a perfect-square trinomial.

a) $x^2 + 6x + 9$ **b)** $t^2 - 8t - 9$ **c)** $16x^2 + 49 - 56x$

Solution

a) To see if $x^2 + 6x + 9$ is a perfect-square trinomial, note that:

1. Two terms, x^2 and 9, are squares.
2. Neither x^2 nor 9 is being subtracted.
3. The remaining term, $6x$, is $2 \cdot x \cdot 3$, where x and 3 are the square roots of x^2 and 9.

Thus, $x^2 + 6x + 9$ *is* a perfect-square trinomial.

b) To see if $t^2 - 8t - 9$ is a perfect-square trinomial, note that:

1. Two terms, t^2 and 9, are squares. But:
2. Since 9 is being subtracted, $t^2 - 8t - 9$ *is not* a perfect-square trinomial.

c) To see if $16x^2 + 49 - 56x$ is a perfect-square trinomial, it helps to first write it in descending order:

$$16x^2 - 56x + 49.$$

Next, note that:

1. Two terms, $16x^2$ and 49, are squares.
2. There is no minus sign before $16x^2$ or 49.
3. Twice the product of the square roots, $2 \cdot 4x \cdot 7$, is $56x$, the opposite of the remaining term, $-56x$.

Thus, $16x^2 + 49 - 56x$ *is* a perfect-square trinomial.

Student Notes

If you're not already quick to recognize the squares that represent $1^2, 2^2, 3^2, \ldots, 12^2$, this would be a good time to familiarize yourself with these numbers.

Study Skills

Fill in Your Blanks

Don't hesitate to write out any missing steps that you'd like to see included. For instance, in Example 1(c), we state (in red) that $16x^2$ is a square. To solidify your understanding, you may want to write in $4x \cdot 4x = 16x^2$.

Factoring Perfect-Square Trinomials

Either of the factoring methods from Section 5.3 can be used to factor perfect-square trinomials, but a faster method is to recognize the following patterns.

Factoring a Perfect-Square Trinomial

$$A^2 + 2AB + B^2 = (A + B)^2; \qquad A^2 - 2AB + B^2 = (A - B)^2$$

Each factorization uses the square roots of the squared terms and the sign of the remaining term. To verify these equations, you should compute $(A + B)(A + B)$ and $(A - B)(A - B)$.

EXAMPLE 2 Factor: **(a)** $x^2 + 6x + 9$; **(b)** $t^2 + 49 - 14t$; **(c)** $16x^2 - 40x + 25$.

Solution

a) $x^2 + 6x + 9 = x^2 + 2 \cdot x \cdot 3 + 3^2 = (x + 3)^2$ The sign of the middle term is positive.

$$\uparrow \quad \uparrow \; \uparrow \; \uparrow \quad \uparrow \; \uparrow$$

$$A^2 + 2\;A\;\;B + B^2 = (A + B)^2$$

b) $t^2 + 49 - 14t = t^2 - 14t + 49$ Using a commutative law to write in descending order

$$= t^2 - 2 \cdot t \cdot 7 + 7^2 = (t - 7)^2$$

$$\uparrow \quad \uparrow\ \uparrow\ \uparrow \quad \uparrow\ \uparrow$$

$$A^2 - 2\ A\ B + B^2 = (A - B)^2$$

c) $16x^2 - 40x + 25 = (4x)^2 - 2 \cdot 4x \cdot 5 + 5^2 = (4x - 5)^2$ Recall that $(4x)^2 = 16x^2$.

$$\uparrow \quad \uparrow\ \uparrow\ \uparrow\ \uparrow \quad \uparrow\ \uparrow$$

$$A^2 - 2\ A\ B + B^2 = (A - B)^2$$

With practice, it is possible to spot perfect-square trinomials as they occur and factor them quickly.

EXAMPLE 3 Factor: $4p^2 - 12pq + 9q^2$.

Solution We have

$$4p^2 - 12pq + 9q^2 = (2p)^2 - 2(2p)(3q) + (3q)^2$$ Recognizing the perfect-square trinomial

$$= (2p - 3q)^2.$$ The sign of the middle term is negative.

Check: $(2p - 3q)(2p - 3q) = 4p^2 - 12pq + 9q^2$.

The factorization is $(2p - 3q)^2$.

EXAMPLE 4 Factor: $-75m^3 - 60m^2 - 12m$.

Solution *Always* look first for a common factor. This time there is one. We factor out $-3m$ so that the leading coefficient of the polynomial inside the parentheses is positive:

$$-75m^3 - 60m^2 - 12m = -3m[25m^2 + 20m + 4]$$ Factoring out the largest common factor

$$= -3m[(5m)^2 + 2(5m)(2) + 2^2]$$ Recognizing the perfect-square trinomial. Try to do this mentally.

$$= -3m(5m + 2)^2.$$

Check: $-3m(5m + 2)^2 = -3m(5m + 2)(5m + 2)$

$$= -3m(25m^2 + 20m + 4)$$

$$= -75m^3 - 60m^2 - 12m.$$

The factorization is $-3m(5m + 2)^2$.

Recognizing Differences of Squares

Some binomials represent the difference of two squares. For example, the binomial $16x^2 - 9$ is a difference of two expressions, $16x^2$ and 9, that are squares. To see this, note that $16x^2 = (4x)^2$ and $9 = 3^2$.

Any expression, like $16x^2 - 9$, that can be written in the form $A^2 - B^2$ is called a **difference of squares**. Note that for a binomial to be a difference of squares, it must have the following.

1. There must be two expressions, both squares, such as

$$25x^2, \quad 9, \quad 4x^2y^2, \quad 1, \quad x^6, \quad 49y^8.$$

2. The terms in the binomial must have different signs.

Note that in order for a term to be a square, its coefficient must be a perfect square and the power(s) of the variable(s) must be even.

EXAMPLE 5 Determine whether each of the following is a difference of squares.

a) $9x^2 - 64$ **b)** $25 - t^3$ **c)** $-4x^{10} + 36$

Solution

a) To see if $9x^2 - 64$ is a difference of squares, note that:

1. The first expression is a square: $9x^2 = (3x)^2$.
The second expression is a square: $64 = 8^2$.

2. The terms have different signs.

Thus, $9x^2 - 64$ is a difference of squares, $(3x)^2 - 8^2$.

b) To see if $25 - t^3$ is a difference of squares, note that:

1. The expression t^3 is not a square.

Thus, $25 - t^3$ is not a difference of squares.

c) To see if $-4x^{10} + 36$ is a difference of squares, note that:

1. The expressions $4x^{10}$ and 36 are squares: $4x^{10} = (2x^5)^2$ and $36 = 6^2$.

2. The terms have different signs.

Thus, $-4x^{10} + 36$ is a difference of squares, $6^2 - (2x^5)^2$. It is often useful to rewrite $-4x^{10} + 36$ in the equivalent form $36 - 4x^{10}$.

Factoring Differences of Squares

To factor a difference of squares, we reverse a pattern from Section 4.5:

Factoring a Difference of Squares

$$A^2 - B^2 = (A + B)(A - B).$$

Once we have identified the expressions that are playing the roles of A and B, the factorization can be written directly. To verify this equation, simply multiply $(A + B)(A - B)$.

EXAMPLE 6 Factor: **(a)** $x^2 - 4$; **(b)** $m^2 - 9p^2$; **(c)** $9 - 16t^{10}$; **(d)** $50x^2 - 8x^8$.

Solution

a) $x^2 - 4 = x^2 - 2^2 = (x + 2)(x - 2)$

$$\uparrow \quad \uparrow \quad \uparrow \quad \uparrow \quad \uparrow \quad \uparrow$$

$$\mathbf{A^2 - B^2 = (A + B)(A - B)}$$

b) $m^2 - 9p^2 = m^2 - (3p)^2 = (m + 3p)(m - 3p)$

$$\uparrow \quad \uparrow \quad \uparrow \quad \uparrow \quad \uparrow \quad \uparrow$$

$$\mathbf{A^2 \; - \; B^2 \; = (A + B)\,(A - B)}$$

c) $9 - 16t^{10} = 3^2 - (4t^5)^2$ Using the rules for powers

$$\uparrow \quad \uparrow$$

$$\mathbf{A^2 - B^2}$$

$= (3 + 4t^5)(3 - 4t^5)$ Try to go directly to this step.

$$\uparrow \quad \uparrow \quad \uparrow \quad \uparrow$$

$$\mathbf{(A + B)\,(A - B)}$$

d) *Always* look first for a common factor. This time there is one, $2x^2$:

$50x^2 - 8x^8 = 2x^2(25 - 4x^6)$	Factoring out the common factor
$= 2x^2[5^2 - (2x^3)^2]$	Recognizing $A^2 - B^2$. Try to do this mentally.
$= 2x^2(5 + 2x^3)(5 - 2x^3)$.	Factoring the difference of squares

Check: $2x^2(5 + 2x^3)(5 - 2x^3) = 2x^2(25 - 4x^6)$
$= 50x^2 - 8x^8$.

The factorization is $2x^2(5 + 2x^3)(5 - 2x^3)$.

Caution! Note in Example 6 that a difference of squares is *not* the square of the difference; that is,

$A^2 - B^2 \neq (A - B)^2$. To see this, note that $(A - B)^2 = A^2 - 2AB + B^2$.

Factoring Completely

Sometimes, as in Examples 4 and 6(d), a *complete* factorization requires two or more steps. Factoring is complete when no factor can be factored further.

EXAMPLE 7 Factor: $p^4 - 16$.

Solution We have

$p^4 - 16 = (p^2)^2 - 4^2$	Recognizing $A^2 - B^2$
$= (p^2 + 4)(p^2 - 4)$	Factoring a difference of squares. Note that $p^2 - 4$ is not prime.
$= (p^2 + 4)(p + 2)(p - 2).$	Factoring further: $p^2 - 4$ is itself a difference of squares.

Check: $(p^2 + 4)(p + 2)(p - 2) = (p^2 + 4)(p^2 - 4)$
$= p^4 - 16.$

The factorization is $(p^2 + 4)(p + 2)(p - 2)$.

Note in Example 7 that the factor $p^2 + 4$ is a *sum* of squares that cannot be factored further.

Caution! Apart from possibly removing a common factor, you cannot factor a sum of squares. In particular,

$$A^2 + B^2 \neq (A + B)^2.$$

Consider $25x^2 + 100$. Here a sum of squares has a common factor, 25. Factoring, we get $25(x^2 + 4)$, where $x^2 + 4$ is prime.

As you proceed through the exercises, these suggestions may prove helpful.

Tips for Factoring

1. Always look first for a common factor! If there is one, factor it out.
2. Be alert for perfect-square trinomials and for binomials that are differences of squares. Once recognized, they can be factored without trial and error.
3. Always factor completely.
4. Check by multiplying.

5.4 Exercise Set

FOR EXTRA HELP

Student's Solutions Manual | Digital Video Tutor CD 3 Videotape 9 | AW Math Tutor Center | MathXL Tutorials on CD | MathXL | MyMathLab

Concept Reinforcement *Identify each of the following as a perfect-square trinomial, a difference of squares, a prime polynomial, or none of these.*

1. $x^2 - 64$

2. $4x^2 + 49$

3. $x^2 - 5x + 4$

4. $t^2 - 100$

5. $a^2 - 8a + 16$

6. $9x^2 + 6x + 1$

7. $-25x^2 - 9$

8. $2t^2 + 10t + 6$

9. $4r^2 + 20r + 25$

10. $16t^2 - 25$

Determine whether each of the following is a perfect-square trinomial.

11. $x^2 + 18x + 81$

12. $x^2 - 16x + 64$

13. $x^2 - 16x - 64$

14. $x^2 - 14x - 49$

15. $x^2 - 3x + 9$

16. $x^2 + 2x + 4$

17. $9x^2 - 36x + 24$

18. $36x^2 - 24x + 16$

Factor completely. Remember to look first for a common factor and to check by multiplying. If a polynomial is prime, state this.

19. $x^2 + 16x + 64$

20. $x^2 + 14x + 49$

21. $x^2 - 14x + 49$

22. $x^2 - 16x + 64$

23. $3x^2 + 6x + 3$

24. $5x^2 - 10x + 5$

25. $4 - 4x + x^2$

26. $4 + x^2 + 4x$

27. $18x^2 + 12x + 2$

28. $25x^2 + 10x + 1$

29. $49 - 56y + 16y^2$

30. $120m + 75 + 48m^2$

31. $-x^5 + 18x^4 - 81x^3$

32. $-2x^2 + 40x - 200$

33. $2x^3 - 4x^2 + 2x$

34. $x^3 + 24x^2 + 144x$

35. $20x^2 + 100x + 125$

36. $12x^2 + 36x + 27$

37. $49 - 42x + 9x^2$

38. $64 - 112x + 49x^2$

39. $16x^2 + 24x + 9$

40. $2a^2 + 28a + 98$

41. $2 + 20x + 50x^2$

42. $9x^2 + 30x + 25$

43. $4p^2 + 12pq + 9q^2$

44. $25m^2 + 20mn + 4n^2$

45. $a^2 - 12ab + 49b^2$

46. $x^2 - 7xy + 9y^2$

47. $-64m^2 - 16mn - n^2$

48. $-81p^2 + 18pq - q^2$

49. $-32s^2 + 80st - 50t^2$

50. $-36a^2 - 96ab - 64b^2$

Determine whether each of the following is a difference of squares.

51. $x^2 + 100$

52. $x^2 - 36$

53. $x^2 - 81$

54. $x^2 + 4$

55. $-26 + 4t^2$

56. $-1 + 49t^2$

Factor completely. Remember to look first for a common factor. If a polynomial is prime, state this.

57. $y^2 - 4$

58. $x^2 - 36$

59. $p^2 - 9$

60. $q^2 + 1$

61. $-49 + t^2$

62. $-64 + m^2$

63. $6a^2 - 54$

64. $x^2 - 8x + 16$

65. $49x^2 - 14x + 1$

66. $3t^2 - 12$

67. $200 - 2t^2$

68. $98 - 8w^2$

69. $-80a^2 + 45$

70. $25x^2 - 4$

71. $5t^2 - 80$

72. $-4t^2 + 64$

73. $8x^2 - 98$

74. $24x^2 - 54$

75. $36x - 49x^3$

76. $16x - 81x^3$

77. $49a^4 - 20$

78. $25a^4 - 9$

79. $t^4 - 1$

80. $x^4 - 16$

81. $-3x^3 + 24x^2 - 48x$

82. $-2a^4 + 36a^3 - 162a^2$

83. $48t^2 - 27$

84. $125t^2 - 45$

85. $a^8 - 2a^7 + a^6$

86. $x^8 - 8x^7 + 16x^6$

87. $7a^2 - 7b^2$

88. $6p^2 - 6q^2$

89. $25x^2 - 4y^2$

90. $16a^2 - 9b^2$

91. $18t^2 - 8s^2$

92. $49x^2 - 16y^2$

93. Explain in your own words how to determine whether a polynomial is a difference of squares.

94. Explain in your own words how to determine whether a polynomial is a perfect-square trinomial.

SKILL MAINTENANCE

95. About 5 L of oxygen can be dissolved in 100 L of water at 0°C. This is 1.6 times the amount that can be dissolved in the same volume of water at 20°C. How much oxygen can be dissolved at 20°C? [2.5]

96. Bonnie is taking a botany course. To get an A, she must average at least 90 after four exams. Bonnie scored 96, 98, and 89 on the first three tests. Determine (in terms of an inequality) what scores on the last test will earn her an A. [2.7]

Simplify. [4.1]

97. $(x^3y^5)(x^9y^7)$

98. $(5a^2b^3)^2$

Graph. [3.2]

99. $y = \frac{3}{2}x - 3$

100. $3x - 5y = 30$

SYNTHESIS

101. Leon concludes that since $x^2 - 9 = (x - 3)(x + 3)$, it must follow that $x^2 + 9 = (x + 3)(x - 3)$. What mistake(s) is he making?

102. Write directions that would enable someone to construct a polynomial that contains a perfect-square trinomial, a difference of squares, and a common factor.

Factor completely. If a polynomial is prime, state this.

103. $x^8 - 2^8$

104. $3x^2 - \frac{1}{3}$

105. $18x^3 - \frac{8}{25}x$

106. $0.49p - p^3$

107. $(y - 5)^4 - z^8$

108. $x^2 - \left(\frac{1}{x}\right)^2$

109. $-x^4 + 8x^2 + 9$

110. $-16x^4 + 96x^2 - 144$

Aha! 111. $(y + 3)^2 + 2(y + 3) + 1$

112. $49(x + 1)^2 - 42(x + 1) + 9$

113. $27x^3 - 63x^2 - 147x + 343$

114. $a^{2n} - 49b^{2n}$

115. $81 - b^{4k}$

116. $9b^{2n} + 12b^n + 4$

117. Subtract $(x^2 + 1)^2$ from $x^2(x + 1)^2$.

Factor by grouping. Look for a grouping of three terms that is a perfect-square trinomial.

118. $a^2 + 2a + 1 - 9$

119. $y^2 + 6y + 9 - x^2 - 8x - 16$

Find c such that each polynomial is the square of a binomial.

120. $cy^2 + 6y + 1$

121. $cy^2 - 24y + 9$

122. Find the value of a if $x^2 + a^2x + a^2$ factors into $(x + a)^2$.

123. Show that the difference of the squares of two consecutive integers is the sum of the integers. (*Hint*: Use x for the smaller number.)

5.5 Factoring: A General Strategy

Choosing the Right Method

CONNECTING THE CONCEPTS

Thus far, each section in this chapter has examined one or two different methods for factoring polynomials. In practice, when the need for factoring a polynomial arises, we must decide on our own which method to use. As preparation for such a situation, we now encounter polynomials of various types, in random order. Regardless of the polynomial we are faced with, the guidelines listed below can always be used.

To Factor a Polynomial

A. Always look for a common factor first. If there is one, factor out the largest common factor. Be sure to include it in your final answer.

B. Then look at the number of terms.

Two terms: If you have a difference of squares, factor accordingly: $A^2 - B^2 = (A - B)(A + B)$.

Three terms: If the trinomial is a perfect-square trinomial, factor accordingly: $A^2 + 2AB + B^2 = (A + B)^2$ or $A^2 - 2AB + B^2 = (A - B)^2$. If it is not a perfect-square trinomial, try using FOIL or grouping.

Four terms: Try factoring by grouping.

C. Always *factor completely*. When a factor can itself be factored, be sure to factor it. Remember that some polynomials, like $A^2 + B^2$, are prime.

D. Check by multiplying.

Choosing the Right Method

EXAMPLE 1 Factor: $5t^4 - 80$.

Solution

A. We look for a common factor:

$5t^4 - 80 = 5(t^4 - 16)$. 5 is the largest common factor.

B. The factor $t^4 - 16$ is a difference of squares: $(t^2)^2 - 4^2$. We factor it, being careful to rewrite the 5 from step (A):

$5t^4 - 80 = 5(t^2 + 4)(t^2 - 4)$. $t^4 - 16 = (t^2 + 4)(t^2 - 4)$

C. Since $t^2 - 4$ is not prime, we continue factoring:

$$5t^4 - 80 = 5(t^2 + 4)(t^2 - 4) = 5(t^2 + 4)(t - 2)(t + 2)$$

↑ This is a sum of squares with no common factor. It cannot be factored!

D. *Check:* $5(t^2 + 4)(t - 2)(t + 2) = 5(t^2 + 4)(t^2 - 4)$
$= 5(t^4 - 16) = 5t^4 - 80.$

The factorization is $5(t^2 + 4)(t - 2)(t + 2)$.

EXAMPLE 2 Factor: $2x^3 + 10x^2 + x + 5$.

Solution

A. We look for a common factor. There is none.
B. Because there are four terms, we try factoring by grouping:

$2x^3 + 10x^2 + x + 5$	
$= (2x^3 + 10x^2) + (x + 5)$	Separating into two binomials
$= 2x^2(x + 5) + 1(x + 5)$	Factoring out the largest common factor from each binomial. The 1 serves as an aid.
$= (x + 5)(2x^2 + 1)$	Factoring out the common factor, $x + 5$

C. Nothing can be factored further, so we have factored completely.
D. *Check:* $(x + 5)(2x^2 + 1) = 2x^3 + x + 10x^2 + 5$
$= 2x^3 + 10x^2 + x + 5.$

The factorization is $(x + 5)(2x^2 + 1)$.

Study Skills

Keep Your Focus

When studying with someone else, it can be very tempting to prolong conversation that has little to do with the mathematics that you need to study. If you see that this may happen, explain to your partner(s) that you enjoy the nonmathematical conversation, but would enjoy it more later—after the math work has been completed.

EXAMPLE 3 Factor: $-x^5 + 2x^4 + 35x^3$.

Solution

A. We note that there is a common factor, $-x^3$:

$$-x^5 + 2x^4 + 35x^3 = -x^3(x^2 - 2x - 35).$$

B. The factor $x^2 - 2x - 35$ is not a perfect-square trinomial. We factor it using trial and error:

$$-x^5 + 2x^4 + 35x^3 = -x^3(x^2 - 2x - 35)$$
$$= -x^3(x - 7)(x + 5).$$

C. Nothing can be factored further, so we have factored completely.
D. *Check:* $-x^3(x - 7)(x + 5) = -x^3(x^2 - 2x - 35)$
$= -x^5 + 2x^4 + 35x^3.$

The factorization is $-x^3(x - 7)(x + 5)$.

EXAMPLE 4 Factor: $x^2 - 20x + 100$.

Student Notes

Quickly checking the leading and constant terms to see if they are squares can save you time. If they aren't both squares, the trinomial can't possibly be a perfect-square trinomial.

Solution

A. We look first for a common factor. There is none.
B. This polynomial is a perfect-square trinomial. We factor it accordingly:

$$x^2 - 20x + 100 = x^2 - 2 \cdot x \cdot 10 + 10^2 \quad \text{Try to do this step mentally.}$$
$$= (x - 10)^2.$$

C. Nothing can be factored further, so we have factored completely.
D. *Check:* $(x - 10)(x - 10) = x^2 - 20x + 100$.

The factorization is $(x - 10)(x - 10)$, or $(x - 10)^2$.

EXAMPLE 5 Factor: $6x^2y^4 - 21x^3y^5 + 3x^2y^6$.

Solution

A. We first factor out the largest common factor, $3x^2y^4$:

$$6x^2y^4 - 21x^3y^5 + 3x^2y^6 = 3x^2y^4(2 - 7xy + y^2).$$

B. The constant term in $2 - 7xy + y^2$ is not a square, so we do not have a perfect-square trinomial. Note that x appears only in $-7xy$. If $2 - 7xy + y^2$ could be factored into a form like $(1 - y)(2 - y)$, there would be no x in the middle term. Thus, $2 - 7xy + y^2$ cannot be factored.
C. Nothing can be factored further, so we have factored completely.
D. *Check:* $3x^2y^4(2 - 7xy + y^2) = 6x^2y^4 - 21x^3y^5 + 3x^2y^6$.

The factorization is $3x^2y^4(2 - 7xy + y^2)$.

EXAMPLE 6 Factor: $px + py + qx + qy$.

Solution

A. We look first for a common factor. There is none.
B. There are four terms. We try factoring by grouping:

$$px + py + qx + qy = p(x + y) + q(x + y) = (x + y)(p + q).$$

C. Nothing can be factored further, so we have factored completely.
D. *Check:* $(x + y)(p + q) = xp + xq + yp + yq = px + py + qx + qy$.

The factorization is $(x + y)(p + q)$.

EXAMPLE 7 Factor: $25x^2 + 20xy + 4y^2$.

Solution

A. We look first for a common factor. There is none.
B. There are three terms. Note that the first term and the last term are squares: $25x^2 = (5x)^2$ and $4y^2 = (2y)^2$. We see that twice the product of $5x$ and $2y$ is the middle term,

$$2 \cdot 5x \cdot 2y = 20xy,$$

so the trinomial is a perfect square.

To factor, we write a binomial squared:

$$25x^2 + 20xy + 4y^2 = (5x + 2y)^2.$$

C. Nothing can be factored further, so we have factored completely.
D. *Check:* $(5x + 2y)(5x + 2y) = 25x^2 + 20xy + 4y^2$.

The factorization is $(5x + 2y)(5x + 2y)$, or $(5x + 2y)^2$.

EXAMPLE 8 Factor: $p^2q^2 + 7pq + 12$.

Solution

A. We look first for a common factor. There is none.
B. Since only one term is a square, we do not have a perfect-square trinomial. We use trial and error, thinking of the product pq as a single variable:

$$(pq + \quad)(pq + \quad).$$

We factor the last term, 12. All the signs are positive, so we consider only positive factors. Possibilities are 1, 12 and 2, 6 and 3, 4. The pair 3, 4 gives a sum of 7 for the coefficient of the middle term. Thus,

$$p^2q^2 + 7pq + 12 = (pq + 3)(pq + 4).$$

C. Nothing can be factored further, so we have factored completely.
D. *Check:* $(pq + 3)(pq + 4) = p^2q^2 + 7pq + 12$.

The factorization is $(pq + 3)(pq + 4)$.

Compare the variables appearing in Example 7 with those in Example 8. Note that if the leading term contains one variable and a different variable is in the last term, as in Example 7, each binomial contains two variable terms. When two variables appear in the leading term and no variables appear in the last term, as in Example 8, each binomial contains one term that has two variables and one term that is a constant.

EXAMPLE 9 Factor: $a^4 - 16b^4$.

Solution

A. We look first for a common factor. There is none.
B. There are two terms. Since $a^4 = (a^2)^2$ and $16b^4 = (4b^2)^2$, we see that we have a difference of squares. Thus,

$$a^4 - 16b^4 = (a^2 + 4b^2)(a^2 - 4b^2).$$

C. The factor $(a^2 - 4b^2)$ is itself a difference of squares. Thus,

$$a^4 - 16b^4 = (a^2 + 4b^2)(a + 2b)(a - 2b). \qquad \text{Factoring } a^2 - 4b^2$$

D. *Check:* $(a^2 + 4b^2)(a + 2b)(a - 2b) = (a^2 + 4b^2)(a^2 - 4b^2)$
$= a^4 - 16b^4$.

The factorization is $(a^2 + 4b^2)(a + 2b)(a - 2b)$.

5.5 Exercise Set

FOR EXTRA HELP

Student's Solutions Manual | Digital Video Tutor CD 3 Videotape 10 | AW Math Tutor Center | MathXL Tutorials on CD | MathXL | MyMathLab

Concept Reinforcement *In each of Exercises 1–4, complete the sentence.*

1. As a first step when factoring polynomials, always check for a ______________.

2. When factoring a trinomial, if two terms are not squares, it cannot be a ______________.

3. If a polynomial has four terms and no common factor, it may be possible to factor by ______________.

4. It is always possible to check a factorization by ______________.

Factor completely. If a polynomial is prime, state this.

5. $10a^2 - 640$
6. $5x^2 - 45$
7. $y^2 + 49 - 14y$
8. $a^2 + 25 + 10a$
9. $2t^2 + 11t + 12$
10. $8t^2 - 18t - 5$
11. $x^3 - 18x^2 + 81x$
12. $x^3 - 24x^2 + 144x$
13. $x^3 - 5x^2 - 25x + 125$
14. $x^3 + 3x^2 - 4x - 12$
15. $27t^3 - 3t$
16. $98t^2 - 18$
17. $9x^3 + 12x^2 - 45x$
18. $20x^3 - 4x^2 - 72x$
19. $t^2 + 25$
20. $x^2 + 4$
21. $6x^2 + 3x - 45$
22. $2t^2 + 6t - 20$
23. $-2a^6 + 8a^5 - 8a^4$
24. $-x^5 - 14x^4 - 49x^3$
25. $5x^5 - 80x$
26. $4x^4 - 64$
27. $t^4 - 9$
28. $9 + t^8$
29. $-x^6 + 2x^5 - 7x^4$
30. $-x^5 + 4x^4 - 3x^3$
31. $p^2q^2 - r^2$
32. $x^2 - y^2$
33. $ax^2 + ay^2$
34. $12n^2 + 24n^3$
35. $36mn - 9m^2n^2$
36. $ab^2 - a^2b$
37. $2\pi rh + 2\pi r^2$
38. $4\pi r^2 + 2\pi r$

Aha! **39.** $(a + b)5a + (a + b)3b$

40. $5c(a^3 + b) - (a^3 + b)$
41. $x^2 + x + xy + y$
42. $n^2 + 2n + np + 2p$
43. $a^2 - 3a + ay - 3y$
44. $2x^2 - 4x + xz - 2z$
45. $3x^2 + 13xy - 10y^2$
46. $-x^2 - y^2 - 2xy$
47. $4b^2 + a^2 - 4ab$
48. $a^2 - 7a - 6$
49. $16x^2 + 24xy + 9y^2$
50. $7p^4 - 7q^4$
51. $t^2 - 8t + 10$
52. $25z^2 + 10zy + y^2$
53. $a^4b^4 - 16$
54. $a^5 - 4a^4b - 5a^3b^2$
55. $4p^2q - pq^2 + 4p^3$
56. $a^2 + ab + 2b^2$
57. $3b^2 + 17ab - 6a^2$
58. $2mn - 360n^2 + m^2$
59. $-12 - x^2y^2 - 8xy$
60. $m^2n^2 - 4mn - 32$
61. $p^2q^2 + 7pq + 6$
62. $a^5b^2 + 3a^4b - 10a^3$
63. $4ab^5 - 32b^4 + a^2b^6$
64. $8x^2 - 36x + 40$
65. $x^6 + x^5y - 2x^4y^2$
66. $2s^6t^2 + 10s^3t^3 + 12t^4$
67. $36a^2 - 15a + \frac{25}{16}$
68. $a^2 + 2a^2bc + a^2b^2c^2$
69. $\frac{1}{81}x^2 - \frac{8}{27}x + \frac{16}{9}$
70. $\frac{1}{4}a^2 + \frac{1}{3}ab + \frac{1}{9}b^2$
71. $1 - 16x^{12}y^{12}$
72. $b^4a - 81a^5$
73. $4a^2b^2 + 12ab + 9$
74. $9c^2 + 6cd + d^2$
75. $a^4 + 8a^2 + 8a^3 + 64a$
76. $t^4 + 7t^2 - 3t^3 - 21t$

77. Kelly factored $16 - 8x + x^2$ as $(x - 4)^2$, while Tony factored it as $(4 - x)^2$. Are they both correct? Why or why not?

78. Describe in your own words a strategy for factoring polynomials.

SKILL MAINTENANCE

79. Show that the pairs $(-1, 11)$, $(0, 7)$, and $(3, -5)$ are solutions of $y = -4x + 7$. [3.2]

Solve. [2.2]

80. $5x - 4 = 0$

81. $3x + 7 = 0$

82. $2x + 9 = 0$

83. $4x - 9 = 0$

84. Graph: $y = -\frac{1}{2}x + 4$. [3.2]

SYNTHESIS

85. There are third-degree polynomials in x that we are not yet able to factor, despite the fact that they are not prime. Explain how such a polynomial could be created.

86. Describe a method that could be used to find a binomial of degree 16 that can be expressed as the product of prime binomial factors.

Factor.

87. $-(x^5 + 7x^3 - 18x)$

88. $18 + a^3 - 9a - 2a^2$

89. $-3a^4 + 15a^2 - 12$

90. $-x^4 + 7x^2 + 18$

Aha! **91.** $y^2(y + 1) - 4y(y + 1) - 21(y + 1)$

92. $y^2(y - 1) - 2y(y - 1) + (y - 1)$

93. $6(x - 1)^2 + 7y(x - 1) - 3y^2$

94. $(y + 4)^2 + 2x(y + 4) + x^2$

95. $2(a + 3)^4 - (a + 3)^3(b - 2) - (a + 3)^2(b - 2)^2$

96. $5(t - 1)^5 - 6(t - 1)^4(s - 1) + (t - 1)^3(s - 1)^2$

COLLABORATIVE CORNER

*Matching Factorizations**

Focus: Factoring

Time: 20 minutes

Group size: Begin with the entire class. The end result is pairs of students. If there is an odd number of students, the instructor should participate.

Materials: Prepared sheets of paper, pins or tape. On half of the sheets, the instructor writes a polynomial. On the remaining sheets, the instructor writes the factorization of those polynomials. The activity is more interesting if the polynomials and factorizations are similar; for example,

$$x^2 - 2x - 8, \quad (x - 2)(x - 4),$$
$$x^2 - 6x + 8, \quad (x - 1)(x - 8),$$
$$x^2 - 9x + 8, \quad (x + 2)(x - 4).$$

ACTIVITY

1. As class members enter the room, the instructor pins or tapes either a polynomial or a factorization to the back of each student. Class members are told only whether their sheet of paper contains a polynomial or a factorization. All students should remain quiet and not tell others what is on their sheet of paper.
2. After all students are wearing a sheet of paper, they should mingle with one another, attempting to match up their factorization with the appropriate polynomial or vice versa. They may ask "yes/no" questions of one another that relate to factoring and polynomials. Answers to the questions should be yes or no. For example, a legitimate question might be "Is my last term negative?", "Do my factors have opposite signs?", or "Does my factorization include the factors of 6?"
3. The game is over when all factorization/polynomial pairs have "found" one another.

*Thanks to Jann MacInnes of Florida Community College at Jacksonville–Kent Campus for suggesting this activity.

5.6 Solving Quadratic Equations by Factoring

The Principle of Zero Products • Factoring to Solve Equations • Algebraic–Graphical Connection

CONNECTING THE CONCEPTS

Chapter 4 and Sections 5.1–5.5 have been devoted to finding *equivalent expressions.* Whether we are adding, subtracting, multiplying, dividing, or factoring polynomials, the result of our work is an expression that is equivalent to the original expression.

Here in Section 5.6 we return to the task of *solving equations.* This time, however, the equations will contain a variable raised to a power greater than 1 and will usually have more than one solution. Our ability to factor will play a pivotal role in solving such equations.

Second-degree equations like $4t^2 - 9 = 0$ and $x^2 + 6x + 5 = 0$ are called **quadratic equations.**

Study Skills

Identify the Highlights

If you haven't already tried one, consider using a highlighter as you read. By highlighting sentences or phrases that you find especially important, you will make it easier to review important material in the future. Highlighters are only helpful when used, so be sure to keep your highlighter with you whenever you study.

Quadratic Equation

A *quadratic equation* is an equation equivalent to one of the form

$$ax^2 + bx + c = 0,$$

where a, b, and c are constants, with $a \neq 0$.

In order to solve quadratic equations, we need to develop a new principle.

The Principle of Zero Products

Suppose we are told that the product of two numbers is 6. On the basis of this information, it is impossible to know the value of either number—the product could be $2 \cdot 3$, $6 \cdot 1$, $12 \cdot \frac{1}{2}$, and so on. However, if we are told that the product of two numbers is 0, we know that at least one of the two numbers must itself be 0. For example, if $(x + 3)(x - 2) = 0$, we can conclude that either $x + 3$ is 0 or $x - 2$ is 0.

The Principle of Zero Products

An equation $AB = 0$ is true if and only if $A = 0$ or $B = 0$, or both. (A product is 0 if and only if at least one factor is 0.)

EXAMPLE 1 Solve: $(x + 3)(x - 2) = 0$.

Solution We are told that the product of $x + 3$ and $x - 2$ is 0. In order for a product to be 0, at least one factor must be 0. Therefore, either

$x + 3 = 0$ *or* $x - 2 = 0$. Using the principle of zero products

We solve each equation:

$$x + 3 = 0 \quad \text{or} \quad x - 2 = 0$$
$$x = -3 \quad \text{or} \quad x = 2.$$

Both -3 and 2 should be checked in the original equation.

Check: For -3:

$$\begin{array}{r|l} (x + 3)(x - 2) & 0 \\ \hline (-3 + 3)(-3 - 2) & 0 \\ 0(-5) & \\ 0 \stackrel{?}{=} 0 & \text{TRUE} \end{array}$$

For 2:

$$\begin{array}{r|l} (x + 3)(x - 2) & 0 \\ \hline (2 + 3)(2 - 2) & 0 \\ 5(0) & \\ 0 \stackrel{?}{=} 0 & \text{TRUE} \end{array}$$

The solutions are -3 and 2.

When we are using the principle of zero products, the word "or" is meant to emphasize that any one of the factors could be the one that represents 0.

EXAMPLE 2 Solve: $3(5x + 1)(x - 7) = 0$.

Solution Since the factor 3 is constant, the only way for $3(5x + 1)(x - 7)$ to be 0 is for one of the other factors to be 0. That is,

$5x + 1 = 0$ *or* $x - 7 = 0$ Using the principle of zero products

$5x = -1$ *or* $x = 7$ Solving the two equations separately

$x = -\frac{1}{5}$ *or* $x = 7$. The constant factor 3 is *not* a solution.

Check: For $-\frac{1}{5}$:

$$\begin{array}{r|l} 3(5x + 1)(x - 7) & 0 \\ \hline 3\left(5\left(-\frac{1}{5}\right) + 1\right)\left(-\frac{1}{5} - 7\right) & 0 \\ 3(-1 + 1)\left(-7\frac{1}{5}\right) & \\ 3(0)\left(-7\frac{1}{5}\right) & \\ 0 \stackrel{?}{=} 0 & \text{TRUE} \end{array}$$

For 7:

$$\begin{array}{r|l} 3(5x + 1)(x - 7) & 0 \\ \hline 3(5(7) + 1)(7 - 7) & 0 \\ 3(35 + 1)0 & \\ 0 \stackrel{?}{=} 0 & \text{TRUE} \end{array}$$

The solutions are $-\frac{1}{5}$ and 7.

The principle of zero products can be used whenever a product equals 0—even if a factor has only one term.

EXAMPLE 3 Solve: $7t(t - 5) = 0$.

Solution We have

$7 \cdot t(t - 5) = 0$	The factors are 7, t, and $t - 5$.
$t = 0$ *or* $t - 5 = 0$	Using the principle of zero products
$t = 0$ *or* $t = 5$.	Solving. Note that the constant factor, 7, is never 0.

The solutions are 0 and 5. The check is left to the student.

Factoring to Solve Equations

By factoring and using the principle of zero products, we can now solve a variety of quadratic equations.

EXAMPLE 4 Solve: $x^2 + 5x + 6 = 0$.

Solution This equation differs from those solved in Chapter 2. There are no like terms to combine, and there is a squared term. We first factor the polynomial. Then we use the principle of zero products:

$x^2 + 5x + 6 = 0$	
$(x + 2)(x + 3) = 0$	Factoring
$x + 2 = 0$ *or* $x + 3 = 0$	Using the principle of zero products
$x = -2$ *or* $x = -3$.	

Check: For -2:

$$\begin{array}{r|l} x^2 + 5x + 6 & = 0 \\ \hline (-2)^2 + 5(-2) + 6 & 0 \\ 4 - 10 + 6 & \\ -6 + 6 & \\ 0 & \stackrel{?}{=} 0 \quad \text{TRUE} \end{array}$$

For -3:

$$\begin{array}{r|l} x^2 + 5x + 6 & = 0 \\ \hline (-3)^2 + 5(-3) + 6 & 0 \\ 9 - 15 + 6 & \\ -6 + 6 & \\ 0 & \stackrel{?}{=} 0 \quad \text{TRUE} \end{array}$$

The solutions are -2 and -3.

The principle of zero products is used even if the factoring consists of only removing a common factor.

EXAMPLE 5 Solve: $x^2 + 7x = 0$.

Solution Although there is no constant term, because of the x^2-term, the equation is still quadratic. The methods of Chapter 2 are not sufficient, so we try factoring:

$x^2 + 7x = 0$	
$x(x + 7) = 0$	Removing the greatest common factor, x
$x = 0$ *or* $x + 7 = 0$	
$x = 0$ *or* $x = -7$.	

The solutions are 0 and -7. The check is left to the student.

Student Notes

Checking for a common factor is an important step that is often overlooked. Also, be sure to remember that only like terms can be combined.

> *Caution!* We *must* have 0 on one side of the equation before the principle of zero products can be used. Get all nonzero terms on one side and 0 on the other.

EXAMPLE 6

Solve: **(a)** $x^2 - 8x = -16$; **(b)** $4t^2 = 25$.

Solution

a) We first add 16 to get 0 on one side:

$$x^2 - 8x = -16$$

$$x^2 - 8x + 16 = 0 \qquad \text{Adding 16 to both sides to get 0 on one side}$$

$$(x - 4)(x - 4) = 0 \qquad \text{Factoring}$$

$$x - 4 = 0 \quad or \quad x - 4 = 0 \qquad \text{Using the principle of zero products}$$

$$x = 4 \quad or \quad x = 4.$$

There is only one solution, 4. The check is left to the student.

b) We have

$$4t^2 = 25$$

$$4t^2 - 25 = 0 \qquad \text{Subtracting 25 from both sides to get 0 on one side}$$

$$(2t - 5)(2t + 5) = 0 \qquad \text{Factoring a difference of squares}$$

$$\left.\begin{aligned} 2t - 5 = 0 \quad &or \quad 2t + 5 = 0 \\ 2t = 5 \quad &or \quad 2t = -5 \\ t = \tfrac{5}{2} \quad &or \quad t = -\tfrac{5}{2}. \end{aligned}\right\} \text{Solving the two equations separately}$$

The solutions are $\frac{5}{2}$ and $-\frac{5}{2}$. The check is left to the student.

When solving quadratic equations by factoring, remember that a factorization is not useful unless 0 is on the other side of the equation.

EXAMPLE 7

Solve: $(x + 3)(2x - 1) = 9$.

Solution Be careful with an equation like this! Since we need 0 on one side, we multiply out the product on the left and then subtract 9 from both sides:

$$(x + 3)(2x - 1) = 9$$

$$2x^2 + 5x - 3 = 9 \qquad \text{Multiplying on the left}$$

$$2x^2 + 5x - 3 - 9 = 9 - 9 \qquad \text{Subtracting 9 from both sides to get 0 on one side}$$

$$2x^2 + 5x - 12 = 0 \qquad \text{Combining like terms}$$

$$(2x - 3)(x + 4) = 0 \qquad \text{Factoring}$$

$$2x - 3 = 0 \quad or \quad x + 4 = 0 \qquad \text{Using the principle of zero products}$$

$$2x = 3 \quad or \quad x = -4$$

$$x = \tfrac{3}{2} \quad or \quad x = -4.$$

Check: For $\frac{3}{2}$:

$$\begin{array}{c|c} (x+3)(2x-1) & 9 \\ \hline \left(\frac{3}{2}+3\right)\left(2\cdot\frac{3}{2}-1\right) & 9 \\ \left(\frac{9}{2}\right)(2) & \\ 9 & \stackrel{?}{=} 9 \end{array} \quad \text{TRUE}$$

For -4:

$$\begin{array}{c|c} (x+3)(2x-1) & 9 \\ \hline (-4+3)(2(-4)-1) & 9 \\ (-1)(-9) & \\ 9 & \stackrel{?}{=} 9 \end{array} \quad \text{TRUE}$$

The solutions are $\frac{3}{2}$ and -4.

ALGEBRAIC–GRAPHICAL CONNECTION

When graphing a linear equation in Chapter 3, we found the x-intercept by replacing y with 0 and solving for x. This procedure can also be used to find the x-intercepts when graphing an equation of the form $y = ax^2 + bx + c$. Although the details of creating such graphs is left for Chapter 9, we consider them briefly here from the standpoint of finding x-intercepts. The graphs are shaped as shown. Note that each x-intercept represents a solution of $ax^2 + bx + c = 0$.

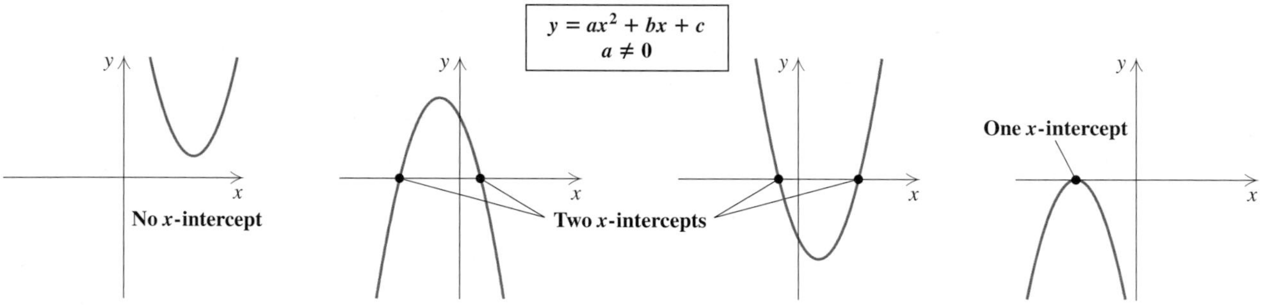

EXAMPLE 8 Find the x-intercepts for the graph of the equation shown. (The grid is intentionally not included.)

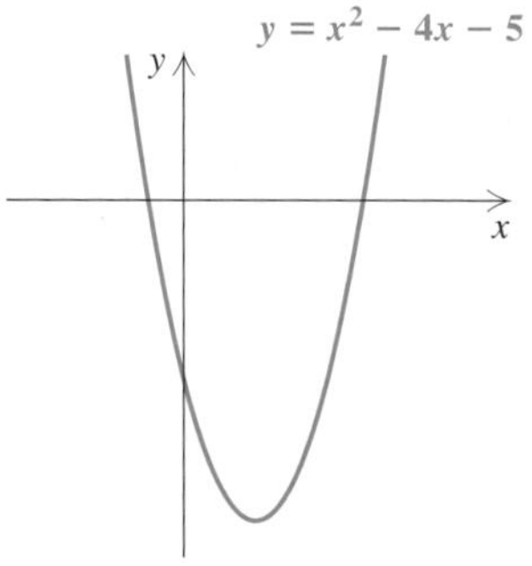

Solution To find the x-intercepts, we let $y = 0$ and solve for x:

$$\begin{aligned} 0 &= x^2 - 4x - 5 && \text{Substituting 0 for } y \\ 0 &= (x-5)(x+1) && \text{Factoring} \\ x - 5 = 0 \quad &or \quad x + 1 = 0 && \text{Using the principle of zero products} \\ x = 5 \quad &or \quad x = -1. && \text{Solving for } x \end{aligned}$$

The x-intercepts are $(5, 0)$ and $(-1, 0)$.

technology connection

A graphing calculator allows us to solve quadratic equations even when an equation cannot be solved by factoring. For example, to solve $x^2 - 3x - 5 = 0$, we can let $y_1 = x^2 - 3x - 5$ and $y_2 = 0$. Selecting a bold line type to the left of y_2 in the Y= window makes the line easier to see. Using the INTERSECT option of the CALC menu, we select the two graphs in which we are interested, along with a guess. The graphing calculator displays the point of intersection.

An alternate method uses only y_1 and the ZERO or ROOT option of the CALC menu. This option requires you to enter an x-value to the left of the x-intercept as a LEFT BOUND. An x-value to the right of the x-intercept is then entered as a RIGHT BOUND. Finally, a GUESS value between the two bounds is entered and the x-intercept, or ZERO or ROOT, is displayed.

$y_1 = x^2 - 3x - 5, \quad y_2 = 0$

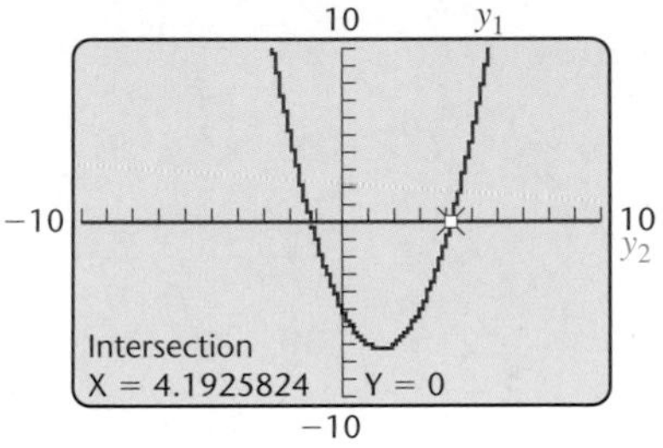

Use a graphing calculator to find the solutions, if they exist, accurate to two decimal places.

1. $x^2 + 4x - 3 = 0$

2. $x^2 - 5x - 2 = 0$

3. $x^2 + 13.54x + 40.95 = 0$

4. $x^2 - 4.43x + 6.32 = 0$

5. $1.235x^2 - 3.409x = 0$

5.6 Exercise Set

FOR EXTRA HELP

Student's Solutions Manual | Digital Video Tutor CD 3 Videotape 10 | AW Math Tutor Center | MathXL Tutorials on CD | MathXL | MyMathLab

Concept Reinforcement *For each of Exercises 1–4, match the phrase with the most appropriate choice from the column on the right.*

1. ____ The name of equations of the type $ax^2 + bx + c = 0$, with $a \neq 0$ — **a)** 2

2. ____ The idea that $A \cdot B = 0$ if and only if $A = 0$ or $B = 0$ — **b)** 0

3. ____ The number of solutions of most quadratic equations — **c)** Quadratic

4. ____ The number that is on one side of a quadratic equation before the principle of zero products is used — **d)** The principle of zero products

Solve using the principle of zero products.

5. $(x + 5)(x + 7) = 0$

6. $(x + 1)(x + 2) = 0$

7. $(x - 3)(x + 6) = 0$

8. $(x + 9)(x - 3) = 0$

9. $(2x - 9)(x + 4) = 0$

10. $(3x - 5)(x + 1) = 0$

11. $(10x - 9)(4x + 7) = 0$

12. $(2x - 7)(3x + 4) = 0$

13. $x(x + 2) = 0$

14. $t(t + 8) = 0$

15. $\left(\frac{2}{3}x - \frac{12}{11}\right)\left(\frac{7}{4}x - \frac{1}{12}\right) = 0$

16. $\left(\frac{1}{9} - 3x\right)\left(\frac{1}{5} + 2x\right) = 0$

17. $5x(2x + 9) = 0$

18. $12x(4x + 5) = 0$

19. $(20 - 0.4x)(7 - 0.1x) = 0$

20. $(1 - 0.05x)(1 - 0.3x) = 0$

Solve by factoring and using the principle of zero products.

21. $x^2 - 7x + 6 = 0$

22. $x^2 - 6x + 5 = 0$

23. $x^2 + 4x - 21 = 0$

24. $x^2 - 7x - 18 = 0$

25. $x^2 + 9x + 14 = 0$

26. $x^2 + 8x + 15 = 0$

27. $x^2 - 6x = 0$

28. $x^2 + 8x = 0$

29. $6t + t^2 = 0$

30. $3t + t^2 = 0$

31. $9x^2 = 4$

32. $4x^2 = 25$

33. $0 = 25 + x^2 + 10x$

34. $0 = 6x + x^2 + 9$

35. $1 + x^2 = 2x$

36. $x^2 + 16 = 8x$

37. $4t^2 = 8t$

38. $12t = 3t^2$

39. $3x^2 - 7x = 20$

40. $6x^2 - 4x = 10$

41. $2y^2 + 12y = -10$

42. $12y^2 - 5y = 2$

43. $(x - 7)(x + 1) = -16$

44. $(x + 2)(x - 7) = -18$

45. $14z^2 - 3 = 21z - 3$

46. $15z^2 + 7 = 20z + 7$

47. $81x^2 - 5 = 20$

48. $36m^2 - 9 = 40$

49. $(x - 1)(5x + 4) = 2$

50. $(x + 3)(3x + 5) = 7$

51. $x^2 - 2x = 18 + 5x$

52. $3x^2 - 2x = 9 - 8x$

53. $(6a + 1)(a + 1) = 21$

54. $(2t + 1)(4t - 1) = 14$

55. Use this graph to solve $x^2 + x - 6 = 0$.

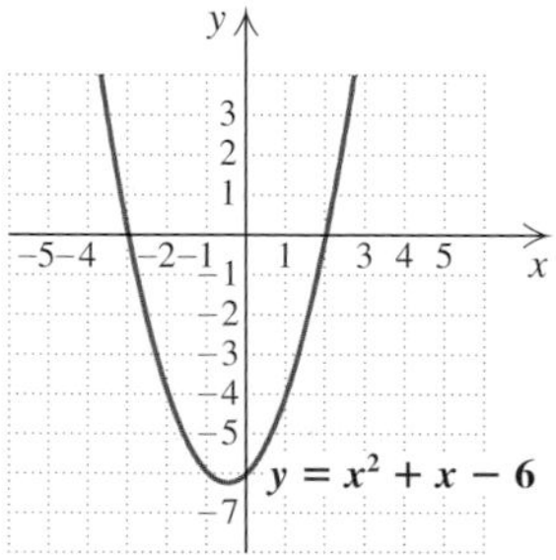

56. Use this graph to solve $x^2 - 3x - 4 = 0$.

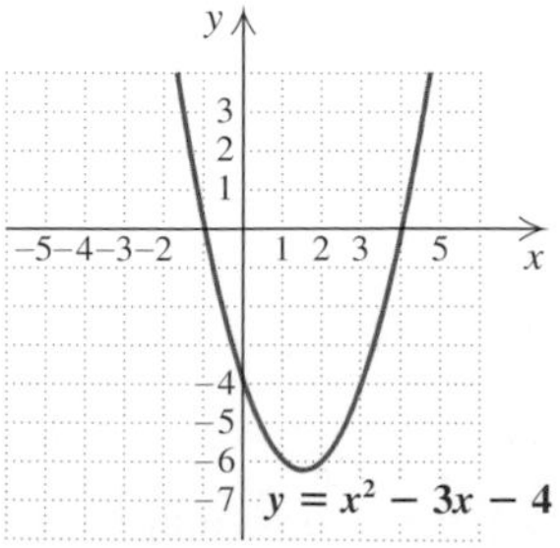

57. Use the following graph to solve $-x^2 + 2x + 3 = 0$.

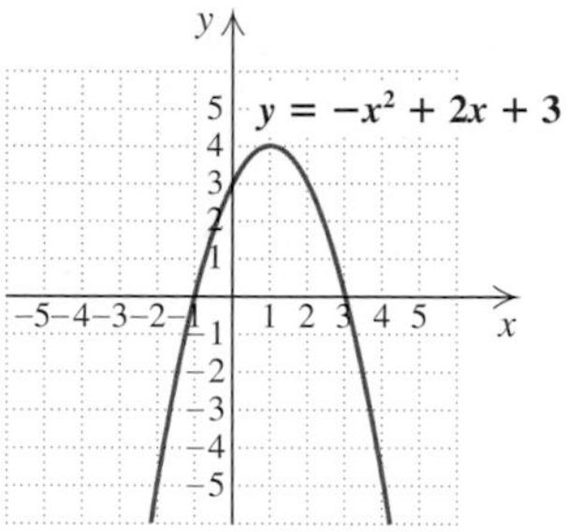

58. Use the following graph to solve $-x^2 - x + 6 = 0$.

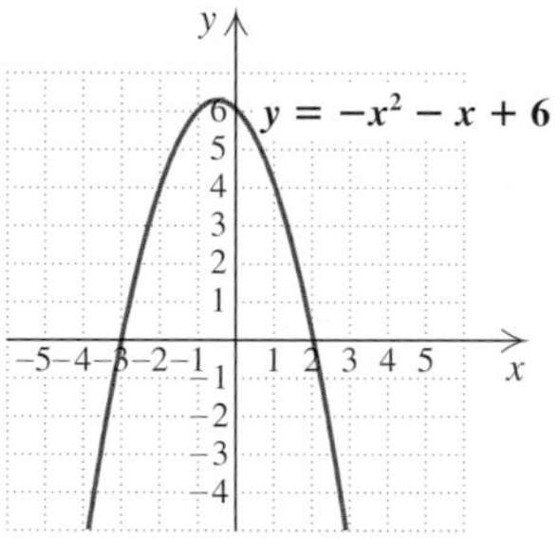

Find the x-intercepts for the graph of each equation. Grids are intentionally not included.

59. $y = x^2 + 3x - 4$

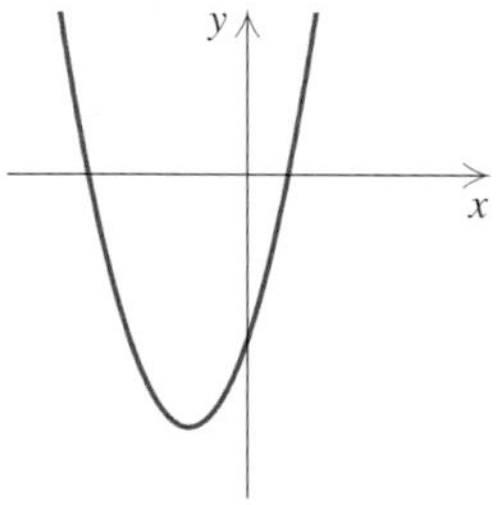

60. $y = x^2 - x - 6$

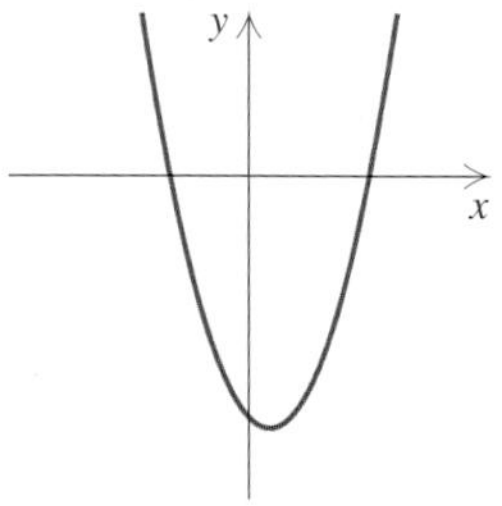

61. $y = x^2 - 2x - 15$

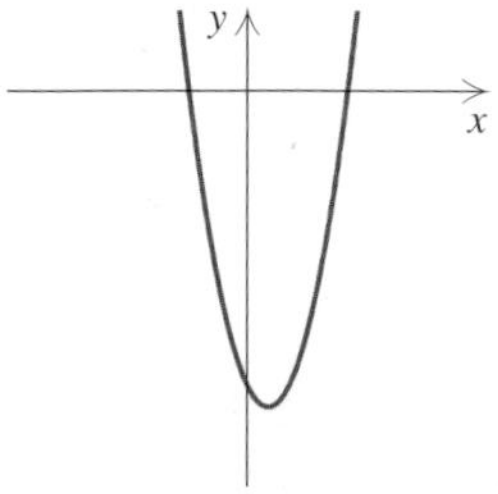

62. $y = x^2 + 2x - 8$

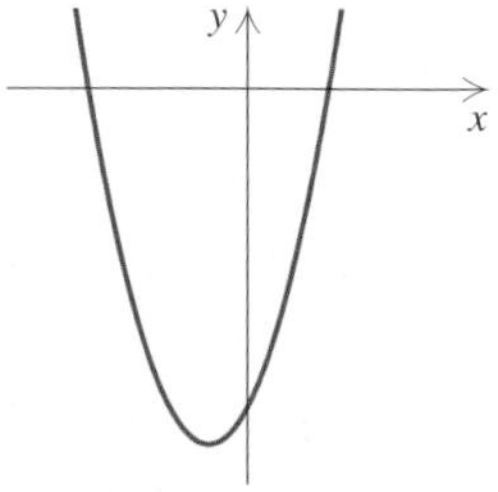

63. $y = 2x^2 + x - 10$

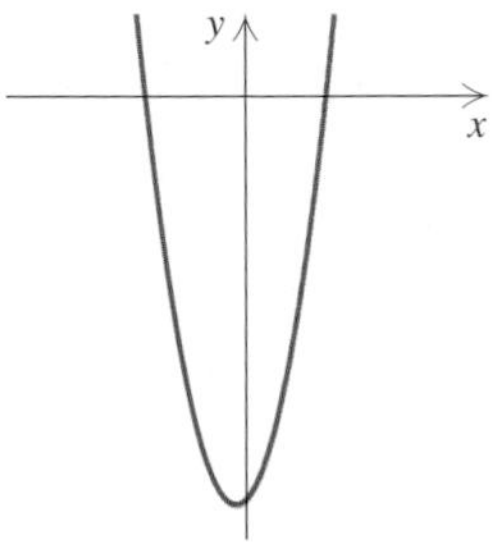

64. $y = 2x^2 + 3x - 9$

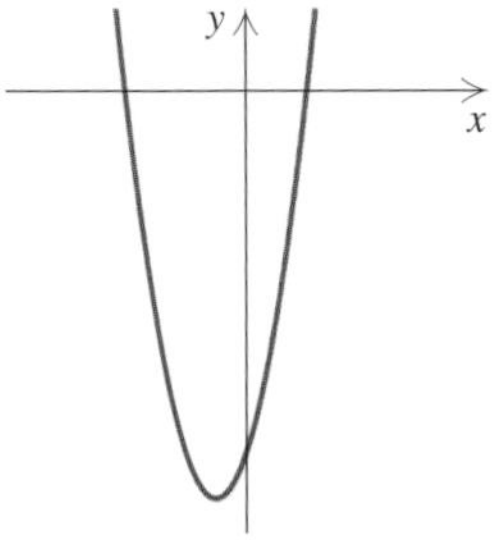

65. The equation $x^2 + 1$ has no real-number solutions. What implications does this have for the graph of $y = x^2 + 1$?

66. What is the difference between a quadratic polynomial and a quadratic equation?

SKILL MAINTENANCE

Translate to an algebraic expression. [1.1]

67. The square of the sum of a and b

68. The sum of the squares of a and b

69. The sum of two consecutive integers

Translate to an inequality. [2.7]

70. 5 more than twice a number is less than 19.

71. 7 less than half of a number exceeds 24.

72. 3 less than a number is at least 34.

SYNTHESIS

73. What is wrong with solving $x^2 = 3x$ by dividing both sides of the equation by x?

74. When the principle of zero products is used to solve a quadratic equation, will there always be two different solutions? Why or why not?

Solve.

75. $(2x - 5)(3x^2 + 29x + 56) = 0$

76. $(4x + 9)(15x^2 - 7x - 2) = 0$

77. Find an equation with integer coefficients that has the given numbers as solutions. For example, 3 and -2 are solutions to $x^2 - x - 6 = 0$.

a) $-4, 5$ **b)** $-1, 7$ **c)** $\frac{1}{4}, 3$
d) $\frac{1}{2}, \frac{1}{3}$ **e)** $\frac{2}{3}, \frac{3}{4}$ **f)** $-1, 2, 3$

Solve.

78. $16(x - 1) = x(x + 8)$

79. $a(9 + a) = 4(2a + 5)$

80. $(t - 5)^2 = 2(5 - t)$

81. $-x^2 + \frac{9}{25} = 0$

82. $-x^2 + \frac{25}{36} = 0$

Aha! **83.** $(t + 1)^2 = 9$

84. $\frac{27}{25}x^2 = \frac{1}{3}$

85. For each equation on the left, find an equivalent equation on the right.

a) $x^2 + 10x - 2 = 0$	$4x^2 + 8x + 36 = 0$
b) $(x - 6)(x + 3) = 0$	$(2x + 8)(2x - 5) = 0$
c) $5x^2 - 5 = 0$	$9x^2 - 12x + 24 = 0$
d) $(2x - 5)(x + 4) = 0$	$(x + 1)(5x - 5) = 0$
e) $x^2 + 2x + 9 = 0$	$x^2 - 3x - 18 = 0$
f) $3x^2 - 4x + 8 = 0$	$2x^2 + 20x - 4 = 0$

86. Explain how to construct an equation that has seven solutions.

87. Explain how the graph in Exercise 57 can be used to visualize the solutions of

$$-x^2 + 2x + 3 = -5.$$

Use a graphing calculator to find the solutions of each equation. Round solutions to the nearest hundredth.

88. $x^2 - 9.10x + 15.77 = 0$

89. $-x^2 + 0.63x + 0.22 = 0$

90. $x^2 + 13.74x + 42.00 = 0$

91. $6.4x^2 - 8.45x - 94.06 = 0$

92. $0.84x^2 - 2.30x = 0$

93. $1.23x^2 + 4.63x = 0$

94. $x^2 + 1.80x - 5.69 = 0$

5.7 Solving Applications

Applications • The Pythagorean Theorem

Applications

We can use the five-step problem-solving process and our new methods of solving quadratic equations to solve new types of problems.

EXAMPLE 1 Race numbers. Roger and Suzanne entered the Twin City Marathon as a two-person team. Their racing bibs were consecutive numbers, the product of which was 156. Find the numbers.

Solution

1. **Familiarize.** Consecutive numbers are one apart, like 49 and 50. Let $x =$ the first bib number; then $x + 1 =$ the next bib number.
2. **Translate.** We reword the problem before translating:

Rewording:	The first bib number	times	the next bib number	is	156.
	↓	↓	↓	↓	↓
Translating:	x	$\cdot$	$(x + 1)$	$=$	156

3. **Carry out.** We solve the equation as follows:

$$x(x + 1) = 156$$
$$x^2 + x = 156 \qquad \text{Multiplying}$$
$$x^2 + x - 156 = 0 \qquad \text{Subtracting 156 to get 0 on one side}$$
$$(x - 12)(x + 13) = 0 \qquad \text{Factoring}$$
$$x - 12 = 0 \quad or \quad x + 13 = 0 \qquad \text{Using the principle of zero products}$$
$$x = 12 \quad or \quad x = -13. \qquad \text{Solving each equation}$$

4. **Check.** The solutions of the equation are 12 and -13. Since bib numbers cannot be negative, -13 must be rejected. On the other hand, if x is 12, then $x + 1$ is 13 and $12 \cdot 13 = 156$. Thus, 12 checks.
5. **State.** The bib numbers for Suzanne and Roger were 12 and 13.

Study Skills

Finishing a Chapter

Try to be aware of when you reach the end of a chapter. Sometimes the end of a chapter signals the arrival of a quiz or test. Almost always, the end of a chapter indicates the end of a particular area of study. Because future work will likely rely on your mastery of the chapter completed, make use of the chapter review and test to solidify your understanding before moving onward.

EXAMPLE 2 Manufacturing. Wooden Work, Ltd., builds cutting boards that are twice as long as they are wide. The most popular board that Wooden Work makes has an area of 800 cm^2. What are the dimensions of the board?

Solution

1. **Familiarize.** We first make a drawing. Recall that the area of any rectangle is Length · Width. We let $x =$ the width of the board, in centimeters. The length is then $2x$, since the board is twice as long as it is wide.

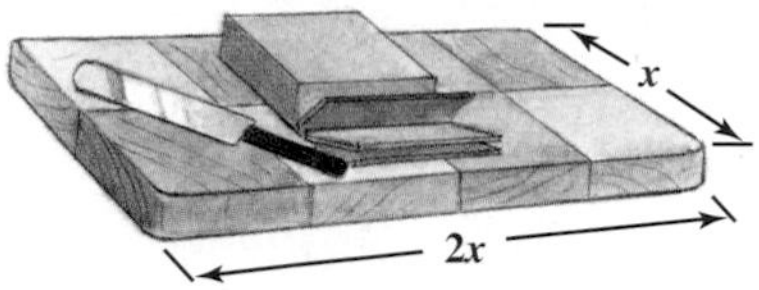

2. **Translate.** We reword and translate as follows:

Rewording:	The area of the rectangle	is	800 cm^2.
Translating:	$2x \cdot x$	$=$	800

3. **Carry out.** We solve the equation as follows:

$$2x \cdot x = 800$$
$$2x^2 = 800$$
$$2x^2 - 800 = 0 \quad \text{Subtracting 800 to get 0 on one side of the equation}$$
$$2(x^2 - 400) = 0 \quad \text{Removing a common factor of 2}$$
$$2(x - 20)(x + 20) = 0 \quad \text{Factoring a difference of squares}$$
$$(x - 20)(x + 20) = 0 \quad \text{Dividing both sides by 2}$$
$$x - 20 = 0 \quad or \quad x + 20 = 0 \quad \text{Using the principle of zero products}$$
$$x = 20 \quad or \quad x = -20. \quad \text{Solving each equation}$$

4. **Check.** The solutions of the equation are 20 and -20. Since the width must be positive, -20 cannot be a solution. To check 20 cm, we note that if the width is 20 cm, then the length is $2 \cdot 20$ cm $= 40$ cm and the area is 20 cm · 40 cm $= 800$ cm^2. Thus the solution 20 checks.

5. **State.** The cutting board is 20 cm wide and 40 cm long.

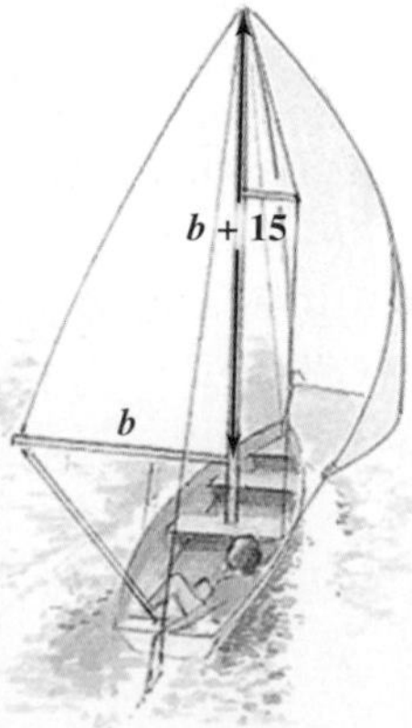

EXAMPLE 3 Dimensions of a sail. The mainsail of Stacey's Lightning-styled sailboat has an area of 125 ft^2. If the sail is 15 ft taller than it is wide, find the height and the width of the sail.

Solution

1. **Familiarize.** We first make a drawing. The formula for the area of a triangle is Area $= \frac{1}{2} \cdot$ (base) · (height). We let $b =$ the width, in feet, of the triangle's base and $b + 15 =$ the height, in feet.

2. **Translate.** We reword and translate as follows:

Rewording: The area of the sail is 125 ft^2.

Translating: $\frac{1}{2} \cdot b(b + 15) = 125.$

3. **Carry out.** We solve the equation as follows:

$$\frac{1}{2} \cdot b \cdot (b + 15) = 125$$

$$\frac{1}{2}(b^2 + 15b) = 125 \quad \text{Multiplying}$$

$$b^2 + 15b = 250 \quad \text{Multiplying by 2 to clear fractions}$$

$$b^2 + 15b - 250 = 0 \quad \text{Subtracting 250 to get 0 on one side}$$

$$(b + 25)(b - 10) = 0 \quad \text{Factoring}$$

$$b + 25 = 0 \quad or \quad b - 10 = 0 \quad \text{Using the principle of zero products}$$

$$b = -25 \quad or \quad b = 10.$$

4. **Check.** The width must be positive, so -25 cannot be a solution. Suppose the base is 10 ft. The height would be $10 + 15$, or 25 ft, and the area $\frac{1}{2}(10)(25)$, or 125 ft^2. These numbers check in the original problem.
5. **State.** Stacey's mainsail is 25 ft tall and 10 ft wide.

EXAMPLE 4 Medicine. For certain people suffering an extreme allergic reaction, the drug epinephrine (adrenaline) is sometimes prescribed. The number of micrograms N of epinephrine in an adult's bloodstream t minutes after 250 micrograms have been injected can be approximated by

$$-10t^2 + 100t = N$$

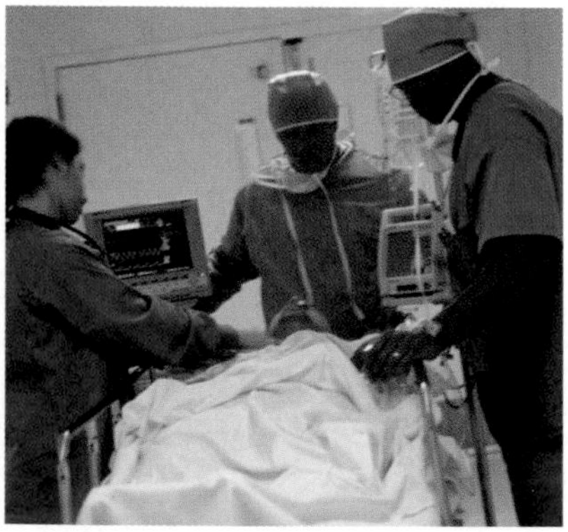

(*Source*: Based on information in Chohan, Naina, Rita M. Doyle, and Patricia Nayle (eds.), *Nursing Handbook*, 21st ed. Springhouse, PA: Springhouse Corporation, 2001). How long after an injection will there be about 210 micrograms of epinephrine in the bloodstream?

Solution

1. **Familiarize.** To familiarize ourselves with this problem, we could calculate N for different choices of t. We leave this for the student. We could also speak with a healthcare professional to learn that injections of epinephrine are very quick-acting. Note that there may be two solutions, one on each side of the time at which the drug's effect peaks.
2. **Translate.** To find the length of time after injection when 210 micrograms are in the bloodstream, we replace N with 210 in the formula above:

$$-10t^2 + 100t = 210. \quad \text{Substituting 210 for } N\text{. This is now an equation in one variable.}$$

technology connection

As a visual check for Example 4, we can either let $y_1 = -10x^2 + 100x$ and $y_2 = 210$, or let $y_1 = -10x^2 + 100x - 210$ and $y_2 = 0$. In either case, the points of intersection occur at $x = 3$ and $x = 7$, as shown.

$y_1 = -10x^2 + 100x, \quad y_2 = 210$

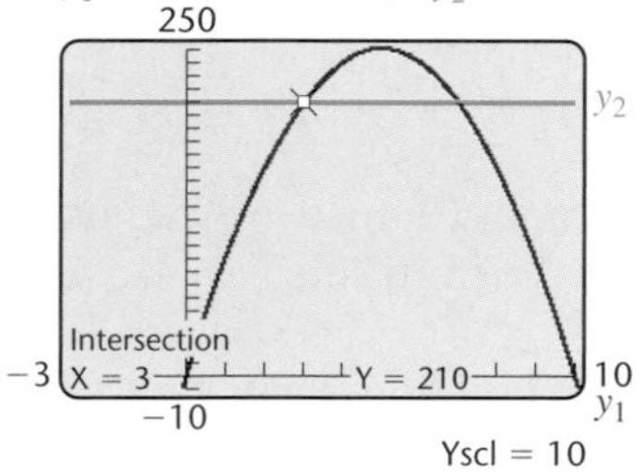

$y_1 = -10x^2 + 100x - 210, \quad y_2 = 0$

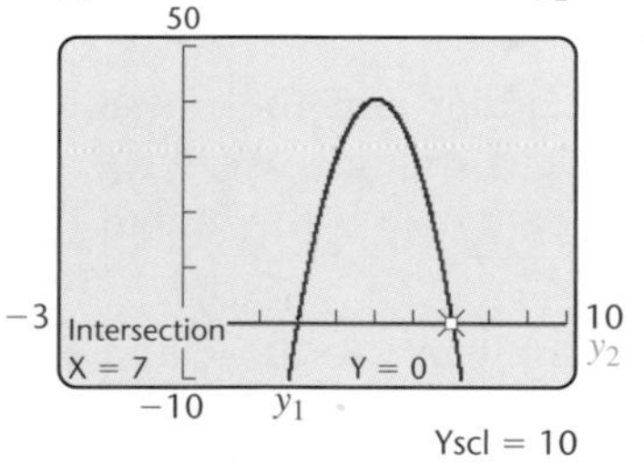

3. Carry out. We solve the equation as follows:

$$-10t^2 + 100t = 210$$

$-10t^2 + 100t - 210 = 0$ Subtracting 210 from both sides to get 0 on one side

$-10(t^2 - 10t + 21) = 0$ Factoring out the largest common factor, -10

$-10(t - 3)(t - 7) = 0$ Factoring

$t - 3 = 0$ *or* $t - 7 = 0$ Using the principle of zero products

$t = 3$ *or* $t = 7$.

4. Check. Since $-10 \cdot 3^2 + 100 \cdot 3 = -90 + 300 = 210$, the number 3 checks. Since $-10 \cdot 7^2 + 100 \cdot 7 = -490 + 700 = 210$, the number 7 also checks.

5. State. There will be 210 micrograms of epinephrine in the bloodstream approximately 3 minutes and 7 minutes after injection.

The Pythagorean Theorem

The following problems involve the Pythagorean theorem, which relates the lengths of the sides of a *right* triangle. A triangle is a **right triangle** if it has a 90°, or *right*, angle. The side opposite the 90° angle is called the **hypotenuse**. The other sides are called **legs**.

The Pythagorean Theorem

In any right triangle, if a and b are the lengths of the legs and c is the length of the hypotenuse, then

$$a^2 + b^2 = c^2, \quad \text{or}$$

$$(\text{Leg})^2 + (\text{Other leg})^2 = (\text{Hypotenuse})^2.$$

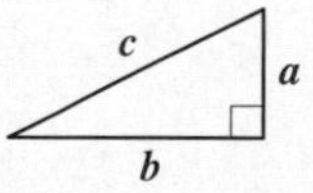

The equation $a^2 + b^2 = c^2$ is called the **Pythagorean equation.***

The Pythagorean theorem is named for the Greek mathematician Pythagoras (569?–500? B.C.). We can think of this relationship as adding areas.

*The *converse* of the Pythagorean theorem is also true. That is, if $a^2 + b^2 = c^2$, then the triangle is a right triangle.

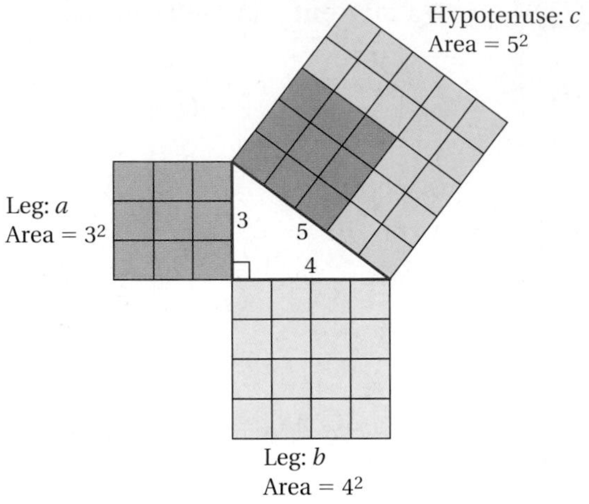

$$a^2 + b^2 = c^2$$
$$3^2 + 4^2 = 5^2$$
$$9 + 16 = 25$$

If we know the lengths of any two sides of a right triangle, we can use the Pythagorean equation to determine the length of the third side.

EXAMPLE 5 Ladder settings. A 13-ft ladder is placed against a building in such a way that the distance from the top of the ladder to the ground is 7 ft more than the distance from the bottom of the ladder to the building. Find both distances.

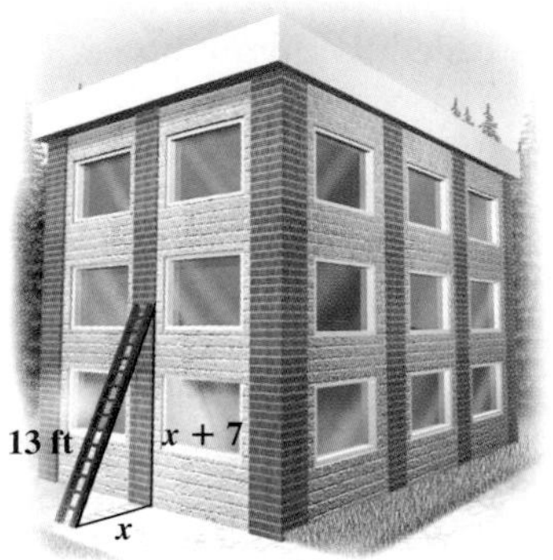

Solution

1. **Familiarize.** We first make a drawing. The ladder and the missing distances form the hypotenuse and legs of a right triangle. We let $x =$ the length of the side (leg) across the bottom. Then $x + 7 =$ the length of the other side (leg). The hypotenuse has length 13 ft.
2. **Translate.** Since a right triangle is formed, we can use the Pythagorean theorem:
$$a^2 + b^2 = c^2$$
$$x^2 + (x + 7)^2 = 13^2. \qquad \text{Substituting}$$
3. **Solve.** We solve the equation as follows:
$$x^2 + (x^2 + 14x + 49) = 169 \qquad \text{Squaring the binomial and 13}$$
$$2x^2 + 14x + 49 = 169 \qquad \text{Combining like terms}$$
$$2x^2 + 14x - 120 = 0 \qquad \text{Subtracting 169 to get 0 on one side}$$
$$2(x^2 + 7x - 60) = 0 \qquad \text{Factoring out a common factor}$$
$$2(x + 12)(x - 5) = 0 \qquad \text{Factoring}$$
$$x + 12 = 0 \quad or \quad x - 5 = 0 \qquad \text{Using the principle of zero products}$$
$$x = -12 \quad or \quad x = 5.$$
4. **Check.** The integer -12 cannot be a length of a side because it is negative. When $x = 5$, $x + 7 = 12$, and $5^2 + 12^2 = 13^2$. So 5 checks.
5. **State.** The distance from the top of the ladder to the ground is 12 ft. The distance from the bottom of the ladder to the building is 5 ft.

EXAMPLE 6 Roadway design. Elliott Street is 24 ft wide when it ends at Main Street in Brattleboro, Vermont. A 40-ft long diagonal crosswalk allows pedestrians to cross Main Street to or from either corner of Elliott Street (see the figure). Determine the width of Main Street.

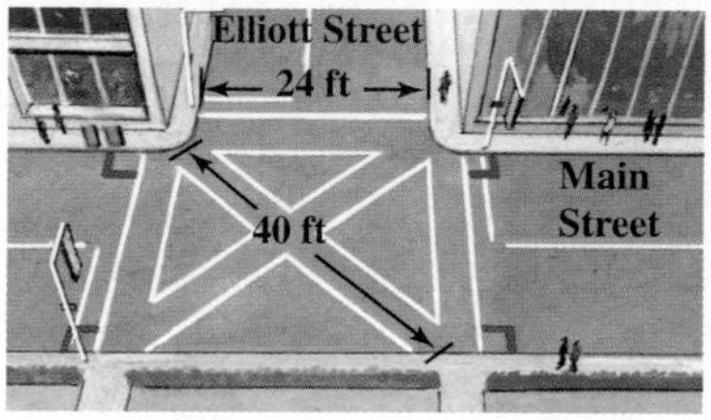

Solution

1. **Familiarize.** A drawing has already been provided, but we can redraw and label the relevant part. Note that the two streets intersect at a right angle. We let $x =$ the width of Main Street, in feet.

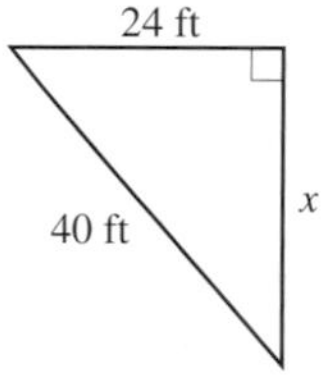

2. **Translate.** Since a right triangle is formed, we can use the Pythagorean theorem:

$$a^2 + b^2 = c^2$$

$$x^2 + 24^2 = 40^2. \quad \text{Substituting}$$

3. **Carry out.** We solve the equation as follows:

$x^2 + 576 = 1600$ Squaring 24 and 40

$x^2 - 1024 = 0$ Subtracting 1600 from both sides

$(x - 32)(x + 32) = 0$ Note that $1024 = 32^2$. A calculator might be helpful here.

$x - 32 = 0$ *or* $x + 32 = 0$ Using the principle of zero products

$x = 32$ *or* $x = -32$.

4. **Check.** Since the width of a street must be positive, -32 is not a solution. If the width is 32 ft, we have $32^2 + 24^2 = 1024 + 576 = 1600$, which is 40^2. Thus, 32 checks.

5. **State.** The width of Main Street is 32 ft.

5.7 Exercise Set

FOR EXTRA HELP

Student's Solutions Manual | Digital Video Tutor CD 3 Videotape 10 | AW Math Tutor Center | MathXL Tutorials on CD | MathXL | MyMathLab

Solve. Use the five-step problem-solving approach.

1. A number is 20 less than its square. Find all such numbers.

2. A number is 2 less than its square. Find all such numbers.

3. One leg of a right triangle is 3 cm longer than the other leg. The length of the hypotenuse is 15 cm. Find the length of each side.

4. One leg of a right triangle is 2 cm shorter than the other leg. The length of the hypotenuse is 10 cm. Find the length of each side.

5. *Locker numbers.* The product of two consecutive locker numbers is 90. Find the locker numbers.

6. *Page numbers.* The product of the page numbers on two facing pages of a book is 210. Find the page numbers.

7. The product of two consecutive odd integers is 255. Find the integers.

8. The product of two consecutive even integers is 224. Find the integers.

9. *Furnishings.* A rectangular table in Arlo's House of Tunes is six times as long as it is wide. If the area of the table is 24 ft^2, find the length and the width of the table.

10. *Framing.* A rectangular picture frame is twice as long as it is wide. If the area of the frame is 288 in^2, find its dimensions.

11. *Design.* The screen of the TI-84 Plus graphing calculator is nearly rectangular. The length of the rectangle is 2 cm more than the width. If the area of the rectangle is 24 cm^2, find the length and the width.

12. *Area of a garden.* The length of a rectangular garden is 4 m greater than the width. The area of the garden is 96 m^2. Find the length and the width.

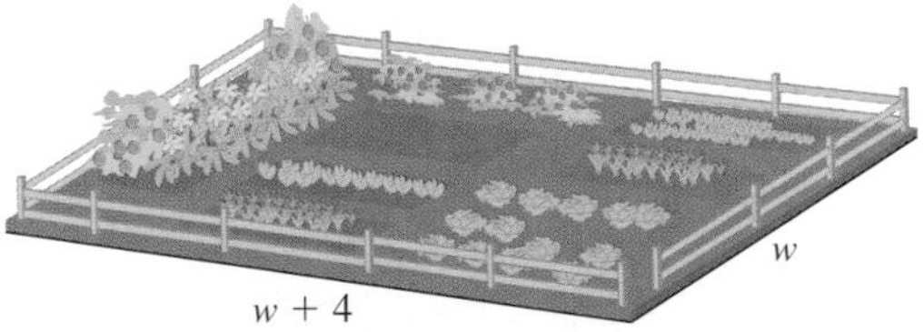

13. *Dimensions of a triangle.* A triangle is 10 cm wider than it is tall. The area is 28 cm^2. Find the height and the base.

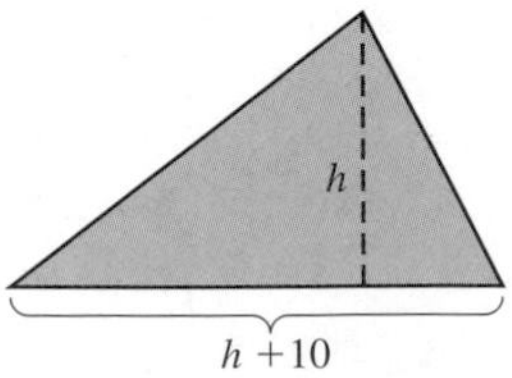

14. *Dimensions of a triangle.* The height of a triangle is 3 cm less than the length of the base. If the area of the triangle is 35 cm^2, find the height and the length of the base.

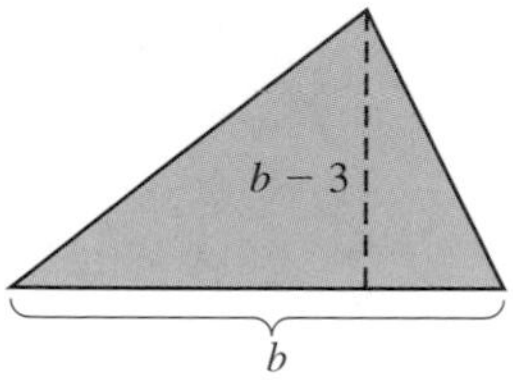

15. *Dimensions of a sail.* The height of the jib sail on a Lightning sailboat is 5 ft greater than the length of its "foot." If the area of the sail is 42 ft^2, find the length of the foot and the height of the sail.

16. *Road design.* A triangular traffic island has a base half as long as its height. Find the base and the height if the island has an area of 64 m^2.

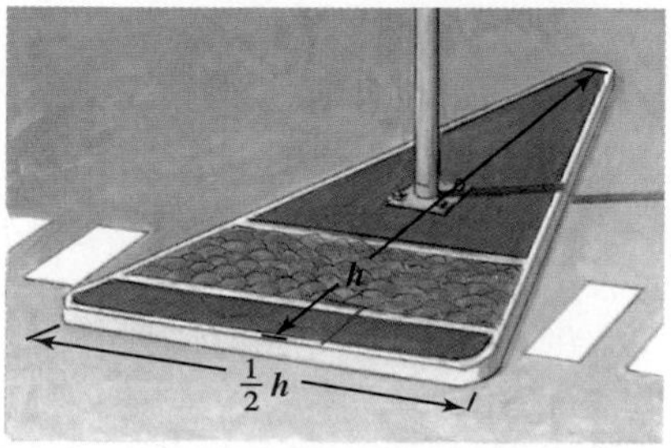

17. *Medicine.* For many people suffering from constricted bronchial muscles, the drug Albuterol is prescribed. The number of micrograms A of Albuterol in a person's bloodstream t minutes after 200 micrograms have been inhaled can be approximated by

$$A = -50t^2 + 200t.$$

How long after an inhalation will there be about 150 micrograms of Albuterol in the bloodstream?
Source: Based on information in Chohan, Naina, Rita M. Doyle, and Patricia Nayle (eds.), *Nursing Handbook*, 21st ed. Springhouse, PA: Springhouse Corporation, 2001

18. *Medicine.* For adults with certain heart conditions, the drug Primacor (milrinone lactate) is prescribed. The number of milligrams M of Primacor in the bloodstream of a 132-lb patient t hours after a 3-mg dose has been injected can be approximated by

$$M = -\frac{1}{2}t^2 + \frac{5}{2}t.$$

How long after an injection will there be about 2 mg in the bloodstream?
Source: Based on information in Chohan, Naina, Rita M. Doyle, and Patricia Nayle (eds.), *Nursing Handbook*, 21st ed. Springhouse, PA: Springhouse Corporation, 2001

Games in a league's schedule. *In a sports league of x teams in which all teams play each other twice, the total number N of games played is given by*

$$x^2 - x = N.$$

Use this formula for Exercises 19 and 20.

19. The Colchester Youth Soccer League plays a total of 240 games, with all teams playing each other twice. How many teams are in the league?

20. A women's softball league plays a total of 132 games. How many teams are in the league?

Number of handshakes. *The number of possible handshakes H within a group of n people is given by $H = \frac{1}{2}(n^2 - n)$. Use this formula for Exercises 21–24.*

21. At a meeting, there are 15 people. How many handshakes are possible?

22. At a party, there are 30 people. How many handshakes are possible?

23. *High-fives.* After winning the championship, all Los Angeles Lakers teammates exchanged "high-fives." Altogether there were 66 high-fives. How many players were there?

24. *Toasting.* During a toast at a party, there were 190 "clicks" of glasses. How many people took part in the toast?

25. *Construction.* The diagonal braces in a lookout tower are 15 ft long and span a distance of 12 ft. How high does each brace reach vertically?

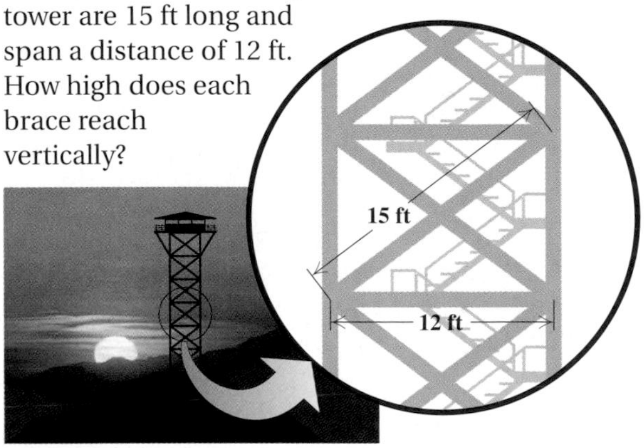

26. *Reach of a ladder.* Twyla has a 26-ft ladder leaning against her house. If the bottom of the ladder is 10 ft from the base of the house, how high does the ladder reach?

27. *Physical education.* An outdoor-education ropes course includes a cable that slopes downward from a height of 37 ft to a height of 30 ft. The trees that the cable connects are 24 ft apart. How long is the cable?

28. *Aviation.* Engine failure forced Geraldine to pilot her Cessna 150 to an emergency landing. To land, Geraldine's plane glided 17,000 ft over a 15,000-ft stretch of deserted highway. From what altitude did the descent begin?

29. *Architecture.* An architect has allocated a rectangular space of 264 ft^2 for a square dining room and a 10-ft wide kitchen, as shown in the figure. Find the dimensions of each room.

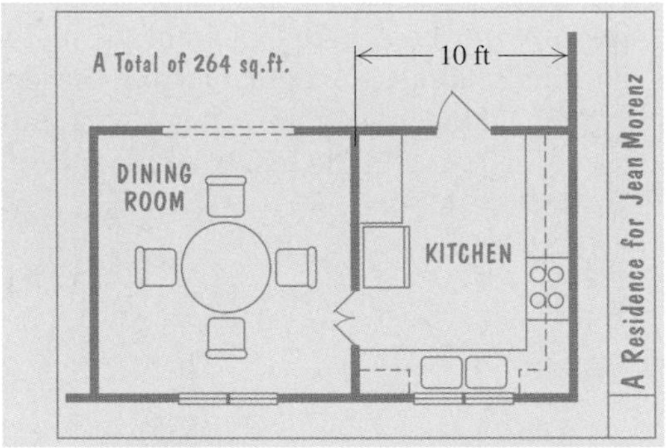

30. *Guy wire.* The guy wire on a TV antenna is 1 m longer than the height of the antenna. If the guy wire is anchored 3 m from the foot of the antenna, how tall is the antenna?

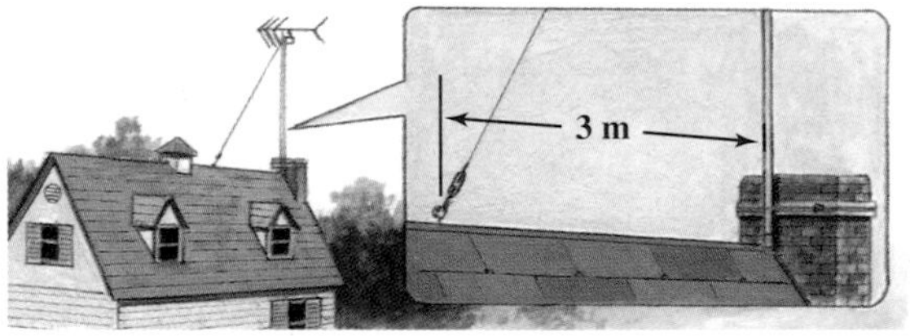

Height of a rocket. *For Exercises 31–34, assume that a water rocket is launched upward with an initial velocity of 48 ft/sec. Its height h, in feet, after t seconds, is given by $h = 48t - 16t^2$.*

31. Determine the height of the rocket $\frac{1}{2}$ sec after it has been launched.

32. Determine the height of the rocket 1.5 sec after it has been launched.

33. When will the rocket be exactly 32 ft above the ground?

34. When will the rocket crash into the ground?

35. Do we now have the ability to solve *any* problem that translates to a quadratic equation? Why or why not?

36. Write a problem for a classmate to solve such that only one of two solutions of a quadratic equation can be used as an answer.

SKILL MAINTENANCE

Simplify.

37. $-\frac{2}{3} \cdot \frac{4}{7}$ [1.7]

38. $-\frac{4}{5} \cdot \frac{2}{9}$ [1.7]

39. $\frac{5}{6}\left(\frac{-7}{9}\right)$ [1.7]

40. $\frac{3}{8}\left(-\frac{5}{6}\right)$ [1.7]

41. $-\frac{2}{3} + \frac{4}{7}$ [1.5]

42. $-\frac{4}{5} + \frac{2}{9}$ [1.5]

43. $\frac{5}{6} + \frac{-7}{9}$ [1.5]

44. $\frac{3}{8} + \left(-\frac{5}{6}\right)$ [1.5]

SYNTHESIS

The converse of the Pythagorean theorem is also true. That is, if $a^2 + b^2 = c^2$, then the triangle is a right triangle (where a and b are the lengths of the legs and c is the length of the hypotenuse). Use this result to answer Exercises 45 and 46.

45. An archaeologist has measuring sticks of 3 ft, 4 ft, and 5 ft. Explain how she could draw a 7-ft by 9-ft rectangle on a piece of land being excavated.

46. Explain how measuring sticks of 5 cm, 12 cm, and 13 cm can be used to draw a right triangle that has two 45° angles.

47. *Sailing.* The mainsail of a Lightning sailboat is a right triangle in which the hypotenuse is called the leech. If a 24-ft tall mainsail has a leech length of 26 ft and if Dacron® sailcloth costs $10 per square foot, find the cost of a new mainsail.

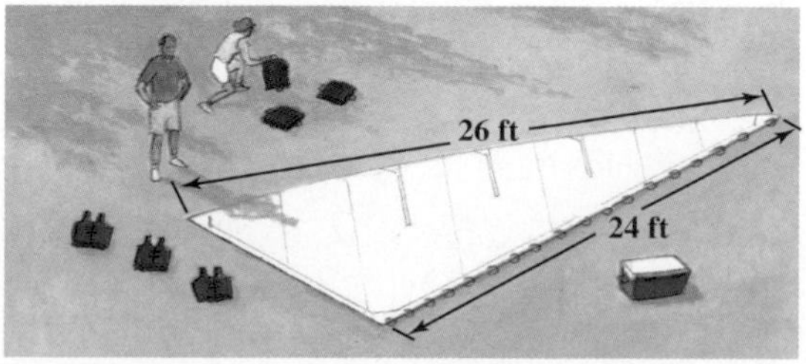

48. *Roofing.* A *square* of shingles covers 100 ft^2 of surface area. How many squares will be needed to reshingle the house shown?

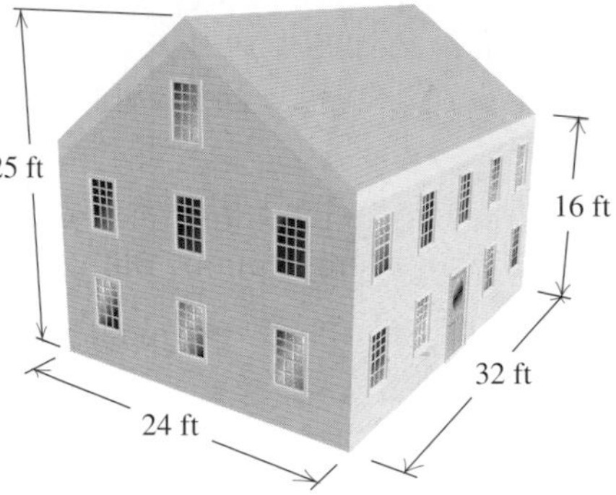

49. Solve for x.

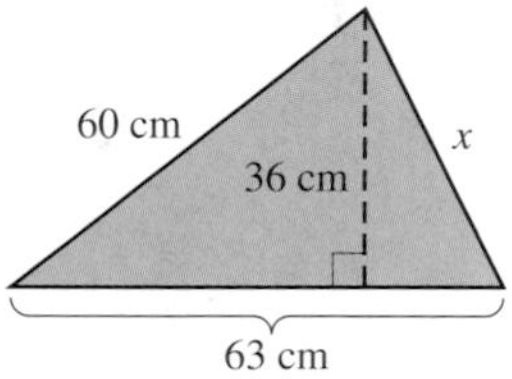

50. *Pool sidewalk.* A cement walk of uniform width is built around a 20-ft by 40-ft rectangular pool. The total area of the pool and the walk is 1500 ft^2. Find the width of the walk.

51. *Dimensions of an open box.* A rectangular piece of cardboard is twice as long as it is wide. A 4-cm square is cut out of each corner, and the sides are turned up to make a box with an open top. The volume of the box is 616 cm^3. Find the original dimensions of the cardboard.

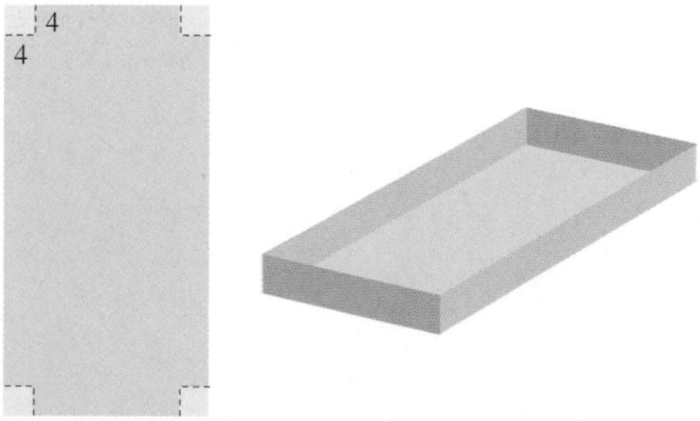

52. Find a polynomial for the shaded area in the figure below.

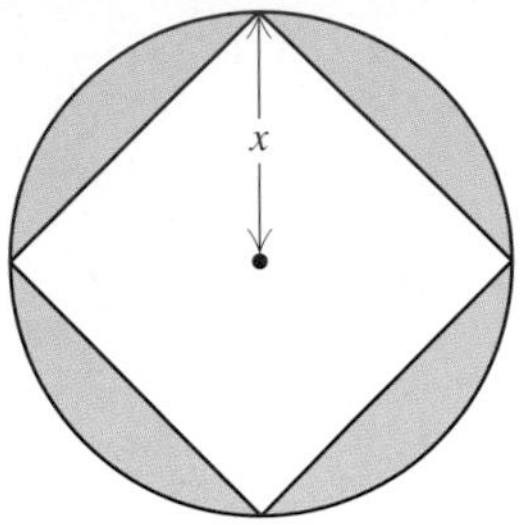

53. *Telephone service.* Use the information in the figure below to determine the height of the telephone pole.

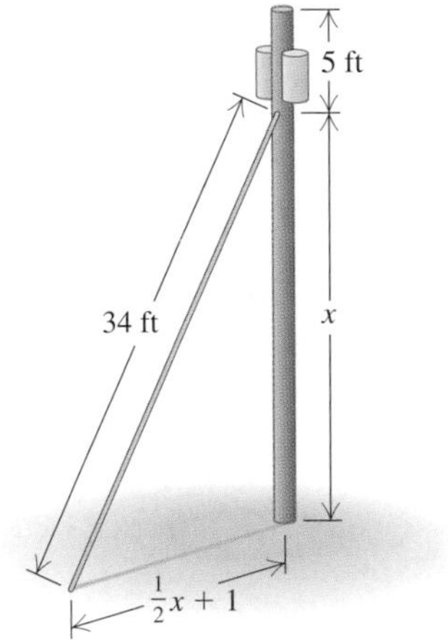

54. *Dimensions of a closed box.* The total surface area of a closed box is 350 m^2. The box is 9 m high and has a square base and lid. Find the length of a side of the base.

Medicine. For certain people with acid reflux, the drug Pepcid (famotidine) is used. The number of milligrams N of Pepcid in an adult's bloodstream t hours after a 20-mg tablet is swallowed can be approximated by

$$N = -0.009t(t - 12)^3.$$

Use a graphing calculator with the window $[-1, 13, -1, 25]$ *and the* TRACE *feature to answer Exercises 55–57.*

Source: Based on information in Chohan, Naina, Rita M. Doyle, and Patricia Nayle (eds.), *Nursing Handbook*, 21st ed. Springhouse, PA: Springhouse Corporation, 2001

55. Approximately how long after a tablet is swallowed will there be 18 mg in the bloodstream?

56. Approximately how long after a tablet is swallowed will there be 10 mg in the bloodstream?

57. Approximately how long after a tablet is swallowed will the peak dosage in the bloodstream occur?

5 Study Summary

Like whole numbers, many polynomials can be expressed as products. The process of writing a polynomial as a product is called **factoring** and the polynomials used in the product are called **factors** (p. 300). In some instances, all terms in the polynomial being factored share a **common factor** that can be factored out by using the distributive law (p. 301). Other times, the polynomial being factored may be a **perfect-square trinomial** or a **difference of squares** and can be factored using a recognized pattern (pp. 326–329). Often trinomials can be factored by either **trial and error**, using FOIL, or **grouping** (pp. 308, 317, and 322). A polynomial that cannot be factored is said to be **prime** (p. 312). In order for a polynomial to be **factored completely**, each factor in the factorization must be prime (p. 330).

$3x^2 + 12x = 3x(x + 4)$	⟵ $3x$ is the largest common factor.
$ad + ac + bc + bd = (a + b)(c + d)$	⟵ Factoring by grouping
$4t^2 + 20t + 25 = (2t + 5)^2$	⟵ Factoring a perfect-square trinomial
$9x^2 - 1 = (3x - 1)(3x + 1)$	⟵ Factoring a difference of squares
$4t^2 - 21t - 18 = (4t + 3)(t - 6)$	⟵ Using trial and error (FOIL) or grouping

(For a general strategy for factoring, see p. 334.)

Certain equations can be solved by factoring and using **the principle of zero products** (p. 340). Often **quadratic equations** can be solved in this manner (p. 340):

$$\begin{aligned} 3x^2 - 4x - 4 &= 0 \\ (3x + 2)(x - 2) &= 0 \\ 3x + 2 = 0 \quad &or \quad x - 2 = 0 \\ 3x = -2 \quad &or \quad x = 2 \\ x = -\tfrac{2}{3} \quad &or \quad x = 2. \end{aligned}$$

The solutions are $-\frac{2}{3}$ and 2.

Quadratic equations sometimes arise from use of the **Pythagorean theorem** (p. 351):

$$a^2 + b^2 = c^2.$$

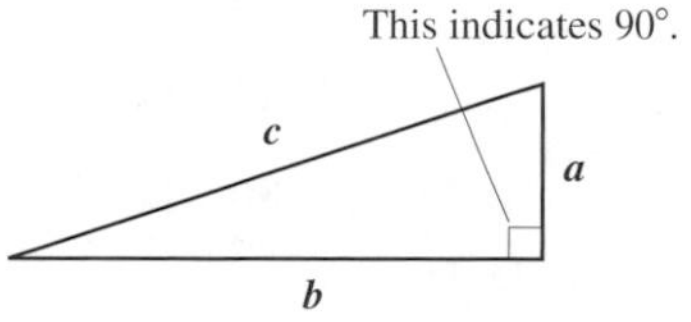

5 Review Exercises

Concept Reinforcement *Classify each statement as either true or false.*

1. Every polynomial has a common factor other than 1 or −1. [5.1]
2. A prime polynomial has no common factor other than 1 or −1. [5.2]
3. Every perfect-square trinomial can be expressed as a binomial squared. [5.4]
4. Every binomial can be regarded as a difference of squares. [5.4]
5. In a right triangle, the hypotenuse is always longer than either leg. [5.7]
6. Every quadratic equation has two different solutions. [5.6]
7. The principle of zero products can be applied whenever a product equals 0. [5.6]
8. The Pythagorean theorem can be applied to any triangle that has an angle measuring at least 90°. [5.7]

Find three factorizations of each monomial. [5.1]

9. $36x^3$
10. $-20x^5$

Factor completely. If a polynomial is prime, state this.

11. $12x^4 - 18x^3$ [5.1]
12. $8a^2 - 12a$ [5.1]
13. $4t^2 - 9$ [5.4]
14. $x^2 + 4x - 12$ [5.2]
15. $x^2 + 14x + 49$ [5.4]
16. $12x^3 + 12x^2 + 3x$ [5.4]
17. $6x^3 + 9x^2 + 2x + 3$ [5.1]
18. $6t^2 - 5t - 1$ [5.3]
19. $25t^2 + 9 - 30t$ [5.4]
20. $48t^2 - 28t + 6$ [5.1]
21. $81a^4 - 1$ [5.4]
22. $9x^3 + 12x^2 - 45x$ [5.3]
23. $2x^2 - 50$ [5.4]
24. $x^4 + 4x^3 - 2x - 8$ [5.1]
25. $a^2b^4 - 36$ [5.4]
26. $-8x^6 + 32x^5 - 4x^4$ [5.1]
27. $75 + 12x^2 - 60x$ [5.4]
28. $a^2 + 4$ [5.4]
29. $-x^3 + x^2 + 30x$ [5.2]
30. $4x^2 - 25$ [5.4]
31. $4z^2 - 6z$ [5.1]
32. $15z + 10z^2$ [5.1]
33. $4t^2 + 13t + 10$ [5.3]
34. $2t^2 - 7t - 4$ [5.3]
35. $7x^3 + 35x^2 + 28x$ [5.2]
36. $5x^3 + 35x^2 + 50x$ [5.2]
37. $18x^2 - 12x + 2$ [5.4]
38. $-3x^2 + 27$ [5.4]
39. $15 - 8x + x^2$ [5.2]
40. $25x^2 - 20x + 4$ [5.4]
41. $x^2y^2 + xy - 12$ [5.2]
42. $12a^2 + 84ab + 147b^2$ [5.4]
43. $m^2 + 5m + mt + 5t$ [5.1]
44. $32x^4 - 128y^4z^4$ [5.4]
45. $6m^2 + 2mn + n^2 + 3mn$ [5.1], [5.3]
46. $r^2 - 3rt - 15t^2$ [5.2]

Solve. [5.6]

47. $(x - 7)(x + 8) = 0$
48. $x^2 + 2x - 35 = 0$
49. $9x^2 = 1$
50. $3x^2 + 2 = 5x$
51. $2x^2 - 5x = 12$
52. $(x + 1)(x - 2) = 4$
53. $6t - 8t^2 = 0$
54. $12t^2 - 16t = 0$
55. The square of a number is 12 more than the number. Find all such numbers. [5.7]

56. The formula $x^2 - x = N$ can be used to determine the total number of games played, N, in a league of x teams in which all teams play each other twice. Serena referees for a soccer league in which all teams play each other twice and a total of 90 games is played. How many teams are in the league? [5.7]

57. Find the x-intercepts for the graph of $y = 2x^2 - 3x - 5$. [5.6]

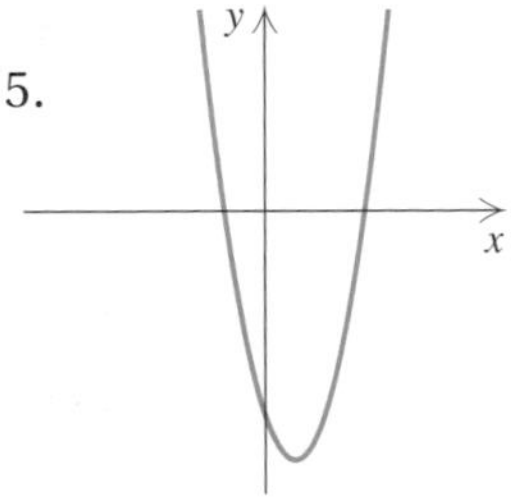

58. A triangular sign is as wide as it is tall. Its area is 800 cm^2. Find the height and the base. [5.7]

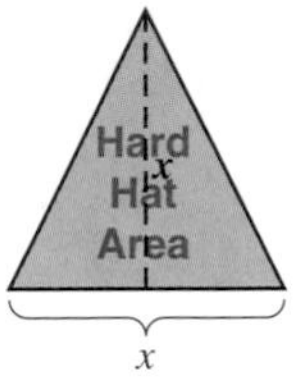

59. Nigel has a 26-ft ladder leaning against his house. If the bottom of the ladder is 10 ft from the base of the house, how high does the ladder reach? [5.7]

SYNTHESIS

60. On a quiz, Edith writes the factorization of $4x^2 - 100$ as $(2x - 10)(2x + 10)$. If this were a 10-point question, how many points would you give Edith? Why? [5.4]

61. How do the equations solved in this chapter differ from those solved in previous chapters? [5.6]

Solve.

62. The pages of a book measure 15 cm by 20 cm. Margins of equal width surround the printing on each page and constitute one half of the area of the page. Find the width of the margins. [5.7]

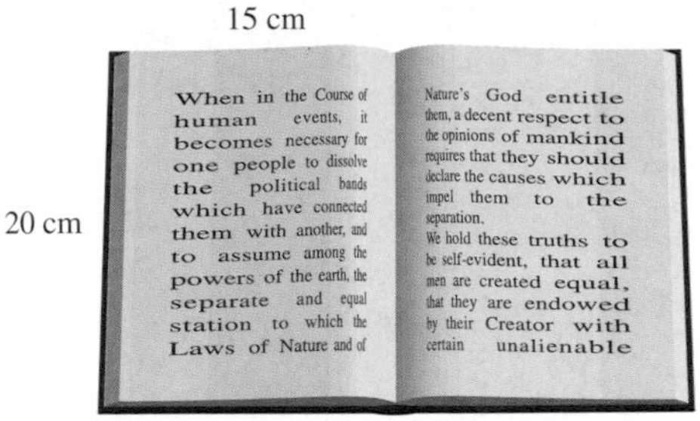

63. The cube of a number is the same as twice the square of the number. Find the number. [5.7]

64. The length of a rectangle is two times its width. When the length is increased by 20 cm and the width is decreased by 1 cm, the area is 160 cm^2. Find the original length and width. [5.7]

65. The length of each side of a square is increased by 5 cm to form a new square. The area of the new square is $2\frac{1}{4}$ times the area of the original square. Find the area of each square. [5.7]

Solve. [5.6]

66. $(x - 2)2x^2 + x(x - 2) - (x - 2)15 = 0$

Aha! **67.** $x^2 + 25 = 0$

5 Chapter Test

1. Find three factorizations of $8x^4$.

Factor completely.

2. $x^2 - 7x + 10$

3. $x^2 + 25 - 10x$

4. $6y^2 - 8y^3 + 4y^4$

5. $x^3 + x^2 + 2x + 2$

6. $t^7 - 3t^5$

7. $x^3 + 2x^2 - 3x$

8. $28x - 48 + 10x^2$

9. $4t^2 - 25$

10. $x^2 - x - 12$

11. $-6m^3 - 9m^2 - 3m$

12. $3w^2 - 75$

13. $45r^2 + 60r + 20$

14. $3x^4 - 48$

15. $49t^2 + 36 + 84t$

16. $5x^2 - 26x + 5$

17. $x^4 + 2x^3 - 3x - 6$

18. $80 - 5x^4$

19. $4x^2 - 4x - 15$

20. $6t^3 + 9t^2 - 15t$

21. $3m^2 - 9mn - 30n^2$

Solve.

22. $x^2 + x - 20 = 0$

23. $2x^2 - 7x = 15$

24. $x(x - 3) = 28$

25. Find the x-intercepts for the graph of $y = 3x^2 - 5x - 8$.

26. The length of a rectangle is 2 m more than the width. The area of the rectangle is 48 m^2. Find the length and the width.

27. A mason wants to be sure she has a right corner in a building's foundation. She marks a point 3 ft from the corner along one wall and another point 4 ft from the corner along the other wall. If the corner is a right angle, what should the distance be between the two marked points?

SYNTHESIS

28. An open rectangular gutter is made by turning up the sides of a piece of metal 20 in. wide. The area of the cross-section of the gutter is 48 in^2. Find the possible depths of the gutter.

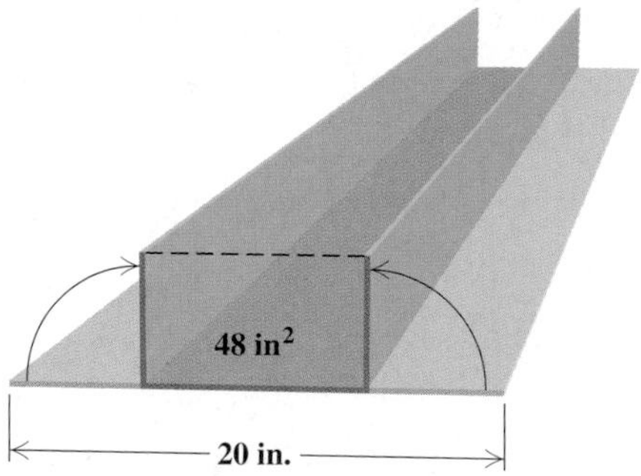

29. The length of a rectangle is five times its width. When the length is decreased by 3 and the width is increased by 2, the area of the new rectangle is 60. Find the original length and width.

30. Factor: $(a + 3)^2 - 2(a + 3) - 35$.

31. Solve: $20x(x + 2)(x - 1) = 5x^3 - 24x - 14x^2$.

6 Rational Expressions and Equations

AN APPLICATION

In South Africa, the design of every woven handbag, or *gipatsi*, is created by repeating two or more patterns around the bag. If a weaver uses a four-strand, a six-strand, and an eight-strand pattern, what is the smallest number of strands needed in order for all three patterns to repeat a whole number of times?

This problem appears as Exercise 80 in Section 6.3.

Estelle Carlson
HANDWEAVER AND DESIGNER
Los Angeles, California

Weavers use math when designing patterns, from calculating the size of the pattern and number of times it repeats to figuring the number of threads per inch and the weight of the thread. I also use math to convert between English and metric units when dyeing warps and woofs.

Just as fractions are needed to solve certain arithmetic problems, rational expressions *similar to those in the following pages are needed to solve certain algebra problems. We now learn how to simplify, add, subtract, multiply, and divide rational expressions. These skills will then be used to solve the equations that arise from real-life problems like the one on the preceding page.*

6.1 Rational Expressions

Simplifying Rational Expressions • Factors That Are Opposites

Just as a rational number is any number that can be written as a quotient of two integers, a **rational expression** is any expression that can be written as a quotient of two polynomials. The following are examples of rational expressions:

$$\frac{7}{3}, \quad \frac{5}{x+6}, \quad \frac{t^2-5t+6}{4t^2-7}, \quad 2x+7+\frac{1}{x}.$$

Rational expressions are examples of *algebraic fractions*. They are also examples of *fractional expressions*.

Because rational expressions indicate division, we must be careful to avoid denominators that are 0. When a variable is replaced with a number that produces a denominator of 0, the rational expression is undefined. For example, in the expression

$$\frac{x+3}{x-7},$$

when x is replaced with 7, the denominator is 0, and the expression is undefined:

$$\frac{x+3}{x-7} = \frac{7+3}{7-7} = \frac{10}{0}. \leftarrow$$ As explained in Chapter 1, division by 0 is undefined.

When x is replaced with a number other than 7—say, 6—the expression *is* defined because the denominator is not zero:

$$\frac{x+3}{x-7} = \frac{6+3}{6-7} = \frac{9}{-1} = -9.$$

Study Skills

Try an Exercise Break

Often the best way to regain your energy or focus is to take a break from your studies in order to exercise. Jogging, biking, or walking briskly are just a few of the activities that can improve your concentration.

EXAMPLE 1 Find all numbers for which the rational expression

$$\frac{x+4}{x^2-3x-10}$$

is undefined.

Solution The value of the numerator has no bearing on whether or not a rational expression is defined. To determine which numbers make the rational expression undefined, we set the *denominator* equal to 0 and solve:

$x^2 - 3x - 10 = 0$	We must originate this equation.
$(x - 5)(x + 2) = 0$	Factoring
$x - 5 = 0 \quad or \quad x + 2 = 0$	Using the principle of zero products
$x = 5 \quad or \quad x = -2.$	Solving each equation

Check:

For $x = 5$:

$$\frac{x + 4}{x^2 - 3x - 10} = \frac{5 + 4}{5^2 - 3 \cdot 5 - 10}$$ There are no restrictions on the numerator.

$$= \frac{9}{25 - 15 - 10} = \frac{9}{0}.$$ This expression is undefined, as expected.

For $x = -2$:

$$\frac{x + 4}{x^2 - 3x - 10} = \frac{-2 + 4}{(-2)^2 - 3(-2) - 10}$$

$$= \frac{2}{4 + 6 - 10} = \frac{2}{0}.$$ This expression is undefined, as expected.

Thus, $\dfrac{x + 4}{x^2 - 3x - 10}$ is undefined for $x = 5$ and $x = -2$.

technology connection

To check Example 1 with a graphing calculator, let $y_1 = x^2 - 3x - 10$ and $y_2 = (x + 4)/(x^2 - 3x - 10)$ or $(x + 4)/y_1$ and use the TABLE feature. Since $x^2 - 3x - 10$ is 0 for $x = 5$, it is impossible to evaluate y_2 for $x = 5$.

TBL MIN = 0 ΔTBL = 1

X	Y1	Y2
0	−10	−.4
1	−12	−.4167
2	−12	−.5
3	−10	−.7
4	−6	−1.333
5	0	ERROR
6	8	1.25

X = 5

Simplifying Rational Expressions

A rational expression is said to be *simplified* when the numerator and the denominator have no factors (other than 1) in common. To simplify a rational expression, we first factor the numerator and the denominator. We then identify factors common to the numerator and the denominator, rewrite the expression as a product of two rational expressions (one of which is equal to 1), and then remove the factor equal to 1. The process is identical to that used in Section 1.3 to simplify $\frac{15}{40}$:

$\frac{15}{40} = \frac{3 \cdot 5}{8 \cdot 5}$	Factoring the numerator and the denominator. Note the common factor, 5.
$= \frac{3}{8} \cdot \frac{5}{5}$	Rewriting as a product of two fractions
$= \frac{3}{8} \cdot 1$	$\frac{5}{5} = 1$
$= \frac{3}{8}.$	Using the identity property of 1 to remove the factor 1

Similar steps are followed when simplifying rational expressions: We factor and remove a factor equal to 1, using the fact that

$$\frac{ab}{cb} = \frac{a}{c} \cdot \frac{b}{b}.$$

EXAMPLE 2 Simplify: $\frac{8x^2}{24x}$.

Solution

$$\frac{8x^2}{24x} = \frac{8 \cdot x \cdot x}{3 \cdot 8 \cdot x}$$ Factoring the numerator and the denominator. Note the common factor of $8 \cdot x$.

$$= \frac{x}{3} \cdot \frac{8x}{8x}$$ Rewriting as a product of two rational expressions

$$= \frac{x}{3} \cdot 1$$ $\frac{8x}{8x} = 1$

$$= \frac{x}{3}$$ Removing the factor 1

We say that $\frac{8x^2}{24x}$ *simplifies* to $\frac{x}{3}$.* In the work that follows, we assume that all denominators are nonzero.

EXAMPLE 3 Simplify: $\frac{5a + 15}{10}$.

Solution

$$\frac{5a + 15}{10} = \frac{5(a + 3)}{5 \cdot 2}$$ Factoring the numerator and the denominator. Note the common factor of 5.

$$= \frac{5}{5} \cdot \frac{a + 3}{2}$$ Rewriting as a product of two rational expressions

$$= 1 \cdot \frac{a + 3}{2}$$ $\frac{5}{5} = 1$

$$= \frac{a + 3}{2}$$ Removing the factor 1

Sometimes the common factor has two or more terms.

EXAMPLE 4 Simplify.

a) $\frac{6x + 12}{7x + 14}$ **b)** $\frac{6a^2 + 4a}{2a^2 + 2a}$ **c)** $\frac{x^2 + 3x + 2}{x^2 - 1}$

Solution

a) $$\frac{6x + 12}{7x + 14} = \frac{6(x + 2)}{7(x + 2)}$$ Factoring the numerator and the denominator. Note the common factor of $x + 2$.

$$= \frac{6}{7} \cdot \frac{x + 2}{x + 2}$$ Rewriting as a product of two rational expressions

*In more advanced courses, we would *not* say that $8x^2/(24x)$ simplifies to $x/3$, but would instead say that $8x^2/(24x)$ simplifies to $x/3$ *with the restriction that* $x \neq 0$.

$$= \frac{6}{7} \cdot 1 \qquad \frac{x+2}{x+2} = 1$$

$$= \frac{6}{7} \qquad \text{Removing the factor 1}$$

b) $\dfrac{6a^2 + 4a}{2a^2 + 2a} = \dfrac{2a(3a+2)}{2a(a+1)}$ Factoring the numerator and the denominator. Note the common factor of $2a$.

$= \dfrac{2a}{2a} \cdot \dfrac{3a+2}{a+1}$ Rewriting as a product of two rational expressions

$= 1 \cdot \dfrac{3a+2}{a+1}$ $\quad \dfrac{2a}{2a} = 1$

$= \dfrac{3a+2}{a+1}$ Removing the factor 1. No common factors of the numerator and the denominator exist, so simplification is complete.

c) $\dfrac{x^2 + 3x + 2}{x^2 - 1} = \dfrac{(x+1)(x+2)}{(x+1)(x-1)}$ Factoring; $x + 1$ is the common factor.

$= \dfrac{x+1}{x+1} \cdot \dfrac{x+2}{x-1}$ Rewriting as a product of two rational expressions

$= 1 \cdot \dfrac{x+2}{x-1}$ $\quad \dfrac{x+1}{x+1} = 1$

$= \dfrac{x+2}{x-1}$ Removing the factor 1

Canceling is a shortcut that can be used—and easily *misused*—to simplify rational expressions. As stated in Section 1.3, canceling must be done with care and understanding. Essentially, canceling streamlines the process of removing a factor equal to 1. Example 4(c) could have been streamlined as follows:

$\dfrac{x^2 + 3x + 2}{x^2 - 1} = \dfrac{\cancel{(x+1)}(x+2)}{\cancel{(x+1)}(x-1)}$ When a factor equal to 1 is noted, it is "canceled": $\dfrac{x+1}{x+1} = 1$

$= \dfrac{x+2}{x-1}.$ Simplifying

> ***Caution!*** Canceling is often used incorrectly. The following cancellations are *incorrect*:
>
> $$\cancel{\frac{\cancel{x}+2}{\cancel{x}+3}}; \quad \cancel{\frac{a^2 - \cancel{5}}{\cancel{5}}}; \quad \cancel{\frac{6\cancel{x}^2 + 5\cancel{x} + 1}{4\cancel{x}^2 - 3\cancel{x}}}.$$
>
> Wrong! Wrong! Wrong!
>
> None of the above cancellations removes a factor equal to 1. Factors are parts of products. For example, in $x \cdot 2$, x and 2 are factors, but in $x + 2$, x and 2 are terms, *not* factors. If it is not a factor, it cannot be canceled.

technology connection

We can use the TABLE feature as a partial check that rational expressions have been simplified correctly. To check the simplification in Example 4(c),

$$\frac{x^2 + 3x + 2}{x^2 - 1} = \frac{x+2}{x-1},$$

we enter $y_1 = (x^2 + 3x + 2)/(x^2 - 1)$ and $y_2 = (x + 2)/(x - 1)$ and select the mode AUTO to look at a table of values of y_1 and y_2. The values should match for all allowable replacements.

X	Y1	Y2
−4	.4	.4
−3	.25	.25
−2	0	0
−1	ERROR	−.5
0	−2	−2
1	ERROR	ERROR
2	4	4

X = −4

The ERROR messages indicate that −1 and 1 are not allowable replacements in y_1 and 1 is not an allowable replacement in y_2. For all other numbers, y_1 and y_2 are the same, so the simplification appears to be correct.

Use the TABLE feature to determine which of the following appear to be correct.

1. $\dfrac{8x^2}{24x} = \dfrac{x}{3}$
2. $\dfrac{5x + 15}{10} = \dfrac{x+3}{2}$
3. $\dfrac{x+3}{x} = 3$
4. $\dfrac{x^2 + 3x - 4}{x^2 - 16} = \dfrac{x-1}{x+4}$

EXAMPLE 5 Simplify: $\dfrac{3x^2 - 2x - 1}{x^2 - 3x + 2}$.

Solution We factor the numerator and the denominator and look for common factors:

$$\frac{3x^2 - 2x - 1}{x^2 - 3x + 2} = \frac{(3x + 1)\cancel{(x - 1)}}{(x - 2)\cancel{(x - 1)}}$$

Try to visualize this as $\dfrac{3x + 1}{x - 2} \cdot \dfrac{x - 1}{x - 1}$.

$$= \frac{3x + 1}{x - 2}.$$

Removing a factor equal to 1: $\dfrac{x - 1}{x - 1} = 1$

When a rational expression is simplified, the result is an equivalent expression. Example 3 says that

$$\frac{5a + 15}{10} \text{ is equivalent to } \frac{a + 3}{2}.$$

This result can be partially checked using a replacement for a. For instance, if $a = 2$, then

$$\frac{5a + 15}{10} = \frac{5 \cdot 2 + 15}{10} = \frac{25}{10} = \frac{5}{2}$$

and

$$\frac{a + 3}{2} = \frac{2 + 3}{2} = \frac{5}{2}.$$

To see why this check is not foolproof, see Exercise 65.

If evaluating both expressions yields differing results, we know that a mistake has been made. For example, if $(5a + 15)/10$ is incorrectly simplified as $(a + 15)/2$ and we evaluate using $a = 2$, we have

$$\frac{5a + 15}{10} = \frac{5 \cdot 2 + 15}{10} = \frac{5}{2}$$

and

$$\frac{a + 15}{2} = \frac{2 + 15}{2} = \frac{17}{2},$$

Different results

which demonstrates that a mistake has been made.

Factors That Are Opposites

Consider

$$\frac{x - 4}{8 - 2x}, \quad \text{or, equivalently,} \quad \frac{x - 4}{2(4 - x)}.$$

At first glance, the numerator and the denominator do not appear to have any common factors. But $x - 4$ and $4 - x$ are opposites, or additive inverses, of each other. Thus we can find a common factor by factoring out -1 in one expression.

EXAMPLE 6 Simplify $\dfrac{x-4}{8-2x}$ and check by evaluating.

Solution We have

$$\frac{x-4}{8-2x} = \frac{x-4}{2(4-x)} \qquad \text{Factoring}$$

$$= \frac{x-4}{2(-1)(x-4)} \qquad \text{Note that } 4-x = -x+4 = -1(x-4).$$

$$= \frac{x-4}{-2(x-4)} \qquad \text{Had we originally factored out } -2 \text{, we could have gone directly to this step.}$$

$$= \frac{1}{-2}\cdot\frac{x-4}{x-4} \qquad \text{Rewriting as a product. It is important to write the 1 in the numerator.}$$

$$= -\frac{1}{2}. \qquad \text{Removing a factor equal to 1: } (x-4)/(x-4) = 1$$

As a partial check, note that for any choice of x other than 4, the value of the rational expression is $-\frac{1}{2}$. For example, if $x = 6$, then

$$\frac{x-4}{8-2x} = \frac{6-4}{8-2\cdot 6}$$

$$= \frac{2}{-4} = -\frac{1}{2}.$$

6.1 Exercise Set

FOR EXTRA HELP

Student's Solutions Manual | Digital Video Tutor CD 4 Videotape 11 | AW Math Tutor Center | MathXL Tutorials on CD | MathXL | MyMathLab

Concept Reinforcement In each of Exercises 1–6, match the rational expression with the list of numbers in the column on the right for which the rational expression is undefined.

1. ____ $\dfrac{x-5}{(x-2)(x+3)}$

2. ____ $\dfrac{3t}{(t+1)(t-4)}$

3. ____ $\dfrac{a+7}{a^2-a-12}$

4. ____ $\dfrac{m-3}{m^2-2m-15}$

5. ____ $\dfrac{2t+7}{(2t-1)(3t+4)}$

6. ____ $\dfrac{4x-1}{(3x-1)(3x-2)}$

a) $-1, 4$ **b)** $-3, 5$ **c)** $-\dfrac{4}{3}, \dfrac{1}{2}$

d) $-3, 4$ **e)** $-3, 2$ **f)** $\dfrac{1}{3}, \dfrac{2}{3}$

List all numbers for which each rational expression is undefined.

7. $\frac{12}{-7x}$

8. $\frac{14}{-5y}$

9. $\frac{t-6}{t+8}$

10. $\frac{a-8}{a+7}$

11. $\frac{a-4}{3a-12}$

12. $\frac{x^2-9}{4x-12}$

13. $\frac{x^2-25}{x^2-3x-28}$

14. $\frac{p^2-9}{p^2-7p+10}$

15. $\frac{t^2-4}{2t^2+11t-6}$

16. $\frac{x^2-9}{3x^2-x-14}$

Simplify by removing a factor equal to 1. Show all steps.

17. $\frac{50a^2b}{40ab^3}$

18. $\frac{45x^3y^2}{9x^5y}$

19. $\frac{28x^2y}{21x^3y^5}$

20. $\frac{12a^5b^6}{18a^3b}$

21. $\frac{9x+15}{12x+20}$

22. $\frac{14x-7}{10x-5}$

23. $\frac{a^2-9}{a^2+4a+3}$

24. $\frac{a^2+5a+6}{a^2-9}$

Simplify, if possible. Then check by evaluating, as in Example 6.

25. $\frac{36x^6}{24x^9}$

26. $\frac{75a^5}{50a^3}$

27. $\frac{-2y+6}{-8y}$

28. $\frac{4x-12}{6x}$

29. $\frac{6a^2-3a}{7a^2-7a}$

30. $\frac{3m^2+3m}{6m^2+9m}$

31. $\frac{t^2-16}{t^2+t-20}$

32. $\frac{a^2-4}{a^2+5a+6}$

33. $\frac{3a^2+9a-12}{6a^2-30a+24}$

34. $\frac{2t^2-6t+4}{4t^2+12t-16}$

35. $\frac{x^2+8x+16}{x^2-16}$

36. $\frac{x^2-25}{x^2-10x+25}$

37. $\frac{t^2-1}{t+1}$

38. $\frac{a^2-1}{a-1}$

39. $\frac{y^2+4}{y+2}$

40. $\frac{x^2+1}{x+1}$

41. $\frac{5x^2+20}{10x^2+40}$

42. $\frac{6x^2+54}{4x^2+36}$

43. $\frac{y^2+6y}{2y^2+13y+6}$

44. $\frac{t^2+2t}{2t^2+t-6}$

45. $\frac{4x^2-12x+9}{10x^2-11x-6}$

46. $\frac{4x^2-4x+1}{6x^2+5x-4}$

47. $\frac{x-9}{9-x}$

48. $\frac{6-x}{x-6}$

49. $\frac{7t-14}{2-t}$

50. $\frac{4a-12}{3-a}$

51. $\frac{a-b}{3b-3a}$

52. $\frac{q-p}{2p-2q}$

53. $\frac{3x^2-3y^2}{2y^2-2x^2}$

54. $\frac{7a^2-7b^2}{3b^2-3a^2}$

Aha! **55.** $\frac{7s^2-28t^2}{28t^2-7s^2}$

56. $\frac{9m^2-4n^2}{4n^2-9m^2}$

57. Explain how simplifying is related to the identity property of 1.

58. If a rational expression is undefined for $x = 5$ and $x = -3$, what is the degree of the denominator? Why?

SKILL MAINTENANCE

Simplify.

59. $-\frac{2}{3} \cdot \frac{6}{7}$ [1.7]

60. $\frac{5}{9}\left(\frac{-6}{11}\right)$ [1.7]

61. $\frac{5}{8} \div \left(-\frac{1}{6}\right)$ [1.7]

62. $\frac{7}{10} \div \left(-\frac{8}{15}\right)$ [1.7]

63. $\frac{7}{9} - \frac{2}{3} \cdot \frac{6}{7}$ [1.8]

64. $\frac{2}{3} - \left(\frac{3}{4}\right)^2$ [1.8]

SYNTHESIS

65. Terry *incorrectly* simplifies

$$\frac{x^2+x-2}{x^2+3x+2} \quad \text{as} \quad \frac{x-1}{x+2}.$$

He then checks his simplification by evaluating both expressions for $x = 1$. Use this situation to explain why evaluating is not a foolproof check.

66. How could you convince someone that $a - b$ and $b - a$ are opposites of each other?

Simplify.

67. $\dfrac{16y^4 - x^4}{(x^2 + 4y^2)(x - 2y)}$

68. $\dfrac{(x - 1)(x^4 - 1)(x^2 - 1)}{(x^2 + 1)(x - 1)^2(x^4 - 2x^2 + 1)}$

69. $\dfrac{x^5 - 2x^3 + 4x^2 - 8}{x^7 + 2x^4 - 4x^3 - 8}$

70. $\dfrac{10t^4 - 8t^3 + 15t - 12}{8 - 10t + 12t^2 - 15t^3}$

71. $\dfrac{(t^4 - 1)(t^2 - 9)(t - 9)^2}{(t^4 - 81)(t^2 + 1)(t + 1)^2}$

72. $\dfrac{(t + 2)^3(t^2 + 2t + 1)(t + 1)}{(t + 1)^3(t^2 + 4t + 4)(t + 2)}$

73. $\dfrac{(x^2 - y^2)(x^2 - 2xy + y^2)}{(x + y)^2(x^2 - 4xy - 5y^2)}$

74. $\dfrac{x^4 - y^4}{(y - x)^4}$

75. Select any number x, multiply by 2, add 5, multiply by 5, subtract 25, and divide by 10. What do you get? Explain how this procedure can be used for a number trick.

6.2 Multiplication and Division

Multiplication • Division

Multiplication and division of rational expressions are similar to multiplication and division with fractions. In this section, we again assume that all denominators are nonzero.

Multiplication

Recall that to multiply fractions, we multiply numerator times numerator and denominator times denominator. Rational expressions are multiplied in a similar way.

Study Skills

Strike While the Iron's Hot

Make an effort to do your homework as soon as possible after each class. Make this part of your routine, choosing a time and a place where you can focus with a minimum of interruptions.

The Product of Two Rational Expressions

To multiply rational expressions, multiply numerators and multiply denominators:

$$\frac{A}{B} \cdot \frac{C}{D} = \frac{AC}{BD}.$$

Then factor and simplify the result if possible.

For example,

$$\frac{3}{5} \cdot \frac{8}{11} = \frac{24}{55} \quad \text{and} \quad \frac{x}{3} \cdot \frac{x + 2}{y} = \frac{x(x + 2)}{3y}.$$

Fraction bars are grouping symbols, so parentheses are needed when writing some products. Because we generally simplify, we often leave the product in factored form. There is no need to multiply further.

EXAMPLE 1 Multiply and, if possible, simplify.

a) $\dfrac{5a^3}{4} \cdot \dfrac{2}{5a}$ **b)** $\dfrac{x^2 + 6x + 9}{x^2 - 4} \cdot \dfrac{x - 2}{x + 3}$ **c)** $\dfrac{x^2 + x - 2}{15} \cdot \dfrac{5}{2x^2 - 3x + 1}$

Solution

a) $\dfrac{5a^3}{4} \cdot \dfrac{2}{5a} = \dfrac{5a^3(2)}{4(5a)}$ Forming the product of the numerators and the product of the denominators

$= \dfrac{5 \cdot a \cdot a \cdot a \cdot 2}{2 \cdot 2 \cdot 5 \cdot a}$ Factoring the numerator and the denominator

$= \dfrac{\not{5} \cdot a \cdot \not{a} \cdot a \cdot \not{2}}{\not{2} \cdot 2 \cdot \not{5} \cdot \not{a}}$

$= \dfrac{a^2}{2}$

Removing a factor equal to 1: $\dfrac{2 \cdot 5 \cdot a}{2 \cdot 5 \cdot a} = 1$

b) $\dfrac{x^2 + 6x + 9}{x^2 - 4} \cdot \dfrac{x - 2}{x + 3} = \dfrac{(x^2 + 6x + 9)(x - 2)}{(x^2 - 4)(x + 3)}$ Multiplying the numerators and the denominators

$= \dfrac{(x + 3)(x + 3)(x - 2)}{(x + 2)(x - 2)(x + 3)}$ Factoring the numerator and the denominator

$= \dfrac{\cancel{(x + 3)}(x + 3)\cancel{(x - 2)}}{(x + 2)\cancel{(x - 2)}\cancel{(x + 3)}}$

$= \dfrac{x + 3}{x + 2}$

Removing a factor equal to 1: $\dfrac{(x + 3)(x - 2)}{(x + 3)(x - 2)} = 1$

c) $\dfrac{x^2 + x - 2}{15} \cdot \dfrac{5}{2x^2 - 3x + 1} = \dfrac{(x^2 + x - 2)5}{15(2x^2 - 3x + 1)}$ Multiplying the numerators and the denominators

$= \dfrac{(x + 2)(x - 1)5}{5(3)(x - 1)(2x - 1)}$ Factoring the numerator and the denominator. Try to go directly to this step.

$= \dfrac{(x + 2)\cancel{(x - 1)}\not{5}}{\not{5}(3)\cancel{(x - 1)}(2x - 1)}$

$= \dfrac{x + 2}{3(2x - 1)}$

Removing a factor equal to 1: $\dfrac{5(x - 1)}{5(x - 1)} = 1$

Student Notes

Neatness is important for work with rational expressions. Consider using the lines on your notebook paper to indicate where the fraction bars should be drawn in each example.

Because our results are often used in addition or subtraction problems that require factored form, there is no need to multiply out the numerator or the denominator.

Division

As with fractions, reciprocals of rational expressions are found by interchanging the numerator and the denominator. For example,

the reciprocal of $\dfrac{2}{7}$ is $\dfrac{7}{2}$, and the reciprocal of $\dfrac{3x}{x + 5}$ is $\dfrac{x + 5}{3x}$.

The Quotient of Two Rational Expressions

To divide by a rational expression, multiply by its reciprocal:

$$\frac{A}{B} \div \frac{C}{D} = \frac{A}{B} \cdot \frac{D}{C} = \frac{AD}{BC}.$$

Then factor and, if possible, simplify.

EXAMPLE 2 Divide: **(a)** $\frac{x}{5} \div \frac{7}{y}$; **(b)** $(x + 2) \div \frac{x - 1}{x + 3}$.

Solution

a) $\frac{x}{5} \div \frac{7}{y} = \frac{x}{5} \cdot \frac{y}{7}$ Multiplying by the reciprocal of the divisor

$= \frac{xy}{35}$ Multiplying rational expressions

b) $(x + 2) \div \frac{x - 1}{x + 3} = \frac{x + 2}{1} \cdot \frac{x + 3}{x - 1}$ Multiplying by the reciprocal of the divisor. Writing $x + 2$ as $\frac{x + 2}{1}$ can be helpful.

$= \frac{(x + 2)(x + 3)}{x - 1}$

As usual, we should simplify when possible. Often that requires us to factor one or more polynomials. Our hope is to discover a common factor that appears in both the numerator and the denominator.

EXAMPLE 3 Divide and, if possible, simplify: $\frac{x + 1}{x^2 - 1} \div \frac{x + 1}{x^2 - 2x + 1}$.

Solution

$\frac{x + 1}{x^2 - 1} \div \frac{x + 1}{x^2 - 2x + 1} = \frac{x + 1}{x^2 - 1} \cdot \frac{x^2 - 2x + 1}{x + 1}$ Multiplying by the reciprocal of the divisor

$= \frac{(x + 1)(x - 1)(x - 1)}{(x + 1)(x - 1)(x + 1)}$ Multiplying rational expressions and factoring numerators and denominators

$= \frac{\cancel{(x + 1)}\cancel{(x - 1)}(x - 1)}{\cancel{(x + 1)}\cancel{(x - 1)}(x + 1)}$

$= \frac{x - 1}{x + 1}$

Removing a factor equal to 1: $\frac{(x+1)(x-1)}{(x+1)(x-1)} = 1$

EXAMPLE 4 Divide and, if possible, simplify.

a) $\dfrac{a^2 + 3a + 2}{a^2 + 4} \div (5a^2 + 10a)$ **b)** $\dfrac{x^2 - 2x - 3}{x^2 - 4} \div \dfrac{x + 1}{x + 5}$

Solution

a) $\dfrac{a^2 + 3a + 2}{a^2 + 4} \div (5a^2 + 10a)$

$= \dfrac{a^2 + 3a + 2}{a^2 + 4} \cdot \dfrac{1}{5a^2 + 10a}$ Multiplying by the reciprocal of the divisor

$= \dfrac{(a + 2)(a + 1)}{(a^2 + 4)5a(a + 2)}$ Multiplying rational expressions and factoring

$= \dfrac{\cancel{(a + 2)}(a + 1)}{(a^2 + 4)5a\cancel{(a + 2)}}$

$= \dfrac{a + 1}{(a^2 + 4)5a}$

Removing a factor equal to 1: $\dfrac{a + 2}{a + 2} = 1$

b) $\dfrac{x^2 - 2x - 3}{x^2 - 4} \div \dfrac{x + 1}{x + 5} = \dfrac{x^2 - 2x - 3}{x^2 - 4} \cdot \dfrac{x + 5}{x + 1}$ Multiplying by the reciprocal of the divisor

$= \dfrac{(x - 3)(x + 1)(x + 5)}{(x - 2)(x + 2)(x + 1)}$ Multiplying rational expressions and factoring

$= \dfrac{(x - 3)\cancel{(x + 1)}(x + 5)}{(x - 2)(x + 2)\cancel{(x + 1)}}$

$= \dfrac{(x - 3)(x + 5)}{(x - 2)(x + 2)}$

Removing a factor equal to 1: $\dfrac{x + 1}{x + 1} = 1$

---

technology connection

In performing a partial check of Example 4(b), care must be taken in placing parentheses. For example, we enter the original expression in Example 4(b) as $y_1 = ((x^2 - 2x - 3)/(x^2 - 4))/((x + 1)/(x + 5))$ and the simplified expression as $y_2 = ((x - 3)(x + 5))/((x - 2)(x + 2))$. Comparing values of y_1 and y_2, we see that the simplification is probably correct.

X	Y1	Y2
−5	ERROR	0
−4	−.5833	−.5833
−3	−2.4	−2.4
−2	ERROR	ERROR
−1	ERROR	5.3333
0	3.75	3.75
1	4	4

X = −5

1. Check Example 4(a).
2. Why are there 3 ERROR messages shown for y_1 on the screen above, and only 1 for y_2?

6.2 Exercise Set

FOR EXTRA HELP

Student's Solutions Manual | Digital Video Tutor CD 4 Videotape 11 | AW Math Tutor Center | MathXL Tutorials on CD | MathXL | MyMathLab

Multiply. Leave each answer in factored form.

1. $\dfrac{7x}{5} \cdot \dfrac{x - 5}{2x + 1}$

2. $\dfrac{3x}{4} \cdot \dfrac{5x + 2}{x - 1}$

3. $\dfrac{a - 4}{a + 6} \cdot \dfrac{a + 2}{a + 6}$

4. $\dfrac{a + 3}{a + 6} \cdot \dfrac{a + 3}{a - 1}$

5. $\dfrac{2x + 3}{4} \cdot \dfrac{x + 1}{x - 5}$

6. $\dfrac{x + 2}{3x - 4} \cdot \dfrac{4}{5x + 6}$

7. $\dfrac{a - 4}{a^2 + 4} \cdot \dfrac{a + 4}{a^2 - 4}$

8. $\dfrac{t + 3}{t^2 - 2} \cdot \dfrac{t + 3}{t^2 - 4}$

9. $\dfrac{x + 6}{3 + x} \cdot \dfrac{x - 1}{x + 1}$

10. $\dfrac{m + 4}{m + 8} \cdot \dfrac{2 + m}{m + 5}$

Multiply and, if possible, simplify.

11. $\dfrac{5a^4}{6a} \cdot \dfrac{2}{a}$

12. $\dfrac{10}{t^7} \cdot \dfrac{3t^2}{25t}$

13. $\frac{3c}{d^2} \cdot \frac{8d}{6c^3}$

14. $\frac{3x^2y}{2} \cdot \frac{4}{xy^3}$

15. $\frac{x^2 - 3x - 10}{(x - 2)^2} \cdot \frac{x - 2}{x - 5}$

16. $\frac{t + 2}{t - 2} \cdot \frac{t^2 - 5t + 6}{(t + 2)^2}$

17. $\frac{a^2 + 25}{a^2 - 4a + 3} \cdot \frac{a - 5}{a + 5}$

18. $\frac{x + 3}{x^2 + 9} \cdot \frac{x^2 + 5x + 4}{x + 9}$

19. $\frac{a^2 - 9}{a^2} \cdot \frac{7a}{a^2 + a - 12}$

20. $\frac{x^2 + 10x - 11}{9x} \cdot \frac{x^3}{x + 11}$

21. $\frac{4a^2}{3a^2 - 12a + 12} \cdot \frac{3a - 6}{2a}$

22. $\frac{5v + 5}{v - 2} \cdot \frac{2v^2 - 8v + 8}{v^2 - 1}$

23. $\frac{t^2 + 2t - 3}{t^2 + 4t - 5} \cdot \frac{t^2 - 3t - 10}{t^2 + 5t + 6}$

24. $\frac{x^2 + 5x + 4}{x^2 - 6x + 8} \cdot \frac{x^2 + 5x - 14}{x^2 + 8x + 7}$

25. $\frac{5a^2 - 180}{10a^2 - 10} \cdot \frac{20a + 20}{2a - 12}$

26. $\frac{2t^2 - 98}{4t^2 - 4} \cdot \frac{8t + 8}{16t - 112}$

Aha! 27. $\frac{x^2 + 4x + 4}{(x - 1)^2} \cdot \frac{x^2 - 2x + 1}{(x + 2)^2}$

28. $\frac{x^2 + 7x + 12}{x^2 + 6x + 8} \cdot \frac{4 - x^2}{x^2 + x - 6}$

29. $\frac{5t^2 + 12t + 4}{t^2 + 4t + 4} \cdot \frac{t^2 + 8t + 16}{5t^2 + 22t + 8}$

30. $\frac{3y^2 - y - 2}{y^2 - 2y + 1} \cdot \frac{y^2 - 4y + 4}{6y^2 - 13y + 2}$

31. $\frac{2x^2 - 5x + 3}{6x^2 - 5x - 1} \cdot \frac{6x^2 + 13x + 2}{2x^2 + 3x - 9}$

32. $\frac{10x^2 - x - 2}{4x^2 - 12x + 5} \cdot \frac{4x^2 - 8x + 3}{10x^2 - 11x - 6}$

Find the reciprocal of each expression.

33. $\frac{3x}{7}$

34. $\frac{3 - x}{x^2 + 4}$

35. $a^3 - 8a$

36. $\frac{7}{a^2 - b^2}$

37. $\frac{x^2 + 2x - 5}{x^2 - 4x + 7}$

38. $\frac{x^2 - 3xy + y^2}{x^2 + 7xy - y^2}$

Divide and, if possible, simplify.

39. $\frac{5}{8} \div \frac{3}{7}$

40. $\frac{4}{9} \div \frac{5}{7}$

41. $\frac{x}{4} \div \frac{5}{x}$

42. $\frac{5}{x} \div \frac{x}{12}$

43. $\frac{a^5}{b^4} \div \frac{a^2}{b}$

44. $\frac{x^5}{y^2} \div \frac{x^2}{y}$

45. $\frac{y + 5}{4} \div \frac{y}{2}$

46. $\frac{a + 2}{a - 3} \div \frac{a - 1}{a + 3}$

47. $\frac{4y - 8}{y + 2} \div \frac{y - 2}{y^2 - 4}$

48. $\frac{x^2 - 1}{x} \div \frac{x + 1}{x - 1}$

49. $\frac{a}{a - b} \div \frac{b}{b - a}$

50. $\frac{x - y}{6} \div \frac{y - x}{3}$

51. $(y^2 - 9) \div \frac{y^2 - 2y - 3}{y^2 + 1}$

52. $(x^2 - 5x - 6) \div \frac{x^2 - 1}{x + 6}$

53. $\frac{-3 + 3x}{16} \div \frac{x - 1}{5}$

54. $\frac{-4 + 2x}{15} \div \frac{x - 2}{3}$

55. $\frac{-6 + 3x}{5} \div \frac{4x - 8}{25}$

56. $\frac{-12 + 4x}{12} \div \frac{-6 + 2x}{6}$

57. $\frac{a + 2}{a - 1} \div \frac{3a + 6}{a - 5}$

58. $\frac{t - 3}{t + 2} \div \frac{4t - 12}{t + 1}$

59. $(2x - 1) \div \dfrac{2x^2 - 11x + 5}{4x^2 - 1}$

60. $(a + 7) \div \dfrac{3a^2 + 14a - 49}{a^2 + 8a + 7}$

61. $\dfrac{a^2 - 10a + 25}{2a^2 - a - 21} \div \dfrac{a^2 - a - 20}{3a^2 + 5a - 12}$

62. $\dfrac{3a^2 + 7a - 20}{a^2 - 2a + 1} \div \dfrac{3a^2 - 8a + 5}{a^2 - 5a - 6}$

63. $\dfrac{c^2 + 10c + 21}{c^2 - 2c - 15} \div (5c^2 + 32c - 21)$

64. $\dfrac{z^2 - 2z + 1}{z^2 - 1} \div (4z^2 - z - 3)$

65. $\dfrac{x - y}{x^2 + 2xy + y^2} \div \dfrac{x^2 - y^2}{x^2 - 5xy + 4y^2}$

66. $\dfrac{a^2 - b^2}{a^2 - 4ab + 4b^2} \div \dfrac{a^2 - 3ab + 2b^2}{a - 2b}$

67. Why is it important to insert parentheses when multiplying rational expressions in which the numerators and the denominators contain more than one term?

68. A student claims to be able to divide, but not multiply, rational expressions. Why is this claim difficult to believe?

SKILL MAINTENANCE

Simplify.

69. $\dfrac{3}{4} + \dfrac{5}{6}$ [1.3]

70. $\dfrac{7}{8} + \dfrac{5}{6}$ [1.3]

71. $\dfrac{2}{9} - \dfrac{1}{6}$ [1.3]

72. $\dfrac{3}{10} - \dfrac{7}{15}$ [1.3]

73. $\dfrac{2}{5} - \left(\dfrac{3}{2}\right)^2$ [1.8]

74. $\dfrac{5}{9} + \dfrac{2}{3} \cdot \dfrac{4}{5}$ [1.8]

SYNTHESIS

75. Is the reciprocal of a product the product of the two reciprocals? Why or why not?

76. Explain why the quotient

$$\frac{x + 3}{x - 5} \div \frac{x - 7}{x + 1}$$

is undefined for $x = 5$, $x = -1$, and $x = 7$, but *is* defined for $x = -3$.

Simplify.

77. $\dfrac{2a^2 - 5ab}{c - 3d} \div (4a^2 - 25b^2)$

78. $(x - 2a) \div \dfrac{a^2x^2 - 4a^4}{a^2x + 2a^3}$

79. $\dfrac{3a^2 - 5ab - 12b^2}{3ab + 4b^2} \div (3b^2 - ab)^2$

80. $\dfrac{3x^2 - 2xy - y^2}{x^2 - y^2} \div (3x^2 + 4xy + y^2)^2$

Aha! 81. $\dfrac{a^2 - 3b}{a^2 + 2b} \cdot \dfrac{a^2 - 2b}{a^2 + 3b} \cdot \dfrac{a^2 + 2b}{a^2 - 3b}$

82. $\dfrac{y^2 - 4xy}{y - x} \div \dfrac{16x^2y^2 - y^4}{4x^2 - 3xy - y^2} \div \dfrac{4}{x^3y^3}$

83. $\dfrac{z^2 - 8z + 16}{z^2 + 8z + 16} \div \dfrac{(z - 4)^5}{(z + 4)^5} \div \dfrac{3z + 12}{z^2 - 16}$

84. $\dfrac{x^2 - x + xy - y}{x^2 + 6x - 7} \div \dfrac{x^2 + 2xy + y^2}{4x + 4y}$

85. $\dfrac{3x + 3y + 3}{9x} \div \dfrac{x^2 + 2xy + y^2 - 1}{x^4 + x^2}$

86. $\dfrac{(t + 2)^3}{(t + 1)^3} \div \dfrac{t^2 + 4t + 4}{t^2 + 2t + 1} \cdot \dfrac{t + 1}{t + 2}$

87. $\dfrac{3y^3 + 6y^2}{y^2 - y - 12} \div \dfrac{y^2 - y}{y^2 - 2y - 8} \cdot \dfrac{y^2 + 5y + 6}{y^2}$

88. $\dfrac{a^4 - 81b^4}{a^2c - 6abc + 9b^2c} \cdot \dfrac{a + 3b}{a^2 + 9b^2} \div \dfrac{a^2 + 6ab + 9b^2}{(a - 3b)^2}$

89. Use a graphing calculator to check that

$$\frac{x - 1}{x^2 + 2x + 1} \div \frac{x^2 - 1}{x^2 - 5x + 4}$$

is equivalent to

$$\frac{x^2 - 5x + 4}{(x + 1)^3}.$$

COLLABORATIVE CORNER

Currency Exchange

Focus: Least common multiples and proportions

Time: 20 minutes

Group size: 2

Travel between different countries usually necessitates an exchange of currencies. Recently one Canadian dollar was worth 76 U.S. cents. Use this exchange rate for the activity that follows.

ACTIVITY

1. Within each group of two students, one student should play the role of a U.S. citizen planning a visit to Canada. The other student should play the role of a Canadian planning a visit to the United States. Use the exchange rate of one Canadian dollar for 76 U.S. cents.
2. Determine how much Canadian money the U.S. citizen would receive in exchange for \$76 U.S. (this should be easy). Then determine how much U.S. money the Canadian would receive in exchange for \$76 Canadian. Finally, determine how much the Canadian would receive in exchange for \$100 Canadian and how much the U.S. citizen would receive for \$100 U.S.
3. The answers to part (2) should indicate that coins smaller than a dollar are needed to exchange \$76 Canadian for U.S. funds, or to exchange \$100 U.S. for Canadian money. What is the smallest amount of Canadian dollars that can be exchanged for a whole-number amount of U.S. dollars? What is the smallest amount of U.S. dollars that can be exchanged for a whole-number amount of Canadian dollars? (*Hint*: See part 2.)
4. Use the results from part (3) to find two other amounts of U.S. dollars that can be exchanged for a whole-number amount of Canadian dollars. Answers may vary.
5. Find the smallest number a for which both conversions—from a Canadian dollars to U.S. funds and from a U.S. dollars to Canadian funds—use only whole numbers. (*Hint*: Use LCMs and the results of part 2 above.)
6. At one time in 2004, one New Zealand dollar was worth about 60 U.S. cents. Find the smallest number a for which both conversions—from a New Zealand dollars to U.S. funds and from a U.S. dollars to New Zealand funds—use only whole numbers. (*Hint*: See part 5.)

6.3 Addition, Subtraction, and Least Common Denominators

Addition When Denominators Are the Same • Subtraction When Denominators Are the Same • Least Common Multiples and Denominators

Addition When Denominators Are the Same

Recall that to add fractions having the same denominator, like $\frac{2}{7}$ and $\frac{3}{7}$, we add the numerators and keep the common denominator: $\frac{2}{7} + \frac{3}{7} = \frac{5}{7}$. The same procedure is used when rational expressions share a common denominator.

The Sum of Two Rational Expressions

To add when the denominators are the same, add the numerators and keep the common denominator:

$$\frac{A}{B} + \frac{C}{B} = \frac{A + C}{B}.$$

In this section, we again assume that all denominators are nonzero.

EXAMPLE 1 Add. Simplify the result, if possible.

a) $\frac{4}{a} + \frac{3 + a}{a}$

b) $\frac{3x}{x - 5} + \frac{2x + 1}{x - 5}$

c) $\frac{2x^2 + 3x - 7}{2x + 1} + \frac{x^2 + x - 8}{2x + 1}$

d) $\frac{x - 5}{x^2 - 9} + \frac{2}{x^2 - 9}$

Solution

a) $\frac{4}{a} + \frac{3 + a}{a} = \frac{7 + a}{a}$ When the denominators are alike, add the numerators and keep the common denominator.

b) $\frac{3x}{x - 5} + \frac{2x + 1}{x - 5} = \frac{5x + 1}{x - 5}$ The denominators are alike, so we add the numerators.

c) $\frac{2x^2 + 3x - 7}{2x + 1} + \frac{x^2 + x - 8}{2x + 1} = \frac{(2x^2 + 3x - 7) + (x^2 + x - 8)}{2x + 1}$

$= \frac{3x^2 + 4x - 15}{2x + 1}$ Combining like terms

d) $\frac{x - 5}{x^2 - 9} + \frac{2}{x^2 - 9} = \frac{x - 3}{x^2 - 9}$ Combining like terms in the numerator: $x - 5 + 2 = x - 3$

$= \frac{x - 3}{(x - 3)(x + 3)}$ Factoring

$= \frac{1 \cdot \cancel{(x - 3)}}{\cancel{(x - 3)}(x + 3)}$

$= \frac{1}{x + 3}$

Removing a factor equal to 1: $\frac{x - 3}{x - 3} = 1$

Study Skills

Visualize the Steps

If you have completed all assignments and are studying for a quiz or test, don't feel that you need to redo every assigned problem. A more productive use of your time would be simply to reread the assigned problems, making certain that you can visualize the steps that lead to a solution. When you are unsure of how to solve a problem, redo that problem in its entirety, seeking outside help as needed.

Subtraction When Denominators Are the Same

When two fractions have the same denominator, we subtract one numerator from the other and keep the common denominator: $\frac{5}{7} - \frac{2}{7} = \frac{3}{7}$. The same procedure is used with rational expressions.

The Difference of Two Rational Expressions

To subtract when the denominators are the same, subtract the second numerator from the first and keep the common denominator:

$$\frac{A}{B} - \frac{C}{B} = \frac{A - C}{B}.$$

Caution! The fraction bar under a numerator is a grouping symbol, just like parentheses. Thus, when a numerator is subtracted, it is important to subtract *every* term in that numerator.

EXAMPLE 2 Subtract and, if possible, simplify: **(a)** $\frac{3x}{x+2} - \frac{x-5}{x+2}$; **(b)** $\frac{x^2}{x-4} - \frac{x+12}{x-4}$.

Solution

a) $\frac{3x}{x+2} - \frac{x-5}{x+2} = \frac{3x - (x-5)}{x+2}$ The parentheses are needed to make sure that we subtract both terms.

$= \frac{3x - x + 5}{x+2}$ Removing the parentheses and changing signs (using the distributive law)

$= \frac{2x+5}{x+2}$ Combining like terms

b) $\frac{x^2}{x-4} - \frac{x+12}{x-4} = \frac{x^2 - (x+12)}{x-4}$ Remember the parentheses!

$= \frac{x^2 - x - 12}{x-4}$ Removing parentheses (using the distributive law)

$= \frac{(x-4)(x+3)}{x-4}$ Factoring, in hopes of simplifying

$= \frac{\cancel{(x-4)}(x+3)}{\cancel{x-4}}$ Removing a factor equal to 1: $\frac{x-4}{x-4} = 1$

$= x + 3$

Least Common Multiples and Denominators

Thus far, every pair of rational expressions that we have added or subtracted shared a common denominator. To add or subtract rational expressions that have different denominators, we must first find equivalent rational expressions that *do* have a common denominator.

In algebra, we find a common denominator much as we do in arithmetic. Recall that to add $\frac{1}{12}$ and $\frac{7}{30}$, we first identify the smallest number that contains both 12 and 30 as factors. Such a number, the **least common multiple (LCM)** of the denominators, is then used as the **least common denominator (LCD)**.

Let's find the LCM of 12 and 30 using a method that can also be used with polynomials. We begin by writing the prime factorization of 12:

$$12 = 2 \cdot 2 \cdot 3.$$

Next, we write the prime factorization of 30:

$$30 = 2 \cdot 3 \cdot 5.$$

The LCM must include the factors of each number, so it must include each prime factor the greatest number of times that it appears in either of the factorizations. To find the LCM for 12 and 30, we select one factorization, say

$$2 \cdot 2 \cdot 3,$$

and note that because it lacks a factor of 5, it does not contain the entire factorization of 30. If we multiply $2 \cdot 2 \cdot 3$ by 5, every prime factor occurs just often enough to contain both 12 and 30 as factors.

12 is a factor of the LCM.

$$\text{LCM} = 2 \cdot 2 \cdot 3 \cdot 5$$

30 is a factor of the LCM.

Note that each prime factor—2, 3, and 5—is used the greatest number of times that it appears in either of the individual factorizations. The factor 2 occurs twice and the factors 3 and 5 once each.

To Find the Least Common Denominator (LCD)

1. Write the prime factorization of each denominator.
2. Select one of the factorizations and inspect it to see if it contains the other.
   a) If it does, it represents the LCM of the denominators.
   b) If it does not, multiply that factorization by any factors of the other denominator that it lacks. The final product is the LCM of the denominators.

The LCD is the LCM of the denominators. It should contain each factor the greatest number of times that it occurs in any of the individual factorizations.

Let's finish adding $\frac{1}{12}$ and $\frac{7}{30}$:

$$\frac{1}{12} + \frac{7}{30} = \frac{1}{2 \cdot 2 \cdot 3} + \frac{7}{2 \cdot 3 \cdot 5}.$$ The least common denominator (LCD) is $2 \cdot 2 \cdot 3 \cdot 5$.

We found above that the LCD is $2 \cdot 2 \cdot 3 \cdot 5$, or 60. To get the LCD, we see that the first denominator needs a factor of 5, and the second denominator needs another factor of 2. To accomplish this, we multiply $\frac{1}{12}$ by 1, using $\frac{5}{5}$, and we multiply $\frac{7}{30}$ by 1, using $\frac{2}{2}$. We can do this because $a \cdot 1 = a$, for any number a:

$$\frac{1}{12} + \frac{7}{30} = \frac{1}{2 \cdot 2 \cdot 3} \cdot \frac{5}{5} + \frac{7}{2 \cdot 3 \cdot 5} \cdot \frac{2}{2} \qquad \frac{5}{5} = 1 \text{ and } \frac{2}{2} = 1$$

$$= \frac{5}{60} + \frac{14}{60} \qquad \text{Both denominators are now the LCD.}$$

$$= \frac{19}{60}. \qquad \text{Adding the numerators and keeping the LCD}$$

Expressions like $\dfrac{5}{36x^2}$ and $\dfrac{7}{24x}$ are added in much the same manner.

EXAMPLE 3 Find the LCD of $\dfrac{5}{36x^2}$ and $\dfrac{7}{24x}$.

Solution

1. We begin by writing the prime factorizations of $36x^2$ and $24x$:

$$36x^2 = 2 \cdot 2 \cdot 3 \cdot 3 \cdot x \cdot x;$$

$$24x = 2 \cdot 2 \cdot 2 \cdot 3 \cdot x.$$

2. Except for a third factor of 2, the factorization of $36x^2$ contains the entire factorization of $24x$. To find the smallest product that contains both $36x^2$ and $24x$ as factors, we multiply $36x^2$ by a third factor of 2:

$$\text{LCM} = 2 \cdot 2 \cdot 3 \cdot 3 \cdot x \cdot x \cdot 2$$

$36x^2$ is a factor of the LCM.

Note that each factor appears the greatest number of times that it occurs in either of the above factorizations.

$24x$ is a factor of the LCM.

The LCM of the denominators is thus $2^3 \cdot 3^2 \cdot x^2$, or $72x^2$, so the LCD is $72x^2$.

We can now add $\dfrac{5}{36x^2}$ and $\dfrac{7}{24x}$:

$$\frac{5}{36x^2} + \frac{7}{24x} = \frac{5}{2 \cdot 2 \cdot 3 \cdot 3 \cdot x \cdot x} + \frac{7}{2 \cdot 2 \cdot 2 \cdot 3 \cdot x}.$$

In Example 3, we found that the LCD is $2 \cdot 2 \cdot 2 \cdot 3 \cdot 3 \cdot x \cdot x$, or $72x^2$. To obtain equivalent expressions with this LCD, we multiply each expression by 1, using the missing factors of the LCD to write 1:

$$\frac{5}{36x^2} + \frac{7}{24x} = \frac{5}{2 \cdot 2 \cdot 3 \cdot 3 \cdot x \cdot x} \cdot \frac{2}{2} + \frac{7}{2 \cdot 2 \cdot 2 \cdot 3 \cdot x} \cdot \frac{3 \cdot x}{3 \cdot x}$$

The LCD requires another factor of 2.

The LCD requires additional factors of 3 and x.

$$= \frac{10}{72x^2} + \frac{21x}{72x^2}$$

Both denominators are now the LCD.

$$= \frac{21x + 10}{72x^2}.$$

You now have the "big picture" of why LCMs are needed when adding rational expressions. For the remainder of this section, we will practice finding LCMs and rewriting rational expressions so that they have the LCD as the denominator. In Section 6.4, we will return to the addition and subtraction of rational expressions.

EXAMPLE 4 For each pair of polynomials, find the least common multiple.

a) $15a$ and $35b$

b) $21x^3y^6$ and $7x^5y^2$

c) $x^2 + 5x - 6$ and $x^2 - 1$

Solution

a) We write the prime factorizations and then construct the LCM:

$$15a = 3 \cdot 5 \cdot a$$
$$35b = 5 \cdot 7 \cdot b$$

$$\text{LCM} = 3 \cdot 5 \cdot a \cdot 7 \cdot b$$

$15a$ is a factor of the LCM.

Each factor appears the greatest number of times that it occurs in either of the above factorizations.

$35b$ is a factor of the LCM.

The LCM is $3 \cdot 5 \cdot a \cdot 7 \cdot b$, or $105ab$.

b) $21x^3y^6 = 3 \cdot 7 \cdot x \cdot x \cdot x \cdot y \cdot y \cdot y \cdot y \cdot y \cdot y$

$7x^5y^2 = 7 \cdot x \cdot x \cdot x \cdot x \cdot x \cdot y \cdot y$

Try to visualize the factors of x and y mentally.

$$\text{LCM} = 3 \cdot 7 \cdot x \cdot x \cdot x \cdot y \cdot y \cdot y \cdot y \cdot y \cdot y \cdot x \cdot x$$

$21x^3y^6$ is a factor of the LCM.

$7x^5y^2$ is a factor of the LCM.

Note that we used the highest power of each factor in $21x^3y^6$ and $7x^5y^2$. The LCM is $21x^5y^6$.

c) $x^2 + 5x - 6 = (x - 1)(x + 6)$

$x^2 - 1 = (x - 1)(x + 1)$

$$\text{LCM} = (x - 1)(x + 6)(x + 1)$$

$x^2 + 5x - 6$ is a factor of the LCM.

$x^2 - 1$ is a factor of the LCM.

The LCM is $(x - 1)(x + 6)(x + 1)$. There is no need to multiply this out.

The above procedure can be used to find the LCM of three or more polynomials as well. We factor each polynomial and then construct the LCM using each factor the greatest number of times that it appears in any one factorization.

EXAMPLE 5

For each group of polynomials, find the LCM.

a) $12x$, $16y$, and $8xyz$

b) $x^2 + 4$, $x + 1$, and 5

Student Notes

If you prefer, the LCM for a group of three polynomials can be found by finding the LCM of two of them and then finding the LCM of that result and the remaining polynomial.

Solution

a) $12x = 2 \cdot 2 \cdot 3 \cdot x$

$16y = 2 \cdot 2 \cdot 2 \cdot 2 \cdot y$

$8xyz = 2 \cdot 2 \cdot 2 \cdot x \cdot y \cdot z$

$$\text{LCM} = 2 \cdot 2 \cdot 3 \cdot x \cdot 2 \cdot 2 \cdot y \cdot z$$

$12x$ is a factor of the LCM.

$16y$ is a factor of the LCM.

$8xyz$ is a factor of the LCM.

The LCM is $2^4 \cdot 3 \cdot xyz$, or $48xyz$.

b) Since $x^2 + 4$, $x + 1$, and 5 are not factorable, the LCM is their product: $5(x^2 + 4)(x + 1)$.

To add or subtract rational expressions with different denominators, we must be able to write equivalent expressions that have the LCD. Doing so usually requires multiplying each rational expression by a carefully constructed form of 1.

EXAMPLE 6

Find equivalent expressions that have the LCD:

$$\frac{x + 3}{x^2 + 5x - 6}, \quad \frac{x + 7}{x^2 - 1}.$$

Solution From Example 4(c), we know that the LCD is

$$(x+6)(x-1)(x+1).$$

Since

$$x^2+5x-6=(x+6)(x-1),$$

the factor of the LCD that is missing from the first denominator is $x+1$. We multiply by 1 using $(x+1)/(x+1)$:

$$\left.\begin{aligned}\frac{x+3}{x^2+5x-6}&=\frac{x+3}{(x+6)(x-1)}\cdot\frac{x+1}{x+1}\\&=\frac{(x+3)(x+1)}{(x+6)(x-1)(x+1)}.\end{aligned}\right\}$$ Finding an equivalent expression that has the least common denominator

For the second expression, we have

$$x^2-1=(x+1)(x-1).$$

The factor of the LCD that is missing is $x+6$. We multiply by 1 using $(x+6)/(x+6)$:

$$\left.\begin{aligned}\frac{x+7}{x^2-1}&=\frac{x+7}{(x+1)(x-1)}\cdot\frac{x+6}{x+6}\\&=\frac{(x+7)(x+6)}{(x+1)(x-1)(x+6)}.\end{aligned}\right\}$$ Finding an equivalent expression that has the least common denominator

We leave the results in factored form. In Section 6.4, we will carry out the actual addition and subtraction of such rational expressions.

6.3 Exercise Set

FOR EXTRA HELP

Student's Solutions Manual | Digital Video Tutor CD 4 Videotape 11 | AW Math Tutor Center | MathXL Tutorials on CD | MathXL | MyMathLab

Concept Reinforcement *Use one or more words to complete each of the following sentences.*

1. To add two rational expressions when the denominators are the same, add __________ and keep the common __________.
2. When a numerator is being subtracted, be sure to treat its fraction bar as a __________ symbol and subtract every __________ in that numerator.
3. The least common multiple of two denominators is usually referred to as the __________ and is abbreviated __________.
4. The least common denominator of two fractions must contain the prime __________ of both __________.

Perform the indicated operation. Simplify, if possible.

5. $\frac{6}{x}+\frac{4}{x}$
6. $\frac{4}{a^2}+\frac{9}{a^2}$
7. $\frac{x}{12}+\frac{2x+5}{12}$
8. $\frac{a}{7}+\frac{3a-4}{7}$
9. $\frac{4}{a+3}+\frac{5}{a+3}$
10. $\frac{5}{x+2}+\frac{8}{x+2}$

11. $\frac{8}{a+2} - \frac{2}{a+2}$

12. $\frac{8}{x+7} - \frac{2}{x+7}$

13. $\frac{3y+8}{2y} - \frac{y+1}{2y}$

14. $\frac{5+3t}{4t} - \frac{2t+1}{4t}$

15. $\frac{7x+8}{x+1} + \frac{4x+3}{x+1}$

16. $\frac{3a+13}{a+4} + \frac{2a+7}{a+4}$

17. $\frac{7x+8}{x+1} - \frac{4x+3}{x+1}$

18. $\frac{3a+13}{a+4} - \frac{2a+7}{a+4}$

19. $\frac{a^2}{a-4} + \frac{a-20}{a-4}$

20. $\frac{x^2}{x+5} + \frac{7x+10}{x+5}$

21. $\frac{x^2}{x-2} - \frac{6x-8}{x-2}$

22. $\frac{a^2}{a+3} - \frac{2a+15}{a+3}$

Aha! 23. $\frac{t^2-5t}{t-1} + \frac{5t-t^2}{t-1}$

24. $\frac{y^2+6y}{y+2} + \frac{2y+12}{y+2}$

25. $\frac{x-6}{x^2+5x+6} + \frac{9}{x^2+5x+6}$

26. $\frac{x-5}{x^2-4x+3} + \frac{2}{x^2-4x+3}$

27. $\frac{t^2-5t}{t^2+6t+9} + \frac{4t-12}{t^2+6t+9}$

28. $\frac{y^2-7y}{y^2+8y+16} + \frac{6y-20}{y^2+8y+16}$

29. $\frac{2x^2+x}{x^2-8x+12} - \frac{x^2-2x+10}{x^2-8x+12}$

30. $\frac{2x^2+3}{x^2-6x+5} - \frac{3+2x^2}{x^2-6x+5}$

31. $\frac{3-2x}{x^2-6x+8} + \frac{7-3x}{x^2-6x+8}$

32. $\frac{1-2t}{t^2-5t+4} + \frac{4-3t}{t^2-5t+4}$

33. $\frac{x-9}{x^2+3x-4} - \frac{2x-5}{x^2+3x-4}$

34. $\frac{5-3x}{x^2-2x+1} - \frac{x+1}{x^2-2x+1}$

Find the LCM.

35. 15, 27

36. 10, 15

37. 8, 9

38. 12, 15

39. 6, 9, 21

40. 8, 36, 40

Find the LCM.

41. $12x^2$, $6x^3$

42. $10t^3$, $5t^4$

43. $15a^4b^7$, $10a^2b^8$

44. $6a^2b^7$, $9a^5b^2$

45. $2(y-3)$, $6(y-3)$

46. $4(x-1)$, $8(x-1)$

47. x^2-4, x^2+5x+6

48. x^2+3x+2, x^2-4

49. t^3+4t^2+4t, t^2-4t

50. y^3-y^2, y^4-y^2

51. $10x^2y$, $6y^2z$, $5xz^3$

52. $8x^3z$, $12xy^2$, $4y^5z^2$

53. $a+1$, $(a-1)^2$, a^2-1

54. x^2-9, $x+3$, $(x-3)^2$

55. m^2-5m+6, m^2-4m+4

56. $2x^2+5x+2$, $2x^2-x-1$

57. $6x^3-24x^2+18x$, $4x^5-24x^4+20x^3$

58. $9x^3-9x^2-18x$, $6x^5-24x^4+24x^3$

Find equivalent expressions that have the LCD.

59. $\frac{3}{10a^3}$, $\frac{b}{5a^6}$

60. $\frac{5}{6x^5}$, $\frac{y}{12x^3}$

61. $\frac{7}{3x^4y^2}$, $\frac{4}{9xy^3}$

62. $\frac{3}{2a^2b}$, $\frac{7}{8ab^2}$

63. $\frac{2x}{x^2-4}$, $\frac{4x}{x^2+5x+6}$

64. $\frac{5x}{x^2-9}$, $\frac{2x}{x^2+11x+24}$

65. Explain why the product of two numbers is not always their least common multiple.

66. If the LCM of two numbers is their product, what can you conclude about the two numbers?

SKILL MAINTENANCE

Write each number in two equivalent forms. [1.7]

67. $\frac{7}{-9}$

68. $-\frac{3}{2}$

Simplify. [1.3]

69. $\frac{5}{18} - \frac{7}{12}$

70. $\frac{8}{15} - \frac{13}{20}$

Find a polynomial that can represent the shaded area of each figure. [4.6]

71.

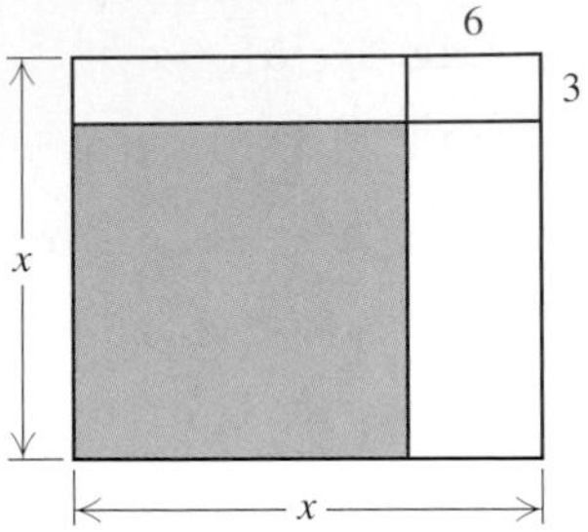

72.

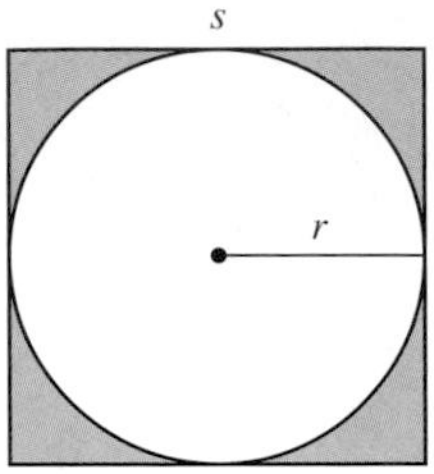

SYNTHESIS

73. If the LCM of two third-degree polynomials is a sixth-degree polynomial, what can be concluded about the two polynomials?

74. If the LCM of a binomial and a trinomial is the trinomial, what relationship exists between the two expressions?

Perform the indicated operations. Simplify, if possible.

75. $\dfrac{6x-1}{x-1}+\dfrac{3(2x+5)}{x-1}+\dfrac{3(2x-3)}{x-1}$

76. $\dfrac{2x+11}{x-3}\cdot\dfrac{3}{x+4}+\dfrac{-1}{4+x}\cdot\dfrac{6x+3}{x-3}$

77. $\dfrac{x^2}{3x^2-5x-2}-\dfrac{2x}{3x+1}\cdot\dfrac{1}{x-2}$

78. $\dfrac{x+y}{x^2-y^2}+\dfrac{x-y}{x^2-y^2}-\dfrac{2x}{x^2-y^2}$

South African artistry. *In South Africa, the design of every woven handbag, or* gipatsi *(plural,* sipatsi *) is created by repeating two or more geometric patterns.*

Each pattern encircles the bag, sharing the strands of fabric with any pattern above or below. The length, or period, of each pattern is the number of strands required to construct the pattern. For a gipatsi to be considered beautiful, each individual pattern must fit a whole number of times around the bag.

Source: Gerdes, Paulus, *Women, Art and Geometry in Southern Africa.* Asmara, Eritrea: Africa World Press, Inc., p. 5

79. A weaver is using two patterns to create a gipatsi. Pattern A is 10 strands long, and pattern B is 3 strands long. What is the smallest number of strands that can be used to complete the gipatsi?

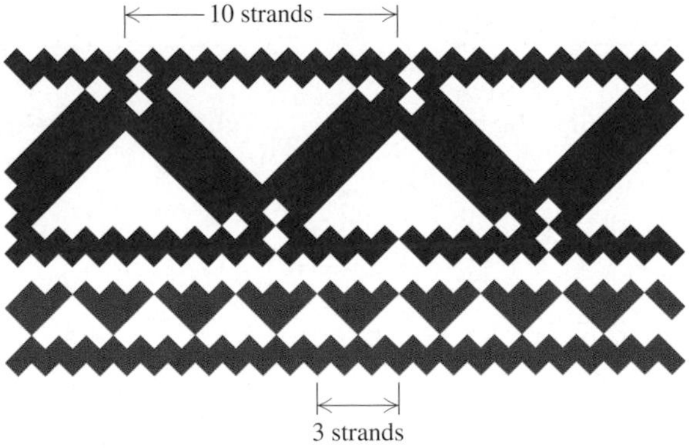

80. A weaver is using a four-strand pattern, a six-strand pattern, and an eight-strand pattern. What is the smallest number of strands that can be used to complete the gipatsi?

81. For technical reasons, the number of strands is generally a multiple of 4. Answer Exercise 79 with this additional requirement in mind.

Find the LCM.

82. 72, 90, 96

83. $6t^2-6,\ (3t^2-6t+3)^2,\ 8t-8$

84. $9x^2-16,\ 6x^2-x-12,\ (4x^2-12x+9)^2$

85. *Copiers.* The Brother® DCP-1000 copier can print 10 pages per minute. The Sharp® AL-1540CS copier can print 14 pages per minute. If both machines begin printing at the same instant, how long will it be until they again begin copying a page at exactly the same time?

86. *Running.* Kim and Jed leave the starting point of a fitness loop at the same time. Kim jogs a lap in 6 min and Jed jogs one in 8 min. Assuming they continue to run at the same pace, when will they next meet at the starting place?

87. *Bus schedules.* Beginning at 5:00 A.M., a hotel shuttle bus leaves Salton Airport every 25 min, and the downtown shuttle bus leaves the airport every 35 min. What time will it be when both shuttles again leave at the same time?

88. *Appliances.* Dishwashers last an average of 10 yr, clothes washers an average of 14 yr, and refrigerators an average of 20 yr. If an apartment house is equipped with new dishwashers, clothes washers, and refrigerators in 2005, in what year will all three appliances need to be replaced at once?
Source: *Energy Savers: Tips on Saving Energy and Money at Home,* produced for the U.S. Department of Energy by the National Renewable Energy Laboratory, 2003

89. Explain how evaluating can be used to perform a partial check on the result of Example 1(d):

$$\frac{x-5}{x^2-9}+\frac{2}{x^2-9}=\frac{1}{x+3}.$$

90. On p. 380, the second step in finding an LCD is to select one of the factorizations of the denominators. Does it matter which one is selected? Why or why not?

6.4 Addition and Subtraction with Unlike Denominators

Adding and Subtracting with LCDs • When Factors Are Opposites

Adding and Subtracting with LCDs

We now know how to rewrite two rational expressions in equivalent forms that use the LCD. Once rational expressions share a common denominator, they can be added or subtracted just as in Section 6.3.

To Add or Subtract Rational Expressions Having Different Denominators

1. Find the LCD.
2. Multiply each rational expression by a form of 1 made up of the factors of the LCD missing from that expression's denominator.
3. Add or subtract the numerators, as indicated. Write the sum or difference over the LCD.
4. Simplify, if possible.

EXAMPLE 1 Add: $\dfrac{5x^2}{8} + \dfrac{7x}{12}$.

Study Skills

If a Question Stumps You

Unless you know the material "cold," don't be surprised if a quiz or test includes a question that you feel unsure about. Should this happen, do not get rattled—simply skip the question and continue with the quiz or test, returning to the trouble spot after the other questions have been answered.

Solution

1. First, we find the LCD:

$$\left.\begin{aligned} 8 &= 2 \cdot 2 \cdot 2 \\ 12 &= 2 \cdot 2 \cdot 3 \end{aligned}\right\} \quad \text{LCD} = 2 \cdot 2 \cdot 2 \cdot 3, \text{ or } 24.$$

2. The denominator 8 needs to be multiplied by 3 in order to obtain the LCD. The denominator 12 needs to be multiplied by 2 in order to obtain the LCD. Thus we multiply the first expression by $\frac{3}{3}$ and the second expression by $\frac{2}{2}$ to get the LCD:

$$\begin{aligned} \frac{5x^2}{8} + \frac{7x}{12} &= \frac{5x^2}{2 \cdot 2 \cdot 2} + \frac{7x}{2 \cdot 2 \cdot 3} \\ &= \frac{5x^2}{2 \cdot 2 \cdot 2} \cdot \frac{3}{3} + \frac{7x}{2 \cdot 2 \cdot 3} \cdot \frac{2}{2} \qquad \text{Multiplying each expression by a form of 1 to get the LCD} \\ &= \frac{15x^2}{24} + \frac{14x}{24}. \end{aligned}$$

3. Next, we add the numerators:

$$\frac{15x^2}{24} + \frac{14x}{24} = \frac{15x^2 + 14x}{24}.$$

4. Since $15x^2 + 14x$ and 24 have no common factor,

$$\frac{15x^2 + 14x}{24}$$

cannot be simplified any further.

Subtraction is performed in much the same way.

EXAMPLE 2 Subtract: $\dfrac{7}{8x} - \dfrac{5}{12x^2}$.

Solution We follow the four steps shown above. First, we find the LCD:

$$\left.\begin{aligned} 8x &= 2 \cdot 2 \cdot 2 \cdot x \\ 12x^2 &= 2 \cdot 2 \cdot 3 \cdot x \cdot x \end{aligned}\right\} \quad \text{LCD} = 2 \cdot 2 \cdot 3 \cdot x \cdot x \cdot 2, \text{ or } 24x^2.$$

The denominator $8x$ must be multiplied by $3x$ in order to obtain the LCD. The denominator $12x^2$ must be multiplied by 2 in order to obtain the LCD.

Thus we multiply by $\frac{3x}{3x}$ and $\frac{2}{2}$ to get the LCD. Then we subtract and, if possible, simplify.

$$\frac{7}{8x} - \frac{5}{12x^2} = \frac{7}{8x} \cdot \frac{3x}{3x} - \frac{5}{12x^2} \cdot \frac{2}{2}$$

$$= \frac{21x}{24x^2} - \frac{10}{24x^2}$$

Caution! Do not simplify *these* rational expressions or you will lose the LCD.

$$= \frac{21x - 10}{24x^2}$$ This cannot be simplified, so we are done.

When denominators contain polynomials with two or more terms, the same steps are used.

EXAMPLE 3 Add: $\frac{2a}{a^2 - 1} + \frac{1}{a^2 + a}$.

Solution First, we find the LCD:

$$\left.\begin{aligned} a^2 - 1 &= (a - 1)(a + 1) \\ a^2 + a &= a(a + 1). \end{aligned}\right\} \quad \text{LCD} = (a - 1)(a + 1)a$$

We multiply by a form of 1 to get the LCD in each expression:

$$\frac{2a}{a^2 - 1} + \frac{1}{a^2 + a} = \frac{2a}{(a - 1)(a + 1)} \cdot \frac{a}{a} + \frac{1}{a(a + 1)} \cdot \frac{a - 1}{a - 1}$$ Multiplying by $\frac{a}{a}$ and $\frac{a-1}{a-1}$ to get the LCD

$$= \frac{2a^2}{(a - 1)(a + 1)a} + \frac{a - 1}{a(a + 1)(a - 1)}$$

$$= \frac{2a^2 + a - 1}{a(a - 1)(a + 1)}$$ Adding numerators

$$= \frac{(2a - 1)\cancel{(a + 1)}}{a(a - 1)\cancel{(a + 1)}}$$

$$= \frac{2a - 1}{a(a - 1)}.$$

Simplifying by factoring and removing a factor equal to 1: $\frac{a + 1}{a + 1} = 1$

EXAMPLE 4 Perform the indicated operations.

a) $\frac{x + 4}{x - 2} - \frac{x - 7}{x + 5}$

b) $\frac{t}{t^2 + 11t + 30} + \frac{-5}{t^2 + 9t + 20}$

c) $\frac{x}{x^2 + 5x + 6} - \frac{2}{x^2 + 3x + 2}$

Solution

a) First, we find the LCD. It is just the product of the denominators:

$$\text{LCD} = (x - 2)(x + 5).$$

We multiply by a form of 1 to get the LCD in each expression. Then we subtract and try to simplify.

$$\frac{x+4}{x-2} - \frac{x-7}{x+5} = \frac{x+4}{x-2} \cdot \frac{x+5}{x+5} - \frac{x-7}{x+5} \cdot \frac{x-2}{x-2}$$

$$= \frac{x^2 + 9x + 20}{(x-2)(x+5)} - \frac{x^2 - 9x + 14}{(x-2)(x+5)}$$ Multiplying out numerators (but not denominators)

$$= \frac{x^2 + 9x + 20 - (x^2 - 9x + 14)}{(x-2)(x+5)}$$ When subtracting a numerator with more than one term, parentheses are important.

$$= \frac{x^2 + 9x + 20 - x^2 + 9x - 14}{(x-2)(x+5)}$$ Removing parentheses and subtracting every term

$$= \frac{18x + 6}{(x-2)(x+5)}$$

Factoring $18x + 6$ as $6(3x + 1)$ would not enable us to simplify our result, so it need not be written in that form.

b) $$\frac{t}{t^2 + 11t + 30} + \frac{-5}{t^2 + 9t + 20}$$

$$= \frac{t}{(t+5)(t+6)} + \frac{-5}{(t+5)(t+4)}$$ Factoring the denominators in order to find the LCD. The LCD is $(t + 5)(t + 6)(t + 4)$.

$$= \frac{t}{(t+5)(t+6)} \cdot \frac{t+4}{t+4} + \frac{-5}{(t+5)(t+4)} \cdot \frac{t+6}{t+6}$$ Multiplying to get the LCD

$$= \frac{t^2 + 4t}{(t+5)(t+6)(t+4)} + \frac{-5t - 30}{(t+5)(t+6)(t+4)}$$ Multiplying in each numerator

$$= \frac{t^2 + 4t - 5t - 30}{(t+5)(t+6)(t+4)}$$ Adding numerators

$$= \frac{t^2 - t - 30}{(t+5)(t+6)(t+4)}$$ Combining like terms in the numerator

$$= \frac{\cancel{(t+5)}(t-6)}{\cancel{(t+5)}(t+6)(t+4)}$$

$$= \frac{t-6}{(t+6)(t+4)}$$

Always simplify the result, if possible, by removing a factor equal to 1; here $\frac{t+5}{t+5} = 1$.

Student Notes

As you can see, adding or subtracting rational expressions can involve many steps. Therefore, it is important to double-check each step of your work as you work through each problem. Waiting to check your work at the end of the problems is usually a less efficient use of your time.

c) $\frac{x}{x^2 + 5x + 6} - \frac{2}{x^2 + 3x + 2}$

$= \frac{x}{(x + 2)(x + 3)} - \frac{2}{(x + 2)(x + 1)}$ Factoring denominators. The LCD is $(x + 2)(x + 3)(x + 1)$.

$= \frac{x}{(x + 2)(x + 3)} \cdot \frac{x + 1}{x + 1} - \frac{2}{(x + 2)(x + 1)} \cdot \frac{x + 3}{x + 3}$

$= \frac{x^2 + x}{(x + 2)(x + 3)(x + 1)} - \frac{2x + 6}{(x + 2)(x + 3)(x + 1)}$

$= \frac{x^2 + x - (2x + 6)}{(x + 2)(x + 3)(x + 1)}$ Don't forget the parentheses!

$= \frac{x^2 + x - 2x - 6}{(x + 2)(x + 3)(x + 1)}$ Remember to subtract each term in $2x + 6$.

$= \frac{x^2 - x - 6}{(x + 2)(x + 3)(x + 1)}$ Combining like terms in the numerator

$= \frac{(x + 2)(x - 3)}{(x + 2)(x + 3)(x + 1)}$

$= \frac{x - 3}{(x + 3)(x + 1)}$

Factoring and simplifying; $\frac{x + 2}{x + 2} = 1$

When Factors Are Opposites

When one denominator is the opposite of the other, we can first multiply either expression by 1 using $-1/-1$.

EXAMPLE 5 Add: **(a)** $\frac{t}{2} + \frac{3}{-2}$; **(b)** $\frac{x}{x - 5} + \frac{7}{5 - x}$.

Solution

a) $\frac{t}{2} + \frac{3}{-2} = \frac{t}{2} + \frac{3}{-2} \cdot \frac{-1}{-1}$ Multiplying by 1 using $\frac{-1}{-1}$

$= \frac{t}{2} + \frac{-3}{2}$ The denominators are now the same.

$= \frac{t + (-3)}{2}$

$= \frac{t - 3}{2}$

b) Recall that when an expression of the form $a - b$ is multiplied by -1, the subtraction is reversed: $-1(a - b) = -a + b = b + (-a) = b - a$. Since $x - 5$ and $5 - x$ are opposites, we can find a common denominator by multiplying one of the rational expressions by $-1/-1$. Because polynomials are usually written in descending order, we choose to reverse the subtraction in the second denominator:

$$\frac{x}{x-5} + \frac{7}{5-x} = \frac{x}{x-5} + \frac{7}{5-x} \cdot \frac{-1}{-1}$$ Writing 1 as $-1/-1$ and multiplying to obtain a common denominator

$$= \frac{x}{x-5} + \frac{-7}{-5+x}$$

$$= \frac{x}{x-5} + \frac{-7}{x-5}$$ Note that $-5 + x = x + (-5) = x - 5$.

$$= \frac{x-7}{x-5}.$$

Sometimes, after factoring to find the LCD, we find a factor in one denominator that is the opposite of a factor in the other denominator. When this happens, multiplication by $-1/-1$ can again be helpful.

EXAMPLE 6 Perform the indicated operations and simplify.

a) $\dfrac{x}{x^2 - 25} + \dfrac{3}{5 - x}$

b) $\dfrac{x + 9}{x^2 - 4} + \dfrac{6 - x}{4 - x^2} - \dfrac{1 + x}{x^2 - 4}$

Solution

a) $$\frac{x}{x^2-25} + \frac{3}{5-x} = \frac{x}{(x-5)(x+5)} + \frac{3}{5-x}$$ Factoring

$$= \frac{x}{(x-5)(x+5)} + \frac{3}{5-x} \cdot \frac{-1}{-1}$$ Multiplying by $-1/-1$ changes $5 - x$ to $x - 5$.

$$= \frac{x}{(x-5)(x+5)} + \frac{-3}{x-5}$$ $(5 - x)(-1) = x - 5$

$$= \frac{x}{(x-5)(x+5)} + \frac{-3}{(x-5)} \cdot \frac{x+5}{x+5}$$ The LCD is $(x - 5)(x + 5)$.

$$= \frac{x}{(x-5)(x+5)} + \frac{-3x-15}{(x-5)(x+5)}$$

$$= \frac{-2x-15}{(x-5)(x+5)}$$

technology connection

The TABLE feature can be used to check addition or subtraction of rational expressions, much as we did on p. 374 of Section 6.2. Below we check Example 6(a), using $y_1 = x/(x^2 - 25) + 3/(5 - x)$ and $y_2 = (-2x - 15)/((x - 5)(x + 5))$.

ΔTBL = 1

X	Y1	Y2
1	.70833	.70833
2	.90476	.90476
3	1.3125	1.3125
4	2.5556	2.5556
5	ERROR	ERROR
6	−2.455	−2.455
7	−1.208	−1.208
X = 1		

Because the values for y_1 and y_2 match, we have a check.

b) Since $4 - x^2$ is the opposite of $x^2 - 4$, multiplying the second rational expression by $-1/-1$ will lead to a common denominator:

$$\frac{x+9}{x^2-4} + \frac{6-x}{4-x^2} - \frac{1+x}{x^2-4} = \frac{x+9}{x^2-4} + \frac{6-x}{4-x^2} \cdot \frac{-1}{-1} - \frac{1+x}{x^2-4}$$

$$= \frac{x+9}{x^2-4} + \frac{x-6}{x^2-4} - \frac{1+x}{x^2-4}$$

$$= \frac{x+9+x-6-1-x}{x^2-4} \quad \text{Adding and subtracting numerators}$$

$$= \frac{x+2}{x^2-4}$$

$$= \frac{\cancel{(x+2)} \cdot 1}{\cancel{(x+2)}(x-2)} \quad \text{Simplifying}$$

$$= \frac{1}{x-2}.$$

6.4 Exercise Set

FOR EXTRA HELP

Student's Solutions Manual | Digital Video Tutor CD 4 Videotape 11 | AW Math Tutor Center | MathXL Tutorials on CD | MathXL | MyMathLab

Concept Reinforcement *In Exercises 1–4, the four steps for adding rational expressions with different denominators are listed. Fill in the missing word or words for each step.*

1. To add or subtract when the denominators are different, first find the ______________.

2. Multiply each rational expression by a form of 1 made up of the factors of the LCD that are ______________ from that expression's ______________.

3. Add or subtract the ______________, as indicated. Write the sum or difference over the ______________.

4. ______________, if possible.

Perform the indicated operation. Simplify, if possible.

5. $\frac{4}{x} + \frac{9}{x^2}$

6. $\frac{5}{x} + \frac{6}{x^2}$

7. $\frac{1}{6r} - \frac{3}{8r}$

8. $\frac{4}{9t} - \frac{7}{6t}$

9. $\frac{2}{c^2d} + \frac{7}{cd^3}$

10. $\frac{4}{xy^2} + \frac{2}{x^2y}$

11. $\frac{-2}{3xy^2} - \frac{6}{x^2y^3}$

12. $\frac{8}{9t^3} - \frac{5}{6t^2}$

13. $\frac{x-4}{9} + \frac{x+5}{6}$

14. $\frac{x+5}{8} + \frac{x-3}{12}$

15. $\dfrac{x-2}{6} - \dfrac{x+1}{3}$

16. $\dfrac{a+2}{2} - \dfrac{a-4}{4}$

17. $\dfrac{a+4}{16a} + \dfrac{3a+4}{4a^2}$

18. $\dfrac{2a-1}{3a^2} + \dfrac{5a+1}{9a}$

19. $\dfrac{4z-9}{3z} - \dfrac{3z-8}{4z}$

20. $\dfrac{x-1}{4x} - \dfrac{2x+3}{x}$

21. $\dfrac{x+y}{xy^2} + \dfrac{3x+y}{x^2y}$

22. $\dfrac{2c-d}{c^2d} + \dfrac{c+d}{cd^2}$

23. $\dfrac{4x+2t}{3xt^2} - \dfrac{5x-3t}{x^2t}$

24. $\dfrac{5x+3y}{2x^2y} - \dfrac{3x+4y}{xy^2}$

25. $\dfrac{3}{x-2} + \dfrac{3}{x+2}$

26. $\dfrac{5}{x-1} + \dfrac{5}{x+1}$

27. $\dfrac{5}{x+5} - \dfrac{3}{x-5}$

28. $\dfrac{4}{z-1} - \dfrac{2}{z+1}$

29. $\dfrac{3}{x+1} + \dfrac{2}{3x}$

30. $\dfrac{2}{x+5} + \dfrac{3}{4x}$

31. $\dfrac{3}{2t^2-2t} - \dfrac{5}{2t-2}$

32. $\dfrac{8}{3t^2-15t} - \dfrac{3}{2t-10}$

33. $\dfrac{2x}{x^2-16} + \dfrac{x}{x-4}$

34. $\dfrac{4x}{x^2-25} + \dfrac{x}{x+5}$

35. $\dfrac{6}{z+4} - \dfrac{2}{3z+12}$

36. $\dfrac{t}{t-3} - \dfrac{5}{4t-12}$

37. $\dfrac{3}{x-1} + \dfrac{2}{(x-1)^2}$

38. $\dfrac{2}{x+3} + \dfrac{4}{(x+3)^2}$

39. $\dfrac{3}{x+2} - \dfrac{8}{x^2-4}$

40. $\dfrac{2t}{t^2-9} - \dfrac{3}{t-3}$

41. $\dfrac{3a}{4a-20} + \dfrac{9a}{6a-30}$

42. $\dfrac{4a}{5a-10} + \dfrac{3a}{10a-20}$

Aha! 43. $\dfrac{x}{x-5} + \dfrac{x}{5-x}$

44. $\dfrac{x+4}{x} + \dfrac{x}{x+4}$

45. $\dfrac{6}{a^2+a-2} + \dfrac{4}{a^2-4a+3}$

46. $\dfrac{x}{x^2+2x+1} + \dfrac{1}{x^2+5x+4}$

47. $\dfrac{x}{x^2+9x+20} - \dfrac{4}{x^2+7x+12}$

48. $\dfrac{x}{x^2+5x+6} - \dfrac{2}{x^2+3x+2}$

49. $\dfrac{3z}{z^2-4z+4} + \dfrac{10}{z^2+z-6}$

50. $\dfrac{3}{x^2-9} + \dfrac{2}{x^2-x-6}$

Aha! 51. $\dfrac{-5}{x^2+17x+16} - \dfrac{0}{x^2+9x+8}$

52. $\dfrac{x}{x^2+15x+56} - \dfrac{1}{x^2+13x+42}$

53. $\dfrac{4x}{5} - \dfrac{x-3}{-5}$

54. $\dfrac{x}{4} - \dfrac{3x-5}{-4}$

55. $\dfrac{y^2}{y-3} + \dfrac{9}{3-y}$

56. $\dfrac{t^2}{t-2} + \dfrac{4}{2-t}$

57. $\dfrac{b-7}{b^2-16} + \dfrac{7-b}{16-b^2}$

58. $\dfrac{a-3}{a^2-25} + \dfrac{a-3}{25-a^2}$

59. $\dfrac{4-p}{25-p^2} + \dfrac{p+1}{p-5}$

60. $\dfrac{y+2}{y-7} + \dfrac{3-y}{49-y^2}$

61. $\dfrac{8x}{16-x^2} - \dfrac{5}{x-4}$

62. $\dfrac{5x}{x^2-9} - \dfrac{4}{3-x}$

63. $\dfrac{a}{a^2-1} + \dfrac{2a}{a-a^2}$

64. $\dfrac{3x+2}{3x+6} + \dfrac{x}{4-x^2}$

65. $\dfrac{4x}{x^2-y^2} - \dfrac{6}{y-x}$

66. $\dfrac{4-a^2}{a^2-9} - \dfrac{a-2}{3-a}$

Perform the indicated operations. Simplify, if possible.

67. $\dfrac{x-3}{2-x} - \dfrac{x+3}{x+2} + \dfrac{x+6}{4-x^2}$

68. $\dfrac{t-5}{1-t} - \dfrac{t+4}{t+1} + \dfrac{t+2}{t^2-1}$

69. $\dfrac{x+5}{x+3} + \dfrac{x+7}{x+2} - \dfrac{7x+19}{(x+3)(x+2)}$

70. $\dfrac{2x+5}{x+1} + \dfrac{x+7}{x+5} - \dfrac{5x+17}{(x+1)(x+5)}$

71. $\dfrac{1}{x+y} + \dfrac{1}{x-y} - \dfrac{2x}{x^2-y^2}$

72. $\dfrac{2r}{r^2-s^2} + \dfrac{1}{r+s} - \dfrac{1}{r-s}$

73. What is the advantage of using the *least* common denominator—rather than just *any* common denominator—when adding or subtracting rational expressions?

74. Describe a procedure that can be used to add any two rational expressions.

SKILL MAINTENANCE

Simplify.

75. $-\frac{3}{7} \div \frac{6}{13}$ [1.7]

76. $\frac{5}{12} \div \left(-\frac{3}{4}\right)$ [1.7]

77. $\dfrac{\frac{2}{9}}{\frac{5}{3}}$ [1.3]

78. $\dfrac{\frac{7}{10}}{\frac{3}{5}}$ [1.3]

Graph. [3.2]

79. $y = -\frac{1}{2}x - 5$

80. $y = \frac{1}{2}x - 5$

SYNTHESIS

81. How could you convince someone that

$$\frac{1}{3 - x} \quad \text{and} \quad \frac{1}{x - 3}$$

are opposites of each other?

82. Are parentheses as important for adding rational expressions as they are for subtracting rational expressions? Why or why not?

Write expressions for the perimeter and the area of each rectangle.

83.

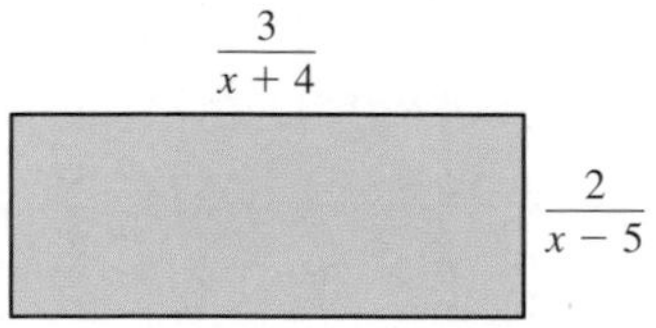

84.

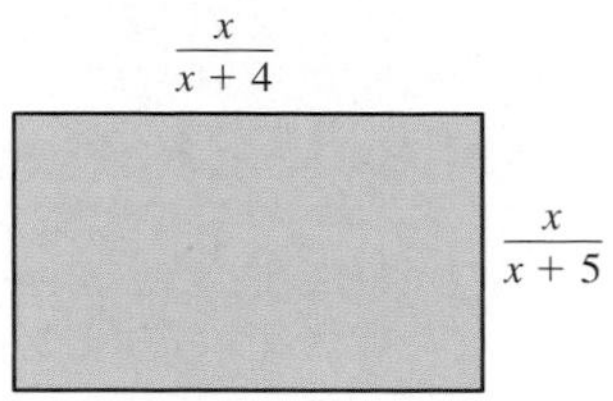

Perform the indicated operations.

85. $\frac{2x + 11}{x - 3} \cdot \frac{3}{x + 4} + \frac{2x + 1}{4 + x} \cdot \frac{3}{3 - x}$

86. $\frac{x^2}{3x^2 - 5x - 2} - \frac{2x}{3x + 1} \cdot \frac{1}{x - 2}$

Aha! **87.** $\left(\frac{x}{x + 7} - \frac{3}{x + 2}\right)\left(\frac{x}{x + 7} + \frac{3}{x + 2}\right)$

88. $\frac{1}{ay - 3a + 2xy - 6x} - \frac{xy + ay}{a^2 - 4x^2}\left(\frac{1}{y - 3}\right)^2$

89. $\frac{2x^2 + 5x - 3}{2x^2 - 9x + 9} + \frac{x + 1}{3 - 2x} + \frac{4x^2 + 8x + 3}{x - 3} \cdot \frac{x + 3}{9 - 4x^2}$

90. $\left(\frac{a}{a - b} + \frac{b}{a + b}\right)\left(\frac{1}{3a + b} + \frac{2a + 6b}{9a^2 - b^2}\right)$

91. Express

$$\frac{a - 3b}{a - b}$$

as a sum of two rational expressions with denominators that are opposites of each other. Answers may vary.

92. Use a graphing calculator to check the answer to Exercise 29.

93. Why does the word ERROR appear in the table displayed on p. 393?

6.5 Complex Rational Expressions

Using Division to Simplify • Multiplying by the LCD

A **complex rational expression** is a rational expression that has one or more rational expressions within its numerator or denominator. Here are some examples:

$$\frac{1 + \frac{2}{x}}{3}, \quad \frac{\frac{x + y}{7}}{\frac{2x}{x + 1}}, \quad \frac{\frac{4}{3} + \frac{1}{5}}{\frac{2}{x} - \frac{x}{y}}.$$

These are rational expressions within the complex rational expression.

Study Skills

If You Miss a Class

If you must miss a class, find out what the new assignment is. Try to determine what problems were reviewed, what new concepts were discussed, and what announcements (regarding quizzes, hand-in assignments, schedule of class meetings, etc.) you may have missed. If possible, borrow notes from a classmate who attended the class.

We will consider two methods for simplifying complex rational expressions. Each method offers certain advantages.

Using Division to Simplify (Method 1)

Our first method for simplifying complex rational expressions involves rewriting the expression as a quotient of two rational expressions.

To Simplify a Complex Rational Expression by Dividing

1. Add or subtract, as needed, to get a single rational expression in the numerator.
2. Add or subtract, as needed, to get a single rational expression in the denominator.
3. Divide the numerator by the denominator (invert and multiply).
4. If possible, simplify by removing a factor equal to 1.

The key here is to express a complex rational expression as one rational expression divided by another. We can then proceed as in Section 6.2.

EXAMPLE 1 Simplify: $\dfrac{\frac{x}{x - 3}}{\frac{4}{5x - 15}}$.

Solution Here the numerator and the denominator are already single rational expressions. This allows us to start by dividing (step 3), as in Section 6.2:

$$\frac{\frac{x}{x-3}}{\frac{4}{5x-15}} = \frac{x}{x-3} \div \frac{4}{5x-15}$$ Rewriting with a division symbol

$$= \frac{x}{x-3} \cdot \frac{5x-15}{4}$$ Multiplying by the reciprocal of the divisor (inverting and multiplying)

$$= \frac{x}{\cancel{x-3}} \cdot \frac{5(\cancel{x-3})}{4}$$ Factoring and removing a factor equal to 1: $\frac{x-3}{x-3} = 1$

$$= \frac{5x}{4}.$$

To use this method, we must sometimes add or subtract in the numerator and/or the denominator before we can divide.

EXAMPLE 2 Simplify.

a) $\dfrac{\frac{5}{2a} + \frac{1}{a}}{\frac{1}{4a} - \frac{5}{6}}$ **b)** $\dfrac{\frac{x^2}{y} - \frac{5}{x}}{xz}$

Solution

a) $$\frac{\frac{5}{2a} + \frac{1}{a}}{\frac{1}{4a} - \frac{5}{6}} = \frac{\frac{5}{2a} + \frac{1}{a} \cdot \frac{2}{2}}{\frac{1}{4a} \cdot \frac{3}{3} - \frac{5}{6} \cdot \frac{2a}{2a}}$$

← Multiplying by 1 to get the LCD, $2a$, for the numerator of the complex rational expression

← Multiplying by 1 to get the LCD, $12a$, for the denominator of the complex rational expression

$$= \frac{\frac{5}{2a} + \frac{2}{2a}}{\frac{3}{12a} - \frac{10a}{12a}} = \frac{\frac{7}{2a}}{\frac{3-10a}{12a}}$$

← Adding

← Subtracting

$$= \frac{7}{2a} \div \frac{3-10a}{12a}$$ Rewriting with a division symbol. This is often done mentally.

$$= \frac{7}{2a} \cdot \frac{12a}{3-10a}$$ Multiplying by the reciprocal of the divisor (inverting and multiplying)

$$= \frac{7}{\cancel{2a}} \cdot \frac{\cancel{2a} \cdot 6}{3-10a}$$ Removing a factor equal to 1: $\frac{2a}{2a} = 1$

$$= \frac{42}{3-10a}$$

b) $$\frac{\frac{x^2}{y} - \frac{5}{x}}{xz} = \frac{\frac{x^2}{y}\cdot\frac{x}{x} - \frac{5}{x}\cdot\frac{y}{y}}{xz}$$ ← Multiplying by 1 to get the LCD, xy, for the numerator of the complex rational expression

$$= \frac{\frac{x^3}{xy} - \frac{5y}{xy}}{xz}$$

$$= \frac{\frac{x^3 - 5y}{xy}}{xz}$$ ← Subtracting; ← If you prefer, write xz as $\frac{xz}{1}$.

$$= \frac{x^3 - 5y}{xy} \div (xz)$$ Rewriting with a division symbol

$$= \frac{x^3 - 5y}{xy} \cdot \frac{1}{xz}$$ Multiplying by the reciprocal of the divisor (inverting and multiplying)

$$= \frac{x^3 - 5y}{x^2yz}$$

Multiplying by the LCD (Method 2)

A second method for simplifying complex rational expressions relies on multiplying by a carefully chosen expression that is equal to 1. This multiplication by 1 will lead to a simpler, but equivalent, expression.

To Simplify a Complex Rational Expression by Multiplying by the LCD

1. Find the LCD of *all* rational expressions within the complex rational expression.
2. Multiply the complex rational expression by a factor equal to 1. Write 1 as the LCD over itself (LCD/LCD).
3. Simplify. No fractional expressions should remain within the complex rational expression.
4. Factor and, if possible, simplify.

EXAMPLE 3 Simplify: $$\frac{\frac{1}{2} + \frac{3}{4}}{\frac{5}{6} - \frac{3}{8}}.$$

Solution

1. Unlike Method 1, in which $\frac{1}{2} + \frac{3}{4}$ would be treated separately from $\frac{5}{6} - \frac{3}{8}$, here we look for the LCD of *all* four fractions. That LCD is 24.

2. We multiply by a form of 1, using the LCD:

$$\frac{\frac{1}{2}+\frac{3}{4}}{\frac{5}{6}-\frac{3}{8}} = \frac{\frac{1}{2}+\frac{3}{4}}{\frac{5}{6}-\frac{3}{8}} \cdot \frac{24}{24}$$

Multiplying by a factor equal to 1, using the LCD: $\frac{24}{24} = 1$

3. Using the distributive law, we perform the multiplication:

$$\frac{\frac{1}{2}+\frac{3}{4}}{\frac{5}{6}-\frac{3}{8}} \cdot \frac{24}{24} = \frac{\left(\frac{1}{2}+\frac{3}{4}\right)24}{\left(\frac{5}{6}-\frac{3}{8}\right)24}$$

← Multiplying the numerator by 24
Don't forget the parentheses!
← Multiplying the denominator by 24

$$= \frac{\frac{1}{2}(24)+\frac{3}{4}(24)}{\frac{5}{6}(24)-\frac{3}{8}(24)}$$

Using the distributive law

$$= \frac{12+18}{20-9}, \quad \text{or} \quad \frac{30}{11}.$$

Simplifying

4. The result, $\frac{30}{11}$, cannot be factored or simplified, so we are done.

Multiplying like this effectively clears fractions in both the top and the bottom of the complex rational expression. In Example 4 we follow, but do not number, the same four steps.

EXAMPLE 4 Simplify.

a) $\dfrac{\frac{3}{x}+\frac{1}{2x}}{\frac{1}{3x}-\frac{3}{4x}}$ **b)** $\dfrac{1-\frac{1}{x}}{1-\frac{1}{x^2}}$

Solution

a) The denominators within the complex expression are x, $2x$, $3x$, and $4x$, so the LCD is $12x$. We multiply by 1 using $(12x)/(12x)$:

$$\frac{\frac{3}{x}+\frac{1}{2x}}{\frac{1}{3x}-\frac{3}{4x}} = \frac{\frac{3}{x}+\frac{1}{2x}}{\frac{1}{3x}-\frac{3}{4x}} \cdot \frac{12x}{12x} = \frac{\frac{3}{x}(12x)+\frac{1}{2x}(12x)}{\frac{1}{3x}(12x)-\frac{3}{4x}(12x)}.$$

Using the distributive law

When we multiply by $12x$, all fractions in the numerator and the denominator of the complex rational expression are cleared:

$$\frac{\frac{3}{x}(12x)+\frac{1}{2x}(12x)}{\frac{1}{3x}(12x)-\frac{3}{4x}(12x)} = \frac{36+6}{4-9} = -\frac{42}{5}.$$

technology connection

Be careful to place parentheses properly when entering complex rational expressions into a graphing calculator. Remember to enclose the entire numerator of the complex rational expression in one set of parentheses and the entire denominator in another. For example, we enter the expression in Example 4(a) as

$$y_1 = (3/x + 1/(2x))$$
$$/(1/(3x) - 3/(4x)).$$

1. Write Example 4(b) as you would to enter it into a graphing calculator.
2. When must the numerator of a rational expression be enclosed in parentheses? the denominator?

b) $\dfrac{1-\dfrac{1}{x}}{1-\dfrac{1}{x^2}} = \dfrac{1-\dfrac{1}{x}}{1-\dfrac{1}{x^2}} \cdot \dfrac{x^2}{x^2}$ The LCD is x^2 so we multiply by 1 using x^2/x^2.

$= \dfrac{1 \cdot x^2 - \dfrac{1}{x} \cdot x^2}{1 \cdot x^2 - \dfrac{1}{x^2} \cdot x^2}$ Using the distributive law

$= \dfrac{x^2 - x}{x^2 - 1}$ All fractions have been cleared within the complex rational expression.

$= \dfrac{x(x-1)}{(x+1)(x-1)}$ Factoring and simplifying: $\dfrac{x-1}{x-1} = 1$

$= \dfrac{x}{x+1}$

It is important to understand both of the methods studied in this section. Sometimes, as in Example 1, the complex rational expression is either given as—or easily written as—a quotient of two rational expressions. In these cases, Method 1 (using division) is probably the easier method to use. Other times, as in Example 4(a), it is not difficult to find the LCD of all denominators in the complex rational expression. When this occurs, it is usually easier to use Method 2 (multiplying by the LCD). The more practice you get using both methods, the better you will be at selecting the easier method for any given problem.

6.5 Exercise Set

FOR EXTRA HELP

Student's Solutions Manual | Digital Video Tutor CD 4 Videotape 12 | AW Math Tutor Center | MathXL Tutorials on CD | MathXL | MyMathLab

Concept Reinforcement *In each of Exercises 1–4, use the method listed to match the accompanying expression with the expression in the column on the right that arises when that method is used.*

1. ____ $\dfrac{\dfrac{5}{x^2}+\dfrac{1}{x}}{\dfrac{7}{2}-\dfrac{3}{4x}}$; Multiplying by the LCD (Method 2)

2. ____ $\dfrac{\dfrac{5}{x^2}+\dfrac{1}{x}}{\dfrac{7}{2}-\dfrac{3}{4x}}$; Using division to simplify (Method 1)

3. ____ $\dfrac{\dfrac{4}{5x}-\dfrac{1}{10}}{\dfrac{8}{x^2}+\dfrac{7}{2}}$; Using division to simplify (Method 1)

4. ____ $\dfrac{\dfrac{4}{5x}-\dfrac{1}{10}}{\dfrac{8}{x^2}+\dfrac{7}{2}}$; Multiplying by the LCD (Method 2)

a) $\dfrac{\dfrac{5+x}{x^2}}{\dfrac{14x-3}{4x}}$

b) $\dfrac{\dfrac{8-x}{10x}}{\dfrac{16+7x^2}{2x^2}}$

c) $\dfrac{\dfrac{4}{5x}\cdot 10x^2 - \dfrac{1}{10}\cdot 10x^2}{\dfrac{8}{x^2}\cdot 10x^2 + \dfrac{7}{2}\cdot 10x^2}$

d) $\dfrac{\dfrac{5}{x^2}\cdot 4x^2 + \dfrac{1}{x}\cdot 4x^2}{\dfrac{7}{2}\cdot 4x^2 - \dfrac{3}{4x}\cdot 4x^2}$

Simplify. Use either method or the method specified by your instructor.

5. $\dfrac{1 + \dfrac{1}{2}}{1 + \dfrac{1}{4}}$

6. $\dfrac{1 + \dfrac{3}{4}}{1 + \dfrac{1}{2}}$

7. $\dfrac{4 + \dfrac{1}{3}}{1 - \dfrac{5}{27}}$

8. $\dfrac{3 + \dfrac{1}{5}}{1 - \dfrac{2}{15}}$

9. $\dfrac{\dfrac{s}{3} + s}{\dfrac{3}{s} + s}$

10. $\dfrac{\dfrac{1}{x} - 5}{\dfrac{1}{x} + 3}$

11. $\dfrac{\dfrac{4}{x}}{\dfrac{3}{x} + \dfrac{2}{x^2}}$

12. $\dfrac{\dfrac{5}{x} - \dfrac{2}{x^2}}{\dfrac{2}{x^2}}$

13. $\dfrac{\dfrac{2a - 5}{3a}}{\dfrac{a - 7}{6a}}$

14. $\dfrac{\dfrac{a + 5}{a^2}}{\dfrac{a - 2}{3a}}$

15. $\dfrac{\dfrac{x}{4} - \dfrac{4}{x}}{\dfrac{1}{4} + \dfrac{1}{x}}$

16. $\dfrac{\dfrac{3}{x} + \dfrac{3}{8}}{\dfrac{x}{8} - \dfrac{3}{x}}$

17. $\dfrac{\dfrac{1}{6} - \dfrac{1}{x}}{\dfrac{6 - x}{6}}$

18. $\dfrac{\dfrac{1}{7} + \dfrac{1}{a}}{\dfrac{7 + a}{7}}$

19. $\dfrac{\dfrac{1}{t^2} + 1}{\dfrac{1}{t} - 1}$

20. $\dfrac{2 + \dfrac{1}{x}}{2 - \dfrac{1}{x^2}}$

21. $\dfrac{\dfrac{x^2}{x^2 - y^2}}{\dfrac{x}{x + y}}$

22. $\dfrac{\dfrac{a^2}{a - 3}}{\dfrac{2a}{a^2 - 9}}$

23. $\dfrac{\dfrac{7}{a^2} + \dfrac{2}{a}}{\dfrac{5}{a^3} - \dfrac{3}{a}}$

24. $\dfrac{\dfrac{5}{x^3} - \dfrac{1}{x^2}}{\dfrac{2}{x} + \dfrac{3}{x^2}}$

25. $\dfrac{\dfrac{2}{7a^4} - \dfrac{1}{14a}}{\dfrac{3}{5a^2} + \dfrac{2}{15a}}$

26. $\dfrac{\dfrac{5}{4x^3} - \dfrac{3}{8x}}{\dfrac{3}{2x} + \dfrac{3}{4x^3}}$

Aha! **27.** $\dfrac{\dfrac{x}{5y^3} + \dfrac{3}{10y}}{\dfrac{3}{10y} + \dfrac{x}{5y^3}}$

28. $\dfrac{\dfrac{a}{6b^3} + \dfrac{4}{9b^2}}{\dfrac{5}{6b} - \dfrac{1}{9b^3}}$

29. $\dfrac{\dfrac{3}{ab^4} + \dfrac{4}{a^3b}}{\dfrac{5}{a^3b} - \dfrac{3}{ab}}$

30. $\dfrac{\dfrac{2}{x^2y} + \dfrac{3}{xy^2}}{\dfrac{3}{xy^2} + \dfrac{2}{x^2y}}$

31. $\dfrac{2 - \dfrac{3}{x^2}}{2 + \dfrac{3}{x^4}}$

32. $\dfrac{3 - \dfrac{2}{a^4}}{2 + \dfrac{3}{a^3}}$

33. $\dfrac{t - \dfrac{2}{t}}{t + \dfrac{5}{t}}$

34. $\dfrac{x + \dfrac{3}{x}}{x - \dfrac{2}{x}}$

35. $\dfrac{5 + \dfrac{4}{ab^3}}{\dfrac{3 + a}{a^2b}}$

36. $\dfrac{5 + \dfrac{3}{x^2y}}{\dfrac{3 + x}{x^3y}}$

37. $\dfrac{t + 5 + \dfrac{3}{t}}{t + 2 + \dfrac{1}{t}}$

38. $\dfrac{a + 3 + \dfrac{2}{a}}{a + 2 + \dfrac{5}{a}}$

39. $\dfrac{x - 2 - \dfrac{1}{x}}{x - 5 - \dfrac{4}{x}}$

40. $\dfrac{x - 3 - \dfrac{2}{x}}{x - 4 - \dfrac{3}{x}}$

41. Is it possible to simplify complex rational expressions without knowing how to divide rational expressions? Why or why not?

42. Why is the distributive law important when simplifying complex rational expressions?

SKILL MAINTENANCE

Solve.

43. $3x - 5 + 2(4x - 1) = 12x - 3$ [2.2]

44. $(x - 1)7 - (x + 1)9 = 4(x + 2)$ [2.2]

45. $\dfrac{3}{4}x - \dfrac{5}{8} = \dfrac{3}{8}x + \dfrac{7}{4}$ [2.2]

46. $\dfrac{5}{9} - \dfrac{2x}{3} = \dfrac{5x}{6} + \dfrac{4}{3}$ [2.2]

47. $x^2 - 7x - 30 = 0$ [5.6]

48. $x^2 + 8x - 20 = 0$ [5.6]

SYNTHESIS

49. Which of the two methods presented would you use to simplify Exercise 30? Why?

50. Which of the two methods presented would you use to simplify Exercise 22? Why?

In Exercises 51–54, find all x-values for which the given expression is undefined.

51. $\dfrac{\dfrac{x - 5}{x - 6}}{\dfrac{x - 7}{x - 8}}$

52. $\dfrac{\dfrac{x + 1}{x + 2}}{\dfrac{x + 3}{x + 4}}$

53. $\dfrac{\dfrac{2x + 3}{5x + 4}}{\dfrac{3}{7} - \dfrac{2x}{21}}$

54. $\dfrac{\dfrac{3x - 5}{2x - 7}}{\dfrac{4x}{5} - \dfrac{8}{15}}$

55. The formula

$$\frac{P\left(1+\dfrac{i}{12}\right)^2}{\dfrac{\left(1+\dfrac{i}{12}\right)^2-1}{\dfrac{i}{12}}},$$

where P is a loan amount and i is an interest rate, arises in certain business situations. Simplify this expression. (*Hint*: Expand the binomials.)

56. Find the simplified form for the reciprocal of

$$\frac{2}{x-1}-\frac{1}{3x-2}.$$

Simplify.

57. $\dfrac{\dfrac{5}{x+2}-\dfrac{3}{x-2}}{\dfrac{x}{x-1}+\dfrac{x}{x+1}}$

58. $\dfrac{\dfrac{x}{x+5}+\dfrac{3}{x+2}}{\dfrac{2}{x+2}-\dfrac{x}{x+5}}$

Aha! **59.** $\left[\dfrac{\dfrac{x-1}{x-1}-1}{\dfrac{x+1}{x-1}+1}\right]^5$

60. $1+\dfrac{1}{1+\dfrac{1}{1+\dfrac{1}{x}}}$

61. $\dfrac{\dfrac{z}{1-\dfrac{z}{2+2z}}-2z}{\dfrac{2z}{5z-2}-3}$

62. Under what circumstance(s) will there be no restrictions on the variable appearing in a complex rational expression?

63. Use a graphing calculator to check Example 2(a).

6.6 Solving Rational Equations

Solving a New Type of Equation • A Visual Interpretation

Our study of rational expressions allows us to solve a type of equation that we could not have solved prior to this chapter.

CONNECTING THE CONCEPTS

In Sections 6.1–6.5, we learned how to *simplify expressions* like

$$\frac{4x^2-9}{6x+9},\quad \frac{t^2-1}{8t}\cdot\frac{4t^2}{3},\quad \text{and}\quad \frac{\dfrac{5}{x}}{\dfrac{2}{x^2}+\dfrac{3}{x}}.$$

In this section, we will return to *solving equations*. These equations will look like the following:

$$x+\frac{6}{x}=-5\quad\text{and}\quad\frac{3}{x-5}+\frac{1}{x+5}=\frac{2}{x^2-25}.$$

As always, be careful not to confuse simplifying an expression with solving an equation. When expressions are simplified, the result is an equivalent expression. When equations are solved, the result is a solution.

Solving a New Type of Equation

A **rational**, or **fractional**, **equation** is an equation containing one or more rational expressions, often with the variable in a denominator. Here are some examples:

$$\frac{2}{3}+\frac{5}{6}=\frac{x}{9}, \qquad t+\frac{7}{t}=-5, \qquad \frac{x^2}{x-1}=\frac{1}{x-1}.$$

To Solve a Rational Equation

1. List any restrictions that exist. Numbers that make a denominator equal 0 cannot possibly be solutions.
2. Clear the equation of fractions by multiplying both sides by the LCM of the denominators.
3. Solve the resulting equation using the addition principle, the multiplication principle, and the principle of zero products, as needed.
4. Check the possible solution(s) in the original equation.

When clearing an equation of fractions, we use the terminology LCM instead of LCD because we are *not* adding or subtracting rational expressions.

Study Skills

Does More Than One Solution Exist?

Keep in mind that many problems—in math and elsewhere—have more than one solution. When asked to solve an equation, we are expected to find any and all solutions of the equation.

EXAMPLE 1 Solve: $\frac{x}{6}-\frac{x}{8}=\frac{1}{12}$.

Solution Because no variable appears in a denominator, no restrictions exist. The LCM of 6, 8, and 12 is 24, so we multiply both sides by 24:

$$24\left(\frac{x}{6}-\frac{x}{8}\right)=24\cdot\frac{1}{12}$$ Using the multiplication principle to multiply both sides by the LCM. Parentheses are important!

$$24\cdot\frac{x}{6}-24\cdot\frac{x}{8}=24\cdot\frac{1}{12}$$ Using the distributive law

Be sure to multiply *each* term by the LCM.

$$\frac{24x}{6}-\frac{24x}{8}=\frac{24}{12}$$
$$4x-3x=2$$
Simplifying. Note that all fractions have been cleared. If fractions remain, we have either made a mistake or have not used the LCM of the denominators.

$$x=2.$$

Check:

$$\frac{x}{6} - \frac{x}{8} = \frac{1}{12}$$

$$\frac{2}{6} - \frac{2}{8} \;\Big|\; \frac{1}{12}$$

$$\frac{1}{3} - \frac{1}{4}$$

$$\frac{4}{12} - \frac{3}{12}$$

$$\frac{1}{12} \stackrel{?}{=} \frac{1}{12} \quad \text{TRUE}$$

This checks, so the solution is 2.

Recall that the multiplication principle states that $a = b$ is equivalent to $a \cdot c = b \cdot c$, *provided c is not zero*. Because rational equations often have variables in a denominator, clearing fractions will now require us to multiply both sides by a variable expression. Since a variable expression could represent 0, *multiplying both sides of an equation by a variable expression does not always produce an equivalent equation.* Thus checking each solution in the original equation is essential.

EXAMPLE 2 Solve.

a) $\dfrac{2}{3x} + \dfrac{1}{x} = 10$

b) $x + \dfrac{6}{x} = -5$

c) $1 + \dfrac{3x}{x+2} = \dfrac{-6}{x+2}$

d) $\dfrac{3}{x-5} + \dfrac{1}{x+5} = \dfrac{2}{x^2-25}$

e) $\dfrac{x^2}{x-1} = \dfrac{1}{x-1}$

Solution

a) Note that x cannot be 0. The LCM is $3x$, so we multiply both sides by $3x$:

$$\frac{2}{3x} + \frac{1}{x} = 10$$
The LCM of $3x$ and x is $3x$; $x \neq 0$.

$$3x\left(\frac{2}{3x} + \frac{1}{x}\right) = 3x \cdot 10$$
Using the multiplication principle to multiply both sides by the LCM. *Don't forget the parentheses!*

$$\cancel{3x} \cdot \frac{2}{\cancel{3x}} + 3\cancel{x} \cdot \frac{1}{\cancel{x}} = 3x \cdot 10$$
Using the distributive law

$$2 + 3 = 30x$$
Removing factors equal to 1: $3x/(3x) = 1$ and $x/x = 1$. This clears all fractions.

$$5 = 30x$$

$$\frac{5}{30} = x, \quad \text{so } x = \frac{1}{6}.$$
Dividing both sides by 30, or multiplying both sides by 1/30

Since $\frac{1}{6} \neq 0$, and 0 is the only restricted value, $\frac{1}{6}$ *should* check.

Check:

$$\frac{2}{3x} + \frac{1}{x} = 10$$

$$\begin{array}{c|c} \dfrac{2}{3 \cdot \frac{1}{6}} + \dfrac{1}{\frac{1}{6}} & 10 \\ \dfrac{2}{\frac{1}{2}} + \dfrac{1}{\frac{1}{6}} & \\ 2 \cdot \frac{2}{1} + 1 \cdot \frac{6}{1} & \\ 4 + 6 & \end{array}$$

$$10 \stackrel{?}{=} 10 \quad \text{TRUE}$$

The solution is $\frac{1}{6}$.

b) Again, note that x cannot be 0. We multiply both sides by x to clear fractions:

$$x + \frac{6}{x} = -5$$ We cannot have $x = 0$.

$$x\left(x + \frac{6}{x}\right) = x(-5)$$ Multiplying both sides by x. *Don't forget the parentheses!*

$$x \cdot x + \not{x} \cdot \frac{6}{\not{x}} = -5x$$ Using the distributive law

$$x^2 + 6 = -5x$$ Removing a factor equal to 1: $x/x = 1$. We are left with a quadratic equation.

$$x^2 + 5x + 6 = 0$$ Using the addition principle to add $5x$ to both sides

$$(x + 3)(x + 2) = 0$$ Factoring

$$x + 3 = 0 \quad \text{or} \quad x + 2 = 0$$ Using the principle of zero products

$$x = -3 \quad \text{or} \quad x = -2.$$ Since neither solution is 0, the restriction in the first step, both answers should check.

Check: For -3:

$$x + \frac{6}{x} = -5$$

$$\begin{array}{c|c} -3 + \dfrac{6}{-3} & -5 \\ -3 - 2 & \end{array}$$

$$-5 \stackrel{?}{=} -5 \quad \text{TRUE}$$

For -2:

$$x + \frac{6}{x} = -5$$

$$\begin{array}{c|c} -2 + \dfrac{6}{-2} & -5 \\ -2 - 3 & \end{array}$$

$$-5 \stackrel{?}{=} -5 \quad \text{TRUE}$$

Both of these check, so there are two solutions, -3 and -2.

Student Notes

Not all checking is for finding errors in computation. For these equations, the solution process itself can introduce numbers that do not check.

c) To avoid division by 0, we must have $x + 2 \neq 0$, or $x \neq -2$. With this restriction in mind, we multiply both sides of the equation by the LCM:

$$1 + \frac{3x}{x + 2} = \frac{-6}{x + 2} \qquad \text{We cannot have } x = -2.$$

$$(x + 2)\left(1 + \frac{3x}{x + 2}\right) = (x + 2)\frac{-6}{x + 2} \qquad \text{Multiplying both sides by } x + 2\text{. Don't forget the parentheses.}$$

$$(x + 2) \cdot 1 + \cancel{(x + 2)}\frac{3x}{\cancel{x + 2}} = \cancel{(x + 2)}\frac{-6}{\cancel{x + 2}} \qquad \text{Using the distributive law; removing a factor equal to 1: } (x + 2)/(x + 2) = 1$$

$$x + 2 + 3x = -6$$

$$4x + 2 = -6$$

$$4x = -8$$

$$x = -2. \qquad \text{Above, we stated that } x \neq -2.$$

Because of the above restriction, -2 must be rejected as a solution. The check below simply confirms this.

Check:

$$\begin{array}{c|c} 1 + \dfrac{3x}{x + 2} & \dfrac{-6}{x + 2} \\ \hline 1 + \dfrac{3(-2)}{-2 + 2} & \dfrac{-6}{-2 + 2} \end{array}$$

$$1 + \frac{-6}{0} \stackrel{?}{=} \frac{-6}{0} \qquad \text{FALSE}$$

The equation has no solution.

d)

$$\frac{3}{x - 5} + \frac{1}{x + 5} = \frac{2}{x^2 - 25} \qquad \text{Note that } x \neq 5 \text{ and } x \neq -5\text{. The LCM of } x - 5,\ x + 5, \text{ and } x^2 - 25 \text{ is } (x - 5)(x + 5).$$

$$(x - 5)(x + 5)\left(\frac{3}{x - 5} + \frac{1}{x + 5}\right) = (x - 5)(x + 5)\frac{2}{(x - 5)(x + 5)}$$

$$\frac{\cancel{(x - 5)}(x + 5)3}{\cancel{x - 5}} + \frac{(x - 5)\cancel{(x + 5)}}{\cancel{x + 5}} = \frac{2\cancel{(x - 5)}\cancel{(x + 5)}}{\cancel{(x - 5)}\cancel{(x + 5)}} \qquad \text{Using the distributive law}$$

$$(x + 5)3 + (x - 5) = 2 \qquad \left\{\text{Removing factors equal to 1: } \frac{x - 5}{x - 5} = 1,\ \frac{x + 5}{x + 5} = 1, \text{ and } \frac{(x - 5)(x + 5)}{(x - 5)(x + 5)} = 1\right.$$

$$3x + 15 + x - 5 = 2 \qquad \text{Using the distributive law}$$

$$4x + 10 = 2$$

$$4x = -8$$

$$x = -2 \qquad -2 \neq 5 \text{ and } -2 \neq -5, \text{ so } -2 \textit{ should} \text{ check.}$$

We leave it to the student to check that -2 is the solution.

e) To avoid division by 0, we must have $x - 1 \neq 0$, or $x \neq 1$. With this restriction in mind, we multiply both sides by $x - 1$ to clear fractions:

$\dfrac{x^2}{x-1} = \dfrac{1}{x-1}$	We cannot have $x = 1$.
$(x-1) \cdot \dfrac{x^2}{x-1} = (x-1) \cdot \dfrac{1}{x-1}$	Multiplying both sides by $x - 1$
$x^2 = 1$	Removing a factor equal to 1: $(x-1)/(x-1) = 1$
$x^2 - 1 = 0$	Subtracting 1 from both sides
$(x-1)(x+1) = 0$	Factoring
$x - 1 = 0 \quad or \quad x + 1 = 0$	Using the principle of zero products
$x = 1 \quad or \quad x = -1.$	Above, we stated that $x \neq 1$.

Because of the above restriction, 1 must be rejected as a solution. The student should check in the original equation that -1 *does* check. The solution is -1.

A Visual Interpretation

ALGEBRAIC–GRAPHICAL CONNECTION

We can obtain a visual check of the solutions of a rational equation by graphing. For example, consider the equation

$$\frac{x}{4} + \frac{x}{2} = 6.$$

We can examine the solution by graphing the equations

$$y = \frac{x}{4} + \frac{x}{2} \quad \text{and} \quad y = 6$$

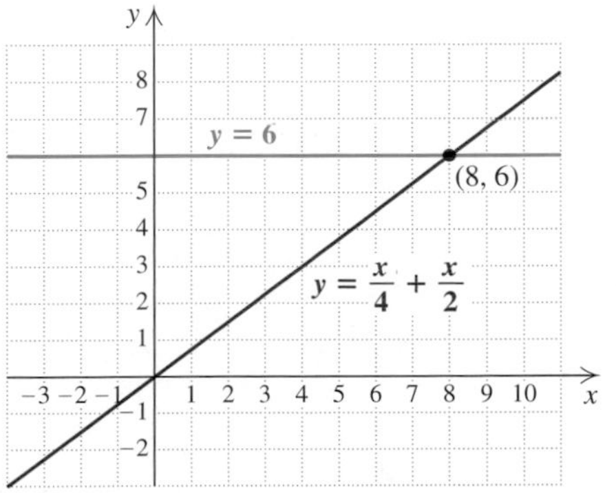

using the same set of axes, as shown at left.

The y-values for each equation will be the same where the graphs intersect. The x-value of that point will yield that value, so it will be the solution of the equation. It appears from the graph that when $x = 8$, the value of $x/4 + x/2$ is 6. We can check by substitution:

$$\frac{x}{4} + \frac{x}{2} = \frac{8}{4} + \frac{8}{2} = 2 + 4 = 6.$$

Thus the solution is 8.

technology connection

We can use a table to check possible solutions of rational equations. Consider the equation in Example 2(e),

$$\frac{x^2}{x-1} = \frac{1}{x-1},$$

and the possible solutions that were found, 1 and -1. To check these solutions, we enter $y_1 = x^2/(x-1)$ and $y_2 = 1/(x-1)$. After setting Indpnt to Ask and Depend to Auto in the TBLSET menu, we display the table and enter $x = 1$. The ERROR messages indicate that 1 is not a solution because it is not an allowable replacement for x in the equation. Next, we enter $x = -1$. Since y_1 and y_2 have the same value, we know that the equation is true when $x = -1$, and thus -1 is a solution.

X	Y1	Y2
1	ERROR	ERROR
−1	−.5	−.5

X =

Use a graphing calculator to check the possible solutions of Example 1 and Example 2, parts (a)–(d).

6.6 Exercise Set

FOR EXTRA HELP

Student's Solutions Manual | Digital Video Tutor CD 4 Videotape 12 | AW Math Tutor Center | MathXL Tutorials on CD | MathXL | MyMathLab

Concept Reinforcement *Classify each statement as either true or false.*

1. Every rational equation has at least one solution.
2. It is possible for a rational equation to have more than one solution.
3. When both sides of an equation are multiplied by a variable expression, the result is not always an equivalent equation.
4. All the equation-solving principles studied thus far may be needed when solving a rational equation.

Solve. If no solution exists, state this.

5. $\frac{3}{5} - \frac{5}{8} = \frac{x}{20}$

6. $\frac{4}{5} - \frac{2}{3} = \frac{x}{9}$

7. $\frac{1}{3} + \frac{5}{6} = \frac{1}{x}$

8. $\frac{3}{5} + \frac{1}{8} = \frac{1}{x}$

9. $\frac{1}{6} + \frac{1}{8} = \frac{1}{t}$

10. $\frac{1}{8} + \frac{1}{10} = \frac{1}{t}$

11. $x + \frac{5}{x} = -6$

12. $x + \frac{6}{x} = -7$

13. $\frac{x}{6} - \frac{6}{x} = 0$

14. $\frac{x}{7} - \frac{7}{x} = 0$

15. $\frac{5}{x} = \frac{6}{x} - \frac{1}{3}$

16. $\frac{4}{t} = \frac{5}{t} - \frac{1}{2}$

17. $\frac{5}{3t} + \frac{3}{t} = 1$

18. $\frac{3}{4x} + \frac{5}{x} = 1$

19. $\frac{x-8}{x+3} = \frac{1}{4}$

20. $\frac{a-4}{a+5} = \frac{3}{8}$

21. $x + \frac{12}{x} = -7$

22. $x + \frac{8}{x} = -9$

23. $\frac{2}{x+1} = \frac{1}{x-2}$

24. $\frac{5}{x-1} = \frac{3}{x+2}$

25. $\frac{a}{6} - \frac{a}{10} = \frac{1}{6}$

26. $\frac{t}{8} - \frac{t}{12} = \frac{1}{8}$

27. $\frac{x+1}{3} - 1 = \frac{x-1}{2}$

28. $\frac{x+2}{5} - 1 = \frac{x-2}{4}$

29. $\frac{4}{t-5} = \frac{t-1}{t-5}$

30. $\frac{2}{t-9} = \frac{t-7}{t-9}$

31. $\frac{3}{x+4} = \frac{5}{x}$

32. $\frac{2}{x+3} = \frac{7}{x}$

33. $\frac{a-4}{a-1} = \frac{a+2}{a-2}$

34. $\frac{x-2}{x-3} = \frac{x-1}{x+1}$

35. $\frac{5}{t-2} + \frac{3t}{t-2} = \frac{4}{t^2-4t+4}$

36. $\frac{4}{t-3} + \frac{2t}{t-3} = \frac{12}{t^2-6t+9}$

37. $\frac{4}{x-3} + \frac{2x}{x^2-9} = \frac{1}{x+3}$

38. $\frac{x}{x+4} - \frac{4}{x-4} = \frac{x^2+16}{x^2-16}$

39. $\frac{5}{y-3} - \frac{30}{y^2-9} = 1$

40. $\frac{1}{x+3} + \frac{1}{x-3} = \frac{1}{x^2-9}$

41. $\frac{4}{8-a} = \frac{4-a}{a-8}$

42. $\frac{t+10}{7-t} = \frac{3}{t-7}$

Aha! 43. $\frac{-2}{x+2} = \frac{x}{x+2}$

44. $\frac{3}{2x-6} = \frac{x}{2x-6}$

45. When solving rational equations, why do we multiply each side by the LCM of the denominators?

46. Explain the difference between adding rational expressions and solving rational equations.

SKILL MAINTENANCE

47. The sum of two consecutive odd numbers is 276. Find the numbers. [2.5]

48. The length of a rectangular picture window is 3 yd greater than the width. The area of the rectangle is 10 yd^2. Find the perimeter. [5.7]

49. The height of a triangle is 3 cm longer than its base. If the area of the triangle is 54 cm^2, find the measurements of the base and the height. [5.7]

50. The product of two consecutive even integers is 48. Find the numbers. [5.7]

51. *Human physiology.* Between June 9 and June 24, Seth's beard grew 0.9 cm. Find the rate at which Seth's beard grows. [3.4]

52. *Gardening.* Between July 7 and July 12, Carla's string beans grew 1.4 in. Find the string beans' growth rate. [3.4]

SYNTHESIS

53. Describe a method that can be used to create rational equations that have no solution.

54. How can a graph be used to determine how many solutions an equation has?

Solve.

55. $1 + \frac{x-1}{x-3} = \frac{2}{x-3} - x$

56. $\frac{4}{y-2} + \frac{3}{y^2-4} = \frac{5}{y+2} + \frac{2y}{y^2-4}$

57. $\frac{x}{x^2+3x-4} + \frac{x+1}{x^2+6x+8} = \frac{2x}{x^2+x-2}$

58. $\frac{12-6x}{x^2-4} = \frac{3x}{x+2} - \frac{3-2x}{2-x}$

59. $\frac{x^2}{x^2-4} = \frac{x}{x+2} - \frac{2x}{2-x}$

60. $7 - \frac{a-2}{a+3} = \frac{a^2-4}{a+3} + 5$

61. $\frac{1}{x-1} + x - 5 = \frac{5x-4}{x-1} - 6$

62. $\frac{5-3a}{a^2+4a+3} - \frac{2a+2}{a+3} = \frac{3-a}{a+1}$

63. Use a graphing calculator to check your answers to Exercises 13, 21, 31, and 55.

6.7 Applications Using Rational Equations and Proportions

Problems Involving Work • Problems Involving Motion • Problems Involving Proportions

In many areas of study, applications involving rates, proportions, or reciprocals translate to rational equations. By using the five steps for problem solving and the lessons of Section 6.6, we can now solve such problems.

Problems Involving Work

EXAMPLE 1 Sorting recyclables. Cecilia and Aaron work as volunteers at a town's recycling depot. Cecilia can sort a day's accumulation of recyclables in 4 hr, while Aaron requires 6 hr to do the same job. How long would it take them, working together, to sort the recyclables?

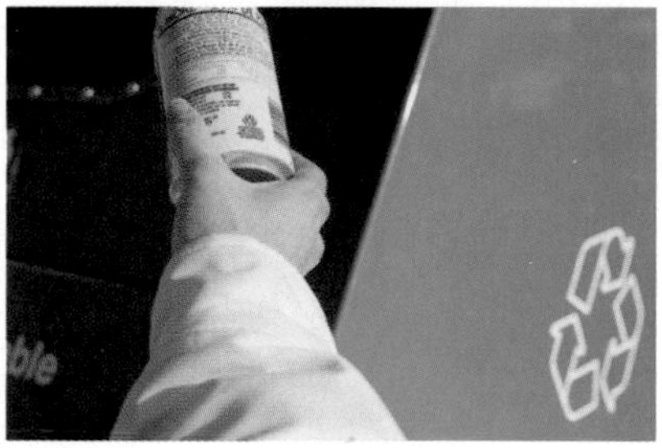

Solution

1. **Familiarize.** We familiarize ourselves with the problem by exploring two common, but *incorrect*, approaches.

   a) One common incorrect approach is to simply add the two times:

   $4\text{ hr} + 6\text{ hr} = 10\text{ hr}.$

   Let's think about this. If Cecilia can do the sorting *alone* in 4 hr, then Cecilia and Aaron *together* should take *less* than 4 hr. Thus we reject 10 hr as a solution and reason that the answer must be less than 4 hr.

   b) Another incorrect approach is to assume that Cecilia does half the sorting and Aaron does the other half. Then

   Cecilia sorts $\frac{1}{2}$ of the accumulation in $\frac{1}{2}(4\text{ hr})$, or 2 hr, and
   Aaron sorts $\frac{1}{2}$ of the accumulation in $\frac{1}{2}(6\text{ hr})$, or 3 hr.

   This would waste time since Cecilia would finish 1 hr earlier than Aaron. In reality, Cecilia would help Aaron after completing her half, so that Aaron would actually sort less than half of the accumulation. This tells us that the entire job will take them between 2 hr and 3 hr.

   A correct approach is to consider how much of the sorting is finished in 1 hr, 2 hr, 3 hr, and so on. It takes Cecilia 4 hr to sort the recyclables alone, so her *rate* is $\frac{1}{4}$ of the job per hour. It takes Aaron 6 hr to do the sorting alone, so his *rate* is $\frac{1}{6}$ of the job per hour. Working together, they can complete

   $\frac{1}{4} + \frac{1}{6}$, or $\frac{5}{12}$ of the sorting in 1 hr. Their rate working together is the sum of their individual rates.

Study Skills

Plug It In

Every solution of an equation can be checked by substituting that value in the original equation. Take advantage of the opportunity to determine (without consulting the back of the book) if your answers are correct. When solving applied problems, check to make sure that your answer checks in the original statement of the problem.

In 2 hr, Cecilia can do $\frac{1}{4} \cdot 2$ of the sorting and Aaron can do $\frac{1}{6} \cdot 2$ of the sorting. Working together, they can complete

$$\frac{1}{4} \cdot 2 + \frac{1}{6} \cdot 2, \quad \text{or } \frac{5}{6} \text{ of the sorting in 2 hr.}$$

Note that $\frac{5}{12} \cdot 2 = \frac{5}{6}$.

Continuing this reasoning, we can form a table.

Time	Fraction of the Sorting Completed		
	Cecilia	**Aaron**	**Together**
1 hr	$\frac{1}{4}$	$\frac{1}{6}$	$\frac{1}{4} + \frac{1}{6}$, or $\frac{5}{12}$
2 hr	$\frac{1}{4} \cdot 2$	$\frac{1}{6} \cdot 2$	$\left(\frac{1}{4} + \frac{1}{6}\right)2$, or $\frac{5}{12} \cdot 2$, or $\frac{5}{6}$ ← This is too little.
3 hr	$\frac{1}{4} \cdot 3$	$\frac{1}{6} \cdot 3$	$\left(\frac{1}{4} + \frac{1}{6}\right)3$, or $\frac{5}{12} \cdot 3$, or $1\frac{1}{4}$ ← This is too much.
t hr	$\frac{1}{4} \cdot t$	$\frac{1}{6} \cdot t$	$\left(\frac{1}{4} + \frac{1}{6}\right)t$, or $\frac{5}{12} \cdot t$

From the table, we see that if they work 3 hr, the fraction of the sorting that they complete is $1\frac{1}{4}$, which is more of the job than needs to be done. We need to find a number t for which the fraction of the sorting that is completed in t hours is exactly 1, no more and no less.

2. **Translate.** From the table, we see that the time we want is some number t for which

Portion of work done by Cecilia in t hr: $\frac{1}{4} \cdot t$; Portion of work done by Aaron in t hr: $\frac{1}{6} \cdot t$

$$\frac{1}{4} \cdot t + \frac{1}{6} \cdot t = 1$$

or

$$\left(\frac{1}{4} + \frac{1}{6}\right)t = 1 \quad \text{or} \quad \frac{5}{12} \cdot t = 1.$$

Portion of work done together in t hr

3. **Carry out.** We can choose any one of the above equations to solve:

$$\frac{5}{12} \cdot t = 1$$

$$\frac{12}{5} \cdot \frac{5}{12} \cdot t = \frac{12}{5} \cdot 1 \qquad \text{Multiplying both sides by } \tfrac{12}{5}$$

$$t = \frac{12}{5}, \quad \text{or} \quad 2\frac{2}{5} \text{ hr.}$$

4. **Check.** The check can be done following the pattern used in the table of the *Familiarize* step above:

$$\frac{1}{4} \cdot \frac{12}{5} + \frac{1}{6} \cdot \frac{12}{5} = \frac{3}{5} + \frac{2}{5} = \frac{5}{5} = 1.$$

A second, partial, check is that (as we predicted in step 1) the answer is between 2 hr and 3 hr.

5. **State.** Together, it takes Cecilia and Aaron $2\frac{2}{5}$ hr to complete the sorting.

The Work Principle

Suppose that A requires a units of time to complete a task and B requires b units of time to complete the same task. Then

A works at a rate of $\dfrac{1}{a}$ tasks per unit of time,

B works at a rate of $\dfrac{1}{b}$ tasks per unit of time, and

A and B together work at a rate of $\dfrac{1}{a} + \dfrac{1}{b}$ tasks per unit of time.

If A and B, working together, require t units of time to complete the task, then their rate is $1/t$ and the following equations hold:

$$\frac{1}{a} \cdot t + \frac{1}{b} \cdot t = 1; \quad \left(\frac{1}{a} + \frac{1}{b}\right)t = 1; \quad \frac{t}{a} + \frac{t}{b} = 1; \quad \frac{1}{a} + \frac{1}{b} = \frac{1}{t}.$$

Problems Involving Motion

Problems that deal with distance, speed (or rate), and time are called **motion problems**. Translation of these problems involves the distance formula, $d = r \cdot t$, and/or the equivalent formulas $r = d/t$ and $t = d/r$.

EXAMPLE 2 Flight speed. Because of a tailwind, a Delta Boeing 777 is able to fly 200 mph faster than a Northwest 777 that is flying *into* the wind. In the same time that it takes the Delta plane to travel 1800 mi, the Northwest plane flies 1200 mi. How fast is each plane traveling?

Solution

1. **Familiarize.** Suppose that the Northwest plane is traveling 300 mph. Then the Delta plane would be flying 300 + 200, or 500 mph. Thus if r is the speed of the Northwest plane, in miles per hour, then the Delta plane is traveling $r + 200$ mph.

   At 300 mph, the Northwest flight would travel 1200 mi in 1200/300, or 4 hr. At 500 mph, the Delta plane would travel 1800 mi in 1800/500, or $3\frac{3}{5}$ hr. Since both planes spend the same amount of time traveling, and since 4 hr $\neq 3\frac{3}{5}$ hr, we see that our guess of 300 mph is incorrect. Rather than check another guess, we form a table.

	Distance =	*Rate* ·	*Time*
	Distance (in miles)	**Speed (in miles per hour)**	**Time (in hours)**
Northwest	1200	r	
Delta	1800	$r + 200$	

2. Translate. Examine how we checked our guess. We found, and then compared, the two flight times. The times were found by dividing the distances, 1200 mi and 1800 mi, by the rates, 300 mph and 500 mph, respectively. Thus the blanks in the table above can be filled, using *time* = *distance*/*rate*. This yields a table that uses only one variable.

	Distance (in miles)	**Speed (in miles per hour)**	**Time (in hours)**
Northwest	1200	r	$1200/r$
Delta	1800	$r + 200$	$1800/(r + 200)$

The times must be the same.

Since the times must be the same for both planes, we have the equation

$$\frac{1200}{r} = \frac{1800}{r + 200}.$$

Note that $\frac{\text{mi}}{\text{mph}} = \frac{\text{mi}}{\text{mi/hr}} = \cancel{\text{mi}} \cdot \frac{\text{hr}}{\cancel{\text{mi}}} = \text{hr}$, so we are indeed comparing two times.

3. Carry out. To solve the equation, we first multiply both sides by the LCM of the denominators, $r(r + 200)$:

$$r(r + 200) \cdot \frac{1200}{r} = r(r + 200) \cdot \frac{1800}{r + 200}$$ Multiplying both sides by the LCM, $r(r + 200)$. Note that we must have $r \neq 0$ and $r \neq -200$.

$(r + 200)1200 = 1800r$ Simplifying

$1200r + 240{,}000 = 1800r$ Using the distributive law

$240{,}000 = 600r$ Subtracting $1200r$ from both sides

$400 = r.$ Dividing both sides by 600

We now have a possible solution. The speed of the Northwest plane is 400 mph, and the speed of the Delta plane is 400 + 200, or 600 mph.

4. **Check.** We first reread the problem to confirm that we were to find the speeds. Note that, at 600 mph, the Delta flight would indeed be traveling 200 mph faster than the Northwest flight. At 600 mph, the Delta plane would cover 1800 mi in 1800/600, or 3 hr. If the Northwest plane flies 1200 mi at 400 mph, it is flying for 1200/400, or 3 hr. Since the times are the same, the speeds check.
5. **State.** The Northwest 777 is flying 400 mph and the Delta 777 is flying 600 mph.

Problems Involving Proportions

A **ratio** of two quantities is their quotient. For example, 37% is the ratio of 37 to 100, or $\frac{37}{100}$. A **proportion** is an equation stating that two ratios are equal.

Proportion

An equality of ratios, $A/B = C/D$, is called a *proportion*. The numbers within a proportion are said to be *proportional* to each other.

Proportions arise in geometry when we are studying *similar triangles*. If two triangles are **similar**, then their corresponding angles have the same measure and their corresponding sides are proportional. To illustrate, if triangle ABC is similar to triangle RST, then angles A and R have the same measure, angles B and S have the same measure, angles C and T have the same measure, and

$$\frac{a}{r} = \frac{b}{s} = \frac{c}{t}.$$

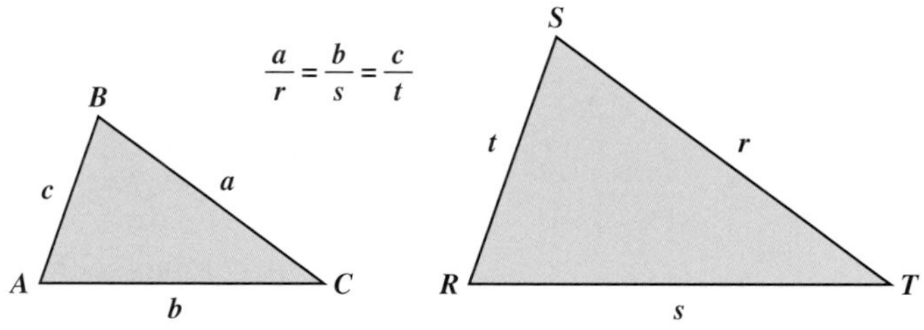

EXAMPLE 3 Similar triangles. Triangles ABC and XYZ are similar. Solve for z if $x = 10$, $a = 8$, and $c = 5$.

Solution We make a drawing, write a proportion, and then solve. Note that side a is always opposite angle A, side x is always opposite angle X, and so on.

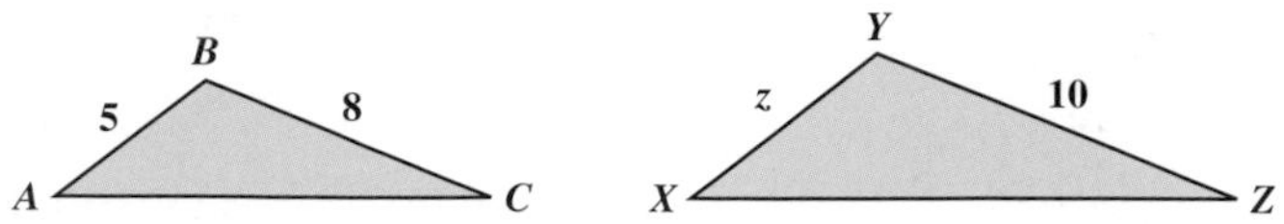

We have

$$\frac{z}{5} = \frac{10}{8}$$ The proportions $\frac{5}{z} = \frac{8}{10}$, $\frac{5}{8} = \frac{z}{10}$, or $\frac{8}{5} = \frac{10}{z}$ could also be used.

$$z = \frac{10}{8} \cdot 5$$ Multiplying both sides by 5

$$z = \frac{50}{8}, \text{ or } 6.25.$$

EXAMPLE 4 Architecture. A *blueprint* is a scale drawing of a building representing an architect's plans. Emily is adding 12 ft to the length of an apartment and needs to indicate the addition on an existing blueprint. If a 10-ft long bedroom is represented by $2\frac{1}{2}$ in. on the blueprint, how much longer should Emily make the drawing in order to represent the addition?

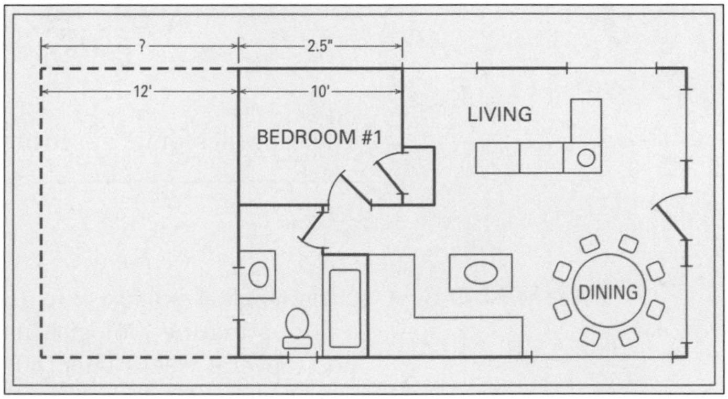

Solution We let w represent the width, in inches, of the addition that Emily is drawing. Because the drawing must be to scale, we have

$$\begin{matrix}\text{Inches on drawing} \longrightarrow \\ \text{Feet in real life} \longrightarrow\end{matrix} \frac{w}{12} = \frac{2.5}{10}. \begin{matrix}\longleftarrow \text{Inches on drawing} \\ \longleftarrow \text{Feet in real life}\end{matrix}$$

To solve for w, we multiply both sides by the LCM of the denominators, 60:

$$60 \cdot \frac{w}{12} = 60 \cdot \frac{2.5}{10}$$

$$5w = 6 \cdot 2.5$$ Simplifying

$$w = \frac{15}{5}, \text{ or } 3.$$

Emily should make the blueprint 3 in. longer.

Proportions can be used to solve a variety of applied problems.

EXAMPLE 5 Mileage. The 2004 Toyota Prius is a gasoline–electric car that travels approximately 220 mi on 4 gal of gas (*Source*: www.Toyota.com). Find the amount of gas required for a 700-mi trip.

Solution By assuming that the car always burns gas at the same rate, we can form a proportion in which the ratio of miles to gallons is expressed in two ways:

$$\begin{matrix}\text{Miles} \longrightarrow \\ \text{Gallons} \longrightarrow\end{matrix} \frac{220}{4} = \frac{700}{x}. \begin{matrix}\longleftarrow \text{Miles} \\ \longleftarrow \text{Gallons}\end{matrix}$$

To solve for x, we multiply both sides of the equation by the LCD, $4x$:

$$4x \cdot \frac{220}{4} = 4x \cdot \frac{700}{x}$$ We could also simplify first and solve $55 = \frac{700}{x}$.

$$\cancel{4} \cdot \frac{220x}{\cancel{4}} = \cancel{x} \cdot \frac{4 \cdot 700}{\cancel{x}}$$ Removing factors equal to 1: $\frac{4}{4} = 1$ and $\frac{x}{x} = 1$

$$220x = 4 \cdot 700$$

$$x = \frac{4 \cdot 700}{220}$$ Dividing both sides by 220

$$x \approx 12.7.$$ Simplifying

The trip will require approximately 12.7 gal of gasoline.

EXAMPLE 6 Environmental science. To determine the number of humpback whales in a pod, a marine biologist, using tail markings, identifies 27 members of the pod. Several weeks later, 40 whales from the pod are randomly sighted. Of the 40 sighted, 12 are from the 27 originally identified. Estimate the number of whales in the pod.

Solution

1. **Familiarize.** If we knew that the 27 whales that were first identified constituted, say, 10% of the pod, we could easily calculate the pod's population from the proportion

$$\frac{27}{W} = \frac{10}{100},$$

where W is the size of the pod's population. Unfortunately, we are *not* told the percentage of the pod identified. We must reread the problem, looking for numbers that could be used to approximate this percentage.

2. **Translate.** Since 12 of the 40 whales that were later sighted were among those originally identified, the ratio 12/40 estimates the percentage of the pod originally identified. We can then translate to a proportion:

$$\begin{matrix}\text{Whales originally identified} \longrightarrow \\ \text{Entire pod} \longrightarrow\end{matrix} \frac{27}{W} = \frac{12}{40}. \begin{matrix}\longleftarrow \text{Original whales sighted later} \\ \longleftarrow \text{Whales sighted later}\end{matrix}$$

3. Carry out. To solve the proportion, we multiply by the LCD, $40W$.

$$40\cancel{W} \cdot \frac{27}{\cancel{W}} = \cancel{40}W \cdot \frac{12}{\cancel{40}} \qquad \text{Multiplying both sides by } 40W$$

$$40 \cdot 27 = W \cdot 12 \qquad \text{Removing factors equal to 1: } W/W = 1 \text{ and } 40/40 = 1$$

$$\frac{40 \cdot 27}{12} = W \quad \text{or} \quad W = 90. \qquad \text{Dividing both sides by 12}$$

4. Check. The check is left to the student.

5. State. There are about 90 whales in the pod.

6.7 Exercise Set

FOR EXTRA HELP

Student's Solutions Manual | Digital Video Tutor CD 4 Videotape 12 | AW Math Tutor Center | MathXL Tutorials on CD | MathXL | MyMathLab

Solve.

1. *Volunteerism.* As a "Flynn Spirit," it takes Ned 20 min to fold up all the seats in the Flynn Theater following a performance. Linda requires 30 min to do the job when she volunteers as a Flynn Spirit. How long would it take Ned and Linda to fold up the seats working together?

2. *Construction.* It takes Fontella 4 hr to put up paneling in a room. Omar takes 5 hr to do the same job. How long would it take them, working together, to panel the room?

3. *Carpentry.* By checking work records, a carpenter finds that Juanita can build a small shed in 12 hr. Anton can do the same job in 16 hr. How long would it take if they worked together?

4. *Shoveling.* Vern can shovel the snow from his driveway in 45 min. Nina can do the same job in 60 min. How long would it take Nina and Vern to shovel the driveway if they worked together?

5. *Raking.* Zoe can rake her yard in 4 hr. Steffi does the same job in 3 hr. How long would it take the two of them, working together, to rake the yard?

6. *Masonry.* By checking work records, a contractor finds that it takes Kenny Dewitt 8 hr to construct a wall of a certain size. It takes Betty Wohnt 6 hr to construct the same wall. How long would it take if they worked together?

7. *Plumbing.* By checking work records, a plumber finds that Raul can plumb a house in 48 hr. Mira can do the same job in 36 hr. How long would it take if they worked together?

8. *Gardening.* Nicole can weed her vegetable garden in 50 min, while Glen can weed the same garden in 40 min. How long would it take if they worked together?

9. *Fence construction.* It takes Jorge, working alone, 4 days to construct a fence around a 2-acre parcel of land. Carla can construct the fence in 5 days. How long would it take the two of them, working together, to construct the fence?

10. *Harvesting.* Bobbi can pick a quart of raspberries in 20 min. Blanche can pick a quart in 25 min. How long would it take if Bobbi and Blanche worked together?

11. *Multifunction copiers.* The Sharp AL-1540CS can copy Charlotte's dissertation in 12 min. The Brother DCP-1000 can copy the same document in 18 min. If the two machines work together, how long would they take to copy the dissertation?
Source: Manufacturers' marketing brochures

12. *Fax machines.* The Canon Imageclass D680 can fax a year-end report in 7 min while the HP Officejet 6110 can fax the same report in 14 min. How long would it take the two machines, working together, to fax the report? (Assume that the recipient has at least two machines for incoming faxes.)
Source: Manufacturers' marketing brochures

13. *Train speeds.* A B & M freight train is traveling 14 km/h slower than an AMTRAK passenger train. The B & M train travels 330 km in the same time that it takes the AMTRAK train to travel 400 km. Find their speeds. Complete the following table as part of the familiarization.

	Distance =	***Rate*** ·	***Time***
	Distance (in km)	**Speed (in km/h)**	**Time (in hours)**
B & M	330		
AMTRAK	400	r	$\frac{400}{r}$

14. *Speed of travel.* A loaded Roadway truck is moving 40 mph faster than a New York Railways freight train. In the time that it takes the train to travel 150 mi, the truck travels 350 mi. Find their speeds. Complete the following table as part of the familiarization.

	Distance =	***Rate*** ·	***Time***
	Distance (in miles)	**Speed (in miles per hour)**	**Time (in hours)**
Truck	350	r	$\frac{350}{r}$
Train	150		

15. *Driving speed.* Hillary's Lexus travels 30 mph faster than Bill's Harley. In the same time that Bill travels 75 mi, Hillary travels 120 mi. Find their speeds.

16. *Bicycle speed.* Hank bicycles 5 km/h slower than Kelly. In the time that it takes Hank to bicycle 42 km, Kelly can bicycle 57 km. How fast does each bicyclist travel?

17. *Walking speed.* Bonnie walks 3 km/h faster than Ralph. In the time that it takes Ralph to walk 7.5 km, Bonnie walks 12 km. Find their speeds.

18. *Cross-country skiing.* Gerard cross-country skis 4 km/h faster than Sally. In the time that it takes Sally to ski 18 km, Gerard skis 24 km. Find their speeds.

Aha! **19.** *Tractor speed.* Manley's tractor is just as fast as Caledonia's. It takes Manley 1 hr more than it takes Caledonia to drive to town. If Manley is 20 mi from town and Caledonia is 15 mi from town, how long does it take Caledonia to drive to town?

20. *Boat speed.* Tory and Emilio's motorboats both travel at the same speed. Tory pilots her boat 40 km before docking. Emilio continues for another 2 hr, traveling a total of 100 km before docking. How long did it take Tory to navigate the 40 km?

Geometry. ***For each pair of similar triangles, find the value of the indicated letter.***

21. b

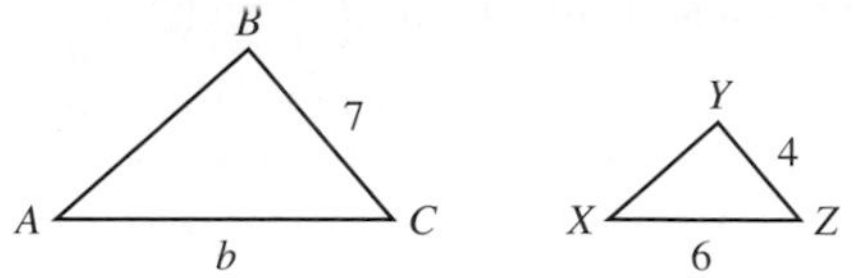

22. a

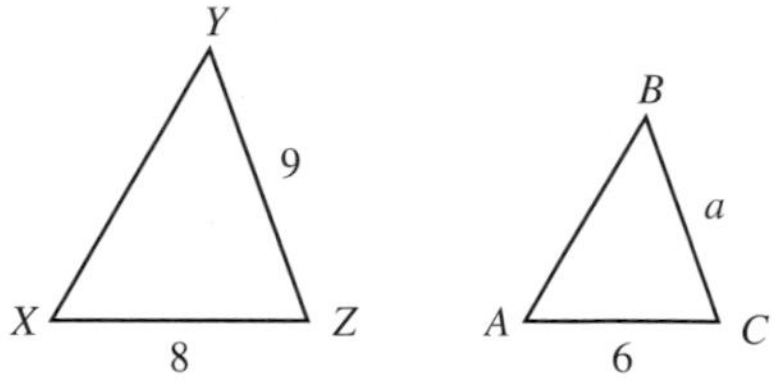

23. f

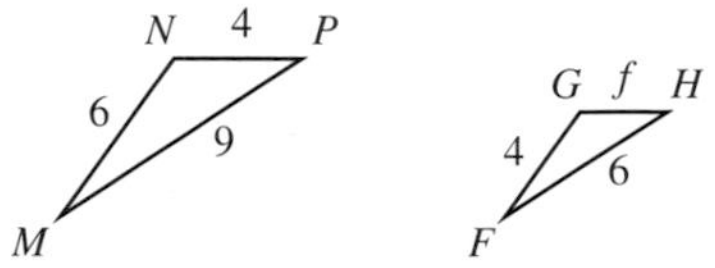

24. r

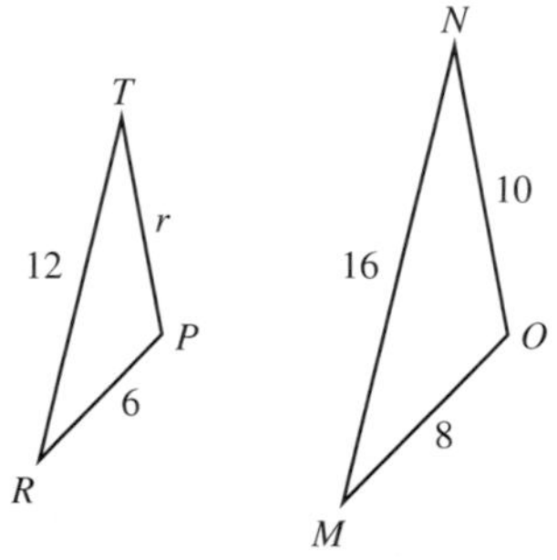

Architecture. ***Use the blueprint below to find the indicated length.***

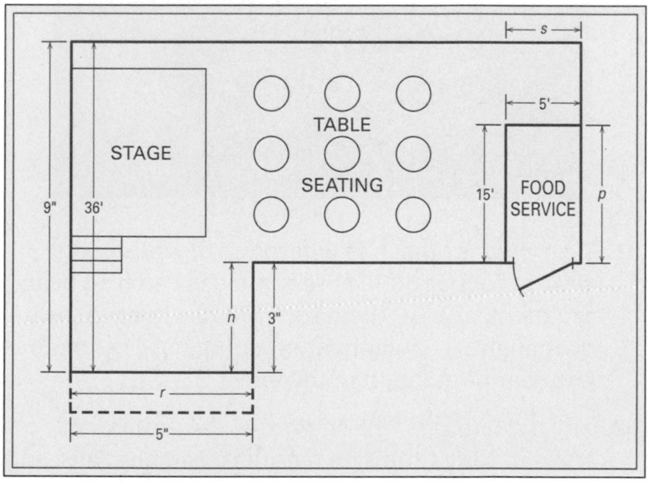

25. p, in inches on blueprint

26. s, in inches on blueprint

27. r, in feet on actual building

28. n, in feet on actual building

Construction. ***Find the indicated length.***

29. h

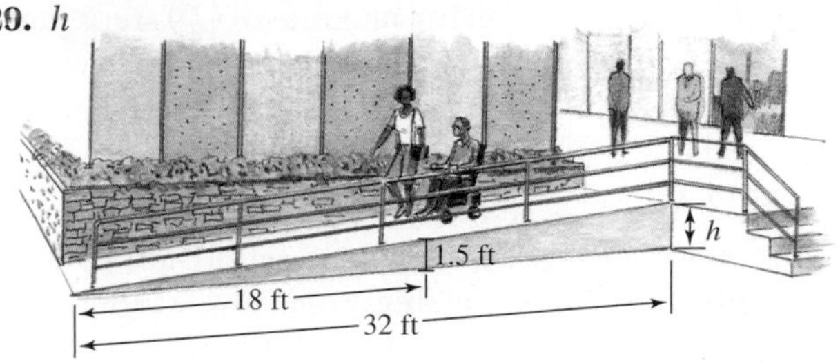

30. l

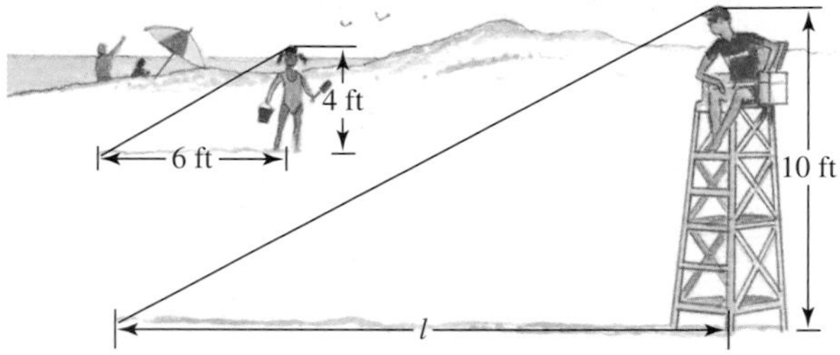

Geometry. ***When three parallel lines are crossed by two or more lines (transversals), the lengths of corresponding segments are proportional (see the following figure).***

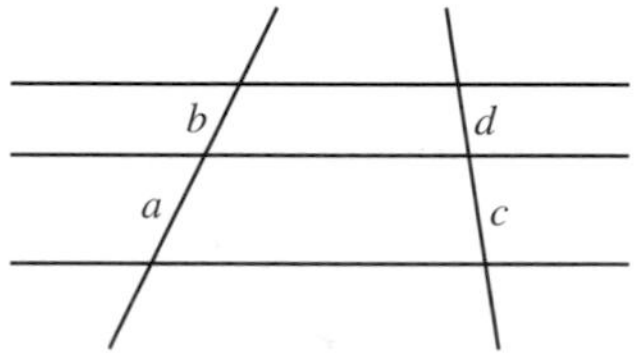

31. If a is 8 cm when b is 5 cm, find d when c is 6 cm.

32. If d is 7 cm when c is 10 cm, find a when b is 9 cm.

Graphing. ***Find the indicated length.***

33. r

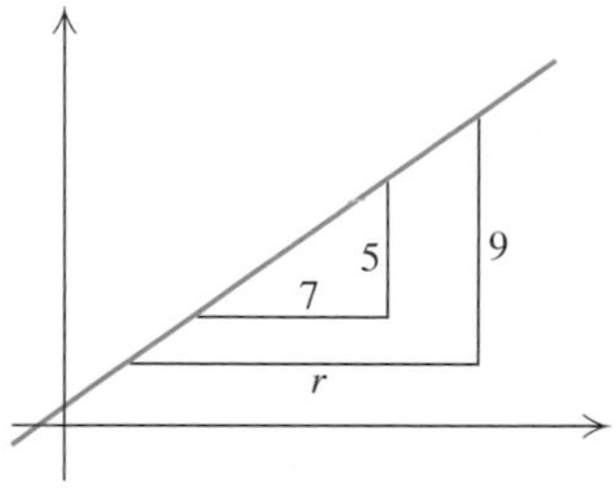

34. s

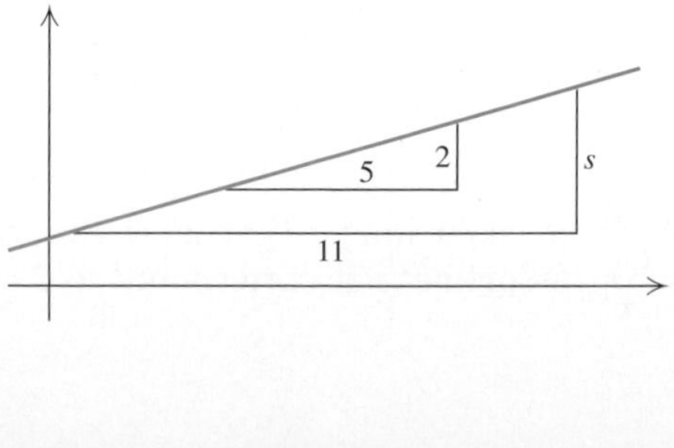

35. *Walking speed.* For adults with an average stride that is $2\frac{1}{2}$ ft long, walking at a rate of 140 steps per minute corresponds to a speed of 4 mph. How many steps per minute would correspond to a speed of 3 mph?
Source: Runnersworld.com

36. *Burning calories.* The average 150-lb adult burns about 360 calories walking 4 mi. How far should the average 150-lb adult walk in order to burn 20 calories?
Source: Runnersworld.com

37. *Coffee harvest.* The coffee beans from 14 trees are needed to produce 7.7 kg of coffee. (This is the average amount that each person in the United States consumes each year.) How many trees are needed to produce 308 kg of coffee?

Aha! **38.** *Photography.* Wanda snapped 234 photos over a period of 14 days. At this rate, how many would she take in 42 days?

39. *Hemoglobin.* A normal 10-cc specimen of human blood contains 1.2 g of hemoglobin. How much hemoglobin would 16 cc of the same blood contain?

40. *Baking.* In a potato bread recipe, the ratio of milk to flour is $\frac{3}{13}$. If 5 cups of milk are used, how many cups of flour are used?

41. *Wages.* For comparable work, U.S. women earn 77 cents for each dollar earned by a man. If a male sales manager earns $42,000, how much would a female earn for comparable work?
Source: U.S. Bureau of the Census, Public Information Office, 9/26/03

Aha! **42.** *Money.* The ratio of the weight of copper to the weight of zinc in a U.S. penny is $\frac{1}{39}$. If 50 kg of zinc is being turned into pennies, how much copper is needed?
Source: United States Mint

Hat sizes. U.S. hat sizes typically range between 6 and 8 and are proportional to the circumference of one's head. In Europe, and increasingly in North America, hat size is given in centimeters.

43. A motorcycle helmet that is 53.8 cm in circumference is size $6\frac{3}{4}$ in the United States. What U.S. size corresponds to a 59.8-cm helmet?

44. A 53.8-cm ski helmet is U.S. hat size $6\frac{3}{4}$. What European helmet size corresponds to U.S. hat size $7\frac{3}{8}$?

45. *Firecrackers.* A sample of 144 firecrackers contained 9 "duds." How many duds would you expect in a sample of 320 firecrackers?

46. *Light bulbs.* A sample of 184 light bulbs contained 6 defective bulbs. How many defective bulbs would you expect in a sample of 1288 bulbs?

47. *Fish population.* To determine the number of trout in a lake, a naturalist catches 112 trout, tags them, and throws them back into the lake. Later, 82 trout are caught; 32 of them have tags. Estimate the number of trout in the lake.

48. *Miles driven.* Emmanuel is allowed to drive his leased car for 45,000 mi in 4 yr without penalty. In the first $1\frac{1}{2}$ yr, Emmanuel has driven 16,000 mi. At this rate will he exceed the mileage allowed for 4 yr?

49. *Moose population.* To determine the size of Pine County's moose population, naturalists catch 69 moose, tag them, and then set them free. Months later, 40 moose are caught, of which 15 have tags. Estimate the size of the moose population.

50. *Deer population.* To determine the number of deer in the Great Gulf Wilderness, a game warden catches 318 deer, tags them, and lets them loose. Later, 168 deer are caught; 56 of them have tags. Estimate the number of deer in the preserve.

51. *Bear population.* To determine the number of bear in Sachee State Forest, rangers catch 16 bears, tag them, and set them free. Months later, 20 bears are caught, 8 of whom are wearing tags. Estimate the bear population of the forest.

52. *Fox population.* To determine the number of foxes in King County, a naturalist catches, tags, and then releases 25 foxes. Later, 36 foxes are caught; 4 of them have tags. Estimate the fox population of the county.

53. *Weight on the moon.* The ratio of the weight of an object on the moon to the weight of that object on Earth is 0.16 to 1.

a) How much would a 12-ton rocket weigh on the moon?
b) How much would a 180-lb astronaut weigh on the moon?

54. *Weight on Mars.* The ratio of the weight of an object on Mars to the weight of that object on Earth is 0.4 to 1.
a) How much would a 12-ton rocket weigh on Mars?
b) How much would a 120-lb astronaut weigh on Mars?

55. Is it correct to assume that two workers will complete a task twice as quickly as one person working alone? Why or why not?

56. If two triangles are exactly the same shape and size, are they similar? Why or why not?

SKILL MAINTENANCE

Graph. [3.2]

57. $y = 2x - 6$

58. $y = -2x + 6$

59. $3x + 2y = 12$

60. $x - 3y = 6$

61. $y = -\frac{3}{4}x + 2$

62. $y = \frac{2}{5}x - 4$

SYNTHESIS

63. Write a problem similar to Example 1 for a classmate to solve. Design the problem so that the translation step is

$$\frac{t}{7} + \frac{t}{5} = 1.$$

64. Write a problem similar to Example 2 for a classmate to solve. Design the problem so that the translation step is

$$\frac{30}{r + 4} = \frac{18}{r}.$$

65. *Quilting.* Ricki and Maura work together and sew a quilt in 4 hr. Working alone, Maura would need 6 hr more than Ricki to sew a quilt. How long would it take each of them working alone?

66. *Car cleaning.* Together, Michelle, Sal, and Kristen can clean and wax a car in 1 hr 20 min. To complete the job alone, Michelle needs twice the time that Sal needs and 2 hr more than Kristen. How long would it take each to clean and wax the car working alone?

67. *Programming.* Rosina, Ng, and Oscar can write a computer program in 3 days. Rosina can write the program in 8 days and Ng can do it in 10 days. How many days will it take Oscar to write the program?

68. *Wiring.* Janet can wire a house in 28 hr. Linus can wire a house in 34 hr. How long will it take Janet and Linus, working together, to wire *two* houses?

Aha! 69. *Roofing.* Working alone, Russ can reshingle a roof in 12 hr. When Joan works with Russ, the job takes 6 hr. How long would it take Joan, working alone, to reshingle the roof?

70. *Grading.* Alma can grade a batch of placement exams in 3 hr. Kevin can grade a batch in 4 hr. If they work together to grade a batch of exams, what percentage of the exams will have been graded by Alma?

71. *Home maintenance.* Fuel used in lawn mowers and chain saws is made by pouring a 3.2-oz bottle of 2-cycle oil into 160 oz of gasoline. Gus accidentally poured 5.6 oz of 2-cycle oil into 200 oz of gasoline. How much more oil or gasoline should he add in order for the fuel to have the proper ratio of oil to gasoline?

72. *Boating.* The speed of a boat in still water is 10 mph. It travels 24 mi upstream and 24 mi downstream in a total time of 5 hr. What is the speed of the current?

73. *Commuting.* To reach an appointment 50 mi away, Dr. Wright allowed 1 hr. After driving 30 mi, she realized that her speed would have to be increased 15 mph for the remainder of the trip. What was her speed for the first 30 mi?

74. *Distances.* The shadow from a 40-ft cliff just reaches across a water-filled quarry at the same time that a 6-ft tall diver casts a 10-ft shadow. How wide is the quarry?

75. Simplest fraction notation for a rational number is $\frac{9}{17}$. Find an equivalent ratio where the sum of the numerator and the denominator is 104.

76. How soon after 5 o'clock will the hands on a clock first be together?

77. Given that

$$\frac{A}{B} = \frac{C}{D},$$

write three other proportions using *A, B, C,* and *D.*

78. If two triangles are similar, are their areas and perimeters proportional? Why or why not?

79. Are the equations

$$\frac{A+B}{B} = \frac{C+D}{D} \quad \text{and} \quad \frac{A}{B} = \frac{C}{D}$$

equivalent? Why or why not?

COLLABORATIVE CORNER

Sharing the Workload

Focus: Modeling, estimation, and work problems

Time: 20–25 minutes

Group size: 3

Materials: Paper, pencils, textbooks, and a watch

Many tasks can be done by two people working together. If both people work at the same rate, each does half the task, and the project is completed in half the time. However, when the work rates differ, the faster worker performs more than half of the task.

ACTIVITY

1. The project is to write down (but not answer) Review Exercises 9–42 from Chapter 6 (pp. 424–425) on a sheet of paper. The problems should be spaced apart and written clearly so that they can be used for studying in the future. Two of the members in each group should write down the exercises, one working slowly and one working quickly. The third group member should record the time required for each to write down all 34 exercises.
2. Using the times from step (1), calculate how long it will take the two workers, working together, to complete the task.
3. Next, have the same workers as in step (1)—working at the same speeds as in step (1)—perform the task together. To do this, one person should begin writing with Exercise 9, while the other worker begins with Exercise 42 and lists the problems counting backward. The third worker is again the timekeeper and should observe when the two workers have written all the exercises. To avoid collision, each of the two writers should use a separate sheet of paper.
4. Compare the actual experimental time from part (3) with the time predicted by the model in part (2). List reasons that might account for any discrepancy.
5. Let t_1, t_2, and t_3 represent the times required for the first worker, the second worker, and the two workers together, respectively, to complete a task. Then develop a model that can be used to find t_3 when t_1 and t_2 are known.

Time Required for Worker A, Working Alone	Time Required for Worker B, Working Alone	Estimated Time for the Two Workers, Working Together	Actual Time Required for the Two Workers, Working Together

6 Study Summary

Like the fractions in arithmetic, **rational expressions** can be **simplified, added, subtracted, multiplied**, and **divided** (pp. 364, 365, 371, 373, 378, 379):

$$\frac{A}{B} \cdot \frac{C}{D} = \frac{AC}{BD}; \qquad \frac{A}{B} \div \frac{C}{D} = \frac{A}{B} \cdot \frac{D}{C} = \frac{AD}{BC};$$

$$\frac{A}{B} + \frac{C}{B} = \frac{A + C}{B}; \qquad \frac{A}{B} - \frac{C}{B} = \frac{A - C}{B}.$$

When adding or subtracting rational expressions, we must first make certain that the expressions being added or subtracted have a common denominator. The simplest common denominator to work with is the **least common denominator** (p. 380). To find the least common denominator (LCD), we use the **least common multiple** (LCM) of the denominators (p. 380).

Sometimes rational expressions appear within a rational expression, as in

$$\frac{\dfrac{2}{x + 1} - \dfrac{1}{x}}{\dfrac{3}{2x}} \quad \text{or} \quad \frac{5 - \dfrac{t}{t + 3}}{t^2}.$$

Such expressions are called **complex rational expressions** and can be simplified either by division or by multiplication involving the least common denominator (pp. 396, 398).

When a rational expression appears in an equation, as in

$$\frac{3}{x + 1} + \frac{2}{x} = 7 \quad \text{or} \quad \frac{5}{t} = \frac{7}{9},$$

we have what is called a **rational equation** (p. 403). The multiplication principle is used to solve rational equations and, because it now involves multiplying both sides by a variable expression, checking potential solutions in the original equation is very important. A variety of real-world problems translate to rational equations. Among these are **work problems, motion problems,** and **proportions** (pp. 410, 412, 414).

---

6 Review Exercises

Concept Reinforcement *Classify each statement as either true or false.*

1. Every rational expression can be simplified. [6.1]
2. The expression $(t - 3)/(t^2 - 4)$ is undefined for $t = 2$. [6.1]
3. The expression $(t - 3)/(t^2 - 4)$ is undefined for $t = 3$. [6.1]
4. To multiply rational expressions, a common denominator is never required. [6.2]
5. To divide rational expressions, a common denominator is never required. [6.2]
6. To add rational expressions, a common denominator is never required. [6.3]
7. To subtract rational expressions, a common denominator is never required. [6.3]
8. Every rational equation has at least one solution. [6.6]

List all numbers for which each expression is undefined. [6.1]

9. $\dfrac{17}{-x^2}$

10. $\dfrac{9}{a - 4}$

11. $\dfrac{x - 5}{x^2 - 36}$

12. $\dfrac{x^2 + 3x + 2}{x^2 + x - 30}$

13. $\dfrac{-6}{(t + 2)^2}$

Simplify. [6.1]

14. $\dfrac{4x^2 - 8x}{4x^2 + 4x}$

15. $\dfrac{14x^2 - x - 3}{2x^2 - 7x + 3}$

16. $\dfrac{(y - 5)^2}{y^2 - 25}$

17. $\dfrac{5x^2 - 20y^2}{2y - x}$

Multiply or divide and, if possible, simplify. [6.2]

18. $\dfrac{a^2 - 36}{10a} \cdot \dfrac{2a}{a + 6}$

19. $\dfrac{8t + 8}{2t^2 + t - 1} \cdot \dfrac{t^2 - 1}{t^2 - 2t + 1}$

20. $\dfrac{16 - 8t}{3} \div \dfrac{t - 2}{12t}$

21. $\dfrac{4x^4}{x^2 - 1} \div \dfrac{2x^3}{x^2 - 2x + 1}$

22. $\dfrac{x^2 + 1}{x - 2} \cdot \dfrac{2x + 1}{x + 1}$

23. $(t^2 + 3t - 4) \div \dfrac{t^2 - 1}{t + 4}$

Find the LCM. [6.3]

24. $8a^2b^9,\ 6a^5b^3$

25. $x^2 - x,\ x^5 - x^3,\ x^4$

26. $y^2 - y - 2,\ y^2 - 4$

Add or subtract and, if possible, simplify.

27. $\dfrac{x + 6}{x + 3} + \dfrac{9 - 4x}{x + 3}$ [6.3]

28. $\dfrac{3}{3x - 9} + \dfrac{x - 2}{3 - x}$ [6.4]

29. $\dfrac{6x - 3}{x^2 - x - 12} - \dfrac{2x - 15}{x^2 - x - 12}$ [6.3]

30. $\dfrac{3x - 1}{2x} - \dfrac{x - 3}{x}$ [6.4]

31. $\dfrac{x + 5}{x - 2} - \dfrac{x}{2 - x}$ [6.4]

32. $\dfrac{2a}{a + 1} - \dfrac{4a}{1 - a^2}$ [6.4]

33. $\dfrac{d^2}{d-c} + \dfrac{c^2}{c-d}$ [6.4]

34. $\dfrac{1}{x^2-25} - \dfrac{x-5}{x^2-4x-5}$ [6.4]

35. $\dfrac{3x}{x+2} - \dfrac{x}{x-2} + \dfrac{8}{x^2-4}$ [6.4]

36. $\dfrac{2}{5x} + \dfrac{3}{2x+4}$ [6.4]

Simplify. [6.5]

37. $\dfrac{\frac{1}{z}+1}{\frac{1}{z^2}-1}$

38. $\dfrac{2+\frac{1}{xy^2}}{\frac{1+x}{x^4y}}$

39. $\dfrac{\frac{c}{d}-\frac{d}{c}}{\frac{1}{c}+\frac{1}{d}}$

Solve. [6.6]

40. $\dfrac{3}{y} - \dfrac{1}{4} = \dfrac{1}{y}$

41. $\dfrac{5}{x+3} = \dfrac{3}{x+2}$

42. $\dfrac{15}{x} - \dfrac{15}{x+2} = 2$

43. Jackson can sand the oak floors and stairs in a two-story home in 12 hr. Olga can do the same job in 9 hr. How long would it take if they worked together? (Assume that two sanders are available.) [6.7]

44. The distance by highway between Richmond and Waterbury is 70 km, and the distance by rail is 60 km. A car and a train leave Richmond at the same time and arrive in Waterbury at the same time, the car having traveled 15 km/h faster than the train. Find the speed of the car and the speed of the train. [6.7]

45. To estimate the frog population in a pond, a scientist captures, tags, and releases 24 frogs. Weeks later, 20 frogs are caught and 8 of them are wearing tags. Estimate the frog population of the pond. [6.7]

46. Triangles *ABC* and *XYZ* are similar. Find the value of *x*. [6.7]

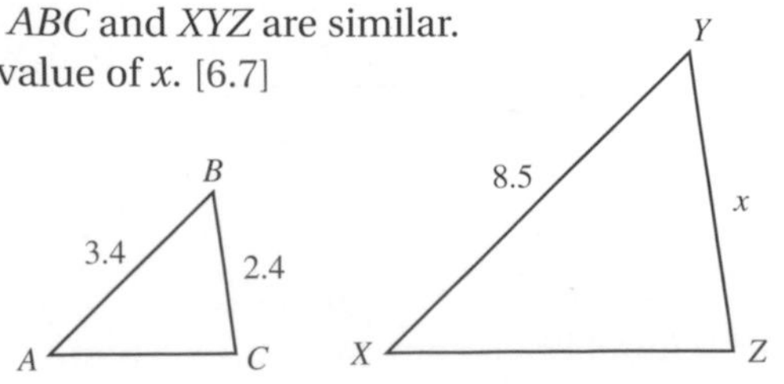

47. A sample of 25 doorbells contained 2 defective ones. How many defective doorbells would you expect in a batch of 350? [6.7]

SYNTHESIS

48. For what procedures in this chapter is the LCM of denominators used to clear fractions? [6.1], [6.4], [6.6]

49. A student insists on finding a common denominator by always multiplying the denominators of the expressions being added. How could this approach be improved? [6.3]

Simplify.

50. $\dfrac{2a^2+5a-3}{a^2} \cdot \dfrac{5a^3+30a^2}{2a^2+7a-4} \div \dfrac{a^2+6a}{a^2+7a+12}$ [6.2]

51. $\dfrac{12a}{(a-b)(b-c)} - \dfrac{2a}{(b-a)(c-b)}$ [6.4]

Aha! **52.** $\dfrac{5(x-y)}{(x-y)(x+2y)} - \dfrac{5(x-3y)}{(x+2y)(x-3y)}$ [6.3]

53. It has been over 60 yr since a major-league baseball player went an entire season averaging 4 hits in every 10 at-bats. Suppose that Hideki currently has 153 hits after 395 at-bats. If he is assured 125 more at-bats, what percentage of those must be hits if he is to average 4 hits for every 10 at-bats? [6.7]

6 Chapter Test

List all numbers for which each expression is undefined.

1. $\dfrac{2 - x}{5x}$

2. $\dfrac{5}{x + 8}$

3. $\dfrac{x - 7}{x^2 - 49}$

4. $\dfrac{x^2 + x - 30}{x^2 - 3x + 2}$

5. Simplify: $\dfrac{6x^2 + 17x + 7}{2x^2 + 7x + 3}$.

Multiply or divide and, if possible, simplify.

6. $\dfrac{a^2 - 25}{9a} \cdot \dfrac{6a}{5 - a}$

7. $\dfrac{25y^2 - 1}{9y^2 - 6y} \div \dfrac{5y^2 + 9y - 2}{3y^2 + y - 2}$

8. $\dfrac{4x^2 - 1}{x^2 - 2x + 1} \div \dfrac{x - 2}{x^2 + 1}$

9. $(x^2 + 6x + 9) \cdot \dfrac{(x - 3)^2}{x^2 - 9}$

10. Find the LCM:
$y^2 - 9,\ y^2 + 10y + 21,\ y^2 + 4y - 21.$

Add or subtract, and, if possible, simplify.

11. $\dfrac{2 + x}{x^3} + \dfrac{7 - 4x}{x^3}$

12. $\dfrac{5 - t}{t^2 + 1} - \dfrac{t - 3}{t^2 + 1}$

13. $\dfrac{x - 4}{x - 3} + \dfrac{x - 1}{3 - x}$

14. $\dfrac{x - 4}{x - 3} - \dfrac{x - 1}{3 - x}$

15. $\dfrac{7}{t - 2} + \dfrac{4}{t}$

16. $\dfrac{1}{x^2 - 16} - \dfrac{x + 4}{x^2 - 3x - 4}$

17. $\dfrac{1}{x - 1} + \dfrac{4}{x^2 - 1} - \dfrac{2}{x^2 - 2x + 1}$

Simplify.

18. $\dfrac{9 - \dfrac{1}{y^2}}{3 - \dfrac{1}{y}}$

19. $\dfrac{\dfrac{3}{a^2b} - \dfrac{2}{ab^3}}{\dfrac{1}{ab} + \dfrac{2}{a^4b}}$

Solve.

20. $\dfrac{7}{y} - \dfrac{1}{3} = \dfrac{1}{4}$

21. $\dfrac{15}{x} - \dfrac{15}{x - 2} = -2$

22. Kopy Kwik has 2 copiers. One can copy a year-end report in 20 min. The other can copy the same document in 30 min. How long would it take both machines, working together, to copy the report?

23. A recipe for pizza crust calls for $3\frac{1}{2}$ cups of whole wheat flour and $1\frac{1}{4}$ cups of warm water. If 6 cups of whole wheat flour are used, how much water should be used?

24. Craig drives 20 km/h faster than Marilyn. In the same time that Marilyn drives 225 km, Craig drives 325 km. Find the speed of each car.

SYNTHESIS

25. Reggie and Rema work together to mulch the flower beds around an office complex in $2\frac{6}{7}$ hr. Working alone, it would take Reggie 6 hr more than it would take Rema. How long would it take each of them to complete the landscaping working alone?

26. Simplify: $1 - \dfrac{1}{1 - \dfrac{1}{1 - \dfrac{1}{a}}}$.

27. The square of a number is the opposite of the number's reciprocal. Find the number.

1–6 Cumulative Review

1. Use the commutative law of addition to write an expression equivalent to $a + 2b$. [1.2]

2. Write a true sentence using either $<$ or $>$:
   $-3.1 \; \blacksquare \; -3.15$. [1.4]

3. Evaluate $(y - 1)^2$ for $y = -4$. [1.8]

4. Simplify: $-4[2(x - 3) - 1]$. [1.8]

Simplify.

5. $-\frac{1}{2} + \frac{3}{8} + (-6) + \frac{3}{4}$ [1.5]

6. $-\frac{72}{108} \div \left(-\frac{2}{3}\right)$ [1.7]

7. $-6.262 \div 1.01$ [1.7]

8. $4 \div (-2) \cdot 2 + 3 \cdot 4$ [1.8]

Solve.

9. $5(x - 2) = 40$ [2.2]

10. $49 = x^2$ [5.6]

11. $-6t = 20$ [2.1]

12. $3x - 4 = 7x + 8$ [2.2]

13. $4(y - 5) = -2(y + 2)$ [2.2]

14. $x^2 + 11x + 10 = 0$ [5.6]

15. $\frac{4}{9}t + \frac{2}{3} = \frac{1}{3}t - \frac{2}{9}$ [2.2]

16. $\frac{4}{x} + x = 5$ [6.6]

17. $6 - y \geq 2y + 8$ [2.6]

18. $\frac{2}{x - 3} = \frac{5}{3x + 1}$ [6.6]

19. $2x^2 + 7x = 4$ [5.6]

20. $4(x + 7) < 5(x - 3)$ [2.6]

21. $\frac{t^2}{t + 5} = \frac{25}{t + 5}$ [6.6]

22. $(2x + 7)(x - 5) = 0$ [5.6]

23. $\frac{2}{x^2 - 9} + \frac{5}{x - 3} = \frac{3}{x + 3}$ [6.6]

Solve each formula. [2.3]

24. $3a - b + 9 = c$, for b

25. $\frac{3}{4}(x + 2y) = z$, for y

Combine like terms. [1.6]

26. $x + 2y - 2z + \frac{1}{2}x - z$

27. $2x^3 - 7 + \frac{3}{7}x^2 - 6x^3 - \frac{4}{7}x^2 + 5$

Graph. [3.2], [3.3]

28. $y = \frac{3}{4}x + 5$

29. $x = -3$

30. $4x + 5y = 20$

31. $y = 6$

32. Find the slope of the line containing the points $(1, 5)$ and $(2, 3)$. [3.5]

Simplify.

33. $\frac{x^{-5}}{x^{-3}}$ [4.8]

34. $y^2 \cdot y^{-8}$ [4.8]

35. $-(2a^2b^7)^2$ [4.1]

36. Subtract: [4.3]
    $(-8y^2 - y + 2) - (y^3 - 6y^2 + y - 5)$.

Multiply.

37. $5(3a - 2b + c)$ [1.2]

38. $(2x^2 - 1)(x^3 + x - 3)$ [4.4]

39. $(6x - 5y)^2$ [4.5]

40. $(x + 8)(2x - 5)$ [4.5]

41. $(2x^3 + 1)(2x^3 - 1)$ [4.5]

Factor.

42. $6x - 2x^2 - 24x^4$ [5.1]

43. $16x^2 - 81$ [5.4]

44. $t^2 - 10t + 24$ [5.2]

45. $8x^2 + 10x + 3$ [5.3]

46. $6x^2 - 28x + 16$ [5.3]

$4t^2 - 36$ [5.4]

48. $25t^2 + 40t + 16$ [5.4]

49. $3x^2 + 10x - 8$ [5.3]

50. $x^4 + 2x^3 - 3x - 6$ [5.1]

Simplify.

51. $\frac{y^2 - 36}{2y + 8} \cdot \frac{y + 4}{y - 6}$ [6.2]

52. $\frac{x^2 - 1}{x^2 - x - 2} \div \frac{x - 1}{x - 2}$ [6.2]

53. $\frac{5ab}{a^2 - b^2} + \frac{a + b}{a - b}$ [6.4]

54. $\frac{x + 2}{4 - x} - \frac{x + 3}{x - 4}$ [6.4]

55. $\frac{1 + \frac{2}{x}}{1 - \frac{4}{x^2}}$ [6.5]

56. $\frac{\frac{1}{t} + 2t}{t - \frac{2}{t^2}}$ [6.5]

Divide. [4.7]

57. $\frac{18x^4 - 15x^3 + 6x^2 + 12x + 3}{3x^2}$

58. $(15x^4 - 12x^3 + 6x^2 + 2x + 18) \div (x + 3)$

Solve.

59. Linnae has \$36 budgeted for stationery. Engraved stationery costs \$20 for the first 25 sheets and \$0.08 for each additional sheet. How many sheets of stationery can Linnae order and still stay within her budget? [2.7]

60. The price of a box of granola increased 15% to \$4.14. What was the price of the granola before the increase? [2.4]

61. If the sides of a square are increased by 2 ft, the area of the original square plus the area of the enlarged square is 452 ft^2. Find the length of a side of the original square. [5.7]

62. The sum of two consecutive even integers is -554. Find the integers. [2.5]

63. It takes Dina 50 min to shovel 9 in. of snow from her driveway. It takes Nell 75 min to do the same job. How long would it take if they worked together? [6.7]

64. A game warden catches, tags, and then releases 15 zebras. A month later, a sample of 20 zebras is collected and 6 of them have tags. Use this information to estimate the size of the zebra population in that area. [6.7]

65. A 78-in. board is to be cut into two pieces. One piece must be twice as long as the other. How long should the shorter piece be? [2.5]

SYNTHESIS

66. Simplify: $(x + 7)(x - 4) - (x + 8)(x - 5)$. [4.3], [4.5]

67. Solve: $\frac{1}{3}|n| + 8 = 56$. [1.4], [2.2]

Aha! **68.** Multiply: $[4y^3 - (y^2 - 3)][4y^3 + (y^2 - 3)]$. [4.5]

69. Factor: $2a^{32} - 13{,}122b^{40}$. [5.4]

70. Solve: $x(x^2 + 3x - 28) - 12(x^2 + 3x - 28) = 0$. [5.6]

71. Simplify: $-|0.875 - (-\frac{1}{8}) - 8|$. [1.4], [1.6]

72. Solve: $\frac{2}{x - 3} \cdot \frac{3}{x + 3} - \frac{4}{x^2 - 7x + 12} = 0$. [6.6]

73. Jesse can peel a bushel of potatoes in 60 min. When Jesse and Priscilla work together, the job takes 20 min. When working together with Jesse, what percentage of the work is performed by Priscilla? [6.7]

7 Systems and More Graphing

AN APPLICATION

In 2000, about 33.1 billion photos were printed from film and that number was declining at a rate of 1.1 billion per year. There were 2.8 billion digital photos printed or stored in 2000 and that number was growing at a rate of 2.9 billion per year. (*Source*: *Deseret Morning News*, Nov. 16, 2003) In what year will the numbers of filmed photos and digital photos be the same?

This problem appears as Exercise 67 in Section 7.1.

Laurie Wood
PROFESSIONAL PHOTOGRAPHER
Los Angeles, California

As a photographer, I use math every day without thinking about it! I use fractions to set exposures and use math in the darkroom when developing or printing pictures. Depending on how the film was exposed, I may need to add or subtract time in the development.

In fields ranging from business to zoology, problems arise that are most easily solved using a system of equations. *Section 7.1 examines how graphing can be used to solve a system of equations, and Sections 7.2 and 7.3 discuss algebraic methods of solving systems. These three methods are then used in a variety of applications and as an aid in solving systems of inequalities.*

7.1 Systems of Equations and Graphing

Solutions of Systems • Solving Systems of Equations by Graphing

Solutions of Systems

A **system of equations** is a set of two or more equations that are to be solved simultaneously. We will find that it is often easier to translate real-world situations to a system of two equations that use two variables, or unknowns, than it is to represent the situation with one equation using one variable. To see this, let's see how the following problem from Section 2.5 can be represented by two equations using two unknowns:

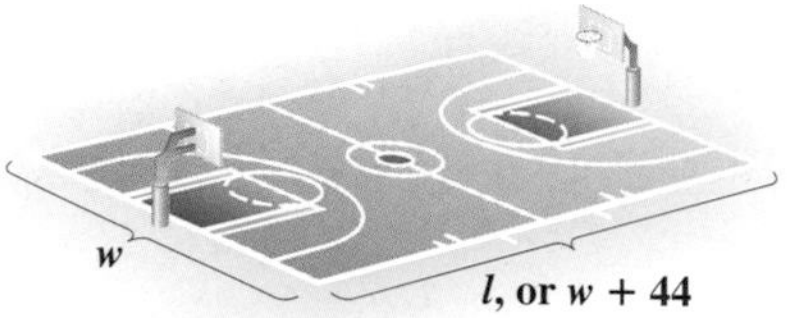

> The perimeter of an NBA basketball court is 288 ft. The length is 44 ft longer than the width. (*Source*: National Basketball Association) Find the dimensions of the court.

If we let w = the width of the court, in feet, and l = the length of the court, in feet, the problem translates to the following system of equations:

$$2l + 2w = 288, \quad \text{The perimeter is 288.}$$
$$l = w + 44. \quad \text{The length is 44 more than the width.}$$

To solve a system of equations is to find all ordered pairs (if any exist) for which *both* equations are true. Thus a solution of the system listed above is an ordered pair of the form (l, w). Note that variables are listed in alphabetical order within an ordered pair unless stated otherwise.

EXAMPLE 1 Consider the system from above:

$$2l + 2w = 288,$$
$$l = w + 44.$$

Determine whether each pair is a solution of the system: **(a)** (94, 50); **(b)** (90, 46).

Solution

a) We check by substituting (alphabetically) 94 for l and 50 for w:

$2l + 2w = 288$	
$2 \cdot 94 + 2 \cdot 50$	288
$188 + 100$	
$288 \stackrel{?}{=} 288$	TRUE

$l = w + 44$	
94	$50 + 44$
$94 \stackrel{?}{=} 94$	TRUE

Since (94, 50) checks in *both* equations, it is a solution of the system.

b) We substitute 90 for l and 46 for w:

$2l + 2w = 288$	
$2 \cdot 90 + 2 \cdot 46$	288
$180 + 92$	
$272 \stackrel{?}{=} 288$	FALSE

$l = w + 44$	
90	$46 + 44$
$90 \stackrel{?}{=} 90$	TRUE

Since (90, 46) is not a solution of *both* equations, it is not a solution of the system.

Study Skills

And Now for Something Completely Different

When a new topic, like systems of equations, is introduced, try to master any new concepts as they arise. By staying in command of this new material, you will ultimately save yourself time and build confidence as you move forward.

In Example 1, we demonstrated that (94, 50) is a solution of the system, but we did not show how the pair (94, 50) was found. One way to find such a solution uses graphs.

Solving Systems of Equations by Graphing

Recall that a graph of an equation is a set of points representing its solution set. Each point on the graph corresponds to an ordered pair that is a solution of the equation. By graphing two equations using one set of axes, we can identify a solution of both equations by looking for a point of intersection.

EXAMPLE 2 Solve this system of equations by graphing:

$$x + y = 7,$$
$$y = 3x - 1.$$

Solution We graph the equations using any method studied earlier. The equation $x + y = 7$ can be graphed easily using the intercepts, $(0, 7)$ and $(7, 0)$. The equation $y = 3x - 1$ is in slope–intercept form, so it can be graphed by plotting its y-intercept, $(0, -1)$, and "counting off" a slope of 3.

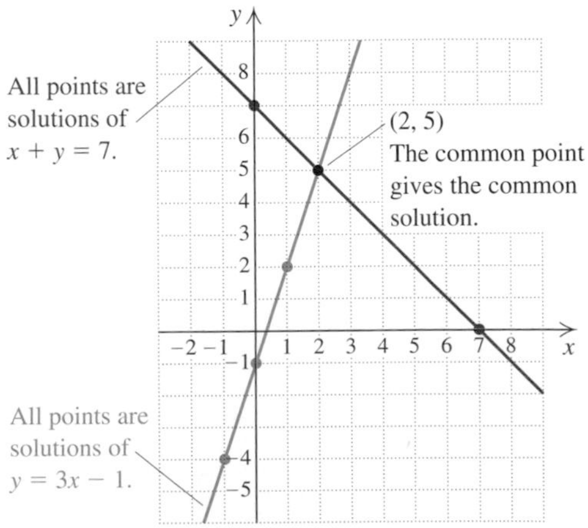

The "apparent" solution of the system, (2, 5), should be checked in both equations.

Student Notes

Because it is so critical to accurately identify any point(s) of intersection, use graph paper, a ruler or other straightedge, and a pencil to graph each line as neatly as possible.

Check:

$x + y = 7$	
$2 + 5$	7
$7 \stackrel{?}{=} 7$	TRUE

$y = 3x - 1$	
5	$3 \cdot 2 - 1$
$5 \stackrel{?}{=} 5$	TRUE

Since it checks in both equations, (2, 5) is a solution of the system.

A system of equations that has at least one solution, like the systems in Examples 1 and 2, is said to be **consistent**. A system for which there is no solution is said to be **inconsistent**.

EXAMPLE 3 Solve this system of equations by graphing:

$$y = \frac{5}{2}x + 4,$$
$$y = \frac{5}{2}x - 3.$$

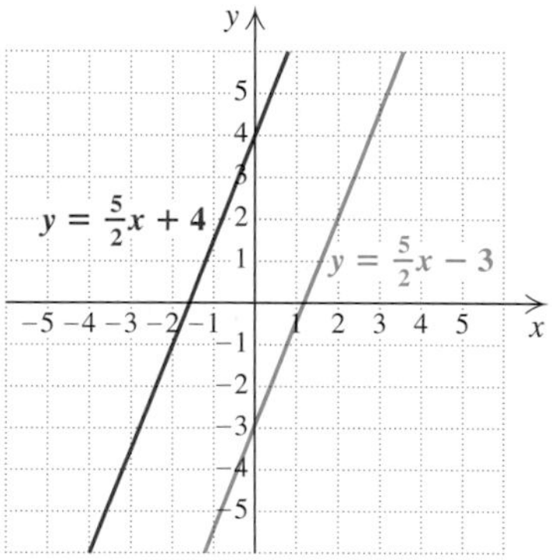

Solution Both equations are in slope–intercept form so it is easy to see that both lines have the same slope, $\frac{5}{2}$. The y-intercepts differ so the lines are parallel, as shown in the figure at right.

Because the lines are parallel, there is no point of intersection. Thus the system is inconsistent and has no solution.

Sometimes both equations in a system have the same graph.

EXAMPLE 4 Solve this system of equations by graphing:

$$2x + 3y = 6,$$
$$-8x - 12y = -24.$$

Solution Graphing the equations, we see that they both represent the same line. This can also be seen by solving each equation for y, obtaining the equivalent slope–intercept form, $y = -\frac{2}{3}x + 2$. Because the equations are equivalent, any solution of one equation is a solution of the other equation as well. We show four such solutions.

We check one solution, (0, 2), in each of the original equations.

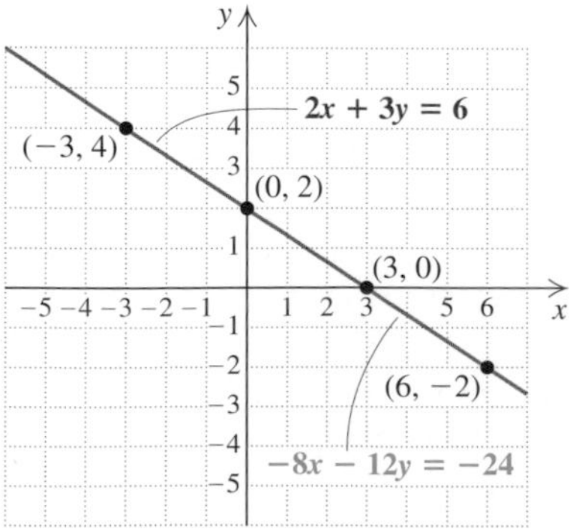

$2x + 3y = 6$	
$2(0) + 3(2)$	6
$0 + 6$	
$6 \stackrel{?}{=} 6$	TRUE

$-8x - 12y = -24$	
$-8(0) - 12(2)$	-24
$0 - 24$	
$-24 \stackrel{?}{=} -24$	TRUE

On your own, check that (3, 0) is also a solution of the system. If two points are solutions, then all points on the line containing them are solutions. The lines coincide, so there is an infinite number of solutions. Since a solution exists, the system is consistent.

When one equation can be obtained by multiplying both sides of another equation by a nonzero constant, the two equations are called **dependent**. Thus the equations in Example 4 are dependent, but those in Examples 2 and 3 are **independent**. For systems of two equations, when two equations are dependent, they are equivalent. For systems containing more than two equations, the definition of dependent is slightly different and it is possible for dependent equations to not be equivalent.

When a system of two linear equations in two variables is graphed, one of the following must occur:

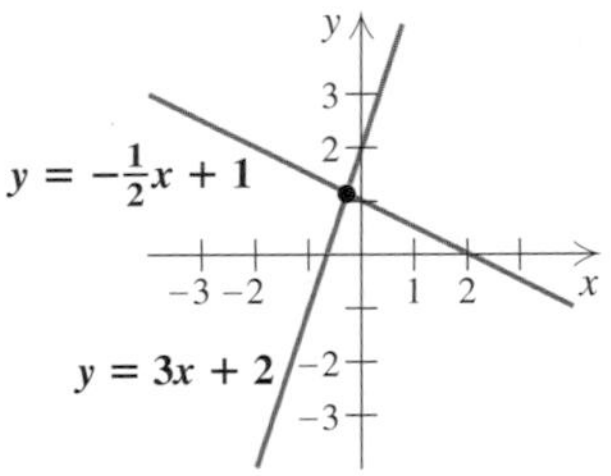

Graphs intersect at one point. The system is *consistent* and has one solution. Since neither equation is a multiple of the other, the equations are *independent.*

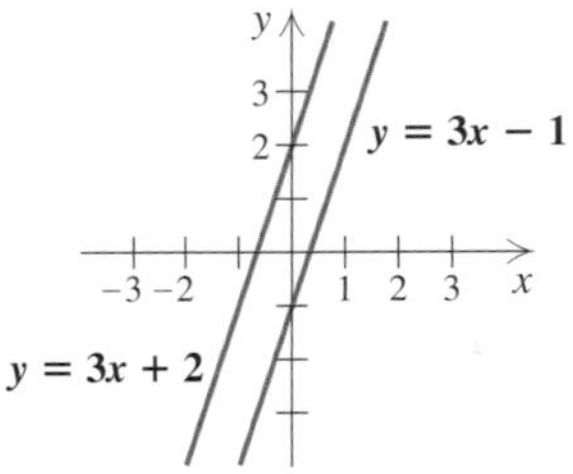

Graphs are parallel. The system is *inconsistent* because there is no solution. Since neither equation is a multiple of the other, the equations are *independent.*

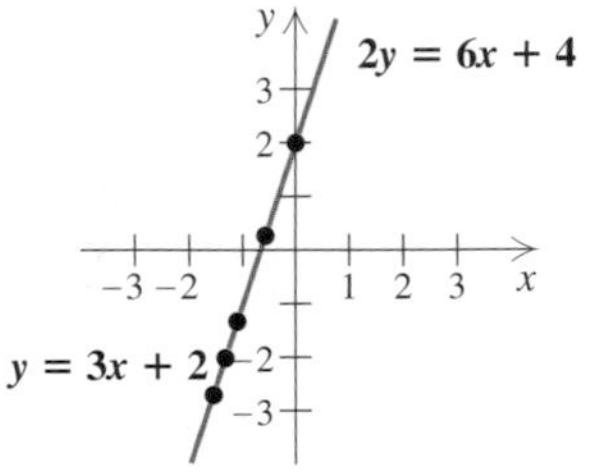

Equations have the same graph. The system is *consistent* and has an infinite number of solutions. Since one equation is two times the other, the equations are *dependent.*

technology connection

Graphing calculators can be used to solve systems of equations, provided each equation has been solved for y. Thus, to solve Example 2, we must rewrite $x + y = 7$ as $y = -x + 7$ to form the equivalent system

$$y = -x + 7,$$
$$y = 3x - 1.$$

We then enter the two equations as y_1 and y_2. After the equations have been graphed, we use the INTERSECT option of the CALC menu to identify and display the point of intersection.

1. Use a graphing calculator to check Example 2.
2. Graph the system

$$y_1 = 0.23x + 1.49,$$
$$y_2 = 0.23x + 3.49$$

and then, using the Y-VARS option of the VARS menu, let $y_3 = y_1 - y_2$. Because the graphs of y_1 and y_2 are parallel, we expect y_3 to be a constant. Use TRACE or the TABLE feature to confirm that this is the case.

ALGEBRAIC–GRAPHICAL CONNECTION

To bring together the concepts of Chapters 1–6, let's take an algebraic–graphical look at equation solving. Such interpretation is useful when you are using a graphing calculator or computer graphing software.

Consider the equation $2x - 5 = 3$. Let's solve it algebraically as we did in Chapter 2:

$2x - 5 = 3$	
$2x = 8$	Adding 5 to both sides
$x = 4.$	Dividing both sides by 2

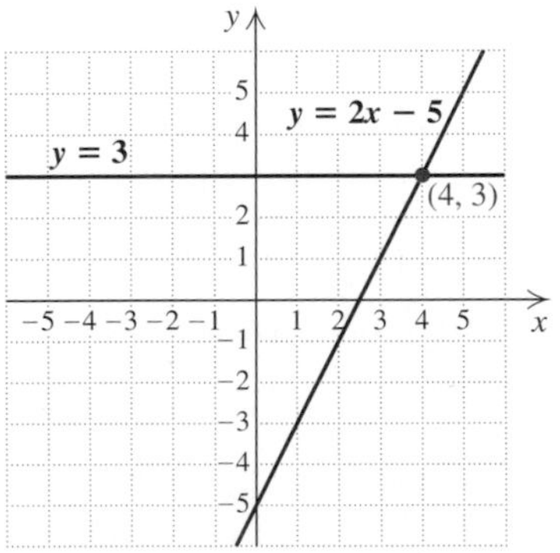

To solve $2x - 5 = 3$ graphically, we graph the equations $y = 2x - 5$ and $y = 3$, as shown at right. The point of intersection, (4, 3), indicates that when x is 4, the value of $2x - 5$ is 3. Thus the solution of $2x - 5 = 3$ is 4.

EXAMPLE 5 Solve graphically: $5 - x = x - 1$.

Solution We graph $y = 5 - x$ and $y = x - 1$, as shown. The graphs intersect at (3, 2), indicating that for the x-value 3 both $5 - x$ and $x - 1$ share the same value (in this case, 2). As a check, note that $5 - 3 = 3 - 1$ is true. The solution is 3.

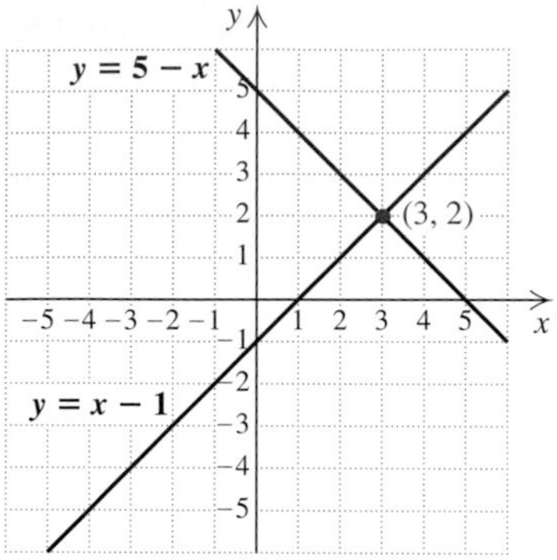

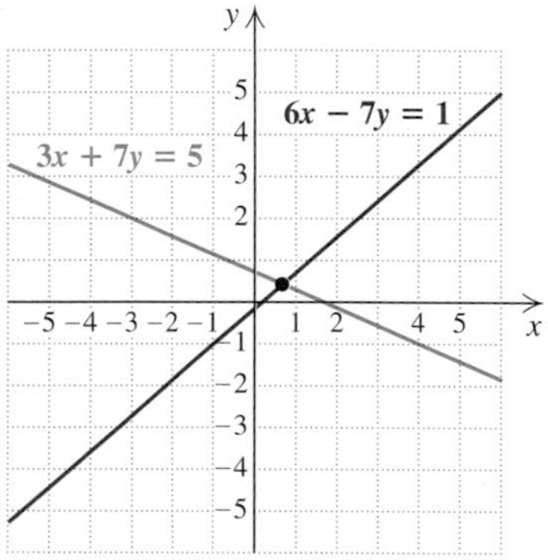

Although graphing lets us "see" the solution of a system, it does not always allow us to find a precise solution. For example, the solution of the system

$$3x + 7y = 5,$$
$$6x - 7y = 1$$

is $\left(\frac{2}{3}, \frac{3}{7}\right)$, but finding that precise solution from a graph—*even with a computer or graphing calculator*—can be difficult. Fortunately, systems like this can be solved accurately with methods discussed in Sections 7.2 and 7.3.

7.1 Exercise Set

FOR EXTRA HELP

Student's Solutions Manual | Digital Video Tutor CD 4 Videotape 13 | AW Math Tutor Center | MathXL Tutorials on CD | MathXL | MyMathLab

Concept Reinforcement *Choose the correct word(s) to complete each sentence.*

1. A solution of a system of two equations is an ordered pair that is a solution of ______ equation(s). (both/at least one)

2. A solution of a system of two equations can be found by identifying where the two graphs ______. (intersect/cross the y-axis)

3. A system of equations that has at least one solution is said to be ______. (inconsistent/consistent)

4. When one equation in a system can be obtained by multiplying both sides of another equation in the system by a nonzero constant, the equations are said to be ______. (dependent/independent)

Determine whether each ordered pair is a solution of the system of equations. Use alphabetical order of the variables.

5. (3, 2); $2x + 3y = 12,$ $x - 4y = -5$

6. (1, 5); $5x - 2y = -5,$ $3x - 7y = -32$

7. (3, 2); $3b - 2a = 0,$ $b + 2a = 15$

8. (2, −2); $b + 2a = 2,$ $b - a = -4$

9. (15, 20); $3x - 2y = 5,$ $6x - 5y = -10$

10. (−1, −3); $3r + s = -6,$ $2r = 1 + s$

Solve each system of equations by graphing. If there is no solution or an infinite number of solutions, state this.

11. $x + y = 7,$
$x - y = 1$

12. $x - y = 1,$
$x + y = 3$

13. $y = -2x + 5,$
$x + y = 4$

14. $y = 2x - 5,$
$x + y = 4$

15. $y = x - 3,$
$y = -2x + 3$

16. $y = -3x + 2,$
$y = x - 2$

17. $4x - 20 = 5y,$
$8x - 10y = 12$

18. $6x + 12 = 2y,$
$6 - y = -3x$

19. $x = 6,$
$y = -1$

20. $x = -2,$
$y = 5$

21. $2x + y = 8,$
$x - y = 7$

22. $3x + y = 4,$
$x - y = 4$

23. $x - y = 5,$
$2x + y = 4$

24. $x - y = 8,$
$3x + y = 12$

25. $x + 2y = 7,$
$3x + 6y = 21$

26. $x + 3y = 6,$
$4x + 12y = 24$

27. $2x = 3y - 6,$
$x = 3y$

28. $3y - 9 = 6x,$
$y = x$

Aha! **29.** $y = \frac{1}{5}x + 4,$
$2y = \frac{2}{5}x + 8$

30. $y = \frac{1}{3}x + 2,$
$y = \frac{1}{3}x - 7$

31. $2x + y = -1,$
$y = 3x - 6$

32. $2x - y = 5,$
$y = \frac{1}{2}x + 1$

33. $2x - 3y = 5,$
$x - 2y = 6$

34. $3x + 4y = 8,$
$x + 2y = 10$

35. $3x + 2y = 1,$
$2x + 5y = -14$

36. $4x + 2y = -2,$
$5x + 4y = 5$

37. $x = \frac{1}{3}y,$
$y = 6$

38. $x = \frac{1}{2}y,$
$x = 3$

Solve graphically.

39. $2x - 1 = 3$

40. $3x - 1 = 2$

41. $x - 4 = 6 - x$

42. $x - 3 = 1 - x$

43. $2x - 1 = -x + 5$

44. $-x + 4 = 2x - 5$

45. $\frac{1}{2}x + 3 = -\frac{1}{2}x - 1$

46. $\frac{3}{2}x + 5 = -\frac{1}{2}x + 1$

47. Suppose that the equations in a system of two linear equations are dependent. Does it follow that the system is consistent? Why or why not?

48. Why is slope–intercept form especially useful when solving systems of equations by graphing?

SKILL MAINTENANCE

Solve. [2.2]

49. $4x - 5(9 - 2x) = 7$

50. $5x - (7 + 3x) = 8$

51. $3(4 - 2y) - 5y = 6$

52. $2(8 - 3y) - 4y = 7$

53. Solve $3a - 5b = 7$ for b. [2.3]

54. Solve $5r + 6s = -8$ for r. [2.3]

SYNTHESIS

55. Is it possible for a system of two linear equations to have exactly two solutions? Why or why not?

56. Explain how it is possible to determine whether or not the system

$$Ax + By = C,$$
$$Dx + Ey = F$$

is inconsistent by simply examining $A, B, C, D, E,$ and F.

57. Which of the systems in Exercises 11–38 contain dependent equations?

58. Which of the systems in Exercises 11–38 are consistent?

59. Which of the systems in Exercises 11–38 are inconsistent?

60. Which of the systems in Exercises 11–38 contain independent equations?

61. Write an equation that can be paired with $5x + 2y = 3$ to form a system that has $(-1, 4)$ as the solution. Answers may vary.

62. Write an equation that can be paired with $4x + 3y = 6$ to form a system that has $(3, -2)$ as the solution. Answers may vary.

63. The solution of the following system is $(2, -3)$. Find A and B.

$$Ax - 3y = 13,$$
$$x - By = 8$$

64. Solve by graphing:

$$4x - 8y = -7,$$
$$2x + 3y = 7.$$

(*Hint*: Use four squares per unit on your graph.)

65. *Copying costs.* Shelby occasionally goes to The UPS Store® with small copying jobs. He can purchase a "copy card" for $20 that will entitle him to 500 copies, or he can simply pay 6¢ per page.

a) Create cost equations for each method of paying for a number (up to 500) of copies.

b) Graph both cost equations on the same set of axes.

c) Use the graph to determine how many copies Shelby must make if the card is to be more economical.

Aha! **66.** Solve:

$$3x - 4y = 2,$$
$$-6x + 8y = -6.$$

67. *Photography.* In 2000, about 33.1 billion photos were printed from film and that number was declining at a rate of 1.1 billion per year. There were 2.8 billion digital photos printed or stored in 2000 and that number was growing at a rate of 2.9 billion per year.

Source: *Deseret Morning News*, Nov. 16, 2003

a) Write two equations that can be used to predict n, the number of filmed or digital photos, in billions, t years after 2000.

b) Use a graphing calculator to determine the year in which the numbers of filmed photos and digital photos are the same.

68. Use a graphing calculator to solve the system

$$y = 1.2x - 32.7,$$
$$y = -0.7x + 46.15.$$

69. Use a graphing calculator to solve $1.3x - 4.9 = 6.3 - 3.7x$.

COLLABORATIVE CORNER

Conserving Energy and Money

Focus: System of linear equations (two variables)

Time: 20 minutes

Group size: 2

Materials: Graph paper

Jean, a condo owner, has an old electric water heater that consumes $100 of electricity per month. To replace it with a new gas water heater that consumes only $25 of gas per month will cost $250 plus $150 for installation. Jean wants to know how long it will take for the new gas water heater to "pay for itself," in other words, to produce savings.

ACTIVITY

1. The "break-even" point occurs when the costs of the two water heaters are equal. Determine, by "guessing and checking," the number of months before Jean breaks even.
2. One of the group members should create a cost equation of the form $y = mx + b$ for the electric heater, where y is the cost, in dollars, and x is the time, in months. He or she should also graph the equation on the graph paper provided.
3. The second group member should create a cost equation of the form $y = mx + b$ for the gas heater, where y is the cost, in dollars, and x is the time, in months. This equation should be graphed on the same graph used in part (2).
4. Working together, the group should determine the coordinates of the point of intersection of the two lines. This is the break-even point. Which coordinate indicates the number of months before Jean breaks even? What does the other coordinate indicate? Compare the answer found graphically with the estimate made in part (1).

7.2 Systems of Equations and Substitution

The Substitution Method • Solving for the Variable First • Problem Solving

Near the end of Section 7.1, we mentioned that graphing can be an imprecise method for solving systems. In this section and the next, we develop methods of finding exact solutions using algebra.

The Substitution Method

One method for solving systems is known as the **substitution method**. It uses algebra instead of graphing and is thus considered an *algebraic* method.

Study Skills

Avoid Overconfidence

Sometimes a topic that seems familiar may arise and you find yourself tempted to take a vacation from your studies, thinking "I know this already." Try to resist this temptation. Often a new wrinkle is included that will catch the unsuspecting student by surprise. If indeed the material is review, use this as a chance to review other more challenging material.

EXAMPLE 1 Solve the system

$x + y = 7,$ (1) We have numbered the equations (1) and

$y = 3x - 1.$ (2) (2) for easy reference.

Solution The second equation says that y and $3x - 1$ represent the same value. Thus, in the first equation, we can substitute $3x - 1$ for y:

$x + y = 7,$ Equation (1)

$x + 3x - 1 = 7.$ Substituting $3x - 1$ (from equation 2) for y (in equation 1)

The equation $x + 3x - 1 = 7$ has only one variable, for which we now solve:

$4x - 1 = 7$ Combining like terms

$4x = 8$ Adding 1 to both sides

$x = 2.$ Dividing both sides by 4

We have found the x-value of the solution. To find the y-value, we return to the original pair of equations. Substituting into either equation will give us the y-value. We choose equation (1):

$x + y = 7$ Equation (1)

$2 + y = 7$ Substituting 2 for x

$y = 5.$ Subtracting 2 from both sides

The ordered pair (2, 5) appears to be a solution. We check:

$x + y = 7$		$y = 3x - 1$	
$2 + 5 \mid 7$		$5 \mid 3 \cdot 2 - 1$	
$7 \stackrel{?}{=} 7$	TRUE	$5 \stackrel{?}{=} 5$	TRUE

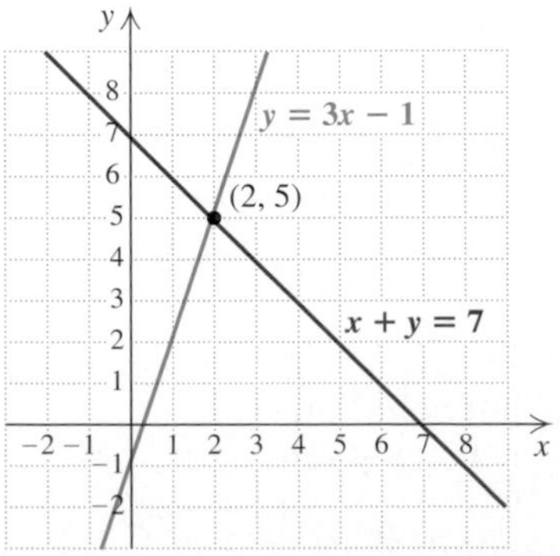

Since (2, 5) checks, it is the solution. For this particular system, we can also check by examining the graph from Example 2 in Section 7.1, as shown at left.

> *Caution!* A solution of a system of equations in two variables is an ordered *pair* of numbers. Once you have solved for one variable, don't forget the other. A common mistake is to solve for only one variable.

EXAMPLE 2 Solve:

$$x = 3 - 2y, \quad (1)$$
$$y - 3x = 5. \quad (2)$$

Solution We substitute $3 - 2y$ for x in the second equation:

$y - 3x = 5$	Equation (2)
$y - 3(3 - 2y) = 5.$	Substituting $3 - 2y$ for x. The parentheses are very important.

Now we solve for y:

$y - 9 + 6y = 5$	Using the distributive law
$7y - 9 = 5$	
$7y = 14$	Solving for y
$y = 2.$	

Next, we substitute 2 for y in equation (1) of the original system:

$x = 3 - 2y$	Equation (1)
$x = 3 - 2 \cdot 2$	Substituting 2 for y
$x = -1.$	Simplifying

We check the ordered pair $(-1, 2)$.

Check:

$x = 3 - 2y$			$y - 3x = 5$		
-1	$3 - 2 \cdot 2$		$2 - 3(-1)$	5	
	$3 - 4$		$2 + 3$		
$-1 \stackrel{?}{=} -1$		TRUE	$5 \stackrel{?}{=} 5$		TRUE

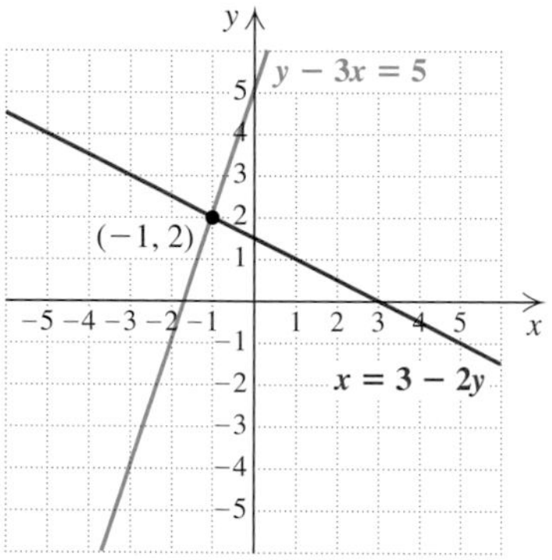

The pair $(-1, 2)$ is the solution. A graph is shown at left as another check.

Solving for the Variable First

Sometimes neither equation has a variable alone on one side. In that case, we solve one equation for one of the variables and then proceed as before.

EXAMPLE 3 Solve:

$$x - 2y = 6, \quad (1)$$
$$3x + 2y = 4. \quad (2)$$

Solution We can solve either equation for either variable. Since the coefficient of x is 1 in equation (1), it is easier to solve that equation for x:

$x - 2y = 6$		Equation (1)
$x = 6 + 2y.$	(3)	Adding $2y$ to both sides

technology connection

To check Example 3 with a graphing calculator, we must first solve each equation for y. When we do so, equation (1) becomes $y = (6 - x)/(-2)$ and equation (2) becomes $y = (4 - 3x)/2$.

1. Use the INTERSECT option of the CALC menu to determine the solution of the system.
2. What happens when parentheses are deleted from the two equations above?

We substitute $6 + 2y$ for x in equation (2) of the original pair and solve for y:

$$3x + 2y = 4 \qquad \text{Equation (2)}$$

$$3(6 + 2y) + 2y = 4 \qquad \text{Substituting } 6 + 2y \text{ for } x$$

Remember to use parentheses when you substitute.

$$18 + 6y + 2y = 4 \qquad \text{Using the distributive law}$$

$$18 + 8y = 4 \qquad \text{Combining like terms}$$

$$8y = -14 \qquad \text{Subtracting 18 from both sides}$$

$$y = \frac{-14}{8} = -\frac{7}{4}. \qquad \text{Dividing both sides by 8}$$

To find x, we can substitute $-\frac{7}{4}$ for y in equation (1), (2), or (3). Because it is generally easier to use an equation that has already been solved for a specific variable, we decide to use equation (3):

$$x = 6 + 2y = 6 + 2\left(-\tfrac{7}{4}\right) = 6 - \tfrac{7}{2} = \tfrac{12}{2} - \tfrac{7}{2} = \tfrac{5}{2}.$$

We check the ordered pair $\left(\frac{5}{2}, -\frac{7}{4}\right)$.

Check:

$x - 2y = 6$	
$\frac{5}{2} - 2\left(-\frac{7}{4}\right)$	6
$\frac{5}{2} + \frac{7}{2}$	
$\frac{12}{2}$	
$6 \stackrel{?}{=} 6$ TRUE	

$3x + 2y = 4$	
$3 \cdot \frac{5}{2} + 2\left(-\frac{7}{4}\right)$	4
$\frac{15}{2} - \frac{7}{2}$	
$\frac{8}{2}$	
$4 \stackrel{?}{=} 4$ TRUE	

Since $\left(\frac{5}{2}, -\frac{7}{4}\right)$ checks, it is the solution.

Some systems have no solution and some have an infinite number of solutions.

EXAMPLE 4 Solve each system.

a) $y = \frac{5}{2}x + 4, \quad (1)$
$y = \frac{5}{2}x - 3 \quad (2)$

b) $2y = 6x + 4, \quad (1)$
$y = 3x + 2 \quad (2)$

Solution

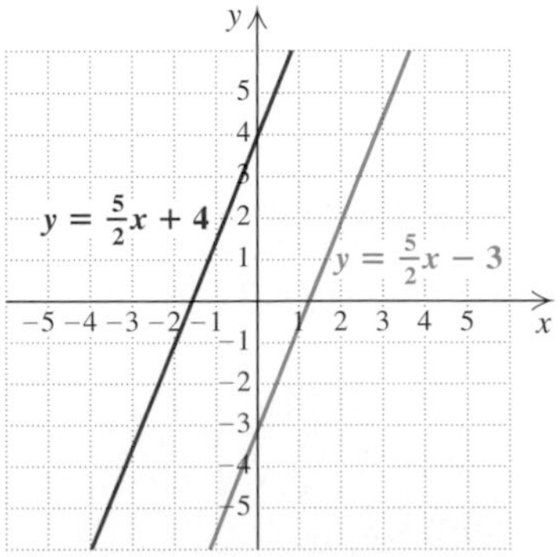

a) We solved this system graphically in Example 3 of Section 7.1. The lines are parallel and the system has no solution. Let's see what happens if we try to solve this system by substituting $\frac{5}{2}x - 3$ for y in the first equation:

$$y = \tfrac{5}{2}x + 4 \qquad \text{Equation (1)}$$

$$\tfrac{5}{2}x - 3 = \tfrac{5}{2}x + 4 \qquad \text{Substituting } \tfrac{5}{2}x - 3 \text{ for } y$$

$$-3 = 4. \qquad \text{Subtracting } \tfrac{5}{2}x \text{ from both sides}$$

When we subtract $\frac{5}{2}x$ from both sides, we obtain a *false* equation. In such a case, when solving algebraically leads to a false equation, we state that the system has no solution and thus is inconsistent.

b) A graph of this system first appeared on p. 433. The lines coincide, so the system has an infinite number of solutions. If we use substitution to solve the system, we can substitute $3x + 2$ for y in equation (1):

$$2y = 6x + 4 \quad \text{Equation (1)}$$
$$2(3x + 2) = 6x + 4 \quad \text{Substituting } 3x + 2 \text{ for } y$$
$$6x + 4 = 6x + 4.$$

This last equation is true for *any* choice of x, indicating that for any choice of x, a solution can be found. When the algebraic solution of a system of two equations leads to an equation that is true for all real numbers, we state that the system has an infinite number of solutions.

To Solve a System Using Substitution

1. Solve for a variable in either one of the equations if neither equation already has a variable isolated.
2. Using the result of step (1), substitute in the *other* equation for the variable isolated in step (1).
3. Solve the equation from step (2).
4. Substitute the solution from step (3) into one of the other equations to solve for the other variable.
5. Check that the ordered pair resulting from steps (3) and (4) checks in both of the original equations.

Problem Solving

Now let's use the substitution method in problem solving.

EXAMPLE 5 Supplementary angles. Two angles are supplementary. One angle measures 30° more than twice the other. Find the measures of the two angles.

Solution

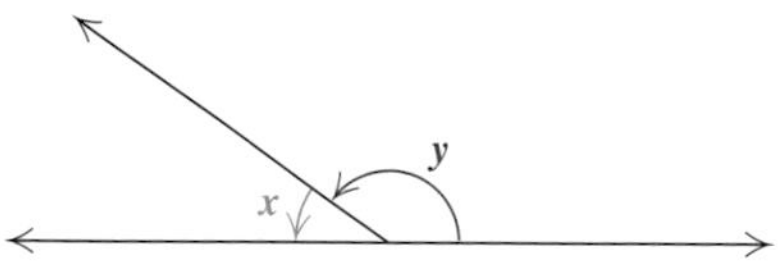

Supplementary angles

1. **Familiarize.** Recall that two angles are supplementary if the sum of their measures is 180°. We could try to guess a solution, but instead we make a drawing and translate. Let x and y represent the measures of the two angles.
2. **Translate.** Since we are told that the angles are supplementary, one equation is

$$x + y = 180. \qquad (1)$$

The second sentence can be rephrased and translated as follows:

Rewording: One angle is 30° more than two times the other.

Translating: $y = 2x + 30$ (2)

We now have a system of two equations in two unknowns:

$$x + y = 180, \quad (1)$$
$$y = 2x + 30. \quad (2)$$

3. **Carry out.** We substitute $2x + 30$ for y in equation (1):

$$\begin{aligned} x + y &= 180 && \text{Equation (1)} \\ x + (2x + 30) &= 180 && \text{Substituting} \\ 3x + 30 &= 180 \\ 3x &= 150 && \text{Subtracting 30 from both sides} \\ x &= 50. && \text{Dividing both sides by 3} \end{aligned}$$

Substituting 50 for x in equation (1) then gives us

$$\begin{aligned} x + y &= 180 && \text{Equation (1)} \\ 50 + y &= 180 && \text{Substituting 50 for } x \\ y &= 130. \end{aligned}$$

4. **Check.** If one angle is 50° and the other is 130°, then the sum of the measures is 180°. Thus the angles are supplementary. If 30° is added to twice the measure of the smaller angle, we have $2 \cdot 50° + 30°$, or 130°, which is the measure of the other angle. The numbers check.
5. **State.** One angle measures 50° and the other 130°.

7.2 Exercise Set

FOR EXTRA HELP

Student's Solutions Manual | Digital Video Tutor CD 4 Videotape 13 | AW Math Tutor Center | MathXL Tutorials on CD | MathXL | MyMathLab

Concept Reinforcement *Classify each statement as either true or false.*

1. The substitution method requires that we solve for the variables in the order in which they occur alphabetically.
2. The substitution method often requires us to first solve for a variable, much as we did when solving for a letter in a formula.
3. When solving a system of equations algebraically leads to a false equation, the system has no solution.
4. When solving a system of two equations algebraically leads to an equation that is always true, the system has an infinite number of solutions.

Solve each system using the substitution method. If a system has no solution or an infinite number of solutions, state this.

5. $x + y = 7,$ $y = x + 3$
6. $x + y = 9,$ $x = y + 1$
7. $x = y + 1,$ $x + 2y = 4$
8. $y = x - 3,$ $3x + y = 5$
9. $y = 2x - 5,$ $3y - x = 5$
10. $y = 2x + 1,$ $x + y = 4$
11. $3x + y = 2,$ $y = -2x$
12. $r = -3s,$ $r + 4s = 10$
13. $2x + 3y = 8,$ $x = y - 6$
14. $x = y - 8,$ $3x + 2y = 1$

15. $x = 2y + 1,$
$3x - 6y = 2$

16. $y = 3x - 1,$
$6x - 2y = 2$

17. $s + t = -4,$
$s - t = 2$

18. $x - y = 6,$
$x + y = -2$

19. $x - y = 5,$
$x + 2y = 7$

20. $y - 2x = -6,$
$2y - x = 5$

21. $x - 2y = 7,$
$3x - 21 = 6y$

22. $x - 4y = 3,$
$2x - 6 = 8y$

23. $y = 2x + 5,$
$-2y = -4x - 10$

24. $y = -2x + 3,$
$3y = -6x + 9$

25. $2x + 3y = -2,$
$2x - y = 9$

26. $x + 2y = 10,$
$3x + 4y = 8$

27. $x - y = -3,$
$2x + 3y = -6$

28. $3a + 2b = 2,$
$-2a + b = 8$

29. $r - 2s = 0,$
$4r - 3s = 15$

30. $y - 2x = 0,$
$3x + 7y = 17$

31. $x - 3y = 7,$
$-4x + 12y = 28$

32. $8x + 2y = 6,$
$y = 3 - 4x$

33. $x - 2y = 5,$
$2y - 3x = 1$

34. $x - 3y = -1,$
$5y - 2x = 4$

Aha! **35.** $2x - y = 0,$
$2x - y = -2$

36. $5x = y - 3,$
$5x = y + 5$

Solve using a system of equations.

37. The sum of two numbers is 83. One number is 5 more than the other. Find the numbers.

38. The sum of two numbers is 76. One number is 2 more than the other. Find the numbers.

39. Find two numbers for which the sum is 93 and the difference is 9.

40. Find two numbers for which the sum is 76 and the difference is 12.

41. The difference between two numbers is 16. Three times the larger number is seven times the smaller. What are the numbers?

42. The difference between two numbers is 18. Twice the smaller number plus three times the larger is 74. What are the numbers?

43. *Supplementary angles.* Two angles are supplementary. One angle is 15° more than twice the other. Find the measure of each angle.

44. *Supplementary angles.* Two angles are supplementary. One angle is 8° less than three times the other. Find the measure of each angle.

45. *Complementary angles.* Two angles are complementary. Their difference is 18°. Find the measure of each angle. (*Complementary angles* are angles for which the sum is 90°.)

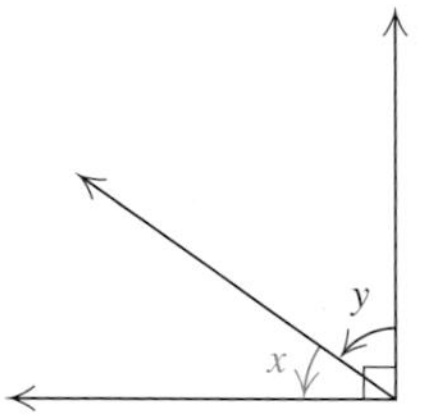

Complementary angles

46. *Complementary angles.* Two angles are complementary. One angle is 42° more than one-half the other. Find the measure of each angle.

47. *Two-by-four.* The perimeter of a cross section of a "two-by-four" piece of lumber is $10\frac{1}{2}$ in. The length is twice the width. Find the actual dimensions of the cross section of a two-by-four.

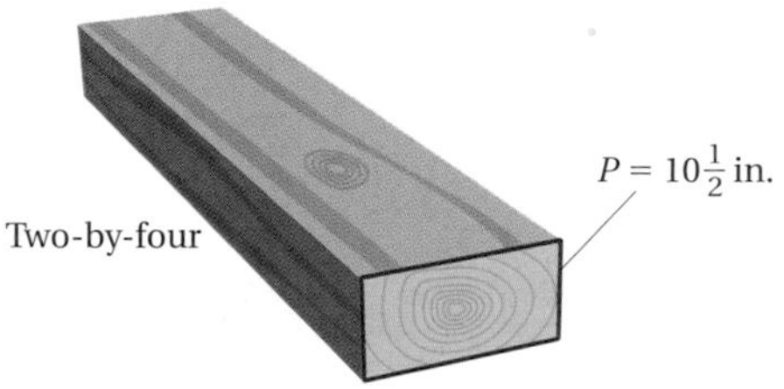

48. *Standard billboard.* A standard rectangular highway billboard has a perimeter of 124 ft. The length is 34 ft more than the width. Find the length and the width.
Source: Eller Sign Company

49. *Dimensions of Colorado.* The state of Colorado is roughly in the shape of a rectangle whose perimeter is 1300 mi. The width is 110 mi less than the length. Find the length and the width.

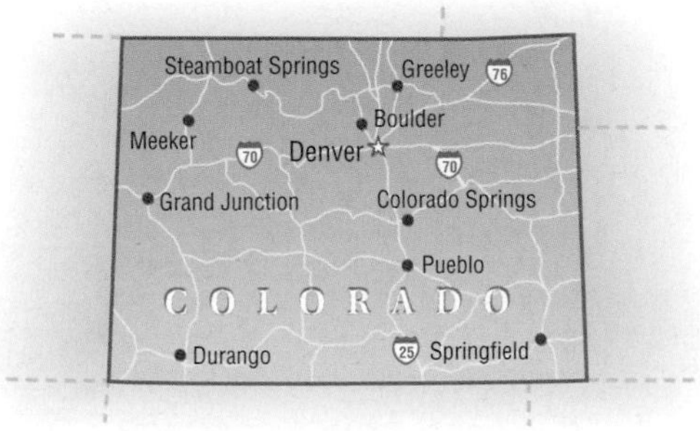

50. *Dimensions of Wyoming.* The state of Wyoming is a rectangle with a perimeter of 1280 mi. The width is 90 mi less than the length. Find the length and the width.

51. *Soccer.* The perimeter of a soccer field is 280 yd. The width is 5 more than half the length. Find the length and the width.

52. *Racquetball.* A regulation racquetball court has a perimeter of 120 ft, with a length that is twice the width. Find the length and the width of a court.

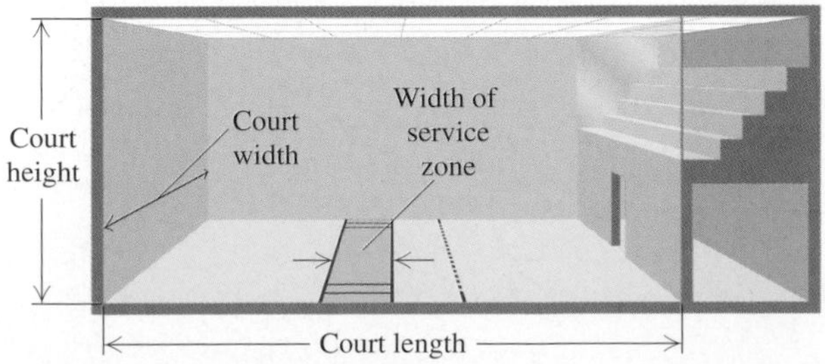

53. *Racquetball.* The height of the front wall of a standard racquetball court is four times the width of the service zone (see the figure). Together, these measurements total 25 ft. Find the height and the width.

54. *Lacrosse.* The perimeter of a lacrosse field is 340 yd. The length is 10 yd less than twice the width. Find the length and the width.

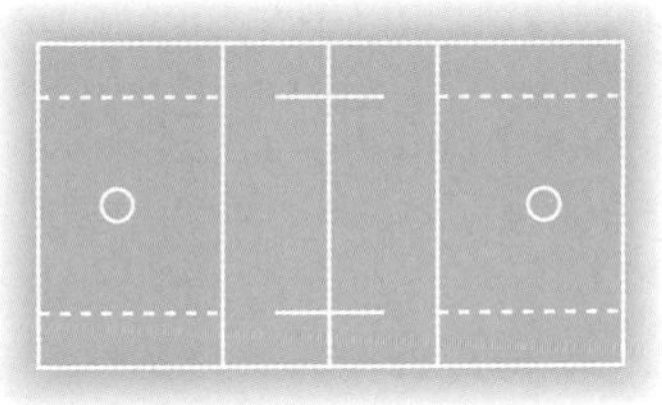

55. Joel solves every system of two equations (in x and y) by first solving for y in the first equation and then substituting into the second equation. Is he using the best approach? Why or why not?

56. Describe two advantages of the substitution method over the graphing method for solving systems of equations.

SKILL MAINTENANCE

Simplify. [1.8]

57. $2(5x + 3y) - 3(5x + 3y)$

58. $5(2x + 3y) - 3(7x + 5y)$

59. $4(5x + 6y) - 5(4x + 7y)$

60. $2(7x + 5 - 3y) - 7(2x + 5)$

61. $2(5x - 3y) - 5(2x + y)$

62. $4(2x + 3y) + 3(5x - 4y)$

SYNTHESIS

63. Janine can tell by inspection that the system

$$x = 2y - 1,$$
$$x = 2y + 3$$

has no solution. How can she tell?

64. Under what circumstances can a system of equations be solved more easily by graphing than by substitution?

Solve by the substitution method.

65. $\frac{1}{6}(a+b)=1,$
$\frac{1}{4}(a-b)=2$

66. $\frac{x}{5}-\frac{y}{2}=3,$
$\frac{x}{4}+\frac{3y}{4}=1$

67. $y+5.97=2.35x,$
$2.14y-x=4.88$

68. $a+4.2b=25.1,$
$9a-1.8b=39.78$

69. *Age at marriage.* Trudy is 20 yr younger than Dennis. She feels that she needs to be 7 more than half of Dennis's age before they can marry. What is the youngest age at which Trudy can marry Dennis and honor this requirement?

Exercises 70 and 71 contain systems of three equations in three variables. A solution is an ordered triple of the form (x, y, z). Use the substitution method to solve.

70. $x+y+z=4,$
$x-2y-z=1,$
$y=-1$

71. $x+y+z=180,$
$x=z-70,$
$2y-z=0$

72. *Softball.* The perimeter of a softball diamond is two-thirds of the perimeter of a baseball diamond. Together, the two perimeters measure 200 yd. Find the distance between the bases in each sport.

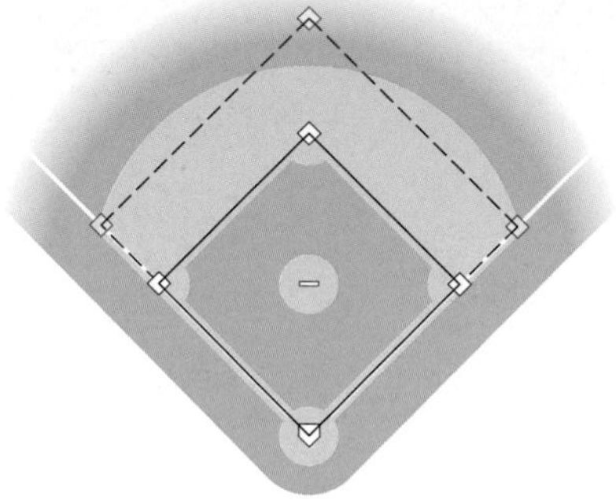

73. Solve Example 3 by first solving for $2y$ in equation (1) and then substituting for $2y$ in equation (2). Is this method easier than the procedure used in Example 3? Why or why not?

74. Write a system of two linear equations that can be solved more quickly—but still precisely—by a graphing calculator than by substitution. Time yourself using both methods to solve the system.

7.3 Systems of Equations and Elimination

Solving by the Elimination Method • Problem Solving

Study Skills

Use What You Know

An excellent strategy for solving any new type of problem is to rewrite the problem in an equivalent form that we already know how to solve. Although this is not always feasible, when it is—as in some of the problems in this section—it can make a new topic much easier to learn.

We have seen that graphing is not always a precise method of solving a system of equations, especially when fraction solutions are involved. The substitution method, considered in Section 7.2, is precise but sometimes difficult to use. For example, to solve the system

$$2x+3y=13, \quad (1)$$
$$4x-3y=17 \quad (2)$$

by substitution, we would need to first solve for a variable in one of the equations. Were we to solve equation (1) for y, we would find (after several steps) that $y=\frac{13}{3}-\frac{2}{3}x$. We could then use the expression $\frac{13}{3}-\frac{2}{3}x$ in equation (2) as a replacement for y:

$$4x-3\left(\frac{13}{3}-\frac{2}{3}x\right)=17.$$

As you will see, although substitution *could* be used to solve this system, another method, *elimination*, is simpler to use on problems like this.

Solving by the Elimination Method

The **elimination method** for solving systems of equations makes use of the addition principle. To see how it works, we use it to solve the system above.

EXAMPLE 1 Solve the system

$$2x + 3y = 13, \quad (1)$$
$$4x - 3y = 17. \quad (2)$$

Solution According to equation (2), $4x - 3y$ and 17 are the same number. Thus we can add $4x - 3y$ to the left side of equation (1) and 17 to the right side:

$$\begin{aligned} 2x + 3y &= 13 && (1) \\ \underline{4x - 3y = 17} & && (2) \\ 6x + 0y &= 30. && \text{Adding. Note that } y \text{ has been "eliminated."} \end{aligned}$$

The resulting equation has just one variable:

$$6x = 30.$$

Dividing both sides of this equation by 6, we find that $x = 5$.

Next, we substitute 5 for x in either of the original equations:

$$\begin{aligned} 2x + 3y &= 13 && \text{Equation (1)} \\ 2 \cdot 5 + 3y &= 13 && \text{Substituting 5 for } x \\ 10 + 3y &= 13 \\ 3y &= 3 \\ y &= 1. && \text{Solving for } y \end{aligned}$$

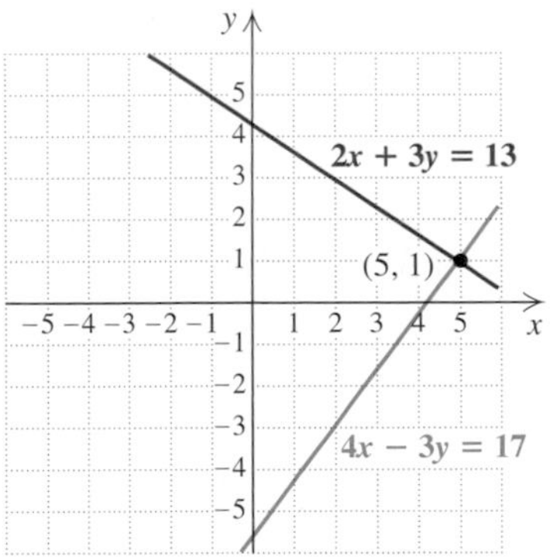

We check the ordered pair (5, 1). The graph shown at left also serves as a check.

Check:

$2x + 3y = 13$	
$2(5) + 3(1)$	13
$10 + 3$	
$13 \stackrel{?}{=} 13$	TRUE

$4x - 3y = 17$	
$4(5) - 3(1)$	17
$20 - 3$	
$17 \stackrel{?}{=} 17$	TRUE

Since (5, 1) checks in both equations, it is the solution.

The system in Example 1 is easier to solve by elimination than by substitution because two terms, $-3y$ in equation (2) and $3y$ in equation (1), are opposites. Most systems have no pair of terms that are opposites. When this occurs, we can multiply one or both of the equations by appropriate numbers to create a pair of terms that are opposites.

EXAMPLE 2 Solve:

$$2x + 3y = 8, \qquad (1)$$
$$x + 3y = 7. \qquad (2)$$

Solution Adding these equations as they now appear will not eliminate a variable. However, if the $3y$ were $-3y$ in one equation, we could eliminate y. We multiply both sides of equation (2) by -1 to find an equivalent equation that contains $-3y$, and then add:

$$\begin{aligned} 2x + 3y &= 8 && \text{Equation (1)} \\ -x - 3y &= -7 && \text{Multiplying both sides of equation (2) by } -1 \\ \hline x \quad &= 1. && \text{Adding} \end{aligned}$$

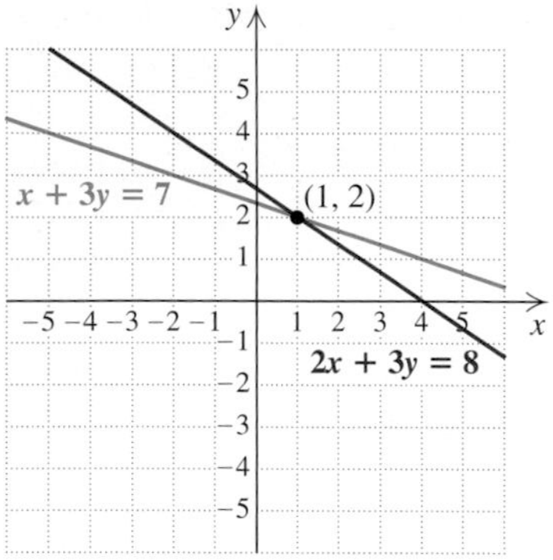

Next, we substitute 1 for x in either of the original equations:

$$\begin{aligned} x + 3y &= 7 && \text{Equation (2)} \\ 1 + 3y &= 7 && \text{Substituting 1 for } x \\ 3y &= 6 && \text{Solving for } y \\ y &= 2. && \end{aligned}$$

We can check the ordered pair (1, 2). The graph shown at left is also a check.

Check:

$2x + 3y = 8$	
$2 \cdot 1 + 3 \cdot 2$	8
$2 + 6$	
$8 \stackrel{?}{=} 8$	TRUE

$x + 3y = 7$	
$1 + 3 \cdot 2$	7
$1 + 6$	
$7 \stackrel{?}{=} 7$	TRUE

Since (1, 2) checks in both equations, it is the solution.

When deciding which variable to eliminate, we inspect the coefficients in both equations. If one coefficient is a multiple of the coefficient of the same variable in the other equation, that is the easiest variable to eliminate.

EXAMPLE 3 Solve:

$$3x + 6y = -6, \qquad (1)$$
$$5x - 2y = 14. \qquad (2)$$

Solution No terms are opposites, but if both sides of equation (2) are multiplied by 3 (or if both sides of equation (1) are multiplied by $\frac{1}{3}$), the coefficients of y will be opposites. Note that 6 is the LCM of 2 and 6:

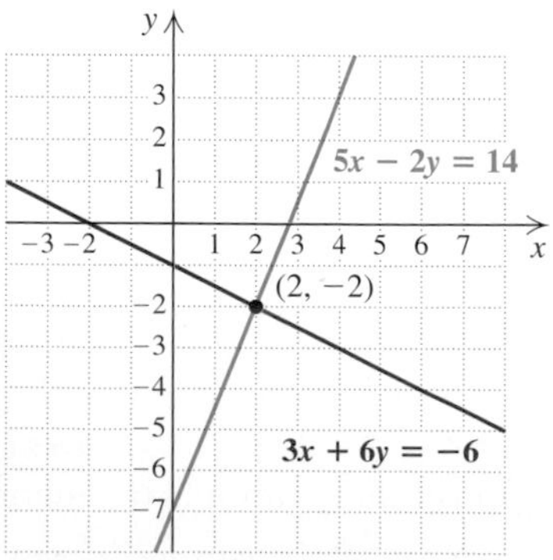

$$\begin{aligned} 3x + 6y &= -6 && \text{Equation (1)} \\ 15x - 6y &= 42 && \text{Multiplying both sides of equation (2) by 3} \\ \hline 18x \quad &= 36 && \text{Adding} \\ x &= 2. && \text{Solving for } x \end{aligned}$$

We then substitute 2 for x in either equation (1) or equation (2):

$$\begin{aligned} 3 \cdot 2 + 6y &= -6 && \text{Substituting 2 for } x \text{ in equation (1)} \\ 6 + 6y &= -6 && \\ 6y &= -12 && \text{Solving for } y \\ y &= -2. && \end{aligned}$$

We leave it to the student to confirm that $(2, -2)$ checks and is the solution. The graph in the margin also serves as a check.

Sometimes both equations must be multiplied to find the least common multiple of two coefficients.

EXAMPLE 4 Solve:

$$3y + 1 + 2x = 0, \qquad (1)$$
$$5x = 7 - 4y. \qquad (2)$$

Solution It is often helpful to write both equations in the form $Ax + By = C$ before attempting to eliminate a variable:

$2x + 3y = -1,$ (3) Subtracting 1 from both sides and rearranging the terms of the first equation

$5x + 4y = 7.$ (4) Adding $4y$ to both sides of equation (2)

Since neither coefficient of x is a multiple of the other and neither coefficient of y is a multiple of the other, we use the multiplication principle with *both* equations. Note that we can eliminate the x-term by multiplying both sides of equation (3) by 5 and both sides of equation (4) by -2:

$10x + 15y = -5$ Multiplying both sides of equation (3) by 5

$-10x - 8y = -14$ Multiplying both sides of equation (4) by -2

$7y = -19$ Adding

$y = \frac{-19}{7} = -\frac{19}{7}.$ Dividing by 7

We substitute $-\frac{19}{7}$ for y in equation (3):

$2x + 3y = -1$ Equation (3)

$2x + 3\left(-\frac{19}{7}\right) = -1$ Substituting $-\frac{19}{7}$ for y

$2x - \frac{57}{7} = -1$

$2x = -1 + \frac{57}{7}$ Adding $\frac{57}{7}$ to both sides

$2x = -\frac{7}{7} + \frac{57}{7} = \frac{50}{7}$

$x = \frac{50}{7} \cdot \frac{1}{2} = \frac{25}{7}.$ Solving for x

We check the ordered pair $\left(\frac{25}{7}, -\frac{19}{7}\right)$.

Check:

$3y + 1 + 2x = 0$	
$3\left(-\frac{19}{7}\right) + 1 + 2 \cdot \frac{25}{7}$	0
$-\frac{57}{7} + \frac{7}{7} + \frac{50}{7}$	
$0 \stackrel{?}{=} 0$	TRUE

$5x = 7 - 4y$	
$5 \cdot \frac{25}{7}$	$7 - 4\left(-\frac{19}{7}\right)$
$\frac{125}{7}$	$\frac{49}{7} + \frac{76}{7}$
$\frac{125}{7} \stackrel{?}{=} \frac{125}{7}$	TRUE

The solution is $\left(\frac{25}{7}, -\frac{19}{7}\right)$.

Student Notes

Before diving into a problem, spend some time deciding which variable to eliminate. Always try to select the approach that will minimize your calculations.

Next, we consider a system with no solution and see what happens when the elimination method is used.

EXAMPLE 5 Solve:

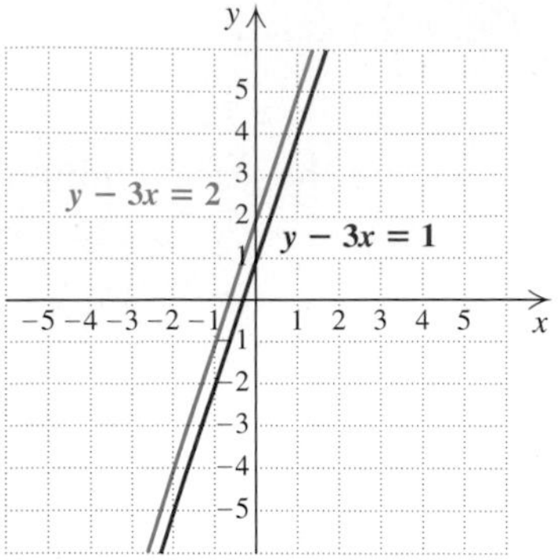

$$y - 3x = 2, \quad (1)$$
$$y - 3x = 1. \quad (2)$$

Solution To eliminate y, we multiply both sides of equation (2) by -1. Then we add:

$$\begin{aligned} y - 3x &= 2 \\ -y + 3x &= -1 \quad \text{Multiplying both sides of equation (2) by } -1 \\ \hline 0 &= 1. \quad \text{Adding} \end{aligned}$$

Note that in eliminating y, we eliminated x as well. The resulting equation, $0 = 1$, is false for any pair (x, y), so there is *no solution*.

Sometimes there is an infinite number of solutions. Consider a system that we graphed in Example 4 of Section 7.1.

EXAMPLE 6 Solve:

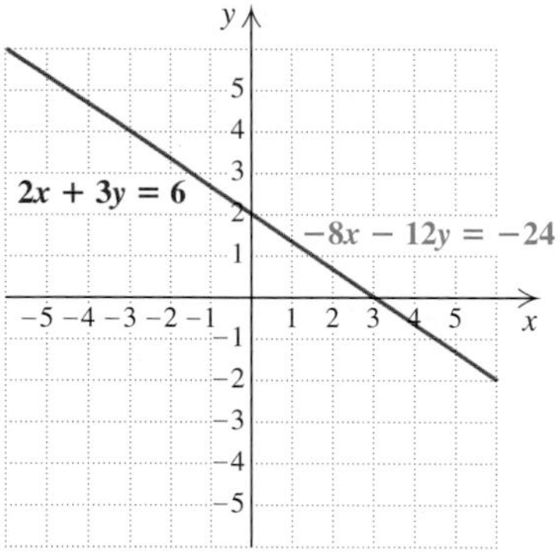

$$2x + 3y = 6, \quad (1)$$
$$-8x - 12y = -24. \quad (2)$$

Solution To eliminate x, we multiply both sides of equation (1) by 4 and then add the two equations:

$$\begin{aligned} 8x + 12y &= 24 \quad \text{Multiplying both sides of equation (1) by 4} \\ -8x - 12y &= -24 \\ \hline 0 &= 0. \quad \text{Adding} \end{aligned}$$

Again, we have eliminated *both* variables. The resulting equation, $0 = 0$, is always true, indicating that the equations are dependent. Such a system has an infinite number of solutions.

When decimals or fractions appear, we can first multiply to clear them. Then we proceed as before.

EXAMPLE 7 Solve:

$$\tfrac{1}{2}x + \tfrac{3}{4}y = 2, \quad (1)$$
$$x + 3y = 7. \quad (2)$$

Solution The number 4 is the LCD for equation (1). Thus we multiply both sides of equation (1) by 4 to clear fractions:

$$\begin{aligned} 4\left(\tfrac{1}{2}x + \tfrac{3}{4}y\right) &= 4 \cdot 2 \quad \text{Multiplying both sides of equation (1) by 4} \\ 4 \cdot \tfrac{1}{2}x + 4 \cdot \tfrac{3}{4}y &= 8 \quad \text{Using the distributive law} \\ 2x + 3y &= 8. \end{aligned}$$

The resulting system is

$$2x + 3y = 8, \qquad \text{This equation is equivalent to equation (1).}$$
$$x + 3y = 7.$$

As we saw in Example 2, the solution of this system is (1, 2).

Problem Solving

We now use the elimination method to solve a problem.

EXAMPLE 8 Phone cards. A calling-card company offers two prepaid cards for domestic calls, the Liberty Prepaid Card and the USA Calling Card. The Liberty Card has a 50¢ connection fee per call and a 1¢ per minute rate. The USA Card has a 13.6¢ connection fee per call and a 2.2¢ per minute rate. (*Source:* www.PrepaidPhoneCardsUSA.com) For what length of call will the costs be the same?

Solution

1. **Familiarize.** To become familiar with the problem, we make and check a guess of 20 min. A 20-min Liberty call would cost $1 \cdot 20 + 50$, or 70¢. Using the USA card, a 20-min call would cost $2.2(20) + 13.6$, or 57.6¢. Since $70 \neq 57.6$, our guess is incorrect. However, from the check, we can see how equations can be written to model the situation. We let m = the length of a phone call, in minutes, and c = the cost of the call, in cents.
2. **Translate.** We reword the problem and translate as follows:

Rewording:	Liberty's cost	is	50¢	plus	1¢	times	the length of the call, in minutes.
	↓	↓	↓	↓	↓	↓	↓
Translating:	c	$=$	50	$+$	1	$\cdot$	m

Note that cents are used as the monetary unit. We write a second equation representing the cost of a call on the USA card:

Rewording:	USA's cost	is	13.6¢	plus	2.2¢	times	the length of the call, in minutes.
	↓	↓	↓	↓	↓	↓	↓
Translating:	c	$=$	13.6	$+$	2.2	$\cdot$	m

We now have the system of equations

$$c = 50 + m,$$
$$c = 13.6 + 2.2m.$$

3. **Carry out.** To solve the system, we multiply the second equation by -1 and add to eliminate c:

$$\begin{aligned} c &= 50 + m \\ -c &= -13.6 - 2.2m \\ \hline 0 &= 36.4 - 1.2m. \end{aligned}$$

We can now solve for m:

$$\begin{aligned} 1.2m &= 36.4 \\ m &= 30.\overline{3} \\ m &\approx 30. \end{aligned}$$

4. **Check.** For 30 min, the cost of a Liberty Card call would be

$$50 + 1 \cdot 30, \quad \text{or} \quad 50 + 30¢, \quad \text{or} \quad 80¢,$$

and the cost of a USA Card call would be

$$13.6 + 2.2 \cdot 30, \quad \text{or} \quad 13.6 + 66¢, \quad \text{or} \quad 80¢.$$ Rounding to the nearest cent

Thus the costs are the same for a 30-min call.

5. **State.** For a 30-min call, the costs are the same.

7.3 Exercise Set

FOR EXTRA HELP

Student's Solutions Manual | Digital Video Tutor CD 4 Videotape 13 | AW Math Tutor Center | MathXL Tutorials on CD | MathXL | MyMathLab

Concept Reinforcement *Classify each statement as either true or false.*

1. The elimination method is never easier to use than the substitution method.

2. The elimination method works especially well when the coefficients of one variable are opposites of each other.

3. When the elimination method yields an equation, like $0 = 0$, that is always true, there is an infinite number of solutions.

4. When the elimination method yields an equation, like $0 = 3$, that is never true, the system has no solution.

Solve using the elimination method. If a system has no solution or an infinite number of solutions, state this.

5. $x - y = 6,$
$x + y = 12$

6. $x + y = 3,$
$x - y = 7$

7. $x + y = 6,$
$-x + 3y = -2$

8. $x + y = 6,$
$-x + 2y = 15$

9. $4x - y = 1,$
$3x + y = 13$

10. $3x - y = 9,$
$2x + y = 6$

11. $5a + 4b = 7,$
$-5a + b = 8$

12. $7c + 4d = 16,$
$c - 4d = -4$

13. $8x - 5y = -9,$
$3x + 5y = -2$

14. $3a - 3b = -15,$
$-3a - 3b = -3$

15. $3a - 6b = 8,$
$-3a + 6b = -8$

16. $8x + 3y = 4,$
$-8x - 3y = -4$

17. $-x - y = 8,$
$2x - y = -1$

18. $x + y = -7,$
$3x + y = -9$

19. $x + 3y = 19,$
$x - y = -1$

20. $3x - y = 8,$
$x + 2y = 5$

21. $x + y = 5,$
$4x - 3y = 13$

22. $x - y = 7,$
$3x - 5y = 15$

23. $2w - 3z = -1,$
$-4w + 6z = 5$

24. $7p + 5q = 2,$
$8p - 9q = 17$

25. $2a + 3b = -1,$
$3a + 5b = -2$

26. $3x - 4y = 16,$
$5x + 6y = 14$

27. $3y = x,$
$5x + 14 = y$

28. $5a = 2b,$
$2a + 11 = 3b$

29. $4x - 10y = 13,$
$-2x + 5y = 8$

30. $2p + 5q = 9,$
$3p - 2q = 4$

31. $8n + 6 - 3m = 0,$
$32 = m - n$

32. $6x - 8 + y = 0,$
$11 = 3y - 8x$

33. $3x + 5y = 4,$
$-2x + 3y = 10$

34. $2x + y = 13,$
$4x + 2y = 23$

35. $0.06x + 0.05y = 0.07,$
$0.4x - 0.3y = 1.1$

36. $x - \frac{3}{2}y = 13,$
$\frac{3}{2}x - y = 17$

37. $x + \frac{9}{2}y = \frac{15}{4},$
$\frac{9}{10}x - y = \frac{9}{20}$

38. $1.8x - 2y = 0.9,$
$0.04x + 0.18y = 0.15$

Solve.

39. *Local truck rentals.* Budget rents a 15-ft truck for \$39.95 plus 79¢ per mile. Penske rents a 15-ft van for \$49.95 plus 59¢ per mile. For what mileage is the cost the same?
Source: Budget Truck Rental and Penske Truck Leasing, November 2003

40. *Local truck rentals.* U-Haul rents a 14-ft truck for \$29.95 plus 79¢ per mile. Penske rents a 15-ft van for \$49.95 plus 59¢ per mile. For what mileage is the cost the same?
Source: Penske Truck Leasing and U-Haul International, November 2003

41. *Complementary angles.* Two angles are complementary. One angle is 12° more than twice the other. Find the measure of each angle.

42. *Complementary angles.* Two angles are complementary. Their difference is 26°. Find the measure of each angle.

43. *Phone rates.* Recently, AT&T offered two long-distance calling plans. The One-Rate® 7¢ Plus Plan costs \$4.95 per month plus 7¢ a minute. Another plan has no monthly fee, but costs 10¢ a minute. For what number of minutes will the two plans cost the same?

44. *Phone rates.* Recently, MCI offered one calling plan that charges 45¢ a minute for calling-card calls. Sprint offered a plan charging 25¢ a minute for calling-card calls, but costs an additional \$1 per month. For what number of minutes will the two plans cost the same?

45. *Supplementary angles.* Two angles are supplementary. One angle measures 5° less than four times the measure of the other. Find the measure of each angle.

46. *Supplementary angles.* Two angles are supplementary. One angle measures 45° more than twice the measure of the other. Find the measure of each angle.

47. *Baking.* Maple Branch Bakers sells 175 loaves of bread each day—some white and the rest whole-wheat. Because of a regular order from a local sandwich shop, Maple Branch consistently bakes 9 more loaves of white bread than whole-wheat. How many loaves of each type of bread do they bake?

48. *Planting grapes.* South Wind Vineyards uses 820 acres to plant Chardonnay and Riesling grapes. The vintner knows the profits will be greatest by planting 140 more acres of Chardonnay than Riesling. How many acres of each type of grape should be planted?

49. *Framing.* Angel has 18 ft of molding from which he needs to make a rectangular frame. Because of the dimensions of the mirror being framed, the frame must be twice as long as it is wide. What should the dimensions of the frame be?

50. *Gardening.* Patrice has 108 ft of fencing for a rectangular garden. If the garden's length is to be $1\frac{1}{2}$ times its width, what should the garden's dimensions be?

51. Describe a method that could be used for writing a system that contains dependent equations.

52. Describe a method that could be used for writing an inconsistent system of equations.

SKILL MAINTENANCE

Convert to decimal notation. [2.4]

53. 8% **54.** 7.3% **55.** 0.4%

Solve. [2.4]

56. What percent of 45 is 18?

57. What number is 9% of 350?

58. 24 is what percent of 150?

SYNTHESIS

59. If a system has an infinite number of solutions, does it follow that *any* ordered pair is a solution? Why or why not?

60. Explain how the multiplication and addition principles are used in this section. Then count the number of times that these principles are used in Example 4.

Solve using substitution, elimination, or graphing.

61. $x + y = 7,$
$3(y - x) = 9$

62. $y = 3x + 4,$
$3 + y = 2(y - x)$

63. $2(5a - 5b) = 10,$
$-5(2a + 6b) = 10$

64. $0.05x + y = 4,$
$\frac{x}{2} + \frac{y}{3} = 1\frac{1}{3}$

Aha! **65.** $y = -\frac{2}{7}x + 3,$
$y = \frac{4}{5}x + 3$

66. $y = \frac{2}{5}x - 7,$
$y = \frac{2}{5}x + 4$

Solve for x and y.

67. $y = ax + b,$
$y = x + c$

68. $ax + by + c = 0,$
$ax + cy + b = 0$

69. *Caged rabbits and pheasants.* Several ancient Chinese books included problems that can be solved by translating to systems of equations. *Arithmetical Rules in Nine Sections* is a book of 246 problems compiled by a Chinese mathematician, Chang Tsang, who died in 152 B.C. One of the problems is: Suppose there are a number of rabbits and pheasants confined in a cage. In all, there are 35 heads and 94 feet. How many rabbits and how many pheasants are there? Solve the problem.

70. *Age.* Patrick's age is 20% of his mother's age. Twenty years from now, Patrick's age will be 52% of his mother's age. How old are Patrick and his mother now?

71. *Age.* If 5 is added to a man's age and the total is divided by 5, the result will be his daughter's age. Five years ago, the man's age was eight times his daughter's age. Find their present ages.

72. *Dimensions of a triangle.* When the base of a triangle is increased by 1 ft and the height is increased by 2 ft, the height changes from being two-thirds of the base to being four-fifths of the base. Find the original dimensions of the triangle.

7.4 More Applications Using Systems

Total-Value Problems • Mixture Problems

CONNECTING THE CONCEPTS

We now have three distinctly different ways to solve a system. Each method has certain strengths and weaknesses.

Method	Strengths	Weaknesses
Graphical	Solutions are displayed visually. Works with any system that can be graphed.	Inexact when solutions involve numbers that are not integers or are very large and off the graph.
Substitution	Always yields exact solutions. Easy to use when a variable is alone on one side of an equation.	Introduces extensive computations with fractions when solving more complicated systems. Solutions are not graphically displayed.
Elimination	Always yields exact solutions. Easy to use when fractions or decimals appear in the system.	Solutions are not graphically displayed.

When selecting the best method to use for a particular system, consider the strengths and weaknesses listed above. As you gain experience with these methods, it will become easier to choose the best method for any given system.

The five steps for problem solving and the methods for solving systems of equations can be used in a variety of applications.

Total-Value Problems

EXAMPLE 1

Basketball scores. In one game during the 2004 NBA playoffs, the Indiana Pacers scored 87 points. Of those, 22 points were from free throws. The remaining 65 points were a result of 28 two- and three-point baskets. (*Source: Burlington Free Press*, 5/11/04) How many baskets of each type were made?

Heat 94, Pacers 87

INDIANA (87)
Artest 4-18 4-7 14, O'Neal 9-21 11-16 29, Foster 1-2 1-2 3, Tinsley 6-8 0-0 16, Miller 1-2 1-1 4, Harrington 5-12 2-4 13, F.Jones 0-2 1-2 1, Johnson 1-3 0-0 3, Bender 1-4 2-2 4. Totals 28-72 22-34 87.
MIAMI (94)
C.Butler 2-8 8-8 12, Odom 5-9 5-12 16, Grant 3-7 0-0 6, Wade 7-15 11-12 25, E.Jones 4-12 2-2 12, Allen 6-9 1-2 13, Alston 2-4 0-0 5, Haslem 1-1 0-0 2, R.Butler 1-1 0-0 3. Totals 31-66 27-36 94.

Indiana	**20**	**15**	**25**	**27—87**
Miami	**14**	**25**	**25**	**30—94**

Solution

1. **Familiarize.** Suppose that of the 28 baskets, 24 were two-pointers and 4 were three-pointers. These 28 baskets would then amount to a total of

$$24 \cdot 2 + 4 \cdot 3 = 48 + 12 = 60 \text{ points.}$$

Although our guess is incorrect, checking the guess has familiarized us with the problem. We let $w =$ the number of two-pointers made and $r =$ the number of three-pointers made.

2. **Translate.** Since a total of 28 baskets was made, we must have

$$w + r = 28.$$

To find a second equation, we reword some information and focus on the points scored, just as when we checked our guess above.

Rewording:	The points scored from two-pointers	plus	the points scored from three-pointers	totaled	65.
Translating:	$w \cdot 2$	$+$	$r \cdot 3$	$=$	65

The problem has been translated to the following system of equations:

$$w + r = 28, \quad (1)$$
$$2w + 3r = 65. \quad (2)$$

3. **Carry out.** For purposes of review, we solve by substitution. First we solve equation (1) for w:

$$w + r = 28 \qquad \text{Equation (1)}$$
$$w = 28 - r. \quad (3) \qquad \text{Solving for } w$$

Next, we replace w in equation (2) with $28 - r$:

$$2w + 3r = 65 \qquad \text{Equation (2)}$$
$$2(28 - r) + 3r = 65 \qquad \text{Substituting } 28 - r \text{ for } w$$
$$56 - 2r + 3r = 65$$
$$\left.\begin{aligned} 56 + r &= 65 \\ r &= 9. \end{aligned}\right\} \quad \text{Solving for } r$$

We find w by substituting 9 for r in equation (3):

$$w = 28 - r = 28 - 9 = 19.$$

4. **Check.** If the Pacers made 19 two-pointers and 9 three-pointers, they would have made 28 shots, for a total of

$$19 \cdot 2 + 9 \cdot 3 = 38 + 27 = 65 \text{ points.}$$

The numbers check.

5. **State.** The Pacers made 19 two-pointers and 9 three-pointers.

Study Skills

Putting Math to Use

One excellent way to study math is to use it in your everyday life. The concepts of this section can be easily reinforced if you look for real-life situations in which systems of equations can be used. Keep this in mind when you are shopping at a grocery or hardware store and buying multiple items of two or more types.

EXAMPLE 2 Film processing. Ritz Camera One Hour Photo® recently charged \$10.99 for processing a 24-exposure roll and \$14.99 for processing a 36-exposure roll (*Source*: Ritz Camera One Hour Photo, So. Burlington, VT, 2004). After a field trip to a nature preserve, Amanda's photography class dropped off 19 rolls of film at Ritz and paid \$232.81 for processing. How many rolls of each type were processed?

Solution

1. **Familiarize.** When faced with a new problem, it is often useful to compare it to a similar problem that you have already solved. Here instead of counting two- and three-point baskets, as in Example 1, we are counting 24-exposure and 36-exposure rolls of film. We let w = the number of 24-exposure rolls that were processed and r = the number of 36-exposure rolls that were processed.

2. **Translate.** Since a total of 19 rolls was processed, we have

$$w + r = 19.$$

To find a second equation, we reword some information, focusing on the amount of money paid.

Rewording:	The money paid for the 24-exposure processing	plus	the money paid for the 36-exposure processing	totaled	\$232.81.
	↓	↓	↓	↓	↓
Translating:	$w \cdot 10.99$	$+$	$r \cdot 14.99$	$=$	232.81

Presenting the information in a table can be helpful.

	24-exposure	36-exposure	Total
Cost per Roll	\$10.99	\$14.99	
Number of Rolls	w	r	19
Money Paid	$10.99w$	$14.99r$	232.81

Number of Rolls → $w + r = 19$

Money Paid → $10.99w + 14.99r = 232.81$

We have translated to a system of equations:

$$w + r = 19, \quad (1)$$
$$10.99w + 14.99r = 232.81. \quad (2)$$

3. **Carry out.** The system can be solved using elimination:

$-10.99w - 10.99r = -208.81$	Multiplying both sides of equation (1) by -10.99
$10.99w + 14.99r = 232.81$	Equation (2)
$4r = 24$	Adding
$r = 6$	Dividing both sides by 4

To solve for w, we substitute 6 for r:

$$w + r = 19 \qquad \text{Using equation (1)}$$
$$w + 6 = 19$$
$$w = 13. \qquad \text{Subtracting 6 from both sides}$$

4. **Check.** If $w = 13$ and $r = 6$, a total of 19 rolls was developed. The amount paid was 13($10.99), or $142.87, for the 24-exposure rolls, and 6($14.99), or $89.94, for the 36-exposure rolls. The total paid was therefore $142.87 + $89.94, or $232.81. The numbers check.

5. **State.** The class had 13 rolls of 24-exposure film and 6 rolls of 36-exposure film developed.

Mixture Problems

EXAMPLE 3 Blending coffees. The Java Joint wants to mix organic Kenyan beans that sell for $8.25 per pound with organic Venezuelan beans that sell for $9.50 per pound to form a 50-lb batch of Morning Blend that sells for $9.00 per pound. How many pounds of each type of bean should go into the blend?

Solution

1. **Familiarize.** This problem seems similar to Example 2. Instead of two types of film, we have Kenyan coffee and Venezuelan coffee. Instead of two different prices for processing, we have two different prices per pound. Finally, instead of knowing the total amount paid, we know the weight and price per pound of the batch of Morning Blend being made. Note that we can easily calculate the value of the batch of Morning Blend by multiplying 50 lb times $9.00 per pound. We let k = the number of pounds of organic Kenyan coffee used and v = the number of pounds of organic Venezuelan coffee used.

2. **Translate.** Since a 50-lb batch is being made, we must have

$$k + v = 50.$$

To find a second equation, we consider the total value of the 50-lb batch. That value must be the same as the value of the Kenyan beans and the value of the Venezuelan beans that go into the blend.

Rewording:	The value of the Kenyan beans	plus	the value of the Venezuelan beans	is	the value of the Morning Blend.
	↓	↓	↓	↓	↓
Translating:	$k \cdot 8.25$	$+$	$v \cdot 9.50$	$=$	$50 \cdot 9.00$

This information can be presented in a table.

	Kenyan	Venezuelan	Morning Blend	
Number of Pounds	k	v	50	$\rightarrow k + v = 50$
Price per Pound	\$8.25	\$9.50	\$9.00	
Value of Beans	$8.25k$	$9.50v$	$50 \cdot 9$, or 450	$\rightarrow 8.25k + 9.50v = 450$

We have translated to a system of equations:

$$k + v = 50, \qquad (1)$$
$$8.25k + 9.50v = 450. \qquad (2)$$

3. **Carry out.** When equation (1) is solved for k, we have $k = 50 - v$. We then substitute $50 - v$ for k in equation (2):

$$8.25(50 - v) + 9.50v = 450 \qquad \text{Solving by substitution}$$
$$412.50 - 8.25v + 9.50v = 450 \qquad \text{Using the distributive law}$$
$$1.25v = 37.50 \qquad \text{Combining like terms; subtracting 412.50 from both sides}$$
$$v = 30. \qquad \text{Dividing both sides by 1.25}$$

If $v = 30$, we see from equation (1) that $k = 20$.

4. **Check.** If 20 lb of organic Kenyan beans and 30 lb of organic Venezuelan beans are mixed, a 50-lb blend will result. The value of 20 lb of Kenyan beans is 20(\$8.25), or \$165. The value of 30 lb of Venezuelan beans is 30(\$9.50), or \$285, so the value of the blend is \$165 + \$285 = \$450. A 50-lb blend priced at \$9.00 a pound is also worth \$450, so our answer checks.

5. **State.** The Morning Blend should be made by combining 20 lb of organic Kenyan beans with 30 lb of organic Venezuelan beans.

EXAMPLE 4 Paint colors. At a local "paint swap," Madison found large supplies of Skylite Pink (12.5% red pigment) and MacIntosh Red (20% red pigment). How many gallons of each color should be mixed in order to create a 15-gal batch of Summer Rose (17% red pigment)?

Solution

1. **Familiarize.** This problem is similar to Example 3. Instead of mixing two types of coffee and keeping an eye on the price of the mixture, we are mixing two types of paint and keeping an eye on the amount of pigment in the mixture.

To visualize this problem, think of the pigment as a solid that, given time, would settle to the bottom of each can. Let's guess that 3 gal of Skylite Pink and 12 gal of MacIntosh Red are mixed. How much pigment would be in the mixture? The Skylite Pink would contribute 12.5% of 3 gal, or 0.375 gal of pigment, and the MacIntosh Red would contribute 20% of 12 gal, or 2.4 gal of pigment. Thus the 15-gal mixture would contain $0.375 + 2.4 = 2.775$ gal of pigment. Since Madison needs the 15 gal of Summer Rose to be 17% pigment, and since 17% of 15 gal is 2.55 gal, our guess is incorrect. Rather than guess again, we let $p =$ the number of gallons of Skylite Pink used and $m =$ the number of gallons of MacIntosh Red used.

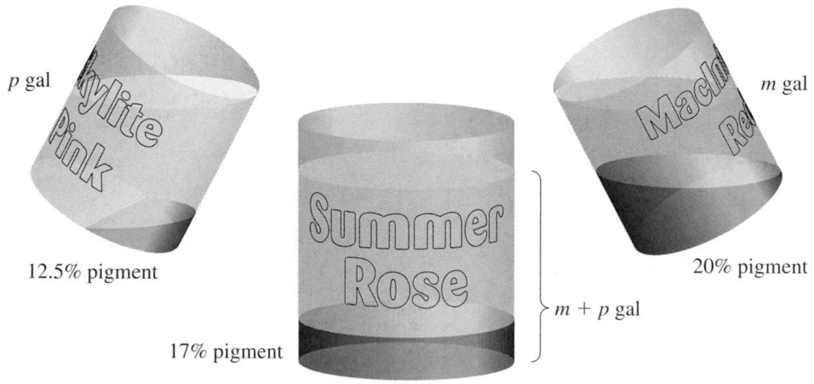

2. **Translate.** As in Example 3, the information given can be arranged in a table.

	Skylite Pink	MacIntosh Red	Summer Rose
Amount of Paint (in gallons)	p	m	15
Percent Pigment	12.5%	20%	17%
Amount of Pigment (in gallons)	$0.125p$	$0.2m$	0.17×15, or 2.55

A system of two equations can be formed by reading across the first and third rows of the table. Since Madison needs 15 gal of mixture, we must have

$$p + m = 15. \longleftarrow \text{Total amount of paint}$$

Madison also needs 2.55 gal of pigment. Since the amount of pigment in the Summer Rose paint comes from the pigment in the Skylite Pink and the MacIntosh Red paint, we have

$$0.125p + 0.2m = 2.55. \longleftarrow \text{Total amount of pigment}$$

We have translated to a system of equations:

$$\begin{aligned} p + \quad m &= 15, & (1)\\ 0.125p + 0.2m &= 2.55. & (2) \end{aligned}$$

3. Carry out. We note that if we multiply both sides of equation (2) by -5, we can eliminate m (other approaches will also work):

$$\begin{aligned} p + m &= 15 \\ -0.625p - m &= -12.75 \qquad \text{We observed that } (-5)(0.2m) = -m. \\ \hline 0.375p \quad &= 2.25 \\ p &= 6. \qquad \text{Dividing both sides by 0.375} \end{aligned}$$

If $p = 6$, we see from equation (1) that $m = 9$.

4. Check. Clearly, 6 gal of Skylite Pink and 9 gal of MacIntosh Red do add up to a total of 15 gal. To determine whether the mixture is the right color, Summer Rose, we calculate the amount of pigment in the mixture: $0.125 \cdot 6 + 0.2 \cdot 9 = 0.75 + 1.8 = 2.55$ gal. Since 2.55 is indeed 17% of 15, the mixture is the correct color.

5. State. Madison needs 6 gal of Skylite Pink and 9 gal of MacIntosh Red in order to make 15 gal of Summer Rose.

Re-examine Examples 1–4, looking for similarities. Examples 3 and 4 are often called *mixture problems,* but they have much in common with Examples 1 and 2.

> *Problem-Solving Tip*
>
> When solving a problem, see if it is patterned or modeled after a problem that you have already solved.

7.4 Exercise Set

FOR EXTRA HELP

Student's Solutions Manual | Digital Video Tutor CD 5 Videotape 14 | AW Math Tutor Center | MathXL Tutorials on CD | MathXL | MyMathLab

Solve. Use the five steps for problem solving.

1. *Basketball scoring.* In a recent game, Baron Davis of the New Orleans Hornets scored 25 points on a combination of 11 two- and three-point baskets. How many shots of each type were made?
Source: National Basketball Association

2. *Basketball scoring.* In a recent game, the Indiana Pacers scored 72 points on a combination of 35 two- and three-point baskets. How many shots of each type were made?
Source: National Basketball Association

3. *Basketball scoring.* In clinching the Eastern Conference championship, the New Jersey Nets once scored 88 of their points on a combination of 42 two- and three-point baskets. How many shots of each type were made?
Source: National Basketball Association

4. *Basketball scoring.* In winning the Western Conference finals, the San Antonio Spurs once scored 76 of their points on a combination of 36 two- and three-pointers. How many shots of each type did they make?
Source: National Basketball Association

5. *College credits.* Each course at Pease County Community College is worth either 3 or 4 credits. The members of the women's swim team are taking a total of 27 courses that are worth a total of 89 credits. How many 3-credit courses and how many 4-credit courses are being taken?

6. *College credits.* Each course at Mt. Regis College is worth either 3 or 4 credits. The members of the men's soccer team are taking a total of 48 courses that are worth a total of 155 credits. How many 3-credit courses and how many 4-credit courses are being taken?

7. *Returnable bottles.* As part of a fundraiser, the Cobble Hill Daycare collected 430 returnable bottles and cans, some worth 5 cents each and the rest worth 10 cents each. If the total value of the cans and bottles was $26.20, how many 5-cent bottles or cans and how many 10-cent bottles or cans were collected?

8. *Ice cream cones.* A busload of campers stopped at a dairy stand for ice cream. They ordered 40 cones, some soft-serve at $1.75 and the rest hard-pack at $2.00. If the total bill was $74, how many of each type of cone were ordered?

9. *Yellowstone Park admissions.* Entering Yellowstone National Park costs $20 for a car and $15 for a motorcycle. On a typical day, 5950 cars or motorcycles enter and pay a total of $107,875. How many motorcycles enter on a typical day?
Source: National Park Service, U.S. Department of the Interior, 11/10

10. *Disneyland admissions.* A two-day Park Hopper ticket to Disneyland costs $78 for children ages 3–9 and $98 for adults and children ages 10 and older. A bus full of 23 kindergartners and parents paid a total of $1974 for their tickets. How many children and how many adults were on the bus?

11. *Zoo admissions.* From October 27 through April 2, the Bronx Zoo charges $8 for adults and $6 for children and seniors. One December day, a total of $2610 was collected from 394 admissions. How many adult admissions were there?
Source: Bronx Zoo

12. *Zoo admissions.* During the summer months, the Bronx Zoo charges $11 for adults and $8 for children and seniors. One July day, a total of $8700 was collected from 960 admissions. How many adult admissions were there?
Source: Bronx Zoo

13. *Music lessons.* Alice charges $25 for a private guitar lesson and $18 for a group guitar lesson. One day in August, Alice earned $265 from 12 students. How many students of each type did Alice teach?

14. *Dance lessons.* Jean charges $20 for a private tap lesson and $12 for a group class. One Wednesday, Jean earned $216 from 14 students. How many students of each type did Jean teach?

15. *Music and movies.* Freedom Tunes sells used CDs for $5.99 and used videos for $7.99. Holly recently purchased a total of 14 CDs and videos for $93.86 (before tax). How many CDs and how many videos did she buy?

16. *Books.* The yearly book sale for the Northfield Public Library charges $1.25 for used hardbacks and 50¢ for used paperbacks. Keith purchased a total of 23 books for $19.75. How many books of each type did he buy?

17. *Coffee blends.* Cafe Europa mixes Brazilian coffee worth $19 per kilogram with Turkish coffee worth $22 per kilogram. The mixture should be worth $20 per kilogram. How much of each type of coffee should be used to make a 300-kg mixture?

18. *Seed mix.* Sunflower seed is worth $1.00 per pound and rolled oats are worth $1.35 per pound. How much of each would you use to make 50 lb of a mixture worth $1.14 per pound?

19. *Mixed nuts.* A grocer wishes to mix peanuts worth \$2.52 per pound with Brazil nuts worth \$3.80 per pound to make 480 lb of a mixture worth \$3.44 per pound. How much of each should be used?

20. *Mixed nuts.* The Nuthouse has 10 kg of mixed cashews and pecans worth \$8.40 per kilogram. Cashews alone sell for \$8.00 per kilogram, and pecans sell for \$9.00 per kilogram. How many kilograms of each are in the mixture?

21. *Acid mixtures.* Jerome's experiment requires him to mix a 50%-acid solution with an 80%-acid solution to create 200 mL of a 68%-acid solution. How much 50%-acid solution and how much 80%-acid solution should he use? Complete the following table as part of the *Translate* step.

Type of Solution	**50%-Acid**	**80%-Acid**	**68%-Acid Mix**
Amount of Solution	x	y	
Percent Acid	50%		68%
Amount of Acid in Solution		$0.8y$	

22. *Production.* Streakfree window cleaner is 12% alcohol and Sunstream window cleaner is 30% alcohol. How much of each should be used to make 90 oz of a cleaner that is 20% alcohol?

23. *Horticulture.* A solution containing 28% fungicide is to be mixed with a solution containing 40% fungicide to make 300 L of a solution containing 36% fungicide. How much of each solution should be used?

24. *Chemistry.* E-Chem Testing has a solution that is 80% base and another that is 30% base. A technician needs 200 L of a solution that is 62% base. The 200 L will be prepared by mixing the two solutions on hand. How much of each should be used?

25. *Octane ratings.* When a tanker delivers gas to a gas station, it brings only two grades of gasoline, the highest and the lowest, filling two large underground tanks. If you purchase a middle grade, the pump's computer mixes the other two grades appropriately. How much 87-octane gas and 93-octane gas should be blended in order to make 12 gal of 91-octane gas?
Source: Champlain Electric and Petroleum Equipment

26. *Octane ratings.* Refer to Exercise 25. If a gas station is supplied with 87-octane gas and 95-octane gas, how much of each should be blended in order to make 10 gal of 93-octane gas?

27. *Printing.* Using some pages that hold 1300 words per page and others that hold 1850 words per page, a typesetter is able to completely fill 12 pages with an 18,350-word document. How many pages of each kind were used?

28. *Coin value.* A collection of quarters and nickels is worth \$1.25. There are 13 coins in all. How many of each are there?

29. *Basketball scoring.* Wilt Chamberlain once scored a record 100 points on a combination of 64 foul shots (each worth one point) and two-pointers. How many shots of each type did he make?

30. *Basketball scoring.* Shaquille O'Neal recently scored 34 points on a combination of 21 foul shots and two-pointers. How many shots of each type did he make?

31. *Suntan lotion.* Lisa has a tube of Kinney's suntan lotion that is rated 15 spf and a second tube of Coppertone that is 30 spf. How many fluid ounces of each type of lotion should be mixed in order to create 50 fluid ounces of sunblock that is rated 20 spf?

32. *Cough syrup.* Dr. Zeke's cough syrup is 2% alcohol. Vitabrite cough syrup is 5% alcohol. How much of each type should be used in order to prepare an 80-oz batch of cough syrup that is 3% alcohol?

Aha! 33. *Nutrition.* New England Natural Bakers Muesli gets 20% of its calories from fat. Breadshop Supernatural granola gets 35% of its calories from fat. How much of each type should be used to create a 40-lb mixture that gets 27.5% of its calories from fat?
Source: Onion River Cooperative, Burlington VT

34. *Textile production.* DRG Outdoor Products uses one insulation that is 20% goose down and another that is 34% goose down. How many pounds of each should be used to create 50 lb of insulation that is 25% goose down?

35. Why might fraction answers be acceptable on problems like Examples 3 and 4, but not on problems like Examples 1 and 2?

36. Write a problem for a classmate to solve by translating to a system of two equations in two unknowns.

SKILL MAINTENANCE

Solve. [2.6]

37. $7 - 3x < 22$

38. $4 - 5x \geq 39$

Graph on a number line. [2.6]

39. $x + 2 \geq 6$

40. $3x + 3 < 9$

41. $6 < -\frac{1}{2}x + 1$

42. $4 > -\frac{1}{3}x + 2$

SYNTHESIS

43. In Exercise 30, suppose that some of O'Neal's 21 baskets were three-pointers. Could the problem still be solved? Why or why not?

44. In Exercise 28, suppose that some of the 13 coins may have been half-dollars. Could the problem still be solved? Why or why not?

45. *Coffee.* Kona coffee, grown only in Hawaii, is highly desired and quite expensive. To create a blend of beans that is 30% Kona, the Brewtown Beanery is adding pure Kona beans to a 45-lb sack of Columbian beans. How many pounds of Kona should be added to the 45 lb of Columbian?

46. *Chemistry.* A tank contains 8000 L of a solution that is 40% acid. How much water should be added in order to make a solution that is 30% acid?

47. *Automobile maintenance.* The radiator in Candy's Honda Accord contains 6.3 L of antifreeze and water. This mixture is 30% antifreeze. How much should be drained and replaced with pure antifreeze so that the mixture will be 50% antifreeze?

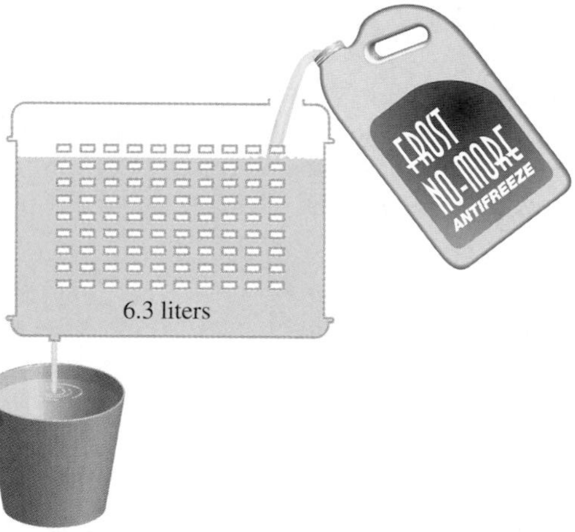

48. *Investing.* One year Shannon made $288 from two investments: $1100 was invested at one yearly rate and $1800 at a rate that was 1.5% higher. Find the two rates of interest.

49. *Octane rating.* Many cars need gasoline with an octane rating of at least 87. After mistakenly putting 5 gal of 85-octane gas in her empty gas tank, Kim plans to add 91-octane gas until the mixture's octane rating is 87. How much 91-octane gas should she add?

50. *Sporting-goods prices.* Together, a bat, ball, and glove cost $99.00. The bat costs $9.95 more than the ball, and the glove costs $65.45 more than the bat. How much does each cost?

51. *Overtime pay.* Juanita is paid "time and a half" for any time she works in excess of 40 hr per week. The week before Christmas she worked 55 hr and was paid $812.50. What was her normal hourly wage?

52. *Investing.* Eduardo invested $54,000, part of it at 6% and the rest at 6.5%. The total yield after one year is $3385. How much was invested at each rate?

53. *Dairy farming.* The Benson Cooperative Creamery has 1000 gal of milk that is 4.6% butterfat. How much skim milk (no butterfat) should be added to make milk that is 2% butterfat?

54. *Payroll.* Ace Engineering pays a total of $325 an hour when employing some workers at $20 an hour and others at $25 an hour. When the number of $20 workers is increased by 50% and the number of $25 workers is decreased by 20%, the cost per hour is $400. How many workers were originally employed at each rate?

55. A two-digit number is six times the sum of its digits. The tens digit is 1 more than the ones digit. Find the number.

56. The sum of the digits of a two-digit number is 12. When the digits are reversed, the number is decreased by 18. Find the original number.

57. *Literature.* In Lewis Carroll's *Through the Looking Glass*, Tweedledum says to Tweedledee, "The sum of your weight and twice mine is 361 pounds." Then Tweedledee says to Tweedledum, "Contrariwise, the sum of your weight and twice mine is 362 pounds." Find the weights of Tweedledum and Tweedledee.

COLLABORATIVE CORNER

Sunoco's Custom Blending Pump

Focus: Mixture problems
Time: 30 minutes
Group size: 3
Materials: Calculators

Sunoco® gasoline stations pride themselves on offering customers the "custom blending pump." While most competitors offer just three octane levels—87, 93, and a blend that is 89—Sunoco customers can select an octane level of 86, 87, 89, 92, or 94. The Sunoco supplier brings 86- and 94-octane gasoline to each station and a computerized pump mixes the two to create the blend that a customer desires.

ACTIVITY

1. Assume that your group's gas station has an abundant supply of 86-octane and 94-octane gasoline. Each group member should select a different one of the custom blends: 87, 89, or 92.
2. Each member will be asked to determine the number of gallons of 86-octane gas and 94-octane gas needed to form 100 gal of his or her selected blend. Before doing so, however, the group should outline a series of steps that each member will use to solve his or her problem. Group members should agree on the letters chosen as variables, the variable that will be solved for first, and the sequence of steps that will be followed. For the purposes of this activity, it is best to use substitution to solve the system of equations that will be created.
3. *Following the agreed-upon series of steps,* each group member should determine how many gallons of 86-octane gas and how many gallons of 94-octane gas should be mixed in order to form 100 gal of his or her selected blend. Check that all work is done correctly and consistently.
4. The pumps in use at most gas stations blend mixtures in $\frac{1}{10}$-gal "batches." How can the results of part (3) be adjusted so that $\frac{1}{10}$-gal, not 100-gal, blends are formulated?

7.5 Linear Inequalities in Two Variables

Graphing Linear Inequalities • Linear Inequalities in One Variable

Study Skills

When Something Seems Easy

Every so often, you may encounter a lesson that you remember from a previous math course. When this occurs, make sure that *all* of that lesson is understood. If anything is amiss, be sure to review all tricky spots.

Just as the solutions of linear equations like $5x + 4y = 13$ or $y = \frac{1}{2}x + 1$ can be graphed, so too can the solutions of *linear inequalities* like $5x + 4y < 13$ or $y > \frac{1}{2}x + 1$ be represented graphically.

Graphing Linear Inequalities

In Section 2.6, we found that solutions of inequalities like $5x + 9 \le 4x + 3$ can be represented by a shaded portion of a number line. When a solution included an endpoint, we drew a solid dot, and when the endpoint was excluded, we drew an open dot. To graph inequalities like $y > \frac{1}{2}x + 1$ or $2x + 3y \le 6$, we will shade a region of a plane. That region will be either above or below the graph of a "boundary line" (in this case, the graph of $y = \frac{1}{2}x + 1$ or $2x + 3y = 6$). If the symbol is $\le$ or $\ge$, we will draw the boundary line solid, since it is part of the solution. When the boundary is excluded—that is, if $<$ or $>$ is used—we will draw a dashed line.

EXAMPLE 1 Graph: $y > \frac{1}{2}x + 1$.

Solution We begin by graphing the boundary line $y = \frac{1}{2}x + 1$. The slope is $\frac{1}{2}$ and the y-intercept is $(0, 1)$. This line is drawn dashed since the symbol $>$ is used.

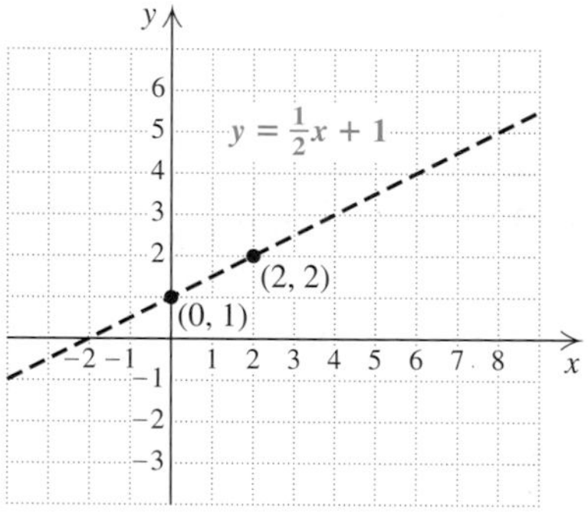

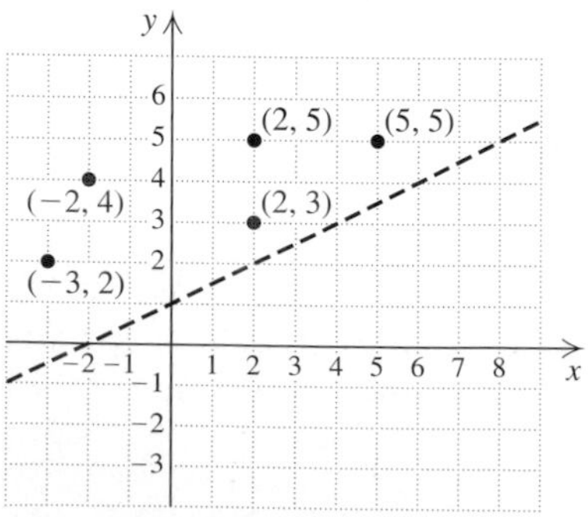

The plane is now split in two. If we consider the coordinates of a few points above the line, we will find that all are solutions of $y > \frac{1}{2}x + 1$.

Here is a check for the points $(2, 3)$ and $(-2, 4)$:

$$\begin{array}{c|l} \multicolumn{2}{c}{y > \frac{1}{2}x + 1} \\ \hline 3 & \frac{1}{2}\cdot 2 + 1 \\ & 1 + 1 \\ \multicolumn{2}{l}{3 \overset{?}{>} 2 \quad \text{TRUE}} \end{array} \qquad \begin{array}{c|l} \multicolumn{2}{c}{y > \frac{1}{2}x + 1} \\ \hline 4 & \frac{1}{2}(-2) + 1 \\ & -1 + 1 \\ \multicolumn{2}{l}{4 \overset{?}{>} 0 \quad \text{TRUE}} \end{array}$$

The student can check that *any* point on the same side of the dashed line as (2, 3) or (−2, 4) is a solution. If one point in a region solves an inequality, then *all* points in that region are solutions. The graph of

$$y > \frac{1}{2}x + 1$$

is shown below. Note that the solution set consists of all points in the shaded region. Furthermore, note that for any inequality of the form $y > mx + b$ or $y \geq mx + b$, we shade the region *above* the boundary line.

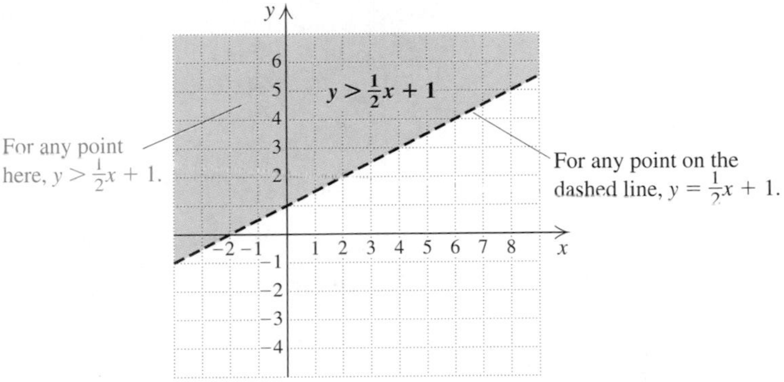

EXAMPLE 2 Graph: $2x + 3y \leq 6$.

Student Notes

A mistake in checking your test point could lead you to shade the wrong region of the plane. For this reason, you may want to use a second test point to assure yourself that the correct region is shaded.

Solution First, we establish the boundary line by graphing $2x + 3y = 6$. This can be done either by using the intercepts, (0, 2) and (3, 0), or by finding slope–intercept form, $y = -\frac{2}{3}x + 2$. Since the inequality contains the symbol $\leq$, we draw a solid boundary line to include all pairs on the line as part of the solution. The graph of $2x + 3y \leq 6$ also includes either the region above or below the line. By using a "test point" that is clearly above or below the line, we can determine which region to shade. The origin, (0, 0), is often a convenient test point:

$$\begin{array}{r|l} 2x + 3y & \leq 6 \\ \hline 2 \cdot 0 + 3 \cdot 0 & 6 \\ 0 & \overset{?}{\leq} 6 \quad \text{TRUE} \end{array}$$

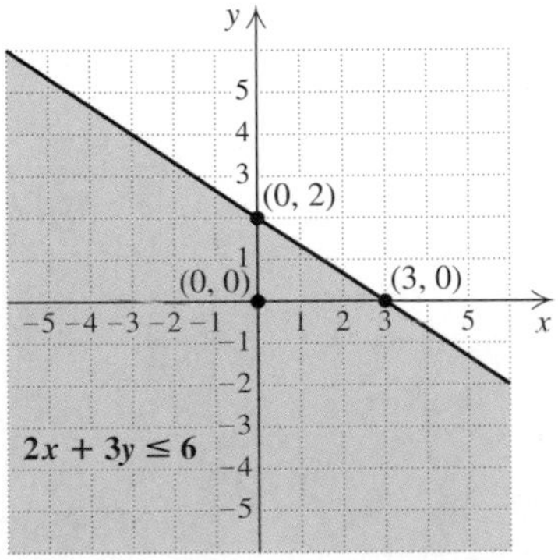

The point (0, 0) is a solution and it appears in the region below the boundary line. Thus this region, along with the line itself, represents the solution.

The original inequality is equivalent to $y \leq -\frac{2}{3}x + 2$. Note that for any inequality of the form $y \leq mx + b$ or $y < mx + b$, we shade the region *below* the boundary line.

To Graph a Linear Inequality

1. Draw the boundary line by replacing the inequality symbol with an equals sign and graphing the resulting equation. If the inequality symbol is $<$ or $>$, the line is dashed. If the symbol is $\leq$ or $\geq$, the line is solid.
2. Shade the region on one side of the boundary line. To determine which side, select a point not on the line as a test point. If that point's coordinates are a solution of the inequality, shade the region containing the point. If not, shade the other region.
3. Inequalities of the form $y < mx + b$ or $y \leq mx + b$ are shaded below the boundary line. Inequalities of the form $y > mx + b$ or $y \geq mx + b$ are shaded above the boundary line.

Linear Inequalities in One Variable

EXAMPLE 3 Graph $y \leq -2$ on a plane.

Solution We graph $y = -2$ as a solid line to indicate that all points on the line are solutions. Again, we select (0, 0) as a test point. It may help to write $y \leq -2$ as $y \leq 0 \cdot x - 2$:

$$\begin{array}{c|c} y \leq 0 \cdot x - 2 & \\ \hline 0 & 0 \cdot 0 - 2 \\ 0 \overset{?}{\leq} -2 & \text{FALSE} \end{array}$$

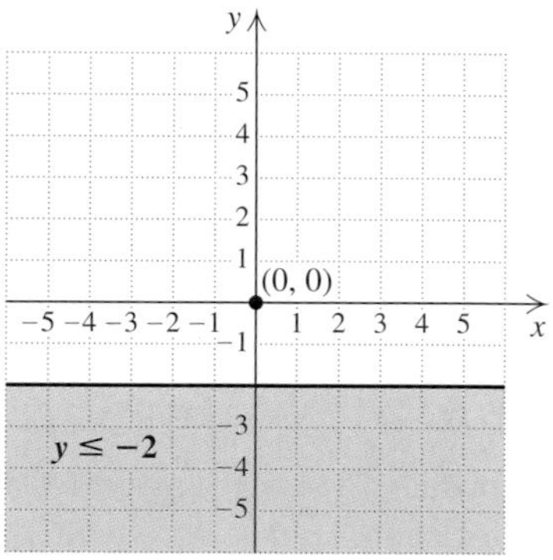

Since (0, 0) is *not* a solution, we do not shade the region in which it appears. Instead, we shade below the boundary line as shown. The solution consists of all ordered pairs with y-coordinates less than or equal to -2.

EXAMPLE 4 Graph $x < 3$ on a plane.

Solution We graph $x = 3$ using a dashed line. To determine which region to shade, we again use the test point (0, 0). It may help to write $x < 3$ as $x + 0 \cdot y < 3$:

$$\begin{array}{c|c} x + 0 \cdot y < 3 & \\ \hline 0 + 0 \cdot 0 & 3 \\ 0 \overset{?}{<} 3 & \text{TRUE} \end{array}$$

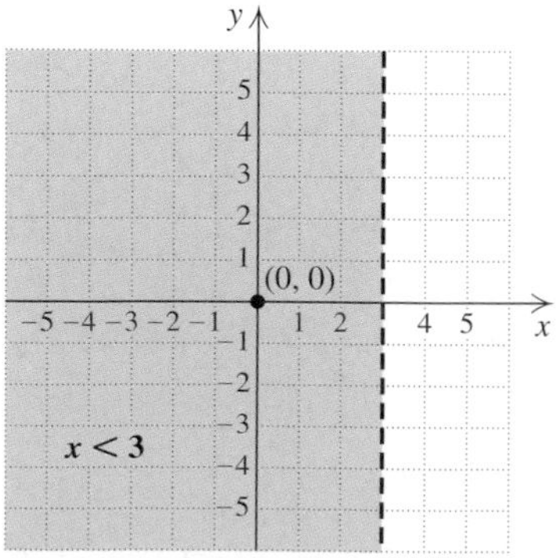

Since (0, 0) is a solution, we shade to the left. The solution consists of all ordered pairs with first coordinates less than 3.

technology connection

To graph $2x + 3y \leq 6$ on a graphing calculator, we must first solve for y. This is precisely what we did in Example 2, where we found that $y \leq -\frac{2}{3}x + 2$. On many graphing calculators, this graph is drawn by entering $(-2/3)x + 2$ as y_1, moving the cursor to the GraphStyle icon just to the left of y_1, pressing ENTER until ◣ appears, and then pressing GRAPH. The symbol ◣ indicates that the area *below* the line is shaded. On some graphing calculators, a SHADE option must be used.

Note that the boundary line always appears solid.

$y_1 \leq (-2/3)x + 2$

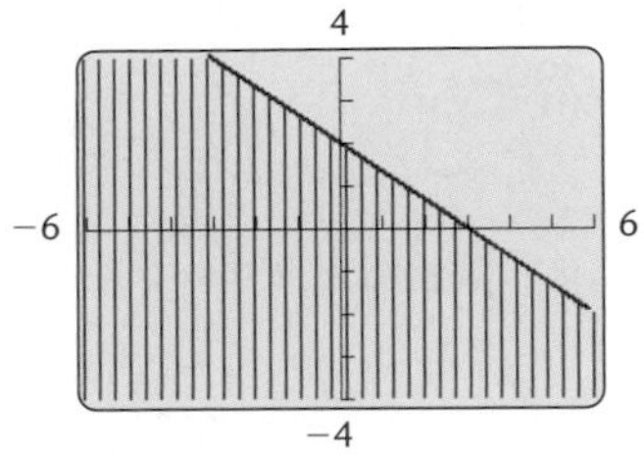

Graph each of the following.

1. $y > \frac{2}{3}x - 2$ **2.** $y - x \leq 5$ **3.** $2x + 5y \geq 25$

7.5 Exercise Set

FOR EXTRA HELP

Student's Solutions Manual | Digital Video Tutor CD 5 Videotape 14 | AW Math Tutor Center | MathXL Tutorials on CD | MathXL | MyMathLab

Concept Reinforcement *In each of Exercises 1–4, classify the statement as either true or false.*

1. To graph a linear inequality, we first graph a line.

2. To determine which region to shade, we must test at least two points.

3. Inequalities of the form $y \geq mx + b$ are shaded above the boundary line.

4. Inequalities of the form $y < mx + b$ are shaded above the boundary line.

5. Determine whether $(-3, -5)$ is a solution of
$x + 3y < -18$.

6. Determine whether $(5, -3)$ is a solution of
$-2x + 4y \leq -2$.

Aha! **7.** Determine whether $\left(\frac{7}{8}, \frac{1}{2}\right)$ is a solution of
$6y + 5x \geq -3$.

8. Determine whether $(-6, 5)$ is a solution of
$x + 0 \cdot y < 3$.

Graph on a plane.

9. $y \leq x + 5$

10. $y \leq x - 1$

11. $y < x - 2$

12. $y < x + 4$

13. $y \geq x - 3$

14. $y \geq x - 1$

15. $y \leq 2x - 1$

16. $y \leq 3x + 2$

17. $x + y \leq 4$

18. $x + y \leq 6$

19. $x - y > 7$

20. $x - y > 5$

21. $y \geq 1 - 2x$

22. $y > 2 - 3x$

23. $y - 3x > 0$

24. $y - 2x \geq 0$

25. $x \geq 4$

26. $x > -4$

27. $y \leq 4$

28. $y > -1$

29. $y \geq -5$

30. $y < 0$

31. $x < 3$

32. $x \leq 5$

33. $x - y < -10$

34. $y - 2x \leq -1$

35. $2x + 3y \leq 12$

36. $5x + 4y \geq 20$

37. Examine the solution of Example 2. Why is the point $(4.5, -1)$ *not* a good choice for a test point?

38. Why is $(0, 0)$ such a "convenient" test point to use?

SKILL MAINTENANCE

Evaluate. [1.8]

39. $3x + 5y$, for $x = -2$ and $y = 4$

40. $2x + 4y$, for $x = 3$ and $y = -1$

The graph below shows the prices paid for a ton of newspaper and for a ton of corrugated cardboard by recyclers in the Northeast.

Source: Chittenden Solid Waste District, Williston, VT

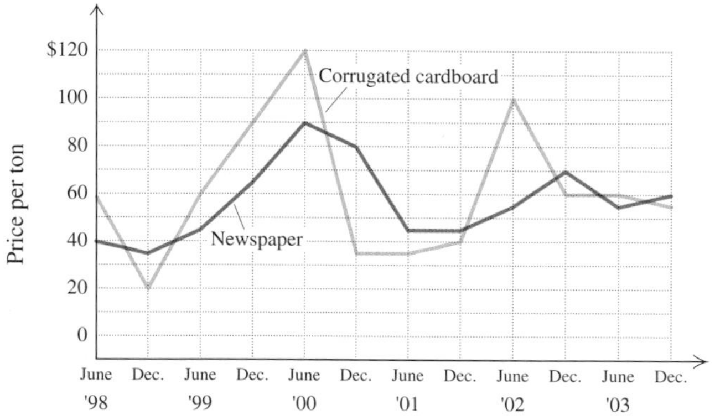

41. How much was being paid for corrugated cardboard in June 2002? [3.1]

42. During what six-month period did the price paid for newspaper first match the price paid for corrugated cardboard? [3.1]

43. When did the value of newspaper peak? [3.1]

44. When was the price paid for corrugated cardboard $20 per ton? [3.1]

45. During what six-month periods did the price paid for corrugated cardboard remain constant? [3.1]

46. During what six-month period did the price paid for corrugated cardboard increase the most? [3.1]

SYNTHESIS

47. Under what circumstances is the graph of $Ax + By > 0$ shaded *above* the line $Ax + By = 0$?

48. Describe a procedure that could be used to graph any inequality of the form $Ax + By < C$.

49. *Elevators.* Many Otis elevators have a capacity of 1000 lb. Suppose that c children, each weighing 75 lb, and a adults, each weighing 150 lb, are on an elevator. Find and graph an inequality that asserts that the elevator is overloaded.

50. *Hockey wins and losses.* A hockey team needs at least 60 points for the season in order to make the playoffs. Suppose that the Coyotes finish with w wins, each worth 2 points, and t ties, each worth 1 point. Find and graph an inequality that indicates that the Coyotes made the playoffs.

51. *Architecture.* Most architects agree that the sum of a step's riser r and tread t, in inches, should not be less than 17 in. Find and graph an inequality that describes the situation.

52. *Photography.* Members of the Ritz Camera® film club recently paid \$9.99 for double prints of a 24-exposure roll of film and \$12.99 for double prints of a 36-exposure roll. Find and graph an inequality indicating that w rolls of 24-exposure film and r rolls of 36-exposure film were developed at a cost exceeding \$140.

Source: Ritz Camera

Find an inequality for each graph shown.

53.

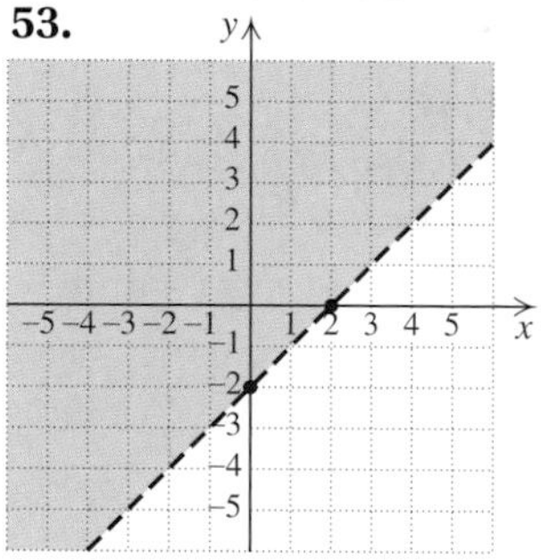

54.

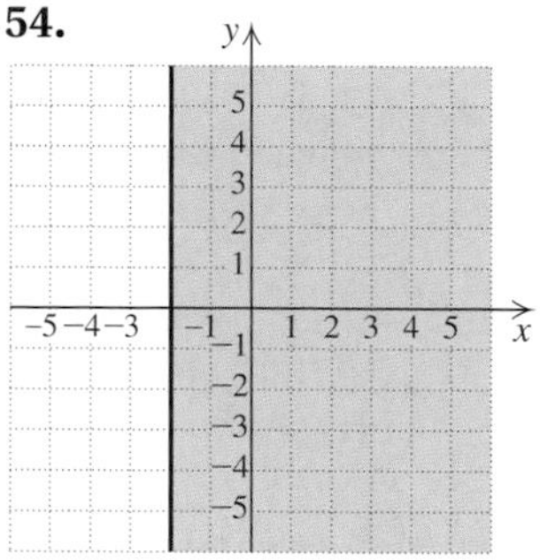

Graph on a plane. (Hint: Use several test points.)

55. $xy \leq 0$

56. $xy \geq 0$

57. Graph: $y + 3x \leq 4.9$.

58. Graph: $0.7x - y \leq 2.3$.

7.6 Systems of Linear Inequalities

Graphing Systems of Inequalities • Locating Solution Sets

Study Skills

Keeping Math Relevant

We have already stated that finding applications of math in your everyday life is a great study aid. Try to extend this idea to the newspapers, periodicals, and books that you read. Look with a critical eye at graphs and their labels. Not only will this help with your math, it will make you a more informed citizen.

Systems of linear equations were graphed in Section 7.1. We now consider **systems of linear inequalities** in two variables, such as

$$x + y \le 3,$$
$$x - y < 3.$$

When systems of equations were solved graphically, we searched for any points common to both lines. To solve a system of inequalities graphically, we again look for points common to both graphs. This is accomplished by graphing each inequality and determining where the graphs overlap.

EXAMPLE 1 Graph the solutions of the system

$$x + y \le 3,$$
$$x - y < 3.$$

Solution To graph $x + y \le 3$, we draw the graph of $x + y = 3$ using a solid line. We graph the line using the intercepts (3, 0) and (0, 3) (see the graph on the left, below). Since (0, 0) is a solution of $x + y \le 3$, we shade (in red) all points on that side of the line. The arrows near the ends of the line also indicate the region that contains solutions.

Next, we superimpose the graph of $x - y < 3$, using a dashed line for $x - y = 3$ and again using (0, 0) as a test point. Since (0, 0) is again a solution, we shade (in blue) the region on the same side of the dashed line as (0, 0).

Student Notes

Unless you have ready access to different colored pencils, using arrows (as in Example 1) or slanted shadings to indicate shaded regions is a good idea.

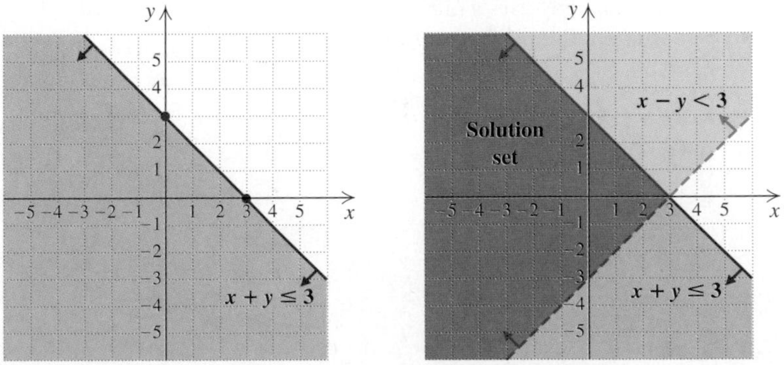

The solution set of the system is the region shaded purple along with the purple portion of the line $x + y = 3$.

EXAMPLE 2 Graph the solutions of the system

$$x \geq 3,$$
$$x - 3y < 6.$$

Solution We graph $x \geq 3$ using blue and $x - 3y < 6$ using red. The solution set is the purple region along with the purple portion of the solid line.

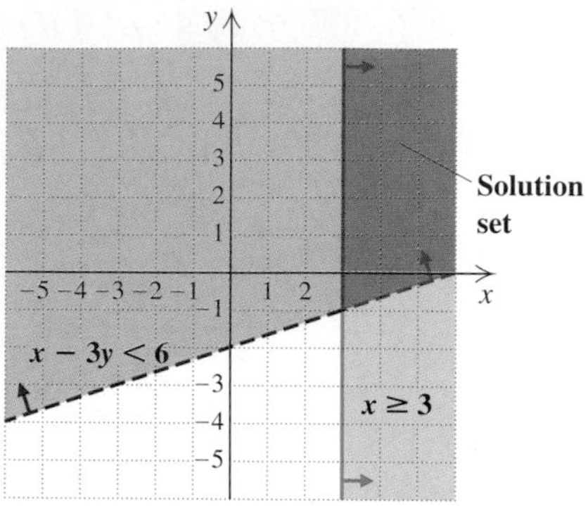

EXAMPLE 3 Graph the solutions of the system

$$x - 2y < 0,$$
$$-2x + y > 2.$$

Solution We graph $x - 2y < 0$ using red and $-2x + y > 2$ using blue. The region that is purple is the solution set of the system since those points solve both inequalities.

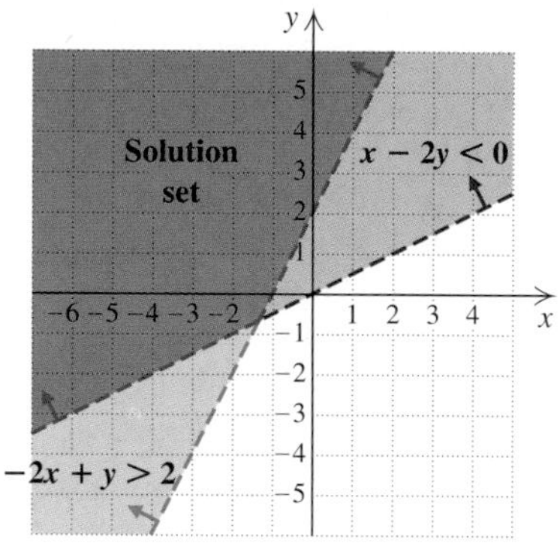

---

technology connection

Many graphing calculators can be used to display systems of linear inequalities. To do so, each inequality is entered along with the side that should be shaded. The graphing calculator automatically uses a different shading for each region. Use your graphing calculator to generate the following graph.

◣ $y_1 = (-2/3)x + 5,$

◥ $y_2 = .5x - 3,$

◣ $y_3 = 3x + 4$

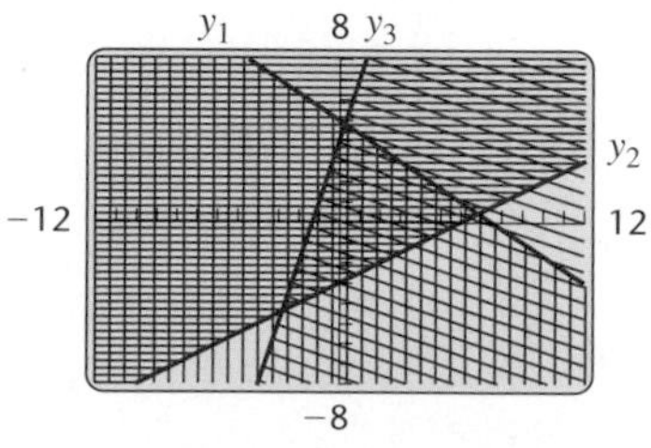

If your calculator has an Inequality application, these inequalities can be entered as

$$y_1 \leq (-2/3)x + 5,$$
$$y_2 \geq .5x - 3,$$
$$y_3 \leq 3x + 4.$$

You may also be able to choose to shade only the intersection of the inequality.

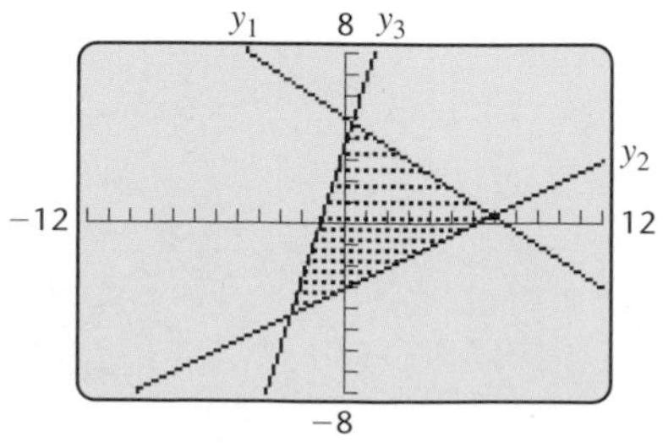

7.6 Exercise Set

FOR EXTRA HELP

Student's Solutions Manual | Digital Video Tutor CD 5 Videotape 14 | AW Math Tutor Center | MathXL Tutorials on CD | MathXL | MyMathLab

Graph the solutions of each system.

1. $x + y \le 7,$
   $x - y \le 4$

2. $x + y \le 3,$
   $x - y \le 5$

3. $y - 2x > 1,$
   $y - 2x < 3$

4. $x + y < 6,$
   $x + y > 0$

5. $y \ge -1,$
   $x > 3 + y$

6. $x > 3,$
   $x + y \le 4$

7. $y > 3x - 2,$
   $y < -x + 4$

8. $y \ge x,$
   $y \le 1 - x$

9. $x \le 4,$
   $y \le 5$

10. $x \ge -5,$
    $y \ge -2$

11. $x \le 0,$
    $y \le 0$

12. $x \ge 0,$
    $y \ge 0$

13. $2x - 3y \ge 9,$
    $2y + x > 6$

14. $3x - 2y \le 8,$
    $2x + y > 6$

15. $y > 4x - 2,$
    $y \le 1 - x$

16. $y > 4,$
    $2y + x \le 4$

17. $x + y \le 5,$
    $x \ge 0,$
    $y \ge 0,$
    $y \le 3$

18. $x + 2y \le 8,$
    $x \le 6,$
    $x \ge 0,$
    $y \ge 0$

19. $y - x \ge 1,$
    $y - x \le 3,$
    $x \le 5,$
    $x \ge 2$

20. $x - 2y \le 0,$
    $y - 2x \le 2,$
    $x \le 2,$
    $y \le 2$

21. $y \le x,$
    $x \ge -2,$
    $x \le -y$

22. $y > 0,$
    $2y + x \ge -6,$
    $x + 2 \le 2y$

23. Will a system of linear inequalities always have a solution? Why or why not?

24. If shadings are used to represent the inequalities in a system, will the most heavily shaded region always represent the solution set (assuming a solution set exists)? Why or why not?

SKILL MAINTENANCE

Solve. [2.1]

25. $7 = \dfrac{k}{5}$

26. $4 = \dfrac{k}{6}$

27. $18 = k \cdot 3$

28. $10 = k \cdot 2$

29. $5 = k \cdot 45$

30. $7 = k \cdot 21$

SYNTHESIS

31. Explain how it would be possible for the solution of a system of linear inequalities to be a line.

32. Explain how it would be possible for the solution of a system of linear inequalities to be a single point.

Graph the solutions of each system. If no solution exists, state this.

33. $3r + 6t \ge 36,$
    $2r + 3t \ge 21,$
    $5r + 3t \ge 30,$
    $t \ge 0,$
    $r \ge 0$

34. $2x + 5y \ge 18,$
    $4x + 3y \ge 22,$
    $2x + y \ge 8,$
    $x \ge 0,$
    $y \ge 0$

35. $x + 3y \le 6,$
    $2x + y \ge 4,$
    $3x + 9y \ge 18$

36. $2x + 5y \ge 10,$
    $x - 3y \le 6,$
    $4x + 10y \le 20$

Aha! 37. $2x + 3y \le 1,$
    $4x + 6y > 9,$
    $5x - 2y \le 8,$
    $x \le 12,$
    $y \ge -15$

38. $5x - 4y \ge 8,$
    $2x + 3y < 9,$
    $2y \ge -8,$
    $x \le -5,$
    $y < -6$

39. Explain how it would be possible for the solution of a system of linear inequalities to be a line segment.

40. Use a graphing calculator to solve Exercise 13.

41. Use a graphing calculator to solve Exercise 14.

7.7 Direct and Inverse Variation

Equations of Direct Variation • Problem Solving with Direct Variation • Equations of Inverse Variation • Problem Solving with Inverse Variation

Study Skills

Take a Power Nap

If you must study when you are tired, consider closing your eyes and resting your head on your arms for a 10-minute "power nap." Often a brief rest like this can greatly improve your concentration.

Many problems lead to equations of the form $y = kx$ or $y = k/x$, where k is a constant. Such equations are called *equations of variation.*

Equations of Direct Variation

A bicycle tour is traveling at a rate of 15 km/h. In 1 hr, it goes 15 km. In 2 hr, it goes 30 km. In 3 hr, it goes 45 km, and so on. In the graph below, we use the number of hours as the first coordinate and the number of kilometers traveled as the second coordinate: (1, 15), (2, 30), (3, 45), (4, 60), and so on. Note that the second coordinate is always 15 times the first.

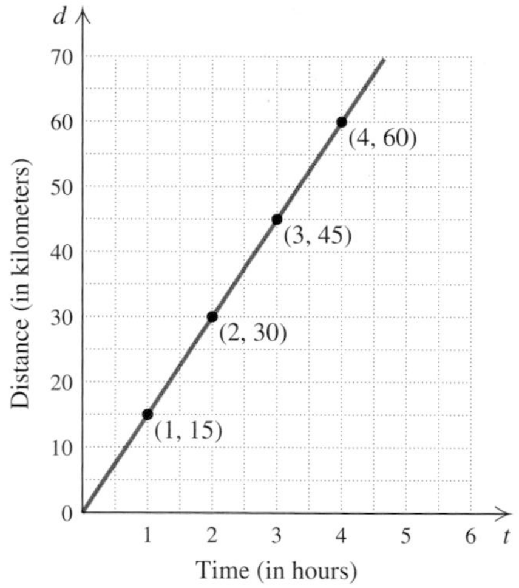

In this example, distance is a constant multiple of time, so we say that there is **direct variation** and that distance **varies directly** as time. The **equation of variation** is $d = 15t$.

> **Direct Variation**
>
> When a situation translates to an equation described by $y = kx$, with k a constant, we say that *y varies directly as x*. The equation $y = kx$ is called an *equation of direct variation.*

Note that for $k > 0$, any equation of the form $y = kx$ indicates that as x increases, y increases as well.

The terminologies

"y varies as x,"

"y is directly proportional to x," and

"y is proportional to x"

also imply direct variation and are used in many situations. The constant k is called the **constant of proportionality** or the **variation constant**. It can be found if one pair of values of x and y is known. Once k is known, other pairs can be determined.

EXAMPLE 1 If y varies directly as x and $y = 2$ when $x = 5$, find the equation of variation.

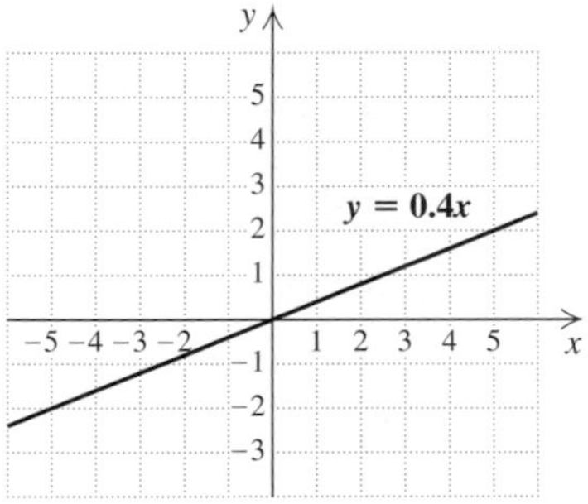

A visualization of Example 1

Solution The words "y varies directly as x" indicate an equation of the form $y = kx$:

$y = kx$	
$2 = k \cdot 5$	Substituting to solve for k
$\frac{2}{5} = k$, or $k = 0.4$.	Dividing both sides by 5

Thus the equation of variation is $y = 0.4x$. A visualization of the situation is shown at left.

From the last two graphs, we see that when y varies directly as x, the constant of proportionality is also the slope of the associated graph—the rate at which y changes with respect to x.

EXAMPLE 2 Find an equation in which s varies directly as t and $s = 10$ when $t = 15$. Then find the value of s when $t = 32$.

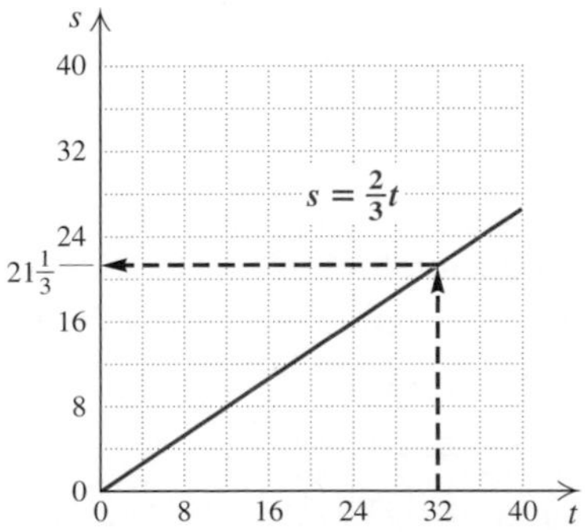

A visualization of Example 2

Solution We have

$s = kt$	We are told "s varies directly as t."
$10 = k \cdot 15$	Substituting 10 for s and 15 for t
$\frac{10}{15} = k$, or $k = \frac{2}{3}$.	Solving for k

Thus the equation of variation is $s = \frac{2}{3}t$. When $t = 32$, we have

$$s = \frac{2}{3}t$$

$$s = \frac{2}{3} \cdot 32 \qquad \text{Substituting 32 for } t \text{ in the equation of variation}$$

$$s = \frac{64}{3}, \text{ or } 21\tfrac{1}{3}.$$

The value of s is $21\frac{1}{3}$ when $t = 32$.

Problem Solving with Direct Variation

In applications, it is often necessary to find an equation of variation and then use it to find other values, much as we did in Example 2.

EXAMPLE 3 The karat rating R of a gold object varies directly as the percentage P of gold in the object. A 14-karat gold chain is 58.25% gold. What is the percentage of gold in a 24-karat gold chain?

Solution

1., 2. Familiarize and **Translate.** The problem states that we have direct variation between R and P. Thus an equation $R = kP$ applies.

3. Carry out. We find an equation of variation:

$$R = kP$$

$$14 = k(0.5825) \quad \text{Substituting 14 for } R \text{ and 58.25\%, or 0.5825, for } P$$

$$\frac{14}{0.5825} = k$$

$$24.03 \approx k. \quad \text{Dividing and rounding to the nearest hundredth}$$

The equation of variation is $R = 24.03P$. When $R = 24$, we have

$$R = 24.03P$$

$$24 = 24.03P \quad \text{Substituting 24 for } R$$

$$\frac{24}{24.03} = P \quad \text{Solving for } P$$

$$0.999 \approx P$$

$$99.9\% \approx P.$$

4. Check. The check might be done by repeating the computations. You might also note that as the karat rating increased from 14 to 24, the percentage increased from 58.25% to 99.9%. The ratios 14/0.5825 and 24/0.999 are both about 24.03.

5. State. A 24-karat gold chain is 99.9% gold.

Equations of Inverse Variation

A car is traveling a distance of 20 mi. At a speed of 5 mph, the trip will take 4 hr. At 20 mph, it will take 1 hr. At 40 mph, it will take $\frac{1}{2}$ hr, and so on. This determines a set of pairs of numbers:

$$(5, 4), \quad (20, 1), \quad \left(40, \tfrac{1}{2}\right), \quad \text{and so on.}$$

Note that the product of speed and time for each of these pairs is 20. Note too that as the speed *increases*, the time *decreases*.

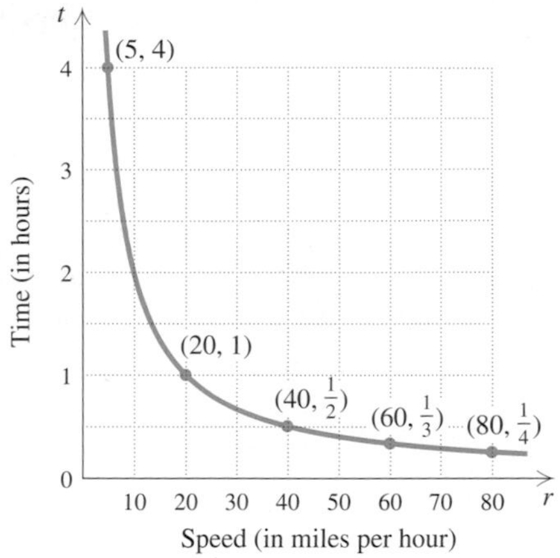

In this case, the product of speed and time is constant so we say that there is **inverse variation** and that time **varies inversely** as speed. The equation of variation is

$$rt = 20 \text{ (a constant)}, \quad \text{or} \quad t = \frac{20}{r}.$$

> **Inverse Variation**
>
> When a situation translates to an equation described by $y = k/x$, with k a constant, we say that *y varies inversely* as x. The equation $y = k/x$ is called an *equation of inverse variation.*

Note that for $k > 0$, any equation of the form $y = k/x$ indicates that as x increases, y decreases.

The terminology

"*y* is inversely proportional to *x*"

also implies inverse variation and is used in some situations. The constant k is again called the *constant of proportionality* or the *variation constant.*

EXAMPLE 4 If y varies inversely as x and $y = 145$ when $x = 0.8$, find the equation of variation.

Solution The words "*y* varies inversely as *x*" indicate an equation of the form $y = k/x$:

$$y = \frac{k}{x}$$

$$145 = \frac{k}{0.8} \qquad \text{Substituting to solve for } k$$

$$(0.8)145 = k \qquad \text{Multiplying both sides by 0.8}$$

$$116 = k.$$

The equation of variation is $y = \dfrac{116}{x}$.

Problem Solving with Inverse Variation

Often in applications, we must decide what kind of variation, if any, applies.

EXAMPLE 5 It takes 4 hr for 20 people to raise a barn. How long would it take 25 people to complete the job? Assume that all people are working at the same rate.

Solution

1. **Familiarize.** Think about the situation. What kind of variation applies? It seems reasonable that the greater the number of people working on a job, the less time it will take. Since everyone is assumed to work at the same rate, and $4 \cdot 20 = 80$, if 8 people worked for 10 hr, the same amount of work would be completed. If $T =$ the time to complete the job, in hours, and $N =$ the number of people working, then as N increases, T decreases and inverse variation applies.
2. **Translate.** Since inverse variation applies, we have

$$T = \frac{k}{N}.$$

3. **Carry out.** We find an equation of variation:

$$T = \frac{k}{N}$$

$$4 = \frac{k}{20} \qquad \text{Substituting 4 for } T \text{ and 20 for } N$$

$$20 \cdot 4 = k \qquad \text{Multiplying both sides by 20}$$

$$80 = k.$$

The equation of variation is $T = \dfrac{80}{N}$. When $N = 25$, we have

$$T = \frac{80}{25} \qquad \text{Substituting 25 for } N$$

$$T = 3.2.$$

4. **Check.** A check might be done by repeating the computations or by noting that $(3.2)(25)$ and $(4)(20)$ are both 80. Also, as the number of people increases, the time needed to complete the job decreases, as expected.
5. **State.** It should take 3.2 hr for 25 people to raise the barn.

To Solve Variation Problems

1. Determine from the language of the problem whether direct or inverse variation applies.
2. Using an equation of the form $y = kx$ for direct variation or $y = k/x$ for inverse variation, substitute known values and solve for k.
3. Write the equation of variation and use it, as needed, to find unknown values.

7.7 Exercise Set

FOR EXTRA HELP

Student's Solutions Manual | Digital Video Tutor CD 5 Videotape 14 | AW Math Tutor Center | MathXL Tutorials on CD | MathXL | MyMathLab

Concept Reinforcement *Determine whether each situation reflects direct variation or inverse variation.*

1. Two copiers can complete the job in 3 hr, whereas three copiers require only 2 hr.

2. Fionna wrote 5 invitations in 30 min and 8 invitations in 48 min.

3. Ralph found 8 flaws on 5 cabinets and 24 flaws on 15 cabinets.

4. Three neighbors collected roadside debris along a mile of roadway in 40 min while another group of five neighbors collected a mile's worth of debris in 24 min.

5. One heater warmed the room to 65° in 21 min when three heaters would have needed only 7 min.

6. Ruth required 4 hr to read 6 term papers and 10 hr to read 15 more.

For each of the following, find an equation of variation in which y varies directly as x and the following are true.

7. $y = 20$, when $x = 4$

8. $y = 30$, when $x = 3$

9. $y = 0.7$, when $x = 0.4$

10. $y = 0.8$, when $x = 0.5$

11. $y = 400$, when $x = 75$

12. $y = 650$, when $x = 175$

13. $y = 200$, when $x = 300$

14. $y = 500$, when $x = 60$

For each of the following, find an equation of variation in which y varies inversely as x and the following are true.

15. $y = 45$, when $x = 2$

16. $y = 8$, when $x = 3$

17. $y = 7$, when $x = 10$

18. $y = 0.125$, when $x = 8$

19. $y = 6.25$, when $x = 25$

20. $y = 42$, when $x = 50$

21. $y = 42$, when $x = 5$

22. $y = 0.2$, when $x = 10$

Solve.

23. *Wages.* Maureen's paycheck P varies directly as the number of hours worked H. For 15 hr of work, the pay is $135. Find the pay for 23 hr of work.

24. *Manufacturing.* The number of bolts B that a machine can make varies directly as the time T that it operates. It can make 6578 bolts in 2 hr. How many can it make in 5 hr?

25. *Gas volume.* The volume V of a gas varies inversely as the pressure P on it. The volume of a gas is 200 cm^3 (cubic centimeters) under a pressure of 32 kg/cm^2. What will be its volume under a pressure of 20 kg/cm^2?

26. *Turkey servings.* The number of servings S of meat that can be obtained from a turkey varies directly as its weight W. From a turkey weighing 15 kg, one can get 40 servings of meat. How many servings can be obtained from a 9-kg turkey?

27. *Lunar weight.* The weight M of an object on the moon varies directly as its weight E on Earth. One of the authors of this book, Marv Bittinger, weighs 192 lb, but would weigh only 32 lb on the moon. The other author, David Ellenbogen, weighs 185 lb. How much would he weigh on the moon?

28. *Electrical current.* The current I in an electrical conductor varies inversely as the resistance R of the conductor. The current is 3 amperes when the resistance is 960 ohms. What is the current when the resistance is 540 ohms?

29. *Musical tones.* The frequency, or pitch P, of a musical tone varies inversely as its wavelength W. A trumpet's concert A has a pitch of 440 vibrations per second and a wavelength of 2.4 ft. A trumpet's E above concert A has a frequency of 660 vibrations per second. What is its wavelength?

30. *Cost of television.* The cost c of operating a television varies directly as the number of hours n that it is in operation. It costs \$14.00 to operate a standard-size color television continuously for 30 days. At this rate, how much would it cost to operate the television for 1 day? for 1 hr?

31. *Filling time.* The time t required to fill a pool varies inversely as the rate r of flow into the pool. A tanker can fill a pool in 90 min at the rate of 1200 L/min. How long would it take to fill the pool at a rate of 2000 L/min?

32. *Answering questions.* The number of minutes m that a student should allow for each question on a quiz is inversely proportional to the number of questions n on the quiz. If a 16-question quiz allows students 2.5 min per question, how many questions would appear on a quiz in which students have 4 min per question?

Aha! **33.** *Chartering a bus.* The cost per person c of a chartered bus is inversely proportional to the number of people n who are chartering the bus. If it costs \$25 per person when 30 people charter a bus, how many people would be on the bus if the cost were \$50 per person?

34. *Weight on Mars.* The weight M of an object on Mars varies directly as its weight E on Earth. In 2002, Zhijuan Song, who weighs 128 lb, set a record for her weight class with a lift (snatch) of 234 lb. On Mars, this lift would be only 89.14 lb. How much would Zhijuan Song weigh on Mars?
Source: 2004 *Guinness Book of World Records*

State whether each situation represents direct variation, inverse variation, or neither. Give reasons for your answers.

35. The cost of mailing a package in the United States and the distance that it travels

36. A runner's speed in a race and the time it takes to run the race

37. The weight of a turkey and its cooking time

38. The number of plays it takes to go 80 yd for a touchdown and the average gain per play

SKILL MAINTENANCE

Simplify.

39. $(-7)^2$ [1.8]
40. $(-5)^2$ [1.8]
41. 13^2 [1.8]
42. 15^2 [1.8]
43. $(3x)^2$ [4.1]
44. $(6a)^2$ [4.1]
45. $(a^2b)^2$ [4.1]
46. $(s^3t)^2$ [4.1]

SYNTHESIS

47. If x varies inversely as y and y varies inversely as z, how does x vary with regard to z? Why?

48. If a varies directly as b and b varies inversely as c, how does a vary with regard to c? Why?

Write an equation of variation for each situation. Use k as the variation constant in each equation.

49. *Wind energy.* The power P in a windmill varies directly as the cube of the wind speed v.

50. *Ecology.* In a stream, the amount of salt S carried varies directly as the sixth power of the speed of the stream v.

51. *Acoustics.* The square of the pitch P of a vibrating string varies directly as the tension t on the string.

52. *Lighting.* The intensity of illumination I from a light source varies inversely as the square of the distance d from the source.

53. *Crowd size.* The number of people attending a First Night celebration N is directly proportional to the temperature T and inversely proportional to the percentage chance of rain or snow, P.

Write an equation of variation for each situation. Include a value for the variation constant in each equation.

54. *Geometry.* The volume V of a sphere varies directly as the cube of the radius r.

55. *Geometry.* The perimeter P of an equilateral octagon varies directly as the length S of a side.

56. *Geometry.* The circumference C of a circle varies directly as the radius r.

57. *Geometry.* The area of a circle varies directly as the square of the length of the radius.

7 Study Summary

Many real-world situations are most easily solved using a **system of equations** (p. 430). A system like

$$2x - 3y = 10,$$
$$7x + 4y = -8,$$

for which at least one solution exists, is **consistent** (p. 432). When the equations in a system of two equations are **dependent** (p. 433), as in

$$2x - 3y = 10,$$
$$4x - 6y = 20,$$

an infinite number of solutions exists. When both equations are **independent** (p. 433), the system has either one solution (as in the case of the first system shown above), or no solution, as in the case of the **inconsistent** (p. 432) system

$$2x - 3y = 10,$$
$$4x - 6y = 30.$$

The **graphing** method for solving systems of equations (p. 431) involves looking for a point of intersection of the graphs of the equations. To use the **substitution** method (p. 440), we solve one equation for a variable and substitute that expression for that variable in the other equation. The **elimination** method (p. 445) is based on the addition principle. We eliminate a variable by adding the same quantity to both sides of an equation. Each method has its strengths and weaknesses (p. 453).

Linear inequalities (p. 464) can also appear in systems (p. 469). These inequalities and systems are solved graphically, using shadings and/or arrows.

In many problems, the value of one quantity varies as another changes. In **direct variation** (p. 472), equations of the form $y = kx$, with $k > 0$, model situations in which one quantity increases when another quantity increases. In **inverse variation** (p. 475), equations of the form $y = k/x$, with $k > 0$, model situations in which one quantity decreases when another quantity increases.

7 Review Exercises

Concept Reinforcement *Complete each sentence.*

1. The solution of a system of two equations in two variables is a(n) ______________ pair of numbers. [7.1]

2. When both equations in a system are equivalent to each other, there is a(n) ______________ number of solutions. [7.1]

3. When the equations in a system have graphs that are ______________, the system has no solution. [7.1]

4. One weakness of the graphical method for solving systems is that it can be ______________ when fractions arise. [7.4]

5. The substitution method is easiest to use when a variable is ______________ on one side of an equation. [7.4]

6. To use the elimination method, the ______________ of one of the variables must be made to be (if they are not already) opposites of each other. [7.3]

7. The graph of an inequality of the form $y < mx + b$ is shaded ______________ the line $y = mx + b$. [7.5]

8. If y varies inversely as x, then as x increases, y ______________. [7.7]

Determine whether each ordered pair is a solution of the system of equations. [7.1]

9. $(-3, 2)$; $x + 2y = 1,$ $x - 3y = -9$

10. $(4, -1)$; $3x - y = 13,$ $2x + y = -9$

Solve by graphing. If there is no solution or an infinite number of solutions, state this. [7.1]

11. $y = 2x - 3,$ $y = 3x - 4$

12. $x - y = 8,$ $x + y = 4$

13. $3x - 4y = 8,$ $4y - 3x = 6$

14. $2x + y = 3,$ $4x + 2y = 6$

Solve using the substitution method. If there is no solution or an infinite number of solutions, state this. [7.2]

15. $y = 4 - x,$ $3x + 4y = 21$

16. $x + 2y = 6,$ $2x + y = 8$

17. $x + y = 5,$ $y = 2 - x$

18. $x + y = 6,$ $y = 3 - 2x$

19. $3x - y = 7,$ $2x + 3y = 23$

20. $3x - y = 5,$ $6x = 2y + 10$

Solve using the elimination method. If there is no solution or an infinite number of solutions, state this. [7.3]

21. $x + 2y = 9,$ $3x - 2y = -3$

22. $x - y = 8,$ $2x + y = 7$

23. $x - \frac{1}{3}y = -\frac{13}{3},$ $3x - y = -13$

24. $2x + 3y = 8,$ $5x + 2y = -2$

25. $5x - 2y = 11,$ $3x - 7y = -5$

26. $-x - y = -5,$ $2x - y = 4$

27. $4x - 6y = 9,$ $-2x + 3y = 6$

28. $2x + 6y = 4,$ $7x + 10y = -8$

Solve.

29. *Perimeter of a rectangle.* The perimeter of a sheet of construction paper is 96 cm. The length is 27 cm more than the width. Find the length and the width. [7.2]

30. *Basketball scoring.* In a recent NBA game, Tracy McGrady scored 20 points on a combination of 9 two- and three-point baskets. How many shots of each type were made? [7.4]
Source: National Basketball Association

31. *Restaurant meals.* Friendly's® Restaurants recently ran a promotion in which a fajita dinner cost \$8.99 and a "Kid's Meal" cost \$3.99. A group of 20 parents and children ordered fajita dinners and Kid's Meals costing a total of \$134.80. How many Kid's Meals and how many fajita dinners were ordered? [7.4]

32. *Fat content.* Café Rich instant flavored coffee gets 40% of its calories from fat. Café Light coffee gets 25% of its calories from fat. How much of each brand of coffee should be mixed in order to make 200 g of instant coffee with 30% of its calories from fat? [7.4]

Graph on a plane. [7.5]

33. $x \le y$

34. $x - 2y \ge 4$

35. $y > -2$

36. $y \ge \frac{2}{3}x - 5$

37. $2x + y < 1$

38. $x < 4$

Graph the solutions of each system. [7.6]

39. $x \ge 1,$
$y \le -1$

40. $x - y > 2,$
$x + y < 1$

41. If y varies inversely as x and $y = 81$ when $x = 3$, find the equation of variation. [7.7]

42. *Catering.* The number of sandwiches S that can be made at a buffet varies directly as the number of pounds of cold cuts C in the buffet. From 6 lb of cold cuts, 25 sandwiches can be made. How many pounds of cold cuts are needed for 40 sandwiches? [7.7]

SYNTHESIS

43. Explain why any solution of a system of equations is a point of intersection of the graphs of each equation in the system. [7.1]

44. Monroe sketches the boundary lines of a system of two linear inequalities and notes that the lines are parallel. Since there is no point of intersection, he concludes that the solution set is empty. What is wrong with this conclusion? [7.6]

45. The solution of the following system is (6, 2). Find C and D.

$$2x - Dy = 6,$$
$$Cx + 4y = 14 \text{ [7.1]}$$

46. Solve using the substitution method:

$$x - y + 2z = -3,$$
$$2x + y - 3z = 11,$$
$$z = -2. \text{ [7.2]}$$

47. Solve:

$$3(x - y) = 4 + x,$$
$$x = 5y + 2. \text{ [7.2]}$$

48. For a two-digit number, the sum of the ones digit and the tens digit is 6. When the digits are reversed, the new number is 18 more than the original number. Find the original number. [7.4]

49. A farmhand agrees to work for one year in exchange for \$24,000 and a horse. After 7 months, the farmhand is transferred and receives the horse and \$10,000. What was the value of her yearly salary? [7.4]

7 Chapter Test

1. Determine whether $(-1, -2)$ is a solution of the following system of equations:

$$3x - 4y = 5,$$
$$2x + 3y = -8.$$

Solve by graphing. If there is no solution or an infinite number of solutions, state this.

2. $y = -2x + 5,$
   $y = 4x - 1$

3. $2y - x = 7,$
   $2x - 4y = 4$

Solve using the substitution method. If there is no solution or an infinite number of solutions, state this.

4. $2x - 22 = 3y,$
   $y = 6 - x$

5. $x + y = 2,$
   $x + 2y = 5$

6. $x = 5y - 10,$
   $15y = 3x + 30$

Solve using the elimination method. If there is no solution or an infinite number of solutions, state this.

7. $x - y = 6,$
   $3x + y = -2$

8. $\frac{3}{2}x - y = 24,$
   $2x + \frac{3}{2}y = 15$

9. $4x + 5y = 5,$
   $6x + 7y = 7$

10. $2x + 3y = 13,$
    $3x - 5y = 10$

Solve.

11. *Complementary angles.* Two angles are complementary. One angle is 18° less than twice the other. Find the angles.

12. *Cooking.* A chef has one vinaigrette that is 40% vinegar and another that is 25% vinegar. How much of each is needed to make 60 L of a vinaigrette that is 30% vinegar?

13. *Taxi fares.* A New York City taxi recently cost \$2.50 plus \$1.00 per half mile. A taxi in Boston cost \$1.45 plus \$1.20 per half mile. For what distance will the taxis cost the same?

Graph on a plane.

14. $y > x - 1$

15. $2x - y \leq 4$

16. $y < -2$

Graph the solutions of each system.

17. $y \geq x - 5,$
    $y < \frac{1}{2}x$

18. $x + y \leq 4,$
    $x \geq 0,$
    $y \geq 0$

19. If y varies directly as x and $y = 9$ when $x = 2$, find the equation of variation.

20. *Work.* It takes 45 min for 2 people to shovel a driveway. How long would it take 5 people to shovel the same driveway?

SYNTHESIS

21. You are in line at a ticket window. There are two more people ahead of you in line than there are behind you. In the entire line, there are three times as many people as there are behind you. How many are in the line?

22. Graph on a plane: $|x| \leq 5$.

23. Find the numbers C and D such that $(-2, 3)$ is a solution of the system

$$Cx - 4y = 7,$$
$$3x + Dy = 8.$$

8 Radical Expressions and Equations

AN APPLICATION

From the peak of a 25-ft tall spruce tree in her front yard, Julia plans to run 10 strands of holiday lights to points in her lawn 15 ft from the tree's center. The lights cost \$5.99 for 25 ft, \$6.99 for 35 ft, and \$11.99 for 68 ft (prices current 12/23/03). What should Julia purchase to make the decorations as economical as possible?

This problem appears as Exercise 51 in Section 8.6.

Claude Minnich

OWNER, HARDWARE BUSINESS

Culpepper, Virginia

Math is very important in the hardware business—I use it every day. A knowledge of fractions is necessary to sell pipes and screws. I often need to figure percentages as well, to measure glass, for example, and just about everything that I sell.

You may already have some familiarity with the notion of square roots. *For example, 3 is a square root of 9 because* $3^2 = 9$. *In this chapter, we learn how to manipulate square roots of polynomials and rational expressions. Later in this chapter, these* radical expressions *will appear in equations and in problem-solving situations.*

8.1 Introduction to Square Roots and Radical Expressions

Square Roots • Radicands and Radical Expressions • Irrational Numbers • Square Roots and Absolute Value • Problem Solving

We begin our study of square roots by examining square roots of numbers, square roots of variable expressions, and an application involving a formula.

Study Skills

Professors Are Human

Even the best professors sometimes make mistakes. If, as you review your notes, you find that something doesn't make sense, it may be due to your instructor having made a mistake. If, after double-checking, you still perceive a mistake, politely ask your instructor about it. In doing so you may be helping *everyone* in your class.

Square Roots

Often in this text we have found the result of squaring a number. When the process is reversed, we say that we are looking for a number's *square root.*

> **Square Root**
>
> The number c is a *square root* of a if $c^2 = a$.

Every positive number has two square roots. For example, the square roots of 25 are 5 and -5 because $5^2 = 25$ and $(-5)^2 = 25$.

EXAMPLE 1 Find the square roots of each number: **(a)** 81; **(b)** 100.

Solution

a) The square roots of 81 are 9 and -9. To check, note that $9^2 = 81$ and $(-9)^2 = (-9)(-9) = 81$.

b) The square roots of 100 are 10 and -10. To check, note that $10^2 = 100$ and $(-10)^2 = 100$.

The nonnegative square root of a number is called the **principal square root** of that number. In Example 1, we showed that the principal square root of 81 is 9 and the principal square root of 100 is 10. A **radical sign**, $\sqrt{}$, indicates the principal square root of the number under the sign (the **radicand**). Thus, $\sqrt{25} = 5$ and $\sqrt{25} \neq -5$.

EXAMPLE 2 Find each of the following: **(a)** $\sqrt{225}$; **(b)** $-\sqrt{64}$.

Solution

a) The principal square root of 225 is its positive square root, so $\sqrt{225} = 15$.

b) The symbol $-\sqrt{64}$ represents the opposite of $\sqrt{64}$. Since $\sqrt{64} = 8$, we have $-\sqrt{64} = -8$.

Radicands and Radical Expressions

A **radical expression** is an algebraic expression that contains at least one radical sign. Here are some examples:

$$\sqrt{14}, \qquad 8 + \sqrt{2x}, \qquad \sqrt{t^2 + 4}, \qquad \sqrt{\frac{x^2 - 5}{2}}.$$

EXAMPLE 3 Identify the radicand in each expression: **(a)** $\sqrt{x}$; **(b)** $\sqrt{y^2 - 5}$.

Solution

a) In $\sqrt{x}$, the radicand is x.

b) In $\sqrt{y^2 - 5}$, the radicand is $y^2 - 5$.

The square of any nonzero real number is always positive. For example, $8^2 = 64$ and $(-11)^2 = 121$. No real number, squared, is equal to a negative number. Thus the following expressions are not real numbers:

$$\sqrt{-100}, \qquad \sqrt{-49}, \qquad -\sqrt{-3}.$$

Numbers like $\sqrt{-100}$, $\sqrt{-49}$, and $-\sqrt{-3}$ are discussed in Chapter 9.

Irrational Numbers

In Section 1.4, we learned that numbers like $\sqrt{2}$ cannot be written as a ratio of two integers. Numbers like $\sqrt{2}$ are real but not rational and are called *irrational*. A number that is the square of some rational number, like 9 or 64, is called a *perfect square*. The square root of a perfect square is always rational; the square root of a number that is not a perfect square is irrational.

EXAMPLE 4 Classify each of the following numbers as rational or irrational.

a) $\sqrt{3}$ **b)** $\sqrt{25}$

c) $\sqrt{35}$ **d)** $-\sqrt{9}$

Solution

a) $\sqrt{3}$ is irrational, since 3 is not a perfect square.

b) $\sqrt{25}$ is rational, since 25 is a perfect square: $\sqrt{25} = 5$.

c) $\sqrt{35}$ is irrational, since 35 is not a perfect square.

d) $-\sqrt{9}$ is rational, since 9 is a perfect square: $-\sqrt{9} = -3$.

For the following list, we have printed the irrational numbers in red: $\sqrt{1}$, $\sqrt{2}$, $\sqrt{3}$, $\sqrt{4}$, $\sqrt{5}$, $\sqrt{6}$, $\sqrt{7}$, $\sqrt{8}$, $\sqrt{9}$, $\sqrt{10}$, $\sqrt{11}$, $\sqrt{12}$, $\sqrt{13}$, $\sqrt{14}$, $\sqrt{15}$, $\sqrt{16}$, $\sqrt{17}$, $\sqrt{18}$, $\sqrt{19}$, $\sqrt{20}$, $\sqrt{21}$, $\sqrt{22}$, $\sqrt{23}$, $\sqrt{24}$, $\sqrt{25}$.

Often, when square roots are irrational, a calculator is used to find decimal approximations.

EXAMPLE 5 Use a calculator to approximate $\sqrt{10}$ to three decimal places.

Solution Calculators vary in their methods of operation. On some, we press (√) and then the number; on others, we enter the number and then press (√).

$\sqrt{10} \approx 3.162277660.$ Using a calculator with a 10-digit display

With most graphing calculators, we press 2ND (√), the radicand (in this case 10), and ENTER.

Decimal representation of an irrational number is nonrepeating and nonending. Rounding to three decimal places, we have $\sqrt{10} \approx 3.162$.

---

technology connection

To approximate $\sqrt{10}$ with a graphing calculator, we press 2ND (√) (1) (0) ( )) ENTER. Note that (√) is the second operation associated with the x^2 key. The keystrokes given assume a calculator that automatically supplies a left parenthesis. Use of the ( )) key is optional here, but is essential when more complex calculations arise.

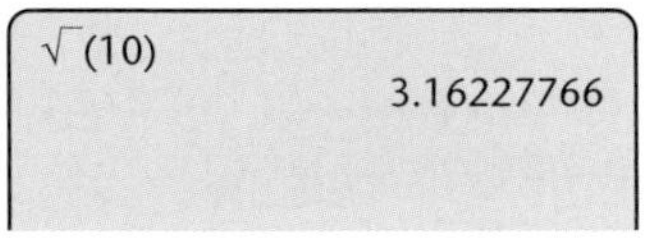

1. Approximate $\sqrt{8}$, $\sqrt{11}$, and $\sqrt{48}$.

Square Roots and Absolute Value

Since $\sqrt{(-5)^2} = \sqrt{25} = 5$ and $\sqrt{5^2} = \sqrt{25} = 5$, we see that squaring a number and then taking the square root is the same as taking the absolute value of the number. In short, the principal square root of the square of A is the absolute value of A:

For any real number A, $\sqrt{A^2} = |A|$.

EXAMPLE 6 Simplify: $\sqrt{(-6)^2}$.

Solution

$\sqrt{(-6)^2} = \sqrt{36} = 6$ Note that $\sqrt{A^2} \neq A$.

EXAMPLE 7 Simplify $\sqrt{(3x)^2}$ given that x can represent any real number.

Solution To simplify $\sqrt{(3x)^2}$, note that if x represents a negative number—say, -2—the result is *not* $3x$. To see this, note that $\sqrt{(3(-2))^2} \neq 3(-2)$, as shown in Example 6. Since the principal square root is always positive, to write $\sqrt{(3x)^2} = 3x$ would be incorrect. Instead, we write

$\sqrt{(3x)^2} = |3x|.$ Note that $3x$ will be negative for $x < 0$.

Fortunately, in many cases, it can be assumed that radicands that are variable expressions do not represent the square of a negative number. When this assumption is made, the need for absolute-value symbols disappears:

For $A \geq 0$, $\sqrt{A^2} = A$.

EXAMPLE 8 Simplify each expression. Assume that all variables represent nonnegative numbers.

a) $\sqrt{(8x)^2}$ **b)** $\sqrt{a^2b^2}$

Solution

a) $\sqrt{(8x)^2} = 8x$ Since $8x$ is assumed to be nonnegative, $|8x| = 8x$.

b) $\sqrt{a^2b^2} = \sqrt{(ab)^2} = ab$ Since ab is assumed to be nonnegative, $|ab| = ab$.

In Sections 8.2–8.6, we will often state assumptions that make absolute-value symbols unnecessary.

Problem Solving

Radical expressions often appear in applications.

EXAMPLE 9

Parking-lot arrival spaces. The attendants at a downtown parking lot use spaces to leave cars before they are taken to long-term parking stalls. The required number N of such spaces is approximated by the formula

$$N = 2.5\sqrt{A},$$

where A is the average number of arrivals in peak hours. Find the number of spaces needed when an average of 43 cars arrive during peak hours.

Solution We substitute 43 into the formula. We use a calculator to find an approximation:

$$\begin{aligned} N &= 2.5\sqrt{43} \\ &\approx 2.5(6.557) \\ &\approx 16.393 \approx 17. \end{aligned}$$

Note that we round *up* to 17 spaces because rounding down would create some overcrowding. Thus, for an average of 43 arrivals, 17 spaces are needed.

Student Notes

In Example 9, the number 16.393 is rounded *up* to 17 because of the real-world situation being modeled. Always make sure that your answers to applications make sense in the real world.

> *Calculator Note.* Generally, when using a calculator, as in Example 9, we round at the *end* of our work. Doing so, we might find
>
> $$N = 2.5\sqrt{43} \approx 2.5(6.557438524) = 16.39359631 \approx 16.394.$$
>
> Note the discrepancy in the third decimal place. When using a calculator for approximation, be aware of possible variations in answers. You may get answers that differ slightly from those at the back of the book. Answers to the exercises have been found by rounding at the end of the calculations.

technology connection

Graphing equations that contain radical expressions often involves approximating irrational numbers. Also, since the square root of a negative number is not real, such graphs may not exist for all choices of x. For example, the graph of $y = \sqrt{x - 1}$ does not exist for $x < 1$.

$y_1 = \sqrt{x - 1}$

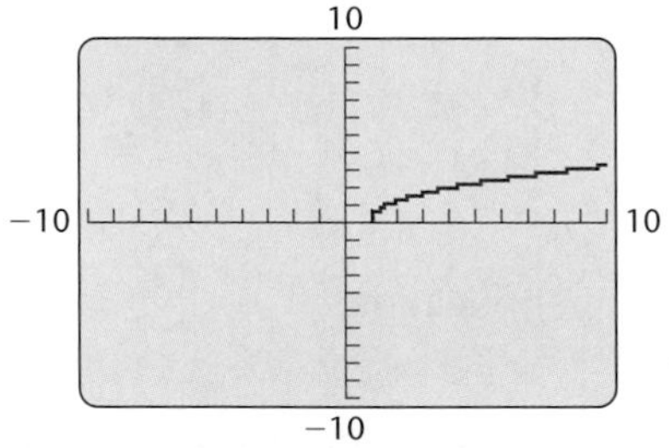

Similarly, the graph of $y = \sqrt{2 - x}$ does not exist for $x > 2$.

$y_1 = \sqrt{2 - x}$

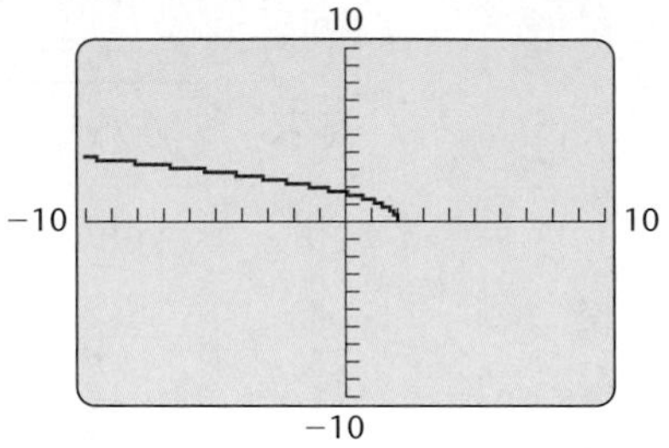

Graph.

1. $y = \sqrt{x}$
2. $y = \sqrt{2x}$
3. $y = \sqrt{x^2}$
4. $y = \sqrt{(2x)^2}$
5. $y = \sqrt{x + 4}$
6. $y = \sqrt{6 - x}$

8.1 Exercise Set

FOR EXTRA HELP

Student's Solutions Manual | Digital Video Tutor CD 5 Videotape 15 | AW Math Tutor Center | MathXL Tutorials on CD | MathXL | MyMathLab

Concept Reinforcement *In each of Exercises 1–6, match the phrase with the most appropriate choice from the column on the right.*

1. ___ The name for an expression written under a radical	**a)** Irrational
2. ___ The name for an algebraic expression that contains at least one radical sign	**b)** Negative
3. ___ The name for a number that is real but not rational	**c)** Radicand
4. ___ The name for a positive number's positive square root	**d)** Positive
5. ___ The sign of $3x$ when x represents a negative number	**e)** Radical expression
6. ___ The sign of $\sqrt{A^2}$ when A represents a negative number	**f)** Principal square root

Classify each statement as either true or false. Do not use a calculator.

7. $\sqrt{67}$ is between 8 and 9.

8. $\sqrt{75}$ is between 7 and 8.

9. $\sqrt{150}$ is between 11 and 12.

10. $\sqrt{103}$ is between 10 and 11.

Find the square roots of each number.

11. 9
12. 4
13. 16
14. 1
15. 49
16. 121
17. 144
18. 169

Simplify.

19. $\sqrt{4}$ **20.** $\sqrt{9}$ **21.** $-\sqrt{1}$

22. $-\sqrt{25}$ **23.** $\sqrt{0}$ **24.** $-\sqrt{81}$

25. $-\sqrt{121}$ **26.** $\sqrt{361}$ **27.** $\sqrt{900}$

28. $\sqrt{441}$ **29.** $\sqrt{144}$ **30.** $\sqrt{169}$

31. $-\sqrt{625}$ **32.** $-\sqrt{400}$

Identify the radicand for each expression.

33. $\sqrt{a + 7}$ **34.** $\sqrt{t + 5}$

35. $5\sqrt{t^3 - 2}$ **36.** $8\sqrt{x^2 + 2}$

37. $x^2y\sqrt{\frac{7}{x + y}}$ **38.** $ab^2\sqrt{\frac{a}{a - b}}$

Classify each number as rational or irrational.

39. $\sqrt{100}$ **40.** $\sqrt{6}$

41. $\sqrt{8}$ **42.** $\sqrt{10}$

43. $\sqrt{32}$ **44.** $\sqrt{49}$

45. $\sqrt{98}$ **46.** $\sqrt{75}$

47. $-\sqrt{4}$ **48.** $-\sqrt{1}$

Aha! **49.** $-\sqrt{19^2}$ **50.** $-\sqrt{14}$

Use a calculator to approximate each of the following numbers. Round to three decimal places.

51. $\sqrt{5}$ **52.** $\sqrt{6}$

53. $\sqrt{17}$ **54.** $\sqrt{19}$

55. $\sqrt{93}$ **56.** $\sqrt{43}$

Simplify. Assume x can represent any real number.

57. $\sqrt{x^2}$ **58.** $\sqrt{(7x)^2}$

59. $\sqrt{(x - 3)^2}$ **60.** $\sqrt{(x - 1)^2}$

61. $\sqrt{(8x)^2}$ **62.** $\sqrt{(4 - x)^2}$

63. $\sqrt{(2x + 1)^2}$ **64.** $\sqrt{(3x + 2)^2}$

Simplify. Assume that all variables represent nonnegative numbers.

65. $\sqrt{t^2}$ **66.** $\sqrt{x^2}$

67. $\sqrt{9x^2}$ **68.** $\sqrt{25a^2}$

69. $\sqrt{(7a)^2}$ **70.** $\sqrt{(4x)^2}$

71. $\sqrt{(x + 1)^2}$ **72.** $\sqrt{(a + 2)^2}$

Parking spaces. *Solve. Use the formula $N = 2.5\sqrt{A}$ of Example 9.*

73. Find the number of spaces needed when the average number of arrivals is **(a)** 36; **(b)** 29.

74. Find the number of spaces needed when the average number of arrivals is **(a)** 49; **(b)** 53.

Hang time. *An athlete's* hang time *(time airborne for a jump), T, in seconds, is given by $T = 0.144\sqrt{V}$,* where V is the athlete's vertical leap, in inches.*

75. LeBron James of the Cleveland Cavaliers can jump 40 in. vertically. Find his hang time.
Source: DallasNews.com

76. Tracy McGrady of the Orlando Magic can jump 42 in. vertically. Find his hang time.
Source: enquirer.com

77. Which is the more exact way to write the square root of 12: 3.464101615 or $\sqrt{12}$? Why?

78. What is the difference between saying "*the* square root of 10" and saying "*a* square root of 10"?

SKILL MAINTENANCE

Simplify. [4.1]

79. $(7x)^2$ **80.** $(-3a)^2$

81. $(4t^7)^2$ **82.** $5x \cdot 9x^6$

83. $3a \cdot 16a^{10}$ **84.** $2t \cdot 4t^8u^6$

SYNTHESIS

85. Explain in your own words why $\sqrt{A^2} \neq A$ when A is negative.

86. One number has only one square root. What is the number and why is it unique in this regard?

*Based on an article by Peter Brancazio, "The Mechanics of a Slam Dunk," *Popular Mechanics*, November 1991. Courtesy of Peter Brancazio, Brooklyn College.

Simplify.

87. $\sqrt{\sqrt{81}}$

88. $\sqrt{3^2 + 4^2}$

Aha! **89.** Between what two consecutive integers is $-\sqrt{33}$?

90. Find a number that is the square of an integer and the cube of a different integer.

Solve. If no real-number solution exists, state this.

91. $\sqrt{t^2} = 7$

92. $\sqrt{y^2} = -5$

93. $-\sqrt{x^2} = -3$

94. $a^2 = 36$

95. For which values of x is $\sqrt{(x+5)^2} = x + 5$ false?

96. For which values of t is $\sqrt{(t-7)^2} = t - 7$ false?

Simplify. Assume that all variables represent positive numbers.

97. $\sqrt{\dfrac{144x^8}{36y^6}}$

98. $\sqrt{\dfrac{y^{12}}{8100}}$

99. $\sqrt{\dfrac{400}{m^{16}}}$

100. $\sqrt{\dfrac{p^2}{3600}}$

101. Use the graph of $y = \sqrt{x}$, shown below, to estimate each of the following to the nearest tenth: **(a)** $\sqrt{3}$; **(b)** $\sqrt{5}$; **(c)** $\sqrt{7}$. Be sure to check by multiplying.

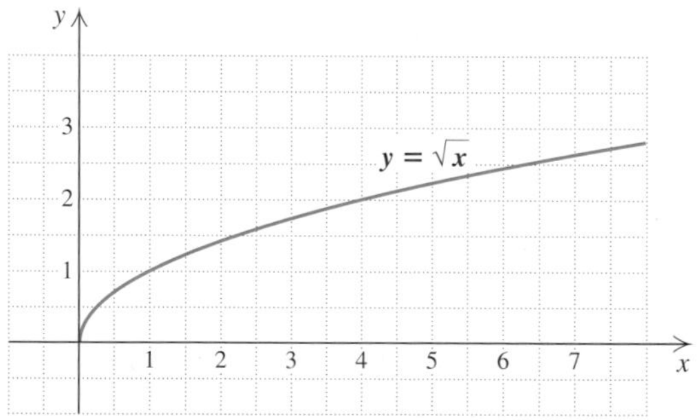

Speed of sound. The speed V of sound traveling through air, in feet per second, is given by

$$V = \frac{1087\sqrt{273 + t}}{16.52},$$

where t is the temperature, in degrees Celsius. Using a calculator, find the speed of sound through air at each of the following temperatures. Round to the nearest tenth.

102. 28°C

103. 5°C

104. −10°C

105. Use a graphing calculator to draw the graphs of $y_1 = \sqrt{x - 2}$, $y_2 = \sqrt{x + 7}$, $y_3 = 5 + \sqrt{x}$, and $y_4 = -4 + \sqrt{x}$. If possible, graph all four equations using the SIMULTANEOUS mode and a $[-10, 10, -10, 10]$ window. Then determine which equation corresponds to each curve.

106. What restrictions on a, if any, are needed in order for

$$\sqrt{64a^{16}} = 8a^8$$

to be true? Explain how you found your answer.

COLLABORATIVE CORNER

Lengths and Cycles of a Pendulum

Focus: Square roots and modeling

Time: 25–35 minutes

Group size: 3

Materials: Rulers, clocks or watches (to measure seconds), pendulums (see below), calculators

A pendulum is simply a string, a rope, or a chain with a weight of some sort attached at one end. When the unweighted end is held, a pendulum can swing freely from side to side. A shoe hanging from a shoelace, a yo-yo, a pendant hanging from a chain, a fishing weight hanging from a fish line, or a hairbrush tied to a length of dental floss are all examples of a pendulum. In this activity, each group will develop a mathematical model (formula) that relates a pendulum's length L to the time T that it takes for one complete swing back and forth (one "cycle").

ACTIVITY

1. The group should design a pendulum (see above). One group member should hold the pendulum so that its length is 1 ft. A second group member should lift the weight to one side and then release (do not throw) the weight. The third group member should find the average time, in seconds, for one swing (cycle) back and forth, by timing *five* cycles and dividing by five. Repeat this for each pendulum length listed, so that the table above is completed.

L **(in feet)**	1	1.5	2	2.5	3	3.5
T **(in seconds)**						

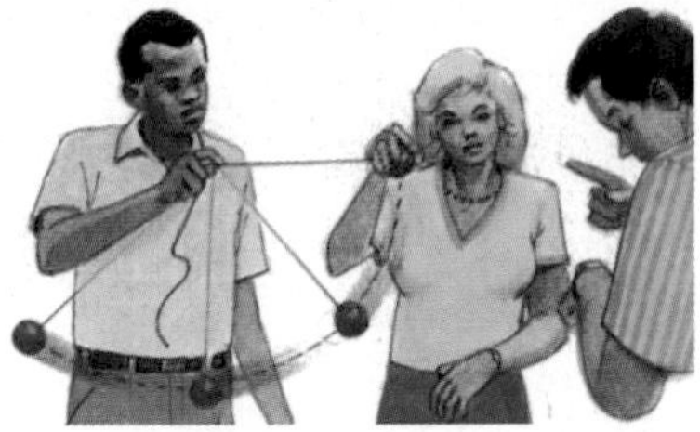

2. Examine the table your group has created. Can you find one number, a, such that $T \approx aL$ for all pairs of values on the chart?
3. To see if a better model can be found, add a third row to the chart and fill in $\sqrt{L}$ for each value of L listed. Can you find one number, b, such that $T \approx b\sqrt{L}$? Does this appear to be a more accurate model than $T = aL$?
4. Use the model for part (3) to predict T when L is 4 ft. Then check your prediction by measuring T as you did in part (1) above. Was your prediction "acceptable"? Compare your results with those of other groups.
5. In Section 8.3, we use a formula equivalent to

$$T = \frac{2\pi}{\sqrt{32}} \cdot \sqrt{L}.$$

How does your value of b from part (3) compare with $2\pi/\sqrt{32}$?

8.2 Multiplying and Simplifying Radical Expressions

Multiplying • Simplifying and Factoring • Simplifying Square Roots of Powers • Multiplying and Simplifying

We now learn to multiply and simplify radical expressions.

Multiplying

To see how to multiply with radical notation, consider the following:

$\sqrt{9} \cdot \sqrt{4} = 3 \cdot 2 = 6;$ This is a product of square roots.

$\sqrt{9 \cdot 4} = \sqrt{36} = 6.$ This is the square root of a product.

Note that $\sqrt{9} \cdot \sqrt{4} = \sqrt{9 \cdot 4}$. This is generalized in the following rule.

Study Skills

Plan Your Future

As you register for next semester's courses, be careful to consider your work and family commitments. Speak to faculty and other students to estimate how demanding each course is before signing up. If in doubt, it is usually better to take one fewer course than one too many.

The Product Rule for Square Roots

For any real numbers $\sqrt{A}$ and $\sqrt{B}$,

$$\sqrt{A} \cdot \sqrt{B} = \sqrt{A \cdot B}.$$

(To multiply square roots, multiply the radicands and take the square root.)

EXAMPLE 1 Multiply: **(a)** $\sqrt{5}\sqrt{7}$; **(b)** $\sqrt{6}\sqrt{6}$; **(c)** $\sqrt{\frac{2}{3}}\sqrt{\frac{7}{5}}$; **(d)** $\sqrt{2x}\sqrt{3y}$.

Solution

a) $\sqrt{5}\sqrt{7} = \sqrt{5 \cdot 7} = \sqrt{35}$

b) $\sqrt{6}\sqrt{6} = \sqrt{6 \cdot 6} = \sqrt{36} = 6$ Try to do this one directly: $\sqrt{6}\sqrt{6} = 6$.

c) $\sqrt{\dfrac{2}{3}}\sqrt{\dfrac{7}{5}} = \sqrt{\dfrac{2}{3} \cdot \dfrac{7}{5}} = \sqrt{\dfrac{14}{15}}$

d) $\sqrt{2x}\sqrt{3y} = \sqrt{6xy}$ Note that in order for $\sqrt{2x}$ and $\sqrt{3y}$ to be real numbers, we must have $x, y \geq 0$.

Simplifying and Factoring

To factor a square root, we can use the product rule in reverse. That is,

$$\sqrt{AB} = \sqrt{A}\sqrt{B}.$$

This property is especially useful when a radicand contains a perfect square as a factor. For example, the radicand in $\sqrt{50}$ is not a perfect square, but one of its factors, 25, *is* a perfect square. Thus,

$\sqrt{50} = \sqrt{25 \cdot 2}$	25 is a perfect-square factor of 50.
$= \sqrt{25} \cdot \sqrt{2}$	$\sqrt{25}$ is a rational factor of $\sqrt{50}$.
$= 5\sqrt{2}.$	Simplifying $\sqrt{25}$; $\sqrt{2}$ cannot be simplified further.

To determine whether a radicand contains a factor that is a perfect square, it may help to write a prime factorization of the radicand. For example, if we did not easily see that 50 contains a perfect square as a factor, we could write

$\sqrt{50} = \sqrt{2 \cdot 5 \cdot 5}$	Factoring into prime factors
$= \sqrt{2} \cdot \sqrt{5 \cdot 5}$	Grouping pairs of like factors; $5 \cdot 5$ is a perfect square.
$= \sqrt{2} \cdot 5.$	

Student Notes

It is extremely important that you take care in locating the radical symbols. There is a great difference between writing $\sqrt{2} \cdot 5$ and $\sqrt{2 \cdot 5}$. It is also important to understand that $5\sqrt{2}$ means $5 \cdot \sqrt{2}$.

To avoid any uncertainty as to what is under the radical sign, it is customary to write the radical factor last. Thus, $\sqrt{50} = 5\sqrt{2}$.

A radical expression, like $\sqrt{26}$, in which the radicand has no perfect-square factors, is considered to be in simplified form.

Simplified Form of a Square Root

A radical expression for a square root is simplified when its radicand has no factor other than 1 that is a perfect square.

Simplifying is always easiest if the *largest* perfect-square factor is identified in the first step.

EXAMPLE 2 Simplify by factoring (remember that all variables are assumed to represent nonnegative numbers).

a) $\sqrt{18}$ **b)** $\sqrt{a^2b}$ **c)** $\sqrt{196t^2u}$

Solution

a) $\sqrt{18} = \sqrt{9 \cdot 2}$	9 is a perfect-square factor of 18.
$= \sqrt{9}\sqrt{2}$	$\sqrt{9}$ is a rational factor of $\sqrt{18}$.
$= 3\sqrt{2}$	$\sqrt{2}$ cannot be simplified further.

b) $\sqrt{a^2b} = \sqrt{a^2}\sqrt{b}$	Identifying a perfect-square factor and factoring into a product of radicals
$= a\sqrt{b}$	No absolute-value signs are necessary since a is assumed to be nonnegative.

c) Most students may not know that 196 is a perfect square. Let's suppose that we noticed only that 4 and t^2 are perfect-square factors of $196t^2u$:

$$\sqrt{196t^2u} = \sqrt{4} \cdot \sqrt{t^2} \cdot \sqrt{49u} \quad \text{Identifying perfect-square factors}$$
$$= 2t\sqrt{49u}. \quad \text{We assume } t \geq 0.$$

Because the radicand still contains a perfect-square factor, we have not simplified completely. To finish simplifying, we rewrite the product and simplify $\sqrt{49u}$:

$$\sqrt{196t^2u} = 2t\sqrt{49u}$$
$$= 2t\sqrt{49}\sqrt{u} \quad \text{Identifying a perfect-square factor of } 49u$$
$$= 2t \cdot 7\sqrt{u}$$
$$= 14t\sqrt{u}.$$

In Chapter 9, problems similar to the next example will arise as we solve certain equations.

EXAMPLE 3 Evaluate $\sqrt{b^2 - 4ac}$ for $a = 3$, $b = 6$, and $c = -5$.

Solution We have

$$\sqrt{b^2 - 4ac} = \sqrt{6^2 - 4 \cdot 3(-5)} \quad \text{Substituting}$$
$$= \sqrt{36 - 12(-5)}$$
$$= \sqrt{36 + 60}$$
$$= \sqrt{96}$$
$$= \sqrt{2 \cdot 2 \cdot 2 \cdot 2 \cdot 2 \cdot 3} \quad \text{The prime factorization always allows us to identify the largest perfect-square factor.}$$
$$= \sqrt{16} \cdot \sqrt{6}$$
$$= 4\sqrt{6}.$$

Simplifying Square Roots of Powers

To take the square root of an even power such as x^{10}, note that $x^{10} = (x^5)^2$. Then

$$\sqrt{x^{10}} = \sqrt{(x^5)^2} = x^5. \quad \text{Remember that we assume } x \geq 0.$$

The exponent of the square root is half the exponent of the radicand. That is,

$$\sqrt{x^{10}} = x^5. \leftarrow \tfrac{1}{2}(10) = 5$$

EXAMPLE 4 Simplify: **(a)** $\sqrt{x^6}$; **(b)** $\sqrt{x^8}$; **(c)** $\sqrt{t^{22}}$.

Solution

a) $\sqrt{x^6} = \sqrt{(x^3)^2} = x^3$ Half of 6 is 3.

b) $\sqrt{x^8} = \sqrt{(x^4)^2} = x^4$ Half of 8 is 4.

c) $\sqrt{t^{22}} = \sqrt{(t^{11})^2} = t^{11}$ Half of 22 is 11.

If a radicand is an odd power, we can simplify by factoring, as in the following example. Note that, for square roots, after we have simplified, the radicand never contains a power of x greater than 1.

EXAMPLE 5 Simplify: **(a)** $\sqrt{x^9}$; **(b)** $\sqrt{32x^{15}}$.

Solution

a) $\sqrt{x^9} = \sqrt{x^8 \cdot x}$ $\quad x^8$ is the largest perfect-square factor of x^9.

$= \sqrt{x^8}\sqrt{x}$

$= x^4\sqrt{x}$

> *Caution!* The square root of x^9 is *not* x^3.

b) $\sqrt{32x^{15}} = \sqrt{16x^{14} \cdot 2x}$ $\quad$ 16 is the largest perfect-square factor of 32; x^{14} is the largest perfect-square factor of x^{15}.

$= \sqrt{16}\sqrt{x^{14}}\sqrt{2x}$

$= 4x^7\sqrt{2x}$ $\quad$ Simplifying. Since $2x$ has no perfect-square factor, we are done.

Multiplying and Simplifying

Sometimes we can simplify after multiplying. To do so, we again try to identify any perfect-square factors of the radicand.

EXAMPLE 6 Multiply and, if possible, simplify. Remember that all variables are assumed to represent nonnegative numbers.

a) $\sqrt{2}\sqrt{14}$ $\qquad$ **b)** $\sqrt{5x}\sqrt{3x}$ $\qquad$ **c)** $\sqrt{2x^8}\sqrt{9x^3}$

Solution

a) $\sqrt{2}\sqrt{14} = \sqrt{2 \cdot 14}$ $\quad$ Multiplying

$= \sqrt{2 \cdot 2 \cdot 7}$ $\quad$ Writing the prime factorization

$= \sqrt{2^2}\sqrt{7}$ $\quad$ Note that $2 \cdot 2$, or 4, is a perfect-square factor.

$= 2\sqrt{7}$ $\quad$ Simplifying

b) $\sqrt{5x}\sqrt{3x} = \sqrt{15x^2}$ $\quad$ Multiplying

$= \sqrt{x^2}\sqrt{15}$
$= x\sqrt{15}$ $\quad$ } Simplifying

c) To simplify $\sqrt{2x^8}\sqrt{9x^3}$, note that x^8 and 9 are perfect-square factors. This allows us to simplify *before* multiplying:

$\sqrt{2x^8}\sqrt{9x^3} = \sqrt{2} \cdot \sqrt{(x^4)^2} \cdot \sqrt{9} \cdot \sqrt{x^3}$ $\quad$ $(x^4)^2$ and 9 are perfect squares.

$= \sqrt{2} \cdot x^4 \cdot 3 \cdot \sqrt{x^3}$ $\quad$ Simplifying

$= 3x^4\sqrt{2}\sqrt{x^3}.$ $\quad$ Using a commutative law

The result, $3x^4\sqrt{2}\,\sqrt{x^3}$, or $3x^4\sqrt{2x^3}$, can be simplified further:

$$\begin{aligned} 3x^4\sqrt{2x^3} &= 3x^4\sqrt{x^2 \cdot 2x} \\ &= 3x^4\sqrt{x^2}\,\sqrt{2x} \end{aligned} \quad \Big\} \; x^3 \text{ has a perfect-square factor, } x^2.$$

$$\begin{aligned} &= 3x^4x\sqrt{2x} \\ &= 3x^5\sqrt{2x}. \end{aligned}$$

8.2 Exercise Set

FOR EXTRA HELP

Student's Solutions Manual | Digital Video Tutor CD 5 Videotape 15 | AW Math Tutor Center | MathXL Tutorials on CD | MathXL | MyMathLab

Concept Reinforcement *In each of Exercises 1–10, match the expression with the equivalent expression from the column on the right. Assume that all variables represent nonnegative numbers.*

1. ___ $\sqrt{3} \cdot \sqrt{7}$	**a)** $3 \cdot 7$
2. ___ $\sqrt{9} \cdot \sqrt{7}$	**b)** $\sqrt{(a^3)^2}$
3. ___ $\sqrt{3 \cdot 49}$	**c)** $\sqrt{b^2ac}$
4. ___ $\sqrt{9 \cdot 49}$	**d)** $\sqrt{a^2} \cdot \sqrt{a}$
5. ___ $\sqrt{a^2}$	**e)** $\sqrt{c^2ab}$
6. ___ $\sqrt{a^3}$	**f)** $\sqrt{3} \cdot 7$
7. ___ $\sqrt{a^6}$	**g)** a^2
8. ___ $\sqrt{a^4}$	**h)** $\sqrt{21}$
9. ___ $\sqrt{ab} \cdot \sqrt{bc}$	**i)** a
10. ___ $\sqrt{ac} \cdot \sqrt{bc}$	**j)** $3\sqrt{7}$

Multiply.

11. $\sqrt{7}\,\sqrt{3}$ **12.** $\sqrt{7}\,\sqrt{5}$ **13.** $\sqrt{4}\,\sqrt{3}$

14. $\sqrt{2}\,\sqrt{9}$ **15.** $\sqrt{\frac{2}{5}}\,\sqrt{\frac{3}{4}}$ **16.** $\sqrt{\frac{3}{8}}\,\sqrt{\frac{1}{5}}$

17. $\sqrt{14} \cdot \sqrt{14}$ **18.** $\sqrt{19}\,\sqrt{19}$ **19.** $\sqrt{25}\,\sqrt{3}$

20. $\sqrt{36}\,\sqrt{2}$ **21.** $\sqrt{2}\,\sqrt{x}$ **22.** $\sqrt{3}\,\sqrt{a}$

23. $\sqrt{7}\,\sqrt{2a}$ **24.** $\sqrt{5}\,\sqrt{7t}$ **25.** $\sqrt{5x}\,\sqrt{7}$

26. $\sqrt{3m}\,\sqrt{5n}$ **27.** $\sqrt{3a}\,\sqrt{2c}$ **28.** $\sqrt{3x}\,\sqrt{yz}$

Simplify by factoring. Assume that all variables represent nonnegative numbers.

29. $\sqrt{20}$ **30.** $\sqrt{28}$ **31.** $\sqrt{50}$

32. $\sqrt{45}$ **33.** $\sqrt{700}$ **34.** $\sqrt{300}$

35. $\sqrt{4t}$ **36.** $\sqrt{9z}$ **37.** $\sqrt{75a}$

38. $\sqrt{40m}$ **39.** $\sqrt{16a}$ **40.** $\sqrt{49b}$

41. $\sqrt{64y^2}$ **42.** $\sqrt{9x^2}$ **43.** $\sqrt{13x^2}$

44. $\sqrt{29t^2}$ **45.** $\sqrt{28t^2}$ **46.** $\sqrt{125a^2}$

In Exercises 47–52, evaluate $\sqrt{b^2 - 4ac}$ for the values of a, b, and c given.

47. $a = 2, b = 4, c = -3$

48. $a = 3, b = 2, c = -4$

49. $a = 1, b = 1, c = -12$

50. $a = 1, b = -3, c = -10$

51. $a = 3, b = -6, c = -4$

52. $a = 1, b = -8, c = -3$

Simplify. Assume that all variables represent nonnegative numbers.

53. $\sqrt{a^{14}}$ **54.** $\sqrt{t^{20}}$ **55.** $\sqrt{x^{16}}$

56. $\sqrt{x^{12}}$ **57.** $\sqrt{r^7}$ **58.** $\sqrt{t^5}$

59. $\sqrt{t^{19}}$ **60.** $\sqrt{p^{17}}$ **61.** $\sqrt{40a^3}$

62. $\sqrt{250y^3}$ **63.** $\sqrt{8a^5}$ **64.** $\sqrt{20b^7}$

65. $\sqrt{104p^{17}}$ **66.** $\sqrt{90m^{23}}$

Multiply and, if possible, simplify.

67. $\sqrt{7} \cdot \sqrt{14}$ **68.** $\sqrt{3}\,\sqrt{6}$

69. $\sqrt{3} \cdot \sqrt{27}$ **70.** $\sqrt{2} \cdot \sqrt{8}$

71. $\sqrt{3x}\,\sqrt{12y}$ **72.** $\sqrt{5x}\,\sqrt{20y}$

73. $\sqrt{17}\,\sqrt{17x}$ **74.** $\sqrt{11}\,\sqrt{11x}$

75. $\sqrt{10b}\,\sqrt{50b}$ **76.** $\sqrt{6a}\,\sqrt{18a}$

Aha! **77.** $\sqrt{8t} \cdot \sqrt{8t}$ **78.** $\sqrt{10a}\,\sqrt{10a}$

79. $\sqrt{ab}\,\sqrt{ac}$ **80.** $\sqrt{xy}\,\sqrt{xz}$

81. $\sqrt{3x^3}\,\sqrt{6x}$ **82.** $\sqrt{15m^7}\,\sqrt{5m}$

83. $\sqrt{x^2y^3}\,\sqrt{xy^4}$ **84.** $\sqrt{x^3y^2}\,\sqrt{xy}$

85. $\sqrt{10ab}\,\sqrt{50a^2b^7}$ **86.** $\sqrt{5xy^2}\,\sqrt{10x^2y^3}$

87. *Cable television.* The number of households h, in millions, served by cable television x years after 1980 can be approximated by the equation

$$h = 10.7 + 13.3\sqrt{x}.$$

Estimate the number of households served by cable television in 2000 and in 2010.

Source: Based on data from Nielsen Media Research

88. *Falling object.* The number of seconds t that it takes for an object to fall d meters when thrown down at a velocity of 9.5 meters per second can be estimated by

$$t = 0.45\sqrt{d + 4.6} - 1.$$

A rock is thrown from the top of Turkey Bluff, 90 m above the Gasconade River in Missouri, at a velocity of 9.5 meters per second. After how many seconds will the rock hit the water?

Speed of a skidding car. *The formula*

$$r = 2\sqrt{5L}$$

can be used to approximate the speed r, in miles per hour, of a car that has left a skid mark L feet long.

89. What was the speed of a car that left skid marks of 20 ft? of 150 ft?

90. What was the speed of a car that left skid marks of 30 ft? of 70 ft?

91. How would you convince someone that the following equation is not true?

$$\sqrt{x^2 - 49} = \sqrt{x^2} - \sqrt{49} = x - 7$$

↑ This is not true.

92. Explain why the rules for manipulating exponents are important when simplifying radical expressions.

SKILL MAINTENANCE

Simplify. [4.1]

93. $\dfrac{a^7b^3}{a^2b}$ **94.** $\dfrac{x^5y^9}{x^2y}$ **95.** $\dfrac{3x}{5y} \cdot \dfrac{2x}{7y}$

96. $\dfrac{7a}{3b} \cdot \dfrac{5a}{2b}$ **97.** $\dfrac{2r^3}{7t} \cdot \dfrac{rt}{rt}$ **98.** $\dfrac{5x^7}{11y} \cdot \dfrac{xy}{xy}$

SYNTHESIS

99. Explain why $\sqrt{16x^4} = 4x^2$, but $\sqrt{4x^{16}} \neq 2x^4$.

100. Simplify $\sqrt{49}$, $\sqrt{490}$, $\sqrt{4900}$, $\sqrt{49{,}000}$, and $\sqrt{490{,}000}$; then describe the pattern you see.

Simplify.

101. $\sqrt{0.01}$ **102.** $\sqrt{0.25}$

103. $\sqrt{0.0625}$ **104.** $\sqrt{0.000001}$

Use the proper symbol ($>$, $<$, or $=$) between each pair of values to make a true sentence. Do not use a calculator.

105. $4\sqrt{14} \square 15$

106. $\sqrt{450} \square 15\sqrt{2}$

107. $3\sqrt{11} \square 7\sqrt{2}$

108. $16 \square \sqrt{15}\sqrt{17}$

109. $8 \square \sqrt{15} + \sqrt{17}$

110. $5\sqrt{7} \square 4\sqrt{11}$

Multiply and then simplify by factoring.

111. $\sqrt{54(x+1)}\sqrt{6y(x+1)^2}$

112. $\sqrt{18(x-2)}\sqrt{20(x-2)^3}$

113. $\sqrt{x^9}\sqrt{2x}\sqrt{10x^5}$

114. $\sqrt{2^{109}}\sqrt{x^{306}}\sqrt{x^{11}}$

Fill in the blank.

115. $\sqrt{21x^9} \cdot$ ______ $= 7x^{14}\sqrt{6x^7}$

116. $\sqrt{35x^7} \cdot$ ______ $= 5x^5\sqrt{14x^3}$

Simplify.

117. $\sqrt{x^{16n}}$

118. $\sqrt{0.04x^{4n}}$

119. Simplify $\sqrt{y^n}$, when n is an odd whole number greater than or equal to 3.

8.3 Quotients Involving Square Roots

Dividing Radical Expressions • Rationalizing Denominators

Study Skills

Review Material on Your Own

Never hesitate to review earlier material in which you feel a lack of confidence. For example, if you feel unsure about how to multiply with fraction notation, be sure to review that material before studying any new material that involves multiplication of fractions. Doing (and checking) some practice problems from that section is also a good way to sharpen any skills that may not have been used for a while.

In this section, we divide radical expressions and simplify quotients containing radicals. As earlier, we assume that no radicands were formed by squaring negative quantities.

Dividing Radical Expressions

To see how to divide with radical notation, consider the following:

$$\frac{\sqrt{25}}{\sqrt{16}} = \frac{5}{4} \text{ since } \sqrt{25} = 5 \text{ and } \sqrt{16} = 4;$$

$$\sqrt{\frac{25}{16}} = \frac{5}{4} \text{ since } \frac{5}{4} \cdot \frac{5}{4} = \frac{25}{16}.$$

Both results are the same, so we see that $\dfrac{\sqrt{25}}{\sqrt{16}} = \sqrt{\dfrac{25}{16}}$.

The Quotient Rule for Square Roots

For any real numbers $\sqrt{A}$ and $\sqrt{B}$ with $B \neq 0$,

$$\frac{\sqrt{A}}{\sqrt{B}} = \sqrt{\frac{A}{B}}.$$

(To divide two square roots, divide the radicands and take the square root.)

EXAMPLE 1 Divide and simplify: **(a)** $\frac{\sqrt{27}}{\sqrt{3}}$; **(b)** $\frac{\sqrt{8a^7}}{\sqrt{2a}}$.

Solution

a) $\frac{\sqrt{27}}{\sqrt{3}} = \sqrt{\frac{27}{3}}$ We can now simplify the radicand: $\frac{27}{3} = 9$.

$= \sqrt{9} = 3$

b) $\frac{\sqrt{8a^7}}{\sqrt{2a}} = \sqrt{\frac{8a^7}{2a}}$ We do this because $\frac{8a^7}{2a}$ can be simplified.

$= \sqrt{4a^6} = 2a^3$ We assume $a > 0$.

The quotient rule for square roots can also be read from right to left:

$$\sqrt{\frac{A}{B}} = \frac{\sqrt{A}}{\sqrt{B}}.$$

We generally select the form that makes simplification easier.

EXAMPLE 2 Simplify by taking square roots in the numerator and the denominator separately.

a) $\sqrt{\frac{25}{9}}$ **b)** $\sqrt{\frac{1}{16}}$ **c)** $\sqrt{\frac{49}{t^2}}$

Solution

a) $\sqrt{\frac{25}{9}} = \frac{\sqrt{25}}{\sqrt{9}} = \frac{5}{3}$ Taking the square root of the numerator and the square root of the denominator. This is sometimes done mentally, in one step.

b) $\sqrt{\frac{1}{16}} = \frac{\sqrt{1}}{\sqrt{16}} = \frac{1}{4}$ Taking the square root of the numerator and the square root of the denominator

c) $\sqrt{\frac{49}{t^2}} = \frac{\sqrt{49}}{\sqrt{t^2}} = \frac{7}{t}$ We assume $t > 0$.

Sometimes a rational expression can be simplified to one that has a perfect-square numerator and/or a perfect-square denominator.

EXAMPLE 3 Simplify: **(a)** $\sqrt{\frac{14}{50}}$; **(b)** $\sqrt{\frac{48x^3}{3x^7}}$.

Solution

a) $\sqrt{\frac{14}{50}} = \sqrt{\frac{7 \cdot 2}{25 \cdot 2}}$

$= \sqrt{\frac{7 \cdot \cancel{2}}{25 \cdot \cancel{2}}}$ Removing a factor equal to 1: $\frac{2}{2} = 1$

$= \frac{\sqrt{7}}{\sqrt{25}} = \frac{\sqrt{7}}{5}$

b) $\sqrt{\dfrac{48x^3}{3x^7}} = \sqrt{\dfrac{16 \cdot 3x^3}{x^4 \cdot 3x^3}}$ Removing a factor equal to 1: $\dfrac{3x^3}{3x^3} = 1$

$= \dfrac{\sqrt{16}}{\sqrt{x^4}} = \dfrac{4}{x^2}$ We assume $x \neq 0$.

Rationalizing Denominators

A procedure for finding an equivalent expression without a radical in the denominator is sometimes useful. Before calculators, this was done to make long division involving decimal approximations easier to perform. The procedure, called **rationalizing the denominator**, relies on multiplying by a carefully selected form of 1 and the fact that $\sqrt{x} \cdot \sqrt{x} = x$.

EXAMPLE 4 Rationalize each denominator: **(a)** $\dfrac{8}{\sqrt{7}}$; **(b)** $\sqrt{\dfrac{5}{a}}$.

Solution

a) By writing 1 as $\sqrt{7}/\sqrt{7}$, we can find an expression that is equivalent to $8/\sqrt{7}$ without a radical in the denominator:

$\dfrac{8}{\sqrt{7}} = \dfrac{8}{\sqrt{7}} \cdot \dfrac{\sqrt{7}}{\sqrt{7}}$ Multiplying by 1, using the denominator, $\sqrt{7}$, to write 1

$= \dfrac{8\sqrt{7}}{7}$. $\sqrt{7} \cdot \sqrt{7} = 7$

b) $\sqrt{\dfrac{5}{a}} = \dfrac{\sqrt{5}}{\sqrt{a}}$ The square root of a quotient is the quotient of the square roots.

$= \dfrac{\sqrt{5}}{\sqrt{a}} \cdot \dfrac{\sqrt{a}}{\sqrt{a}}$ Multiplying by 1, using the denominator, $\sqrt{a}$, to write 1

$= \dfrac{\sqrt{5a}}{a}$ $\sqrt{a} \cdot \sqrt{a} = a$. We assume $a > 0$.

It is usually easiest to rationalize a denominator after the expression has been simplified.

EXAMPLE 5 Rationalize each denominator.

a) $\sqrt{\dfrac{5}{18}}$

b) $\dfrac{\sqrt{7a}}{\sqrt{20}}$

Student Notes

Be careful when writing radical expressions. There is a *big* difference between the expressions $\frac{\sqrt{10}}{6}$ and $\sqrt{\frac{10}{6}}$.

Solution

a) $\sqrt{\frac{5}{18}} = \frac{\sqrt{5}}{\sqrt{18}}$ The square root of a quotient is the quotient of the square roots.

$= \frac{\sqrt{5}}{\sqrt{9}\sqrt{2}}$ Simplifying the denominator. Note that 9 is a perfect square.

$= \frac{\sqrt{5}}{3\sqrt{2}}$

$= \frac{\sqrt{5}}{3\sqrt{2}} \cdot \frac{\sqrt{2}}{\sqrt{2}}$ Multiplying by 1, using $\sqrt{2}$ to write 1

$= \frac{\sqrt{10}}{3 \cdot 2} = \frac{\sqrt{10}}{6}$

b) $\frac{\sqrt{7a}}{\sqrt{20}} = \frac{\sqrt{7a}}{\sqrt{4}\sqrt{5}}$

$= \frac{\sqrt{7a}}{2\sqrt{5}}$ } Simplifying the denominator. Note that 4 is a perfect square.

$= \frac{\sqrt{7a}}{2\sqrt{5}} \cdot \frac{\sqrt{5}}{\sqrt{5}}$ Multiplying by 1

$= \frac{\sqrt{35a}}{2 \cdot 5}$

$= \frac{\sqrt{35a}}{10}$

Caution! Our solutions in Example 5 cannot be simplified any further. A common mistake is to remove a factor of 1 that does not exist. For example, $\frac{\sqrt{10}}{6}$ *cannot* be simplified to $\frac{\sqrt{5}}{3}$ because $\sqrt{10}$ and 6 do not share a common factor.

8.3 Exercise Set

FOR EXTRA HELP

Student's Solutions Manual | Digital Video Tutor CD 5 Videotape 15 | AW Math Tutor Center | MathXL Tutorials on CD | MathXL | MyMathLab

Concept Reinforcement *Classify each statement as either true or false.*

1. To divide one square root by another, we can divide one radicand by the other and then take the square root.

2. The square root of a quotient can be found by dividing the square root of the numerator by the square root of the denominator.

3. Rationalizing the denominator of a fraction relies on squaring both the numerator and the denominator.

4. It is usually easiest to rationalize a denominator before the expression has been simplified.

Simplify. Assume that all variables represent positive numbers.

5. $\dfrac{\sqrt{20}}{\sqrt{5}}$ **6.** $\dfrac{\sqrt{12}}{\sqrt{3}}$ **7.** $\dfrac{\sqrt{75}}{\sqrt{3}}$

8. $\dfrac{\sqrt{72}}{\sqrt{2}}$ **9.** $\dfrac{\sqrt{35}}{\sqrt{5}}$ **10.** $\dfrac{\sqrt{18}}{\sqrt{3}}$

11. $\dfrac{\sqrt{3}}{\sqrt{75}}$ **12.** $\dfrac{\sqrt{5}}{\sqrt{45}}$ **13.** $\dfrac{\sqrt{18}}{\sqrt{32}}$

14. $\dfrac{\sqrt{12}}{\sqrt{75}}$ **15.** $\dfrac{\sqrt{8x}}{\sqrt{2x}}$ **16.** $\dfrac{\sqrt{18b}}{\sqrt{2b}}$

17. $\dfrac{\sqrt{63y^3}}{\sqrt{7y}}$ **18.** $\dfrac{\sqrt{48x^3}}{\sqrt{3x}}$ **19.** $\dfrac{\sqrt{27x^5}}{\sqrt{3x}}$

20. $\dfrac{\sqrt{20a^8}}{\sqrt{5a^2}}$ **21.** $\dfrac{\sqrt{21a^9}}{\sqrt{7a^3}}$ **22.** $\dfrac{\sqrt{35t^{11}}}{\sqrt{5t^5}}$

23. $\sqrt{\dfrac{36}{25}}$ **24.** $\sqrt{\dfrac{9}{49}}$ **25.** $\sqrt{\dfrac{49}{16}}$

26. $\sqrt{\dfrac{100}{49}}$ **27.** $-\sqrt{\dfrac{25}{81}}$ **28.** $-\sqrt{\dfrac{25}{64}}$

29. $\sqrt{\dfrac{2a^5}{50a}}$ **30.** $\sqrt{\dfrac{7a^5}{28a}}$ **31.** $\sqrt{\dfrac{6x^7}{32x}}$

32. $\sqrt{\dfrac{4x^3}{50x}}$ **33.** $\sqrt{\dfrac{21t^9}{28t^3}}$ **34.** $\sqrt{\dfrac{10t^9}{18t^5}}$

Form an equivalent expression by rationalizing each denominator.

35. $\dfrac{5}{\sqrt{3}}$ **36.** $\dfrac{7}{\sqrt{2}}$ **37.** $\dfrac{\sqrt{3}}{\sqrt{7}}$

38. $\dfrac{\sqrt{3}}{\sqrt{11}}$ **39.** $\dfrac{\sqrt{4}}{\sqrt{27}}$ **40.** $\dfrac{\sqrt{9}}{\sqrt{8}}$

41. $\dfrac{\sqrt{7}}{\sqrt{3}}$ **42.** $\dfrac{\sqrt{5}}{\sqrt{7}}$ **43.** $\dfrac{\sqrt{3}}{\sqrt{50}}$

44. $\dfrac{\sqrt{5}}{\sqrt{18}}$ **45.** $\dfrac{\sqrt{2a}}{\sqrt{45}}$ **46.** $\dfrac{\sqrt{3a}}{\sqrt{32}}$

47. $\sqrt{\dfrac{12}{5}}$ **48.** $\sqrt{\dfrac{8}{3}}$ **49.** $\sqrt{\dfrac{5}{z}}$

50. $\sqrt{\dfrac{3}{x}}$ **51.** $\sqrt{\dfrac{t}{32}}$ **52.** $\sqrt{\dfrac{a}{12}}$

53. $\sqrt{\dfrac{x}{90}}$ **54.** $\sqrt{\dfrac{y}{40}}$ Aha! **55.** $\sqrt{\dfrac{3a}{25}}$

56. $\sqrt{\dfrac{7t}{16}}$ **57.** $\sqrt{\dfrac{5x^3}{12x}}$ **58.** $\sqrt{\dfrac{7t^3}{32t}}$

Depreciation of a vehicle. *The resale value of certain cars and trucks that originally sold for \$18,000 can be estimated using the formula*

$$V = \frac{18{,}500}{\sqrt{t + 1.0565}},$$

where V is the value of the vehicle, in dollars, when it is t years old.

59. Estimate the vehicle's value when it is 2 yr old.

60. Estimate the vehicle's value when it is 10 yr old.

61. Estimate the vehicle's value when it is 7 yr old.

62. Estimate the vehicle's value when it is 1 yr old.

Period of a swinging pendulum. *The period T of a pendulum is the time it takes to move from one side to the other and back. A formula for the period is*

$$T = 2\pi\sqrt{\frac{L}{32}},$$

where T is in seconds and L is in feet. Use 3.14 for π.

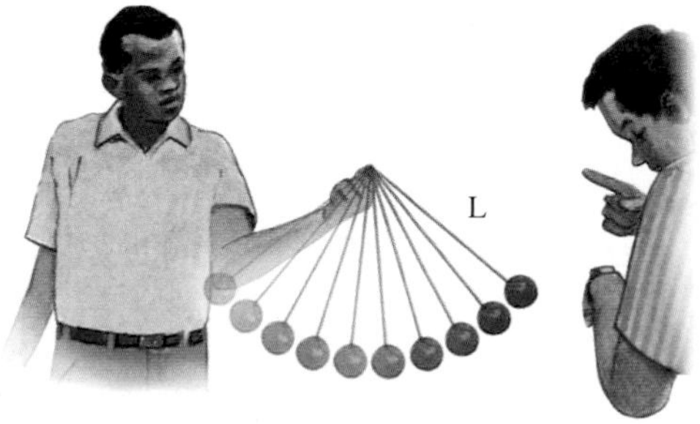

63. Find the periods of pendulums of lengths 32 ft and 50 ft.

64. Find the periods of pendulums of lengths 8 ft and 2 ft.

65. The pendulum of a mantle clock is $2/\pi^2$ ft long. How long does it take to swing from one side to the other and back?

66. The pendulum of a grandfather clock is $98/\pi^2$ ft long. How long does it take to swing from one side to the other and back?

67. Ingrid is swinging at the bottom of a 72-ft long bungee cord. How long does it take her to complete one swing back and forth? (*Hint*: $\sqrt{2.5} \approx 1.6$.)

68. Don is swinging back and forth on an 18-ft long rope swing near the Green River Reservoir. How long does it take him to complete one swing back and forth?

69. Why is it important to know how to multiply radical expressions before learning how to divide them?

70. Describe a method that could be used to rationalize the *numerator* of a radical expression.

SKILL MAINTENANCE

Simplify. [4.2]

71. $5x + 9 + 7x + 4$

72. $7a + 2 + 3a + 4$

73. $2a^3 - a^2 - 3a^3 - 7a^2$

74. $4t - 3t^2 - t - 8t^2$

Multiply. [4.4]

75. $9x(2x - 7)$

76. $2x(3x - 5)$

77. $(3 + 4x)(2 + 5x)$

78. $(7 - 3x)(2 - x)$

SYNTHESIS

79. When calculating approximations by hand using long division, what makes it easier to compute $\sqrt{2}/2$ than $1/\sqrt{2}$? (This is why rationalizing denominators was once so important.)

80. Is it always best to rewrite an expression of the form $\sqrt{a}/\sqrt{b}$ as $\sqrt{a/b}$ before simplifying? Why or why not?

Rationalize each denominator and, if possible, simplify to form an equivalent expression.

81. $\sqrt{\dfrac{7}{1000}}$

82. $\sqrt{\dfrac{3}{800}}$

83. $\sqrt{\dfrac{3x^2}{8x^7y^3}}$

84. $\sqrt{\dfrac{3x^2y}{a^2x^5}}$

85. $\sqrt{\dfrac{2a}{5b^3c^9}}$

86. $\sqrt{\dfrac{1}{5zw^2}}$

Aha! **87.** $\dfrac{3}{\sqrt{\sqrt{7}}}$

88. $\dfrac{2}{\sqrt{\sqrt{5}}}$

Simplify. Assume that $0 < x \le y$ *and* $0 < z \le 1$.

89. $\sqrt{\dfrac{1}{x^2} - \dfrac{2}{xy} + \dfrac{1}{y^2}}$

90. $\sqrt{2 - \dfrac{4}{z^2} + \dfrac{2}{z^4}}$

91. Solve: $\sqrt{\dfrac{2x - 3}{8}} = \dfrac{5}{2}$.

8.4 Radical Expressions with Several Terms

Adding and Subtracting Radical Expressions • More with Multiplication • More with Rationalizing Denominators

We now consider addition and subtraction of radical expressions as well as some new types of multiplication and simplification.

Adding and Subtracting Radical Expressions

The sum of a rational number and an irrational number, like $5 + \sqrt{2}$, *cannot* be simplified. However, the sum of **like radicals**—that is, radical expressions that have the same radical factor—*can* be simplified.

EXAMPLE 1 Add: $3\sqrt{5} + 4\sqrt{5}$.

Solution Recall that to simplify an expression like $3x + 4x$, we use the distributive law, as follows:

$3x + 4x = (3 + 4)x = 7x$. The middle step is usually performed mentally.

In this example, x is replaced with $\sqrt{5}$:

$3\sqrt{5} + 4\sqrt{5} = (3 + 4)\sqrt{5}$ Using the distributive law to factor out $\sqrt{5}$

$= 7\sqrt{5}$. $3\sqrt{5}$ and $4\sqrt{5}$ are like radicals.

To simplify in this manner, the radical factors must be the same.

EXAMPLE 2 Simplify.

a) $9\sqrt{17} - 3\sqrt{17}$

b) $7\sqrt{x} + \sqrt{x}$

c) $5\sqrt{2} - \sqrt{18}$

d) $\sqrt{5} + \sqrt{20} + \sqrt{7}$

Solution

a) $9\sqrt{17} - 3\sqrt{17} = (9 - 3)\sqrt{17}$ Using the distributive law. Try to do this mentally.

$= 6\sqrt{17}$

b) $7\sqrt{x} + \sqrt{x} = (7 + 1)\sqrt{x}$ Using the distributive law. Try to do this mentally.

$= 8\sqrt{x}$

c) $5\sqrt{2} - \sqrt{18} = 5\sqrt{2} - \sqrt{9 \cdot 2}$
$= 5\sqrt{2} - \sqrt{9}\sqrt{2}$ } Simplifying $\sqrt{18}$

$= 5\sqrt{2} - 3\sqrt{2}$ We now have like radicals.

$= 2\sqrt{2}$ Using the distributive law mentally: $5\sqrt{2} - 3\sqrt{2} = (5 - 3)\sqrt{2}$

d) $\sqrt{5} + \sqrt{20} + \sqrt{7} = \sqrt{5} + \sqrt{4}\sqrt{5} + \sqrt{7}$ Simplifying $\sqrt{20}$

$= \sqrt{5} + 2\sqrt{5} + \sqrt{7}$ We now have 2 like radicals.

$= 3\sqrt{5} + \sqrt{7}$ Adding like radicals; $3\sqrt{5} + \sqrt{7}$ cannot be simplified.

Study Skills

Studying Together by Phone

Working with a classmate over the telephone can be a very effective way to receive or give help. The fact that you cannot point to figures on paper forces you to verbalize the mathematics and the act of speaking mathematics will improve your understanding of the material. In some cases, it may be more effective to study with a classmate over the phone than in person.

Caution! It is *not true* that the sum of two square roots is the square root of the sum: $\sqrt{A} + \sqrt{B} \neq \sqrt{A + B}$. For example, $\sqrt{9} + \sqrt{16} \neq \sqrt{9 + 16}$ since $3 + 4 \neq 5$.

More with Multiplication

Radical expressions with more than one term are multiplied in much the same way that polynomials with more than one term are multiplied.

EXAMPLE 3 Multiply.

a) $\sqrt{2}(\sqrt{3} + \sqrt{5})$

b) $(4 + \sqrt{7})(2 + \sqrt{7})$

c) $(2 - \sqrt{5})(2 + \sqrt{5})$

d) $(2 + \sqrt{3})(5 - 4\sqrt{3})$

Solution

a) $\sqrt{2}(\sqrt{3} + \sqrt{5}) = \sqrt{2}\,\sqrt{3} + \sqrt{2}\,\sqrt{5}$ Using the distributive law

$= \sqrt{6} + \sqrt{10}$ Using the product rule for square roots

b) $(4 + \sqrt{7})(2 + \sqrt{7}) = 4 \cdot 2 + 4 \cdot \sqrt{7} + \sqrt{7} \cdot 2 + \sqrt{7} \cdot \sqrt{7}$ Using FOIL

$= 8 + 4\sqrt{7} + 2\sqrt{7} + 7$

$= 15 + 6\sqrt{7}$ Combining like terms

c) Note that $(2 - \sqrt{5})(2 + \sqrt{5})$ is of the form $(A - B)(A + B)$:

$(2 - \sqrt{5})(2 + \sqrt{5}) = 2 \cdot 2 + 2 \cdot \sqrt{5} - \sqrt{5} \cdot 2 - \sqrt{5} \cdot \sqrt{5}$

$= 4 + 2\sqrt{5} - 2\sqrt{5} - 5$ The middle terms are opposites.

$= 4 - 5$ We can use $(A - B)(A + B) = A^2 - B^2$.

$= -1$

d) $(2 + \sqrt{3})(5 - 4\sqrt{3}) = 2 \cdot 5 - 2 \cdot 4\sqrt{3} + \sqrt{3} \cdot 5 - \sqrt{3} \cdot 4\sqrt{3}$

$= 10 - 8\sqrt{3} + 5\sqrt{3} - 4 \cdot 3$ $2 \cdot 5 = 10$; $2 \cdot 4 = 8$; and $\sqrt{3} \cdot \sqrt{3} = 3$

$= 10 - 3\sqrt{3} - 12$ Adding like radicals

$= -2 - 3\sqrt{3}$

More with Rationalizing Denominators

Note in Example 3(c) that the result has no radicals. This will happen whenever expressions like $\sqrt{a} + \sqrt{b}$ and $\sqrt{a} - \sqrt{b}$ are multiplied:

$$(\sqrt{a} + \sqrt{b})(\sqrt{a} - \sqrt{b}) = (\sqrt{a})^2 - (\sqrt{b})^2 = a - b.$$

Expressions such as $\sqrt{3} - \sqrt{5}$ and $\sqrt{3} + \sqrt{5}$ are said to be **conjugates** of each other. So too are expressions like $2 + \sqrt{7}$ and $2 - \sqrt{7}$. Once the conjugate of a denominator has been found, it can be used to rationalize the denominator.

EXAMPLE 4 Rationalize each denominator and, if possible, simplify.

a) $\dfrac{3}{2+\sqrt{5}}$

b) $\dfrac{2}{\sqrt{7}-\sqrt{3}}$

Solution

a) We multiply by a form of 1, using the conjugate of $2+\sqrt{5}$, which is $2-\sqrt{5}$, as the numerator and the denominator:

$$\frac{3}{2+\sqrt{5}} = \frac{3}{2+\sqrt{5}} \cdot \frac{2-\sqrt{5}}{2-\sqrt{5}} \qquad \text{Multiplying by 1}$$

$$= \frac{3(2-\sqrt{5})}{(2+\sqrt{5})(2-\sqrt{5})}$$

$$= \frac{3(2-\sqrt{5})}{2^2-(\sqrt{5})^2} \qquad \text{Using } (A+B)(A-B) = A^2 - B^2$$

$$= \frac{3(2-\sqrt{5})}{-1} \qquad \text{Simplifying the denominator. See Example 3(c): } 4-5=-1.$$

$$= \frac{6-3\sqrt{5}}{-1}$$

$$= -6+3\sqrt{5}. \qquad \text{Dividing } \textit{both} \text{ terms in the numerator by } -1$$

b) $$\frac{2}{\sqrt{7}-\sqrt{3}} = \frac{2}{\sqrt{7}-\sqrt{3}} \cdot \frac{\sqrt{7}+\sqrt{3}}{\sqrt{7}+\sqrt{3}} \qquad \text{Multiplying by 1, using } \sqrt{7}+\sqrt{3}, \text{ the conjugate of } \sqrt{7}-\sqrt{3}$$

$$= \frac{2(\sqrt{7}+\sqrt{3})}{(\sqrt{7}-\sqrt{3})(\sqrt{7}+\sqrt{3})}$$

$$= \frac{2(\sqrt{7}+\sqrt{3})}{(\sqrt{7})^2-(\sqrt{3})^2} \qquad \text{Using } (A-B)(A+B) = A^2 - B^2$$

$$= \frac{2(\sqrt{7}+\sqrt{3})}{7-3} \qquad \text{The denominator is free of radicals.}$$

$$= \frac{2(\sqrt{7}+\sqrt{3})}{4} \qquad \text{Since 2 is a common factor of both the numerator and the denominator, we simplify.}$$

$$\left.\begin{aligned} &= \frac{\cancel{2}(\sqrt{7}+\sqrt{3})}{\cancel{2}\cdot 2} \\ &= \frac{\sqrt{7}+\sqrt{3}}{2} \end{aligned}\right\} \qquad \text{Factoring and removing a factor equal to 1: } \frac{2}{2} = 1$$

---

technology connection

Parentheses are needed to specify the radicand whenever the radicand has more than one term. For example, on most graphing calculators, we would enter the expression $\sqrt{7-2}+8$ as √‾ (7 − 2) + 8. This will give us a different result from √‾ 7 − 2 + 8 or √‾ (7 − 2 + 8.

Use a graphing calculator to approximate each of the following. Remember to use parentheses to enclose numerators and denominators with more than one term.

1. $\dfrac{-3+\sqrt{8}}{2}$
2. $\dfrac{\sqrt{2}+\sqrt{5}}{3}$
3. $\sqrt{\sqrt{7}+5}$
4. Use a graphing calculator to check Examples 4(a) and 4(b).

8.4 Exercise Set

FOR EXTRA HELP

Student's Solutions Manual | Digital Video Tutor CD 5 Videotape 16 | AW Math Tutor Center | MathXL Tutorials on CD | MathXL | MyMathLab

Concept Reinforcement *In each of Exercises 1–4, match the item with the most appropriate choice from the column on the right.*

1. ____ The conjugate of $\sqrt{7}+\sqrt{5}$ — a) $\sqrt{7}+\sqrt{5}$
2. ____ An example of like radicals — b) $\sqrt{7}-\sqrt{5}$
3. ____ The product of $\sqrt{5}-\sqrt{7}$ and its conjugate — c) $3\sqrt{7}$ and $-5\sqrt{7}$
4. ____ The conjugate of $\sqrt{7}-\sqrt{5}$ — d) -2

Add or subtract. Simplify by combining like radical terms, if possible.

5. $2\sqrt{7}+4\sqrt{7}$ **6.** $4\sqrt{3}+8\sqrt{3}$

7. $9\sqrt{5}-6\sqrt{5}$ **8.** $7\sqrt{2}-5\sqrt{2}$

9. $6\sqrt{x}+7\sqrt{x}$ **10.** $9\sqrt{y}+3\sqrt{y}$

11. $9\sqrt{x}-11\sqrt{x}$ **12.** $6\sqrt{a}-12\sqrt{a}$

13. $5\sqrt{2a}+3\sqrt{2a}$ **14.** $5\sqrt{6x}+2\sqrt{6x}$

15. $9\sqrt{10y}-\sqrt{10y}$ **16.** $12\sqrt{14y}-\sqrt{14y}$

17. $6\sqrt{7}+2\sqrt{7}+4\sqrt{7}$ **18.** $2\sqrt{5}+7\sqrt{5}+5\sqrt{5}$

19. $5\sqrt{2}-9\sqrt{2}+8\sqrt{2}$ **20.** $3\sqrt{6}-7\sqrt{6}+2\sqrt{6}$

21. $5\sqrt{3}+\sqrt{8}$ **22.** $2\sqrt{5}+\sqrt{45}$

23. $\sqrt{x}-\sqrt{9x}$ **24.** $\sqrt{25a}-\sqrt{a}$

25. $2\sqrt{3}-4\sqrt{75}$ **26.** $7\sqrt{50}-3\sqrt{2}$

27. $6\sqrt{18}+5\sqrt{8}$ **28.** $3\sqrt{12}+2\sqrt{300}$

29. $\sqrt{72}+\sqrt{98}$ **30.** $\sqrt{45}+\sqrt{80}$

Aha! **31.** $9\sqrt{8}+\sqrt{72}-9\sqrt{8}$ **32.** $4\sqrt{12}+\sqrt{27}-\sqrt{12}$

33. $7\sqrt{12}-2\sqrt{27}+\sqrt{75}$

34. $5\sqrt{18}-2\sqrt{32}-\sqrt{50}$

35. $\sqrt{9x}+\sqrt{49x}-9\sqrt{x}$

36. $\sqrt{16a}-4\sqrt{a}+\sqrt{25a}$

Multiply.

37. $\sqrt{7}(\sqrt{5}+\sqrt{2})$ **38.** $\sqrt{5}(\sqrt{2}+\sqrt{11})$

39. $\sqrt{5}(\sqrt{6}-\sqrt{10})$ **40.** $\sqrt{6}(\sqrt{15}-\sqrt{7})$

41. $(3+\sqrt{2})(4+\sqrt{2})$ **42.** $(5+\sqrt{11})(3+\sqrt{11})$

43. $(\sqrt{7}-2)(\sqrt{7}-5)$ **44.** $(\sqrt{10}+4)(\sqrt{10}-7)$

45. $(\sqrt{5}+4)(\sqrt{5}-4)$ **46.** $(1+\sqrt{5})(1-\sqrt{5})$

47. $(\sqrt{6}-\sqrt{3})(\sqrt{6}+\sqrt{3})$

48. $(\sqrt{2}+\sqrt{6})(\sqrt{2}-\sqrt{6})$

49. $(2+3\sqrt{2})(3-\sqrt{2})$ **50.** $(8-\sqrt{7})(3+2\sqrt{7})$

51. $(7+\sqrt{3})^2$ **52.** $(2+\sqrt{5})^2$

53. $(1-2\sqrt{3})^2$ **54.** $(6-3\sqrt{5})^2$

55. $(\sqrt{x}-\sqrt{10})^2$ **56.** $(\sqrt{a}-\sqrt{6})^2$

Rationalize each denominator and, if possible, simplify to form an equivalent expression.

57. $\dfrac{3}{2+\sqrt{5}}$ **58.** $\dfrac{2}{3+\sqrt{5}}$

59. $\dfrac{6}{2-\sqrt{7}}$ **60.** $\dfrac{3}{4-\sqrt{2}}$

61. $\dfrac{2}{\sqrt{7}+5}$ **62.** $\dfrac{6}{\sqrt{10}+3}$

63. $\dfrac{\sqrt{6}}{\sqrt{6}-5}$ **64.** $\dfrac{\sqrt{10}}{\sqrt{10}-7}$

65. $\dfrac{\sqrt{7}}{\sqrt{7}-\sqrt{3}}$ **66.** $\dfrac{\sqrt{7}}{\sqrt{7}-\sqrt{5}}$

67. $\dfrac{\sqrt{3}}{\sqrt{5}-\sqrt{3}}$ **68.** $\dfrac{\sqrt{6}}{\sqrt{7}+\sqrt{6}}$

69. $\dfrac{2}{\sqrt{7}+\sqrt{2}}$ **70.** $\dfrac{6}{\sqrt{5}-\sqrt{3}}$

71. $\dfrac{\sqrt{6}-\sqrt{x}}{\sqrt{6}+\sqrt{x}}$ **72.** $\dfrac{\sqrt{10}-\sqrt{x}}{\sqrt{10}+\sqrt{x}}$

73. What is the purpose of having the signs differ within each pair of conjugates?

74. Describe a method that could be used to rationalize a numerator that is the sum of two radical expressions.

SKILL MAINTENANCE

Solve.

75. $3x + 5 + 2(x - 3) = 4 - 6x$ [2.2]

76. $3(x - 4) - 2 = 8(2x + 3)$ [2.2]

77. $x^2 - 5x = 6$ [5.6]

78. $x^2 + 10 = 7x$ [5.6]

79. *Mixing juice.* Jolly Juice is 3% real fruit juice, and Real Squeeze is 6% real fruit juice. How many liters of each should be used in order to make an 8-L mixture that is 5.4% real fruit juice? [7.4]

80. *Commuting costs.* Thelma says it costs at least \$7.50 every time she drives to work: \$3 in tolls and \$1.50 per hour for parking. For how long does Thelma park? [2.7]

SYNTHESIS

81. Is it possible to square the sum of two radical expressions without adding like radicals? Why or why not?

82. Why must you know how to add and subtract radical expressions before you can rationalize denominators with two terms?

Add or subtract and, if possible, simplify.

83. $\sqrt{\frac{25}{x}} + \frac{\sqrt{x}}{2x} - \frac{5}{\sqrt{2}}$

84. $5\sqrt{\frac{1}{2}} + \frac{7}{2}\sqrt{18} - 4\sqrt{98}$

85. $\sqrt{8x^6y^3} - x\sqrt{2y^7} - \frac{x}{3}\sqrt{18x^2y^9}$

86. $a\sqrt{a^{17}b^9} - b\sqrt{a^{13}b^{11}} + a\sqrt{a^9b^{15}}$

87. $7x\sqrt{12xy^2} - 9y\sqrt{27x^3} + 5\sqrt{300x^3y^2}$

88. For which pairs of nonnegative numbers a and b does $\sqrt{a} + \sqrt{b} = \sqrt{a + b}$?

89. Three students were asked to simplify $\sqrt{10} + \sqrt{50}$. Their answers were $\sqrt{10}(1 + \sqrt{5})$, $\sqrt{10} + 5\sqrt{2}$, and $\sqrt{2}(5 + \sqrt{5})$. Which answer(s), if any, is correct?

8.5 Radical Equations

Solving Radical Equations • Problem Solving and Applications

CONNECTING THE CONCEPTS

In Sections 8.1–8.4, we learned how to simplify and manipulate radical expressions. We performed this work to find *equivalent expressions.*

Now that we can manipulate radical notation, it is time to learn how to solve a new type of equation. As in our earlier work with equations, finding *equivalent equations* will be part of our strategy. What is different, however, is that now we will use a step that does not always produce equivalent equations. Checking solutions will therefore be more important than ever.

Study Skills

Beginning to Study for the Final Exam

It is never too soon to begin to study for the final examination. Take a few minutes each week to review the highlighted information, such as formulas, properties, and procedures. Make special use of the Study Summaries, Chapter Tests, and Cumulative Reviews, as well as the supplements such as Interact Math Tutorial and MathXL. The Cumulative Reviews at the ends of Chapters 3 and 6 and the Final Examination at the end of Chapter 9 can be used for practice.

An equation in which a variable appears in a radicand is called a **radical equation**. The following are examples:

$$\sqrt{2x} - 4 = 7, \quad 2\sqrt{x+2} = \sqrt{x+10}, \quad \text{and} \quad 3 + \sqrt{27 - 3x} = x.$$

We now learn how to solve such equations and use them in problem solving.

Solving Radical Equations

An equation with a square root can be rewritten without the radical by using *the principle of squaring.*

The Principle of Squaring

If $a = b$, then $a^2 = b^2$.

The principle of squaring does *not* say that if $a^2 = b^2$, then $a = b$. Indeed, if a is replaced with -5 and b with 5, then $a^2 = b^2$ is true (since $(-5)^2 = 5^2$), but the equation $a = b$ is false (since $-5 \neq 5$). Thus, although the principle of squaring *can* lead us to the solutions of a radical equation, it *may* lead us to numbers that are not solutions.

EXAMPLE 1 Solve: **(a)** $\sqrt{x} + 3 = 7$; **(b)** $\sqrt{2x} = -5$.

Solution

a) Our plan is to isolate the radical term on one side of the equation and then use the principle of squaring:

$$\sqrt{x} + 3 = 7$$

$$\sqrt{x} = 4 \qquad \text{Subtracting 3 to get the radical alone on one side}$$

$$(\sqrt{x})^2 = 4^2 \qquad \text{Squaring both sides (using the principle of squaring)}$$

$$x = 16$$

Check:

$$\begin{array}{r|l} \sqrt{x} + 3 & = 7 \\ \hline \sqrt{16} + 3 & 7 \\ 4 + 3 & \\ 7 & \stackrel{?}{=} 7 \quad \text{TRUE} \end{array}$$

The solution is 16.

b)

$$\sqrt{2x} = -5$$

$$(\sqrt{2x})^2 = (-5)^2 \qquad \text{Squaring both sides (using the principle of squaring)}$$

$$\left.\begin{aligned} 2x &= 25 \\ x &= \tfrac{25}{2} \end{aligned}\right\} \qquad \text{Solving for } x$$

Check:

$$\begin{array}{c|c} \sqrt{2x} & -5 \\ \hline \sqrt{2\cdot\frac{25}{2}} & -5 \\ \sqrt{25} & \end{array}$$

$$5 \stackrel{?}{=} -5 \quad \text{FALSE}$$

There are no solutions. You might have suspected this from the start since no number has a principal square root that is negative.

> *Caution!* When the principle of squaring is used to solve an equation, all possible solutions *must* be checked in the original equation!

EXAMPLE 2 Solve: $3\sqrt{x} = \sqrt{x+32}$.

Solution We have

$$3\sqrt{x} = \sqrt{x+32}$$

$$(3\sqrt{x})^2 = (\sqrt{x+32})^2 \qquad \text{Squaring both sides (using the principle of squaring)}$$

$$3^2(\sqrt{x})^2 = x + 32 \qquad \text{Squaring the product on the left; simplifying on the right}$$

$$9x = x + 32 \qquad \text{Simplifying on the left}$$

$$\left.\begin{aligned} 8x &= 32 \\ x &= 4. \end{aligned}\right\} \qquad \text{Solving for } x$$

Check:

$$\begin{array}{c|c} 3\sqrt{x} & \sqrt{x+32} \\ \hline 3\sqrt{4} & \sqrt{4+32} \\ 3\cdot 2 & \sqrt{36} \end{array}$$

$$6 \stackrel{?}{=} 6 \quad \text{TRUE}$$

The number 4 checks. The solution is 4.

We have been using the following strategy.

To Solve a Radical Equation

1. Isolate a radical term.
2. Use the principle of squaring (square both sides).
3. Solve the new equation.
4. Check all possible solutions in the original equation.

In some cases, we may need to apply the principle of zero products (see Section 5.6) after squaring.

EXAMPLE 3 Solve: **(a)** $x - 5 = \sqrt{x + 7}$; **(b)** $3 + \sqrt{27 - 3x} = x$.

Solution

a)

$x - 5 = \sqrt{x + 7}$	
$(x - 5)^2 = (\sqrt{x + 7})^2$	Using the principle of squaring
$x^2 - 10x + 25 = x + 7$	Squaring a binomial on the left side
$x^2 - 11x + 18 = 0$	Adding $-x - 7$ to both sides
$(x - 9)(x - 2) = 0$	Factoring
$x - 9 = 0$ *or* $x - 2 = 0$	Using the principle of zero products
$x = 9$ *or* $x = 2$	

Check: For 9:

$$\begin{array}{c|c} x - 5 & \sqrt{x + 7} \\ \hline 9 - 5 & \sqrt{9 + 7} \\ \multicolumn{2}{c}{4 \stackrel{?}{=} 4} \end{array} \quad \text{TRUE}$$

For 2:

$$\begin{array}{c|c} x - 5 & \sqrt{x + 7} \\ \hline 2 - 5 & \sqrt{2 + 7} \\ \multicolumn{2}{c}{-3 \stackrel{?}{=} 3} \end{array} \quad \text{FALSE}$$

The number 9 checks, but 2 does not. Thus the solution is 9.

b)

$3 + \sqrt{27 - 3x} = x$	
$\sqrt{27 - 3x} = x - 3$	Subtracting 3 to isolate the radical
$(\sqrt{27 - 3x})^2 = (x - 3)^2$	Using the principle of squaring
$27 - 3x = x^2 - 6x + 9$	
$0 = x^2 - 3x - 18$	Adding $3x - 27$ to both sides
$0 = (x - 6)(x + 3)$	Factoring
$x - 6 = 0$ *or* $x + 3 = 0$	Using the principle of zero products
$x = 6$ *or* $x = -3$	

Check: For 6:

$$\begin{array}{r|l} 3 + \sqrt{27 - 3x} & x \\ \hline 3 + \sqrt{27 - 3 \cdot 6} & 6 \\ 3 + \sqrt{9} & \\ 3 + 3 & \\ \multicolumn{2}{c}{6 \stackrel{?}{=} 6} \end{array} \quad \text{TRUE}$$

For -3:

$$\begin{array}{r|l} 3 + \sqrt{27 - 3x} & x \\ \hline 3 + \sqrt{27 - 3 \cdot (-3)} & -3 \\ 3 + \sqrt{27 + 9} & \\ 3 + \sqrt{36} & \\ 3 + 6 & \\ \multicolumn{2}{c}{9 \stackrel{?}{=} -3} \end{array} \quad \text{FALSE}$$

The number 6 checks, but -3 does not. The solution is 6.

technology connection

Solutions of radical equations can be visualized on a graphing calculator. To "see" that 9 is the solution of Example 3(a), we let $y_1 = x - 5$ (the left side of $x - 5 = \sqrt{x + 7}$) and $y_2 = \sqrt{x + 7}$ (the right side of $x - 5 = \sqrt{x + 7}$). Using the INTERSECT option of CALC, we see that (9, 4) is on both curves. This indicates that when $x = 9$, y_1 and y_2 are both 4. No intersection occurs at $x = 2$, which confirms our check.

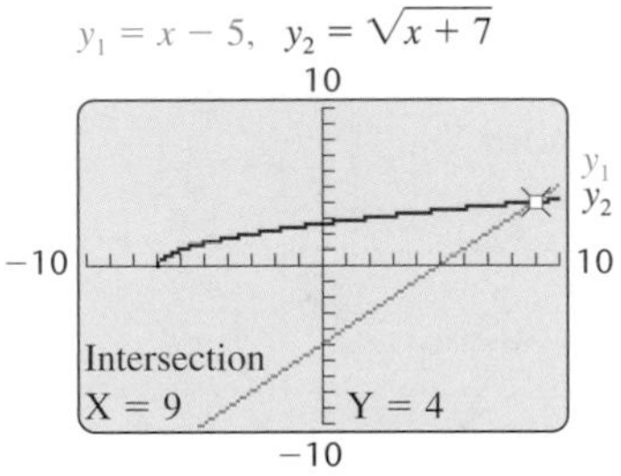

1. Use a graphing calculator to visualize the solution of Example 2.
2. Use a graphing calculator to visualize the solution of Example 3(b).

Problem Solving and Applications

Many applications translate to radical equations. For example, at a temperature of t degrees Fahrenheit, sound travels s feet per second, where

$$s = 21.9\sqrt{5t + 2457}.$$

EXAMPLE 4 Musical performances. The band U2 often performs outdoors for crowds in excess of 20,000 people. An officer stationed at a U2 concert used a radar gun to determine that the sound of the band was traveling at a rate of 1170 ft/sec. What was the air temperature at the concert?

Solution

1. **Familiarize.** If we did not already know the formula relating speed of sound to air temperature (see above), we could consult a reference book, a person in the field, or perhaps the Internet. There is no need to memorize this formula.

2. **Translate.** We substitute 1170 for s in the formula $s = 21.9\sqrt{5t + 2457}$:

$$1170 = 21.9\sqrt{5t + 2457}.$$

3. **Carry out.** We solve the equation for t:

$$1170 = 21.9\sqrt{5t + 2457}$$

$$\frac{1170}{21.9} = \sqrt{5t + 2457} \qquad \text{Dividing both sides by 21.9}$$

$$\left(\frac{1170}{21.9}\right)^2 = (\sqrt{5t + 2457})^2 \qquad \text{Using the principle of squaring}$$

$$2854.2 \approx 5t + 2457 \qquad \text{Simplifying}$$

$$397.2 \approx 5t \qquad \text{Subtracting 2457 from both sides}$$

$$79.4 \approx t. \qquad \text{Dividing both sides by 5}$$

4. **Check.** A temperature of 79.4°F seems reasonable. A complete check is left to the student.

5. **State.** The temperature at the concert was about 79.4°F.

Student Notes

Be careful when checking answers. You don't want to discard a correct answer because of a careless mistake.

8.5 Exercise Set

FOR EXTRA HELP

Student's Solutions Manual | Digital Video Tutor CD 5 Videotape 16 | AW Math Tutor Center | MathXL Tutorials on CD | MathXL | MyMathLab

Concept Reinforcement *Classify each sentence as either true or false.*

1. If $a = b$ is a true statement, then $a^2 = b^2$ must be true.
2. If $a^2 = b^2$ is a true statement, then $a = b$ must be true.
3. Every radical equation has at least one solution.
4. To use the principle of squaring, we square both sides of the equation.

Solve.

5. $\sqrt{x} = 7$
6. $\sqrt{x} = 9$
7. $\sqrt{x} + 4 = 12$
8. $\sqrt{x} + 3 = 15$
9. $\sqrt{2x + 3} = 11$
10. $\sqrt{2x + 4} = 9$
11. $2 + \sqrt{3 - y} = 9$
12. $3 + \sqrt{1 - a} = 5$
13. $6 - 3\sqrt{5n} = 0$
14. $8 - 2\sqrt{3n} = 0$
15. $\sqrt{4x - 6} = \sqrt{x + 9}$
16. $\sqrt{4x + 7} = \sqrt{2x + 13}$

Aha! **17.** $3\sqrt{x} = -7$

18. $2\sqrt{x} + 4 = 0$

19. $\sqrt{2t + 5} = \sqrt{3t + 7}$

20. $\sqrt{4t + 7} = \sqrt{5t + 8}$

21. $\sqrt{3x + 1} = x - 3$

22. $x - 7 = \sqrt{x - 5}$

23. $a - 9 = \sqrt{a - 3}$

24. $\sqrt{t + 18} = t - 2$

25. $x + 1 = 6\sqrt{x - 7}$

26. $x - 5 = \sqrt{15 - 3x}$

27. $\sqrt{5x + 21} = x + 3$

28. $\sqrt{22 - x} = x - 2$

29. $t + 4 = 4\sqrt{t + 1}$

30. $1 + 2\sqrt{y - 1} = y$

31. $\sqrt{x^2 + 6} - x + 3 = 0$

32. $\sqrt{x^2 + 7} - x + 2 = 0$

33. $\sqrt{(p + 6)(p + 1)} - 2 = p + 1$

34. $\sqrt{(4x + 5)(x + 4)} = 2x + 5$

35. $\sqrt{3 - 7x} = \sqrt{5 - 2x}$

36. $\sqrt{8 - 3x} = \sqrt{13 + x}$

37. $x - 1 = \sqrt{(x + 1)(x - 2)}$

38. $x = 1 + \sqrt{1 - x}$

Speed of a skidding car. *The formula $r = 2\sqrt{5L}$ can be used to approximate the speed r, in miles per hour, of a car that has left a skid mark of length L, in feet.*

39. How far will a car skid at 40 mph? at 60 mph?

40. How far will a car skid at 48 mph? at 80 mph?

Temperature and the speed of sound. *Solve, using the formula $s = 21.9\sqrt{5t + 2457}$ from Example 4.*

41. During blasting for avalanche control in Utah's Wasatch Mountains, sound traveled at a rate of 1113 ft/sec. What was the temperature at the time?

42. At a recent concert by the Dave Matthews Band, sound traveled at a rate of 1176 ft/sec. What was the temperature at the time?

Sighting to the horizon. *At a height of h meters, one can see V kilometers to the horizon, where $V = 3.5\sqrt{h}$.*

43. Shari can see 99.4 km to the horizon from her hot-air balloon. What is the height of the balloon?

44. A steeplejack can see 21 km to the horizon from the top of a building. What is the altitude of the steeplejack's eyes?

45. A scout can see 84 km to the horizon from atop a firetower. What is the altitude of the scout's eyes?

46. Amelia can see 378 km to the horizon from an airplane window. How high is the airplane?

Period of a swinging pendulum. *The formula $T = 2\pi\sqrt{L/32}$ can be used to find the period T, in seconds, of a pendulum of length L, in feet.*

47. A playground swing has a period of 4.4 sec. Find the length of the swing's chain. Use 3.14 for π.

48. The pendulum in Alma's regulator clock has a period of 2.0 sec. Find the length of the pendulum. Use 3.14 for π.

49. Do you believe that the principle of squaring can be extended to powers other than 2? That is, if $a = b$, does it follow that $a^n = b^n$ for any integer n? Why or why not?

50. Explain in your own words why possible solutions of radical equations must be checked.

SKILL MAINTENANCE

51. *Test scores.* Amy is taking a test in which items of type A are worth 10 points and items of type B are worth 15 points. She answers 16 questions correctly and scores 180 points. How many questions of each type did Amy answer correctly? [7.4]

52. *Metallurgy.* Francine stocks two alloys that are different purities of gold. The first is three-fourths pure gold and the second is five-twelfths pure gold. How many ounces of each should be combined in order to obtain a 60-oz mixture that is two-thirds pure gold? [7.4]

53. *Driving distances.* A car leaves Parkton traveling west at a speed of 56 km/h. Another car leaves Parkton one hour later, traveling west at 84 km/h. How far from Parkton will the second car overtake the first? [6.3]

54. *Coin value.* A collection of dimes and quarters is worth \$15.25. There are 103 coins in all. How many of each are there? [7.4]

SYNTHESIS

55. Review Example 3 and explain how to create a radical equation for which one "solution" checks and one does not.

56. Explain what would have happened in Example 1(a) if we had not isolated the radical before squaring. Could we still have solved the equation? Why or why not?

57. Find a number such that the opposite of three times its square root is −33.

58. Find a number such that 1 less than the square root of twice the number is 7.

Sometimes the principle of squaring must be used more than once in order to solve an equation. Solve Exercises 59–66 by using the principle of squaring as often as necessary.

59. $1 + \sqrt{x} = \sqrt{x + 9}$

60. $5 - \sqrt{x} = \sqrt{x - 5}$

61. $\sqrt{t + 4} = 1 - \sqrt{3t + 1}$

62. $\sqrt{y + 8} - \sqrt{y} = 2$

63. $\sqrt{y + 1} - \sqrt{y - 2} = \sqrt{2y - 5}$

64. $3 + \sqrt{19 - x} = 5 + \sqrt{4 - x}$

65. $2\sqrt{x - 1} - \sqrt{x - 9} = \sqrt{3x - 5}$

66. $x + (2 - x)\sqrt{x} = 0$

67. *Changing elevations.* A mountain climber pauses to rest and view the horizon. Using the formula $V = 3.5\sqrt{h}$, the climber computes the distance to the horizon and then climbs another 100 m. At this higher elevation, the horizon is 20 km farther than before. At what height was the climber when the first computation was made? (*Hint*: Use a system of equations.)

68. Solve $A = \sqrt{1 + \sqrt{a/b}}$ for b.

Graph. Use at least three ordered pairs.

69. $y = \sqrt{x}$

70. $y = \sqrt{x + 2}$

71. $y = \sqrt{x - 4}$

72. $y = \sqrt{x} + 1$

73. *Safe driving.* The formula $r = 2\sqrt{5L}$ can be used to find the speed, in miles per hour, that a car was traveling when it leaves skid marks L feet long. Police often recommend that drivers allow a space in front of their vehicle of one car length for each 10 miles per hour of speed. Thus a driver traveling 65 mph should leave 6.5 car lengths between his or her vehicle and the car in front of it. Many of today's small cars are approximately 15 ft long. For what speed would the "one car length per 10 mph of speed" rule require a distance equal to that of the skid marks that would be made at that speed?

74. Graph $y = x - 7$ and $y = \sqrt{x - 5}$ using the same set of axes. Determine where the graphs intersect in order to estimate a solution of $x - 7 = \sqrt{x - 5}$.

75. Graph $y = 1 + \sqrt{x}$ and $y = \sqrt{x + 9}$ using the same set of axes. Determine where the graphs intersect in order to estimate a solution of $1 + \sqrt{x} = \sqrt{x + 9}$.

Use a graphing calculator to solve Exercises 76 and 77. Round answers to the nearest hundredth.

76. $\sqrt{x + 3} = 2x - 1$

77. $-\sqrt{x + 3} = 2x - 1$

78. In Example 4, it was stated that the sound was traveling at a rate of 1170 ft/sec. How could this speed be determined by someone in attendance at the concert?

8.6 Applications Using Right Triangles

Right Triangles • Problem Solving

Radicals frequently occur in problem-solving situations in which the Pythagorean theorem is used. In Section 5.7, when we first used the Pythagorean theorem, we had not yet studied square roots. We now know that if $x^2 = n$, then x is a square root of n.

Study Skills

Making Sketches

One need not be an artist to make highly useful mathematical sketches. That said, it is important to make sure that your sketches are drawn accurately enough to represent the relative sizes within each shape. For example, if one side of a triangle is clearly the longest, make sure your drawing reflects this.

Right Triangles

For convenience, we restate the Pythagorean theorem.

The Pythagorean Theorem*

In any right triangle, if a and b are the lengths of the legs and c is the length of the hypotenuse, then

$$a^2 + b^2 = c^2.$$

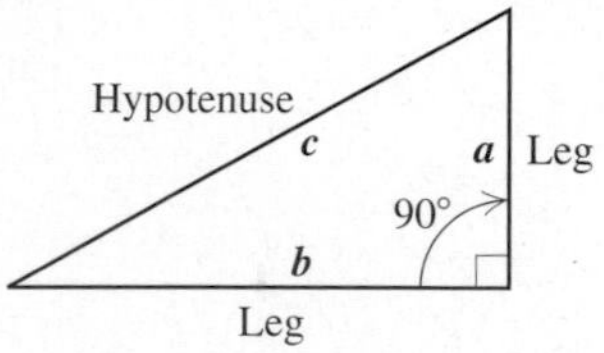

When the Pythagorean theorem is used to find a length, we need not concern ourselves with negative square roots, since length cannot be negative.

EXAMPLE 1 Find the length of the hypotenuse of the triangle shown. Give an exact answer in radical notation, as well as a decimal approximation to the nearest thousandth.

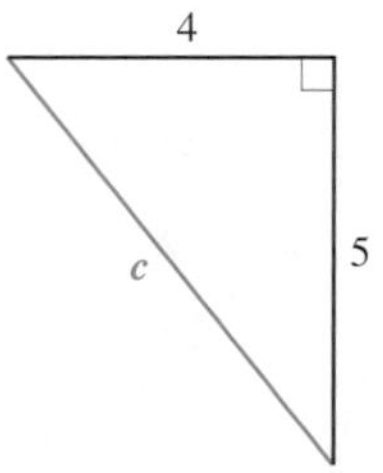

*Recall that the converse of the Pythagorean theorem also holds. That is, if a, b, and c are the lengths of the sides of a triangle and $a^2 + b^2 = c^2$, then the triangle is a right triangle.

Solution We have

$$\begin{aligned} a^2 + b^2 &= c^2 \\ 4^2 + 5^2 &= c^2 && \text{Substituting the lengths of the legs} \\ 16 + 25 &= c^2 \\ 41 &= c^2. \end{aligned}$$

We now use the fact that if $x^2 = n$, then $x = \sqrt{n}$ or $x = -\sqrt{n}$. In this case, since c is a length, it follows that c is the positive square root of 41:

$$\begin{aligned} c &= \sqrt{41} && \text{This is an exact answer.} \\ c &\approx 6.403. && \text{Using a calculator for an approximation} \end{aligned}$$

EXAMPLE 2 Find the length of the indicated leg in each triangle. In each case, give an exact answer in radical notation, as well as a decimal approximation to the nearest thousandth.

a)

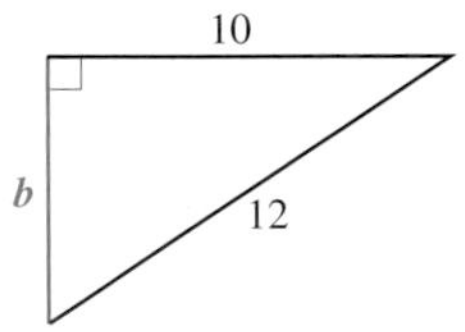

b)

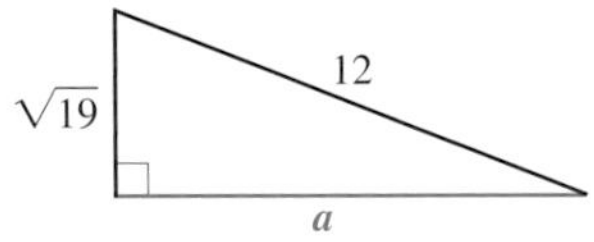

Solution

a)
$$\begin{aligned} 10^2 + b^2 &= 12^2 && \text{Substituting in the Pythagorean theorem} \\ 100 + b^2 &= 144 \\ b^2 &= 44 && \text{Subtracting 100 from both sides} \\ b &= \sqrt{44} && \text{The exact answer is } \sqrt{44}\text{. Since the length is positive, only the principal square root is used.} \\ b &\approx 6.633 && \text{Approximating } \sqrt{44} \text{ with a calculator} \end{aligned}$$

b)
$$\begin{aligned} a^2 + (\sqrt{19})^2 &= 12^2 && \text{Substituting} \\ a^2 + 19 &= 144 \\ a^2 &= 125 && \text{Subtracting 19 from both sides} \\ a &= \sqrt{125} && \text{The exact answer is } \sqrt{125}. \\ a &\approx 11.180 && \text{Using a calculator} \end{aligned}$$

Problem Solving

The five-step process and the Pythagorean theorem can be used for problem solving.

EXAMPLE 3 Prayer flags. To decorate their Santa Cruz sloop, Annabel and Hal plan to run a line with Tibetan prayer flags attached from the top of a 50-ft tall mast to the boat's bow 12 ft from the base of the mast. How long must the line be in order to span that distance?

Solution

1. **Familiarize.** We make a drawing and label the known distances. A right triangle is formed and we let l represent the unknown length, in feet.

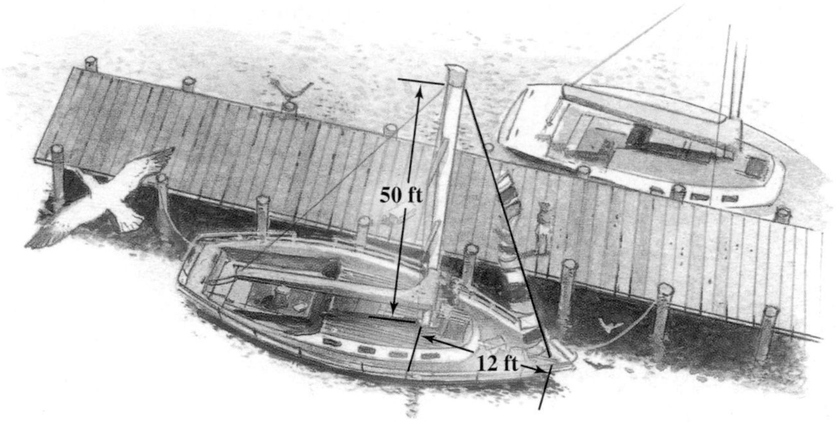

2. **Translate.** We use the Pythagorean theorem, substituting 12 for a, 50 for b, and l for c:

$$12^2 + 50^2 = l^2.$$

3. **Carry out.** We solve the equation:

$$\begin{aligned} 12^2 + 50^2 &= l^2 \\ 144 + 2500 &= l^2 \\ 2644 &= l^2 \\ \sqrt{2644} &= l \qquad \text{This is exact.} \\ 51.420 &\approx l. \qquad \text{Using a calculator to approximate} \end{aligned}$$

4. **Check.** To check, we substitute into the Pythagorean theorem. Note that 51.420 is larger than both 12 and 50, as expected:

$a^2 + b^2 = c^2$	
$12^2 + 50^2$	51.420^2
$144 + 2500$	

$$2644 \stackrel{?}{=} 2644 \qquad \text{TRUE}$$

5. **State.** To span the specified distance, Annabel and Hal's line should be about 51.4 ft long.

EXAMPLE 4 Reach of a ladder. A 32-ft ladder is leaning against a house. The bottom of the ladder is 7 ft from the house. How high is the top of the ladder? Give an exact answer in radical notation and a decimal approximation to the nearest thousandth.

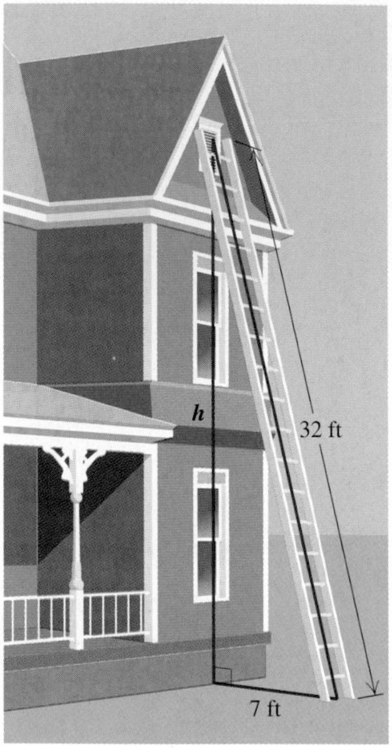

Solution

1. **Familiarize.** First we make a drawing. In it, there is a right triangle. We label the unknown height h.

2. **Translate.** We use the Pythagorean theorem, substituting 7 for a, h for b, and 32 for c:

$$7^2 + h^2 = 32^2.$$

3. **Carry out.** We solve the equation:

$$\begin{aligned} 7^2 + h^2 &= 32^2 \\ 49 + h^2 &= 1024 \\ h^2 &= 975 \\ h &= \sqrt{975} && \text{This answer is exact.} \\ h &\approx 31.225. && \text{Approximating with a calculator} \end{aligned}$$

4. **Check.** We check by substituting 7, $\sqrt{975}$, and 32:

$$\begin{array}{r|l} \multicolumn{2}{c}{a^2 + b^2 = c^2} \\ \hline 7^2 + (\sqrt{975})^2 & 32^2 \\ 49 + 975 & 1024 \\ 1024 & \stackrel{?}{=} 1024 \quad \text{TRUE} \end{array}$$

5. **State.** The top of the ladder is $\sqrt{975}$, or about 31.225 ft from the ground.

8.6 Exercise Set

FOR EXTRA HELP

Student's Solutions Manual | Digital Video Tutor CD 5 Videotape 16 | AW Math Tutor Center | MathXL Tutorials on CD | MathXL | MyMathLab

Concept Reinforcement *Complete each of the following sentences.*

1. In any right triangle, the longest side is opposite the 90° angle and is called the ______________.

2. In any right triangle, the two shortest sides, which form the 90° angle, are called the ______________.

3. The number 6.633 is only a(n) ______________ of $\sqrt{44}$.

4. The ______________ theorem states that if a and b are the lengths of the legs of a right triangle and c is the length of the third side, then $a^2 + b^2 = c^2$.

Find the length of the third side of each triangle. If an answer is not a whole number, use radical notation to give the exact answer and decimal notation for an approximation to the nearest thousandth.

5.
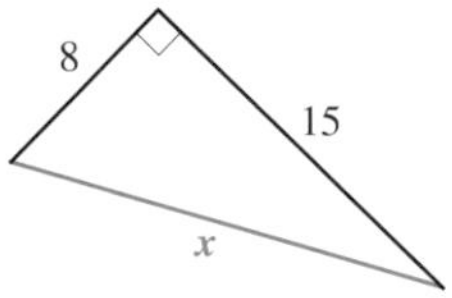

6.
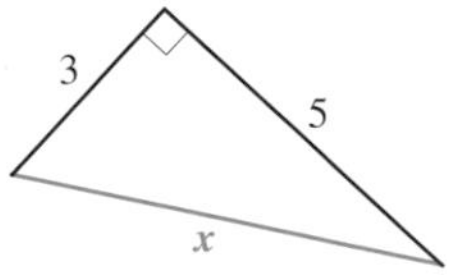

7.
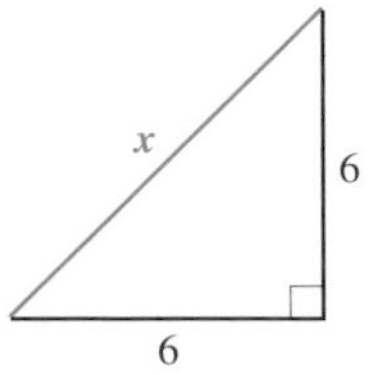

8.
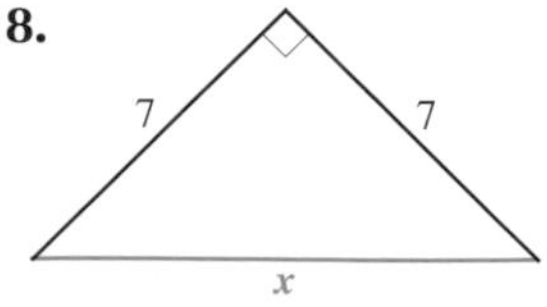

9.

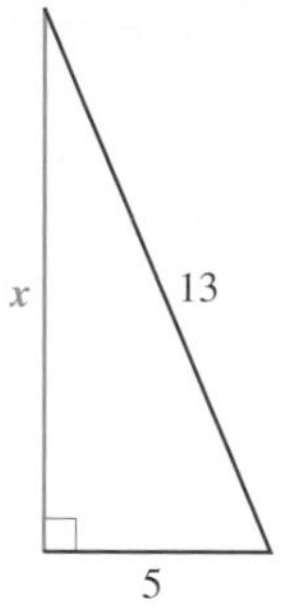

10.

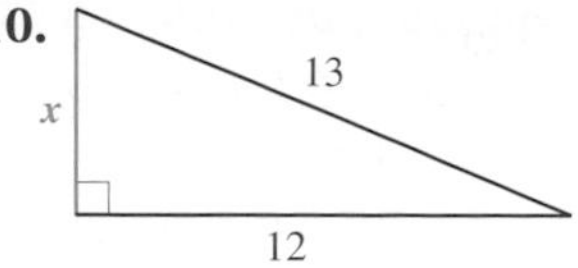

11.

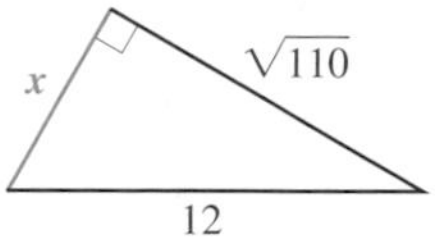

12.

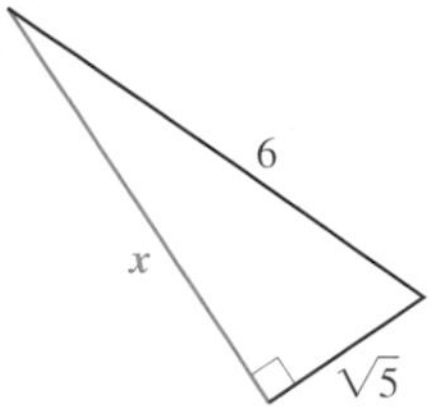

In a right triangle, find the length of the side not given. If an answer is not a whole number, use radical notation to give the exact answer and decimal notation for an approximation to the nearest thousandth. Regard a and b as the lengths of the legs and c as the length of the hypotenuse.

13. $a = 12, b = 5$

14. $a = 24, b = 10$

15. $a = 9, c = 15$

16. $a = 18, c = 30$

17. $b = 1, c = \sqrt{5}$

18. $b = 1, c = \sqrt{2}$

19. $a = 1, c = \sqrt{3}$

20. $a = \sqrt{3}, b = \sqrt{5}$

21. $c = 10, b = 5\sqrt{3}$

22. $a = 5, b = 5$

Solve. Don't forget to make drawings. If an answer is not a rational number, use radical notation to give the exact answer and decimal notation for an approximation to the nearest thousandth.

23. *Decorating.* Royce and Ava want to run a string of blinking lights from the top of a 15-ft sign on their restaurant to the edge of a surrounding garden 8 ft away. How long does the string of lights need to be?

24. *Decorating.* Celia and Bruce wish to run a string of holiday lights from the top of a 12-ft tall post by their front door to the base of a tree 10 ft away. How long does the string of lights need to be?

25. *Roller blading.* Lamar and Nanci are building a rollerblade jump with a base that is 30 in. long and a ramp that is 33 in. long. How high will the back of the jump be?

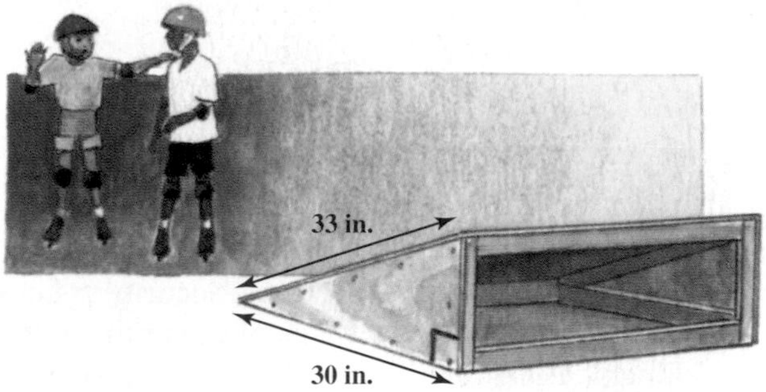

26. *Masonry.* Find the length of a diagonal of a square tile that has sides 4 cm long.

27. *Plumbing.* A new water pipe is being prepared so that it will run diagonally under a kitchen floor. If the kitchen is 8 ft wide and 12 ft long, how long should the pipe be?

28. *Guy wires.* How long must a guy wire be to reach from the top of a 13-m telephone pole to a point on the ground 9 m from the foot of the pole?

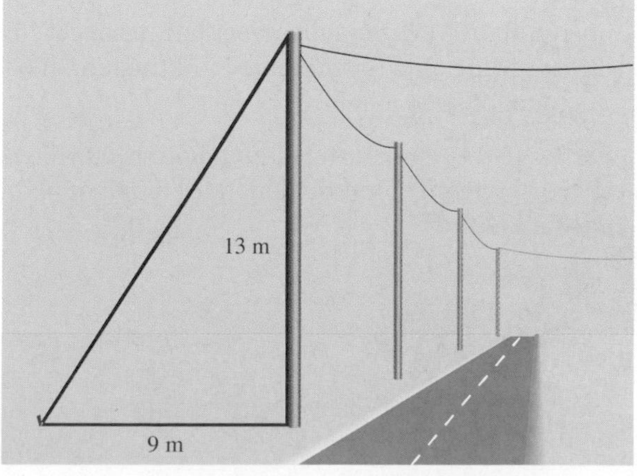

29. *Baseball.* A baseball diamond is a square 90 ft on each side. How far is it from first base to third base?

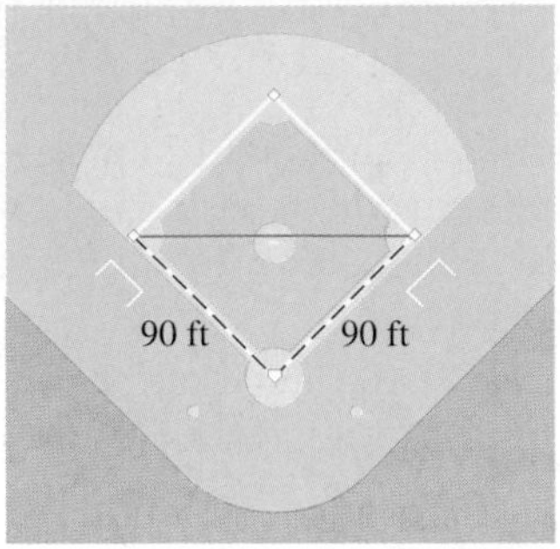

30. *Softball.* A softball diamond is a square 65 ft on each side. How far is it from home plate to second base?

31. *Wiring.* JR Electric is installing a security system with a wire that will run diagonally over the "drop" ceiling of a 10-ft by 16-ft room. How long will that section of wire need to be?

32. *Soccer fields.* The largest regulation soccer field is 100 yd wide and 130 yd long. Find the length of a diagonal of such a field.

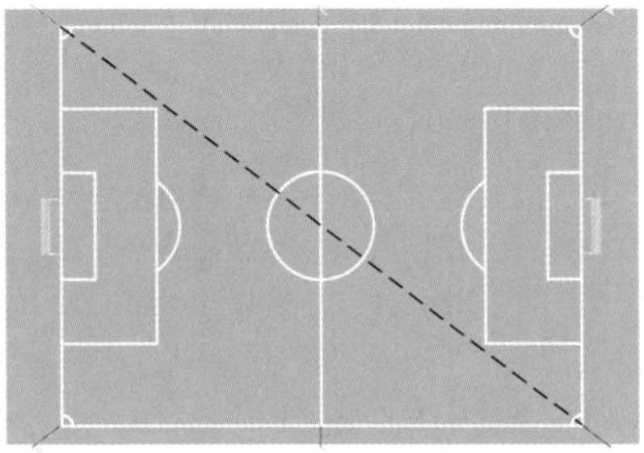

33. *Soccer fields.* The smallest regulation soccer field is 50 yd wide and 100 yd long. Find the length of a diagonal of such a field.

34. *Lacrosse.* A regulation lacrosse field is 60 yd wide and 110 yd long. Find the length of a diagonal of such a field.

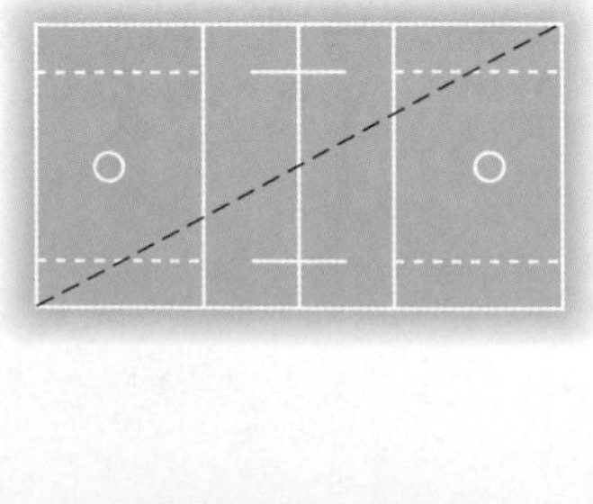

35. *Home maintenance.* The hose on a power washer is 32 ft long. If the compressor to which the hose is attached is located at the corner of a 24-ft wide house, how high can the hose reach up the far corner without moving the compressor?

36. *Surveying.* A surveyor had poles located at points P, Q, and R. The distances that she was able to measure are marked in the figure. What is the approximate length of the lake?

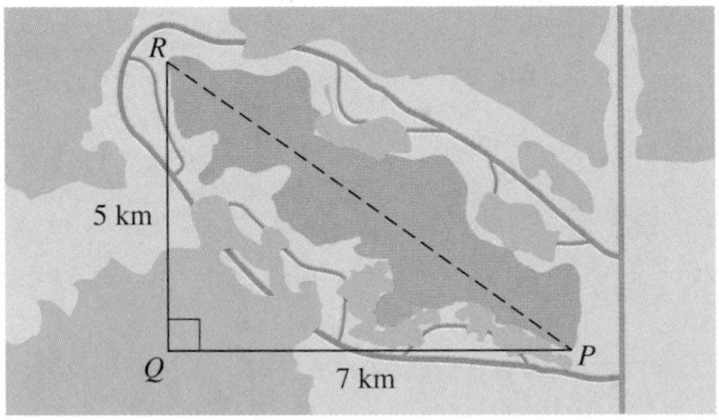

37. In an *isosceles triangle,* two sides have the same length. Can a right triangle be isosceles? Why or why not?

38. In an *equilateral triangle,* all sides have the same length. Can a right triangle be equilateral? Why or why not?

SKILL MAINTENANCE

For Exercises 39–42, consider the following list: [1.4]

$$-45, -9.7, -\sqrt{5}, 0, \tfrac{2}{7}, \sqrt{7}, \pi, 5.09, 19.$$

39. List all rational numbers.

40. List all irrational numbers.

41. List all real numbers.

42. List all integers.

Simplify. [4.1]

43. $(-2)^5$

44. $\left(\frac{7}{2}\right)^2$

45. $(2a)^4$

46. $(-5x)^3$

Factor. [5.4]

47. $x^2 - 10x + 25$

48. $t^2 - 12t + 36$

SYNTHESIS

49. Should a homeowner use a 28-ft ladder to repair clapboard that is 27 ft above ground level? Why or why not?

50. Can the length of a triangle's hypotenuse ever equal the combined lengths of the two legs? Why or why not?

51. *Holiday decorations.* From the peak of a 25-ft tall spruce tree in her front yard, Julia plans to run 10 strands of holiday lights to points in her lawn 15 ft from the tree's center. The lights cost $5.99 for 25 ft, $6.99 for 35 ft, and $11.99 for 68 ft (prices current 12/23/03). What should Julia purchase to make the decorations as economical as possible?

52. *Cordless telephones.* The Panasonic KXTG-2500B cordless phone has a range of one quarter mile. Vance has a corner office in the Empire State Building, 900 ft above street level. Can Vance locate the Panasonic's phone base in his office and use the handset at a restaurant at street level on the opposite corner? Use the figure below and show your work.

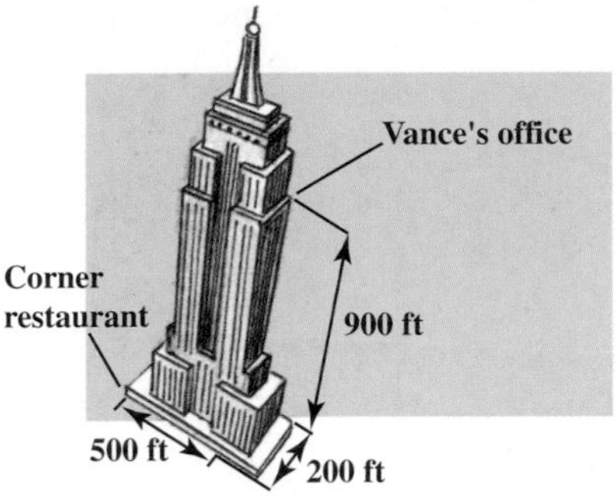

53. *Cordless telephones.* Virginia's AT&T 9002 cordless phone has a range of 1000 ft. Her apartment is a corner unit, located as shown in the figure below. Will Virginia be able to use the phone at the community pool?

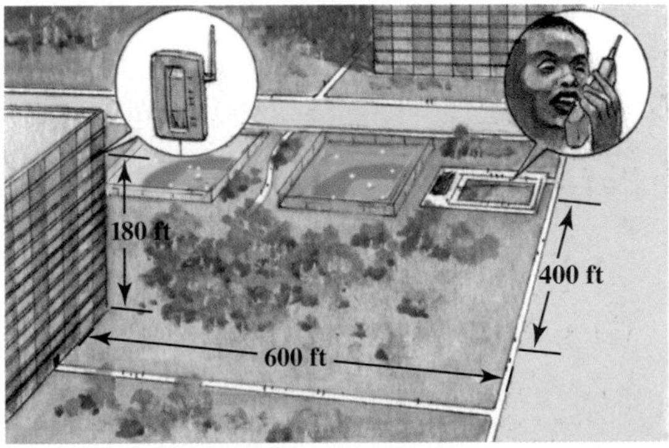

54. *Aviation.* A pilot is instructed to descend from 32,000 ft to 21,000 ft over a horizontal distance of 5 mi. What distance will the plane travel during this descent?

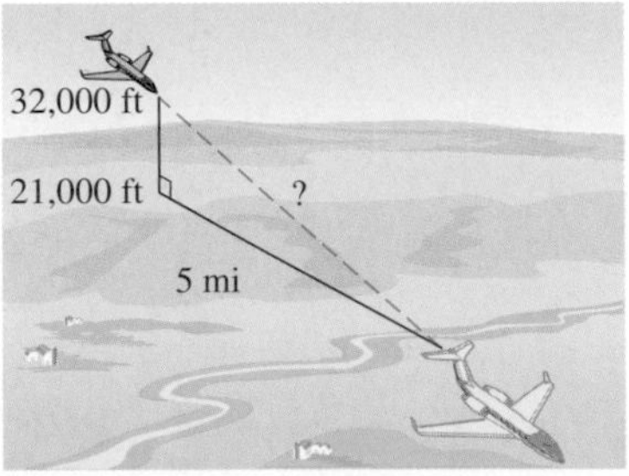

55. The diagonal of a square has a length of $8\sqrt{2}$ ft. Find the length of a side of the square.

56. Find the length of a side of a square that has an area of 7 m^2.

57. A right triangle has sides with lengths that are consecutive even integers. Find the lengths of the sides.

58. Figure *ABCD* is a square. Find the length of a diagonal, $\overline{AC}$.

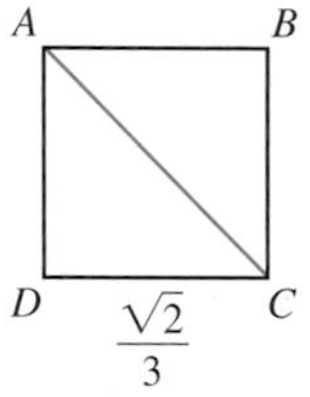

59. Find the length of the diagonal of a cube with sides of length *s*.

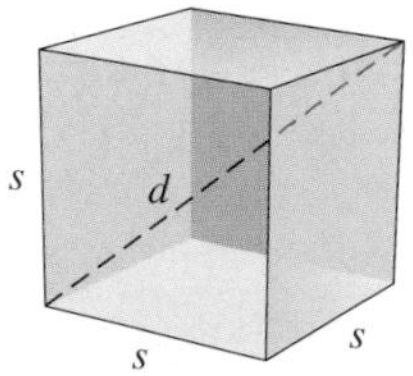

60. The area of square *PQRS* is 100 ft^2, and *A, B, C,* and *D* are midpoints of the sides on which they lie. Find the area of square *ABCD*.

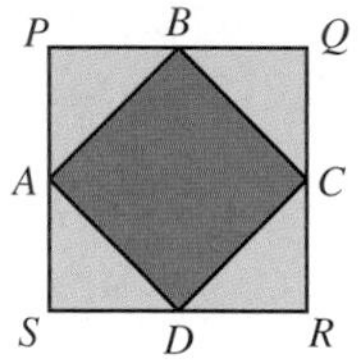

61. Express the height *h* of an equilateral triangle in terms of the length of a side *a*.

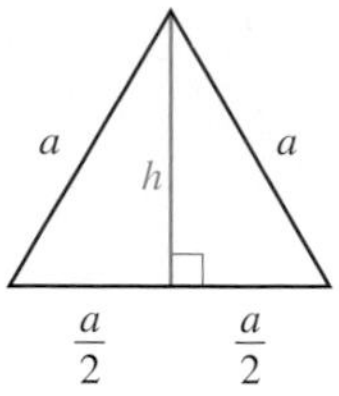

62. *Racquetball.* A racquetball court is 20 ft by 20 ft by 40 ft. What is the longest straight-line distance that can be measured in this racquetball court?

63. *Distance driven.* Two cars leave a service station at the same time. One car travels east at a speed of 50 mph, and the other travels south at a speed of 60 mph. After one half hour, how far apart are they?

64. Solve for *x*.

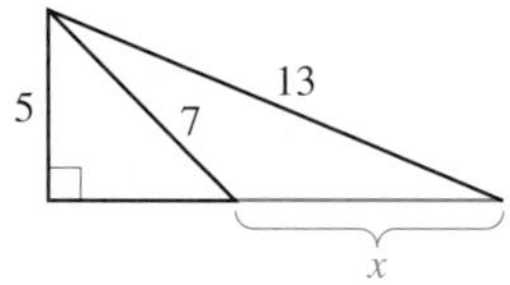

65. *Ranching.* If 2 mi of fencing encloses a square plot of land with an area of 160 acres, how large a square, in acres, will 4 mi of fencing enclose?

COLLABORATIVE CORNER

Pythagorean Triples

Focus: Pythagorean theorem

Time: 15 minutes

Group size: 2–4

Materials: Tape measure and chalk; string and scissors

We mentioned in the footnote on p. 515 that the converse of the Pythagorean theorem is also true: If a, b, and c are the lengths of the sides of a triangle and $a^2 + b^2 = c^2$, then the triangle is a right triangle. Each such set of three numbers is called a *Pythagorean triple*. Since $3^2 + 4^2 = 5^2$ and $5^2 + 12^2 = 13^2$, then (3, 4, 5) and (5, 12, 13) are both Pythagorean triples. Such numbers provide carpenters, masons, archaeologists, and others with a handy way of locating a line that forms a 90° angle with another line.

ACTIVITY

1. Suppose that the group is in the process of building a deck. They determine that they need to position an 8-ft piece of lumber so that it forms a 90° angle with a wall. Use a tape measure, chalk, Pythagorean triples, and—if desired—string and scissors to construct a right angle at a specified point at the base of some wall in or near your classroom.
2. To check that the angle formed in part (1) is truly 90°, repeat the procedure using a different Pythagorean triple.

8.7 Higher Roots and Rational Exponents

Higher Roots • Products and Quotients Involving Higher Roots • Rational Exponents • Calculators

In this section, we study *higher* roots, such as cube roots or fourth roots, and exponents that are not integers.

Higher Roots

Recall that c is a square root of a if $c^2 = a$. A similar definition exists for *cube roots*.

Cube Root

The number c is the *cube root* of a if $c^3 = a$.

The symbolism $\sqrt[3]{a}$ is used to represent the cube root of a. In the radical $\sqrt[3]{a}$, the number 3 is called the **index**, and a is called the **radicand**.

EXAMPLE 1 Find the cube root of each number: **(a)** 8; **(b)** -125.

Solution

a) The cube root of 8 is the number whose cube is 8. Since $2^3 = 2 \cdot 2 \cdot 2 = 8$, the cube root of 8 is 2: $\sqrt[3]{8} = 2$.

b) The cube root of -125 is the number whose cube is -125. Since $(-5)^3 = (-5)(-5)(-5) = -125$, the cube root of -125 is -5: $\sqrt[3]{-125} = -5$.

Study Skills

Abbrevs. cn help u go fst

If you take notes and have trouble keeping up with your instructor, use abbreviations to speed up your work. Consider standard abbreviations like "Ex" for "Example," " ≈ " for "is approximately equal to," "∴" for "therefore," and "⇒" for "implies." Feel free to create your own abbreviations as well.

***n*th Root**

The number c is an nth *root* of a if $c^n = a$.

If n is odd, there is only one nth root and $\sqrt[n]{a}$ represents that root.

If n is even, there are two nth roots, and $\sqrt[n]{a}$ represents the non-negative nth root.

Even roots of negative numbers are not real numbers.

Positive numbers always have *two* nth roots when n is even but when we refer to **the** nth root of a positive number a, denoted $\sqrt[n]{a}$, we mean the *positive* nth root. Thus, although -3 and 3 are both fourth roots of 81 (since $(-3)^4 = 3^4 = 81$), 3 is considered **the** fourth root of 81. In symbols:

$$\sqrt[4]{81} = 3.$$

EXAMPLE 2 Find each root: **(a)** $\sqrt[4]{16}$; **(b)** $\sqrt[5]{-32}$; **(c)** $\sqrt[4]{-16}$; **(d)** $-\sqrt[3]{64}$.

Solution

a) $\sqrt[4]{16} = 2$ Since $2^4 = 2 \cdot 2 \cdot 2 \cdot 2 = 16$

b) $\sqrt[5]{-32} = -2$ Since $(-2)^5 = (-2)(-2)(-2)(-2)(-2) = -32$

c) $\sqrt[4]{-16}$ is not a real number, because it is an even root of a negative number.

d) $-\sqrt[3]{64} = -(\sqrt[3]{64})$ This is the opposite of $\sqrt[3]{64}$.

$= -4$ $4^3 = 4 \cdot 4 \cdot 4 = 64$

Some roots occur so frequently that you may want to memorize them.

Square Roots		Cube Roots	Fourth Roots	Fifth Roots
$\sqrt{1} = 1$	$\sqrt{4} = 2$	$\sqrt[3]{1} = 1$	$\sqrt[4]{1} = 1$	$\sqrt[5]{1} = 1$
$\sqrt{9} = 3$	$\sqrt{16} = 4$	$\sqrt[3]{8} = 2$	$\sqrt[4]{16} = 2$	$\sqrt[5]{32} = 2$
$\sqrt{25} = 5$	$\sqrt{36} = 6$	$\sqrt[3]{27} = 3$	$\sqrt[4]{81} = 3$	$\sqrt[5]{243} = 3$
$\sqrt{49} = 7$	$\sqrt{64} = 8$	$\sqrt[3]{64} = 4$	$\sqrt[4]{256} = 4$	
$\sqrt{81} = 9$	$\sqrt{100} = 10$	$\sqrt[3]{125} = 5$	$\sqrt[4]{625} = 5$	
$\sqrt{121} = 11$	$\sqrt{144} = 12$	$\sqrt[3]{216} = 6$		

Products and Quotients Involving Higher Roots

The rules for working with products and quotients of square roots can be extended to products and quotients of nth roots. Prime factorizations can again be useful as an aid for simplifying.

The Product and Quotient Rules

$$\sqrt[n]{AB} = \sqrt[n]{A}\sqrt[n]{B}, \qquad \sqrt[n]{\frac{A}{B}} = \frac{\sqrt[n]{A}}{\sqrt[n]{B}}$$

EXAMPLE 3 Simplify: **(a)** $\sqrt[3]{40}$; **(b)** $\sqrt[3]{\frac{125}{27}}$; **(c)** $\sqrt[4]{1250}$; **(d)** $\sqrt[5]{\frac{2}{243}}$.

Solution

a) $\sqrt[3]{40} = \sqrt[3]{8 \cdot 5}$ Note that $40 = 2 \cdot 2 \cdot 2 \cdot 5 = 8 \cdot 5$ and 8 is a perfect cube.

$= \sqrt[3]{8} \cdot \sqrt[3]{5}$

$= 2\sqrt[3]{5}$

b) $\sqrt[3]{\frac{125}{27}} = \frac{\sqrt[3]{125}}{\sqrt[3]{27}}$ $125 = 5 \cdot 5 \cdot 5$ and $27 = 3 \cdot 3 \cdot 3$, so 125 and 27 are perfect cubes. See the chart above.

$= \frac{5}{3}$

c) $\sqrt[4]{1250} = \sqrt[4]{625 \cdot 2}$ Note that $1250 = 2 \cdot 5 \cdot 5 \cdot 5 \cdot 5 = 2 \cdot 625$ and 625 is a perfect fourth power.

$= \sqrt[4]{625} \cdot \sqrt[4]{2}$

$= 5\sqrt[4]{2}$

d) $\sqrt[5]{\dfrac{2}{243}} = \dfrac{\sqrt[5]{2}}{\sqrt[5]{243}}$ $\quad 243 = 3 \cdot 3 \cdot 3 \cdot 3 \cdot 3$, so 243 is a perfect fifth power. See the chart on p. 525.

$= \dfrac{\sqrt[5]{2}}{3}$

Student Notes

If you are unsure of the rules for when to add or multiply exponents, this would be a good time to review them in Section 4.1.

Rational Exponents

Expressions containing rational exponents, like $8^{1/3}$, $4^{5/2}$, and $81^{-3/4}$, are defined in a manner that ensures that the laws of exponents still hold. For example, if the product rule, $a^m \cdot a^n = a^{m+n}$, is to hold, then

$$a^{1/2} \cdot a^{1/2} = a^{1/2+1/2}$$
$$= a^1 = a.$$

This says that $a^{1/2}$ times itself is a, which means that $a^{1/2}$ is a square root of a. This idea is generalized as follows.

The Exponent $1/n$

$a^{1/n}$ means $\sqrt[n]{a}$. If a is negative, then the index n must be odd. (Note that $a^{1/2}$ is written $\sqrt{a}$, in which the index 2 is understood.)

Thus, $a^{1/2}$ means $\sqrt{a}$, $a^{1/3}$ means $\sqrt[3]{a}$, and so on.

EXAMPLE 4 Simplify: **(a)** $8^{1/3}$; **(b)** $100^{1/2}$; **(c)** $81^{1/4}$; **(d)** $(-243)^{1/5}$.

Solution

a) $8^{1/3} = \sqrt[3]{8} = 2$

b) $100^{1/2} = \sqrt{100} = 10$

c) $81^{1/4} = \sqrt[4]{81} = 3$

d) $(-243)^{1/5} = \sqrt[5]{-243} = -3$

In order to continue multiplying exponents when raising a power to a power, we must have $a^{2/3} = (a^{1/3})^2$ and $a^{2/3} = (a^2)^{1/3}$. This suggests both that $a^{2/3} = (\sqrt[3]{a})^2$ and that $a^{2/3} = \sqrt[3]{a^2}$.

Positive Rational Exponents

For any natural numbers m and n ($n \neq 1$) and any real number a for which $\sqrt[n]{a}$ exists,

$$a^{m/n} \text{ means } (\sqrt[n]{a})^m, \text{ or equivalently, } a^{m/n} \text{ means } \sqrt[n]{a^m}.$$

In most cases, it is easiest to simplify using $(\sqrt[n]{a})^m$, because smaller numbers are involved.

EXAMPLE 5 Simplify: **(a)** $27^{2/3}$; **(b)** $8^{5/3}$; **(c)** $81^{3/4}$.

Solution

a) $27^{2/3} = (27^{1/3})^2 = (\sqrt[3]{27})^2 = 3^2 = 9$

b) $8^{5/3} = (8^{1/3})^5 = (\sqrt[3]{8})^5 = 2^5 = 32$

c) $81^{3/4} = (81^{1/4})^3 = (\sqrt[4]{81})^3 = 3^3 = 27$

Negative rational exponents are defined in much the same way that negative integer exponents are.

> **Negative Rational Exponents**
>
> For any rational number m/n and any nonzero real number a for which $a^{m/n}$ exists,
>
> $$a^{-m/n} = \frac{1}{a^{m/n}}.$$

EXAMPLE 6 Simplify: **(a)** $16^{-1/2}$; **(b)** $27^{-1/3}$; **(c)** $32^{-2/5}$; **(d)** $64^{-3/2}$.

Solution

a) $16^{-1/2} = \dfrac{1}{16^{1/2}} = \dfrac{1}{\sqrt{16}} = \dfrac{1}{4}$

b) $27^{-1/3} = \dfrac{1}{27^{1/3}} = \dfrac{1}{\sqrt[3]{27}} = \dfrac{1}{3}$

c) $32^{-2/5} = \dfrac{1}{32^{2/5}} = \dfrac{1}{(32^{1/5})^2} = \dfrac{1}{(\sqrt[5]{32})^2} = \dfrac{1}{2^2} = \dfrac{1}{4}$

d) $64^{-3/2} = \dfrac{1}{64^{3/2}} = \dfrac{1}{(\sqrt{64})^3} = \dfrac{1}{8^3} = \dfrac{1}{512}$

> *Caution!* A negative exponent does not indicate that the expression in which it appears is negative.

Calculators

A calculator with a key for finding powers can be used to approximate numbers like $\sqrt[5]{8}$. Generally such keys are labeled [x^y], [a^x], or [^]. We find approximations by entering the radicand, pressing the power key, entering the exponent, and then pressing [=] or [ENTER]. Thus, $\sqrt[5]{8}$ can be approximated by entering 8, pressing the power key, entering 0.2 or $(1 \div 5)$, and pressing [=] to get $\sqrt[5]{8} \approx 1.515716567$. Consult an owner's manual or your instructor if your calculator works differently.

8.7 Exercise Set

FOR EXTRA HELP

Student's Solutions Manual | Digital Video Tutor CD 5 Videotape 16 | AW Math Tutor Center | MathXL Tutorials on CD | MathXL | MyMathLab

Concept Reinforcement *Classify each statement as either true or false.*

1. $4^{1/2}$ is the same as $\sqrt{4}$, or 2.
2. $a^{m/n}$ is the same as $\sqrt[n]{a^m}$.
3. $a^{m/n}$ is the same as $(\sqrt[n]{a})^m$.
4. $5^{-1/2}$ is a negative number.

Simplify. If an expression does not represent a real number, state this.

5. $\sqrt[3]{-8}$ 6. $\sqrt[3]{-64}$ 7. $\sqrt[3]{-125}$
8. $\sqrt[3]{-27}$ 9. $\sqrt[3]{1000}$ 10. $\sqrt[3]{8}$
11. $-\sqrt[3]{216}$ 12. $-\sqrt[3]{-343}$ 13. $\sqrt[4]{625}$
14. $\sqrt[4]{81}$ 15. $\sqrt[5]{0}$ 16. $\sqrt[5]{1}$
17. $\sqrt[5]{-1}$ 18. $\sqrt[5]{-243}$ 19. $\sqrt[4]{-81}$
20. $\sqrt[4]{-1}$ Aha! 21. $\sqrt[4]{10{,}000}$ 22. $\sqrt[5]{100{,}000}$
Aha! 23. $\sqrt[3]{8^3}$ 24. $\sqrt[4]{5^4}$ 25. $\sqrt[6]{64}$
26. $\sqrt[6]{1}$ 27. $\sqrt[9]{a^9}$ 28. $\sqrt[3]{n^3}$
29. $\sqrt[3]{54}$ 30. $\sqrt[3]{32}$ 31. $\sqrt[4]{48}$
32. $\sqrt[5]{160}$ 33. $\sqrt[3]{\frac{64}{125}}$ 34. $\sqrt[3]{\frac{125}{27}}$
35. $\sqrt[5]{\frac{32}{243}}$ 36. $\sqrt[4]{\frac{625}{256}}$ 37. $\sqrt[3]{\frac{7}{8}}$
38. $\sqrt[5]{\frac{15}{32}}$ 39. $\sqrt[4]{\frac{14}{81}}$ 40. $\sqrt[3]{\frac{10}{27}}$

Simplify.

41. $16^{1/2}$ 42. $25^{1/2}$ 43. $125^{1/3}$
44. $1000^{1/3}$ 45. $32^{1/5}$ 46. $16^{1/4}$
47. $16^{3/4}$ 48. $8^{4/3}$ 49. $9^{5/2}$
50. $25^{3/2}$ 51. $64^{2/3}$ 52. $32^{2/5}$
53. $8^{5/3}$ 54. $16^{5/4}$ 55. $4^{5/2}$
56. $36^{-1/2}$ 57. $25^{-1/2}$ 58. $32^{-1/5}$
59. $256^{-1/4}$ 60. $100^{-3/2}$ 61. $16^{-3/4}$
62. $81^{-3/4}$ 63. $81^{-5/4}$ 64. $32^{-2/5}$
65. $8^{-2/3}$ 66. $625^{-3/4}$

67. Expressions of the form $a^{m/n}$ can be rewritten as $(\sqrt[n]{a})^m$ or $\sqrt[n]{a^m}$. Which radical expression would you use when simplifying $25^{3/2}$ and why?

68. Explain in your own words why $\sqrt[n]{a}$ is negative when n is odd and a is negative.

SKILL MAINTENANCE

Solve. [5.6]

69. $x^2 - 5x - 6 = 0$ 70. $x^2 + 4x - 5 = 0$
71. $4t^2 - 9 = 0$ 72. $25t^2 - 4 = 0$
73. $3x^2 + 8x + 4 = 0$ 74. $5x^2 + 13x - 6 = 0$

SYNTHESIS

75. If $a > b$, does it follow that $a^{1/n} > b^{1/n}$? Why or why not?

76. Under what condition(s) will $a^{-3/5}$ be negative?

Using a calculator, approximate each of the following to three decimal places.

77. $10^{4/5}$ 78. $24^{1/4}$
79. $36^{3/8}$ 80. $10^{3/2}$

Simplify.

81. $a^{1/4}a^{3/2}$ 82. $(x^{2/3})^{7/3}$
83. $m^{-2/3}m^{1/4}m^{3/2}$ 84. $\frac{p^{5/6}}{p^{2/3}}$

Graph.

85. $y = \sqrt[3]{x}$ 86. $y = \sqrt[4]{x}$

87. Use a graphing calculator to draw the graphs of $y_1 = x^{2/3}$, $y_2 = x^1$, $y_3 = x^{5/4}$, and $y_4 = x^{3/2}$. Use the window $[-1, 17, -1, 32]$ and the SIMULTANEOUS mode. Then determine which curve corresponds to each equation.

8 Study Summary

The study of **radical expressions** (p. 485) begins with the understanding that if $c^2 = a$, then c is a **square root** (p. 484) of a. A **radical sign**, $\sqrt{}$ (p. 484), is used to indicate the positive or **principal** square root of the **radicand** (p. 484), which is the expression under the radical sign.

Unless a is a **perfect square**, like 25 or $\frac{4}{9}$, the expression $\sqrt{a}$ represents an **irrational number** (p. 485). To facilitate long division, we often will **rationalize the denominator** (p. 500) when an irrational number appears in an expression like $5/\sqrt{2}$. To rationalize a denominator containing two terms, we use the **conjugate** (p. 505) of the denominator to write a form of 1:

$$\frac{3}{5+\sqrt{2}} \cdot \frac{5-\sqrt{2}}{5-\sqrt{2}} = \frac{3 \cdot 5 - 3\sqrt{2}}{25 \underbrace{- 5\sqrt{2} + 5\sqrt{2}} - (\sqrt{2})^2} = \frac{15 - 3\sqrt{2}}{23}.$$

These are **like radicals** (p. 503).

Radical equations (p. 509), like $\sqrt{2x-3} = 3$, can be solved using the **principle of squaring**:

$$(\sqrt{2x-3})^2 = 3^2$$
$$2x - 3 = 9$$
$$2x = 12$$
$$x = 6.$$

The check is left for the student.

Care must be taken to check answers, since the principle of squaring does not always produce an equivalent equation.

Radicals often arise in applications using the **Pythagorean theorem** (p. 515), which states that for any right triangle, the sum of the squares of the lengths of the **legs** (p. 515) is the square of the length of the **hypotenuse** (p. 515).

$$a^2 + b^2 = c^2$$

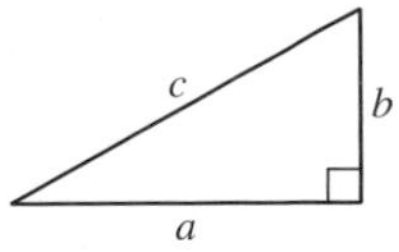

Rational exponents (p. 526) allow us to express **cube roots** (p. 524), like $\sqrt[3]{14}$, using exponents: $\sqrt[3]{14} = 14^{1/3}$. **Higher roots** (p. 523), like $\sqrt[5]{18}$, can also be represented using rational exponents. To do so, the **index** (p. 524)—in this case, 5—becomes the denominator of the exponent: $\sqrt[5]{18} = 18^{1/5}$. In general, the nth root, $\sqrt[n]{a}$, can be expressed as $a^{1/n}$. The rules for multiplying or dividing higher roots parallel the rules for square roots:

The Product Rule: $\sqrt{A}\sqrt{B} = \sqrt{AB}$; $\quad \sqrt[n]{AB} = \sqrt[n]{A}\sqrt[n]{B}$

The Quotient Rule: $\dfrac{\sqrt{A}}{\sqrt{B}} = \sqrt{\dfrac{A}{B}}$; $\quad \sqrt[n]{\dfrac{A}{B}} = \dfrac{\sqrt[n]{A}}{\sqrt[n]{B}}$

8 Review Exercises

Concept Reinforcement *Classify each statement as either true or false.*

1. The sum of two square roots is the square root of the sum of the radicands. [8.4]
2. The product of two square roots is the square root of the product of the radicands. [8.2]
3. The quotient of two cube roots is the cube root of the quotient of the radicands. [8.7]
4. The principal square root of a number is never negative. [8.1]
5. The cube root of a number is never negative. [8.7]
6. The conjugate of $5 - \sqrt{3}$ is $1/(5 - \sqrt{3})$. [8.4]
7. For any triangle, if the lengths of two sides are known, the Pythagorean theorem can be used to determine the length of the third side. [8.6]
8. The rules for adding or multiplying integer exponents also apply to rational exponents. [8.7]
9. It is always possible to add or subtract like radical terms. [8.4]
10. The principle of squaring does not always lead to a solution. [8.5]

Find the square roots of each number. [8.1]

11. 25
12. 196
13. 400
14. 225

Simplify. [8.1]

15. $-\sqrt{144}$
16. $\sqrt{81}$
17. $\sqrt{49}$
18. $-\sqrt{169}$

Identify each radicand. [8.1]

19. $5x\sqrt{2x^2y}$
20. $a\sqrt{\dfrac{a}{b}}$

Determine whether each square root is rational or irrational. [8.1]

21. $-\sqrt{36}$
22. $-\sqrt{34}$
23. $\sqrt{42}$
24. $\sqrt{25}$

Use a calculator to approximate each square root. Round to three decimal places. [8.1]

25. $\sqrt{3}$
26. $\sqrt{99}$

Simplify. Assume that x can be any real number. [8.1]

27. $\sqrt{(5x)^2}$
28. $\sqrt{(x + 1)^2}$

Simplify. Assume for Exercises 29–69 that all variables represent nonnegative numbers. [8.1]

29. $\sqrt{p^2}$
30. $\sqrt{(7x)^2}$
31. $\sqrt{16m^2}$
32. $\sqrt{(ac)^2}$

Simplify by factoring. [8.2]

33. $\sqrt{48}$
34. $\sqrt{98t^2}$
35. $\sqrt{32p}$
36. $\sqrt{x^6}$
37. $\sqrt{12a^{13}}$
38. $\sqrt{36m^{15}}$

Multiply and, if possible, simplify. [8.2]

39. $\sqrt{3}\sqrt{11}$
40. $\sqrt{6}\sqrt{10}$
41. $\sqrt{5x}\sqrt{7t}$
42. $\sqrt{3a}\sqrt{8a}$
43. $\sqrt{5x}\sqrt{10xy^2}$
44. $\sqrt{20a^3b}\sqrt{5a^2b^2}$

Simplify.

45. $\dfrac{\sqrt{35}}{\sqrt{45}}$ [8.3]
46. $\dfrac{\sqrt{30y^9}}{\sqrt{54y}}$ [8.3]
47. $\sqrt{\dfrac{49}{64}}$ [8.3]
48. $\sqrt{\dfrac{20}{45}}$ [8.3]
49. $\sqrt{\dfrac{25}{t^2}}$ [8.3]
50. $10\sqrt{5} + 3\sqrt{5}$ [8.4]
51. $\sqrt{80} - \sqrt{45}$ [8.4]
52. $2\sqrt{x} - \sqrt{25x}$ [8.4]
53. $(2 + \sqrt{3})^2$ [8.4]
54. $(2 + \sqrt{3})(2 - \sqrt{3})$ [8.4]
55. $(1 + 2\sqrt{7})(3 - \sqrt{7})$ [8.4]

Write an equivalent expression by rationalizing each denominator.

56. $\sqrt{\dfrac{1}{2}}$ [8.3]
57. $\dfrac{\sqrt{5}}{\sqrt{8}}$ [8.3]

58. $\sqrt{\dfrac{7}{y}}$ [8.3]

59. $\dfrac{2}{\sqrt{3}}$ [8.3]

60. $\dfrac{4}{2+\sqrt{3}}$ [8.4]

61. $\dfrac{1+\sqrt{5}}{2-\sqrt{5}}$ [8.4]

Solve. [8.5]

62. $\sqrt{x-5}=7$

63. $\sqrt{5x+3}=\sqrt{2x-1}$

64. $\sqrt{x+5}=x-1$

65. $1+x=\sqrt{1+5x}$

66. *Length of a rope swing.* The formula $T=2\pi\sqrt{L/32}$ can be used to find the period T, in seconds, of a pendulum of length L, in feet. A rope swing over a river has a period of 6.6 sec. Find the length of the rope. Use 3.14 for π. [8.5]

In a right triangle, find the length of the side not given. If the answer is not a whole number, use radical notation to give an exact answer and decimal notation to give an approximation to the nearest thousandth. Keep in mind that a and b are the lengths of the legs and c is the length of the hypotenuse. [8.6]

67. $a=15,\ c=25$

68. $a=1,\ b=\sqrt{2}$

69. Four telephone poles form a square that is 48 ft on each side, with the intersection of Blakely Rd and Rt 7 in the center. A traffic light is to be hung from a wire running diagonally from two of the poles. How long should the wire be? [8.6]

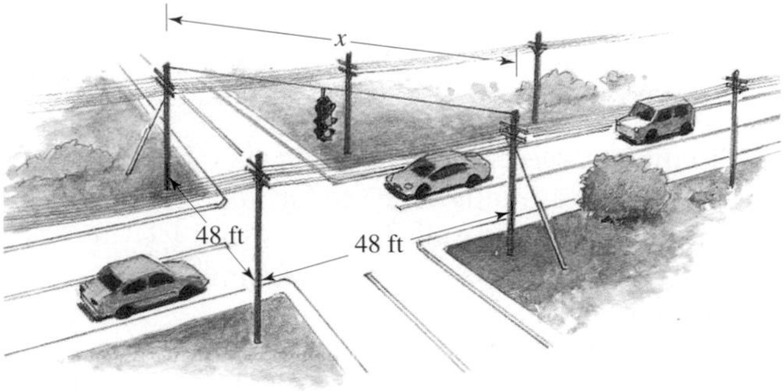

Simplify. If an expression does not represent a real number, state this. [8.7]

70. $\sqrt[5]{32}$

71. $\sqrt[4]{-16}$

72. $\sqrt[3]{-27}$

73. $\sqrt[4]{32}$

Simplify. [8.7]

74. $100^{1/2}$

75. $9^{-1/2}$

76. $16^{3/2}$

77. $81^{-3/4}$

SYNTHESIS

78. Jesse automatically eliminates any possible solutions of a radical equation that are negative. What mistake is he making? [8.5]

79. Why should you simplify each term in a radical expression before attempting to combine like radical terms? [8.4]

80. Simplify: $\sqrt{\sqrt{\sqrt{256}}}$. [8.1]

81. Solve: $\sqrt{x^2}=-10$. [8.1]

82. Use square roots to factor x^2-5. [8.4]

83. Solve $A=\sqrt{a^2+b^2}$ for b. [8.5]

8 Chapter Test

1. Find the square roots of 81.

Simplify.

2. $\sqrt{64}$

3. $-\sqrt{25}$

4. Identify the radicand in $s\sqrt{s^2 - 3}$.

Determine whether each square root is rational or irrational.

5. $\sqrt{20}$

6. $\sqrt{16}$

Approximate using a calculator. Round to three decimal places.

7. $\sqrt{87}$

8. $\sqrt{7}$

Simplify. Assume that a, y $\geq$ 0.

9. $\sqrt{a^2}$

10. $\sqrt{49y^2}$

Simplify by factoring. For Exercises 11–43, assume that all variables represent nonnegative numbers.

11. $\sqrt{40}$

12. $\sqrt{27x^6}$

13. $\sqrt{4t^5}$

Perform the indicated operation and, if possible, simplify.

14. $\sqrt{5}\sqrt{6}$

15. $\sqrt{5}\sqrt{10}$

16. $\sqrt{7x}\sqrt{2y}$

17. $\sqrt{2t}\sqrt{8t}$

18. $\sqrt{3ab}\sqrt{6ab^3}$

19. $\dfrac{\sqrt{18}}{\sqrt{32}}$

20. $\dfrac{\sqrt{35x}}{\sqrt{80xy^2}}$

21. $\sqrt{\dfrac{27}{12}}$

22. $\sqrt{\dfrac{144}{a^2}}$

23. $3\sqrt{18} - 5\sqrt{18}$

24. $\sqrt{27} + 2\sqrt{12}$

25. $(4 - \sqrt{5})^2$

26. $(4 - \sqrt{5})(4 + \sqrt{5})$

Rationalize each denominator to form an equivalent expression.

27. $\sqrt{\dfrac{2}{5}}$

28. $\dfrac{2x}{\sqrt{y}}$

29. $\dfrac{10}{4 - \sqrt{5}}$

30. *Guy wires.* One wire steadying a radio tower stretches from a point 100 ft high on the tower to a point on the ground 25 ft from the base of the tower. How long is the wire?

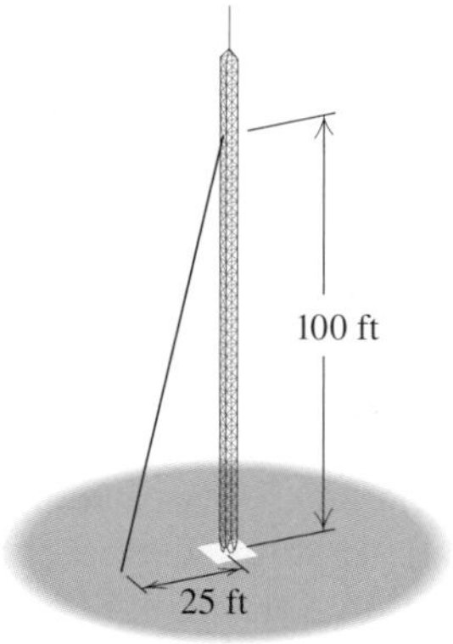

Solve.

31. $\sqrt{3x} + 2 = 14$

32. $\sqrt{6x + 13} = x + 3$

33. Valerie calculates that she can see 247.49 km to the horizon from an airplane window. How high is the airplane? Use the formula $V = 3.5\sqrt{h}$, where h is the altitude, in meters, and V is the distance to the horizon, in kilometers.

Simplify. If an expression does not represent a real number, state this.

34. $\sqrt[4]{16}$

35. $-\sqrt[6]{1}$

36. $\sqrt[3]{-64}$

37. $\sqrt[4]{-81}$

38. $9^{1/2}$

39. $27^{-1/3}$

40. $100^{3/2}$

41. $16^{-5/4}$

SYNTHESIS

42. Solve: $\sqrt{1 - x} + 1 = \sqrt{6 - x}$.

43. Simplify: $\sqrt{y^{16n}}$.

9 Quadratic Equations

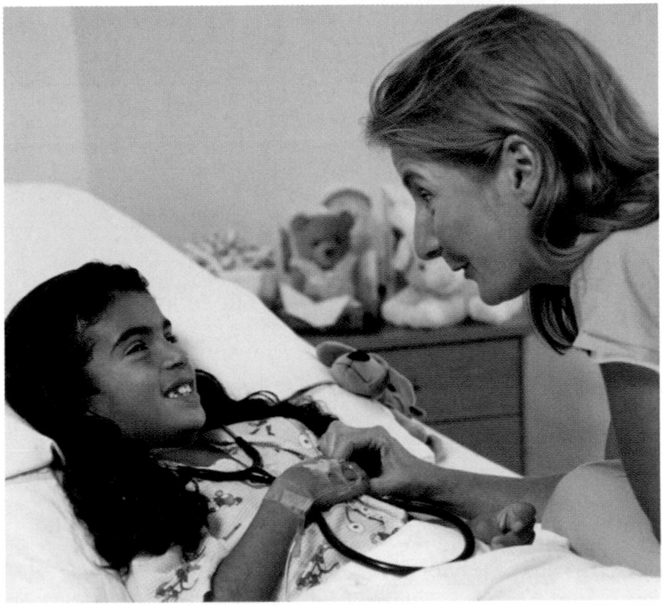

AN APPLICATION

Young's rule for determining the size of a particular child's medicine dosage c is

$$c = \frac{a}{a + 12} \cdot d,$$

where a is the child's age and d is the typical adult dosage (*Source*: Olsen, June Looby, Leon J. Ablon, and Anthony Patrick Giangrasso, *Medical Dosage Calculations*, 6th ed). If a child receives 8 mg of antihistamine when the typical adult dosage is 24 mg, how old is the child?

This problem appears as Exercise 65 in Section 9.4.

Rena J. Webster
REGISTERED NURSE
Indianapolis, Indiana

Nurses dispense medicine on a regular basis. Since medicine often comes in a dosage different from what a doctor prescribes, I must calculate the correct dosage. Math also helps in critical thinking, such as determining dosage on the basis of body weight.

Quadratic equations first appeared in Section 5.6. At that time, we used the principle of zero products because all of the equations could be solved by factoring. In this chapter, we develop methods for solving any *quadratic equation. These methods are then used in applications and in graphing.*

9.1 Solving Quadratic Equations: The Principle of Square Roots

The Principle of Square Roots • Solving Quadratic Equations of the Type $(x + k)^2 = p$

Study Skills

Don't Give Up Now!

Often students are tempted to ease up once the end of a course is in sight. Don't let this happen to you! You have invested a great deal of time and energy thus far. Don't tarnish that hard effort by doing anything less than your best work as the course winds down.

The following are examples of quadratic equations:

$$x^2 - 7x + 9 = 0, \qquad 5t^2 - 4t = 8, \qquad 6y^2 = -9y, \qquad m^2 = 49.$$

We saw in Chapter 5 that one way to solve an equation like $m^2 = 49$ is to subtract 49 from both sides, factor, and then use the principle of zero products:

$$\begin{aligned} m^2 - 49 &= 0 \\ (m + 7)(m - 7) &= 0 \\ m + 7 = 0 \quad &or \quad m - 7 = 0 \\ m = -7 \quad &or \quad m = 7. \end{aligned}$$

This approach relies on our ability to factor. By using the *principle of square roots*, we can develop a method for solving equations like $m^2 = 49$ that allows us to solve equations when factoring is impractical.

The Principle of Square Roots

It is possible to solve $m^2 = 49$ just by noting that m must be a square root of 49, namely, -7 or 7. This approach was used in Section 8.6, but there only positive square roots appeared, since length is never negative.

The Principle of Square Roots

For any nonnegative real number k, if $x^2 = k$, then $x = \sqrt{k}$ or $x = -\sqrt{k}$.

The notation $x = \pm\sqrt{k}$ is often used to indicate $x = \sqrt{k}$ or $x = -\sqrt{k}$.

EXAMPLE 1 Solve: $x^2 = 16$.

Solution We use the principle of square roots:

$$x^2 = 16$$

$$x = \sqrt{16} \quad or \quad x = -\sqrt{16} \qquad \text{Using the principle of square roots}$$

$$x = 4 \quad or \quad x = -4. \qquad \text{Simplifying}$$

We check mentally that $4^2 = 16$ and $(-4)^2 = 16$. The solutions are 4 and -4.

Unlike the principle of zero products, the principle of square roots can be used to solve quadratic equations that have irrational solutions.

EXAMPLE 2 Solve: **(a)** $x^2 = 17$; **(b)** $5t^2 = 15$; **(c)** $-3x^2 + 7 = 0$.

Solution

a)

$$x^2 = 17$$

$$x = \sqrt{17} \quad or \quad x = -\sqrt{17} \qquad \text{Using the principle of square roots}$$

Check: For $\sqrt{17}$:

$$\begin{array}{c|c} x^2 & 17 \\ \hline (\sqrt{17})^2 & 17 \\ 17 & \overset{?}{=} 17 \end{array} \quad \text{TRUE}$$

For $-\sqrt{17}$:

$$\begin{array}{c|c} x^2 & 17 \\ \hline (-\sqrt{17})^2 & 17 \\ 17 & \overset{?}{=} 17 \end{array} \quad \text{TRUE}$$

The solutions are $\sqrt{17}$ and $-\sqrt{17}$.

b)

$$5t^2 = 15$$

$$t^2 = 3 \qquad \text{Dividing both sides by 5 to isolate } t^2$$

$$t = \sqrt{3} \quad or \quad t = -\sqrt{3} \qquad \text{Using the principle of square roots}$$

We leave the check to the student. The solutions are $\sqrt{3}$ and $-\sqrt{3}$.

c)

$$-3x^2 + 7 = 0$$

$$7 = 3x^2 \qquad \text{Adding } 3x^2 \text{ to both sides}$$

$$\frac{7}{3} = x^2 \qquad \text{Dividing both sides by 3}$$

$$x = \sqrt{\frac{7}{3}} \quad or \quad x = -\sqrt{\frac{7}{3}} \qquad \text{Using the principle of square roots}$$

$\left(\text{If we rationalize denominators, these answers can also be written } \frac{\sqrt{21}}{3} \text{ and } -\frac{\sqrt{21}}{3}.\right)$

technology connection

We can visualize Example 2(a) on a graphing calculator by letting $y_1 = x^2$ and $y_2 = 17$ and using the INTERSECT option of the CALC menu to find the x-coordinate at each point of intersection. Below, we show the intersection when $x \approx -\sqrt{17}$.

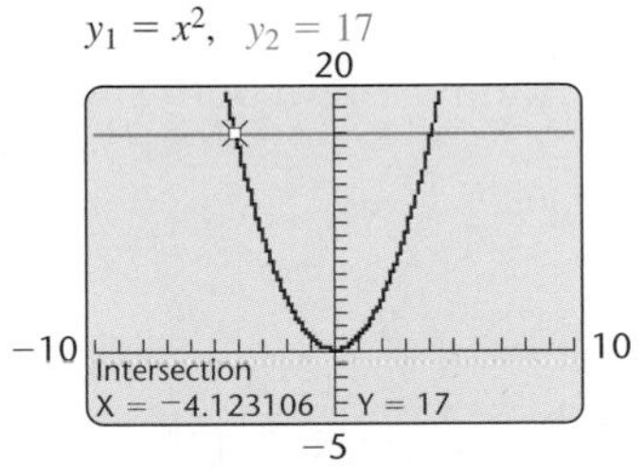

You can confirm that $(-4.123106)^2 \approx 17$. This visualization serves as a check of the algebraic approach.

1. Use a graphing calculator to visualize and check the solutions of Examples 2(b) and 2(c).

Check: For $\sqrt{\frac{7}{3}}$:

$$\begin{array}{r|l} -3x^2 + 7 = 0 & \\ \hline -3\left(\sqrt{\frac{7}{3}}\right)^2 + 7 & 0 \\ -3 \cdot \frac{7}{3} + 7 & \\ -7 + 7 & \\ 0 \stackrel{?}{=} 0 & \text{TRUE} \end{array}$$

For $-\sqrt{\frac{7}{3}}$:

$$\begin{array}{r|l} -3x^2 + 7 = 0 & \\ \hline -3\left(-\sqrt{\frac{7}{3}}\right)^2 + 7 & 0 \\ -3 \cdot \frac{7}{3} + 7 & \\ -7 + 7 & \\ 0 \stackrel{?}{=} 0 & \text{TRUE} \end{array}$$

The solutions of $-3x^2 + 7 = 0$ are $\sqrt{\frac{7}{3}}$ and $-\sqrt{\frac{7}{3}}$.

Solving Quadratic Equations of the Type $(x + k)^2 = p$

Equations like $(x - 5)^2 = 9$ or $(t + 2)^2 = 7$ are of the form $(x + k)^2 = p$. The principle of square roots can be used to solve such equations.

EXAMPLE 3 Solve: **(a)** $(x - 5)^2 = 9$; **(b)** $(t + 2)^2 = 7$.

Solution

a) $(x - 5)^2 = 9$

$x - 5 = 3$ *or* $x - 5 = -3$ — Using the principle of square roots: If $A^2 = 9$, then $A = 3$ or $A = -3$.

$x = 8$ *or* $x = 2$ — Adding 5 to both sides

The solutions are 8 and 2. We leave the check to the student.

b) $(t + 2)^2 = 7$

$t + 2 = \sqrt{7}$ *or* $t + 2 = -\sqrt{7}$ — Using the principle of square roots

$t = -2 + \sqrt{7}$ *or* $t = -2 - \sqrt{7}$ — Adding -2 to both sides

Check: For $-2 + \sqrt{7}$:

$$\begin{array}{r|l} (t + 2)^2 = 7 & \\ \hline (-2 + \sqrt{7} + 2)^2 & 7 \\ (\sqrt{7})^2 & \\ 7 \stackrel{?}{=} 7 & \text{TRUE} \end{array}$$

For $-2 - \sqrt{7}$:

$$\begin{array}{r|l} (t + 2)^2 = 7 & \\ \hline (-2 - \sqrt{7} + 2)^2 & 7 \\ (-\sqrt{7})^2 & \\ 7 \stackrel{?}{=} 7 & \text{TRUE} \end{array}$$

The solutions are $-2 + \sqrt{7}$ and $-2 - \sqrt{7}$, or simply $-2 \pm \sqrt{7}$ (read "-2 plus or minus $\sqrt{7}$").

In Example 3, the left sides of the equations are squares of binomials. Sometimes factoring can be used to express an equation in that form.

EXAMPLE 4 Solve by factoring and using the principle of square roots.

a) $x^2 + 8x + 16 = 49$ **b)** $x^2 + 6x + 9 = 10$

Solution

a) $x^2 + 8x + 16 = 49$ The left side is a perfect-square trinomial.

$(x + 4)^2 = 49$ Factoring

$x + 4 = 7$ *or* $x + 4 = -7$ Using the principle of square roots

$x = 3$ *or* $x = -11$

The solutions are 3 and -11. We leave the check to the student.

b) $x^2 + 6x + 9 = 10$ The left side is a perfect-square trinomial.

$(x + 3)^2 = 10$ Factoring

$x + 3 = \sqrt{10}$ *or* $x + 3 = -\sqrt{10}$ Using the principle of square roots

$x = -3 + \sqrt{10}$ *or* $x = -3 - \sqrt{10}$

The solutions are $-3 + \sqrt{10}$ and $-3 - \sqrt{10}$, or simply $-3 \pm \sqrt{10}$. We leave the check to the student.

9.1 Exercise Set

FOR EXTRA HELP

Student's Solutions Manual | Digital Video Tutor CD 5 Videotape 17 | AW Math Tutor Center | MathXL Tutorials on CD | MathXL | MyMathLab

Concept Reinforcement *Classify each statement as either true or false.*

1. The principle of square roots states that, for $k \geq 0$, if $x^2 = k$, then $x = \sqrt{k}$ or $x = -\sqrt{k}$.
2. The notation $x = \pm\sqrt{5}$ means $x = -\sqrt{5}$ or $x = \sqrt{5}$.
3. The principle of square roots can only be used to find rational solutions.
4. The principle of square roots cannot be used when factoring is possible.

Solve. Use the principle of square roots.

5. $x^2 = 36$ **6.** $x^2 = 100$

7. $a^2 = 25$ **8.** $a^2 = 49$

9. $t^2 = 17$ **10.** $n^2 = 13$

11. $3x^2 = 27$ **12.** $5x^2 = 20$

Aha! **13.** $8t^2 = 0$ **14.** $7t^2 = 21$

15. $4 - 9x^2 = 0$ **16.** $25 - 4a^2 = 0$

17. $49y^2 - 5 = 15$ **18.** $4y^2 - 3 = 9$

19. $8x^2 - 28 = 0$ **20.** $25x^2 - 35 = 0$

21. $(x - 1)^2 = 49$ **22.** $(x - 2)^2 = 25$

23. $(x + 4)^2 = 81$ **24.** $(x + 3)^2 = 36$

25. $(m + 3)^2 = 6$ **26.** $(m - 4)^2 = 21$

Aha! **27.** $(a - 7)^2 = 0$ **28.** $(a + 12)^2 = 81$

29. $(5 - x)^2 = 14$ **30.** $(7 - x)^2 = 12$

31. $(t + 1)^2 = 1$ **32.** $(x + 5)^2 = 25$

33. $\left(y - \frac{3}{4}\right)^2 = \frac{17}{16}$

34. $\left(x + \frac{3}{2}\right)^2 = \frac{13}{4}$

35. $x^2 - 10x + 25 = 100$

36. $x^2 - 6x + 9 = 64$

37. $p^2 + 8p + 16 = 1$

38. $y^2 + 14y + 49 = 4$

39. $t^2 - 6t + 9 = 13$

40. $m^2 - 2m + 1 = 5$

41. $x^2 + 12x + 36 = 18$

42. $x^2 + 4x + 4 = 12$

43. If a quadratic equation can be solved by factoring, what type of number(s) will be solutions? Why?

44. Under what conditions is it easier to use the principle of square roots rather than the principle of zero products to solve a quadratic equation?

SKILL MAINTENANCE

Factor. [5.2]

45. $3x^2 + 12x + 3$

46. $5t^2 + 20t + 25$

47. $t^2 + 16t + 64$

48. $x^2 + 14x + 49$

49. $x^2 - 10x + 25$

50. $t^2 - 8t + 16$

SYNTHESIS

51. Is it possible for a quadratic equation to have $5 + \sqrt{2}$ as a solution, but not $5 - \sqrt{2}$? Why or why not?

52. If a quadratic equation can be solved using the principle of square roots, but not by factoring, what type of number(s) will be solutions? Why?

Factor the left side of each equation. Then solve.

53. $x^2 + \frac{7}{3}x + \frac{49}{36} = \frac{7}{36}$

54. $x^2 - 5x + \frac{25}{4} = \frac{13}{4}$

55. $m^2 - \frac{3}{2}m + \frac{9}{16} = \frac{17}{16}$

56. $t^2 + 3t + \frac{9}{4} = \frac{49}{4}$

57. $x^2 + 2.5x + 1.5625 = 9.61$

58. $a^2 - 3.8a + 3.61 = 27.04$

Use the graph of

$$y = (x + 3)^2$$

to solve each equation.

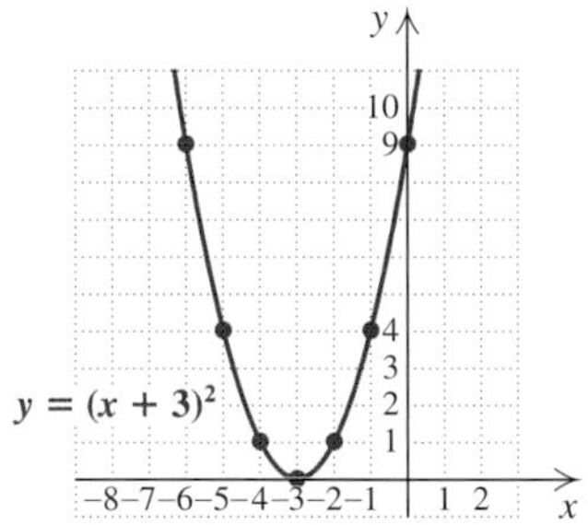

59. $(x + 3)^2 = 1$

60. $(x + 3)^2 = 4$

61. $(x + 3)^2 = 9$

62. $(x + 3)^2 = 0$

63. *Gravitational force.* Newton's law of gravitation states that the gravitational force f between objects of mass M and m, at a distance d from each other, is given by

$$f = \frac{kMm}{d^2},$$

where k is a constant. Solve for d.

COLLABORATIVE CORNER

How Big is Half a Pizza?

Focus: Principle of square roots; formulas

Time: 15–25 minutes

Group size: 3

Materials: Calculators are optional.

Frankie, Johnnie, & Luigi, Too! has the best pizza in the Palo Alto area, according to a poll of Stanford University students. Pizzas there have 12-in., 14-in., and 16-in. diameters.

ACTIVITY

1. Let each member of the group play the role of either Frankie, Johnnie, or Luigi. As part of a promotion, Frankie is offering a "mini" pie that has half the area of a 12-in. pie, Johnnie is offering a "personal" pie that has half the area of a 14-in. pie, and Luigi is offering a "junior" pie that has half the area of a 16-in. pie. Each group member, according to the selected role, should calculate the area of both the original pie and the new offering.
2. Each group member, according to the chosen role, should calculate the radius and then the diameter of the "new" pie. Summarize the group's findings in a table similar to the one below.

	Diameter of Original Pie	**Area of Original Pie**	**Area of New Pie**	**Radius of New Pie**	**Diameter of New Pie**
Frankie					
Johnnie					
Luigi					

3. After checking each other's work, group members should develop a formula that can be used to determine the diameter of a circle that has half the area of a given circle. That is, if a circle has diameter d, what is the diameter of a circle with half the area?
4. If the diameter of one pizza is twice the diameter of another pizza, should the pizza cost twice as much? Why or why not?

9.2 Solving Quadratic Equations: Completing the Square

Completing the Square • Solving by Completing the Square

Study Skills

Preparing for the Final Exam

If you have three or more days to study for a final exam, consider:

- Reviewing the highlighted or boxed information in each chapter.
- Studying the Study Summaries, Review Exercises, Tests, and Cumulative Reviews.
- Re-taking all quizzes and tests that have been returned to you.
- Attending any review sessions being offered.
- Organizing or joining a study group.
- Using the video or software supplements, or asking a tutor or professor about any trouble spots.
- Asking for previous final exams (and answers) for practice.

In Section 9.1, we solved equations like $(x - 5)^2 = 7$ using the principle of square roots. Equations like $x^2 + 8x + 16 = 12$ were similarly solved because the left side of the equation is a perfect-square trinomial. We now learn to solve equations like $x^2 - 8x = 2$, in which the left side is not (yet!) a perfect-square trinomial. The new procedure involves *completing the square* and enables us to solve *any* quadratic equation.

Completing the Square

Recall that

$$\begin{aligned}(x + 3)^2 &= (x + 3)(x + 3)\\ &= x^2 + 3x + 3x + 9\\ &= x^2 + 6x + 9 \qquad \text{This is a perfect-square trinomial.}\end{aligned}$$

and, in general,

$$(x + a)^2 = x^2 + 2ax + a^2. \qquad \text{This is also a perfect-square trinomial.}$$

In $x^2 + 6x + 9$, note that 9 is the square of half of the coefficient of x: $\frac{1}{2} \cdot 6 = 3$, and $3^2 = 9$. Similarly, in $x^2 + 2ax + a^2$, note that a^2 is also the square of half of the coefficient of x: $\frac{1}{2} \cdot 2a = a$ and $a \cdot a = a^2$.

Consider the quadratic equation

$$x^2 + 10x = 4.$$

We need a number that can be added to both sides and that will make the left side a perfect-square trinomial. Such a number is described above as the square of half of the coefficient of x: $\frac{1}{2} \cdot 10 = 5$, and $5^2 = 25$. Thus we add 25 to both sides:

$$\begin{aligned}x^2 + 10x &= 4 &&\textit{Think: } \text{Half of 10 is 5; } 5^2 = 25.\\ x^2 + 10x + 25 &= 4 + 25 &&\text{Adding 25 to both sides}\\ (x + 5)^2 &= 29. &&\text{Factoring the perfect-square trinomial}\end{aligned}$$

By adding 25 to $x^2 + 10x$, we have *completed the square.* The resulting equation contains the square of a binomial on one side. Solutions can then be found using the principle of square roots, as in Section 9.1:

$$(x + 5)^2 = 29$$

$$x + 5 = \sqrt{29} \quad \textit{or} \quad x + 5 = -\sqrt{29} \qquad \text{Using the principle of square roots}$$

$$x = -5 + \sqrt{29} \quad \textit{or} \quad x = -5 - \sqrt{29}.$$

The solutions are $-5 \pm \sqrt{29}$.

technology connection

One way to check that $-5 - \sqrt{29}$ and $-5 + \sqrt{29}$ are both solutions of $x^2 + 10x = 4$ is to store $-5 - \sqrt{29}$ (or $-5 + \sqrt{29}$) as X in the calculator's memory. We then press $X^2 + 10X$ ENTER. The result should be 4.

Completing the Square

To *complete the square* for an expression like $x^2 + bx$, add half of the coefficient of x, squared. That is, add $(b/2)^2$.

A visual interpretation of completing the square is sometimes helpful.

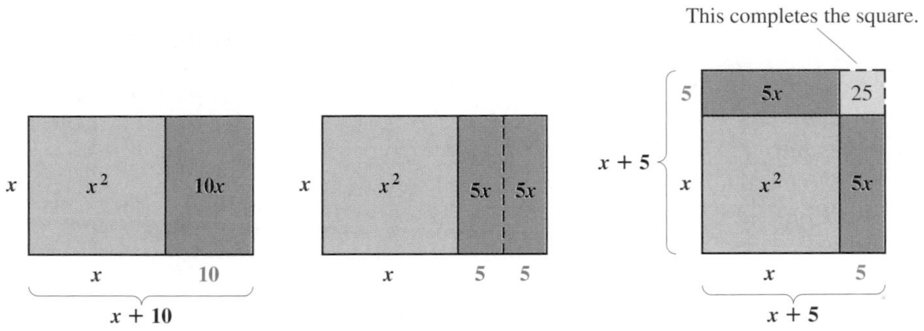

In each figure above, the sum of the pink and purple areas is $x^2 + 10x$. However, by splitting the purple area in half, we can "complete" a square by adding the blue area. The blue area is $5 \cdot 5$, or 25 square units.

Caution! Completing the square does *not* produce an equivalent expression. In future problems, it is performed when using the addition principle to produce equivalent equations.

EXAMPLE 1 Complete the square and check by multiplying: **(a)** $x^2 - 12x$; **(b)** $x^2 + 5x$.

Student Notes

Keep in mind that each time we complete the square, as in Example 1, we are forming a new expression that is *not equivalent* to the original expression.

Solution

a) To complete the square for $x^2 - 12x$, note that the coefficient of x is -12. Half of -12 is -6 and $(-6)^2$ is 36. Thus, $x^2 - 12x$ becomes a perfect-square trinomial when 36 is added:

$$x^2 - 12x + 36 \quad \text{is the square of} \quad x - 6.$$

The number 36 completes the square.

Check: $(x-6)^2 = (x-6)(x-6) = x^2 - 6x - 6x + 36 = x^2 - 12x + 36$

b) To complete the square for $x^2 + 5x$, we take half of the coefficient of x and square it:

$$\left(\tfrac{5}{2}\right)^2 = \tfrac{25}{4}. \qquad \text{Half of 5 is } \tfrac{5}{2};\ \left(\tfrac{5}{2}\right)^2 = \tfrac{5}{2} \cdot \tfrac{5}{2} = \tfrac{25}{4}.$$

Thus, $x^2 + 5x + \frac{25}{4}$ is the square of $x + \frac{5}{2}$. The number $\frac{25}{4}$ completes the square.

Check: $\left(x + \frac{5}{2}\right)^2 = \left(x + \frac{5}{2}\right)\left(x + \frac{5}{2}\right) = x^2 + \frac{5}{2}x + \frac{5}{2}x + \frac{25}{4} = x^2 + 5x + \frac{25}{4}$

> *Caution!* In Example 1, we are neither solving an equation nor writing an equivalent expression. Instead, we are learning how to find the number that completes the square. In Examples 2 and 3, we use the number that completes the square, along with the addition principle, to solve equations.

Solving by Completing the Square

The concept of completing the square can now be used to solve equations like $x^2 + 10x = 4$ much as we did on p. 540, prior to Example 1.

EXAMPLE 2 Solve by completing the square.

a) $x^2 + 6x = -8$ **b)** $x^2 - 10x + 14 = 0$

Solution

a) To solve $x^2 + 6x = -8$, we take half of 6 and square it, to get 9. Then we add 9 to both sides of the equation. This makes the left side the square of a binomial:

$$x^2 + 6x + 9 = -8 + 9$$ Adding 9 to both sides to complete the square

$$(x + 3)^2 = 1$$ Factoring

$$x + 3 = 1 \quad or \quad x + 3 = -1$$ Using the principle of square roots

$$x = -2 \quad or \quad x = -4.$$

The solutions are -2 and -4. The check is left to the student.

b) We have

$$x^2 - 10x + 14 = 0$$

$$x^2 - 10x = -14$$ Subtracting 14 from both sides in preparation for completing the square

$$x^2 - 10x + 25 = -14 + 25$$ Adding 25 to both sides to complete the square: $(-10/2)^2 = 25$

$$(x - 5)^2 = 11$$ Factoring

$$x - 5 = \sqrt{11} \quad or \quad x - 5 = -\sqrt{11}$$ Using the principle of square roots

$$x = 5 + \sqrt{11} \quad or \quad x = 5 - \sqrt{11}.$$

The solutions are $5 + \sqrt{11}$ and $5 - \sqrt{11}$, or simply $5 \pm \sqrt{11}$. The check is left to the student.

To complete the square, the coefficient of x^2 must be 1. When the x^2-coefficient is not 1, we can multiply or divide on both sides to find an equivalent equation with an x^2-coefficient of 1.

EXAMPLE 3 Solve by completing the square.

a) $3x^2 + 24x = 3$

b) $2x^2 - 5x + 1 = 0$

Solution

a)

$$3x^2 + 24x = 3$$

$$\left.\begin{aligned} \tfrac{1}{3}(3x^2 + 24x) &= \tfrac{1}{3} \cdot 3 \\ x^2 + 8x &= 1 \end{aligned}\right\}$$ We multiply by $\frac{1}{3}$ (or divide by 3) on both sides to ensure an x^2-coefficient of 1.

$$x^2 + 8x + 16 = 1 + 16$$ Adding 16 to both sides to complete the square: $(\frac{8}{2})^2 = 16$

$$(x + 4)^2 = 17$$ Factoring

$$x + 4 = \sqrt{17} \quad \textit{or} \quad x + 4 = -\sqrt{17}$$

$$x = -4 + \sqrt{17} \quad \textit{or} \quad x = -4 - \sqrt{17}$$

The solutions are $-4 \pm \sqrt{17}$. The check is left to the student.

b)

$$2x^2 - 5x + 1 = 0$$

$$\frac{1}{2}(2x^2 - 5x + 1) = \frac{1}{2} \cdot 0$$ Multiplying by $\frac{1}{2}$ to make the x^2-coefficient 1

$$x^2 - \frac{5}{2}x + \frac{1}{2} = 0$$

$$x^2 - \frac{5}{2}x = -\frac{1}{2}$$ Subtracting $\frac{1}{2}$ from both sides

$$x^2 - \frac{5}{2}x + \frac{25}{16} = -\frac{1}{2} + \frac{25}{16}$$ Adding $\frac{25}{16}$ to both sides: $[\frac{1}{2}(-\frac{5}{2})]^2 = [-\frac{5}{4}]^2 = \frac{25}{16}$. This completes the square on the left side.

$$\left(x - \frac{5}{4}\right)^2 = \frac{-8}{16} + \frac{25}{16}$$ Factoring and finding a common denominator

$$\left(x - \frac{5}{4}\right)^2 = \frac{17}{16}$$

$$x - \frac{5}{4} = \frac{\sqrt{17}}{4} \quad \textit{or} \quad x - \frac{5}{4} = -\frac{\sqrt{17}}{4}$$ Using the principle of square roots

$$x = \frac{5}{4} + \frac{\sqrt{17}}{4} \quad \textit{or} \quad x = \frac{5}{4} - \frac{\sqrt{17}}{4}$$

The solutions of $2x^2 - 5x + 1 = 0$ are $\frac{5}{4} \pm \frac{\sqrt{17}}{4}$, or $\frac{5 \pm \sqrt{17}}{4}$. The check is left to the student.

The steps in Example 3 can be used to solve *any* quadratic equation.

To Solve $ax^2 + bx + c = 0$ by Completing the Square

1. If $a \neq 1$, multiply both sides of the equation by $1/a$ or divide both sides by a so that the x^2-coefficient is 1.
2. Once the x^2-coefficient is 1, rewrite the equation in the form
$$x^2 + bx = -c, \quad \text{or, if step (1) was needed,}$$
$$x^2 + \frac{b}{a}x = -\frac{c}{a}.$$
3. Take half of the x-coefficient and square it. Add the result to both sides of the equation.
4. Express the left side as the square of a binomial. (Factor.)
5. Use the principle of square roots and complete the solution.

9.2 Exercise Set

FOR EXTRA HELP

Student's Solutions Manual | Digital Video Tutor CD 5 Videotape 17 | AW Math Tutor Center | MathXL Tutorials on CD | MathXL | MyMathLab

Concept Reinforcement *In each of Exercises 1–6, match the equation with the equation from the column on the right to which it is equivalent.*

1. ____	$x^2 + 6x = 2$	**a)** $(x + 3)^2 = 10$
2. ____	$x^2 - 6x + 9 = 10$	**b)** $x^2 - 6x + 9 = 11$
3. ____	$x^2 + 6x + 9 = 10$	**c)** $x^2 + 6x + 9 = 11$
4. ____	$x^2 - 6x = 2$	**d)** $(x + 4)^2 = 18$
5. ____	$x^2 + 8x = 2$	**e)** $(x - 3)^2 = 10$
6. ____	$x^2 - 8x = 2$	**f)** $(x - 4)^2 = 18$

Complete the square. Check by multiplying.

7. $x^2 + 8x$ **8.** $x^2 + 4x$ **9.** $x^2 - 12x$

10. $x^2 - 14x$ **11.** $x^2 - 3x$ **12.** $x^2 - 9x$

13. $t^2 + t$ **14.** $y^2 - y$ **15.** $x^2 + \frac{5}{4}x$

16. $x^2 + \frac{4}{3}x$ **17.** $m^2 - \frac{9}{2}m$ **18.** $r^2 - \frac{2}{5}r$

Solve by completing the square.

19. $x^2 + 8x + 12 = 0$ **20.** $x^2 + 6x - 7 = 0$

21. $x^2 - 24x + 21 = 0$ **22.** $x^2 - 10x + 20 = 0$

23. $3x^2 - 6x - 15 = 0$ **24.** $3x^2 - 12x - 33 = 0$

25. $x^2 - 22x + 102 = 0$ **26.** $t^2 - 18t + 74 = 0$

27. $x^2 + 3x - 3 = 0$ **28.** $t^2 + 8t - 5 = 0$

29. $2x^2 + 6x - 56 = 0$ **30.** $2x^2 - 4x + 1 = 0$

31. $x^2 - \frac{3}{2}x - 2 = 0$ **32.** $x^2 + \frac{5}{2}x - 2 = 0$

33. $2t^2 - 3t - 8 = 0$ **34.** $2x^2 + 3x - 16 = 0$

35. $3x^2 - 4x - 3 = 0$ **36.** $3t^2 + 6t - 1 = 0$

37. $2x^2 = 5 + 9x$ **38.** $2x^2 = 9 + 5x$

39. $6x^2 + 11x = 10$ **40.** $4x^2 + 12x = 7$

41. How does completing the square allow us to solve equations that we could not have otherwise solved?

42. Explain how the addition principle, the multiplication principle, and the square-root principle were used in this section.

SKILL MAINTENANCE

Simplify.

43. $\dfrac{3 + 6x}{3}$ [6.1] **44.** $\dfrac{4 + 2x}{2}$ [6.1]

45. $\dfrac{15 - 10x}{5}$ [6.1] **46.** $\dfrac{18 - 15x}{3}$ [6.1]

47. $\dfrac{24 - 3\sqrt{5}}{9}$ [8.4]

48. $\dfrac{35 - 7\sqrt{6}}{14}$ [8.4]

SYNTHESIS

49. Sal states that "since solving a quadratic equation by completing the square relies on the principle of square roots, the solutions are always opposites of each other." Is Sal correct? Why or why not?

50. When completing the square, what determines if the number being added is a whole number or a fraction?

Find b such that each trinomial is a square.

51. $x^2 + bx + 36$

52. $x^2 + bx + 49$

53. $x^2 + bx + 45$

54. $x^2 + bx + 50$

55. $4x^2 + bx + 16$

56. $x^2 - bx + 48$

Solve each of the following by letting y_1 represent the left side of each equation, letting y_2 represent the right side, and graphing y_1 and y_2 on the same set of axes. INTERSECT *can then be used to determine the x-coordinate at any point of intersection. Find solutions accurate to two decimal places.*

57. $(x + 4)^2 = 13$

58. $(x + 6)^2 = 2$

59. $x^2 - 24x + 21 = 0$ (see Exercise 21)

60. $x^2 + 3x - 3 = 0$ (see Exercise 27)

61. $2x^2 = 9 + 5x$ (see Exercise 38)

62. $2x^2 = 5 + 9x$ (see Exercise 37)

Aha! 63. What is the best way to solve $x^2 + 8x = 0$? Why?

COLLABORATIVE CORNER

Using Areas to Complete the Square

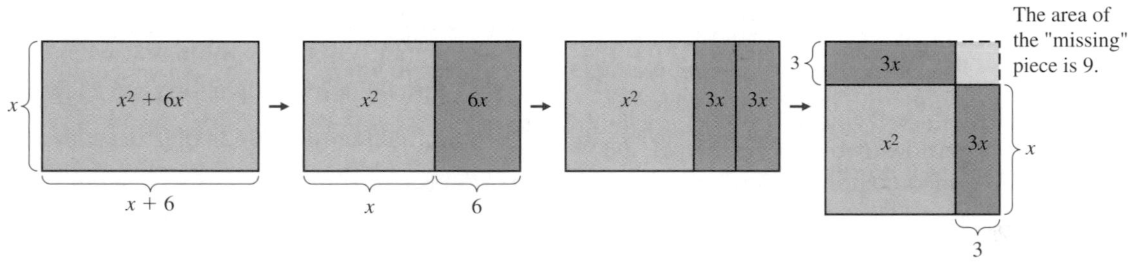

Focus: Visualizing completion of the square
Time: 15–25 minutes
Group size: 2
Materials: Rulers and graph paper may be helpful.

It is not difficult to draw a representation of completing the square. To do so, we use areas and the fact that the area of any rectangle is given by multiplying the length and the width. For example, the above sequence of figures can be drawn to explain why 9 completes the square for $x^2 + 6x$.

ACTIVITY

1. Draw a sequence of four figures, similar to those shown above, to complete the square for $x^2 + 8x$. Group members should take turns, so that each person draws and labels two of the figures.
2. Repeat part (1) to complete the square for $x^2 + 14x$. The person who drew the first drawing in part (1) should take the second turn this time.
3. Keep in mind that when we complete the square, we are not forming an equivalent expression. For this reason, completing the square is generally performed by using the addition principle to form an equivalent *equation*. Use the work in parts (1) and (2) to solve the equations $x^2 + 8x = 9$ and $x^2 + 14x = 15$.
4. Each equation in part (3) has two solutions. Can both be represented geometrically? Why or why not?

9.3 The Quadratic Formula and Applications

The Quadratic Formula • Problem Solving

Study Skills

Crunch Time for the Final

It is always best to study for a final exam over several days or more. If you have only one or two days of study time, however, begin by studying the formulas, problems, properties, and procedures in each chapter's Study Summary. Then do the exercises in the Cumulative Reviews. Make sure to attend a review session if one is offered.

We now derive the *quadratic formula*. In many cases, this formula enables us to solve quadratic equations more quickly than the method of completing the square.

The Quadratic Formula

When mathematicians use a procedure repeatedly, they often try to find a formula for the procedure. The quadratic formula condenses into one calculation the many steps used to solve a quadratic equation by completing the square.

Consider a quadratic equation in *standard form*, $ax^2 + bx + c = 0$, with $a > 0$. Our plan is to solve this equation for x by completing the square. As the steps are performed, compare them with those in Example 3(b) on p. 543:

$$ax^2 + bx + c = 0$$

$$\frac{1}{a}(ax^2 + bx + c) = \frac{1}{a} \cdot 0 \qquad \text{Multiplying by } \frac{1}{a} \text{ to make the } x^2\text{-coefficient 1}$$

$$x^2 + \frac{b}{a}x + \frac{c}{a} = 0$$

$$x^2 + \frac{b}{a}x = -\frac{c}{a} \qquad \text{Adding } -\frac{c}{a} \text{ to both sides}$$

$$x^2 + \frac{b}{a}x + \frac{b^2}{4a^2} = -\frac{c}{a} + \frac{b^2}{4a^2} \qquad \text{Adding } \frac{b^2}{4a^2} \text{ to both sides: } \left[\frac{1}{2} \cdot \frac{b}{a}\right]^2 = \left[\frac{b}{2a}\right]^2 = \frac{b^2}{4a^2}$$

$$\left(x + \frac{b}{2a}\right)^2 = -\frac{4ac}{4a^2} + \frac{b^2}{4a^2} \qquad \text{Factoring and finding a common denominator}$$

$$\left(x + \frac{b}{2a}\right)^2 = \frac{b^2 - 4ac}{4a^2}$$

$$x + \frac{b}{2a} = \sqrt{\frac{b^2 - 4ac}{4a^2}} \quad or \quad x + \frac{b}{2a} = -\sqrt{\frac{b^2 - 4ac}{4a^2}}. \qquad \text{Using the principle of square roots}$$

We assumed $a > 0$, so $\sqrt{4a^2} = 2a$. Thus we can simplify as follows:

$$x + \frac{b}{2a} = \frac{\sqrt{b^2 - 4ac}}{2a} \quad or \quad x + \frac{b}{2a} = -\frac{\sqrt{b^2 - 4ac}}{2a}$$

and

$$x = -\frac{b}{2a} + \frac{\sqrt{b^2 - 4ac}}{2a} \quad or \quad x = -\frac{b}{2a} - \frac{\sqrt{b^2 - 4ac}}{2a}. \qquad \text{Adding } -b/(2a) \text{ to both sides}$$

Thus,

$$x = -\frac{b}{2a} \pm \frac{\sqrt{b^2 - 4ac}}{2a},$$

or

$$x = \frac{-b \pm \sqrt{b^2 - 4ac}}{2a}.$$ Unless $b^2 - 4ac$ is 0, this represents two solutions.

This last equation is the result we sought. It is so useful that it is worth memorizing.

The Quadratic Formula

The solutions of $ax^2 + bx + c = 0$ are given by

$$x = \frac{-b \pm \sqrt{b^2 - 4ac}}{2a}.$$

The quadratic formula also holds when $a < 0$. A similar proof would show this, but we will not consider it here.

EXAMPLE 1 Solve using the quadratic formula.

a) $4x^2 + 5x - 6 = 0$

b) $t^2 = 4t + 7$

c) $x^2 + x = -1$

Student Notes

After identifying which numbers to use as *a, b,* and *c,* be careful to replace only the *letters* in the quadratic formula. The negative sign in $-b$ should be used even when b is negative. Using parentheses, as shown in Example 1, can help in this regard. Also, reading "$-b$" as "the opposite of b" will serve as a reminder of how to substitute correctly.

Solution

a) We identify *a, b,* and *c* and substitute into the quadratic formula:

$$\underset{a}{4}x^2 + \underset{b}{5}x \underset{c}{-6} = 0;$$

$$x = \frac{-b \pm \sqrt{b^2 - 4ac}}{2a}$$

$$x = \frac{-(5) \pm \sqrt{(5)^2 - 4(4)(-6)}}{2(4)}$$ Substituting for *a, b,* and *c*

Be sure to write the fraction bar all the way across.

$$x = \frac{-5 \pm \sqrt{25 - (-96)}}{8}$$

$$x = \frac{-5 \pm \sqrt{121}}{8}$$

$$x = \frac{-5 \pm 11}{8}$$

$$x = \frac{-5 + 11}{8} \quad or \quad x = \frac{-5 - 11}{8}$$

$$x = \frac{6}{8} \quad or \quad x = \frac{-16}{8}$$

$$x = \frac{3}{4} \quad or \quad x = -2.$$

The solutions are $\frac{3}{4}$ and -2.

b) We rewrite $t^2 = 4t + 7$ in standard form, identify a, b, and c, and solve using the quadratic formula:

$$\underset{a}{1}t^2 - \underset{b}{4}t - \underset{c}{7} = 0; \qquad \text{Subtracting } 4t + 7 \text{ from both sides}$$

$$t = \frac{-(-4) \pm \sqrt{(-4)^2 - 4(1)(-7)}}{2 \cdot 1} \qquad \text{Substituting into the quadratic formula}$$

$$t = \frac{4 \pm \sqrt{16 + 28}}{2} = \frac{4 \pm \sqrt{44}}{2}$$

$$t = \frac{4}{2} \pm \frac{\sqrt{44}}{2}$$

$$\left.\begin{aligned} t &= 2 \pm \frac{\sqrt{4}\sqrt{11}}{2} \\ t &= 2 \pm \frac{2\sqrt{11}}{2} \end{aligned}\right\} \quad \text{Simplifying } \sqrt{44}$$

$$t = 2 \pm \sqrt{11}. \qquad \text{Removing a factor equal to 1: } \frac{2}{2} = 1$$

The solutions are $2 + \sqrt{11}$ and $2 - \sqrt{11}$, or $2 \pm \sqrt{11}$.

c) We rewrite $x^2 + x = -1$ in standard form and use the quadratic formula:

$$\underset{a}{1}x^2 + \underset{b}{1}x + \underset{c}{1} = 0; \qquad \text{Adding 1 to both sides}$$

$$x = \frac{-1 \pm \sqrt{1^2 - 4 \cdot 1 \cdot 1}}{2 \cdot 1} \qquad \text{Substituting into the quadratic formula}$$

$$x = \frac{-1 \pm \sqrt{1 - 4}}{2}$$

$$x = \frac{-1 \pm \sqrt{-3}}{2}.$$

Since the radicand, -3, is negative, there are no real-number solutions. In Section 9.5, we will study a number system in which solutions of this equation can be found. For now we simply state, "No real-number solution exists."

technology connection

To see that no real solutions exist for Example 1(c), we let $y_1 = x^2 + x$ and $y_2 = -1$.

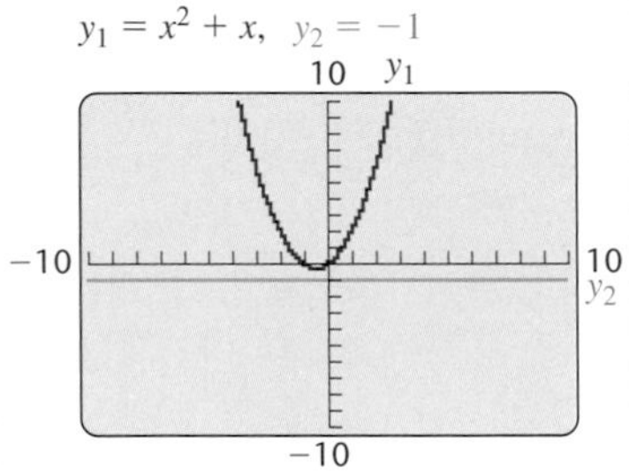

The absence of any point of intersection supports the conclusion that no real-number solution exists.

1. What happens when the INTERSECT feature is used with the graph above?
2. How can the graph of $y = x^2 + x + 1$ be used to provide still another check of Example 1(c)?

CONNECTING THE CONCEPTS

We have now studied four different ways of solving quadratic equations. Each of these methods has certain advantages and disadvantages, as outlined in the chart at right. Note that although the quadratic formula can be used to solve *any* quadratic equation, the other methods are sometimes faster and easier to use.

Method	Advantages	Disadvantages
The quadratic formula	Can be used to solve *any* quadratic equation.	Can be slower than factoring or the principle of square roots.
Completing the square	Works well on equations of the form $x^2 + bx = -c$, where b is even.	Can be complicated when b is odd or a fraction.
The principle of square roots	Fastest way to solve equations of the form $ax^2 = p$, or $(x + k)^2 = p$. Can be used to solve *any* quadratic equation.	Can be slow when completing the square is required.
Factoring	Can be very fast.	Can be used only on certain equations. Many equations are difficult or impossible to solve by factoring.

Problem Solving

EXAMPLE 2 Diagonals in a polygon. The number of diagonals d in a polygon that has n sides is given by the formula

$$d = \frac{n^2 - 3n}{2}.$$

If a polygon has 27 diagonals, how many sides does it have?

Solution

1. **Familiarize.** A sketch can help us to become familiar with the problem. We draw a hexagon (6 sides) and count the diagonals. As the formula predicts, for $n = 6$, there are

$$\frac{6^2 - 3 \cdot 6}{2} = \frac{36 - 18}{2} = \frac{18}{2} = 9 \text{ diagonals.}$$

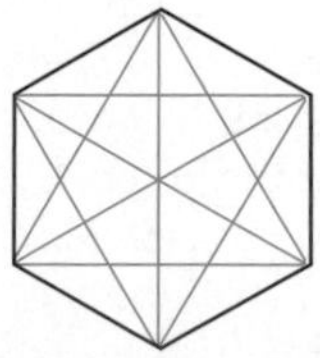

Clearly, the polygon in question must have more than 6 sides. We might suspect that tripling the number of diagonals requires tripling the number of sides. Evaluating the above formula for $n = 18$, you can confirm that this is *not* the case. Rather than continue guessing, we proceed to a translation.

2. **Translate.** Since the number of diagonals is 27, we substitute 27 for d:

$$27 = \frac{n^2 - 3n}{2}.$$

This gives us a translation.

3. **Carry out.** We solve the equation for n, first reversing the equation for convenience:

$$\frac{n^2 - 3n}{2} = 27$$

$$n^2 - 3n = 54 \quad \text{Multiplying both sides by 2 to clear fractions}$$

$$n^2 - 3n - 54 = 0 \quad \text{Subtracting 54 from both sides}$$

$$(n - 9)(n + 6) = 0 \quad \text{Factoring. There is no need for the quadratic formula here.}$$

$$n - 9 = 0 \quad or \quad n + 6 = 0$$

$$n = 9 \quad or \quad n = -6.$$

4. **Check.** Since the number of sides cannot be negative, -6 cannot be a solution. We leave it to the student to show by substitution that 9 checks.

5. **State.** The polygon has 9 sides (it is a nonagon).

EXAMPLE 3

Free-falling objects. The world's highest habitable floor is 1430 ft high at Chicago's Sears Tower (*Source*: *Guinness Book of World Records*, 2004). How many seconds will it take a golf ball to fall from that height? Round to the nearest hundredth.

Solution

1. **Familiarize.** If we did not know anything about this problem, we might consider looking up a formula in a mathematics or physics book. A formula that fits this situation is

$$s = 16t^2, \quad \text{It is useful to remember this formula.}$$

where s is the distance, in feet, traveled by a body falling freely from rest in t seconds. This formula is actually an approximation because it does not account for air resistance. In this problem, we know the distance s to be 1430. We want to determine the time t that it takes the golf ball to reach the ground.

2. **Translate.** The distance is 1430 ft and we need to solve for t. We substitute 1430 for s in the formula above to get the following translation:

$$1430 = 16t^2.$$

3. **Carry out.** Because there is no t-term, we can use the principle of square roots to solve:

$$1430 = 16t^2$$

$$\frac{1430}{16} = t^2 \qquad \text{Solving for } t^2$$

$$\sqrt{\frac{1430}{16}} = t \quad or \quad -\sqrt{\frac{1430}{16}} = t \qquad \text{Using the principle of square roots}$$

$$\frac{\sqrt{1430}}{4} = t \quad or \quad \frac{-\sqrt{1430}}{4} = t$$

$$9.45 \approx t \quad or \quad -9.45 \approx t. \qquad \text{Using a calculator and rounding to the nearest hundredth}$$

4. **Check.** The number -9.45 cannot be a solution because time cannot be negative in this situation. We substitute 9.45 in the original equation:

$$s = 16(9.45)^2 = 16(89.3025) = 1428.84.$$

This is close. Remember that we approximated a solution.

5. **State.** It takes about 9.45 sec for the golf ball to fall to the ground from the top floor of the Sears Tower.

EXAMPLE 4 Right triangles. The hypotenuse of a right triangle is 6 m long. One leg is 1 m longer than the other. Find the lengths of the legs. Round to the nearest hundredth.

Solution

1. **Familiarize.** We first make a drawing and label it. We let $s =$ the length, in meters, of one leg. Then $s + 1 =$ the length, in meters, of the other leg.

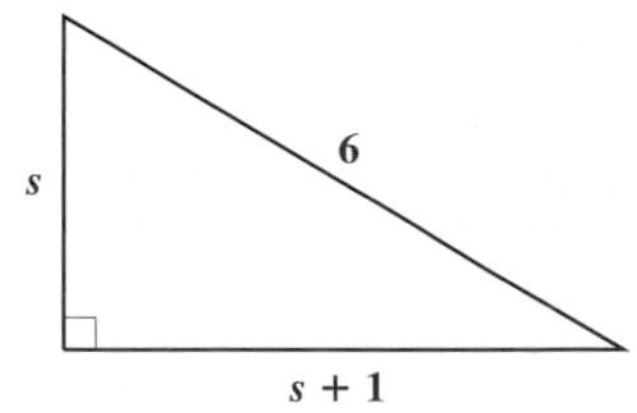

Note that if $s = 3$, then $s + 1 = 4$ and $3^2 + 4^2 = 25 \neq 6^2$. Thus, because of the Pythagorean theorem, we see that $s \neq 3$. Another guess, $s = 4$, is too big since $4^2 + (4 + 1)^2 = 41 \neq 6^2$. Although we have not guessed the solution, we expect s to be between 3 and 4.

2. **Translate.** To translate, we use the Pythagorean theorem:

$$s^2 + (s + 1)^2 = 6^2.$$

3. Carry out. We solve the equation:

$$s^2 + (s + 1)^2 = 6^2$$
$$s^2 + s^2 + 2s + 1 = 36$$
$$\underset{\underset{a}{\uparrow}}{2s^2} + \underset{\underset{b}{\uparrow}}{2s} \underset{\underset{c}{\uparrow}}{- 35} = 0$$

This cannot be factored so we use the quadratic formula.

$$s = \frac{-2 \pm \sqrt{2^2 - 4 \cdot 2(-35)}}{2 \cdot 2}$$

Remember: $s = \dfrac{-b \pm \sqrt{b^2 - 4ac}}{2a}$.

$$s = \frac{-2 \pm \sqrt{4 + 280}}{4} = \frac{-2 \pm \sqrt{284}}{4}$$

$s \approx 3.71$ *or* $s \approx -4.71$. Using a calculator and rounding to the nearest hundredth

4. Check. Length cannot be negative, so -4.71 does not check. Note that if the shorter leg is 3.71 m, the other leg is 4.71 m. Then

$$(3.71)^2 + (4.71)^2 = 13.7641 + 22.1841 = 35.9482$$

and since $35.9482 \approx 6^2$, our answer checks. Also, note that the value of s, 3.71, is between 3 and 4, as predicted in step (1).

5. State. One leg is about 3.71 m long; the other is about 4.71 m long.

9.3 Exercise Set

FOR EXTRA HELP

Student's Solutions Manual | Digital Video Tutor CD 5 Videotape 17 | AW Math Tutor Center | MathXL Tutorials on CD | MathXL | MyMathLab

Concept Reinforcement *In each of Exercises 1–4, match the equation with the method from the column on the right that would most easily solve the equation.*

1. ____ $x^2 + 5x + 6 = 0$
2. ____ $(3t - 1)^2 = 25$
3. ____ $7y^2 + 5y - 4 = 0$
4. ____ $x^2 + 10x = -8$

a) The principle of square roots
b) The quadratic formula
c) Factoring
d) Completing the square

Solve. Try to use factoring, the principle of square roots, or completing the square first. If all of these methods prove difficult, use the quadratic formula. If no real-number solutions exist, state this.

5. $x^2 + 7x = 18$

6. $x^2 - 4x = 21$

7. $x^2 = 8x - 16$

8. $x^2 = 6x - 9$

9. $3y^2 + 7y + 4 = 0$

10. $3y^2 + 2y - 8 = 0$

11. $4x^2 - 12x = 7$

12. $4x^2 + 4x = 15$

13. $t^2 = 64$

14. $t^2 = 81$

15. $x^2 + 4x - 7 = 0$

16. $x^2 + 2x - 2 = 0$

17. $y^2 - 10y + 19 = 0$

18. $y^2 + 6y - 2 = 0$

Aha! **19.** $x^2 + 2x + 1 = 7$

20. $x^2 - 4x + 4 = 5$

21. $3t^2 + 8t + 2 = 0$

22. $3t^2 - 4t - 2 = 0$

23. $2x^2 - 5x = 1$

24. $2x^2 + 2x = 3$

25. $4y^2 + 2y - 3 = 0$

26. $4y^2 - 4y - 3 = 0$

27. $2t^2 - 3t + 2 = 0$

28. $4y^2 + 2y + 3 = 0$

29. $3x^2 - 5x = 4$

30. $2x^2 + 3x = 1$

31. $2y^2 - 6y = 10$

32. $5m^2 = 3 + 11m$

33. $6t^2 + 26t = 20$

34. $7x^2 + 2 = 6x$

35. $5t^2 - 7t = -4$

36. $15t^2 + 10t = 0$

37. $9y^2 = 162$

38. $5t^2 = 100$

Solve using the quadratic formula. Use a calculator to approximate the solutions to the nearest thousandth.

39. $x^2 - 4x - 7 = 0$

40. $x^2 + 2x - 2 = 0$

41. $y^2 - 5y - 1 = 0$

42. $y^2 + 7y + 3 = 0$

43. $4x^2 + 4x = 1$

44. $4x^2 = 4x + 1$

Solve. If an irrational answer occurs, round to the nearest hundredth.

45. A polygon has 35 diagonals. How many sides does it have? (Use $d = (n^2 - 3n)/2$.)

46. A polygon has 20 diagonals. How many sides does it have? (Use $d = (n^2 - 3n)/2$.)

47. *Free-fall time.* At 1482 ft, the Petronas Towers in Malaysia is the world's tallest office building. How long would it take a marble to fall from the top? (Use $s = 16t^2$.)

48. *Free-fall time.* The roof of the Sears Tower in Chicago is 1454 ft high. How long would it take a golf ball to fall from the top? (Use $s = 16t^2$.)

49. *Highest skateboard drop.* The highest drop into a quarterpipe by a skateboarder was 29.6 ft, accomplished by Adil Dyani of Norway. For how long was Dyani airborne? (Use $s = 16t^2$.)
Source: *Guinness Book of World Records*, 2004

50. *Free-fall record.* Stuntman Dar Robinson once fell a record 800 ft from the top of the CN Tower in Toronto before opening a parachute. Approximately how long did the free-fall portion of his jump last? (Use $s = 16t^2$.)
Source: *Guinness Book of World Records*, 2004

51. *Right triangles.* The hypotenuse of a right triangle is 25 ft long. One leg is 17 ft longer than the other. Find the lengths of the legs.

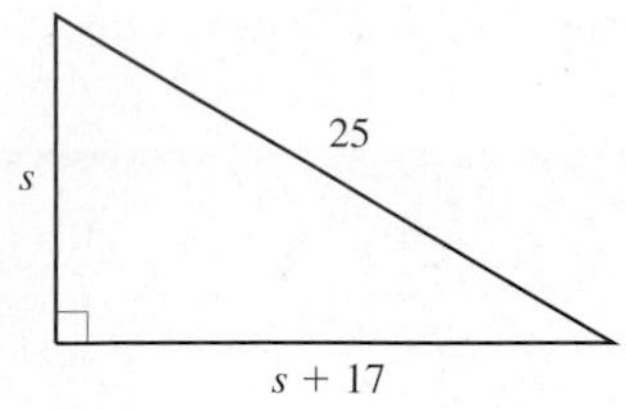

52. *Right triangles.* The hypotenuse of a right triangle is 26 yd long. One leg is 14 yd longer than the other. Find the lengths of the legs.

53. *Area of a rectangle.* The length of a rectangle is 4 cm greater than the width. The area is 60 cm^2. Find the length and the width.

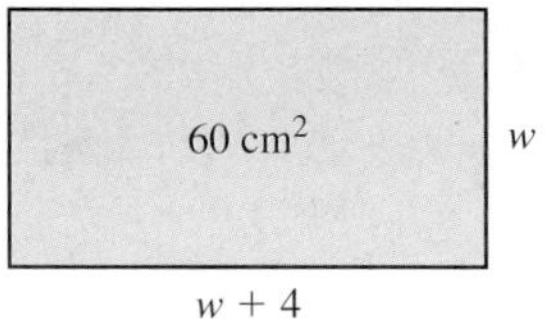

54. *Area of a rectangle.* The length of a rectangle is 3 m greater than the width. The area is 70 m^2. Find the length and the width.

55. *Plumbing.* A drainpipe runs diagonally under a rectangular yard that is 6 m longer than it is wide. If the pipe is 30 m long, determine the dimensions of the yard.

56. *Guy wires.* A 26-ft long guy wire is anchored 10 ft from the base of a telephone pole. How far up the pole does the wire reach?

57. *Right triangles.* The area of a right triangle is 31 m^2. One leg is 2.4 m longer than the other. Find the lengths of the legs.

58. *Right triangles.* The area of a right triangle is 26 cm^2. One leg is 5 cm longer than the other. Find the lengths of the legs.

59. *Area of a rectangle.* The length of a rectangle is 3 in. greater than the width. The area is 30 in^2. Find the length and the width.

60. *Area of a rectangle.* The length of a rectangle is 5 ft greater than the width. The area is 25 ft^2. Find the length and the width.

61. *Area of a rectangle.* The length of a rectangle is twice the width. The area is 16 m^2. Find the length and the width.

62. *Area of a rectangle.* The length of a rectangle is twice the width. The area is 20 cm^2. Find the length and the width.

Investments. The formula $A = P(1 + r)^t$ is used to find the value A to which P dollars grows when invested for t years at an annual interest rate r. In Exercises 63–66, find the interest rate for the given information.

63. \$2000 grows to \$2880 in 2 years

64. \$2560 grows to \$3610 in 2 years

65. \$6000 grows to \$6615 in 2 years

66. \$3125 grows to \$3645 in 2 years

67. *Environmental science.* In 2000, a circular oil slick about 30 km from Cape Town, South Africa, was 20 km^2 in area. How wide was the oil slick?
Source: Environment News Service

68. *Gardening.* Laura has enough mulch to cover 250 ft^2 of garden space. How wide is the largest circular flower garden that Laura can cover with mulch?

69. Under what condition(s) is the quadratic formula *not* the easiest way to solve a quadratic equation?

70. Roy claims to be able to solve any quadratic equation by completing the square. He also claims to be incapable of understanding why the quadratic formula works. Does this strike you as odd? Why or why not?

SKILL MAINTENANCE

Solve.

71. $2x - 7 = 43$ [2.2]

72. $9 - 2x = 1$ [2.2]

73. $\frac{3}{5}t + 6 = 15$ [2.2]

74. $\frac{2}{3}t - 4 = 2$ [2.2]

75. $\sqrt{4x} - 3 = 5$ [8.5]

76. $8 = \sqrt{2x} - 2$ [8.5]

SYNTHESIS

77. Is it possible for a quadratic equation to have one solution that is rational and one that is irrational? Why or why not?

78. Where does the ± symbol in the quadratic formula come from?

Solve.

79. $5x = -x(x - 7)$

80. $x(3x + 7) = 3x$

81. $3 - x(x - 3) = 4$

82. $x(5x - 7) = 1$

83. $(y + 4)(y + 3) = 15$

84. $x^2 + (x + 2)^2 = 7$

85. $\dfrac{x^2}{x + 3} - \dfrac{5}{x + 3} = 0$

86. $\dfrac{x^2}{x + 5} - \dfrac{7}{x + 5} = 0$

87. $\dfrac{1}{x} + \dfrac{1}{x + 1} = \dfrac{1}{3}$

88. $\dfrac{1}{x} + \dfrac{1}{x + 6} = \dfrac{1}{5}$

89. Find r in this figure. Round to the nearest hundredth.

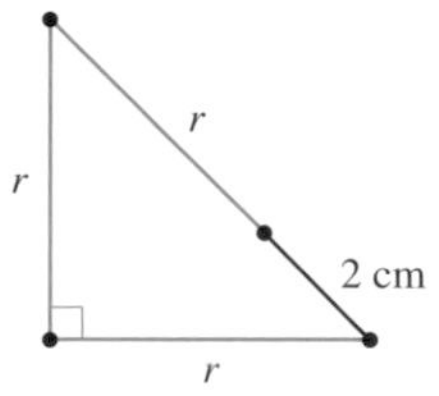

90. *Area of a square.* Find the area of a square for which the diagonal is 3 units longer than the length of the sides.

91. *Golden rectangle.* The so-called *golden rectangle* is said to be extremely pleasing visually and was used often by ancient Greek and Roman architects. The length of a golden rectangle is approximately 1.6 times the width. Find the dimensions of a golden rectangle if its area is 9000 m^2.

92. *Flagpoles.* A 20-ft flagpole is struck by lightning and, while not completely broken, falls over and touches the ground 10 ft from the bottom of the pole. How high up did the pole break?

93. *Investments.* \$4000 is invested at interest rate r for 2 yr. After 1 yr, an additional \$2000 is invested, again at interest rate r. What is the interest rate if \$6510 is in the account at the end of 2 yr?

94. *Investments.* In 2 yr, you want to have \$3000. How much do you need to invest now if you can get an interest rate of 5.75% compounded annually?

95. *Enlarged strike zone.* In baseball, a batter's strike zone is a rectangular area about 15 in. wide and 40 in. high. Many batters subconsciously enlarge this area by 40% when fearful that if they don't swing, the umpire will call the pitch a strike. Assuming that the strike zone is enlarged by an invisible band of uniform width around the actual zone, find the dimensions of the enlarged strike zone.

96. Use a graph to approximate to the nearest thousandth the solutions of Exercises 39–44. Compare your answers with those found using a calculator.

9.4 Formulas and Equations

Solving Formulas

Study Skills

Listen Up!

Many professors make a point of telling their classes what topics or chapters will (or won't) be covered on the final exam. Take special note of this information and base your studying around it.

Formulas arise frequently in the natural and social sciences, business, engineering, and health care. In Section 2.3, we saw that the same steps that are used to solve linear equations can be used to solve a formula that appears in this form. Similarly, the steps that are used to solve a rational, radical, or quadratic equation can also be used to solve a formula that appears in one of these forms. Before turning our attention to these formulas, let's briefly review the steps used to solve each type of equation.

CONNECTING THE CONCEPTS

We have now completed our study of the various types of equations that appear in elementary algebra. Below are examples of each type, along with their solutions.

LINEAR EQUATIONS

$\mathbf{5x + 3 = 2x + 9}$

$3x = 6$	Adding $-2x - 3$ to both sides
$x = 2$	Dividing both sides by 3

The solution is 2.

RADICAL EQUATIONS

$\mathbf{\sqrt{2x+1} - 5 = 2}$

$\sqrt{2x+1} = 7$	Adding 5 to both sides
$2x + 1 = 49$	Squaring both sides
$2x = 48$	Subtracting 1 from both sides
$x = 24$	Dividing both sides by 2

The solution is 24.

RATIONAL EQUATIONS

$\mathbf{\dfrac{5}{2x} + \dfrac{4}{3x} = 2}$	Note that $x \neq 0$.
$6x\left(\dfrac{5}{2x} + \dfrac{4}{3x}\right) = 6x \cdot 2$	Multiplying both sides by the LCD, $6x$
$\dfrac{6x \cdot 5}{2x} + \dfrac{6x \cdot 4}{3x} = 12x$	Using the distributive law
$15 + 8 = 12x$	Simplifying
$23 = 12x$	
$\dfrac{23}{12} = x$	

The solution is $\frac{23}{12}$.

QUADRATIC EQUATIONS

$\mathbf{2x^2 + 3x = 1}$	Subtracting 1 from both sides
$2x^2 + 3x - 1 = 0$	
$x = \dfrac{-3 \pm \sqrt{3^2 - 4(2)(-1)}}{2 \cdot 2}$	Using the quadratic formula
$x = \dfrac{-3 \pm \sqrt{17}}{4}$	

The solutions are $\dfrac{-3}{4} + \dfrac{\sqrt{17}}{4}$ and $\dfrac{-3}{4} - \dfrac{\sqrt{17}}{4}$.

It is always wise to check solutions in the original equation, but this is especially important with radical or rational equations. The checks for the equations above are left to the student.

EXAMPLE 1 Solve: **(a)** $3x + 17 = 8x$; **(b)** $\frac{3}{4x} + \frac{x}{6} = 1$; **(c)** $5 + \sqrt{2x} = 8$.

Solution

a)

$$\begin{aligned} 3x + 17 &= 8x && \text{Recognizing this as a linear equation} \\ 17 &= 5x && \text{Subtracting } 3x \text{ from both sides} \\ \frac{17}{5} &= x && \text{Dividing both sides by 5} \end{aligned}$$

The solution is $\frac{17}{5}$. The check is left to the student.

b)

$$\begin{aligned} \frac{3}{4x} + \frac{x}{6} &= 1 && \text{Recognizing this as a rational equation} \\ 12x\left(\frac{3}{4x} + \frac{x}{6}\right) &= 12x \cdot 1 && \text{Multiplying both sides by the LCD, } 12x \\ \frac{12x \cdot 3}{4x} + \frac{12x \cdot x}{6} &= 12x && \text{Using the distributive law} \\ 9 + 2x^2 &= 12x && \text{Simplifying: } \frac{12x \cdot 3}{4x} = 3 \cdot 3; \frac{12x \cdot x}{6} = 2x \cdot x \\ 2x^2 - 12x + 9 &= 0 && \text{Subtracting } 12x \text{ from both sides} \end{aligned}$$

$$x = \frac{-(-12) \pm \sqrt{(-12)^2 - 4 \cdot 2 \cdot 9}}{2 \cdot 2} \qquad \text{Using the quadratic formula}$$

$$\left.\begin{aligned} x &= \frac{12 \pm \sqrt{72}}{4} = \frac{12}{4} \pm \frac{\sqrt{36}\sqrt{2}}{4} \\ x &= 3 \pm \frac{6\sqrt{2}}{4} = 3 \pm \frac{3}{2}\sqrt{2} \end{aligned}\right\} \quad \text{Simplifying}$$

The solutions are $3 - \frac{3}{2}\sqrt{2}$ and $3 + \frac{3}{2}\sqrt{2}$. Note that neither solution creates a denominator equal to 0. A complete check is left to the student.

c)

$$\begin{aligned} 5 + \sqrt{2x} &= 8 && \text{Recognizing this as a radical equation} \\ \sqrt{2x} &= 3 && \text{Subtracting 5 from both sides} \\ 2x &= 9 && \text{Using the principle of powers: squaring both sides} \\ x &= \tfrac{9}{2} && \text{Dividing both sides by 2} \end{aligned}$$

Check:

$5 + \sqrt{2x} = 8$	
$5 + \sqrt{2 \cdot \frac{9}{2}}$	8
$5 + \sqrt{9}$	

$5 + 3 \overset{?}{=} 8$ TRUE

The solution is $\frac{9}{2}$.

technology connection

To check Example 1(b), let $y_1 = \frac{3}{4x} + \frac{x}{6}$ and $y_2 = 1$.

$y_1 = 3/(4x) + x/6,\ y_2 = 1$

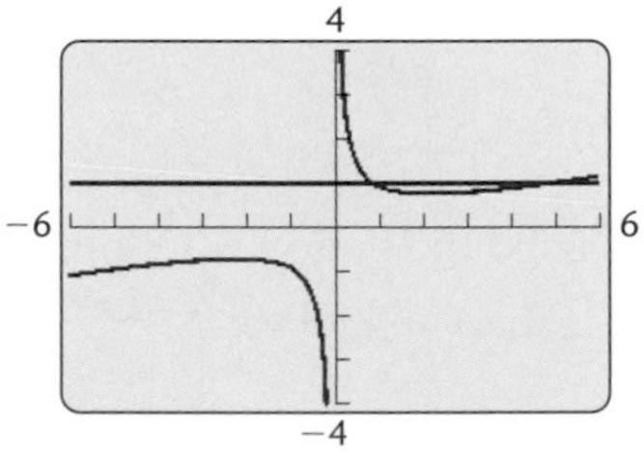

The graph of $y_2 = 1$ appears to intersect the curve in two points.

1. Use the INTERSECT feature to determine the solutions of Example 1(b) to the nearest hundredth.
2. How do your solutions compare with those found using the quadratic formula?

Solving Formulas

Formulas can be linear, rational, radical, or quadratic equations, as well as other types of equations that are beyond the scope of this text. To solve formulas, we use the same steps that we use to solve equations. Probably the greatest difference is that while the solution of an equation is a number, the solution of a formula is generally a variable expression.

EXAMPLE 2 Intelligence quotient. The formula $Q = \dfrac{100m}{c}$ is used to determine the intelligence quotient, Q, of a person of mental age m and chronological age c. Solve for c.

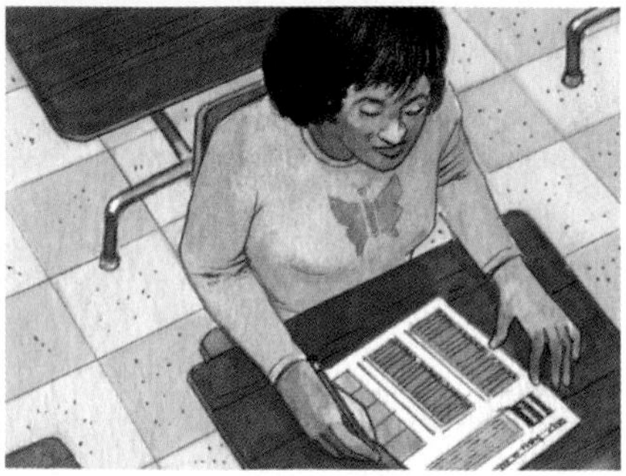

Solution We have

$$Q = \frac{100m}{c}$$

$$c \cdot Q = c \cdot \frac{100m}{c} \qquad \text{Multiplying both sides by } c$$

$$cQ = 100m \qquad \text{Removing a factor equal to 1: } \frac{c}{c} = 1$$

$$c = \frac{100m}{Q}. \qquad \text{Dividing both sides by } Q$$

This formula can be used to determine a person's chronological, or actual, age from his or her mental age and intelligence quotient.

EXAMPLE 3 A work formula. The formula $t/a + t/b = 1$ was used in Section 6.7. Solve this formula for t.

Solution We have

$$\frac{t}{a} + \frac{t}{b} = 1$$

$$ab\left(\frac{t}{a} + \frac{t}{b}\right) = ab \cdot 1 \qquad \text{Multiplying by the LCD, } ab\text{, to clear fractions}$$

$$\left.\begin{aligned} \frac{\cancel{a}bt}{\cancel{a}} + \frac{a\cancel{b}t}{\cancel{b}} &= ab \\ bt + at &= ab. \end{aligned}\right\} \qquad \text{Multiplying to remove parentheses and removing factors equal to 1: } \frac{a}{a} = 1 \text{ and } \frac{b}{b} = 1$$

If the last equation were $3t + 2t = 6$, we would simply combine like terms ($3t + 2t$ is $5t$) and then divide by the coefficient of t (which would be 5). Since $bt + at$ *cannot* be combined, we factor instead:

$$(b + a)t = ab \qquad \text{Factoring out } t\text{, the letter for which we are solving}$$

$$t = \frac{ab}{b + a}. \qquad \text{Dividing both sides by } b + a$$

The answer to Example 3 can be used when the times required to do a job independently (a and b) are known and t represents the time required to complete the task working together.

EXAMPLE 4 Temperature of a fluid. The temperature T of a fluid being heated by a steady flame or burner can be determined by the formula $T = a + b\sqrt{ct}$, where a is the initial temperature of the fluid, b and c are constants determined by the intensity of the heat and the type of fluid used, and t is time. Solve for t.

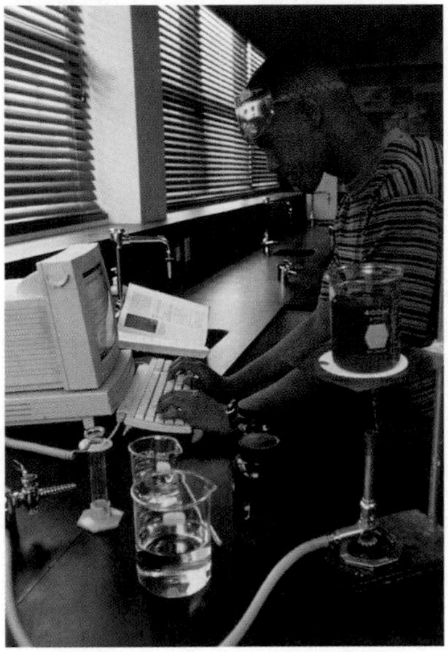

Solution We have

$$T = a + b\sqrt{ct}$$

$$T - a = b\sqrt{ct} \quad \text{Subtracting } a \text{ from both sides}$$

$$\frac{T - a}{b} = \sqrt{ct} \quad \text{Dividing both sides by } b$$

$$\left(\frac{T - a}{b}\right)^2 = ct \quad \text{Using the principle of powers: squaring both sides}$$

$$\frac{T^2 - 2Ta + a^2}{b^2} = ct \quad \text{Squaring } T - a \text{ and } b$$

$$\frac{T^2 - 2Ta + a^2}{b^2c} = t. \quad \text{Dividing both sides by } c$$

This equation can be used to determine the heating time required for an experiment.

In some cases, the quadratic formula is needed.

EXAMPLE 5 A physics formula. The distance s of an object from some established point can be determined using the formula $s = s_0 + v_0t + \frac{1}{2}at^2$, where s_0 is the object's original distance from the point, v_0 is the object's original velocity, a is the object's acceleration, and t is time. Solve for t.

Solution Note first that t appears in two terms, raised to the first and then the second powers. Thus the equation is "quadratic in t," and the quadratic formula is needed:

$$\frac{1}{2}at^2 + v_0t + s_0 = s \quad \text{Rewriting the equation from left to right}$$

$$\underbrace{\tfrac{1}{2}}_{a}at^2 + \underbrace{v_0}_{b}t + \underbrace{s_0 - s}_{c} = 0; \quad \text{Subtracting } s \text{ from both sides and identifying the coefficients needed for the quadratic formula}$$

$$t = \frac{-v_0 \pm \sqrt{v_0^2 - 4\left(\frac{1}{2}a\right)(s_0 - s)}}{2 \cdot \frac{1}{2}a} \quad \text{Substituting into the quadratic formula}$$

$$\left.\begin{aligned} t &= \frac{-v_0 \pm \sqrt{v_0^2 - 2a(s_0 - s)}}{a} \\ t &= \frac{-v_0 \pm \sqrt{v_0^2 - 2as_0 + 2as}}{a}. \end{aligned}\right\} \quad \text{Simplifying}$$

9.4 Exercise Set

FOR EXTRA HELP

Student's Solutions Manual | Digital Video Tutor CD 6 Videotape 18 | AW Math Tutor Center | MathXL Tutorials on CD | MathXL | MyMathLab

Solve.

1. $3x + 8 = 7x + 4$

2. $x - 9 = 5x + 4$

3. $x^2 = 5x - 6$

4. $3x + 4 = x^2$

5. $3 + \sqrt{x} = 8$

6. $7 = \sqrt{x} - 5$

7. $\frac{5}{x} + \frac{3}{4} = 2$

8. $\frac{2}{5} + \frac{3}{x} = 4$

9. $4x - 7 = 2(5x - 3)$

10. $4(2x - 1) = 3x - 5$

11. $\frac{2}{9x} - \frac{5}{6} = 1$

12. $\frac{3}{10x} - \frac{4}{5x} = 6$

13. $3t^2 - 7t + 2 = 0$

14. $2t^2 - 7t + 3 = 0$

15. $11 = 4\sqrt{3t} - 5$

16. $5\sqrt{2t} - 7 = 3$

17. $\frac{3}{10t} + \frac{t}{5} = 1$

18. $\frac{1}{4t} + \frac{t}{6} = 2$

19. $7t - 1 = 2(3 - t) + 5$

20. $5t - 3 = 4(1 - t) + 2$

21. $3\sqrt{2t - 1} = 2\sqrt{5t + 3}$

22. $5\sqrt{3t + 2} = 4\sqrt{2t - 3}$

23. $2n - 1 = 3n^2$

24. $3 - 5n = 2n^2$

25. $1 - \frac{3}{7n} = \frac{5}{14}$

26. $4 - \frac{5}{6n} = \frac{1}{12}$

Solve each formula for the specified variable.

27. $s = \frac{1}{2}gt^2$, for g

(A physics formula for distance)

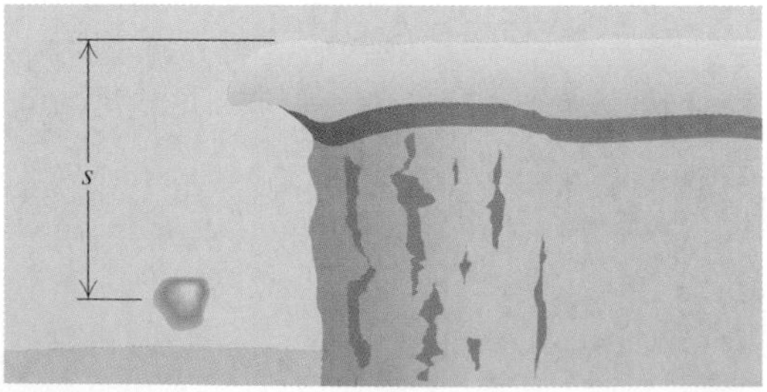

28. $A = \frac{1}{2}bh$, for h

(The area of a triangle)

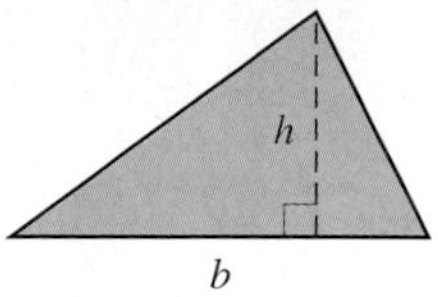

29. $A = P(1 + rt)$, for t

(An investment formula)

30. $S = 2\pi rh$, for h

(A formula for surface area)

31. $d = c\sqrt{h}$, for h

(A formula for distance to the horizon)

32. $n = c + \sqrt{t}$, for t

(A formula for population)

33. $\frac{1}{R} = \frac{1}{r_1} + \frac{1}{r_2}$, for R

(An electricity formula)

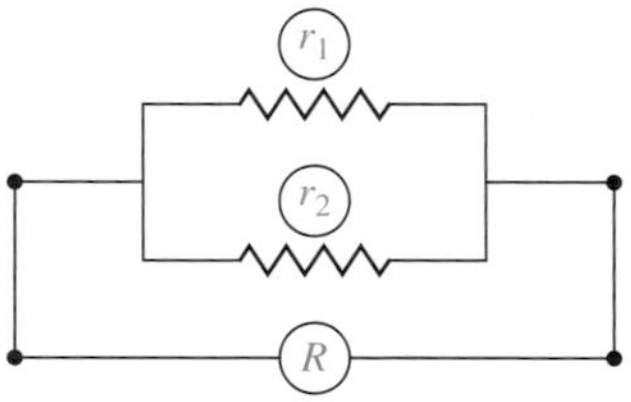

34. $\frac{1}{p} + \frac{1}{q} = \frac{1}{f}$, for f

(An optics formula)

Aha! **35.** $ax^2 + bx + c = 0$, for x

36. $(x - d)^2 = k$, for x

37. $\frac{m}{n} = p - q$, for n

38. $\frac{M - g}{t} = r + s$, for t

39. $Ax + By = C$, for y

(An equation for a line)

40. $T = mg + mf$, for m

41. $S = 2\pi r(r + h)$, for h
(The surface area of a right circular cylinder)

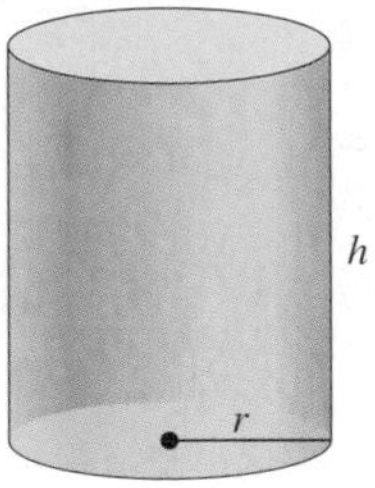

42. $ab = ac + d$, for a

43. $\frac{s}{h} = \frac{h}{t}$, for h
(A geometry formula)

44. $\frac{x}{y} = \frac{z}{x}$, for x

45. $mt^2 + nt - p = 0$, for t
(*Hint*: Use the quadratic formula.)

46. $rs^2 - ts + p = 0$, for s

47. $\frac{m}{n} = r$, for n

48. $s + t = \frac{r}{v}$, for v

49. $m + t = \frac{n}{m}$, for m

50. $x - y = \frac{z}{y}$, for y

51. $n = p - 3\sqrt{t + c}$, for t

52. $M - m\sqrt{ct} = r$, for t

53. $\sqrt{m - n} = \sqrt{3t}$, for n

54. $\sqrt{2t + s} = \sqrt{s - t}$, for t

55. Is it easier to solve

$$\frac{1}{25} + \frac{1}{23} = \frac{1}{x} \text{ for } x,$$

or to solve

$$\frac{1}{p} + \frac{1}{q} = \frac{1}{f} \text{ for } f?$$

Explain why.

56. Explain why someone might want to solve

$$A = \tfrac{1}{2}bh \text{ for } h.$$

(See Exercise 28.)

SKILL MAINTENANCE

Simplify. [8.2]

57. $\sqrt{6} \cdot \sqrt{10}$

58. $\sqrt{21} \cdot \sqrt{15}$

59. $\sqrt{150}$

60. $\sqrt{63}$

61. $\sqrt{4a^7b^4}$

62. $\sqrt{9x^8y^5}$

SYNTHESIS

63. As a step in solving a formula for a certain variable, a student takes the reciprocal on both sides of the equation. Is a mistake being made? Why or why not?

64. Describe a situation in which the result of Example 3,

$$t = \frac{ab}{b + a},$$

would be especially useful.

65. *Health care.* Young's rule for determining the size of a particular child's medicine dosage c is

$$c = \frac{a}{a + 12} \cdot d,$$

where a is the child's age and d is the typical adult dosage. If a child receives 8 mg of antihistamine when the typical adult receives 24 mg, how old is the child?

Source: Olsen, June Looby, Leon J. Ablon, and Anthony Patrick Giangrasso, *Medical Dosage Calculations*, 6th ed., p. A-31

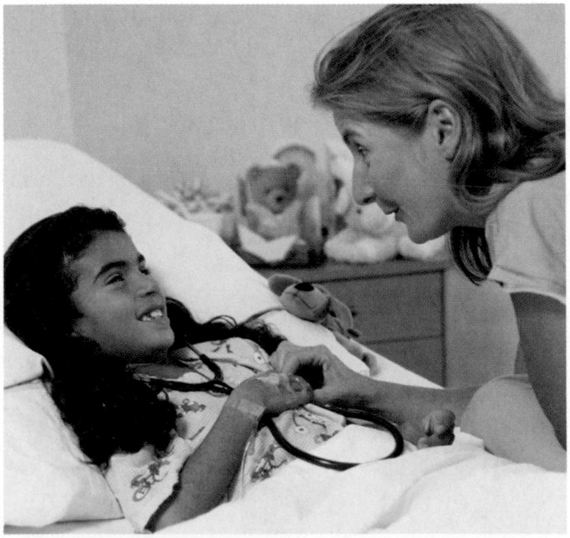

Solve.

66. $Sr = \frac{rl - a}{r - l}$, for r

67. $fm = \frac{gm - t}{m}$, for m

68. $\frac{n_1}{p_1} + \frac{n_2}{p_2} = \frac{n_2 - n_1}{R}$, for n_2

69. *Economics.* The formula

$$V = \frac{k}{\sqrt{at + b}} + c$$

can be used to estimate the value of certain items that depreciate over time. Solve for t.

70. *Marine biology.* The formula

$$N = \frac{(b + d)f_1 - v}{(b - v)f_2}$$

is used when monitoring the water in fisheries. Solve for v.

71. *Meteorology.* The formula

$$C = \tfrac{5}{9}(F - 32)$$

is used to convert the Fahrenheit temperature F to the Celsius temperature C. At what temperature are the Fahrenheit and Celsius readings the same?

9.5 Complex Numbers as Solutions of Quadratic Equations

The Complex-Number System • Solutions of Equations

The Complex-Number System

Because negative numbers do not have square roots that are real numbers, mathematicians have devised a larger set of numbers known as *complex numbers*. In the complex-number system, the number i is used to represent the square root of -1.

The Number i

We define the number $i = \sqrt{-1}$. That is, $i = \sqrt{-1}$ and $i^2 = -1$.

The existence of i allows us to work with numbers like $\sqrt{-3}$.

EXAMPLE 1 Express in terms of i.

a) $\sqrt{-3}$

b) $\sqrt{-25}$

c) $-\sqrt{-10}$

d) $\sqrt{-24}$

Study Skills

Summing It All Up

In preparation for a final exam, many students find it helpful to write up a few pages of notes that represent the most important concepts of the course. After doing so, it is a good idea to try to condense those notes down to just one page. This exercise will help you focus on the most important material.

Student Notes

Do not confuse the a and the b in the expression $a + bi$ with the a and the b used in the quadratic formula.

Solution

a) $\sqrt{-3} = \sqrt{-1 \cdot 3} = \sqrt{-1} \cdot \sqrt{3} = i\sqrt{3}$, or $\sqrt{3}i$ ← *i* is *not* under the radical.

b) $\sqrt{-25} = \sqrt{-1 \cdot 25} = \sqrt{-1} \cdot \sqrt{25} = i \cdot 5 = 5i$

c) $-\sqrt{-10} = -\sqrt{-1 \cdot 10} = -\sqrt{-1} \cdot \sqrt{10} = -i\sqrt{10}$, or $-\sqrt{10}i$

d) $\sqrt{-24} = \sqrt{4(-1)6} = \sqrt{4}\sqrt{-1}\sqrt{6} = 2i\sqrt{6}$, or $2\sqrt{6}i$

Imaginary Numbers

An *imaginary* number* is a number that can be written in the form $a + bi$, where a and b are real numbers and $b \neq 0$.

The following are examples of imaginary numbers:

$$3 + 8i, \qquad \sqrt{7} - 2i, \qquad 4 + \sqrt{6}i, \quad \text{and} \quad 4i \text{ (here } a = 0).^{\dagger}$$

Imaginary numbers can be thought of as "nonreal." Together, the imaginary numbers and the real numbers form the set of **complex numbers**.

Complex Numbers

A *complex number* is any number that can be written as $a + bi$, where a and b are real numbers. (Note that a and b both can be 0.)

It may help to remember that every real number is a complex number ($a + bi$ with $b = 0$), but not every complex number is real ($a + bi$ with $b \neq 0$). For example, numbers like $2 + 3i$ and $-7i$ are complex but not real.

Solutions of Equations

As we saw in Example 1(c) of Section 9.3, not all quadratic equations have real-number solutions. All quadratic equations *do* have complex-number solutions. These solutions are usually written in the form $a + bi$ unless a or b is zero.

*The name "imaginary" should not lead you to believe that these numbers are not useful. Imaginary numbers have important applications in engineering and the physical sciences.

†Numbers like $4i$ are often called *pure imaginary* because they are of the form $0 + bi$.

EXAMPLE 2 Solve: **(a)** $x^2 + 3x + 4 = 0$; **(b)** $x^2 + 2 = 2x$.

Solution

a) We use the quadratic formula:

$$1x^2 + 3x + 4 = 0$$

$$x = \frac{-3 \pm \sqrt{3^2 - 4 \cdot 1 \cdot 4}}{2 \cdot 1} \qquad \text{Remember: } x = \frac{-b \pm \sqrt{b^2 - 4ac}}{2a}.$$

$$x = \frac{-3 \pm \sqrt{-7}}{2} \qquad \text{Simplifying}$$

$$\left.\begin{aligned} x &= \frac{-3 \pm \sqrt{-1}\sqrt{7}}{2} \\ x &= \frac{-3 \pm i\sqrt{7}}{2} \end{aligned}\right\} \quad \text{Rewriting } \sqrt{-7} \text{ as } i\sqrt{7}$$

$$x = -\frac{3}{2} \pm \frac{\sqrt{7}}{2}i. \qquad \text{Writing in the form } a + bi$$

The solutions are $-\frac{3}{2} + \frac{\sqrt{7}}{2}i$ and $-\frac{3}{2} - \frac{\sqrt{7}}{2}i$.

b) We have

$$x^2 + 2 = 2x$$

$$1x^2 - 2x + 2 = 0 \qquad \text{Rewriting in standard form and identifying } a, b, \text{ and } c$$

$$x = \frac{-(-2) \pm \sqrt{(-2)^2 - 4 \cdot 1 \cdot 2}}{2 \cdot 1} \qquad x = \frac{-b \pm \sqrt{b^2 - 4ac}}{2a}$$

$$x = \frac{2 \pm \sqrt{-4}}{2} \qquad \text{Simplifying}$$

$$x = \frac{2 \pm \sqrt{-1}\sqrt{4}}{2}$$

$$x = \frac{2 \pm i2}{2} \qquad \sqrt{-1} = i \text{ and } \sqrt{4} = 2$$

$$x = \frac{2}{2} \pm \frac{2i}{2} \qquad \text{Rewriting in the form } a + bi$$

$$x = 1 \pm i. \qquad \text{Simplifying}$$

The solutions are $1 + i$ and $1 - i$.

9.5 Exercise Set

FOR EXTRA HELP

Student's Solutions Manual | Digital Video Tutor CD 6 Videotape 18 | AW Math Tutor Center | MathXL Tutorials on CD | MathXL | MyMathLab

Concept Reinforcement *Classify each statement as either true or false.*

1. Every complex number is a real number.
2. Many complex numbers are real numbers.
3. Many complex numbers are imaginary numbers.
4. Every complex number is an imaginary number.

Express in terms of i.

5. $\sqrt{-1}$
6. $\sqrt{-36}$
7. $\sqrt{-81}$
8. $\sqrt{-16}$
9. $\sqrt{-50}$
10. $\sqrt{-44}$
11. $-\sqrt{-45}$
12. $-\sqrt{-20}$
13. $-\sqrt{-18}$
14. $-\sqrt{-28}$
15. $4 + \sqrt{-49}$
16. $7 + \sqrt{-4}$
17. $3 + \sqrt{-9}$
18. $-8 - \sqrt{-36}$
19. $5 - \sqrt{-98}$
20. $-2 + \sqrt{-125}$

Solve.

21. $x^2 + 9 = 0$
22. $x^2 + 4 = 0$
23. $x^2 = -28$
24. $x^2 = -48$
25. $t^2 + 4t + 5 = 0$
26. $t^2 - 4t + 6 = 0$
27. $(t + 3)^2 = -16$
28. $(t - 2)^2 = -25$
29. $x^2 + 5 = 2x$
30. $x^2 + 3 = -2x$
31. $t^2 + 7 - 4t = 0$
32. $t^2 + 8 + 4t = 0$
33. $2t^2 + 6t + 5 = 0$
34. $4y^2 + 3y + 2 = 0$
35. $1 + 2m + 3m^2 = 0$
36. $4p^2 + 3 = 6p$
37. Is it possible for a quadratic equation to have one imaginary-number solution and one real-number solution? Why or why not?
38. Under what condition(s) will an equation of the form $x^2 = c$ have imaginary-number solutions?

SKILL MAINTENANCE

Graph. [3.2]

39. $y = \frac{3}{5}x$
40. $2x - 3y = 10$
41. $y = -4x$
42. $x = 2$

Simplify. [1.8]

43. Aha! $(-17)^2 - (8 + 9)^2$
44. $-1(-4)^2(43)0$

SYNTHESIS

45. When using the quadratic formula to solve an equation, if $b^2 < 4ac$, are the solutions imaginary? Why or why not?
46. Can imaginary-number solutions of a quadratic equation be found using the method of completing the square? Why or why not?

Solve.

47. $(x + 1)^2 + (x + 3)^2 = 0$
48. $(p + 5)^2 + (p + 1)^2 = 0$
49. $\dfrac{2x - 1}{5} - \dfrac{2}{x} = \dfrac{x}{2}$
50. $\dfrac{1}{a - 1} - \dfrac{2}{a - 1} = 3a$
51. Use a graphing calculator to confirm that there are no real-number solutions of Examples 2(a) and 2(b).

9.6 Graphs of Quadratic Equations

Graphing Equations of the Form $y = ax^2$ •
Graphing Equations of the Form $y = ax^2 + bx + c$

In this section, we will graph quadratic equations like

$$y = \tfrac{1}{2}x^2, \qquad y = x^2 + 2x - 3, \quad \text{and} \quad y = -5x^2 + 4.$$

Such equations, of the form $y = ax^2 + bx + c$ with $a \neq 0$, have graphs that are either cupped upward or downward. These graphs are symmetric with respect to an **axis of symmetry**, as shown below. When folded along its axis, the graph has two halves that match exactly.

Study Skills

Get Some Rest

The final exam is probably your most important math test of the semester. Do yourself a favor and see to it that you get a good night's sleep the night before. Being well rested will help guarantee that you put forth your best work.

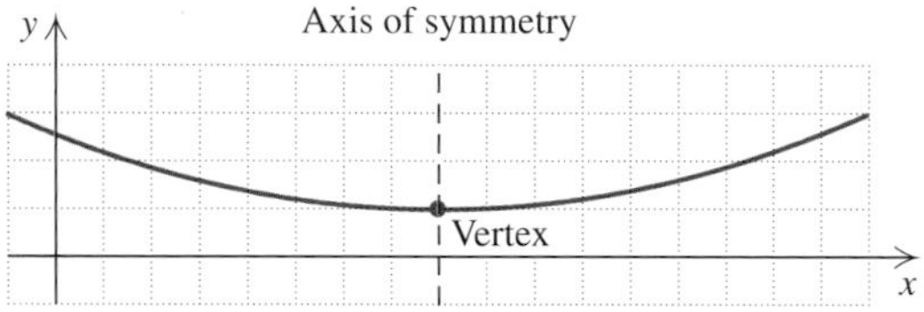

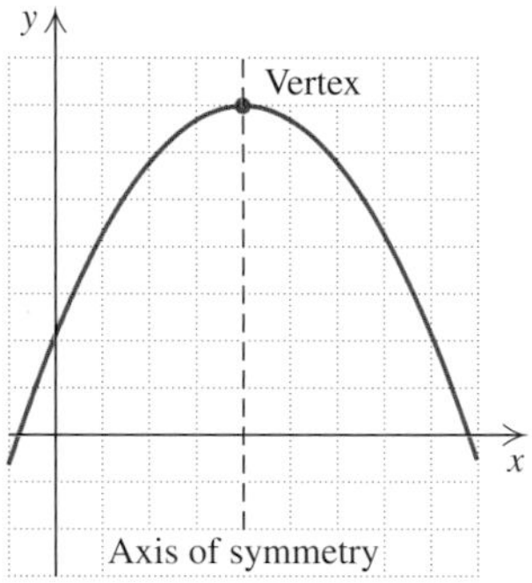

The point at which the graph of a quadratic equation crosses its axis of symmetry is called the **vertex** (plural, vertices). The y-coordinate of the vertex is the graph's largest value of y (if the curve opens downward) or smallest value of y (if the curve opens upward). Graphs of quadratic equations are called **parabolas**.

Graphing Equations of the Form $y = ax^2$

The simplest parabolas to sketch are given by equations of the form $y = ax^2$.

EXAMPLE 1 Graph: $y = x^2$.

Solution We choose numbers for x and find the corresponding values for y.

If $x = -2$, then $y = (-2)^2 = 4$. We get the pair $(-2, 4)$.
If $x = -1$, then $y = (-1)^2 = 1$. We get the pair $(-1, 1)$.
If $x = 0$, then $y = 0^2 = 0$. We get the pair $(0, 0)$.
If $x = 1$, then $y = 1^2 = 1$. We get the pair $(1, 1)$.
If $x = 2$, then $y = 2^2 = 4$. We get the pair $(2, 4)$.

The following table lists these solutions of $y = x^2$. After several ordered pairs are found, we plot them and connect them with a smooth curve.

x	y $y = x^2$	(x, y)
−2	4	(−2, 4)
−1	1	(−1, 1)
0	0	(0, 0)
1	1	(1, 1)
2	4	(2, 4)

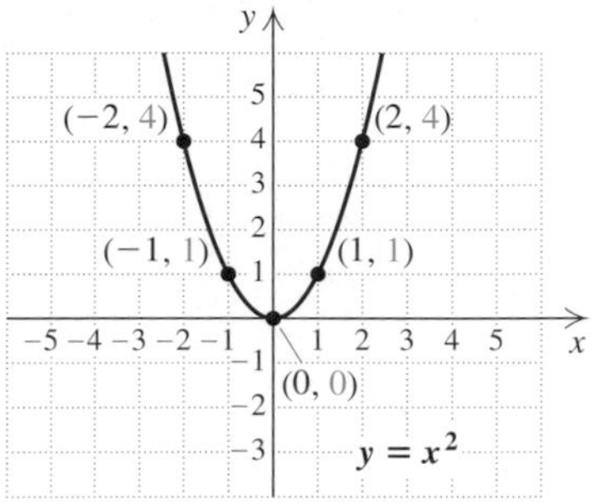

In Example 1, the vertex is (0, 0) and the axis of symmetry is the y-axis. This will be the case for any parabola having an equation of the form $y = ax^2$.

EXAMPLE 2 Graph: $y = -\frac{1}{2}x^2$.

Solution We select numbers for x, find the corresponding y-values, plot the resulting ordered pairs, and connect them with a smooth curve.

x	y $y = -\frac{1}{2}x^2$	(x, y)
−4	−8	(−4, −8)
−2	−2	(−2, −2)
0	0	(0, 0)
2	−2	(2, −2)
4	−8	(4, −8)

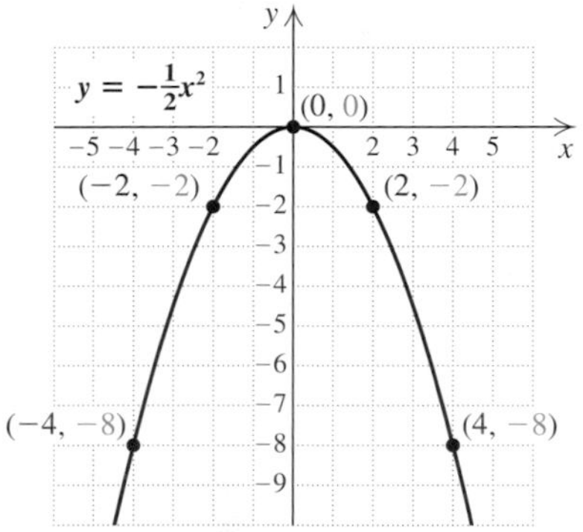

Graphing Equations of the Form $y = ax^2 + bx + c$

Recall from our work with lines that it is often very useful to know the x- and y-intercepts of a line. Intercepts are also useful when graphing parabolas. To find the intercepts of a parabola, we use the same approach we used with lines.

The Intercepts of a Parabola

To find the y-intercept of the graph of $y = ax^2 + bx + c$, replace x with 0 and solve for y. The result will be c.

To find the x-intercept(s) of the graph of $y = ax^2 + bx + c$, if any exist, replace y with 0 and solve for x, To do this, factor or use the quadratic formula. If no real solution exists, there are no x-intercepts.

EXAMPLE 3 Find all y- and x-intercepts of the graph of $y = 2x^2 - x - 28$.

Solution To find the y-intercept, we replace x with 0 and solve for y:

$$y = 2 \cdot 0^2 - 0 - 28$$
$$y = 0 - 0 - 28$$
$$y = -28.$$

When x is 0, we have $y = -28$. Thus the y-intercept is $(0, -28)$.

To find the x-intercept(s), we replace y with 0 and solve for x:

$$0 = 2x^2 - x - 28.$$

The quadratic formula could be used, but factoring is faster:

$$0 = (2x + 7)(x - 4) \quad \text{Factoring}$$
$$2x + 7 = 0 \quad \text{or} \quad x - 4 = 0$$
$$2x = -7 \quad \text{or} \quad x = 4$$
$$x = -\tfrac{7}{2} \quad \text{or} \quad x = 4.$$

Student Notes

The graphs of some parabolas do not cross the horizontal axis. For example, if the parabola in Example 3 had the same vertex, but opened downward instead of upward, no x-intercepts would exist.

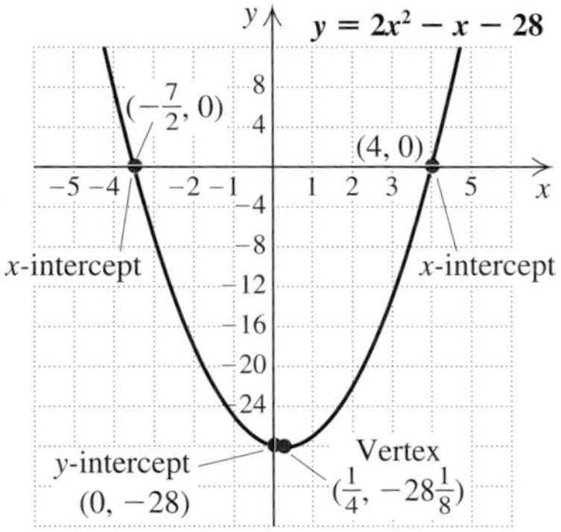

The x-intercepts are $(4, 0)$ and $\left(-\frac{7}{2}, 0\right)$. The y-intercept is $(0, -28)$.

Although we were not asked to graph the equation in Example 3, we did so to show that the x-coordinate of the vertex, $\frac{1}{4}$, is exactly midway between the x-intercepts. The quadratic formula, $x = \dfrac{-b \pm \sqrt{b^2 - 4ac}}{2a}$, can be used to locate x-intercepts when an equation of the form $y = ax^2 + bx + c$ is graphed. If one x-intercept is determined by $\dfrac{-b - \sqrt{b^2 - 4ac}}{2a}$ and the other by $\dfrac{-b + \sqrt{b^2 - 4ac}}{2a}$, then the average of these two values can be used to find the x-coordinate of the vertex. In Exercise 42, you are asked to show that this x-value is $\dfrac{-b}{2a}$. A more complicated approach can be used to show that the x-value of the vertex is $\dfrac{-b}{2a}$ even when no x-intercepts exist.

The Vertex of a Parabola

For a parabola given by the quadratic equation $y = ax^2 + bx + c$:

1. The x-coordinate of the vertex is $-\dfrac{b}{2a}$.
2. The y-coordinate of the vertex is found by substituting $-\dfrac{b}{2a}$ for x and solving for y.

EXAMPLE 4 Graph: $y = x^2 + 2x - 3$.

Solution Our plan is to plot the vertex and some points on either side of the vertex. We will then draw a parabola passing through these points.

To locate the vertex, we use $-b/(2a)$ to find its x-coordinate:

$$\begin{aligned} x\text{-coordinate of the vertex} &= -\frac{b}{2a} = -\frac{2}{2\cdot(1)} \\ &= -1. \end{aligned}$$

We substitute -1 for x to find the y-coordinate of the vertex:

$$\begin{aligned} y\text{-coordinate of the vertex} &= (-1)^2 + 2(-1) - 3 = 1 - 2 - 3 \\ &= -4. \end{aligned}$$

The vertex is $(-1, -4)$. The axis of symmetry is $x = -1$.

We choose some x-values on both sides of the vertex and graph the parabola.

	y	
x	$y = x^2 + 2x - 3$	(x, y)
-4	5	$(-4, 5)$
-3	0	$(-3, 0)$ ← x-intercept
-2	-3	$(-2, -3)$
-1	-4	$(-1, -4)$ ← Vertex
0	-3	$(0, -3)$ ← y-intercept
1	0	$(1, 0)$ ← x-intercept
2	5	$(2, 5)$

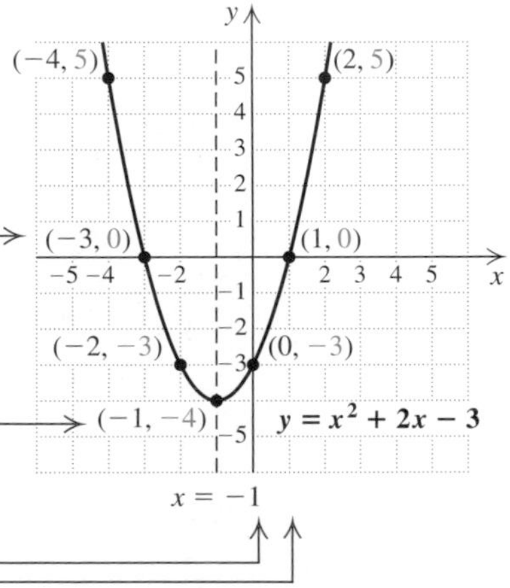

One tip for graphing quadratic equations involves the coefficient of x^2. The sign of a in $y = ax^2 + bx + c$ tells us whether the graph opens upward or downward. When a is positive, as in Examples 1, 3, and 4, the graph opens upward; when a is negative, as in Example 2, the graph opens downward.

EXAMPLE 5 Graph: $y = -2x^2 + 4x + 1$.

Solution Since the coefficient of x^2 is negative, we know that the graph opens downward. To locate the vertex, we first find its x-coordinate:

$$x\text{-coordinate of the vertex} = -\frac{b}{2a} = -\frac{4}{2 \cdot (-2)}$$
$$= 1.$$

We substitute 1 for x to find the y-coordinate of the vertex:

$$y\text{-coordinate of the vertex} = -2 \cdot 1^2 + 4 \cdot 1 + 1 = -2 + 4 + 1$$
$$= 3.$$

The vertex is $(1, 3)$. The axis of symmetry is $x = 1$.

We choose some x-values on both sides of the vertex, calculate their corresponding y-values, and graph the parabola.

	y	
x	$y = -2x^2 + 4x + 1$	(x, y)
3	−5	(3, −5)
2	1	(2, 1)
1	3	(1, 3)
0	1	(0, 1)
−1	−5	(−1, −5)

← This is the vertex.

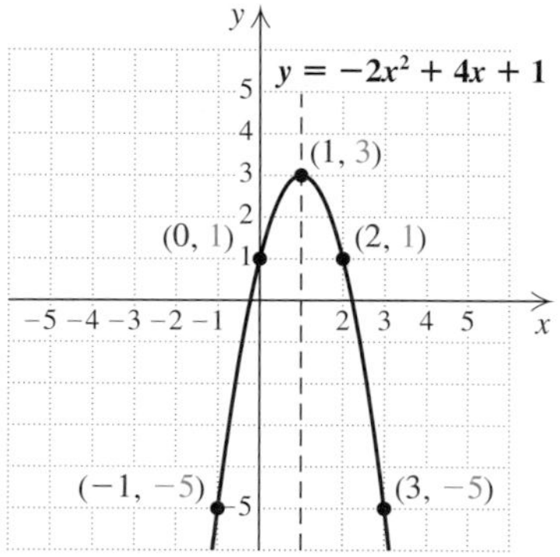

A second tip for graphing quadratic equations can cut our calculation time in half. In Examples 1–5, note that any x-value to the left of the vertex is paired with the same y-value as an x-value the same distance to the right of the vertex. Thus, since the vertex for Example 5 is $(1, 3)$ and since the x-values -1 and 3 are both 2 units from 1, we know that -1 and 3 are both paired with the same y-value. This symmetry provides a useful check and allows us to plot *two* points after calculating just *one*.

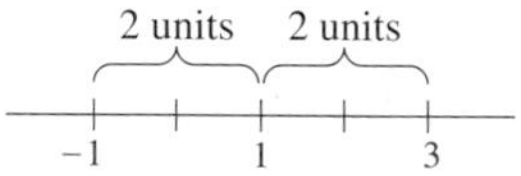

Guidelines for Graphing Quadratic Equations

1. Graphs of quadratic equations, $y = ax^2 + bx + c$, are parabolas. They are cupped upward if $a > 0$ and downward if $a < 0$.
2. Use the formula $x = -b/(2a)$ to find the x-coordinate of the vertex. After calculating the y-coordinate, plot the vertex and some points on either side of it.
3. After a point has been graphed, a second point with the same y-coordinate can be found on the opposite side of the axis of symmetry.
4. Graph the y-intercept and, if requested, any x-intercepts.

9.6 Exercise Set

FOR EXTRA HELP

Student's Solutions Manual | Digital Video Tutor CD 6 Videotape 18 | AW Math Tutor Center | MathXL Tutorials on CD | MathXL | MyMathLab

Graph each quadratic equation, labeling the vertex and the y-intercept.

1. $y = x^2 + 3$

2. $y = x^2 + 2$

3. $y = -2x^2$

4. $y = -1 \cdot x^2$

5. $y = x^2 + x - 6$

6. $y = -x^2 + 2x$

7. $y = x^2 + 2x + 1$

8. $y = x^2 + 2x - 3$

9. $y = 2x^2 - 12x + 13$

10. $y = 3x^2 - 12x + 11$

11. $y = -3x^2 - 2x + 8$

12. $y = -2x^2 - 4x + 1$

13. $y = -\frac{1}{3}x^2$

14. $y = \frac{1}{4}x^2$

15. $y = -\frac{1}{2}x^2 + 5$

16. $y = \frac{1}{2}x^2 - 7$

17. $y = x^2 - 3x$

18. $y = x^2 + 4x$

Graph each equation, labeling the vertex, the y-intercept, and any x-intercepts. If an x-intercept is irrational, round to three decimal places.

19. $y = x^2 + 2x - 8$

20. $y = x^2 + x - 6$

21. $y = 2x^2 - 6x$

22. $y = 2x^2 - 7x$

23. $y = -x^2 - x + 12$

24. $y = -x^2 - 3x + 10$

25. $y = 3x^2 - 6x + 1$

26. $y = 3x^2 + 12x + 11$

27. $y = x^2 + 2x + 3$

28. $y = -x^2 - 2x - 3$

29. $y = 3 - 4x - 2x^2$

30. $y = 1 - 4x - 2x^2$

31. Why is it helpful to know the coordinates of the vertex when graphing a parabola?

32. Suppose that both x-intercepts of a parabola are known. What is the easiest way to find the coordinates of the vertex?

SKILL MAINTENANCE

Evaluate. [4.2]

33. $3a^2 - 5a$, for $a = -1$

34. $4t^2 + 3t$, for $t = 2$

35. $5x^3 - 2x$, for $x = -1$

36. $3t^4 + 5t^2$, for $t = 2$

37. $-9.8x^5 + 3.2x$, for $x = 1$

38. $-32t^2 - 3t$, for $t = 0$

SYNTHESIS

39. Describe a method that could be used to find an equation for a parabola that has x-intercepts at r_1 and r_2.

40. What effect does the size of $|a|$ have on the graph of $y = ax^2 + bx + c$?

41. *Height of a golf ball.* The height H, in feet, of a golf ball with an initial velocity of 96 ft/sec is given by the equation

$$H = -16t^2 + 96t,$$

where t is the number of seconds from launch. Use the graph of this equation, shown below, or any equation-solving technique to answer the following.

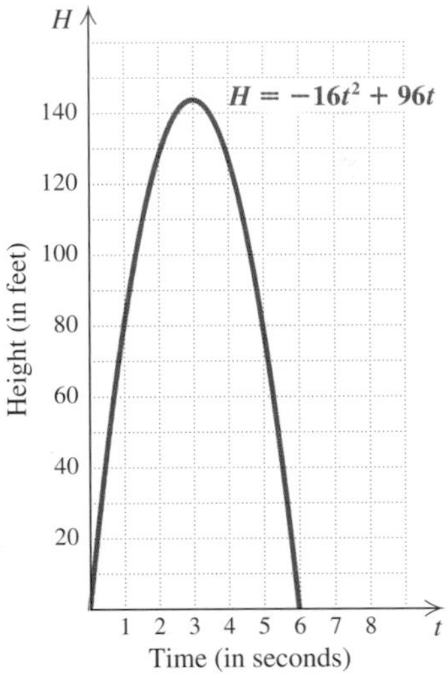

a) How many seconds after launch is the golf ball 128 ft above ground?

b) When does the golf ball reach its maximum height?

Aha! **c)** How many seconds after launch does the golf ball return to the ground?

42. Show that the average of

$$\frac{-b - \sqrt{b^2 - 4ac}}{2a} \quad \text{and} \quad \frac{-b + \sqrt{b^2 - 4ac}}{2a}$$

is $-\dfrac{b}{2a}$.

43. *Stopping distance.* In how many feet can a car stop if it is traveling at a speed of r mph? One estimate, developed in Britain, is as follows. The distance d, in feet, is given by

$$d = \underbrace{\text{Thinking distance (in feet)}}_{r} + \underbrace{\text{Stopping distance (in feet)}}_{0.05r^2}$$

$$d = r + 0.05r^2.$$

a) How many feet would it take to stop a car traveling 25 mph? 40 mph? 55 mph? 65 mph? 75 mph? 100 mph?

b) Graph the equation, assuming $r \geq 0$.

44. On one set of axes, graph $y = x^2$, $y = (x - 3)^2$, and $y = (x + 1)^2$. Describe the effect that h has on the graph of $y = (x - h)^2$.

45. On one set of axes, graph $y = x^2$, $y = x^2 - 5$, and $y = x^2 + 2$. Describe the effect that k has on the graph of $y = x^2 + k$.

46. *Seller's supply.* As the price of a product increases, the seller is willing to sell, or *supply,* more of the product. Suppose that the supply for a certain product is given by

$$S = p^2 + p + 10,$$

where p is the price in dollars and S is the number sold, in thousands, at that price. Graph the equation for values of p such that $0 \leq p \leq 6$.

47. *Consumer's demand.* As the price of a product increases, consumers purchase, or *demand,* less of the product. Suppose that the demand for a certain product is given by

$$D = (p - 6)^2,$$

where p is the price in dollars and D is the number sold, in thousands, at that price. Graph the equation for values of p such that $0 \leq p \leq 6$.

48. *Equilibrium point.* The price p at which the consumer and the seller agree determines the *equilibrium point.* Find p such that

$$D = S$$

for the demand and supply curves in Exercises 46 and 47. How many units of the product will be sold at that price?

49. Use a graphing calculator to draw the graph of $y = x^2 - 5$ and then, using the graph, estimate $\sqrt{5}$ to four decimal places.

9.7 Functions

Identifying Functions • Functions Written as Formulas • Function Notation • Graphs of Functions • Recognizing Graphs of Functions

Functions are enormously important in modern mathematics. The more mathematics you study, the more you will use functions.

Identifying Functions

Functions appear regularly in magazines and newspapers although they are usually not referred to as such. To motivate understanding of functions, consider the numbers and letters on a touch-tone telephone keypad.

Study Skills

Ask to See Your Final

Once the course is over, many students neglect to find out how they fared on the final exam. Please don't overlook this valuable opportunity to extend your learning. It is important for you to find out what mistakes you may have made and to be certain no grading errors have occurred.

Note that to each letter there corresponds *exactly one* number. A correspondence of this type is called a **function**.

> **Function**
>
> A *function* is a correspondence (or rule) that assigns to each member of some set (called the *domain*) exactly one member of a set (called the *range*).

Sometimes the members of the domain are called **inputs**, and the members of the range **outputs**.

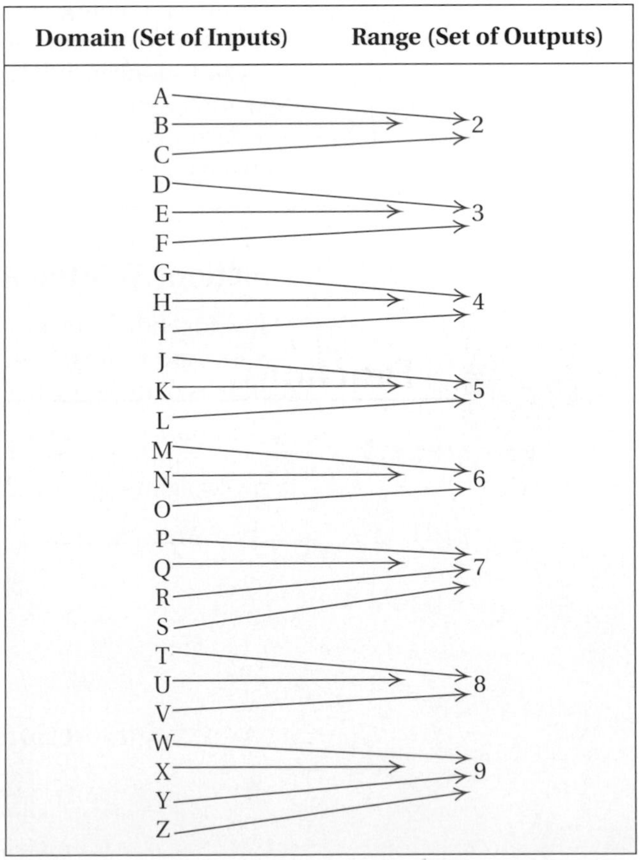

The function above can be written as a set of ordered pairs. Note that each input has exactly *one* output, even though each output is used three or four times:

{(A, 2), (B, 2), (C, 2), (D, 3), (E, 3), (F, 3), (G, 4), (H, 4), (I, 4), (J, 5), (K, 5), (L, 5), (M, 6), (N, 6), (O, 6), (P, 7), (Q, 7), (R, 7), (S, 7), (T, 8), (U, 8), (V, 8), (W, 9), (X, 9), (Y, 9), (Z, 9)}.

EXAMPLE 1 Determine whether or not each of the following correspondences is a function.

f: *Domain* → *Range*
- a → 7
- b → 3
- c → 4

g: *Domain* → *Range*
- 3 → 5
- 4 → 9
- 5 → −7
- 6 → −7

h: *Domain* → *Range*
- New York → Mets
- New York → Yankees
- Florida → Marlins
- Texas → Rangers

p: *Domain* → *Range*
- Cubs → Chicago
- White Sox → Chicago
- Orioles → Baltimore
- Padres → San Diego

Solution Correspondence f *is* a function because each member of the domain is matched to just one member of the range.

Correspondence g *is* also a function because each member of the domain is matched to just one member of the range.

Correspondence h is *not* a function because one member of the domain, New York, is matched to more than one member of the range.

Correspondence p *is* a function because each member of the domain is paired with just one member of the range.

Functions Written as Formulas

Many functions are described by formulas. Equations like $y = x + 3$ and $y = 4x^2$ are examples of such formulas. Outputs are found by substituting members of the domain for x.

EXAMPLE 2 Thunderstorm distance. During a thunderstorm, it is possible to calculate how far away lightning is by using the formula

$$M = \tfrac{1}{5}t.$$

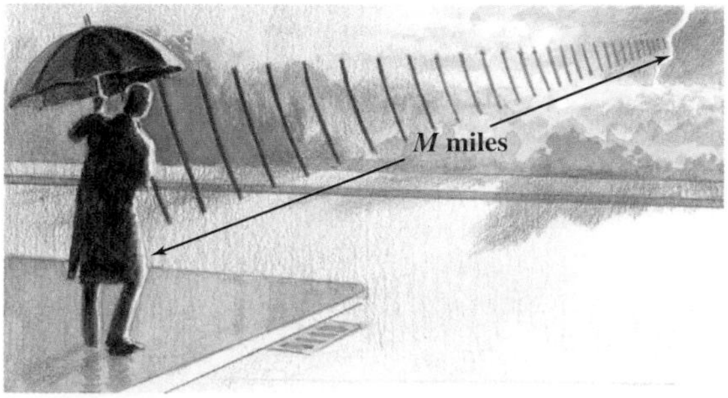

Here M is the distance, in miles, that a storm is from an observer when the sound of thunder arrives t seconds after the lightning has been sighted.

Complete the following table for this function.

t (in seconds)	0	1	2	3	4	5	6	10
M (in miles)	0	$\frac{1}{5}$						

Solution To complete the table, we substitute values of t and compute M.

For $t = 2$, $M = \frac{1}{5} \cdot 2 = \frac{2}{5}$; For $t = 3$, $M = \frac{1}{5} \cdot 3 = \frac{3}{5}$;

For $t = 4$, $M = \frac{1}{5} \cdot 4 = \frac{4}{5}$; For $t = 5$, $M = \frac{1}{5} \cdot 5 = 1$;

For $t = 6$, $M = \frac{1}{5} \cdot 6 = \frac{6}{5}$, or $1\frac{1}{5}$; For $t = 10$, $M = \frac{1}{5} \cdot 10 = 2$.

Function Notation

In Example 2, it was somewhat time-consuming to repeatedly write "For $t = \square$, $M = \frac{1}{5} \cdot \square$." Function notation clearly and concisely presents inputs and outputs together. The notation $M(t)$, read "M of t," denotes the output that is paired with the input t by the function M. Thus, for Example 2,

$M(2) = \frac{1}{5} \cdot 2 = \frac{2}{5}$, $M(3) = \frac{1}{5} \cdot 3 = \frac{3}{5}$, and, in general, $M(t) = \frac{1}{5} \cdot t$.

The notation $M(4) = \frac{4}{5}$ means "when 4 is the input, $\frac{4}{5}$ is the output."

> *Caution!* $M(4)$ *does not* mean M times 4 and should not be read or pronounced that way.

Equations for nonvertical lines can be written in function notation. For example, $f(x) = x + 2$, read "f of x equals x plus 2," can be used instead of $y = x + 2$ when we are discussing functions, although both equations describe the same correspondence.

EXAMPLE 3 For the function given by $f(x) = x + 2$, find each of the following.

a) $f(8)$

b) $f(-3)$

c) $f(0)$

Solution

a) $f(8) = 8 + 2$, or 10 This function adds 2 to each input.

b) $f(-3) = -3 + 2$, or -1 $f(-3)$ is read "f of -3."

c) $f(0) = 0 + 2$, or 2 $f(0)$ *does not mean* $f \cdot 0$.

Student Notes

Functions are so important in mathematics that they will likely be prominent in any subsequent math course you take. The time you invest in studying functions now will pay you dividends in the future.

It is sometimes helpful to think of a function as a machine that gives an output for each input that enters the machine. The following diagram is one way in which the function given by $g(t) = 2t^2 + t$ can be illustrated.

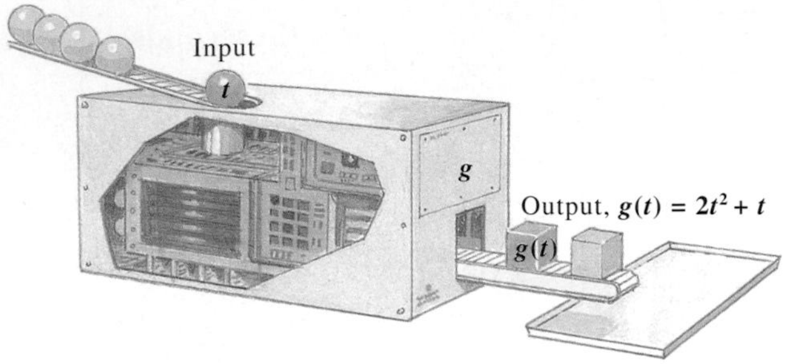

EXAMPLE 4 For the function $g(t) = 2t^2 + t$, find each of the following.

a) $g(3)$ **b)** $g(0)$ **c)** $g(-2)$

Solution

a) $g(3) = 2 \cdot 3^2 + 3$ Using 3 for each occurrence of t
$= 2 \cdot 9 + 3$
$= 21$

b) $g(0) = 2 \cdot 0^2 + 0$ Using 0 for each occurrence of t
$= 0$

c) $g(-2) = 2(-2)^2 + (-2)$ Using -2 for each occurrence of t
$= 2 \cdot 4 - 2$
$= 6$

technology connection

There are several ways in which to check Example 4. We can enter $y_1 = 2x^2 + x$ and use TRACE, and then (on most calculators) enter the desired input. We can also use CALC and VALUE, or the TABLE feature. Yet another way to check is to use the VARS or Y-VARS key to access the function y_1. Parentheses can then be used to complete the writing of $y_1(3)$. When ENTER is pressed, we see the output 21. Use this approach to find $y_1(0)$ and $y_1(-2)$.

Outputs are also called **function values**. In Example 4, $g(-2) = 6$. We can say that the "function value at -2 is 6," or "when x is -2, the value of the function is 6." Most often we say "g of -2 is 6."

Graphs of Functions

To graph a function, we usually calculate ordered pairs of the form (x, y) or $(x, f(x))$, plot them, and connect the points. The symbols y and $f(x)$ are often used interchangeably when working with functions and their graphs.

EXAMPLE 5 Graph: $f(x) = x + 2$.

Solution A list of some function values is shown in the following table. We plot the points and connect them. The graph is a straight line.

x	$f(x)$
−4	−2
−3	−1
−2	0
−1	1
0	2
1	3
2	4
3	5
4	6

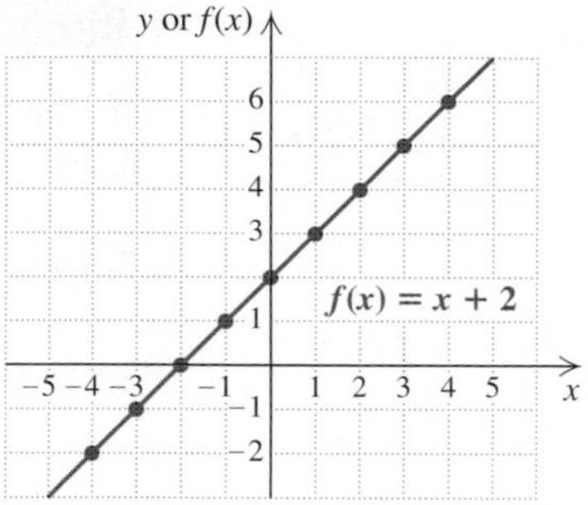

EXAMPLE 6 Graph: $g(x) = 4 - x^2$.

Solution Recall from Section 9.6 that the graph is a parabola. We calculate some function values and draw the curve.

$$g(0) = 4 - 0^2 = 4 - 0 = 4,$$
$$g(-1) = 4 - (-1)^2 = 4 - 1 = 3,$$
$$g(2) = 4 - (2)^2 = 4 - 4 = 0,$$
$$g(-3) = 4 - (-3)^2 = 4 - 9 = -5$$

x	$g(x)$
−3	−5
−2	0
−1	3
0	4
1	3
2	0
3	−5

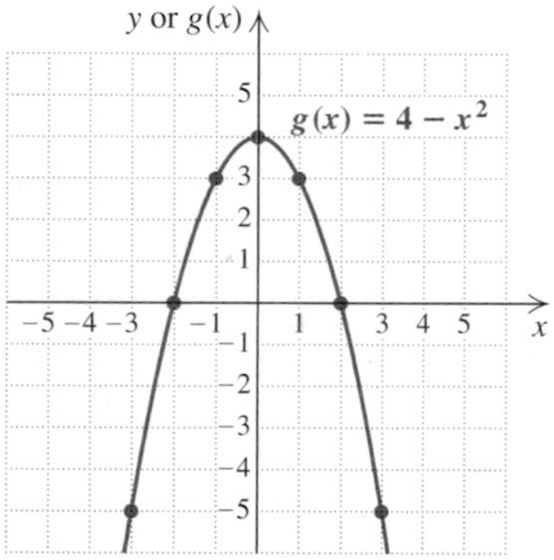

EXAMPLE 7 Graph: $h(x) = |x|$.

Solution A list of some function values is shown in the following table. We plot the points and connect them. The graph is V-shaped and symmetric, rising on either side of the vertical axis.

x	$h(x)$
−3	3
−2	2
−1	1
0	0
1	1
2	2
3	3

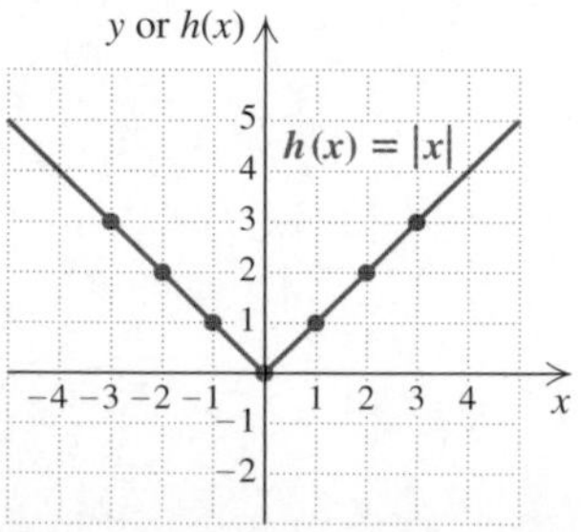

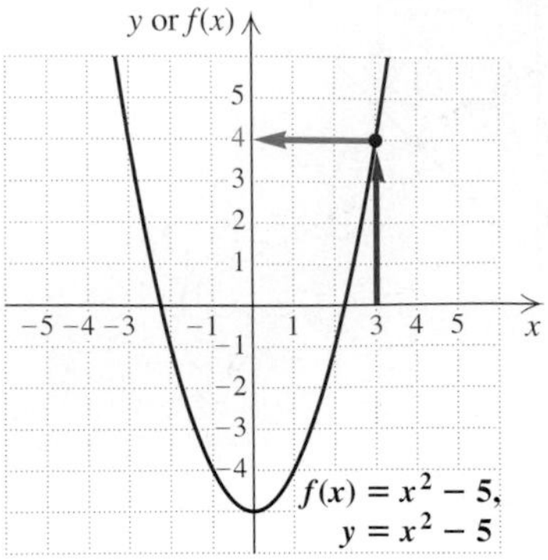

Recognizing Graphs of Functions

Consider the function f described by $f(x) = x^2 - 5$. Its graph is shown at left. It is also the graph of the equation $y = x^2 - 5$.

To find a function value, like $f(3)$, from a graph, we locate the input on the horizontal axis, move vertically to the graph of the function, and then horizontally to find the output on the vertical axis, where members of the range are found.

Recall that when one member of the domain is paired with two or more different members of the range, the correspondence is not a function. Thus, when a graph contains two or more points with the same first coordinate, it cannot represent a function. Points sharing a common first coordinate are vertically above and below each other, as shown in the following figure.

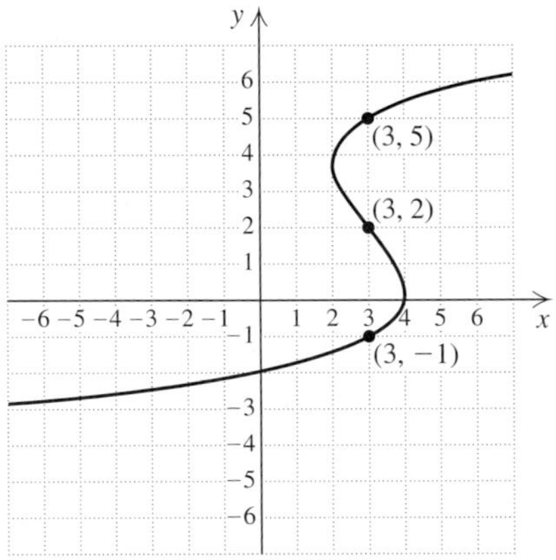

Since 3 is paired with more than one member of the range, the graph does not represent a function.

This observation leads to the *vertical-line test.*

> **The Vertical-Line Test**
>
> A graph represents a function if it is impossible to draw a vertical line that intersects the graph more than once.

EXAMPLE 8 Determine whether each of the following is the graph of a function.

a)

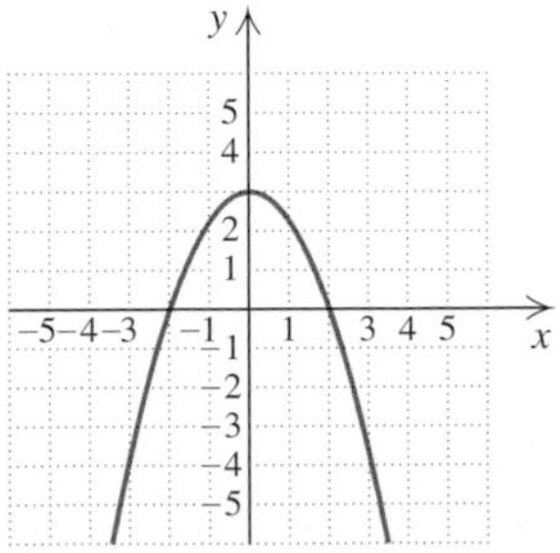

b)

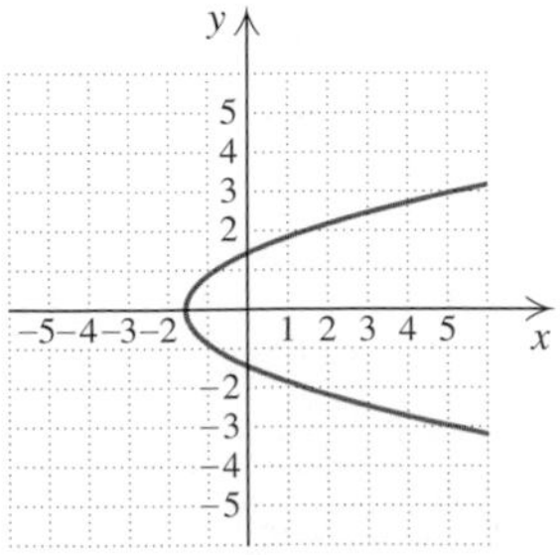

c)

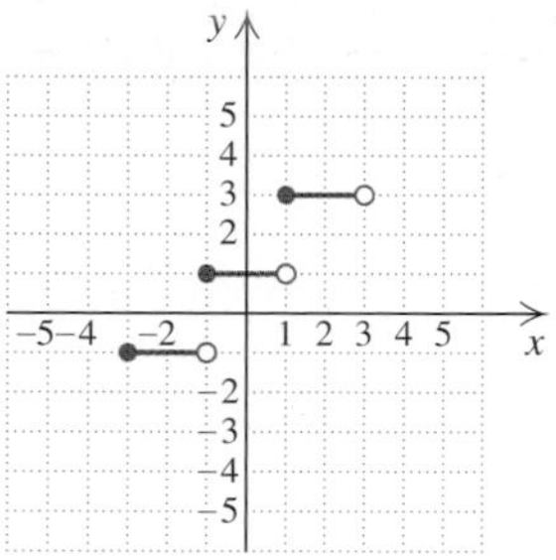

d)

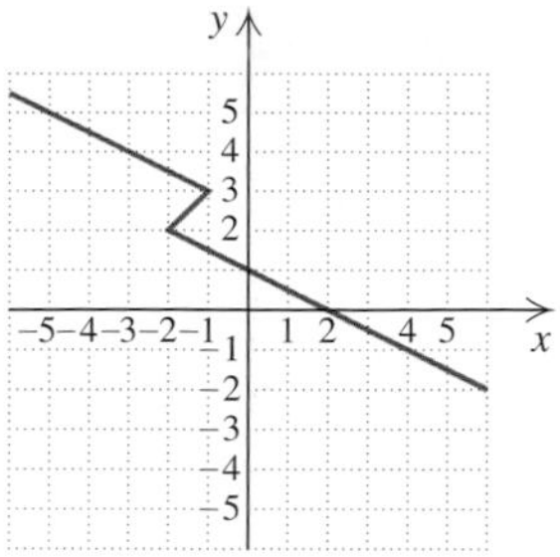

Solution

a) The graph *is* that of a function because it is not possible to draw a vertical line that crosses the graph more than once. This can be confirmed with a ruler or straightedge.

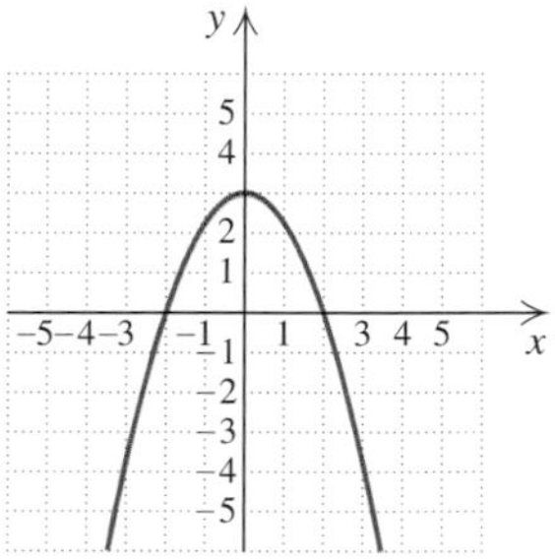

b) The graph is *not* that of a function because a vertical line—say, $x = 1$—crosses the graph at more than one point.

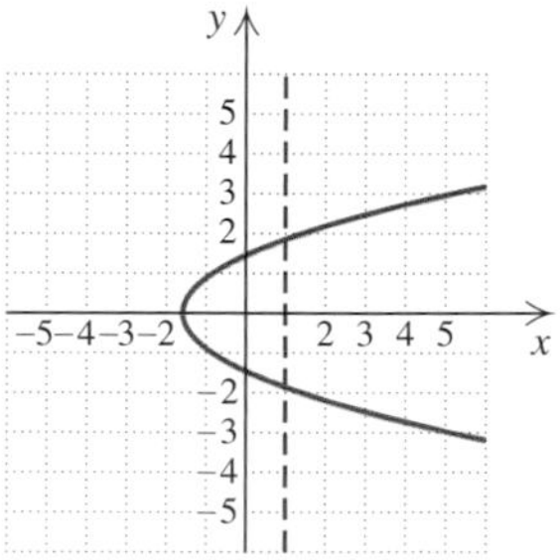

c) The graph *is* that of a function because it is not possible to draw a vertical line that crosses the graph more than once. Note that the open dots indicate the absence of a point.

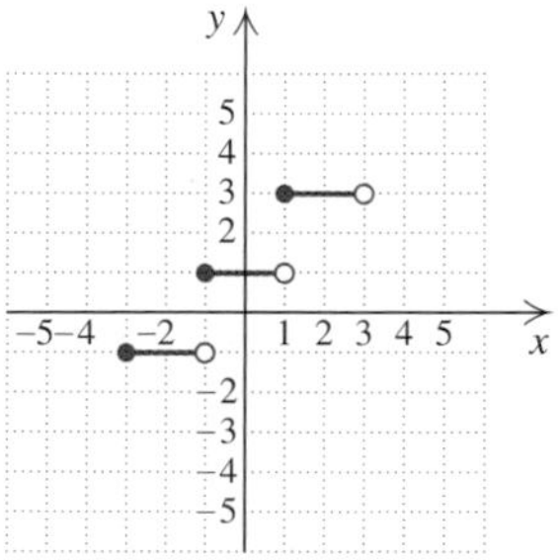

d) The graph is *not* that of a function because a vertical line—say, $x = -2$—crosses the graph at more than one point.

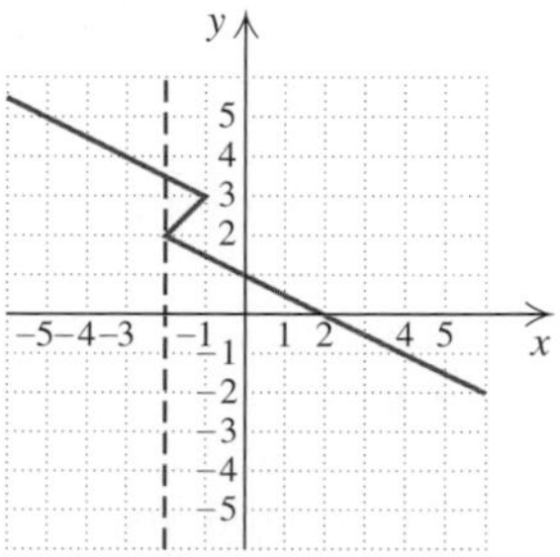

9.7 Exercise Set

FOR EXTRA HELP

Student's Solutions Manual | Digital Video Tutor CD 6 Videotape 18 | AW Math Tutor Center | MathXL Tutorials on CD | MathXL | MyMathLab

Concept Reinforcement *Classify each statement as either true or false.*

1. When we are discussing functions, the notation $f(3)$ does not mean $f \cdot 3$.

2. If $f(x) = x^2$, then $f(-5) = 25$.

3. In order to pass the vertical-line test, a function must score over 70%.

4. If a graph includes both (5, 9) and (5, 7), it cannot represent a function.

Determine whether each correspondence is a function.

5. *Domain* → *Range*
   - 2 → 9
   - −5 → 8
   - 19 → 9

6. *Domain* → *Range*
   - 7 → 1
   - 9 → 1
   - 11 → 1

7. *Domain* → *Range*
   - 5 → 3
   - −3 → 3
   - 7 → 7
   - −7 → 7

8. *Domain* → *Range*
   - 6 → −6
   - 6 → −7
   - 7 → −7
   - 3 → −3

9. *Domain* → *Range*
   - Texas → Austin
   - Texas → Houston
   - Texas → Dallas
   - Ohio → Cleveland
   - Ohio → Toledo
   - Ohio → Cincinnati

10. *Domain* → *Range*
    - Austin → Texas
    - Houston → Texas
    - Dallas → Texas
    - Cleveland → Ohio
    - Toledo → Ohio
    - Cincinnati → Ohio

11. *Domain* (Where college spending money goes, nationally*) → *Range* (Percentage of spending money)
    - Food → 78%
    - Transportation → 7%
    - Books → 1%
    - Clothes → 3%
    - Cigarettes → 1%
    - Social activities → 10%
    - Personal items → 1%

*Due to rounding, total exceeds 100% (*Source*: *USA Today*).

12. *Domain* (Brand of single-serving pizza) → *Range* (Number of calories)
    - Old Chicago Pizza-lite → 324
    - Smart Ones Cheese → 310
    - Banquet Zap Cheese → 310
    - Lean Cuisine Cheese → 310
    - Pizza Hut Supreme Personal Pan → 647
    - Celeste Suprema Pizza-For-One → 678

Find the indicated outputs.

13. $f(4)$, $f(7)$, and $f(-2)$

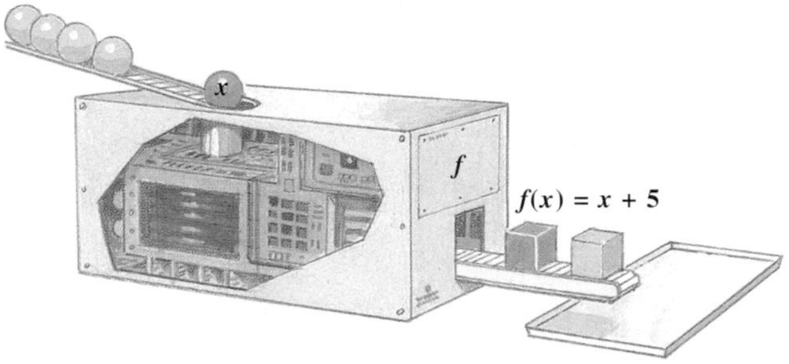

14. $g(1)$, $g(6)$, and $g(13)$

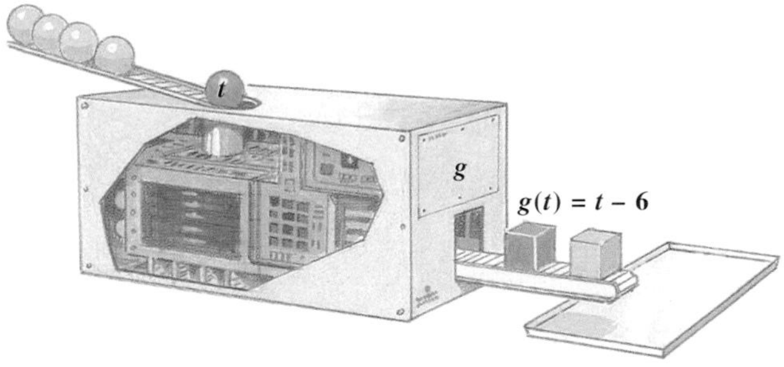

15. $h(-7)$, $h(5)$, and $h(10)$

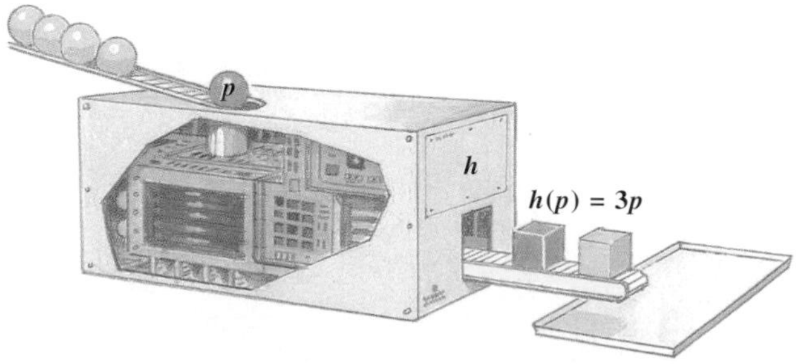

16. $f(6), f\left(-\frac{1}{2}\right)$, and $f(20)$

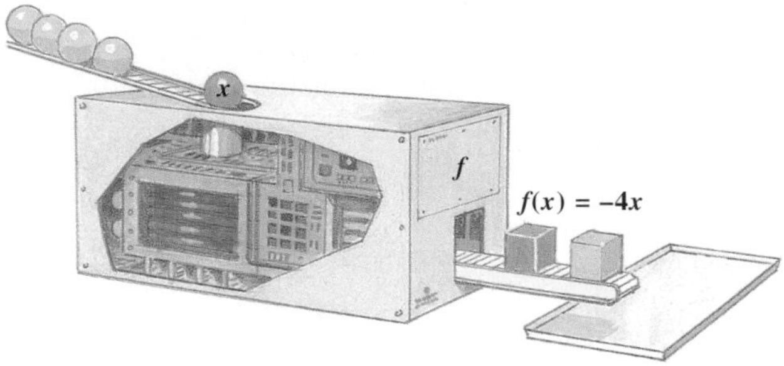

17. $g(s) = 3s + 4$; find $g(1)$, $g(-5)$, and $g(6.7)$.

18. $h(x) = 19$; find $h(4)$, $h(-16)$, and $h(12.5)$.

19. $F(x) = 2x^2 - 3x$; find $F(0)$, $F(-1)$, and $F(2)$.

20. $P(x) = 3x^2 - 2x$; find $P(0)$, $P(-2)$, and $P(3)$.

21. $f(t) = (t + 1)^2$; find $f(-5)$, $f(0)$, and $f\left(-\frac{9}{4}\right)$.

22. $f(x) = (x - 1)^2$; find $f(-3)$, $f(93)$, and $f(-100)$.

23. $g(t) = t^3 + 3$; find $g(1)$, $g(-5)$, and $g(0)$.

24. $h(x) = x^4 - 3$; find $h(0)$, $h(-1)$, and $h(3)$.

25. *Predicting heights.* An anthropologist can estimate the height of a male or a female, given the lengths of certain bones. A *humerus* is the bone from the elbow to the shoulder. The height, in centimeters, of a female with a humerus of x centimeters is given by

$$F(x) = 2.75x + 71.48.$$

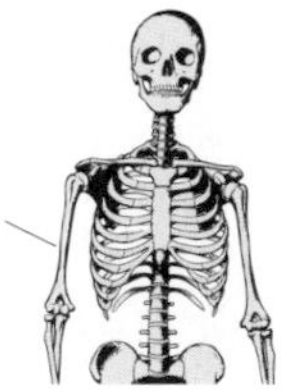

If a humerus is known to be from a female, how tall was the female if the bone is **(a)** 32 cm long? **(b)** 30 cm long?

26. When a humerus (see Exercise 25) is from a male, the function given by $M(x) = 2.89x + 70.64$ is used to find the male's height, in centimeters. If a humerus is known to be from a male, how tall was the male if the bone is **(a)** 30 cm long? **(b)** 35 cm long?

27. *Temperature as a function of depth.* The function given by $T(d) = 10d + 20$ gives the temperature, in degrees Celsius, inside the earth as a function of the depth d, in kilometers. Find the temperature at 5 km, 20 km, and 1000 km.

28. *Melting snow.* The function given by $W(d) = 0.112d$ approximates the amount, in centimeters, of water that results from d centimeters of snow melting. Find the amount of water that results from snow melting from depths of 16 cm, 25 cm, and 100 cm.

29. *Pressure at sea depth.* The function given by $P(d) = 1 + (d/33)$ gives the pressure, in *atmospheres* (atm), at a depth of d feet, in the sea. Note that $P(0) = 1$ atm, $P(33) = 2$ atm, and so on. Find the pressure at 20 ft, 30 ft, and 100 ft.

30. *Temperature conversions.* The function given by $C(F) = \frac{5}{9}(F - 32)$ determines the Celsius temperature that corresponds to F degrees Fahrenheit. Find the Celsius temperature that corresponds to 62°F, 77°F, and 23°F.

Graph each function.

31. $f(x) = 2x - 3$

32. $g(x) = 2x + 5$

33. $g(x) = -x + 4$

34. $f(x) = -\frac{1}{2}x + 2$

35. $f(x) = \frac{1}{2}x + 1$

36. $f(x) = -\frac{3}{4}x - 2$

37. $g(x) = 2|x|$

38. $h(x) = -|x|$

39. $g(x) = x^2$

40. $f(x) = x^2 - 1$

41. $f(x) = x^2 - x - 2$

42. $g(x) = x^2 + 6x + 5$

Determine whether each graph is that of a function.

43.

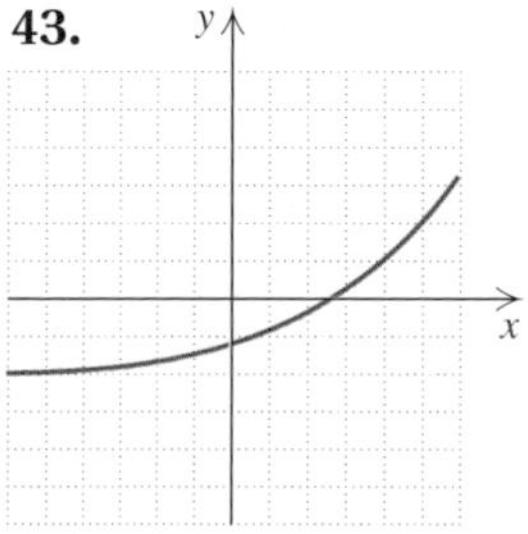

44.

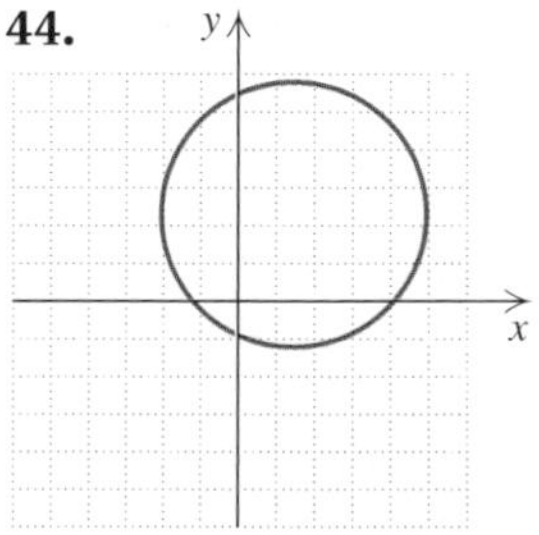

45.
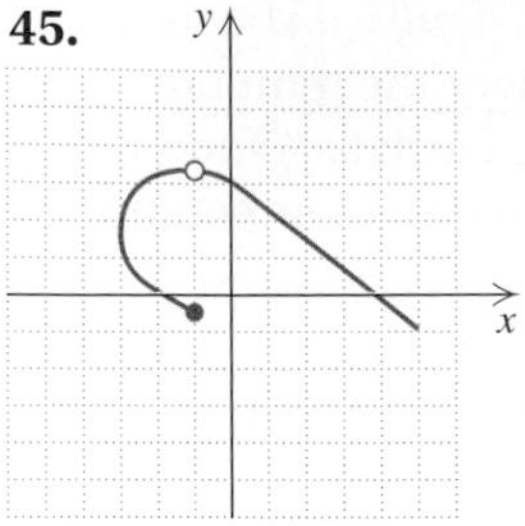

46.
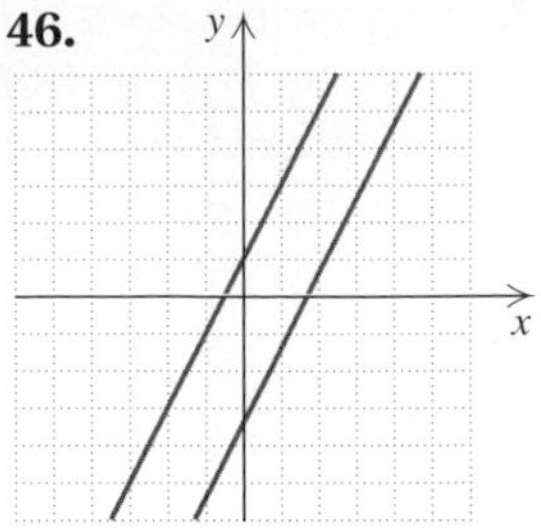

47.
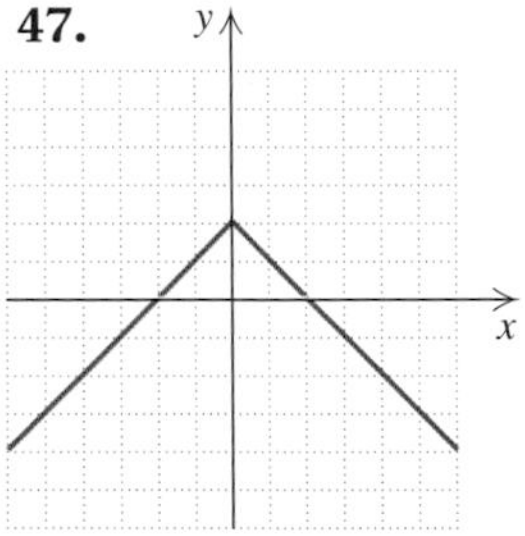

48.
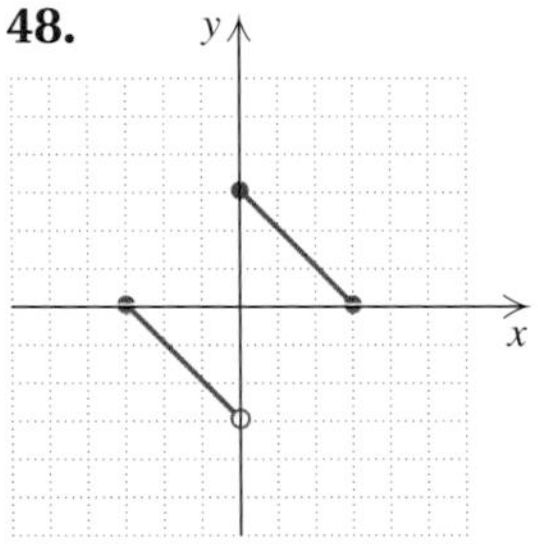

49. Is it possible for a function to have more numbers in the range than in the domain? Why or why not?

50. Is it possible for a function to have more numbers in the domain than in the range? Why or why not?

SKILL MAINTENANCE

Determine whether each pair of equations represents parallel lines. [3.6]

51. $y = \frac{3}{4}x - 7,$
$3x + 4y = 7$

52. $y = \frac{3}{5},$
$y = -\frac{5}{3}$

53. $2x = 3y,$
$4x = 6y - 1$

Solve each system using the substitution method. [7.2]

54. $2x - y = 6,$
$4x - 2y = 5$

55. $x - 3y = 2,$
$3x - 9y = 6$

56. $y = \frac{2}{3}x - 1,$
$y = -3x + 2$

SYNTHESIS

57. Explain in your own words how the vertical-line test works.

58. If $f(x) = g(x) + 2$, how do the graphs of f and g compare?

Graph.

59. $g(x) = x^3$

60. $f(x) = 2 + \sqrt{x}$

61. $f(x) = |x| + x$

62. $g(x) = |x| - x$

63. Sketch a graph that is not that of a function.

64. If $f(-1) = -7$ and $f(3) = 8$, find a linear equation for $f(x)$.

65. If $g(0) = -4$, $g(-2) = 0$, and $g(2) = 0$, find a quadratic equation for $g(x)$.

Find the range of each function for the given domain.

66. $f(x) = 3x + 5$, when the domain is the set of whole numbers less than 4

67. $g(t) = t^2 - 5$, when the domain is the set of integers between -4 and 2

68. $h(x) = |x| - x$, when the domain is the set of integers between -2 and 20

69. $f(m) = m^3 + 1$, when the domain is the set of integers between -3 and 3

70. Use a graphing calculator to check your answers to Exercises 59–62 and 64–69.

9 Study Summary

Any equation that can be written in the form $ax^2 + bx + c = 0$, with a, b, and c constant and $a \neq 0$, is called **quadratic** (p. 534). Quadratic equations written in the form $ax^2 + bx + c = 0$ are said to be in **standard form** (p. 546). There are several methods for solving quadratic equations, as follows.

Factoring (p. 534)

$$\begin{aligned} x^2 - 3x - 10 &= 0 \\ (x + 2)(x - 5) &= 0 \\ x + 2 = 0 \quad &or \quad x - 5 = 0 \\ x = -2 \quad &or \quad x = 5 \end{aligned}$$

Principle of square roots (p. 534)

$$\begin{aligned} x^2 - 8x + 16 &= 25 \\ (x - 4)^2 &= 25 \\ x - 4 = -5 \quad &or \quad x - 4 = 5 \\ x = -1 \quad &or \quad x = 9 \end{aligned}$$

Completing the square (p. 540)

$$\begin{aligned} x^2 + 6x &= 1 \\ x^2 + 6x + \left(\frac{6}{2}\right)^2 &= 1 + \left(\frac{6}{2}\right)^2 \\ x^2 + 6x + 9 &= 1 + 9 \\ (x + 3)^2 &= 10 \\ x + 3 &= \pm\sqrt{10} \\ x &= -3 \pm \sqrt{10} \end{aligned}$$

Quadratic formula (p. 547)

$$3x^2 - 2x - 5 = 0$$

$$x = \frac{-(-2) \pm \sqrt{(-2)^2 - 4 \cdot 3(-5)}}{2 \cdot 3}$$

$$x = \frac{2 \pm \sqrt{4 + 60}}{6}$$

$$x = \frac{2 \pm \sqrt{64}}{6}$$

$$x = \frac{2 \pm 8}{6}$$

$$x = \frac{10}{6} = \frac{5}{3} \quad or \quad x = \frac{-6}{6} = -1$$

Solutions of quadratic equations can include the square root of a negative number. Such numbers are called **imaginary** and/or **complex** (p. 563). Whereas every real number is complex, not every complex number is real.

Quadratic equations of the form $y = ax^2 + bx + c$ can be graphed. The graph is a **parabola** (p. 566) that opens upward for $a > 0$ and downward for $a < 0$. The **axis of symmetry** (p. 566) and the **vertex** (p. 566) occur at $x = -b/(2a)$.

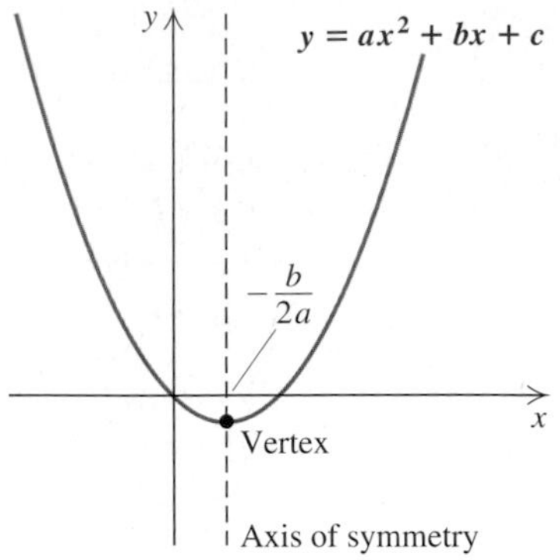

The parabolas in this chapter are examples of **functions** (p. 573) and this can be verified using the **vertical-line test** (p. 578). This test will confirm that each member of the **domain** (p. 573) is paired with exactly one member of the **range** (p. 573). The notation $f(a) = r$ is used to state that the **input** a (p. 573) is paired with the **output** r (p. 573) or **function value** r (p. 576).

9 Review Exercises

In each of Exercises 1–8, match the item with the appropriate item from the column on the right.

1. ____ An equation most easily solved by factoring [9.3]

2. ____ An equation most easily solved using the principle of square roots [9.1]

3. ____ An equation most easily solved by completing the square [9.2]

4. ____ An equation most easily solved by the quadratic formula [9.3]

5. ____ A parabola that is cupped upward [9.6]

6. ____ A parabola that is cupped downward [9.6]

7. ____ An expression for "the input 2 is paired with the output 5" [9.7]

8. ____ An expression for "the input 5 is paired with the output 2" [9.7]

a) $f(2) = 5$

b) $y = 3x^2 + 4x - 7$

c) $f(5) = 2$

d) $y = -3x^2 + 4x - 7$

e) $3x^2 - 4x - 5 = 0$

f) $(x - 7)^2 = 64$

g) $x^2 + 8x = 3$

h) $x^2 - 7x + 6 = 0$

Solve by completing the square. [9.2]

9. $x^2 - 5x = 1$

10. $3x^2 + 2x - 5 = 0$

Solve.

11. $8x^2 = 24$ [9.1]

12. $5x^2 - 8x + 3 = 0$ [9.2]

13. $x^2 - 2x - 10 = 0$ [9.3]

14. $x^2 + 64 = 0$ [9.5]

15. $3y^2 + 5y = 2$ [9.2]

16. $(x + 8)^2 = 13$ [9.1]

17. $(x - 3)^2 = -4$ [9.5]

18. $3x^2 - 6x - 9 = 0$ [9.2]

19. $9x^2 = 0$ [9.1]

20. $x^2 + 6x = 9$ [9.3]

21. $x^2 + x + 1 = 0$ [9.5]

22. $1 + 4x^2 = 8x$ [9.3]

23. $x^2 + 1 = 2x$ [9.2]

24. $40 = 5y^2$ [9.1]

25. $3m = 4 + 5m^2$ [9.5]

26. $6x^2 + 11x = 35$ [9.2]

Solve. [9.4]

27. $2t^2 - s = r$, for t

28. $\sqrt{3m - n} - 1 = 9$, for m

29. $2a - b = c$, for a

30. $\frac{1}{r} + \frac{1}{s} = \frac{1}{t}$, for t

Approximate the solutions to the nearest thousandth. [9.3]

31. $x^2 = 3x - 1$

32. $4y^2 + 8y + 1 = 0$

33. *Right triangles.* The hypotenuse of a right triangle is 7 m long. One leg is 3 m longer than the other. Find the lengths of the legs. Round to the nearest thousandth. [9.3]

34. *Investments.* \$1000 is invested at interest rate r, compounded annually. In 2 years, it grows to \$1102.50. What is the interest rate? [9.3]

35. *Area of a rectangle.* The length of a rectangle is 3 m greater than the width. The area is 108 m^2. Find the length and the width. [9.3]

36. *Free-fall time.* The height of the Lake Point Towers in Chicago is 645 ft. How long would it take an object to fall from the top? (Use $s = 16t^2$.) [9.3]

Express in terms of i. [9.5]

37. $2 - \sqrt{-64}$

38. $\sqrt{-24}$

Graph. Label the vertex, the y-intercept, and any x-intercepts. [9.6]

39. $y = 2 - x^2$

40. $y = x^2 + 4x - 1$

41. $y = 3x^2 - 10x$

42. $y = x^2 - 2x + 1$

43. If $g(x) = 2x - 5$, find $g(2)$, $g(-1)$, and $g(3.5)$. [9.7]

44. If $h(x) = |x| - 1$, find $h(1)$, $h(-1)$, and $h(-20)$. [9.7]

45. *Calories.* Each day a moderately active person needs about 15 calories per pound of body weight. The function given by $C(p) = 15p$ approximates the number of calories that are needed to maintain body weight p, in pounds. How many calories are needed to maintain a body weight of 130 lb? [9.7]

Graph. [9.7]

46. $g(x) = x - 6$

47. $f(x) = x^2 + 2$

48. $h(x) = 3|x|$

Determine whether each graph is that of a function. [9.7]

49.

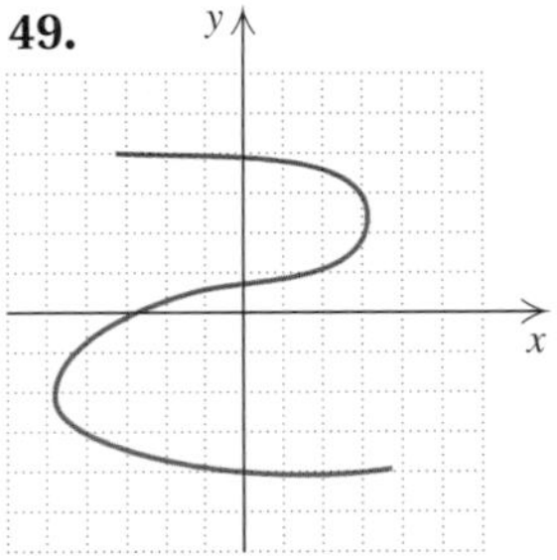

50.

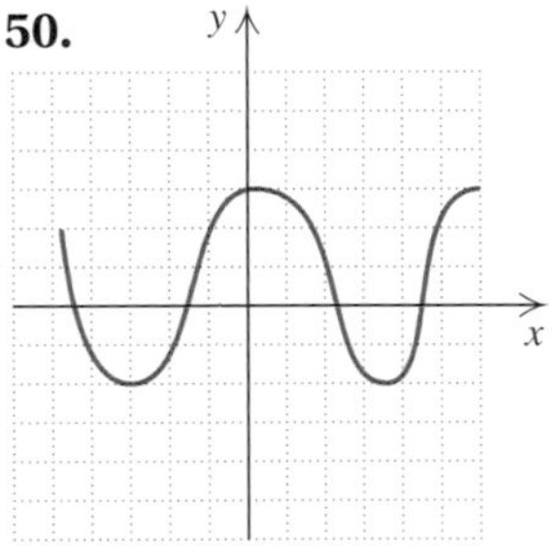

51. How can $b^2 - 4ac$ be used to determine how many x-intercepts the graph of $y = ax^2 + bx + c$ has? [9.6]

SYNTHESIS

52. Explain why it is helpful to know the general shape of a graph before connecting plotted points. [9.6]

53. Is it possible for a rational equation to have more solutions than a quadratic equation? Why or why not? [9.4]

54. Two consecutive integers have squares that differ by 63. Find the integers. [9.3]

55. Find b such that the trinomial $x^2 + bx + 49$ is a square. [9.1]

56. Solve: $x - 4\sqrt{x} - 5 = 0$. [9.3]

57. A square with sides of length s has the same area as a circle with radius 5 in. Find s. [9.3]

9 Chapter Test

Solve.

1. $9x^2 = 27$
2. $3x^2 - 7x = 0$
3. $x^2 = x + 3$
4. $3y^2 + 4y = 15$
5. $48 = t^2 + 2t$
6. $x^2 = -49$
7. $(x - 3)^2 = 7$
8. $x^2 - 4x = -4$
9. $x^2 - 4x = -8$
10. $m^2 - 3m = 7$
11. $10 = 4x + x^2$
12. $3x^2 - 7x + 1 = 0$
13. Solve by completing the square:
$x^2 - 4x - 10 = 0.$

Solve.

14. $3 = n + 2\sqrt{p + 5}$, for p
15. $1 + t = \frac{a}{b}$, for b
16. Approximate the solutions to the nearest thousandth:
$x^2 - 3x - 8 = 0.$
17. *Area of a rectangle.* The width of a rectangle is 4 m less than the length. The area is 16.25 m^2. Find the length and the width.
18. *Diagonals of a polygon.* A polygon has 44 diagonals. How many sides does it have? (*Hint*: $d = (n^2 - 3n)/2$.)

Express in terms of i.

19. $\sqrt{-49}$
20. $3 - \sqrt{-32}$

Graph. Label the vertex, the y-intercept, and any x-intercepts.

21. $y = -x^2 + x - 5$
22. $y = x^2 + 2x - 15$
23. If $f(x) = \frac{1}{2}x + 1$, find $f(0)$, $f(1)$, and $f(2)$.
24. If $g(t) = -2|t| + 3$, find $g(-1)$, $g(0)$, and $g(3)$.
25. *World records.* The world record for the 10,000-m run has been decreasing steadily since 1940. The function given by $R(t) = 30.18 - 0.06t$ estimates the record, in minutes, t years after 1940. Predict what the record will be in 2010.

Graph.

26. $h(x) = x - 4$
27. $g(x) = x^2 - 4$

Determine whether each graph is that of a function.

28.

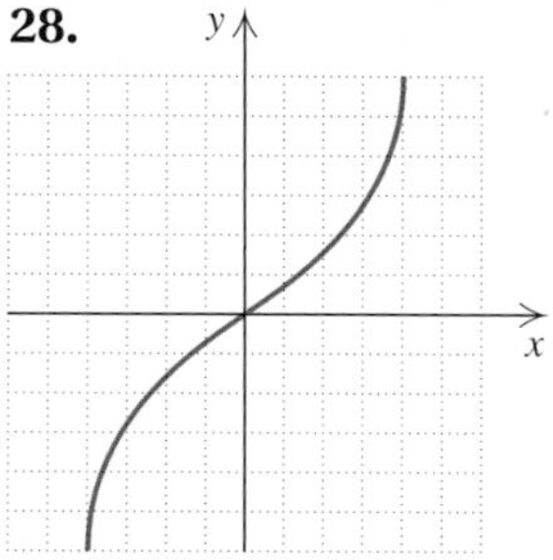

29.

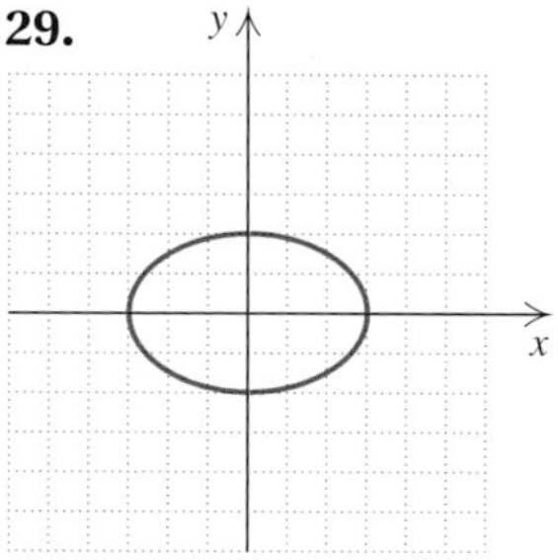

SYNTHESIS

30. Find the area of a square whose diagonal is 5 ft longer than a side.
31. Solve this system for x. Use the substitution method.
$x - y = 2,$
$xy = 4$

1–9 Cumulative Review/Final Exam

1. Write exponential notation for $x \cdot x \cdot x$. [1.8]
2. Evaluate $(x - 1)^2 + 3$ for $x = 9$. [1.8]
3. Use the commutative and associative laws to write an expression equivalent to $6(xy)$. [1.2]
4. Find the LCM of 15 and 48. [6.3]
5. Find the absolute value: $|-7|$. [1.4]

Compute and simplify.

6. $-6 + 12 + (-4) + 7$ [1.5]
7. $2.8 - (-12.2)$ [1.6]
8. $-\frac{3}{8} \div \frac{5}{2}$ [1.7]
9. $13 \cdot 6 \div 3 \cdot 2 \div 13$ [1.8]
10. Remove parentheses and simplify:
    $4m + 9 - (6m + 13)$. [1.8]

Solve. If an equation has no solution, state this.

11. $-5x = 30$ [2.1]
12. $-5x > 30$ [2.6]
13. $3(y - 1) - 2(y + 2) = 0$ [2.2]
14. $x^2 - 8x + 15 = 0$ [5.6]
15. $y - x = 1,$
    $y = 3 - x$ [7.2]
16. $\dfrac{x}{x + 1} = \dfrac{3}{2x} + 1$ [6.6]
17. $4x - 3y = 3,$
    $3x - 2y = 4$ [7.3]
18. $x^2 - x - 6 = 0$ [5.6]
19. $x^2 + 3x = 5$ [9.3]
20. $3 - x = \sqrt{x^2 - 3}$ [8.5]
21. $4 - 9x \leq 18 + 5x$ [2.6]
22. $-\frac{7}{8}x + 7 = \frac{3}{8}x - 3$ [2.2]
23. $0.6x - 1.8 = 1.2x$ [2.2]
24. $x + y = 15,$
    $x - y = 15$ [7.3]
25. $x^2 + 2x + 5 = 0$ [9.5]
26. $3y^2 = 30$ [9.1]
27. $(x - 3)^2 = 6$ [9.1]
28. $\dfrac{6x - 2}{2x - 1} = \dfrac{9x}{3x + 1}$ [6.6]
29. $12x^2 + x = 20$ [5.6]
30. $\dfrac{2x}{x + 3} + \dfrac{6}{x} + 7 = \dfrac{18}{x^2 + 3x}$ [6.6]
31. $\sqrt{x + 9} = \sqrt{2x - 3}$ [8.5]

Solve each formula for the given letter.

32. $A = \dfrac{4s + 3}{t}$, for t [9.4]
33. $\dfrac{1}{t} = \dfrac{1}{m} - \dfrac{1}{n}$, for m [9.4]

Simplify. Write scientific notation for the result.

34. $(2.1 \times 10^7)(1.3 \times 10^{-12})$ [4.8]
35. $\dfrac{5.2 \times 10^{-1}}{2.6 \times 10^{-15}}$ [4.8]

Simplify.

36. $x^{-6} \cdot x^2$ [4.8]
37. $\dfrac{y^3}{y^{-4}}$ [4.8]
38. $(2y^6)^2$ [4.1]
39. Combine like terms and arrange in descending order:
    $2x - 3 + 5x^3 - 2x^3 + 7x^3 + x$. [4.2]

Perform the indicated operation and simplify.

40. $(4x^3 + 3x^2 - 5) + (3x^3 - 5x^2 + 4x - 12)$ [4.3]
41. $(6x^2 - 4x + 1) - (-2x^2 + 7)$ [4.3]
42. $-2y^2(4y^2 - 3y + 1)$ [4.4]
43. $(2t - 3)(3t^2 - 4t + 2)$ [4.4]
44. $\left(t - \frac{1}{4}\right)\left(t + \frac{1}{4}\right)$ [4.5]
45. $(3m - 2)^2$ [4.5]

46. $(15x^2y^3 + 10xy^2 + 5) - (5xy^2 - x^2y^2 - 2)$ [4.6]

47. $(x^2 - 0.2y)(x^2 + 0.2y)$ [4.6]

48. $(3p + 4q^2)^2$ [4.6]

49. $\dfrac{4}{2x - 6} \cdot \dfrac{x - 3}{x + 3}$ [6.2]

50. $\dfrac{3a^4}{a^2 - 1} \div \dfrac{2a^3}{a^2 - 2a + 1}$ [6.2]

51. $\dfrac{3}{3x - 1} + \dfrac{4}{5x}$ [6.4]

52. $\dfrac{2}{x^2 - 16} - \dfrac{x - 3}{x^2 - 9x + 20}$ [6.4]

53. $(x^3 + 7x^2 - 2x + 3) \div (x - 2)$ [4.7]

Factor.

54. $25x^2 - 9$ [5.4]

55. $x^3 - 8x^2 - 5x + 40$ [5.1]

56. $16x^3 - x$ [5.4]

57. $m^2 - 8m + 16$ [5.4]

58. $15x^2 + 14x - 8$ [5.3]

59. $18x^5 + 4x^4 - 10x$ [5.1]

60. $6p^2 - 5p - 6$ [5.3]

61. $2ac - 6ab - 3db + dc$ [5.1]

62. $9x^2 + 30xy + 25y^2$ [5.4]

63. $3t^4 + 6t^2 - 72$ [5.5]

64. $49a^2b^2 - 16$ [5.4]

Simplify.

65. $\dfrac{\dfrac{3}{x} + \dfrac{1}{2x}}{\dfrac{1}{3x} - \dfrac{3}{4x}}$ [6.5]

66. $\sqrt{49}$ [8.1]

67. $-\sqrt[4]{625}$ [8.7]

68. $\sqrt{64x^2}$ [8.2] (Assume $x \geq 0$.)

69. Multiply: $\sqrt{a + b}\,\sqrt{a - b}$. [8.2]

70. Multiply and simplify: $\sqrt{32ab}\,\sqrt{6a^4b^2}$ $(a, b \geq 0)$. [8.2]

Simplify.

71. $8^{-2/3}$ [8.7]

72. $\sqrt{243x^3y^2}$ $(x, y \geq 0)$ [8.2]

73. $\sqrt{\dfrac{100}{81}}$ [8.3]

74. $(2\sqrt{3} + \sqrt{5})(2\sqrt{3} - \sqrt{5})$ [8.4]

75. $4\sqrt{12} + 2\sqrt{48}$ [8.4]

76. Divide and simplify: $\dfrac{\sqrt{72}}{\sqrt{45}}$. [8.3]

77. The hypotenuse of a right triangle is 41 cm long and the length of a leg is 9 cm. Find the length of the other leg. [8.6]

Graph on a plane.

78. $y = \frac{1}{3}x - 5$ [3.6]

79. $2x + 3y = -6$ [3.3]

80. $y = -2$ [3.3]

81. $4x - 3y > 12$ [7.5]

82. $y = x^2 + 2x + 1$ [9.6]

83. $x \geq -3$ [7.6]

84. Solve $9x^2 - 12x - 2 = 0$ by completing the square. [9.2]

85. Approximate the solutions of $4x^2 = 4x + 1$ to the nearest thousandth. [9.3]

86. Graph $y = x^2 + 2x - 5$. Label the vertex, the y-intercept, and the x-intercepts. [9.6]

Solve.

87. *Work force.* In 2000, 55% of the 3.9 million women who gave birth in the previous year returned to the work force. How many women returned to the work force within a year of giving birth? [2.4]

Source: Based on information in the *Statistical Abstract of the United States*, 2003

88. *Two-year college tuition.* The average full-time tuition at a public two-year college was \$1239 in 1996 and \$1905 in 2003. Find the rate at which tuition was increasing. [3.4]

Sources: *Statistical Abstract of the United States*, 2002, and *New York Times* 10/22/03

89. The product of two consecutive even integers is 224. Find the integers. [5.7]

90. The length of a rectangle is 7 m more than the width. The length of a diagonal is 13 m. Find the length. [9.3]

91. *Parking.* Three-fifths of the automobiles entering Dalton each morning will fill the city parking lots. There are 3654 such parking spaces. How many cars enter Dalton each morning? [2.5]

92. *Candy blends.* Good's Candies, in Kennard, Indiana, mixes chocolate creams worth \$11.50 per pound with nut candies worth \$12.50 per pound in order to make 25 lb of a mixture worth \$11.74 per pound. How many pounds of each kind of candy do they use? [7.4]

93. *Warehouse.* Justine and Ken work in a textbook warehouse. Justine can fill an order of 100 books in 40 min. Ken can fill the same order in 60 min. How long would it take them, working together, to fill the order? [6.7]

94. *Cable.* The cumulative cost c of cable television, in dollars, is given by $c = 20t + 25$, where t is the number of months that a household has had cable service. Graph the equation and use the graph to estimate the cost of cable service for 10 months. [3.4]

95. For the function f described by

$$f(x) = 2x^2 + 7x - 4,$$

find $f(0), f(-4)$, and $f\left(\frac{1}{2}\right)$. [9.7]

96. Determine whether the graphs of the following equations are parallel:

$$y - x = 4,$$
$$3y = 5 + 3x. \text{ [3.6]}$$

97. Graph the following system of inequalities: [7.6]

$$x + y \leq 6,$$
$$x + y \geq 2,$$
$$x \leq 3,$$
$$x \geq 1.$$

98. Find the slope and the y-intercept:

$$-6x + 3y = -24. \text{ [3.6]}$$

99. Find the slope of the line containing the points $(-5, -6)$ and $(-4, 9)$. [3.5]

100. Find a point–slope equation for the line containing $(1, -3)$ and having slope $m = -\frac{1}{2}$. [3.7]

101. Simplify: $-\sqrt{-25}$. [9.5]

SYNTHESIS

102. Find b such that the trinomial $x^2 - bx + 225$ is a square. [9.2]

103. Find x. [8.6]

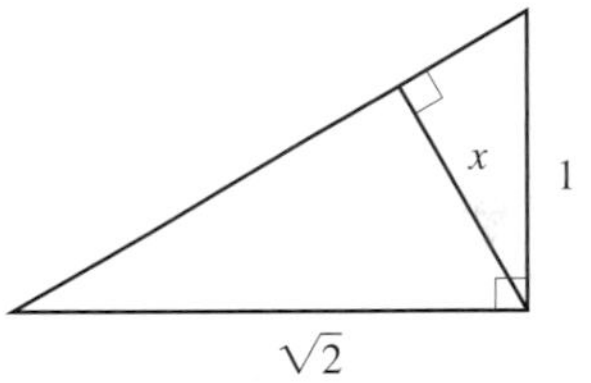

Determine whether each pair of expressions is equivalent.

104. $x^2 - 9$, $(x - 3)(x + 3)$ [4.5]

105. $\dfrac{x + 3}{x - 2}$, $\dfrac{x^2 + x - 6}{x^2 - 4x + 4}$ [6.1]

106. $(x + 5)^2$, $x^2 + 25$ [4.5]

107. $\sqrt{(t - 3)^2}$, $t - 3$ [8.1]

108. $\sqrt{9x^4}$, $3x^2$ [8.1]

Appendixes

A Factoring Sums or Differences of Cubes

Factoring a Sum of Two Cubes • Factoring a Difference of Two Cubes

It is possible to factor both a sum and a difference of two cubes. To see how, consider the following:

$$\begin{aligned}(A + B)(A^2 - AB + B^2) &= A(A^2 - AB + B^2) + B(A^2 - AB + B^2)\\ &= A^3 - A^2B + AB^2 + A^2B - AB^2 + B^3\\ &= A^3 + B^3\end{aligned}$$

and

$$\begin{aligned}(A - B)(A^2 + AB + B^2) &= A(A^2 + AB + B^2) - B(A^2 + AB + B^2)\\ &= A^3 + A^2B + AB^2 - A^2B - AB^2 - B^3\\ &= A^3 - B^3.\end{aligned}$$

These equations show how we can factor a sum or a difference of two cubes.

To Factor a Sum or Difference of Cubes

$$A^3 + B^3 = (A + B)(A^2 - AB + B^2),$$
$$A^3 - B^3 = (A - B)(A^2 + AB + B^2)$$

Remembering this list of cubes may prove helpful when factoring.

N	0.2	0.1	0	1	2	3	4	5	6
N^3	0.008	0.001	0	1	8	27	64	125	216

EXAMPLE 1 Factor: $x^3 - 8$.

Solution We have

$$\begin{array}{c} x^3 - 8 = x^3 - 2^3 = (x - 2)(x^2 + x \cdot 2 + 2^2). \\ \uparrow \quad \uparrow \quad \uparrow \quad \uparrow \quad \uparrow \quad \uparrow \quad \uparrow \quad \uparrow \\ \mathbf{A^3 - B^3 = (A - B)(A^2 + A \quad B + B^2)} \end{array}$$

This tells us that $x^3 - 8 = (x - 2)(x^2 + 2x + 4)$. Note that we cannot factor $x^2 + 2x + 4$. (It is not a perfect-square trinomial nor can it be factored by trial and error or grouping.) The check is left to the student.

EXAMPLE 2 Factor: $x^3 + 125$.

Solution We have

$$\begin{array}{c} x^3 + 125 = x^3 + 5^3 = (x + 5)(x^2 - x \cdot 5 + 5^2). \\ \uparrow \quad \uparrow \quad \uparrow \quad \uparrow \quad \uparrow \quad \uparrow \quad \uparrow \quad \uparrow \\ \mathbf{A^3 + B^3 = (A + B)(A^2 - A \quad B + B^2)} \end{array}$$

Thus, $x^3 + 125 = (x + 5)(x^2 - 5x + 25)$. The check is left to the student.

EXAMPLE 3 Factor: $16a^7b + 54ab^7$.

Solution We first look for a common factor:

$$\begin{aligned} 16a^7b + 54ab^7 &= 2ab[8a^6 + 27b^6] \\ &= 2ab[(2a^2)^3 + (3b^2)^3] \quad \text{This is of the form } A^3 + B^3, \text{ where } A = 2a^2 \text{ and } B = 3b^2. \\ &= 2ab[(2a^2 + 3b^2)(4a^4 - 6a^2b^2 + 9b^4)]. \end{aligned}$$

We check using the distributive law:

$$\begin{aligned} &2ab(2a^2 + 3b^2)(4a^4 - 6a^2b^2 + 9b^4) \\ &\quad = 2ab[2a^2(4a^4 - 6a^2b^2 + 9b^4) + 3b^2(4a^4 - 6a^2b^2 + 9b^4)] \\ &\quad = 2ab[8a^6 - 12a^4b^2 + 18a^2b^4 + 12b^2a^4 - 18a^2b^4 + 27b^6] \\ &\quad = 2ab[8a^6 + 27b^6] \\ &\quad = 16a^7b + 54ab^7. \end{aligned}$$

We have a check. The factorization is

$$2ab(2a^2 + 3b^2)(4a^4 - 6a^2b^2 + 9b^4).$$

EXAMPLE 4 Factor: $y^3 - 0.001$.

Solution Since $0.001 = (0.1)^3$, we have a difference of cubes:

$$y^3 - 0.001 = (y - 0.1)(y^2 + 0.1y + 0.01).$$

The check is left to the student.

Remember the following about factoring sums or differences of squares and cubes:

Difference of cubes: $A^3 - B^3 = (A - B)(A^2 + AB + B^2)$,

Sum of cubes: $A^3 + B^3 = (A + B)(A^2 - AB + B^2)$,

Difference of squares: $A^2 - B^2 = (A + B)(A - B)$.

A Exercise Set

Factor completely.

1. $t^3 + 8$
2. $p^3 + 27$
3. $a^3 - 64$
4. $w^3 - 1$
5. $z^3 + 125$
6. $x^3 + 1$
7. $8a^3 - 1$
8. $27x^3 - 1$
9. $y^3 - 27$
10. $p^3 - 8$
11. $64 + 125x^3$
12. $8 + 27b^3$
13. $125p^3 - 1$
14. $64w^3 - 1$
15. $27m^3 + 64$
16. $8t^3 + 27$
17. $p^3 - q^3$
18. $a^3 + b^3$
19. $x^3 + \frac{1}{8}$
20. $y^3 + \frac{1}{27}$
21. $2y^3 - 128$
22. $3z^3 - 3$
23. $24a^3 + 3$
24. $54x^3 + 2$
25. $rs^3 - 64r$
26. $ab^3 + 125a$
27. $5x^3 + 40z^3$
28. $2y^3 - 54z^3$
29. $x^3 + 0.001$
30. $y^3 + 0.125$

SYNTHESIS

31. Dino incorrectly believes that

$$a^3 - b^3 = (a - b)(a^2 + b^2).$$

How could you convince him that he is wrong?

32. If $x^3 + c$ is prime, what can you conclude about c? Why?

Factor. Assume that variables in exponents represent natural numbers.

33. $125c^6 + 8d^6$
34. $64x^6 + 8t^6$
35. $3x^{3a} - 24y^{3b}$
36. $\frac{8}{27}x^3 - \frac{1}{64}y^3$
37. $\frac{1}{24}x^3y^3 + \frac{1}{3}z^3$
38. $\frac{1}{16}x^{3a} + \frac{1}{2}y^{6a}z^{9b}$

B Mean, Median, and Mode

Mean • Median • Mode

One way to analyze data is to look for a single representative number, called a **center point** or **measure of central tendency**. Those most often used are the **mean** (or **average**), the **median**, and the **mode**.

Mean

Let's first consider the *mean*, or *average*.

Mean, or Average

The *mean*, or *average*, of a set of numbers is the sum of the numbers divided by the number of addends.

EXAMPLE 1 Consider the following data on revenue, in billions of dollars, at McDonald's restaurants in five recent years:

$12.5, $13.2, $14.2, $14.9, $15.9.

What is the mean of the numbers? (*Source*: McDonald's Corporation)

Solution First, we add the numbers:

$$12.5 + 13.2 + 14.2 + 14.9 + 15.9 = 70.7.$$

Then we divide by the number of addends, 5:

$$\frac{(12.5 + 13.2 + 14.2 + 14.9 + 15.9)}{5} = \frac{70.7}{5} = 14.14.$$

The mean, or average, revenue of McDonald's for those five years is $14.14 billion.

Note that 14.14 + 14.14 + 14.14 + 14.14 + 14.14 = 70.7. If we use this center point, 14.14, repeatedly as the addend, we get the same sum that we do when adding individual data numbers.

Median

The *median* is useful when we wish to de-emphasize extreme scores. For example, suppose five workers in a technology company manufactured the following number of computers during one day's work:

Sarah: 88
Matt: 92
Pat: 66
Jen: 94
Mark: 91

Let's first list the scores in order from smallest to largest:

66 88 91 92 94.
↑
Middle number

The middle number—in this case, 91—is the **median**.

> **Median**
>
> Once a set of data has been arranged from smallest to largest, the *median* of the set of data is the middle number if there is an odd number of data numbers. If there is an even number of data numbers, then there are two middle numbers and the median is the *average* of the two middle numbers.

EXAMPLE 2 Find the median of the following set of household incomes:

\$76,000, \$58,000, \$87,000, \$32,500, \$64,800, \$62,500.

Solution We first rearrange the numbers in order from smallest to largest.

\$32,500, \$58,000, \$62,500, \$64,800, \$76,000, \$87,000
↑
Median

There is an even number of numbers. We look for the middle two, which are \$62,500 and \$64,800. In this case, the median is the average of \$62,500 and \$64,800:

$$\frac{\$62{,}500 + \$64{,}800}{2} = \$63{,}650.$$

Mode

The last center point we consider is called the *mode.* A number that occurs most often in a set of data is sometimes considered a representative number or center point.

> **Mode**
>
> The *mode* of a set of data is the number or numbers that occur most often. If each number occurs the same number of times, there is *no* mode.

EXAMPLE 3 Find the mode of the following data:

23, 24, 27, 18, 19, 27.

Solution The number that occurs most often is 27. Thus the mode is 27.

EXAMPLE 4 Find the mode of the following data:

83, 84, 84 84, 85, 86, 87, 87, 87, 88, 89, 90.

Solution There are two numbers that occur most often, 84 and 87. Thus the modes are 84 and 87.

EXAMPLE 5 Find the mode of the following data:

115, 117, 211, 213, 219.

Solution Each number occurs the same number of times. The set of data has *no* mode.

B Exercise Set

For each set of numbers, find the mean (average), the median, and any modes that exist.

1. 17, 19, 29, 18, 14, 29
2. 72, 83, 85, 88, 92
3. 5, 37, 20, 20, 35, 5, 25
4. 13, 32, 25, 27, 13
5. 4.3, 7.4, 1.2, 5.7, 7.4
6. 13.4, 13.4, 12.6, 42.9
7. 234, 228, 234, 229, 234, 278
8. $29.95, $28.79, $30.95, $29.95

9. *Atlantic storms and hurricanes.* The following bar graph shows the number of Atlantic storms or hurricanes that formed in various months from 1980 to 2000. What is the average number for the 9 months given? the median? the mode?

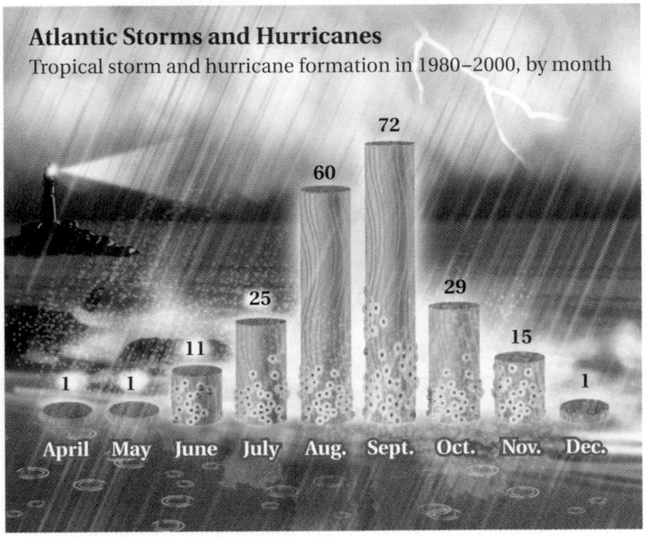

Source: Colorado State University

10. *Cheddar cheese prices.* The following prices per pound of sharp cheddar cheese were found at five supermarkets:

$5.99, $6.79, $5.99, $6.99, $6.79.

What was the average price per pound? the median price? the mode?

11. *Coffee consumption.* The following lists the annual coffee consumption, in number of cups per person, for various countries. Find the mean, the median, and the mode.

Germany	1113
United States	610
Switzerland	1215
France	798
Italy	750

Source: Beverage Marketing Corporation

12. *NBA tall men.* The following is a list of the heights, in inches, of the tallest men in the NBA in a recent year. Find the mean, the median, and the mode.

Shaquille O'Neal	85
Gheorghe Muresan	91
Shawn Bradley	90
Tim Duncan	84
Yao Ming	89
Bruno Sundov	86

Source: National Basketball Association

13. *Salmon prices.* The following prices per pound of Atlantic salmon were found at five fish markets:

$6.99, $8.49, $8.99, $6.99, $9.49.

What was the average price per pound? the median price? the mode?

14. *PBA scores.* Chris Barnes rolled scores of 224, 224, 254, and 187 in a recent tournament of the Professional Bowlers Association. What was his average? his median? his mode?

Source: Professional Bowlers Association

SYNTHESIS

15. *Hank Aaron.* Hank Aaron averaged $34\frac{7}{22}$ home runs per year over a 22-yr career. After 21 yr, Aaron had averaged $35\frac{10}{21}$ home runs per year. How many home runs did Aaron hit in his final year?

16. *Length of pregnancy.* Marta was pregnant 270 days, 259 days, and 272 days for her first three pregnancies. In order for Marta's average length of pregnancy to equal the worldwide average of 266 days, how long must her fourth pregnancy last?
Source: David Crystal (ed.), *The Cambridge Factfinder.* Cambridge CB2 1RP: Cambridge University Press, 1993, p. 84.

17. The ordered set of data 18, 21, 24, a, 36, 37, b has a median of 30 and an average of 32. Find a and b.

18. *Male height.* Jason's brothers are 174 cm, 180 cm, 179 cm, and 172 cm tall. The average male is 176.5 cm tall. How tall is Jason if he and his brothers have an average height of 176.5 cm?

C Sets

Naming Sets • Membership • Subsets • Intersections • Unions

A **set** is a collection of objects. In mathematics the objects, or **elements**, of a set are generally numbers. This section provides a basic introduction to sets.

Naming Sets

To name the set of whole numbers less than 6, we can use *roster notation*, as follows:

$$\{0, 1, 2, 3, 4, 5\}.$$

The set of real numbers x for which x is less than 6 cannot be named by listing all its members because there is an infinite number of them. We name such a set using *set-builder notation*, as follows:

$$\{x \mid x < 6\}.$$

This is read

"The set of all x such that x is less than 6."

See Section 2.6 for more on this notation.

Membership

The symbol $\in$ means *is a member of* or *belongs to*, or *is an element of*. Thus,

$$x \in A$$

means

x is a member of A, or x belongs to A, or x is an element of A.

EXAMPLE 1 Classify each of the following as true or false.

a) $1 \in \{1, 2, 3\}$

b) $1 \in \{2, 3\}$

c) $4 \in \{x \mid x \text{ is an even whole number}\}$

d) $5 \in \{x \mid x \text{ is an even whole number}\}$

Solution

a) Since 1 is listed as a member of the set, $1 \in \{1, 2, 3\}$ is true.

b) Since 1 is *not* a member of $\{2, 3\}$, the statement $1 \in \{2, 3\}$ is false.

c) Since 4 is an even whole number, $4 \in \{x \mid x \text{ is an even whole number}\}$ is true.

d) Since 5 is *not* even, $5 \in \{x \mid x \text{ is an even whole number}\}$ is false.

Set membership can be illustrated with a diagram, as shown below.

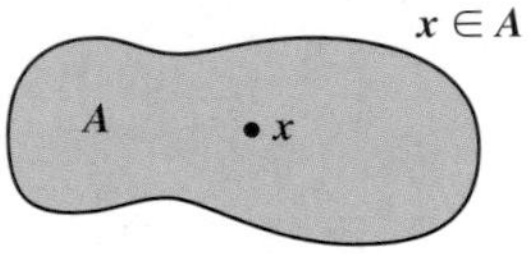

Subsets

If every element of A is also an element of B, then A is a *subset* of B. This is denoted $A \subseteq B$.

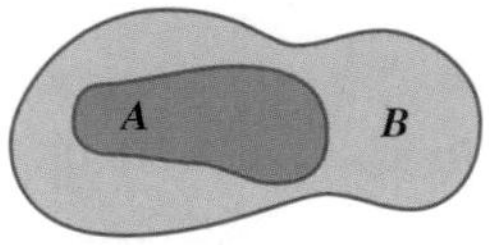

The set of whole numbers is a subset of the set of integers. The set of rational numbers is a subset of the set of real numbers.

EXAMPLE 2 Classify each of the following as true or false.

a) $\{1, 2\} \subseteq \{1, 2, 3, 4\}$

b) $\{p, q, r, w\} \subseteq \{a, p, r, z\}$

c) $\{x \mid x < 6\} \subseteq \{x \mid x \leq 11\}$

Solution

a) Since every element of $\{1, 2\}$ is in the set $\{1, 2, 3, 4\}$, it follows that $\{1, 2\} \subseteq \{1, 2, 3, 4\}$ is true.

b) Since $q \in \{p, q, r, w\}$, but $q \notin \{a, p, r, z\}$, it follows that $\{p, q, r, w\} \subseteq \{a, p, r, z\}$ is false.

c) Since every number that is less than 6 is also less than 11, the statement $\{x \mid x < 6\} \subseteq \{x \mid x \leq 11\}$ is true.

Intersections

The *intersection* of sets A and B, denoted $A \cap B$, is the set of members common to both sets.

EXAMPLE 3 Find each intersection.

a) $\{0, 1, 3, 5, 25\} \cap \{2, 3, 4, 5, 6, 7, 9\}$ b) $\{a, p, q, w\} \cap \{p, q, t\}$

Solution

a) $\{0, 1, 3, 5, 25\} \cap \{2, 3, 4, 5, 6, 7, 9\} = \{3, 5\}$

b) $\{a, p, q, w\} \cap \{p, q, t\} = \{p, q\}$

Set intersection can be illustrated with a diagram, as shown below.

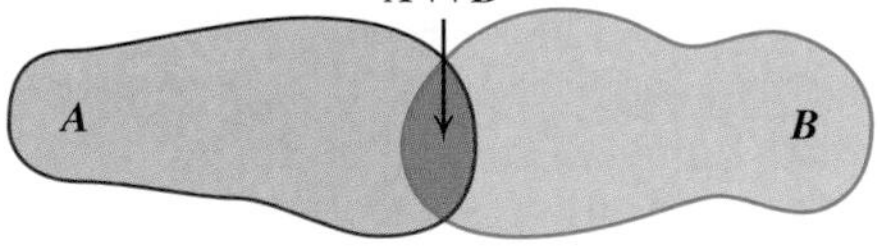

The set without members is known as the *empty set*, and is written $\varnothing$, and sometimes $\{ \quad \}$. Each of the following is a description of the empty set:

The set of all 12-ft–tall people;

$\{2, 3\} \cap \{5, 6, 7\}$;

$\{x \mid x \text{ is an even natural number}\} \cap \{x \mid x \text{ is an odd natural number}\}$.

Unions

Two sets A and B can be combined to form a set that contains the members of both A and B. The new set is called the *union* of A and B, denoted $A \cup B$.

EXAMPLE 4 Find each union.

a) $\{0, 5, 7, 13, 27\} \cup \{0, 2, 3, 4, 5\}$ b) $\{a, c, e, g\} \cup \{b, d, f\}$

Solution

a) $\{0, 5, 7, 13, 27\} \cup \{0, 2, 3, 4, 5\} = \{0, 2, 3, 4, 5, 7, 13, 27\}$

Note that the 0 and the 5 are *not* listed twice in the solution.

b) $\{a, c, e, g\} \cup \{b, d, f\} = \{a, b, c, d, e, f, g\}$

Set union can be illustrated with a diagram, as shown below.

$A \cup B$ is shaded.

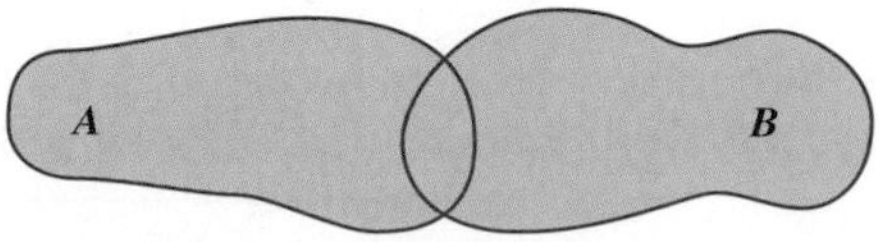

C Exercise Set

Name each set using the roster method.

1. The set of whole numbers 3 through 7
2. The set of whole numbers 83 through 89
3. The set of odd numbers between 40 and 50
4. The set of multiples of 5 between 10 and 40
5. $\{x \mid \text{the square of } x \text{ is } 9\}$
6. $\{x \mid x \text{ is the cube of } 0.2\}$

Classify each statement as true or false.

7. $2 \in \{x \mid x \text{ is an odd number}\}$
8. $7 \in \{x \mid x \text{ is an odd number}\}$
9. Bruce Springsteen $\in$ The set of all rock stars
10. Apple $\in$ The set of all fruit
11. $-3 \in \{-4, -3, 0, 1\}$
12. $0 \in \{-4, -3, 0, 1\}$
13. $\frac{2}{3} \in \{x \mid x \text{ is a rational number}\}$
14. Heads $\in$ The set of outcomes of flipping a penny
15. $\{4, 5, 8\} \subseteq \{1, 3, 4, 5, 6, 7, 8, 9\}$
16. The set of vowels $\subseteq$ The set of consonants
17. $\{-1, -2, -3, -4, -5\} \subseteq \{-1, 2, 3, 4, 5\}$
18. The set of integers $\subseteq$ The set of rational numbers

Find each intersection.

19. $\{a, b, c, d, e\} \cap \{c, d, e, f, g\}$
20. $\{a, e, i, o, u\} \cap \{q, u, i, c, k\}$
21. $\{1, 2, 5, 10\} \cap \{0, 1, 7, 10\}$
22. $\{0, 1, 7, 10\} \cap \{0, 1, 2, 5\}$
23. $\{1, 2, 5, 10\} \cap \{3, 4, 7, 8\}$
24. $\{a, e, i, o, u\} \cap \{m, n, f, g, h\}$

Find each union.

25. $\{a, e, i, o, u\} \cup \{q, u, i, c, k\}$
26. $\{a, b, c, d, e\} \cup \{c, d, e, f, g\}$
27. $\{0, 1, 7, 10\} \cup \{0, 1, 2, 5\}$
28. $\{1, 2, 5, 10\} \cup \{0, 1, 7, 10\}$
29. $\{a, e, i, o, u\} \cup \{m, n, f, g, h\}$
30. $\{1, 2, 5, 10\} \cup \{a, b\}$
31. What advantage(s) does set-builder notation have over roster notation?
32. What advantage(s) does roster notation have over set-builder notation?

SYNTHESIS

33. Find the union of the set of integers and the set of whole numbers.
34. Find the intersection of the set of odd integers and the set of even integers.
35. Find the union of the set of rational numbers and the set of irrational numbers.
36. Find the intersection of the set of even integers and the set of positive rational numbers.
37. Find the intersection of the set of rational numbers and the set of irrational numbers.
38. Find the union of the set of negative integers, the set of positive integers, and the set containing 0.
39. For a set A, find each of the following.
    a) $A \cup \varnothing$
    b) $A \cup A$
    c) $A \cap A$
    d) $A \cap \varnothing$

40. A set is *closed* under an operation if, when the operation is performed on its members, the result is in the set. For example, the set of real numbers is closed under the operation of addition since the sum of any two real numbers is a real number.

a) Is the set of even numbers closed under addition?

b) Is the set of odd numbers closed under addition?

c) Is the set $\{0, 1\}$ closed under addition?

d) Is the set $\{0, 1\}$ closed under multiplication?

e) Is the set of real numbers closed under multiplication?

f) Is the set of integers closed under division?

41. Experiment with sets of various types and determine whether the following distributive law for sets is true:

$$A \cap (B \cup C) = (A \cap B) \cup (A \cap C).$$

Tables

TABLE 1 Fraction and Decimal Equivalents

Fraction Notation	$\frac{1}{10}$	$\frac{1}{8}$	$\frac{1}{6}$	$\frac{1}{5}$	$\frac{1}{4}$	$\frac{3}{10}$	$\frac{1}{3}$	$\frac{3}{8}$	$\frac{2}{5}$	$\frac{1}{2}$
Decimal Notation	0.1	0.125	$0.16\overline{6}$	0.2	0.25	0.3	$0.333\overline{3}$	0.375	0.4	0.5
Percent Notation	10%	12.5%, or $12\frac{1}{2}\%$	$16.6\overline{6}\%$, or $16\frac{2}{3}\%$	20%	25%	30%	$33.3\overline{3}\%$, or $33\frac{1}{3}\%$	37.5%, or $37\frac{1}{2}\%$	40%	50%
Fraction Notation	$\frac{3}{5}$	$\frac{5}{8}$	$\frac{2}{3}$	$\frac{7}{10}$	$\frac{3}{4}$	$\frac{4}{5}$	$\frac{5}{6}$	$\frac{7}{8}$	$\frac{9}{10}$	$\frac{1}{1}$
Decimal Notation	0.6	0.625	$0.666\overline{6}$	0.7	0.75	0.8	$0.83\overline{3}$	0.875	0.9	1
Percent Notation	60%	62.5%, or $62\frac{1}{2}\%$	$66.6\overline{6}\%$, or $66\frac{2}{3}\%$	70%	75%	80%	$83.3\overline{3}\%$, or $83\frac{1}{3}\%$	87.5%, or $87\frac{1}{2}\%$	90%	100%

TABLE 2 Squares and Square Roots with Approximations to Three Decimal Places

N	$\sqrt{N}$	N^2	N	$\sqrt{N}$	N^2	N	$\sqrt{N}$	N^2	N	$\sqrt{N}$	N^2
1	1	1	26	5.099	676	51	7.141	2601	76	8.718	5776
2	1.414	4	27	5.196	729	52	7.211	2704	77	8.775	5929
3	1.732	9	28	5.292	784	53	7.280	2809	78	8.832	6084
4	2	16	29	5.385	841	54	7.348	2916	79	8.888	6241
5	2.236	25	30	5.477	900	55	7.416	3025	80	8.944	6400
6	2.449	36	31	5.568	961	56	7.483	3136	81	9	6561
7	2.646	49	32	5.657	1024	57	7.550	3249	82	9.055	6724
8	2.828	64	33	5.745	1089	58	7.616	3364	83	9.110	6889
9	3	81	34	5.831	1156	59	7.681	3481	84	9.165	7056
10	3.162	100	35	5.916	1225	60	7.746	3600	85	9.220	7225
11	3.317	121	36	6	1296	61	7.810	3721	86	9.274	7396
12	3.464	144	37	6.083	1369	62	7.874	3844	87	9.327	7569
13	3.606	169	38	6.164	1444	63	7.937	3969	88	9.381	7744
14	3.742	196	39	6.245	1521	64	8	4096	89	9.434	7921
15	3.873	225	40	6.325	1600	65	8.062	4225	90	9.487	8100
16	4	256	41	6.403	1681	66	8.124	4356	91	9.539	8281
17	4.123	289	42	6.481	1764	67	8.185	4489	92	9.592	8464
18	4.243	324	43	6.557	1849	68	8.246	4624	93	9.644	8649
19	4.359	361	44	6.633	1936	69	8.307	4761	94	9.695	8836
20	4.472	400	45	6.708	2025	70	8.367	4900	95	9.747	9025
21	4.583	441	46	6.782	2116	71	8.426	5041	96	9.798	9216
22	4.690	484	47	6.856	2209	72	8.485	5184	97	9.849	9409
23	4.796	529	48	6.928	2304	73	8.544	5329	98	9.899	9604
24	4.899	576	49	7	2401	74	8.602	5476	99	9.950	9801
25	5	625	50	7.071	2500	75	8.660	5625	100	10	10,000

TABLE 3 Geometric Formulas

Plane Geometry

Rectangle
Area: $A = lw$
Perimeter: $P = 2l + 2w$

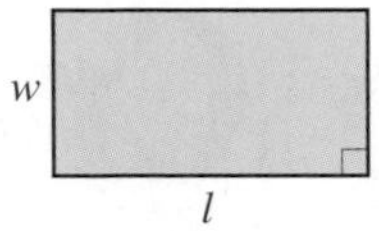

Square
Area: $A = s^2$
Perimeter: $P = 4s$

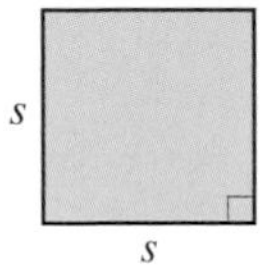

Triangle
Area: $A = \frac{1}{2}bh$

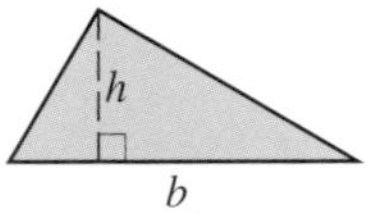

Triangle
Sum of Angle Measures:
$A + B + C = 180°$

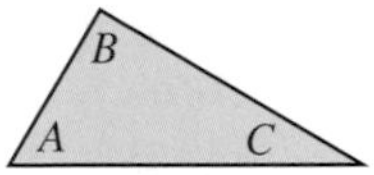

Right Triangle
Pythagorean Theorem (Equation):
$a^2 + b^2 = c^2$

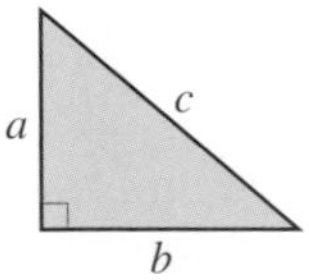

Parallelogram
Area: $A = bh$

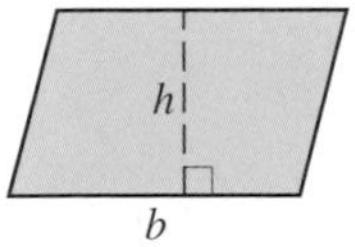

Trapezoid
Area: $A = \frac{1}{2}h(b_1 + b_2)$

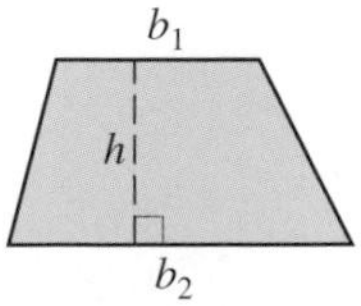

Circle
Area: $A = \pi r^2$
Circumference:
$C = \pi d = 2\pi r$
($\frac{22}{7}$ and 3.14 are different approximations for π)

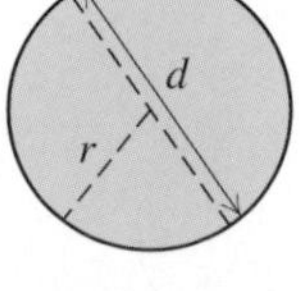

Solid Geometry

Rectangular Solid
Volume: $V = lwh$

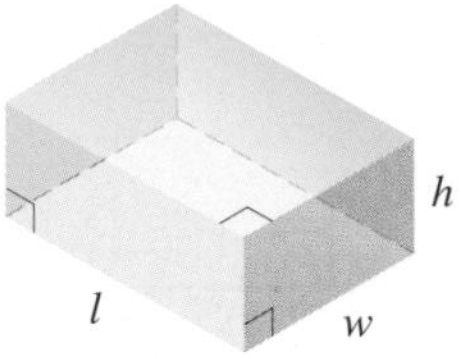

Cube
Volume: $V = s^3$

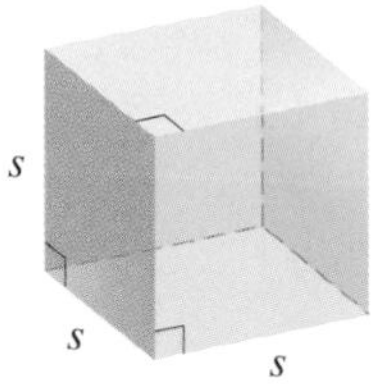

Right Circular Cylinder
Volume: $V = \pi r^2 h$
Total Surface Area:
$S = 2\pi rh + 2\pi r^2$

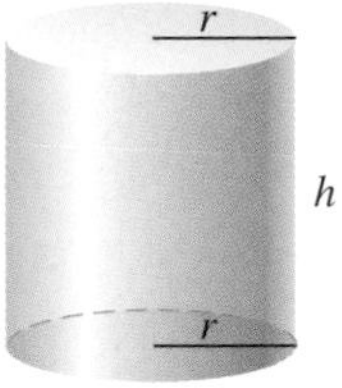

Right Circular Cone
Volume: $V = \frac{1}{3}\pi r^2 h$
Total Surface Area:
$S = \pi r^2 + \pi rs$
Slant Height:
$s = \sqrt{r^2 + h^2}$

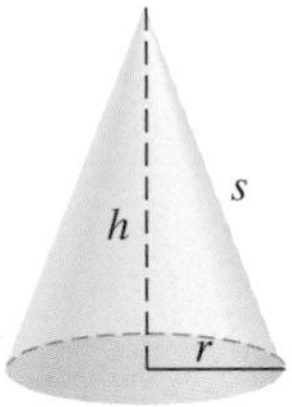

Sphere
Volume: $V = \frac{4}{3}\pi r^3$
Surface Area: $S = 4\pi r^2$

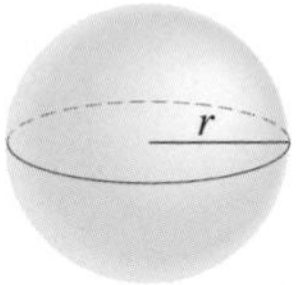

Photo Credits

1, © Peter Turnley/Corbis **7,** Corbis **37 (left),** PhotoDisc **37 (right),** © Tony Roberts/Corbis **42,** PhotoDisc **54,** © Peter Turnley/Corbis **79,** © Ernest H. Robl **98,** © Andrew Holbrooke/Corbis **109,** © Antonio N. Rosario/The Image Bank **110,** Corbis **116,** Appalachian Trail Conference **120,** Ryan McVay, PhotoDisc **123,** © Kevin Horan, Tony Stone **137,** Christine D. Tuff **139,** © Ernest H. Robl **141,** Brand X Pictures (Getty) **147, 179, 180,** Corbis **182,** © David Keaton, The Stock Market **187, 199,** PhotoDisc **200,** Corbis **221,** PhotoDisc **225, 234, 242,** Corbis **299, 350,** Custom Medical Stock Photo, Inc. **355,** Corbis **363, 386,** © Bachmann, Stock, Boston **410, 416,** PhotoDisc **429, 436,** Corbis **454,** © Brent Smith/Reuters/Corbis **474,** Corbis **483,** PhotoDisc **497,** DigitalVision **512,** UPI **513,** Corbis **514, 521, 533,** PhotoDisc **550,** Corbis **553 (top),** Chris-pics **553 (bottom),** The Toronto Star/B. Spremo **559,** Getty One **561,** PhotoDisc **594,** © Ric Ergenbright, Corbis **597 (left),** © Corbis Images **597 (right),** PBA

Answers

CHAPTER 1

Technology Connection, p. 7

1. 3438 **2.** 47,531

Exercise Set 1.1, pp. 9–12

1. Expression **3.** Equation **5.** Equation **7.** Expression **9.** Equation **11.** Expression **13.** 36 **15.** 56 **17.** 5 **19.** 4 **21.** 5 **23.** 6 **25.** 24 ft^2 **27.** 15 cm^2 **29.** 0.368 **31.** Let r represent Ron's age; $r + 5$, or $5 + r$ **33.** $b + 6$, or $6 + b$ **35.** $c - 9$ **37.** $6 + q$, or $q + 6$ **39.** Let p represent Phil's speed; $9p$, or $p \cdot 9$ **41.** $y - x$ **43.** $x \div w$, or $\dfrac{x}{w}$ **45.** $n - m$ **47.** Let l represent the length of the box and h represent the height; $l + h$, or $h + l$ **49.** $9 \cdot 2m$, or $2m \cdot 9$ **51.** Let y represent "some number"; $\frac{1}{4}y$, or $\frac{y}{4}$ **53.** Let w represent the number of women attending; 64% of w, or $0.64w$ **55.** Yes **57.** No **59.** Yes **61.** Yes **63.** Let x represent the unknown number; $73 + x = 201$ **65.** Let x represent the unknown number; $42x = 2352$ **67.** Let s represent the number of unoccupied squares; $s + 19 = 64$ **69.** Let w represent the amount of solid waste generated, in millions of tons; 27% of $w = 56$, or $0.27w = 56$ **71.** (f) **73.** (d) **75.** (g) **77.** (e) **79.** **81.** **83.** \$337.50 **85.** 2 **87.** 6 **89.** $w + 4$ **91.** $l + w + l + w$, or $2l + 2w$ **93.** $t + 8$ **95.**

Exercise Set 1.2, pp. 18–19

1. Commutative **3.** Associative **5.** Distributive **7.** Associative **9.** Commutative **11.** $x + 7$ **13.** $c + ab$ **15.** $3y + 9x$ **17.** $5(1 + a)$ **19.** $a \cdot 2$ **21.** ts **23.** $5 + ba$ **25.** $(a + 1)5$ **27.** $a + (5 + b)$ **29.** $(r + t) + 7$ **31.** $ab + (c + d)$ **33.** $8(xy)$ **35.** $(2a)b$ **37.** $(3 \cdot 2)(a + b)$ **39.** $(r + t) + 6$; $(t + 6) + r$ **41.** $17(ab)$; $b(17a)$

43.
$$\begin{aligned}(5 + x) + 2 &= (x + 5) + 2 && \text{Commutative law}\\ &= x + (5 + 2) && \text{Associative law}\\ &= x + 7 && \text{Simplifying}\end{aligned}$$

45.
$$\begin{aligned}(m \cdot 3)7 &= m(3 \cdot 7) && \text{Associative law}\\ &= m \cdot 21 && \text{Simplifying}\\ &= 21m && \text{Commutative law}\end{aligned}$$

47. $4a + 12$ **49.** $6 + 6x$ **51.** $3x + 3$ **53.** $24 + 8y$ **55.** $18x + 54$ **57.** $5r + 10 + 15t$ **59.** $2a + 2b$ **61.** $5x + 5y + 10$ **63.** x, xyz, 19 **65.** $2a$, $\dfrac{a}{b}$, $5b$ **67.** $2(a + b)$ **69.** $7(1 + y)$ **71.** $3(6x + 1)$ **73.** $5(x + 2 + 3y)$ **75.** $3(4x + 3)$ **77.** $3(a + 3b)$ **79.** $11(4x + y + 2z)$ **81.** s, t **83.** 3, $(x + y)$ **85.** 7, a **87.** $(a - b)$, $(x - y)$ **89.** **91.** Let k represent Kara's salary; $2k$ **92.** $\dfrac{1}{2} \cdot m$, or $\dfrac{m}{2}$ **93.** **95.** Yes; distributive law **97.** Yes; distributive law and commutative law of multiplication **99.** No; for example, let $x = 1$ and $y = 2$. Then $30 \cdot 2 + 1 \cdot 15 = 60 + 15 = 75$ and $5[2(1 + 3 \cdot 2)] = 5[2(7)] = 5 \cdot 14 = 70$. **101.**

Exercise Set 1.3, pp. 28–30

1. Composite **3.** Prime **5.** Composite **7.** Prime **9.** Neither **11.** (b) **13.** (d) **15.** $2 \cdot 25$; $5 \cdot 10$; 1, 2, 5, 10, 25, 50 **17.** $3 \cdot 14$; $6 \cdot 7$; 1, 2, 3, 6, 7, 14, 21, 42 **19.** $2 \cdot 13$ **21.** $2 \cdot 3 \cdot 5$ **23.** $3 \cdot 3 \cdot 3$ **25.** $2 \cdot 3 \cdot 3$ **27.** $2 \cdot 2 \cdot 2 \cdot 5$ **29.** Prime **31.** $2 \cdot 3 \cdot 5 \cdot 7$ **33.** $5 \cdot 23$ **35.** $\frac{2}{3}$ **37.** $\frac{2}{7}$ **39.** $\frac{1}{8}$ **41.** 7 **43.** $\frac{1}{4}$ **45.** 6 **47.** $\frac{21}{25}$ **49.** $\frac{60}{41}$ **51.** $\frac{15}{7}$ **53.** $\frac{3}{14}$ **55.** $\frac{27}{8}$ **57.** $\frac{1}{2}$ **59.** $\frac{7}{6}$ **61.** $\dfrac{3b}{7a}$ **63.** $\dfrac{7}{a}$ **65.** $\frac{5}{6}$ **67.** 1 **69.** $\frac{5}{18}$ **71.** 0 **73.** $\frac{35}{18}$ **75.** $\frac{10}{3}$ **77.** 28 **79.** 1 **81.** $\frac{6}{35}$ **83.** 18 **85.** **87.** $5(3 + x)$; answers may vary

88. $7 + (b + a)$, or $(a + b) + 7$ **89.**
91. Row 1: 7, 2, 36, 14, 8, 8; row 2: 9, 18, 2, 10, 12, 21
93. $\frac{2}{5}$ **95.** $\frac{3q}{t}$ **97.** $\frac{6}{25}$ **99.** $\frac{5ap}{2cm}$ **101.** $\frac{23r}{18t}$ **103.** $\frac{28}{45}\text{m}^2$
105. $14\frac{2}{9}$ m **107.** $27\frac{3}{5}$ cm

Technology Connection, p. 34

1. 2.236067977 **2.** 2.645751311 **3.** 3.605551275
4. 5.196152423 **5.** 6.164414003 **6.** 7.071067812

Exercise Set 1.4, pp. 37–39

1. Repeating **3.** Integer **5.** Rational number
7. Natural number **9.** −1349, 29,035 **11.** 950,000,000, −460 **13.** 2, −6 **15.** 750, −125 **17.** Jets: −34; Strikers: 34
19.
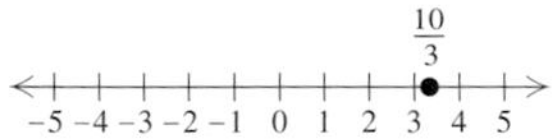

21.
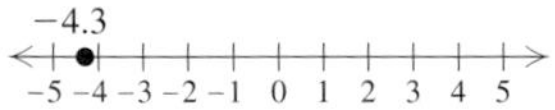

23.
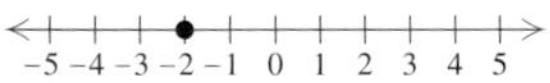

25. 0.875 **27.** −0.75
29. $1.1\overline{6}$ **31.** $0.\overline{6}$ **33.** −0.5 **35.** 0.13 **37.** $<$ **39.** $>$
41. $<$ **43.** $<$ **45.** $>$ **47.** $<$ **49.** $<$ **51.** $x < -7$
53. $y \geq -10$ **55.** True **57.** False **59.** True **61.** 58
63. 17 **65.** 5.6 **67.** 329 **69.** $\frac{9}{7}$ **71.** 0 **73.** 8
75. $-83, -4.7, 0, \frac{5}{9}, 8.31, 62$ **77.** −83, 0, 62
79. $-83, -4.7, 0, \frac{5}{9}, \pi, \sqrt{17}, 8.31, 62$ **81.** **83.** 42
84. $ba + 5$, or $5 + ab$ **85.** **87.** **89.** −23, −17, 0, 4
91. $-\frac{4}{3}, \frac{4}{9}, \frac{4}{8}, \frac{4}{6}, \frac{4}{5}, \frac{4}{3}, \frac{4}{2}$ **93.** $<$ **95.** $=$ **97.** −7, 7
99. −4, −3, 3, 4 **101.** $\frac{3}{3}$ **103.** $\frac{70}{9}$ **105.**

Exercise Set 1.5, pp. 44–46

1. (f) **3.** (e) **5.** (b) **7.** −3 **9.** 4 **11.** 0 **13.** −8
15. −27 **17.** −8 **19.** 0 **21.** −41 **23.** 0 **25.** 7
27. −2 **29.** 11 **31.** −33 **33.** 0 **35.** 18 **37.** −45
39. 0 **41.** 20 **43.** −1.7 **45.** −9.1 **47.** $\frac{1}{5}$ **49.** $\frac{-6}{7}$
51. $-\frac{1}{15}$ **53.** $\frac{2}{9}$ **55.** −3 **57.** 0 **59.** The price rose 9¢.
61. Her new balance was $95. **63.** The total gain was 22 yd. **65.** Lyle owes $85. **67.** The elevation of the peak is 13,796 ft. **69.** $14a$ **71.** $9x$ **73.** $13t$ **75.** $-2m$
77. $-7a$ **79.** $1 - 2x$ **81.** $12x + 17$ **83.** $7r + 8t + 16$
85. $18n + 16$ **87.** **89.** $21z + 7y + 14$ **90.** $\frac{28}{3}$ **91.**
93. $65.25 **95.** $-5y$ **97.** $-7m$ **99.** $-7t, -23$
101. 1 under par

Exercise Set 1.6, pp. 51–54

1. (d) **3.** (f) **5.** (a) **7.** (b) **9.** Four minus ten
11. Two minus negative nine **13.** Nine minus the opposite of t **15.** The opposite of x minus y
17. Negative three minus the opposite of n **19.** −39
21. 9 **23.** 3.14 **25.** −23 **27.** $\frac{14}{3}$ **29.** −0.101 **31.** 72
33. $-\frac{2}{5}$ **35.** 1 **37.** −7 **39.** −2 **41.** −5 **43.** −6
45. −10 **47.** −6 **49.** 0 **51.** −5 **53.** −10 **55.** 2
57. 0 **59.** 0 **61.** 8 **63.** −11 **65.** 16 **67.** −19
69. −1 **71.** 17 **73.** −5 **75.** −3 **77.** −21 **79.** 5
81. −8 **83.** 10 **85.** −23 **87.** −68 **89.** −58
91. −5.5 **93.** −0.928 **95.** $-\frac{7}{11}$ **97.** $-\frac{4}{5}$ **99.** $\frac{5}{17}$
101. $3.8 - (-5.2)$; 9 **103.** $114 - (-79)$; 193 **105.** −58
107. 34 **109.** 41 **111.** −62 **113.** −139 **115.** 0
117. $-7x, -4y$ **119.** $9, -5t, -3st$ **121.** $-3x$
123. $-5a + 4$ **125.** $-7n - 9$ **127.** $-6x + 5$
129. $-8t - 7$ **131.** $-12x + 3y + 9$ **133.** $8x + 66$
135. 150°C **137.** 30,384 ft **139.** 116 m **141.**
143. 432 ft^2 **144.** $2 \cdot 2 \cdot 2 \cdot 2 \cdot 2 \cdot 3 \cdot 3 \cdot 3$ **145.**
147. 11:00 P.M., August 14 **149.** False. For example, let $m = -3$ and $n = -5$. Then $-3 > -5$, but $-3 + (-5) = -8 \not> 0$. **151.** True. For example, for $m = 4$ and $n = -4$, $4 = -(-4)$ and $4 + (-4) = 0$; for $m = -3$ and $n = 3$, $-3 = -3$ and $-3 + 3 = 0$.
153. (−) 9 − (−) 7 ENTER

Exercise Set 1.7, pp. 60–62

1. 1 **3.** 0 **5.** 0 **7.** 1 **9.** 1 **11.** −24 **13.** −56
15. −24 **17.** −72 **19.** 42 **21.** 45 **23.** 190 **25.** −144
27. 1200 **29.** 98 **31.** −78 **33.** 21.7 **35.** $-\frac{2}{5}$ **37.** $\frac{1}{12}$
39. −11.13 **41.** $-\frac{5}{12}$ **43.** 252 **45.** 0 **47.** $\frac{1}{28}$ **49.** 150
51. 0 **53.** −720 **55.** −30,240 **57.** −7 **59.** −4 **61.** −7
63. 4 **65.** −8 **67.** 2 **69.** −12 **71.** −8 **73.** Undefined
75. −4 **77.** 0 **79.** 0 **81.** $-\frac{8}{3}; \frac{8}{-3}$ **83.** $-\frac{29}{35}; \frac{-29}{35}$
85. $\frac{-7}{3}; \frac{7}{-3}$ **87.** $-\frac{x}{2}; \frac{x}{-2}$ **89.** $-\frac{5}{4}$ **91.** $-\frac{13}{47}$ **93.** $-\frac{1}{10}$
95. $\frac{1}{4.3}$, or $\frac{10}{43}$ **97.** $-\frac{4}{9}$ **99.** Does not exist **101.** $\frac{21}{20}$
103. $\frac{12}{55}$ **105.** −1 **107.** 1 **109.** $-\frac{9}{11}$ **111.** $-\frac{7}{4}$
113. −12 **115.** −3 **117.** 1 **119.** 7 **121.** $-\frac{2}{9}$ **123.** $\frac{1}{10}$
125. $-\frac{7}{6}$ **127.** $\frac{6}{7}$ **129.** $-\frac{14}{15}$ **131.** **133.** $\frac{22}{39}$
134. $12x - 2y - 9$ **135.** **137.** For 2 and 3, the reciprocal of the sum is $1/(2 + 3)$ or $1/5$. But $1/5 \neq 1/2 + 1/3$. **139.** Negative **141.** Negative
143. Negative **145.** **(a)** m and n have different signs; **(b)** either m or n is zero; **(c)** m and n have the same sign.
147.

Exercise Set 1.8, pp. 70–72

1. **(a)** Division; **(b)** subtraction; **(c)** addition; **(d)** multiplication; **(e)** subtraction; **(f)** multiplication
3. 2^3 **5.** x^7 **7.** $(3t)^5$ **9.** 9 **11.** 16 **13.** −16 **15.** 64
17. 625 **19.** 7 **21.** $81t^4$ **23.** $-343x^3$ **25.** 26 **27.** 86
29. 7 **31.** 5 **33.** 1 **35.** 298 **37.** 11 **39.** −36
41. 1291 **43.** 14 **45.** 152 **47.** 36 **49.** 1 **51.** −26

53. -2 **55.** $-\frac{9}{2}$ **57.** -11 **59.** -3 **61.** -15 **63.** 9 **65.** 30 **67.** 6 **69.** -17 **71.** $-9x-1$ **73.** $-5+6x$ **75.** $-4a+3b-7c$ **77.** $-3x^2-5x+1$ **79.** $2x-7$ **81.** $-3a+9$ **83.** $5x-6$ **85.** $-3t-11r$ **87.** $9y-25z$ **89.** x^2+2 **91.** $-t^3-2t$ **93.** $37a^2-23ab+35b^2$ **95.** $-22t^3-t^2+9t$ **97.** $2x-25$ **99.** **101.** Let n represent the number; $2n+9$, or $9+2n$ **102.** Let m and n represent the two numbers; $\frac{1}{2}(m+n)$ **103.** **105.** $-6r-5t+21$ **107.** $-2x-f$ **109.** **111.** True **113.** False **115.** 0 **117.** 39,000 **119.** $44x^3$

Review Exercises: Chapter 1, pp. 75–77

1. True **2.** True **3.** False **4.** True **5.** False **6.** False **7.** True **8.** False **9.** False **10.** True **11.** 15 **12.** 4 **13.** -7 **14.** -5 **15.** $z-7$ **16.** xz **17.** Let m and n represent the numbers; $mn+1$, or $1+mn$ **18.** No **19.** Let d represent the number of digital photos taken in 2003, in billions; $29.8 = d + 18.49$ **20.** $t \cdot 3 + 5$ **21.** $2x+(y+z)$ **22.** $(4x)y$, $4(yx)$, $(4y)x$; answers may vary **23.** $18x+30y$ **24.** $40x+24y+16$ **25.** $3(7x+5y)$ **26.** $7(5x+2+y)$ **27.** $2 \cdot 2 \cdot 13$ **28.** $\frac{5}{12}$ **29.** $\frac{9}{4}$ **30.** $\frac{31}{36}$ **31.** $\frac{3}{16}$ **32.** $\frac{3}{5}$ **33.** $\frac{72}{25}$ **34.** $-45, 72$

35.

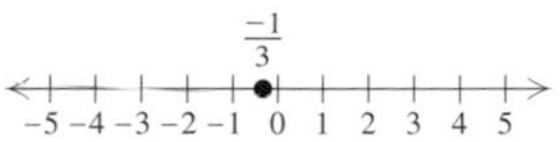

36. $x > -3$

37. True **38.** False **39.** -0.875 **40.** 1 **41.** -9 **42.** -3 **43.** $-\frac{7}{12}$ **44.** 0 **45.** -5 **46.** 5 **47.** $-\frac{7}{5}$ **48.** -7.9 **49.** 54 **50.** -9.18 **51.** $-\frac{2}{7}$ **52.** -140 **53.** -7 **54.** -3 **55.** $\frac{3}{4}$ **56.** 92 **57.** 62 **58.** 48 **59.** 168 **60.** $\frac{21}{8}$ **61.** $\frac{103}{17}$ **62.** $7a-3b$ **63.** $-2x+5y$ **64.** 7 **65.** $-\frac{1}{7}$ **66.** $(2x)^4$ **67.** $-125x^3$ **68.** $-3a+9$ **69.** $-2b+21$ **70.** $-3x+9$ **71.** $12y-34$ **72.** $5x+24$ **73.** The value of a constant never varies. A variable can represent a variety of numbers. **74.** A term is one of the parts of an expression that is separated from the other parts by plus signs. A factor is part of a product. **75.** The distributive law is used in factoring algebraic expressions, multiplying algebraic expressions, combining like terms, finding the opposite of a sum, and subtracting algebraic expressions. **76.** A negative number raised to an even power is positive; a negative number raised to an odd power is negative. **77.** 25,281 **78. (a)** $\frac{3}{11}$; **(b)** $\frac{10}{11}$ **79.** $-\frac{5}{8}$ **80.** -2.1 **81.** (i) **82.** (j) **83.** (a) **84.** (h) **85.** (k) **86.** (b) **87.** (c) **88.** (e) **89.** (d) **90.** (f) **91.** (g)

Test: Chapter 1, p. 78

1. [1.1] 4 **2.** [1.1] Let x represent the number; $x-9$ **3.** [1.1] 240 ft^2 **4.** [1.2] $q+3p$ **5.** [1.2] $(x \cdot 4) \cdot y$ **6.** [1.1] No **7.** [1.1] Let p represent the maximum production capability; $p - 282 = 2518$ **8.** [1.2] $35-7x$ **9.** [1.7] $-5y+10$ **10.** [1.2] $11(1-4x)$ **11.** [1.2] $7(x+3+2y)$ **12.** [1.3] $2 \cdot 2 \cdot 3 \cdot 5 \cdot 5$ **13.** [1.3] $\frac{2}{7}$ **14.** [1.4] $<$ **15.** [1.4] $>$ **16.** [1.4] $\frac{9}{4}$ **17.** [1.4] 2.7 **18.** [1.6] $-\frac{2}{3}$ **19.** [1.7] $-\frac{7}{4}$ **20.** [1.6] 8 **21.** [1.4] $-2 \geq x$ **22.** [1.6] 7.8 **23.** [1.5] -8 **24.** [1.6] -2.5 **25.** [1.6] $\frac{7}{8}$ **26.** [1.7] -48 **27.** [1.7] $\frac{3}{16}$ **28.** [1.7] -6 **29.** [1.7] $\frac{3}{4}$ **30.** [1.7] -9.728 **31.** [1.8] -173 **32.** [1.6] 15 **33.** [1.8] -4 **34.** [1.8] 448 **35.** [1.6] $21a+22y$ **36.** [1.8] $16x^4$ **37.** [1.8] $x+7$ **38.** [1.8] $9a-12b-7$ **39.** [1.8] $68y-8$ **40.** [1.1] 5 **41.** [1.8] $9-(3-4)+5=15$ **42.** [1.8] 15 **43.** [1.8] $4a$ **44.** [1.8] False

CHAPTER 2

Exercise Set 2.1, pp. 87–88

1. (f) **3.** (a) **5.** (d) **7.** 17 **9.** -11 **11.** -21 **13.** -31 **15.** 13 **17.** 19 **19.** -4 **21.** $\frac{7}{3}$ **23.** $-\frac{13}{10}$ **25.** $\frac{41}{24}$ **27.** $-\frac{1}{20}$ **29.** 1.5 **31.** -5 **33.** 14 **35.** 4 **37.** 12 **39.** -23 **41.** 8 **43.** -7 **45.** 8 **47.** -88 **49.** 20 **51.** -54 **53.** $\frac{5}{9}$ **55.** 1 **57.** $\frac{9}{2}$ **59.** -7.6 **61.** -2.5 **63.** -15 **65.** 18 **67.** -6 **69.** -128 **71.** $-\frac{1}{2}$ **73.** -15 **75.** 12 **77.** 310.756 **79.** **81.** -34 **82.** 41 **83.** 1 **84.** -16 **85.** **87.** Identity **89.** 0 **91.** Contradiction **93.** Contradiction **95.** 9.4 **97.** 2 **99.** $-13, 13$ **101.** 9000 **103.** 250

Technology Connection, p. 92

1.

X	Y1	
0	5	
1	4	
2	3	
3	2	
4	1	
5	0	
6	−1	
X = 0		

2.

X	Y1	Y2
0	5	17
1	4	13
2	3	9
3	2	5
4	1	1
5	0	−3
6	−1	−7
X = 0		

3. 4; not reliable because, depending on the choice of ΔTbl, it is easy to scroll past a solution without realizing it.

Exercise Set 2.2, pp. 95–96

1. (c) **3.** (a) **5.** (b) **7.** 8 **9.** 7 **11.** 5 **13.** 14 **15.** -7 **17.** -11 **19.** -24 **21.** 19 **23.** $\frac{10}{9}$ **25.** 3 **27.** 15 **29.** -4 **31.** $-\frac{28}{3}$ **33.** 4 **35.** -3 **37.** 5 **39.** 2 **41.** 0 **43.** 6 **45.** 8 **47.** 0 **49.** 10 **51.** 4 **53.** 0 **55.** 2 **57.** -8 **59.** 2 **61.** $-\frac{2}{5}$ **63.** $\frac{64}{3}$ **65.** $\frac{2}{5}$ **67.** 3 **69.** -4 **71.** $1.\overline{6}$ **73.** $-\frac{40}{37}$ **75.** 11 **77.** 6 **79.** $\frac{16}{15}$ **81.** $-\frac{51}{31}$ **83.** 2 **85.** **87.** -7 **88.** 15 **89.** -15 **90.** -28 **91.** **93.** $\frac{1136}{909}$, or $1.\overline{2497}$ **95.** Contradiction **97.** Identity **99.** $\frac{2}{3}$ **101.** 0 **103.** 0 **105.** -2

Technology Connection, p. 98

1. 72,930

Exercise Set 2.3, pp. 101–104

1. 2 mi **3.** 1423 students **5.** 54,000 Btu's **7.** 255 mg **9.** $b = \frac{A}{h}$ **11.** $r = \frac{d}{t}$ **13.** $P = \frac{I}{rt}$ **15.** $m = 65 - H$ **17.** $l = \frac{P - 2w}{2}$, or $l = \frac{P}{2} - w$ **19.** $\pi = \frac{A}{r^2}$ **21.** $h = \frac{2A}{b}$ **23.** $m = \frac{E}{c^2}$ **25.** $d = 2Q - c$ **27.** $b = 3A - a - c$ **29.** $A = Ms$ **31.** $C = \frac{5}{9}(F - 32)$ **33.** $t = \frac{A}{a + b}$ **35.** $h = \frac{2A}{a + b}$ **37.** $L = W - \frac{N(R - r)}{400}$, or $L = \frac{400W - NR + Nr}{400}$ **39.** **41.** 0 **42.** 9.18 **43.** −13 **44.** 65 **45.** **47.** 35 yr **49.** 27 in^3 **51.** $a = \frac{w}{c} \cdot d$ **53.** $c = \frac{d}{a - b}$ **55.** $a = \frac{c}{3 + b + d}$ **57.** $K = 917 + 13.2276w + 2.3622h - 6a$

Exercise Set 2.4, pp. 109–113

1. (d) **3.** (e) **5.** (c) **7.** (f) **9.** (b) **11.** 0.3 **13.** 0.02 **15.** 0.77 **17.** 0.09 **19.** 0.6258 **21.** 0.007 **23.** 1.25 **25.** 64% **27.** 10.6% **29.** 42% **31.** 90% **33.** 0.49% **35.** 108% **37.** 230% **39.** 80% **41.** 32% **43.** 25% **45.** 24% **47.** $46\frac{2}{3}$, or $\frac{140}{3}$ **49.** 2.5 **51.** 84 **53.** 125% **55.** 0.8 **57.** 50% **59.** \$198 **61.** \$1584 **63.** \$528 **65.** 75 credits **67.** About 626 at-bats **69.** **(a)** 16%; **(b)** \$29 **71.** About 72%; about 28% **73.** \$280 **75.** 285 women **77.** \$18/hr **79.** 150% **81.** \$36 **83.** \$148.50 **85.** About 31.5 lb **87.** 7410 brochures **89.** About 165 calories **91.** **93.** Let n represent the number; $n + 5$ **94.** Let t represent Tino's weight; $t - 4$ **95.** $8 \cdot 2a$ **96.** Let x and y represent the two numbers; $xy + 1$ **97.** **99.** 18,500 people **101.** About 5 ft 6 in. **103.** About 27% **105.**

Exercise Set 2.5, pp. 122–127

1. 8 **3.** 11 **5.** \$85 **7.** \$85 **9.** Approximately $62\frac{2}{3}$ mi **11.** 190 mi **13.** 1204 and 1205 **15.** 396 and 398 **17.** 19, 20, 21 **19.** Bride: 102 yr; groom: 83 yr **21.** Bathrooms: \$$11\frac{2}{3}$ billion; kitchens: \$$23\frac{1}{3}$ billion **23.** 140 and 141 **25.** Width: 100 ft; length: 160 ft; area: 16,000 ft^2 **27.** Width: 50 ft; length: 84 ft **29.** $1\frac{3}{4}$ in. by $3\frac{1}{2}$ in. **31.** 30°, 90°, 60° **33.** 95° **35.** Bottom: 144 ft; middle: 72 ft; top: 24 ft **37.** $10\frac{1}{16}$ mi **39.** $128\frac{1}{3}$ mi **41.** 65°, 25° **43.** Length: 27.9 cm; width: 21.6 cm **45.** \$6600 **47.** 1049 points **49.** 160 chirps per minute **51.** **53.** $<$ **54.** $<$ **55.** $<$ **56.** $>$ **57.** **59.** \$37 **61.** 20 **63.** Half-dollars: 5; quarters: 10; dimes: 20; nickels: 60 **65.** 120 apples **67.** 30 games **69.** 76 **71.** **73.** Width: 23.31 cm; length: 27.56 cm

Exercise Set 2.6, pp. 133–135

1. $\geq$ **3.** $<$ **5.** Equivalent **7.** Equivalent **9.** **(a)** Yes; **(b)** yes; **(c)** yes; **(d)** no; **(e)** yes **11.** **(a)** No; **(b)** no; **(c)** yes; **(d)** yes; **(e)** no **13.**

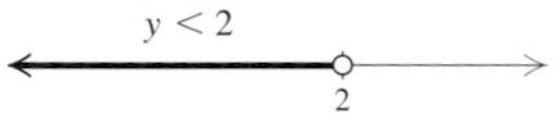

15.

17.

19.

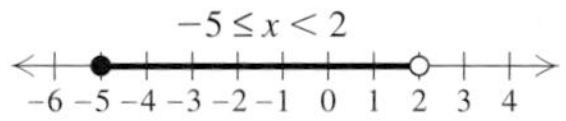

21.

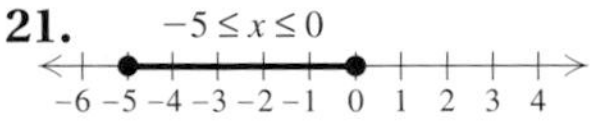

23. $\{x|x > -4\}$ **25.** $\{x|x \leq 2\}$ **27.** $\{x|x < -1\}$ **29.** $\{x|x \geq 0\}$ **31.** $\{y|y > 3\}$,

33. $\{x|x \leq -21\}$,

35. $\{x|x < 17\}$,

37. $\{y|y > -6\}$,

39. $\{x|x \leq 9\}$,

41. $\{y|y \leq \frac{1}{2}\}$,

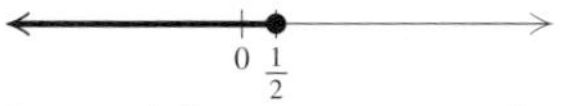

43. $\{t|t > \frac{5}{8}\}$,

45. $\{x|x < 0\}$,

47. $\{t|t < 23\}$,

49. $\{x|x < 7\}$,

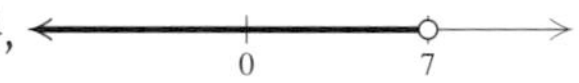

51. $\{x|x > -\frac{13}{7}\}$,

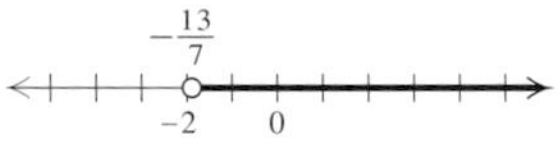

53. $\{t|t < -3\}$,

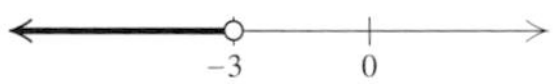

55. $\{y|y \geq -\frac{2}{7}\}$,

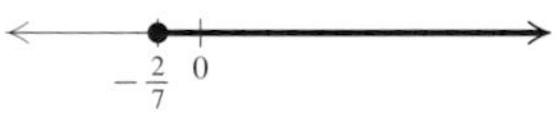

57. $\{y|y \geq -\frac{1}{10}\}$,

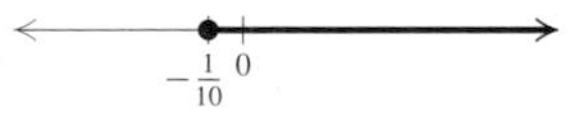

59. $\{x|x > \frac{4}{5}\}$,

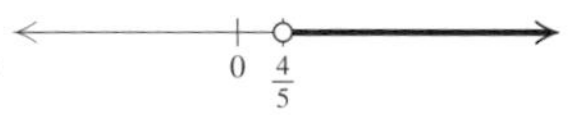

61. $\{x|x < 9\}$ **63.** $\{y|y \geq 4\}$ **65.** $\{t|t \leq 7\}$ **67.** $\{y|y < -4\}$ **69.** $\{x|x > -4\}$ **71.** $\{y|y < -\frac{10}{3}\}$ **73.** $\{x|x > -10\}$ **75.** $\{y|y < 2\}$ **77.** $\{y|y \geq 3\}$ **79.** $\{x|x > -4\}$ **81.** $\{x|x > -4\}$ **83.** $\{n|n \geq 70\}$ **85.** $\{x|x \leq 15\}$ **87.** $\{t|t < 14\}$ **89.** $\{y|y < 6\}$ **91.** $\{t|t \leq -4\}$ **93.** $\{r|r > -3\}$ **95.** $\{x|x \geq 8\}$ **97.** $\{x|x < \frac{11}{18}\}$ **99.** **101.** Let n represent "some number"; $3 + n$ **102.** Let x and y represent the two

numbers; $2(x + y)$ **103.** Let x represent the number; $2x - 3$ **104.** Let y represent the number; $2y + 5$
105. **107.** $\{x \mid x \text{ is a real number}\}$ **109.** $\left\{x \mid x \leq \frac{5}{6}\right\}$
111. $\{x \mid x > 7\}$ **113.** $\left\{x \mid x < \dfrac{y - b}{a}\right\}$
115. $\{x \mid x \text{ is a real number}\}$

Exercise Set 2.7, pp. 138–142

1. $b \leq a$ **3.** $a \leq b$ **5.** $b \leq a$ **7.** $b < a$ **9.** Let n represent the number; $n \geq 8$ **11.** Let t represent the temperature; $t \leq -3$ **13.** Let p represent the price of Pat's PT Cruiser; $p > 21{,}900$ **15.** Let d represent the distance to Normandale Community College; $d \leq 15$ **17.** Let n represent the number; $n > -2$ **19.** Let p represent the number of people attending the Million Man March; $400{,}000 < p < 1{,}200{,}000$ **21.** More than 2.5 hr
23. More than 18 one-way trips per month **25.** Scores greater than or equal to 97 **27.** 8 credits or more
29. 21 calls or more **31.** Lengths greater than 6 cm
33. Depths less than 437.5 ft **35.** Blue-book value is greater than or equal to \$10,625 **37.** Lengths greater than or equal to 5 in. **39.** Temperatures greater than 37°C
41. Heights at least 4 ft **43.** A serving contains at least 16 g of fat. **45.** Dates after September 16 **47.** 14 or fewer copies **49.** Years after 1995 **51.** Mileages less than or equal to 193 **53.** **55.** 2 **56.** $\frac{1}{2}$ **57.** $-\frac{10}{3}$
58. $-\frac{1}{5}$ **59.** **61.** Temperatures between −15°C and $-9\frac{4}{9}$°C **63.** Lengths less than or equal to 8 cm
65. They contain at least 7.5 g of fat per serving.
67. At least \$42 **69.**

Review Exercises: Chapter 2, pp. 144–145

1. True **2.** False **3.** True **4.** True **5.** True **6.** False
7. True **8.** True **9.** −25 **10.** 7 **11.** −65 **12.** 1
13. −5 **14.** 1.11 **15.** $\frac{1}{2}$ **16.** $-\frac{15}{64}$ **17.** $\frac{38}{5}$ **18.** −8
19. −5 **20.** $-\frac{1}{3}$ **21.** 4 **22.** 3 **23.** 4 **24.** 16 **25.** 7
26. $-\frac{7}{5}$ **27.** 12 **28.** 4 **29.** $d = \dfrac{C}{\pi}$ **30.** $B = \dfrac{3V}{h}$
31. $b = 2A - a$ **32.** 0.009 **33.** 44% **34.** 70% **35.** 140
36. Yes **37.** No **38.** Yes **39.**

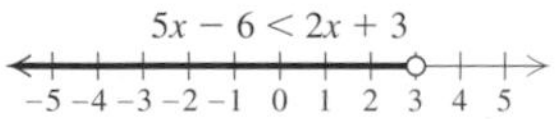

40.

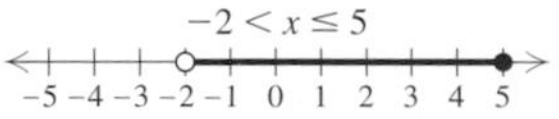

41.

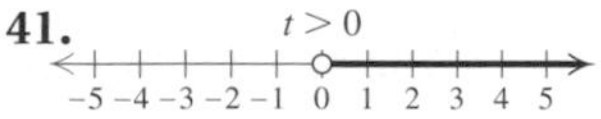

42. $\left\{t \mid t \geq -\frac{1}{2}\right\}$ **43.** $\{x \mid x \geq 7\}$ **44.** $\{y \mid y > 3\}$
45. $\{y \mid y \leq -4\}$ **46.** $\{x \mid x < -11\}$ **47.** $\{y \mid y > -7\}$
48. $\{x \mid x > -6\}$ **49.** $\left\{x \mid x > -\frac{9}{11}\right\}$ **50.** $\{t \mid t \leq -12\}$
51. $\{x \mid x \leq -8\}$ **52.** 20 bottles **53.** 15 ft, 17 ft
54. \$126 billion **55.** 57, 59 **56.** Width: 11 cm; length: 17 cm **57.** \$160 **58.** \$46,987.95 **59.** 35°, 85°, 60°
60. \$105 or less **61.** Widths greater than 17 cm
62. Multiplying both sides of an equation by *any* nonzero number results in an equivalent equation. When multiplying on both sides of an inequality, the sign of the number being multiplied by must be considered. If the number is positive, the direction of the inequality symbol remains unchanged; if the number is negative, the direction of the inequality symbol must be reversed to produce an equivalent inequality. **63.** The solutions of an equation can usually each be checked. The solutions of an inequality are normally too numerous to check. Checking a few numbers from the solution set found cannot guarantee that the answer is correct, although if any number does not check, the answer found is incorrect.
64. 25 hr 39 min **65.** Nile: 6673 km; Amazon: 6440 km
66. \$18,600 **67.** −23, 23 **68.** −20, 20
69. $a = \dfrac{y - 3}{2 - b}$

Test: Chapter 2, p. 146

1. [2.1] 9 **2.** [2.1] 15 **3.** [2.1] −3 **4.** [2.1] 49
5. [2.1] −12 **6.** [2.2] 2 **7.** [2.1] −8 **8.** [2.1] $-\frac{7}{20}$
9. [2.2] 7 **10.** [2.2] $-\frac{5}{3}$ **11.** [2.2] $\frac{23}{3}$ **12.** [2.6] $\{x \mid x > -5\}$
13. [2.6] $\{x \mid x > -13\}$ **14.** [2.6] $\left\{x \mid x < \frac{21}{8}\right\}$
15. [2.6] $\{y \mid y \leq -13\}$ **16.** [2.6] $\{y \mid y \leq -8\}$
17. [2.6] $\left\{x \mid x \leq -\frac{1}{20}\right\}$ **18.** [2.6] $\{x \mid x < -6\}$
19. [2.6] $\{x \mid x \leq -1\}$ **20.** [2.3] $r = \dfrac{A}{2\pi h}$
21. [2.3] $l = 2w - P$ **22.** [2.4] 2.3 **23.** [2.4] 5.4%
24. [2.4] 16 **25.** [2.4] 44%
26. [2.6]

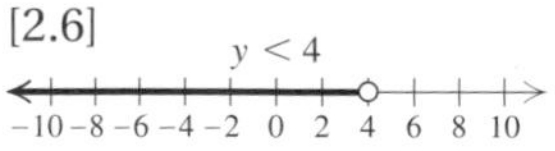

27. [2.6]

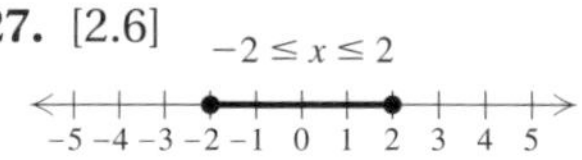

28. [2.5] Width: 7 cm; length: 11 cm **29.** [2.5] 60 mi
30. [2.5] 81 mm, 83 mm, 85 mm **31.** [2.4] \$65
32. [2.7] Mileages less than or equal to 525.8 mi
33. [2.3] $d = \dfrac{a}{3}$ **34.** [1.4], [2.2] −15, 15
35. [2.5] 60 tickets

CHAPTER 3

Exercise Set 3.1, pp. 154–158

1. (a) **3.** (b) **5.** 2 drinks
7. The person weighs more than 200 lb.
9. About 2,920,000 **11.** About 1,460,000
13. About 24.8 million tons
15. About 2.9 million tons
17. 120,000,000 phones
19. 2004

21.

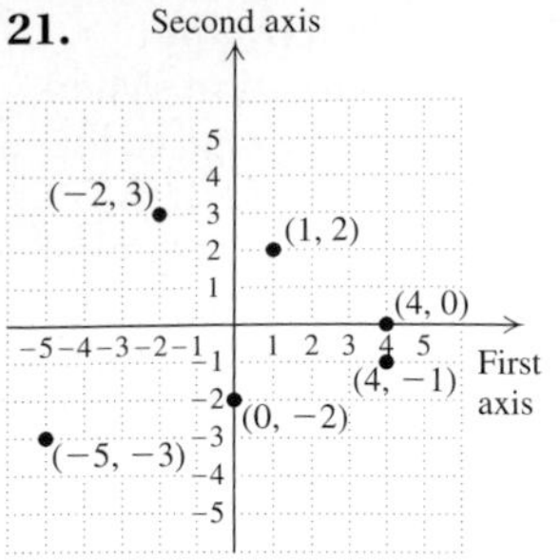

23.

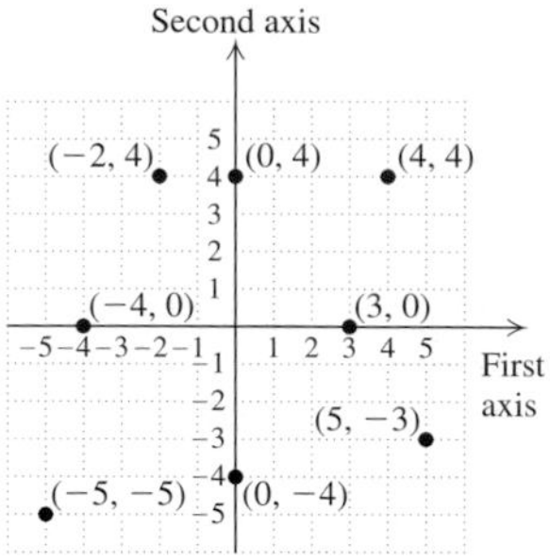

25.

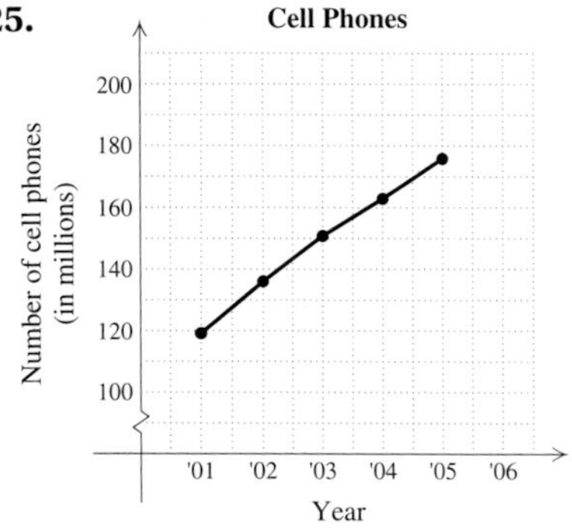

27. $A(-4, 5)$; $B(-3, -3)$; $C(0, 4)$; $D(3, 4)$; $E(3, -4)$
29. $A(4, 1)$; $B(0, -5)$; $C(-4, 0)$; $D(-3, -2)$; $E(3, 0)$

31.

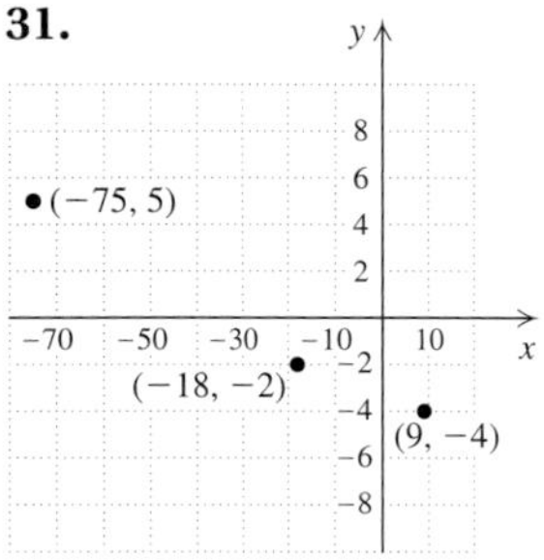

33.

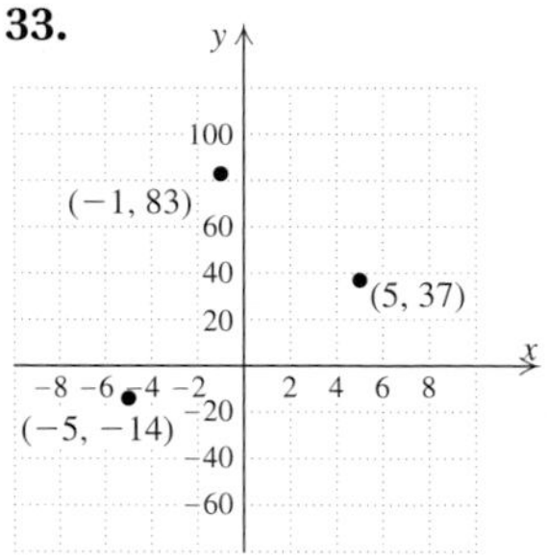

35.

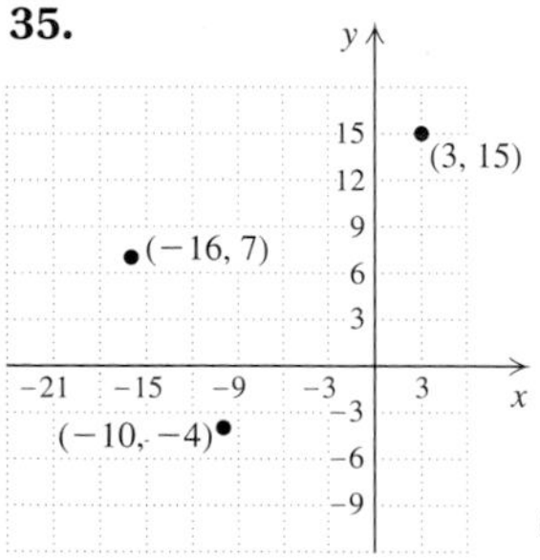

37.

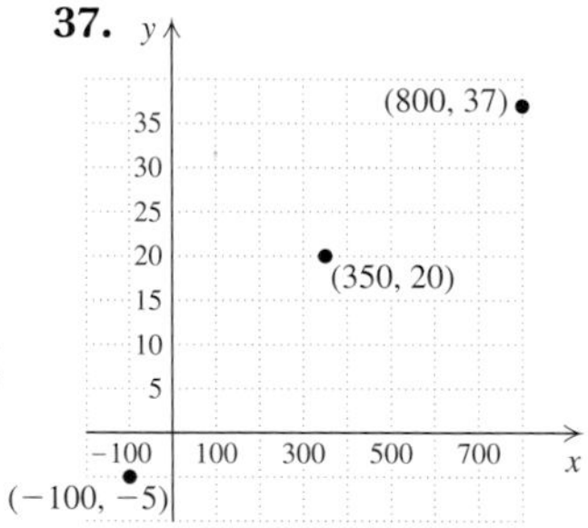

39.

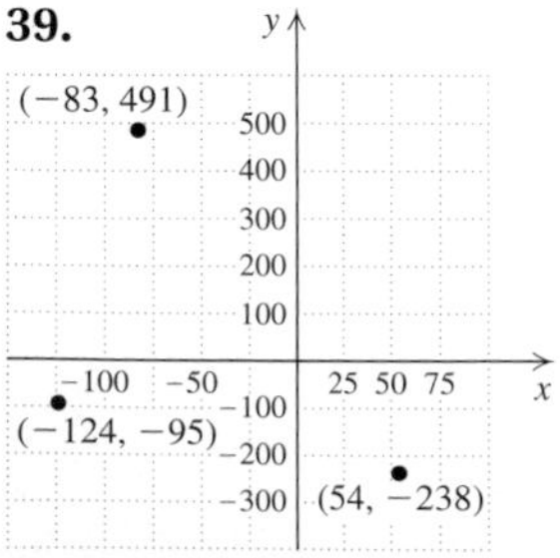

41. IV **43.** III **45.** I

47. II **49.** I and IV **51.** I and III **53.** **55.** −18 **56.** −31 **57.** 6 **58.** 1 **59.** $y = \frac{3}{2}x - 3$ **60.** $y = \frac{7}{4}x - \frac{7}{2}$ **61.** **63.** II or IV **65.** $(-1, -5)$

67.

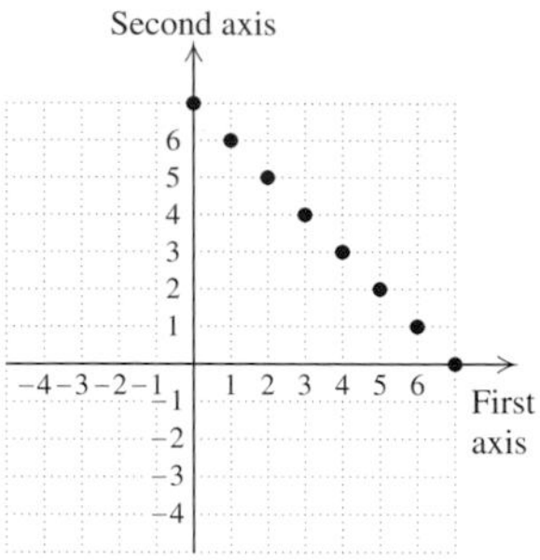

69. $\frac{65}{2}$ sq units

71. Latitude 27°North; longitude 81° West **73.**

Technology Connection, p. 165

1. $y = -5x + 6.5$

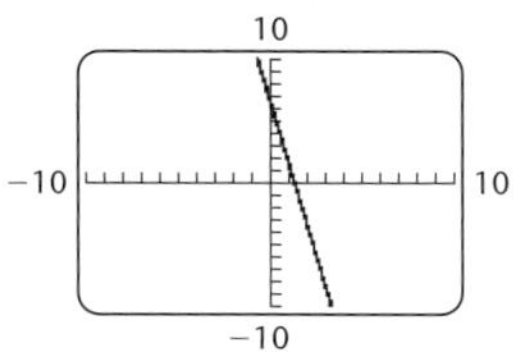

2. $y = 3x + 4.5$

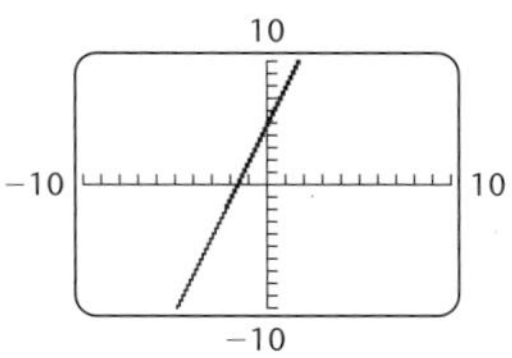

3. $7y - 4x = 22$, or $y = \frac{4}{7}x + \frac{22}{7}$

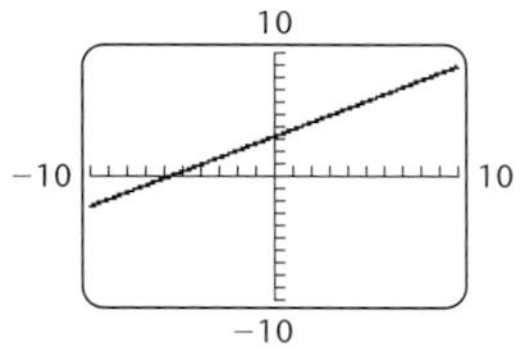

4. $5y + 11x = -20$, or $y = -\frac{11}{5}x - 4$

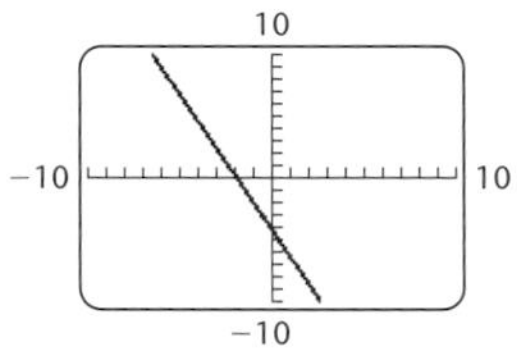

5. $2y - x^2 = 0$, or $y = 0.5x^2$

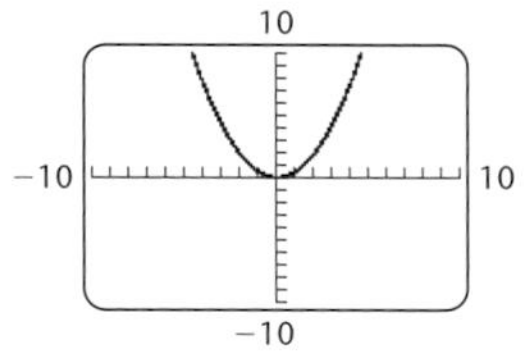

6. $y + x^2 = 8$, or $y = -x^2 + 8$

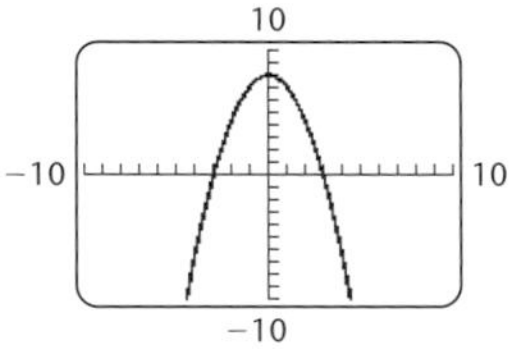

Exercise Set 3.2, pp. 166–168

1. No **3.** No **5.** Yes **7.**

$$\begin{array}{c|c} y = x + 3 & \\ \hline 2 & -1 + 3 \\ 2 \stackrel{?}{=} 2 & \text{True} \end{array} \qquad \begin{array}{c|c} y = x + 3 & \\ \hline 7 & 4 + 3 \\ 7 \stackrel{?}{=} 7 & \text{True} \end{array}$$

(2, 5); answers may vary

9.

$$\begin{array}{c|c} y = \frac{1}{2}x + 3 & \\ \hline 5 & \frac{1}{2} \cdot 4 + 3 \\ & 2 + 3 \\ 5 \stackrel{?}{=} 5 & \text{True} \end{array} \qquad \begin{array}{c|c} y = \frac{1}{2}x + 3 & \\ \hline 2 & \frac{1}{2}(-2) + 3 \\ & -1 + 3 \\ 2 \stackrel{?}{=} 2 & \text{True} \end{array}$$

(0, 3); answers may vary

11.

$y + 3x = 7$	
$1 + 3 \cdot 2$	7
$1 + 6$	

$7 \stackrel{?}{=} 7$ True

$y + 3x = 7$	
$-5 + 3 \cdot 4$	7
$-5 + 12$	

$7 \stackrel{?}{=} 7$ True

(1, 4); answers may vary

13.

$4x - 2y = 10$	
$4 \cdot 0 - 2(-5)$	10
$0 + 10$	

$10 \stackrel{?}{=} 10$ True

$4x - 2y = 10$	
$4 \cdot 4 - 2 \cdot 3$	10
$16 - 6$	

$10 \stackrel{?}{=} 10$ True

(2, −1); answers may vary

15.

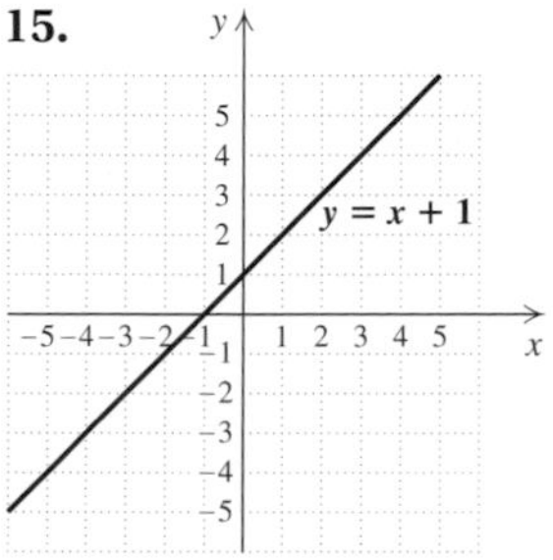

17.

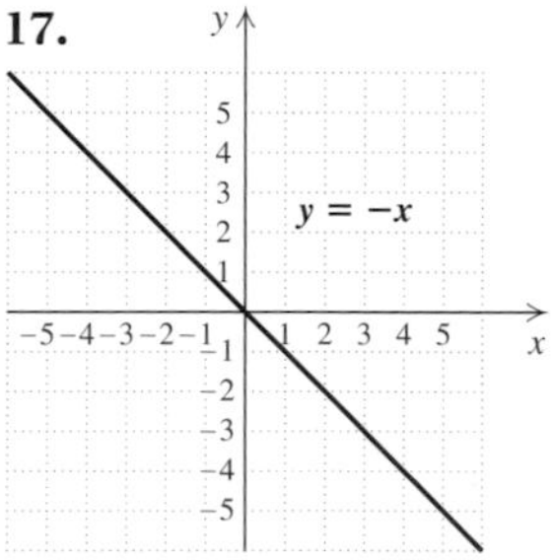

19.

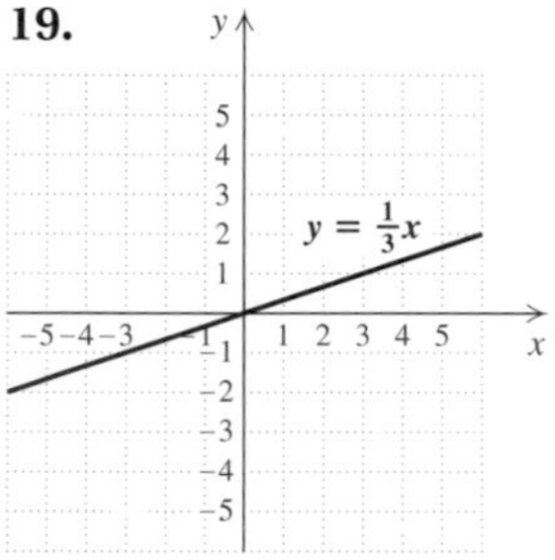

21.

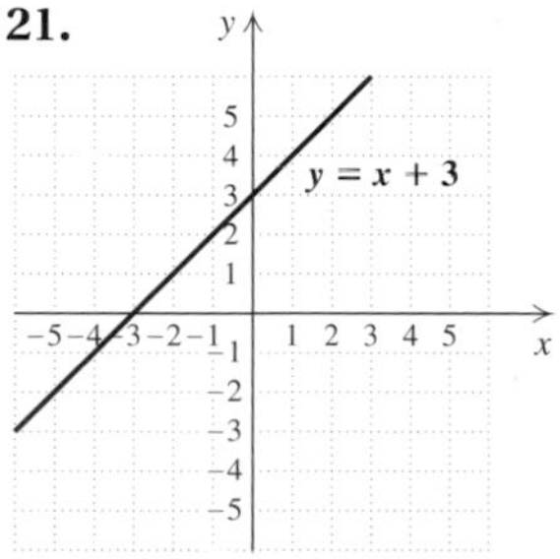

23.

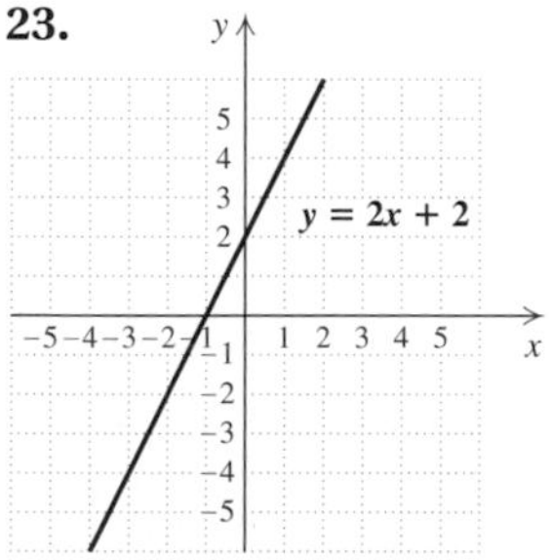

25.

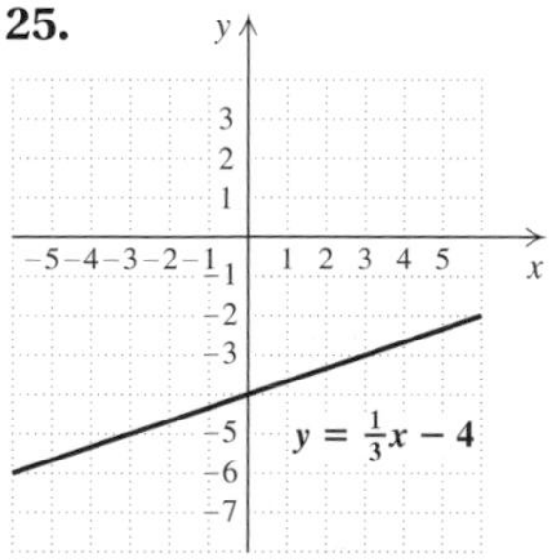

27.

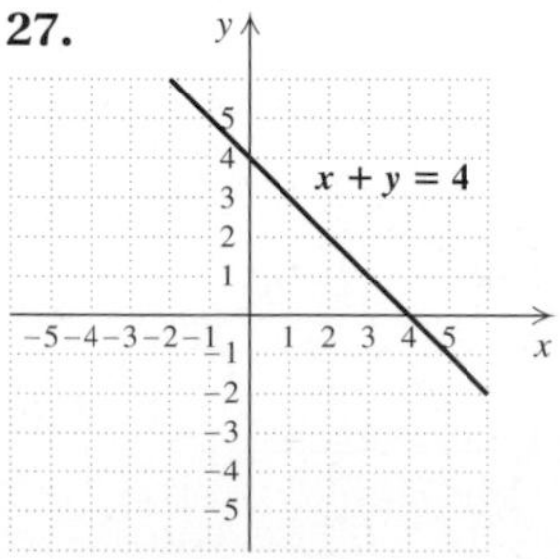

29.

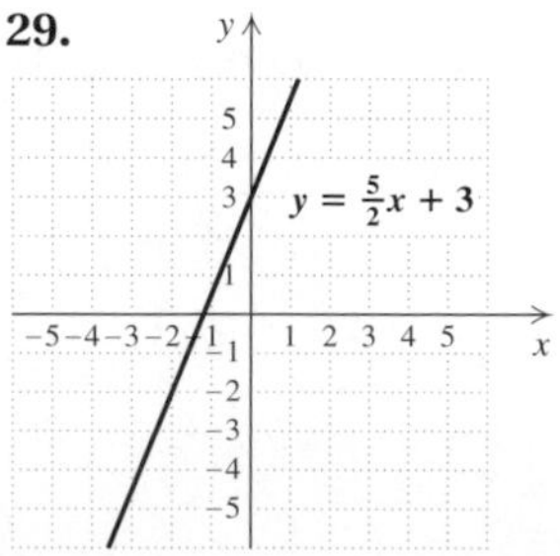

31.

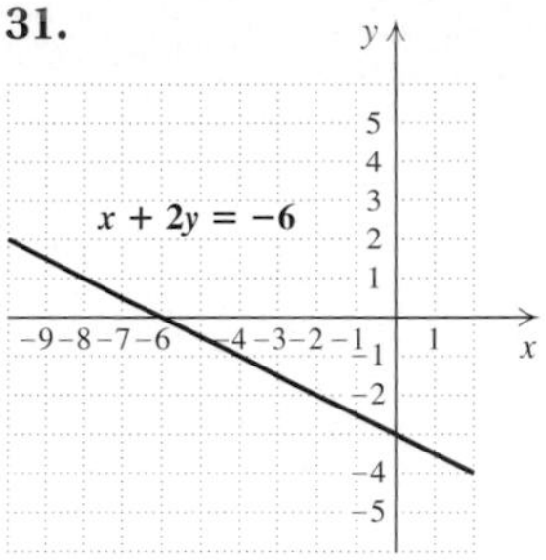

33.

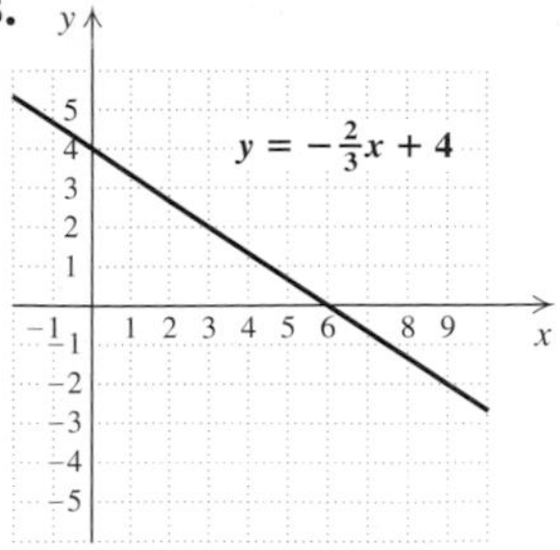

35.

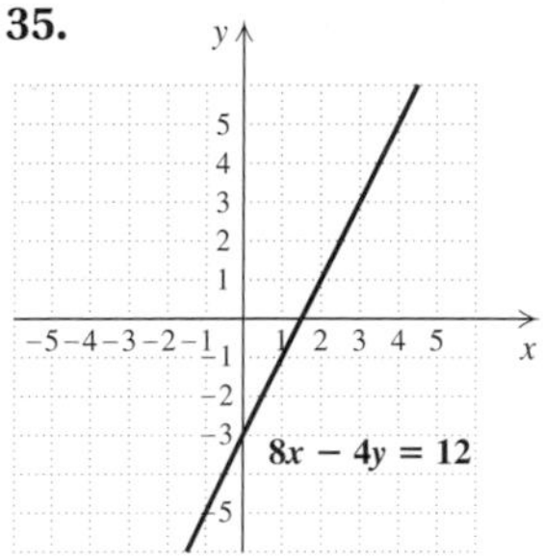

37.

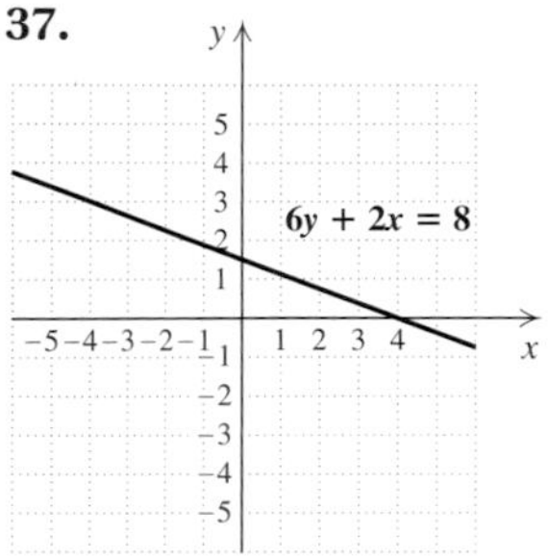

39.

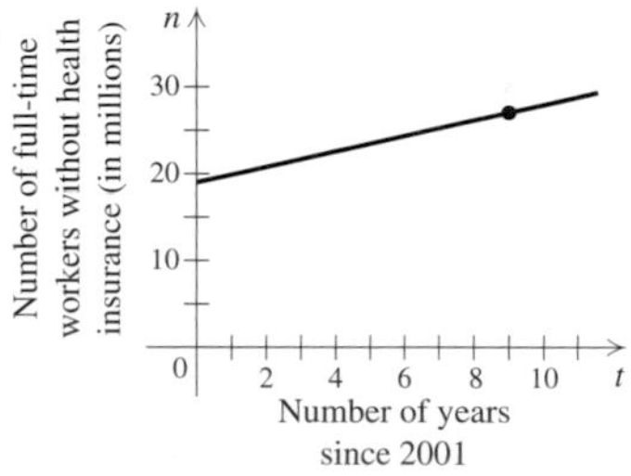

27 million workers

41.

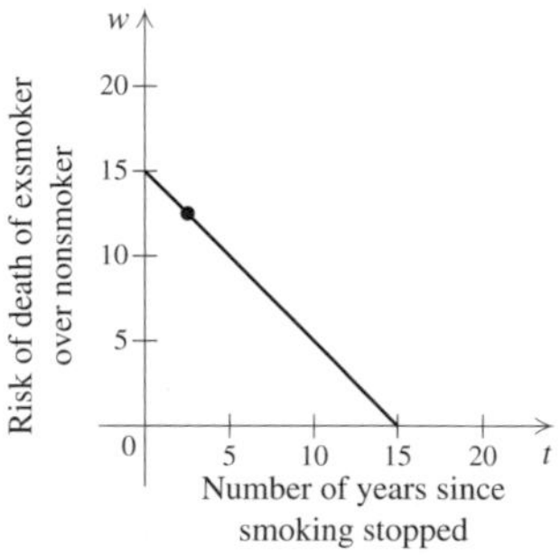

$12\frac{1}{2}$ times

43.

$300

45. $1000

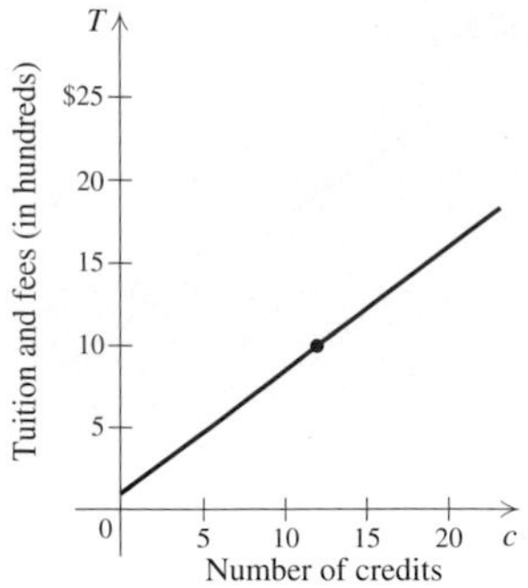

47. 24°F **49.** **51.** $\frac{12}{5}$

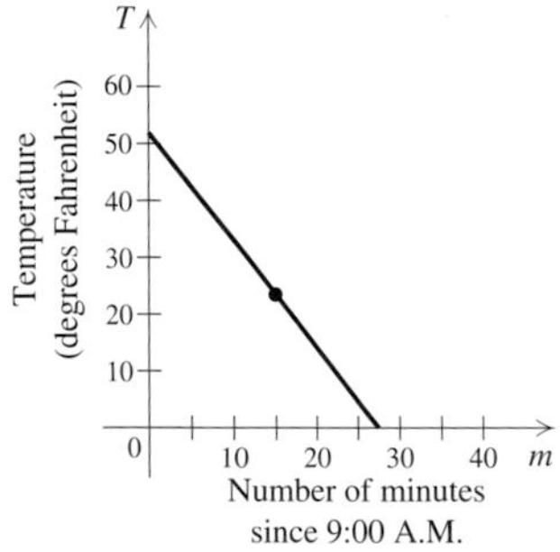

52. $\frac{9}{2}$ **53.** $-\frac{5}{2}$ **54.** $p = \dfrac{w}{q+1}$ **55.** $y = \dfrac{C - Ax}{B}$
56. $Q = 2A - T$ **57.**
59. $s + n = 18$

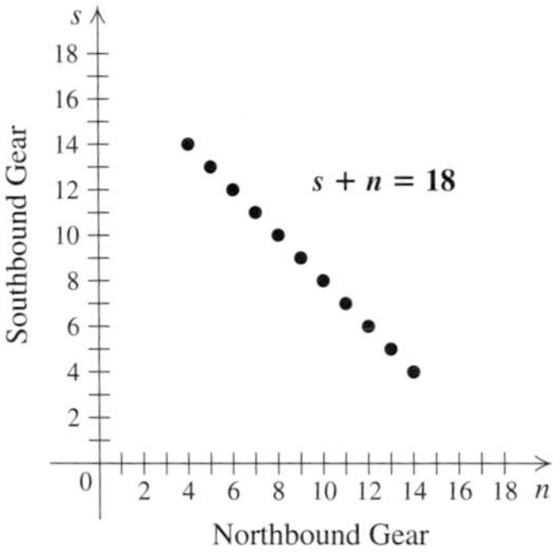

61. $x + y = 2$, or $y = -x + 2$ **63.** $5x - 3y = 15$, or $y = \frac{5}{3}x - 5$ **65.**

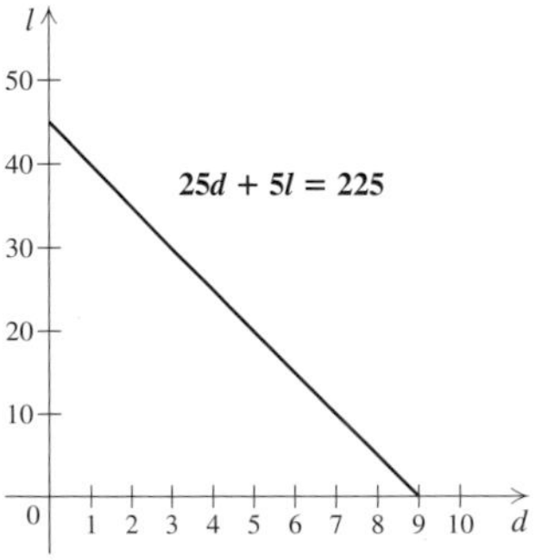

Answers may vary. 1 dinner, 40 lunches; 5 dinners, 20 lunches; 8 dinners, 5 lunches

67.

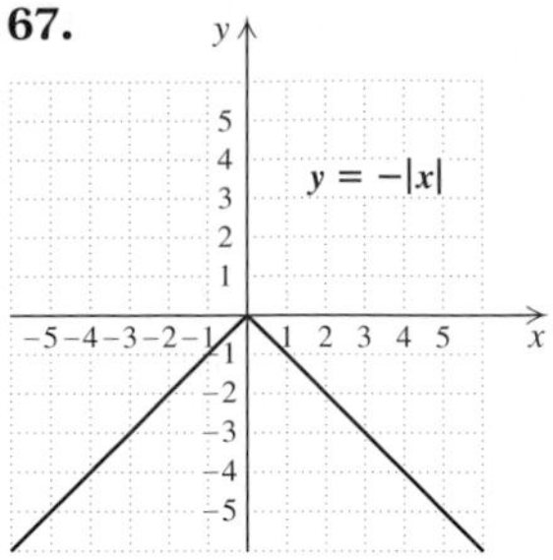

69.

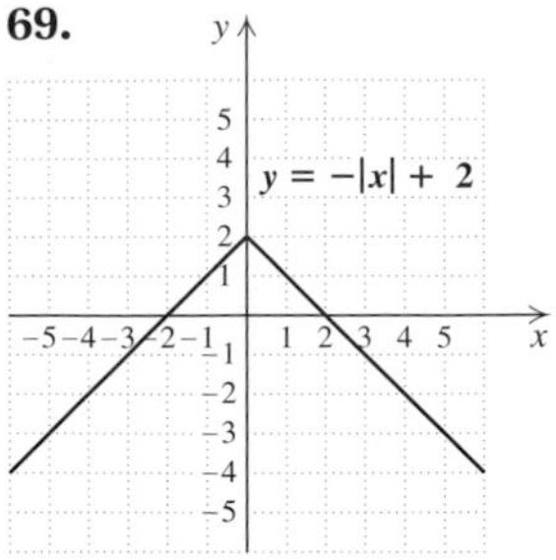

71. $y = -2.8x + 3.5$

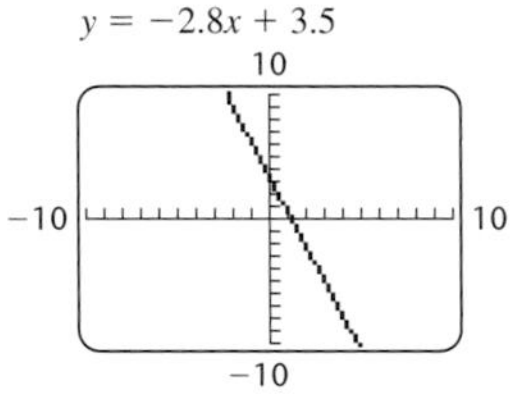

73. $y = 2.8x - 3.5$

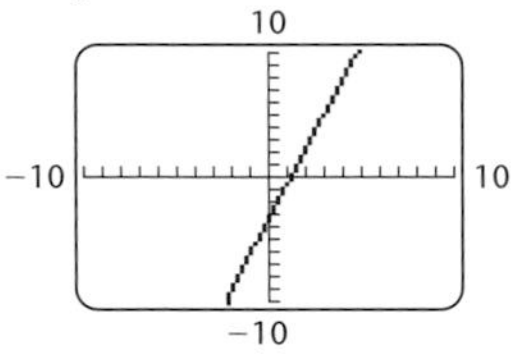

75. $y = x^2 + 4x + 1$

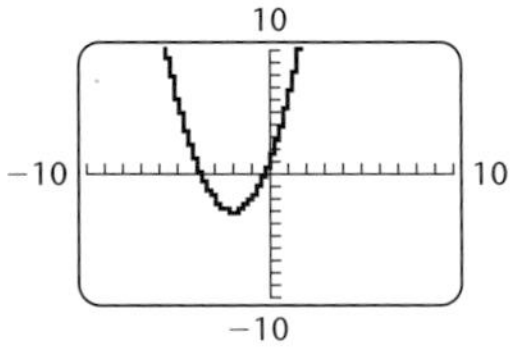

77.

Technology Connection, p. 172

1. $y = -0.72x - 15$

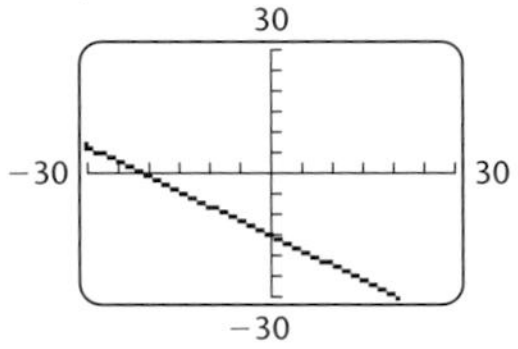

Xscl = 5, Yscl = 5

2. $y - 2.13x = 27$, or $y = 2.13x + 27$

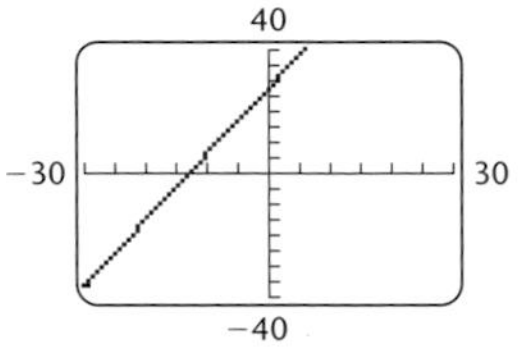

Xscl = 5, Yscl = 5

3. $5x + 6y = 84$, or $y = -\frac{5}{6}x + 14$

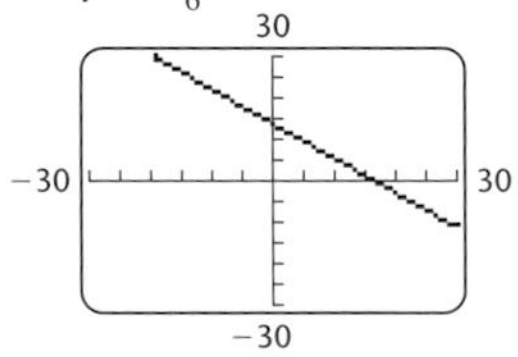

Xscl = 5, Yscl = 5

4. $2x - 7y = 150$, or $y = \frac{2}{7}x - \frac{150}{7}$

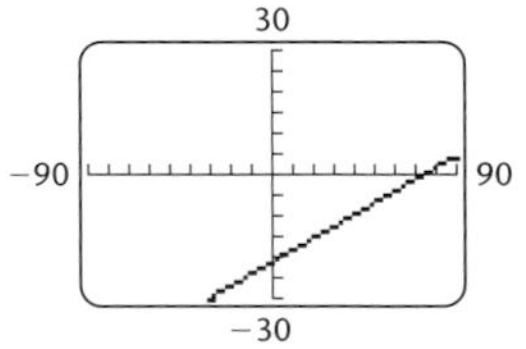

Xscl = 10, Yscl = 5

5. $19x - 17y = 200$, or $y = \frac{19}{17}x - \frac{200}{17}$

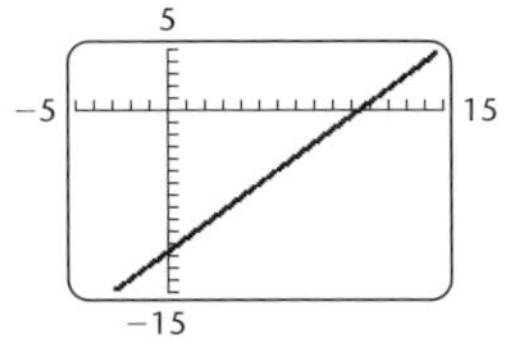

6. $6x + 5y = 159$, or $y = -\frac{6}{5}x + \frac{159}{5}$

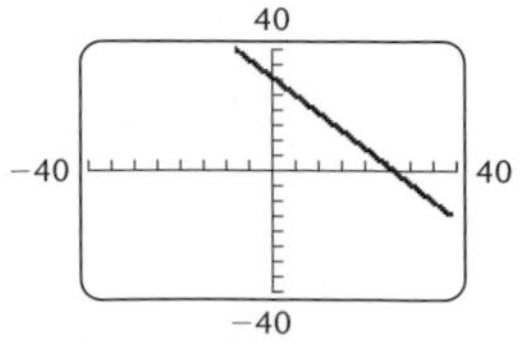

Xscl = 5, Yscl = 5

Exercise Set 3.3, pp. 175–177

1. (f) **3.** (d) **5.** (b) **7.** **(a)** (0, 5); **(b)** (2, 0)
9. **(a)** (0, −4); **(b)** (3, 0) **11.** **(a)** (0, −2); **(b)** (−3, 0)
13. **(a)** (0, 5); **(b)** (3, 0) **15.** **(a)** (0, −14); **(b)** (4, 0)
17. **(a)** (0, 50); **(b)** $\left(-\frac{75}{2}, 0\right)$ **19.** **(a)** (0, 9); **(b)** none
21. **(a)** None; **(b)** (−7, 0)

23.
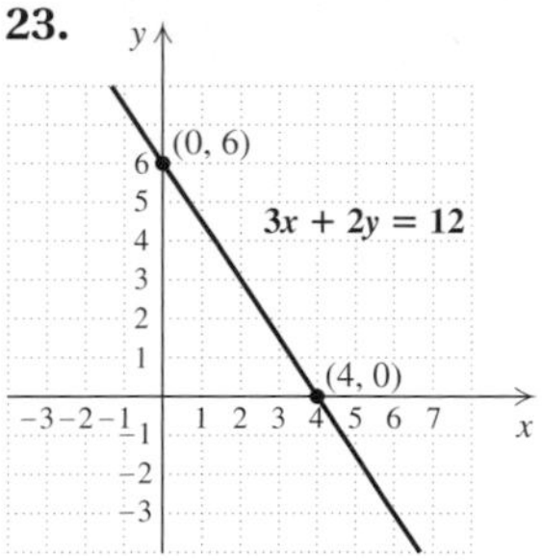

25.
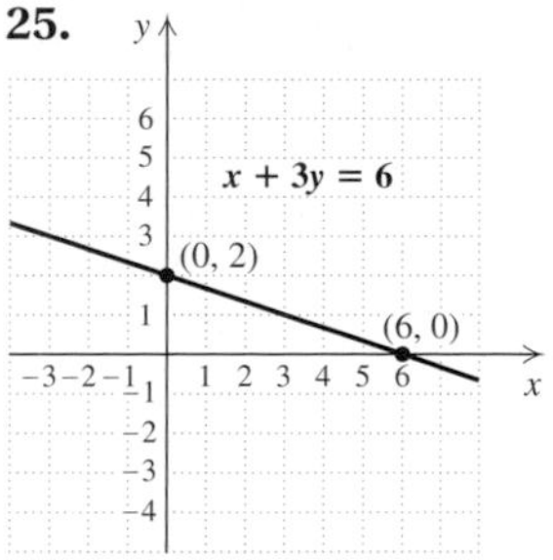

27.
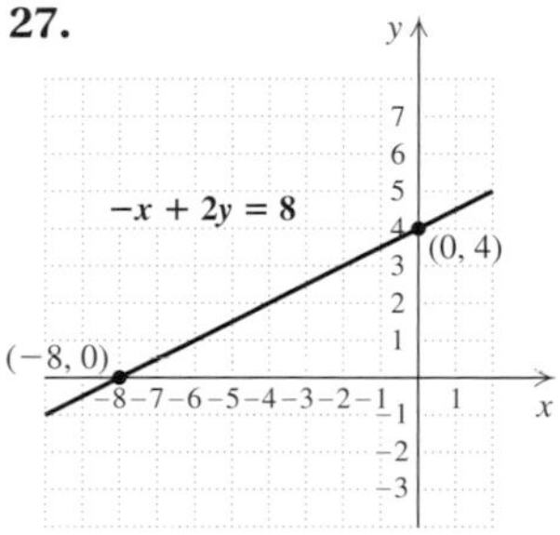

29.
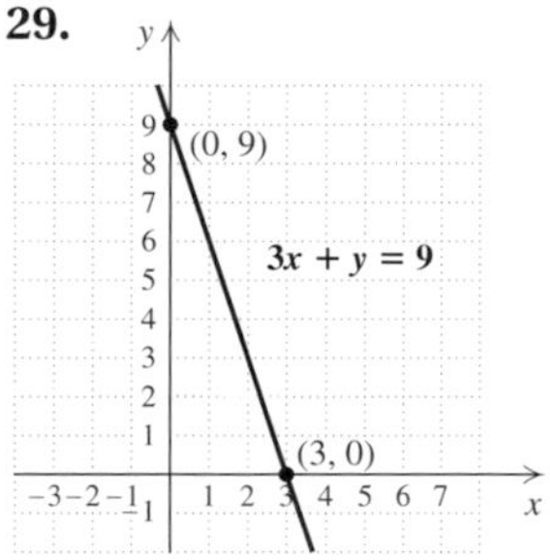

31.
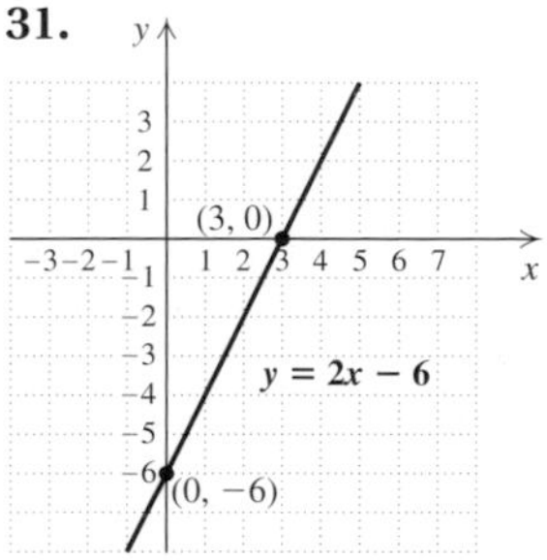

33.
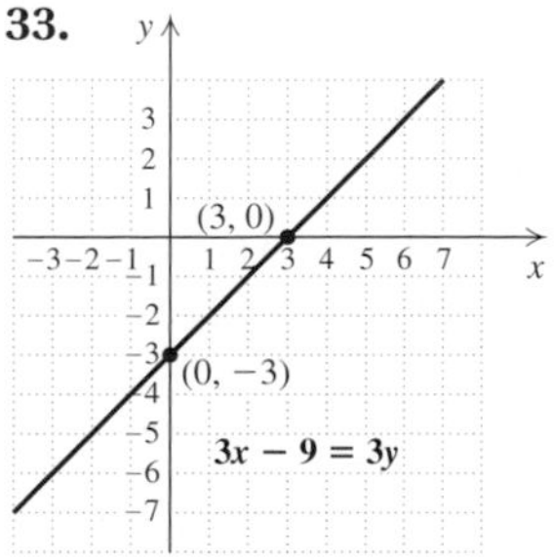

35.
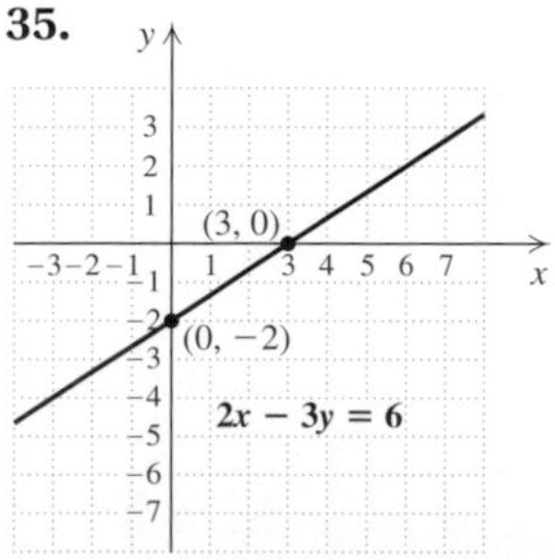

37.
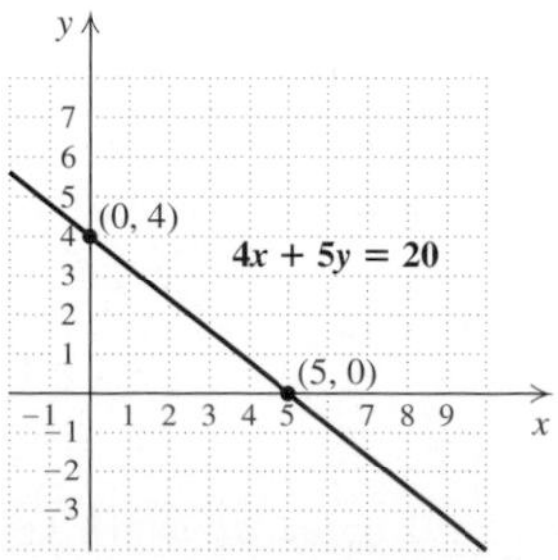

39.
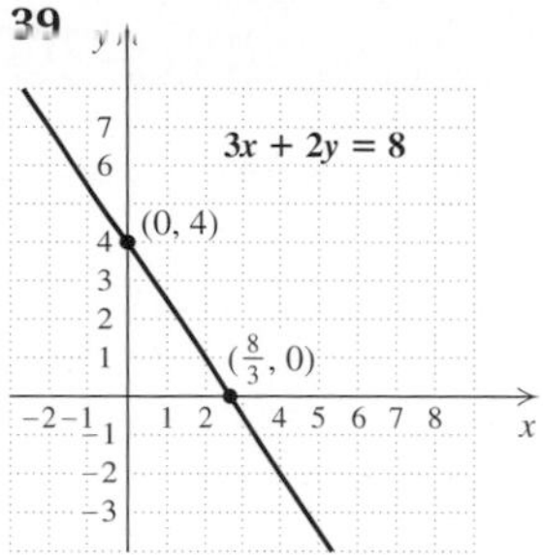

41.
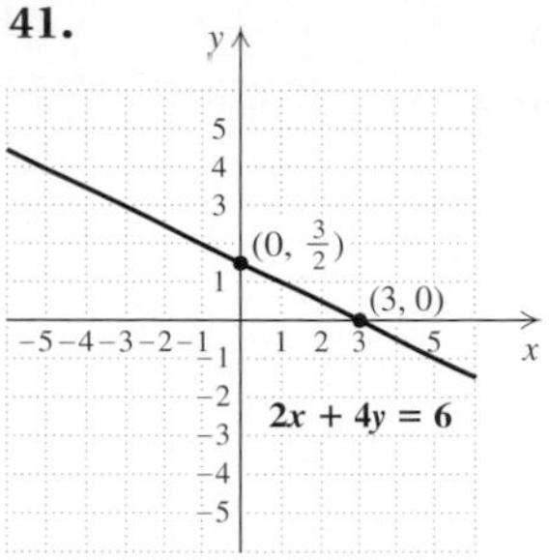

43.
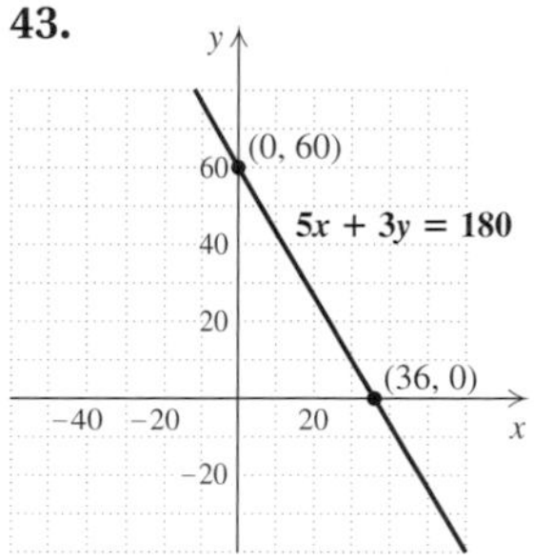

45.
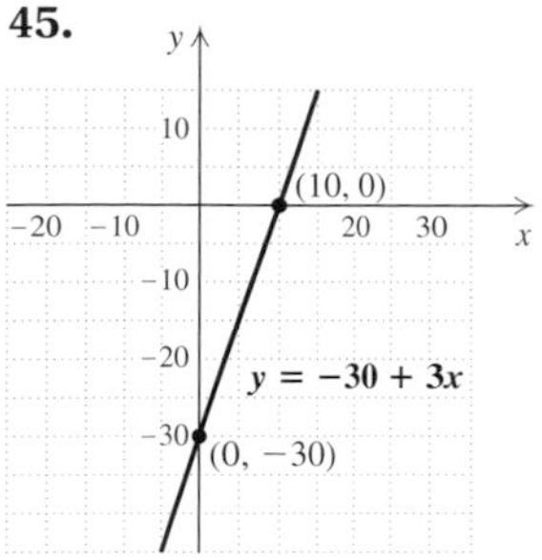

47.
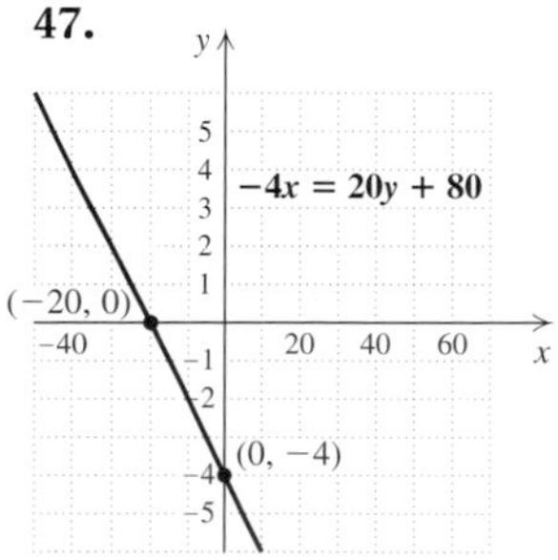

49.
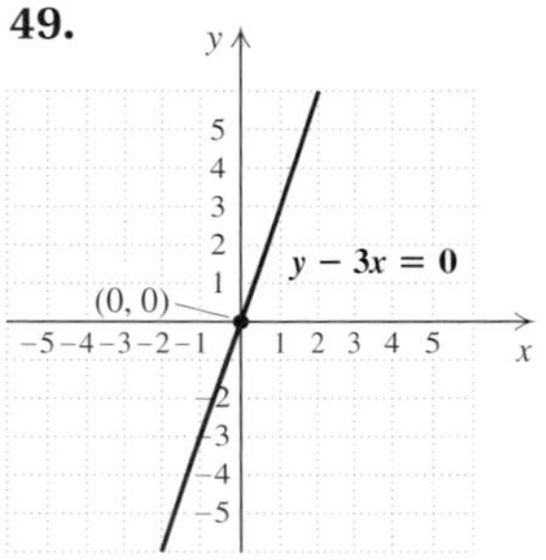

51.
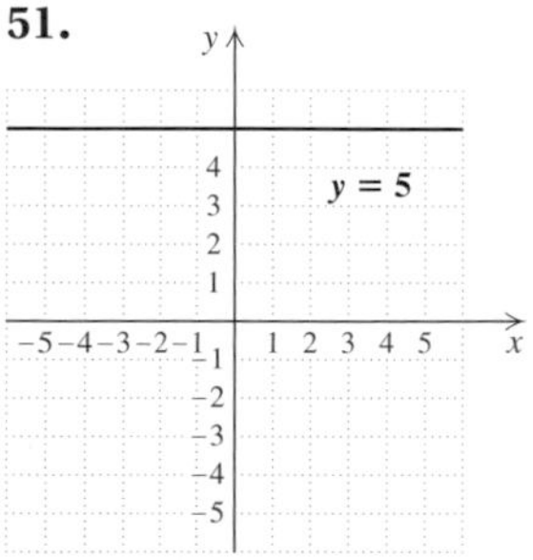

53.
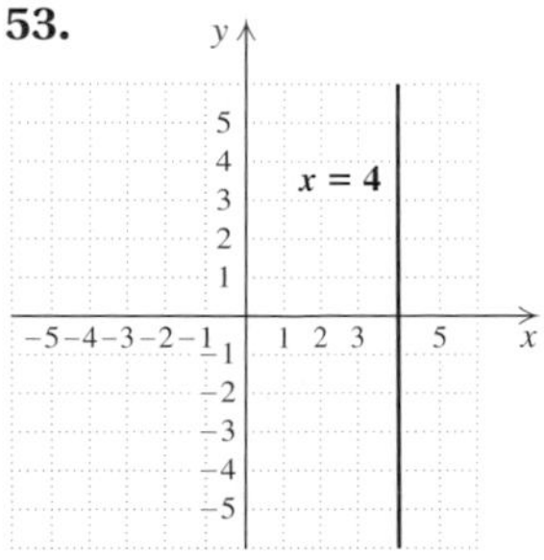

55.
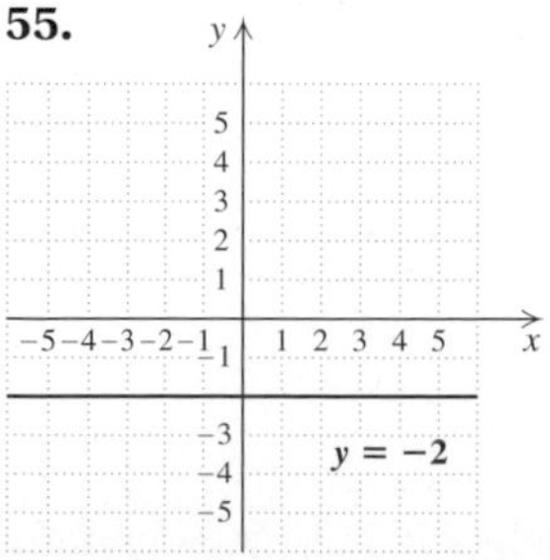

57.
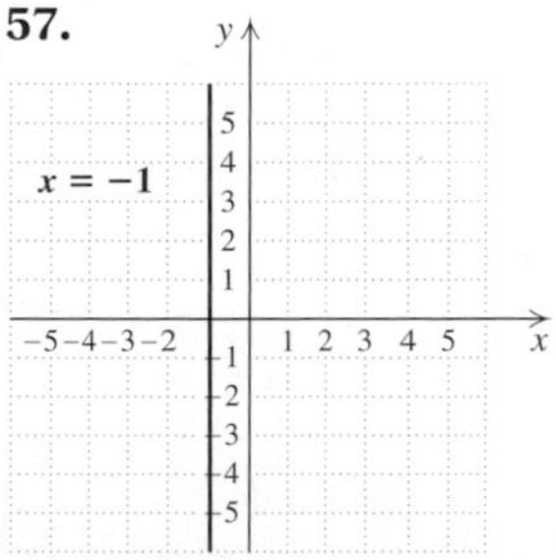

59.
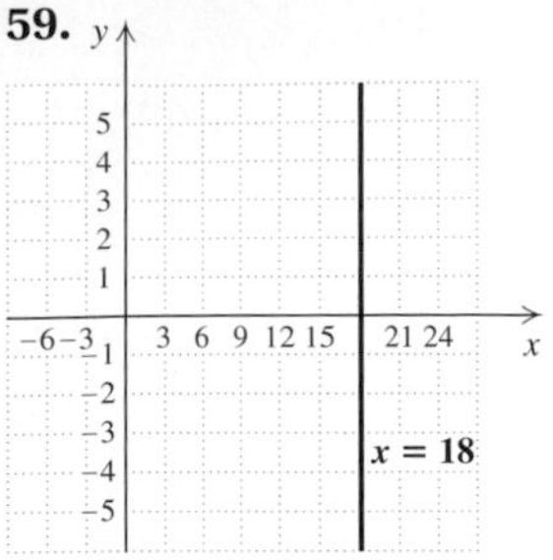

61.
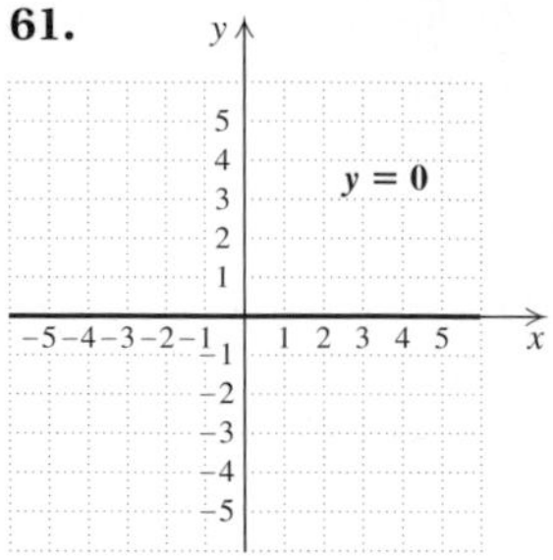

63.
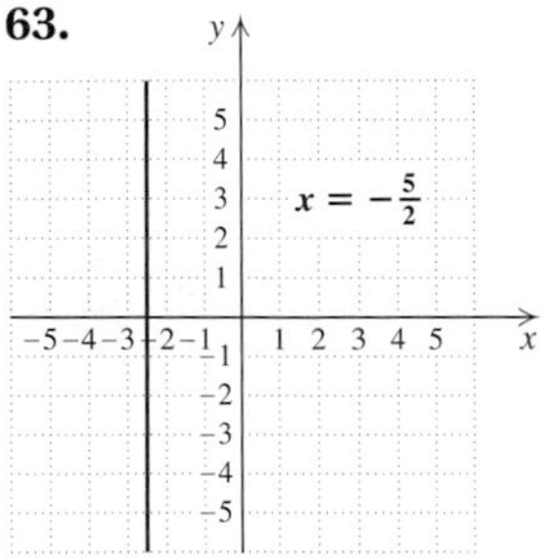

65.
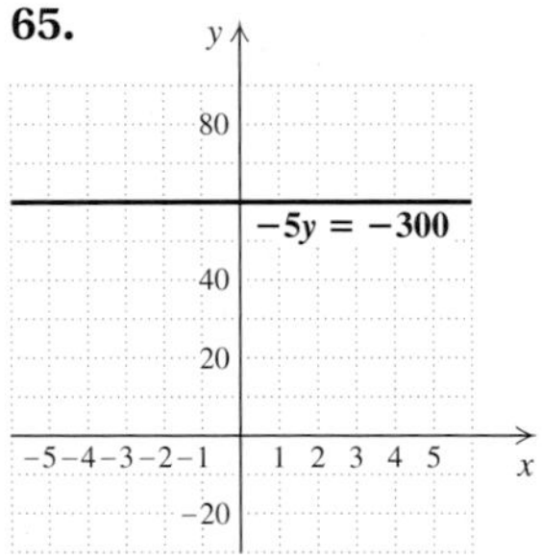

67.
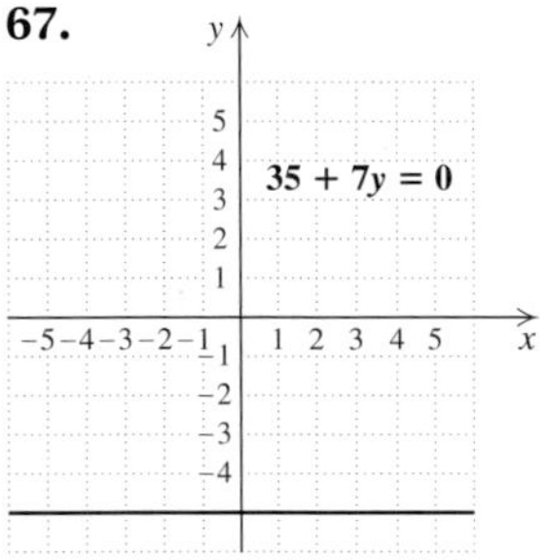

69. $y = -1$ **71.** $x = 4$

73. $y = 0$ **75.** **77.** $d - 7$ **78.** $w + 5$, or $5 + w$ **79.** Let n represent the number; $2 + n$ **80.** Let n represent the number; $3n$ **81.** Let x and y represent the numbers; $2(x + y)$ **82.** Let a and b represent the numbers; $\frac{1}{2}(a + b)$ **83.** **85.** $y = 0$ **87.** $x = -2$ **89.** $(-3, -3)$ **91.** $-5x + 3y = 15$, or $y = \frac{5}{3}x + 5$ **93.** -24 **95.** $(0, 25)$; $\left(\frac{50}{3}, 0\right)$, or $(16.\overline{6}, 0)$ **97.** $(0, -9)$; $(45, 0)$ **99.** $\left(0, -\frac{1}{20}\right)$, or $(0, -0.05)$; $\left(\frac{1}{25}, 0\right)$, or $(0.04, 0)$

Exercise Set 3.4, pp. 181–186

1. **(a)** 21 mpg; **(b)** \$39.33/day; **(c)** 91 mi/day; **(d)** 43¢/mile **3.** **(a)** 6 mph; **(b)** \$4/hr; **(c)** \$0.67/mi **5.** **(a)** \$16/hr; **(b)** 4.5 pages/hr; **(c)** \$3.56/page **7.** \$16/yr **9.** **(a)** 14.5 floors/min; **(b)** 4.14 sec/floor **11.** **(a)** 3.71 ft/min; **(b)** 0.27 min/ft

13.
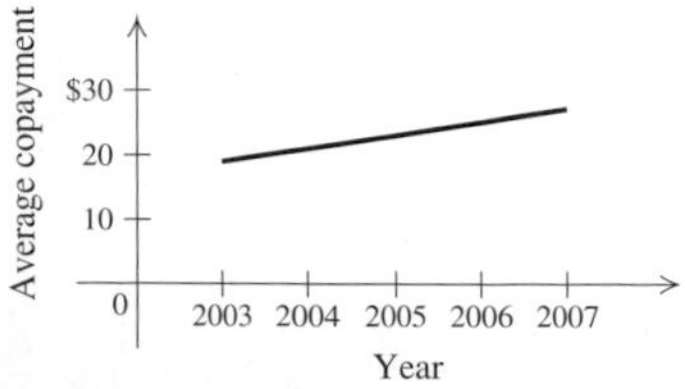

15.
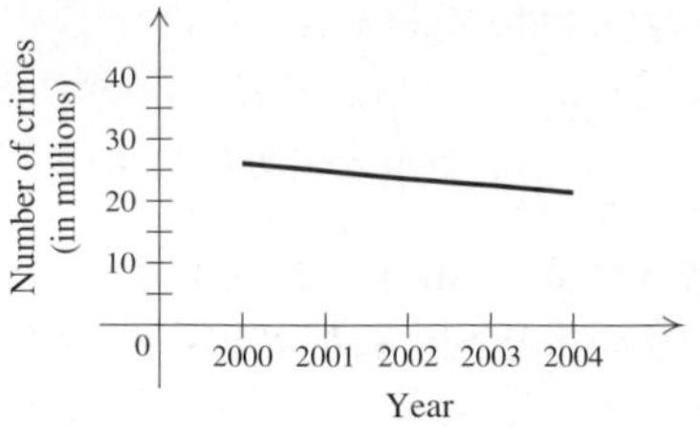

17.
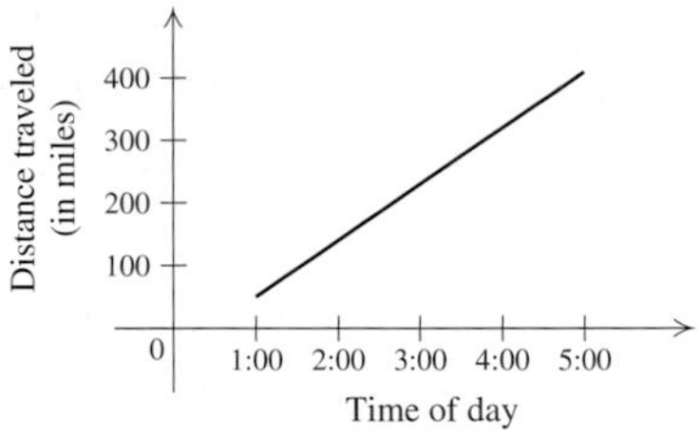

19.
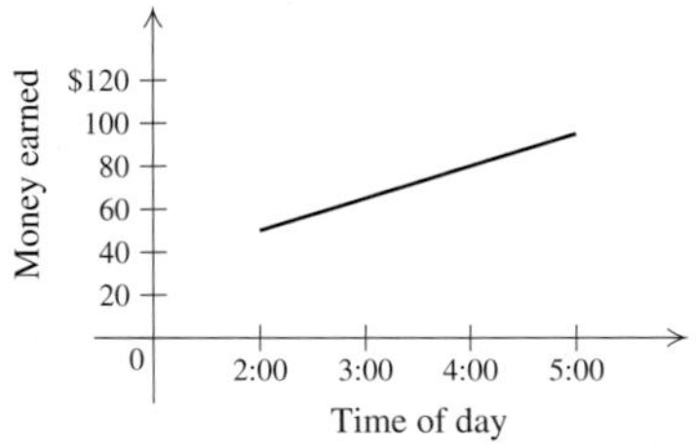

21.
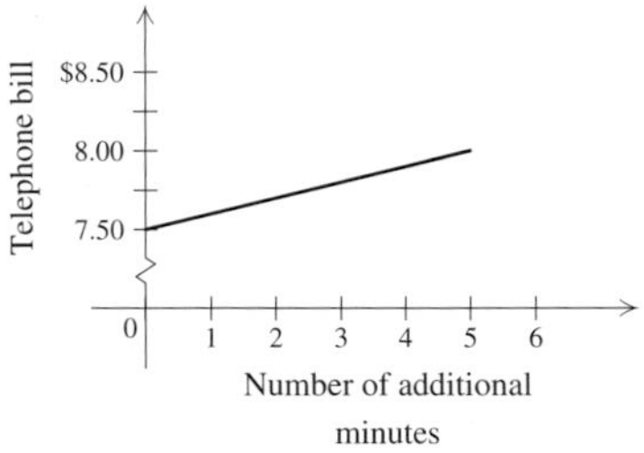

23. 2 haircuts/hr **25.** 75 mi/hr **27.** 7¢/min **29.** −\$500/yr **31.** 0.04 gal/mi **33.** (e) **35.** (d) **37.** (b) **39.** **41.** 5 **42.** -6 **43.** -1 **44.** $-\frac{4}{3}$ **45.** $-\frac{4}{3}$ **46.** $-\frac{4}{5}$ **47.** **49.**

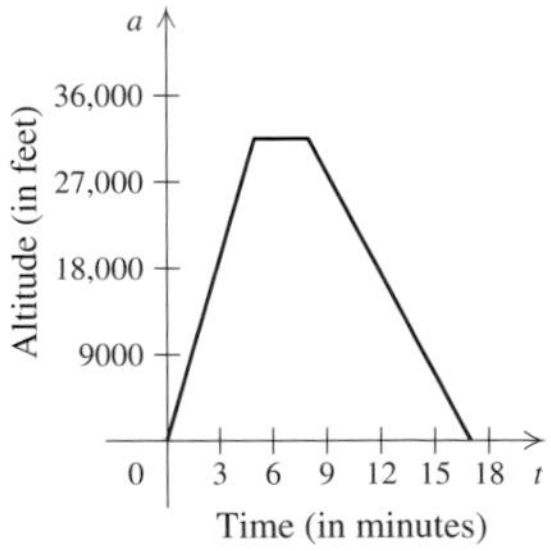

51.
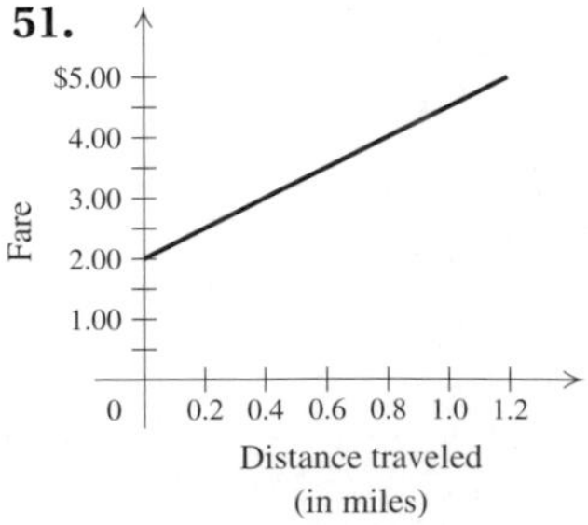

53. 13 ft/sec

55. About 41.7 min **57.** 4:20 PM

Exercise Set 3.5, pp. 194–200

1. Positive **3.** Negative **5.** Positive **7.** Zero **9.** Negative **11.** 2.5 million people/yr **13.** 1.3%/yr **15.** 1 point/$1000 income **17.** −2.1°/min **19.** $\frac{3}{4}$ **21.** $\frac{3}{2}$ **23.** $\frac{1}{3}$ **25.** −1 **27.** 0 **29.** $-\frac{1}{3}$ **31.** Undefined **33.** $-\frac{1}{4}$ **35.** $\frac{3}{2}$ **37.** 0 **39.** −3 **41.** $\frac{3}{2}$ **43.** $-\frac{4}{5}$ **45.** $\frac{7}{9}$ **47.** $-\frac{2}{3}$ **49.** $-\frac{1}{2}$ **51.** 0 **53.** $-\frac{11}{6}$ **55.** Undefined **57.** Undefined **59.** 0 **61.** Undefined **63.** 0 **65.** 8% **67.** $8.\overline{3}\%$ **69.** $\frac{29}{98}$, or about 30% **71.** About 29% **73.** **75.** $y = \dfrac{c - ax}{b}$ **76.** $r = \dfrac{p + mn}{x}$ **77.** $y = \dfrac{ax - c}{b}$ **78.** $t = \dfrac{q - rs}{n}$ **79.** 3 **80.** 2 **81.** **83.** 0.364, or 36.4% **85.** $\{m \mid m \geq \frac{5}{2}\}$ **87.** $\frac{1}{2}$

Technology Connection, p. 206

1. $y_1 = -\frac{3}{4}x - 2,\ y_2 = -\frac{1}{5}x - 2,$
$y_3 = -\frac{3}{4}x - 5,\ y_4 = -\frac{1}{5}x - 5$

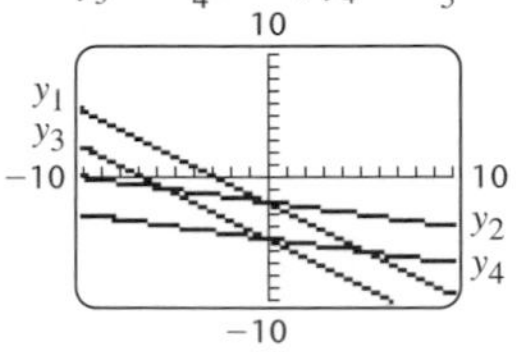

Exercise Set 3.6, pp. 206–209

1. (c) **3.** (f) **5.** (d) **7.**

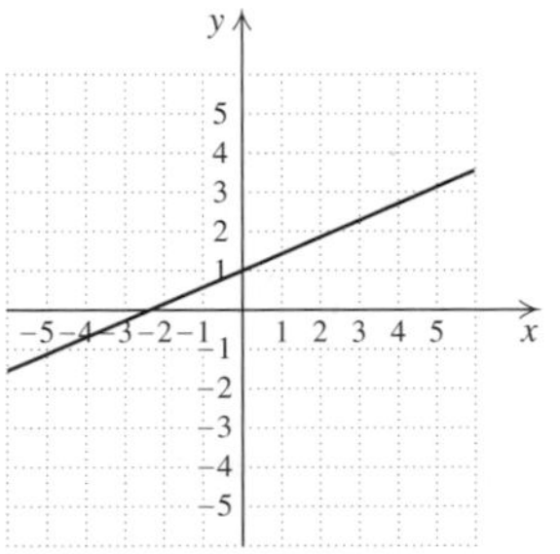

9.

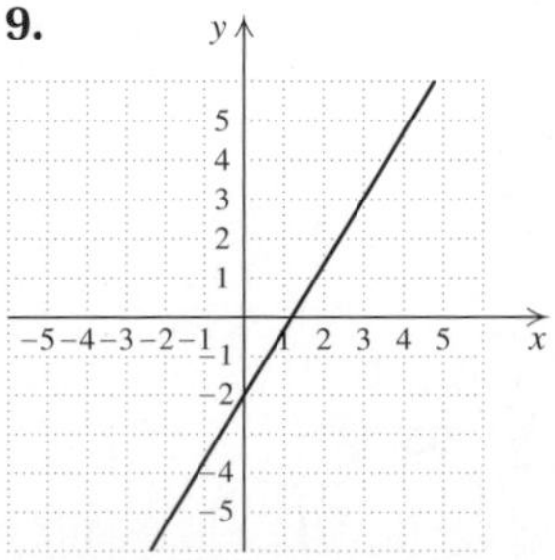

11.

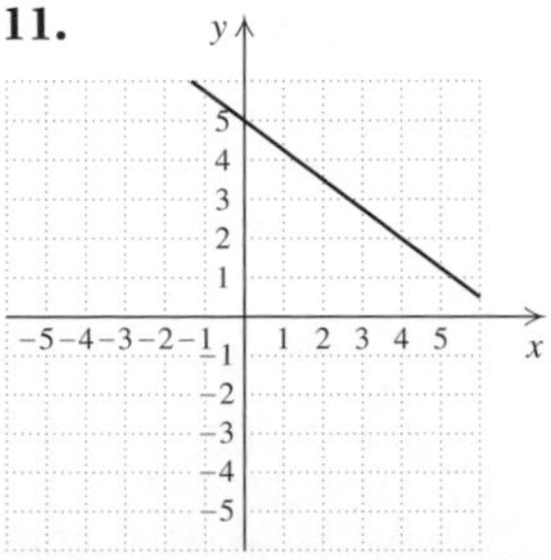

13.

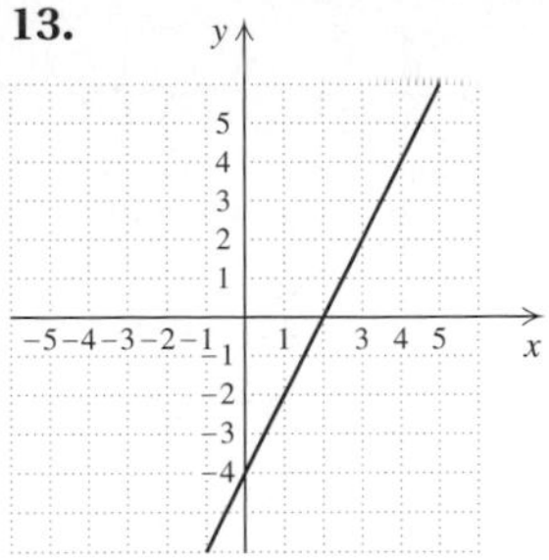

15.

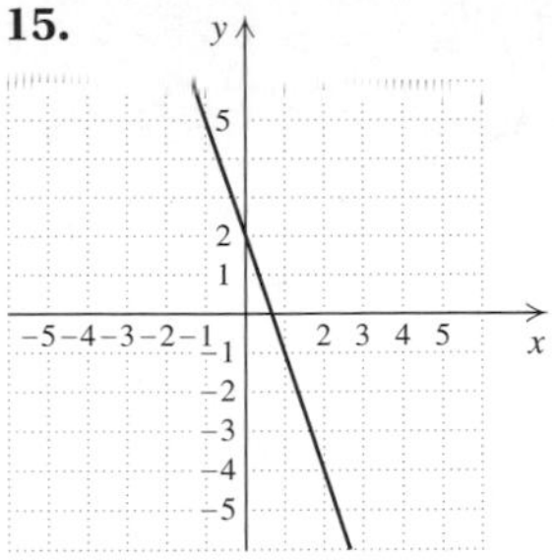

17. $-\frac{2}{7}$; (0, 5) **19.** $\frac{5}{8}$; (0, 3) **21.** $\frac{9}{5}$; (0, −4) **23.** 3; (0, 7) **25.** $-\frac{5}{2}$; (0, 4) **27.** 0; (0, 4) **29.** $\frac{2}{5}$; $\left(0, \frac{8}{5}\right)$ **31.** $y = 3x + 7$ **33.** $y = \frac{7}{8}x - 1$ **35.** $y = -\frac{5}{3}x - 8$ **37.** $y = 3$ **39.** $y = \frac{8}{9}x + 9$, where y is the number of gallons per person and x is the number of years since 1990 **41.** $y = 15x + 250$, where y is the number of jobs, in thousands, and x is the number of years since 1998

43.

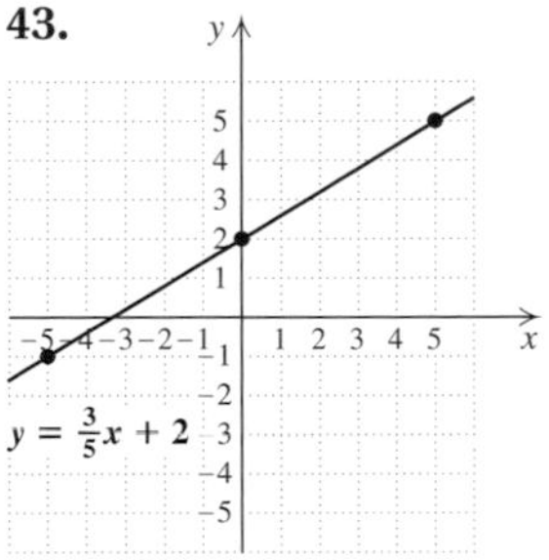

45.

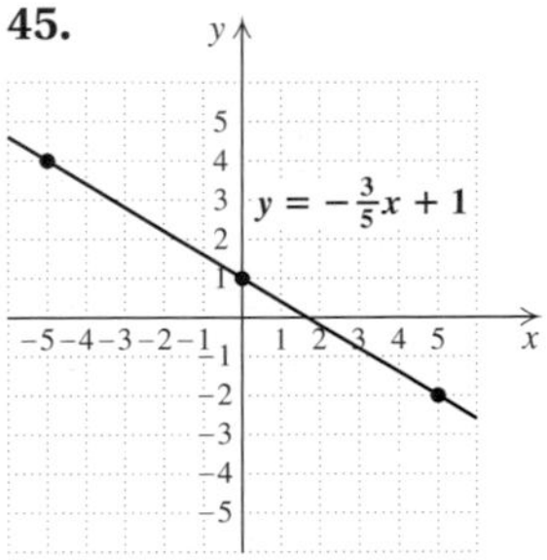

47.

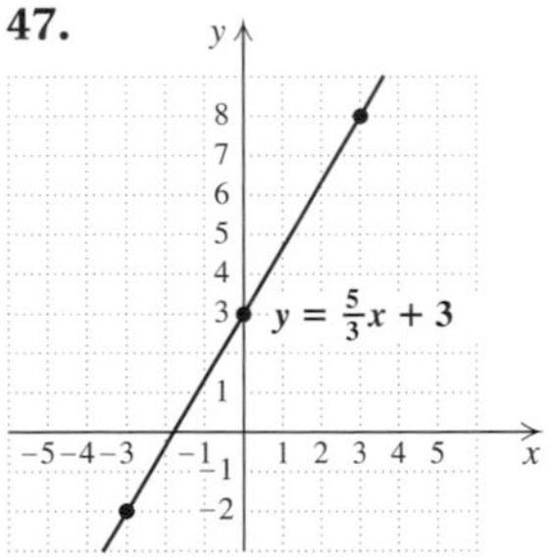

49.

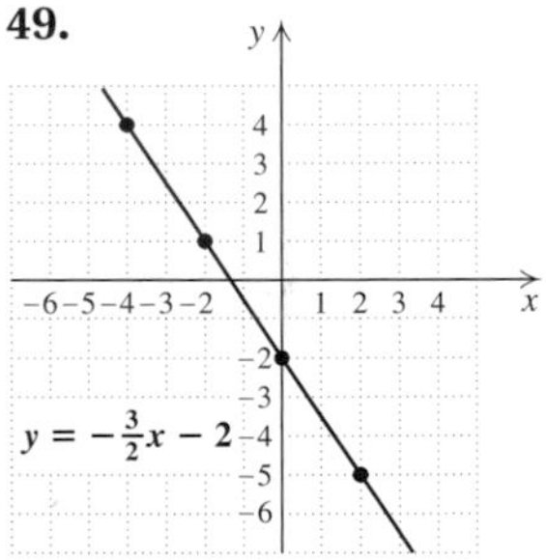

51.

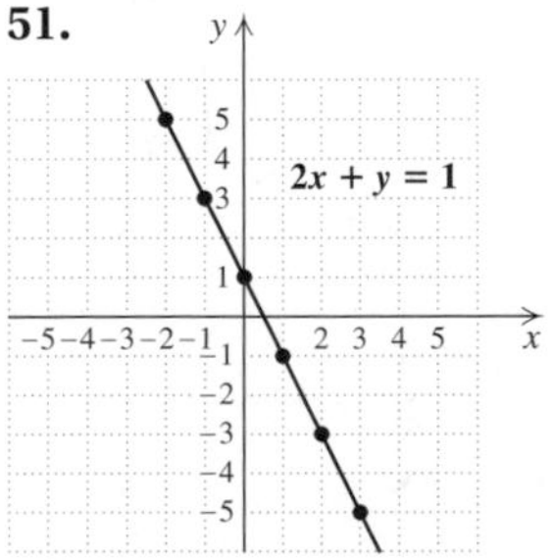

53.

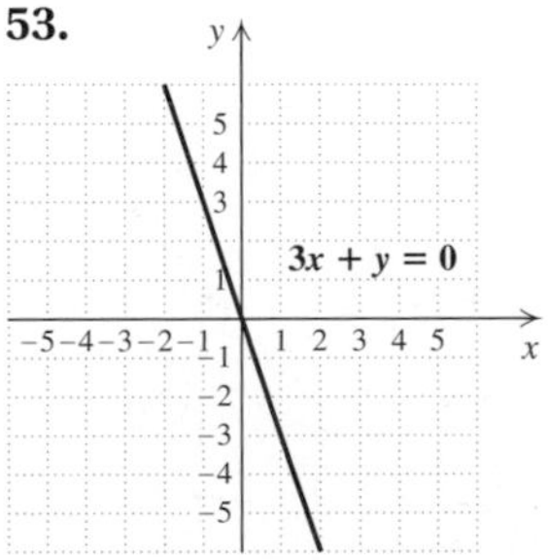

55.

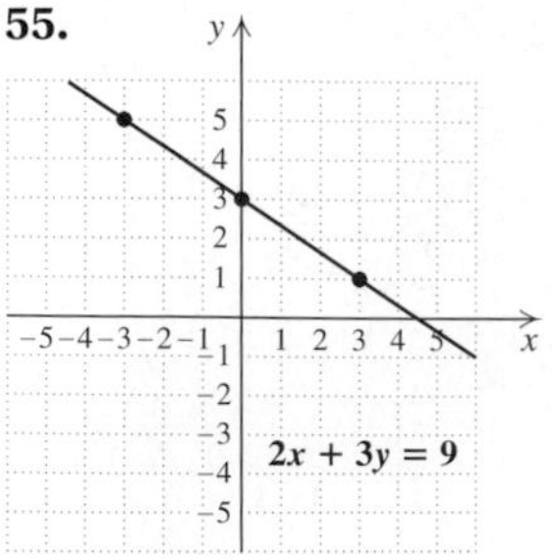

57.

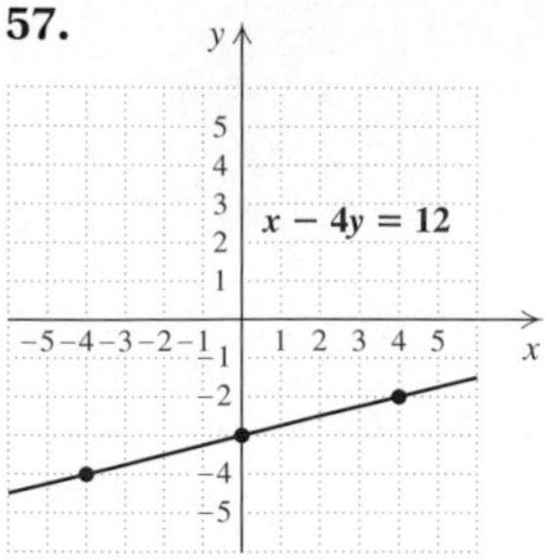

59. Yes **61.** No **63.** Yes **65.**
67. $y = m(x - h) + k$ **68.** $y = -2(x + 4) + 9$
69. 2 **70.** 16 **71.** −9 **72.** −10 **73.**
75. When $x = 0$, $y = b$, so $(0, b)$ is on the line. When $x = 1$, $y = m + b$, so $(1, m + b)$ is on the line. Then

$$\text{slope} = \frac{(m + b) - b}{1 - 0} = m.$$

77. $y = \frac{1}{3}x + 3$ **79.** $y = -\frac{4}{5}x + 4$ **81.** $y = \frac{1}{2}x$ **83.** Yes
85. Yes **87.** No **89.** $y = \frac{3}{2}x + 5$ **91.** $y = \frac{5}{2}x + 1$

Exercise Set 3.7, pp. 215–218

1. (g) **3.** (e) **5.** (b) **7.** (f) **9.** (c) **11.** (d)
13. $y - 2 = 5(x - 6)$ **15.** $y - 3 = \frac{3}{5}(x - 7)$
17. $y - 1 = -4(x - 3)$ **19.** $y - (-4) = \frac{3}{2}(x - 5)$
21. $y - 6 = \frac{5}{4}(x - (-2))$ **23.** $y - (-1) = -2(x - (-4))$
25. $y - 8 = 1(x - (-2))$ **27.** $y = 2x - 3$
29. $y = \frac{7}{4}x - 9$ **31.** $y = -3x + 3$ **33.** $y = -4x - 9$
35. $y = \frac{2}{3}x + 1$ **37.** $y = -\frac{5}{6}x + 4$

39.

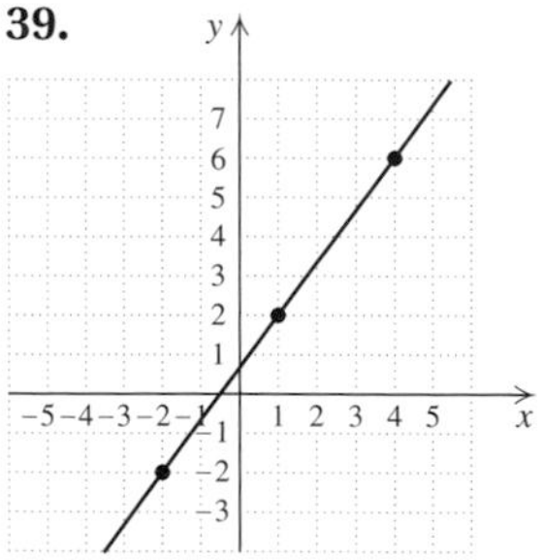

41.

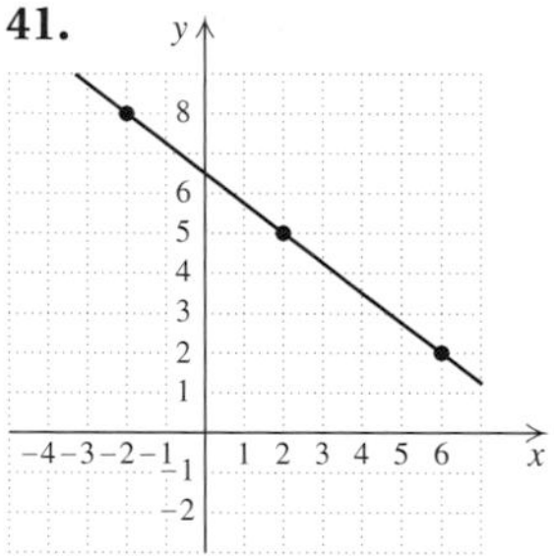

43.

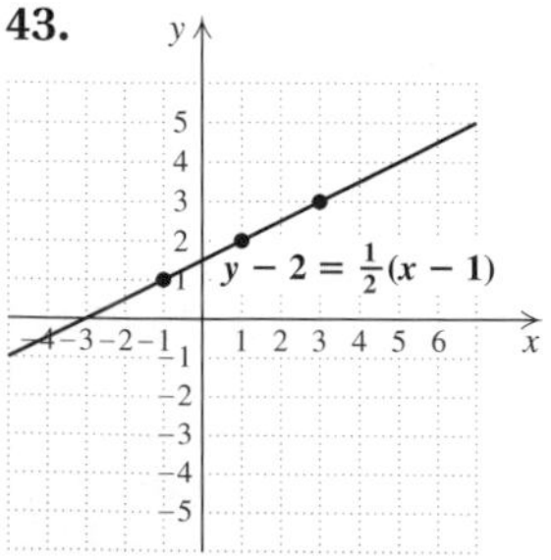

45.

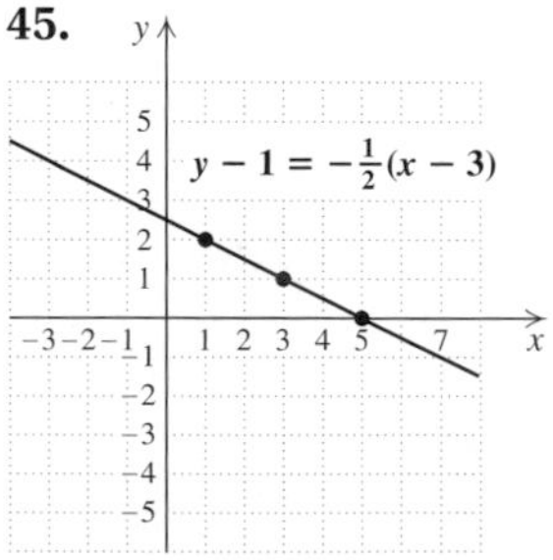

47.

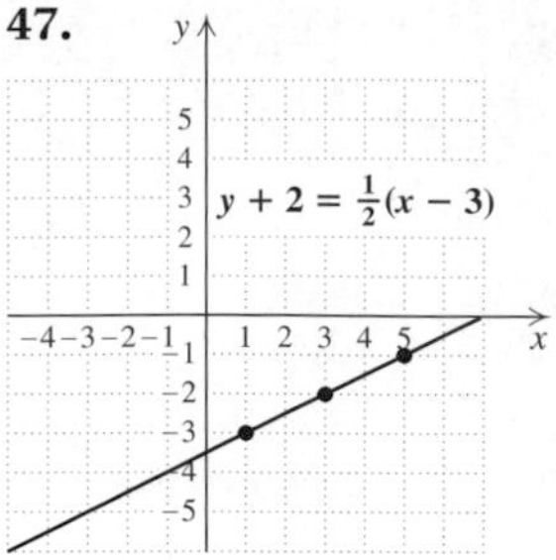

49.

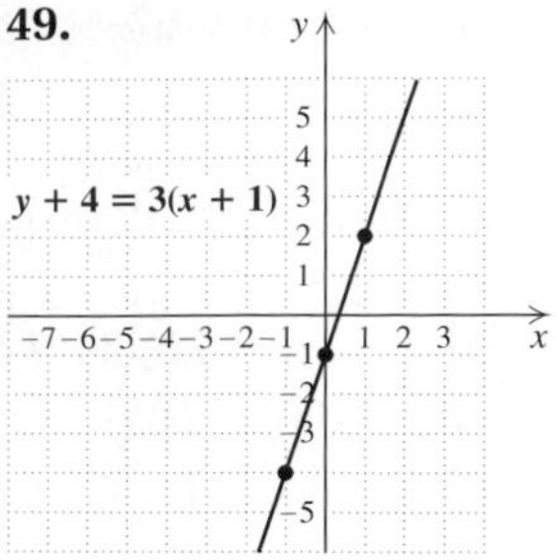

51.

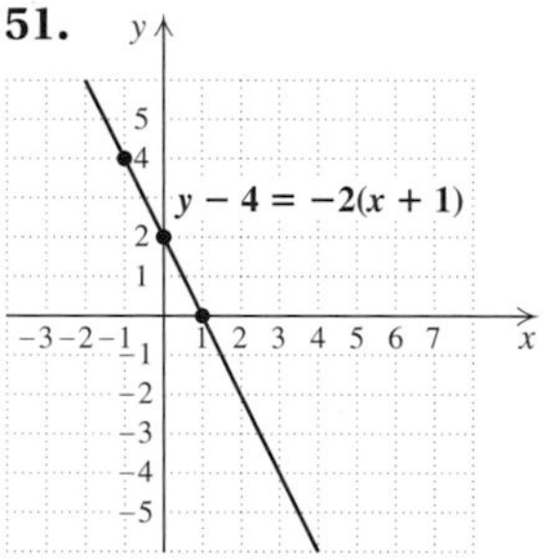

53.

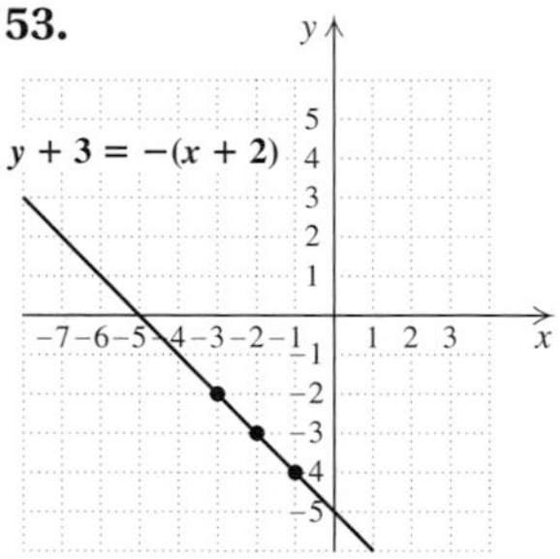

55.

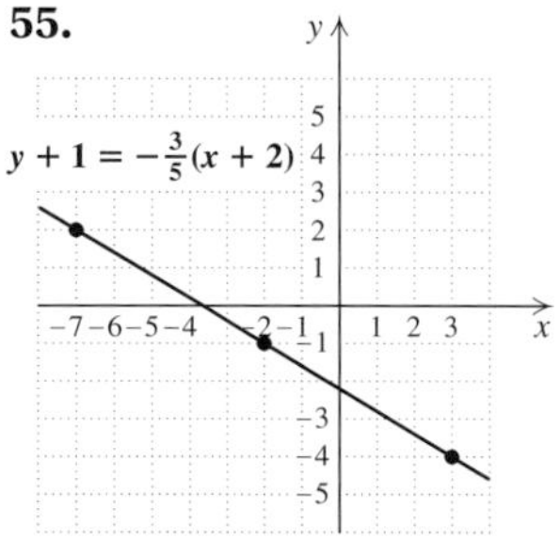

57. **(a)** 49.14 births per 1000 females; **(b)** 34.56 births per 1000 females **59.** **(a)** About 40.6%; **(b)** about 22.3%
61. **(a)** 65.1 million students; **(b)** 72.3 million students
63. **(a)** 33.3 million residents; **(b)** 38.7 million residents
65. $y = -x + 6$ **67.** $y = \frac{2}{3}x + 3$ **69.** $y = \frac{2}{5}x - 2$
71. $y = \frac{3}{4}x - \frac{5}{2}$ **73.** **75.** −125 **76.** 64 **77.** 8
78. 24 **79.** −72 **80.** −4 **81.**
83.

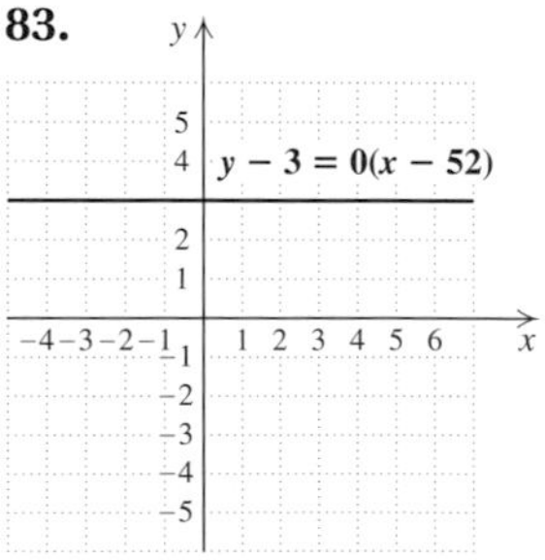

85. $y = 2x - 9$

87. $y = -\frac{4}{3}x + \frac{23}{3}$ **89.** $y - 7 = -\frac{2}{3}(x - (-4))$
91. $y = -4x + 7$ **93.** $y = \frac{10}{3}x + \frac{25}{3}$ **95.**

Review Exercises: Chapter 3, pp. 219–222

1. True **2.** True **3.** False **4.** False **5.** True **6.** True **7.** True **8.** False **9.** True **10.** True **11.** \$54,000 **12.** \$269.50 **13.–15.**

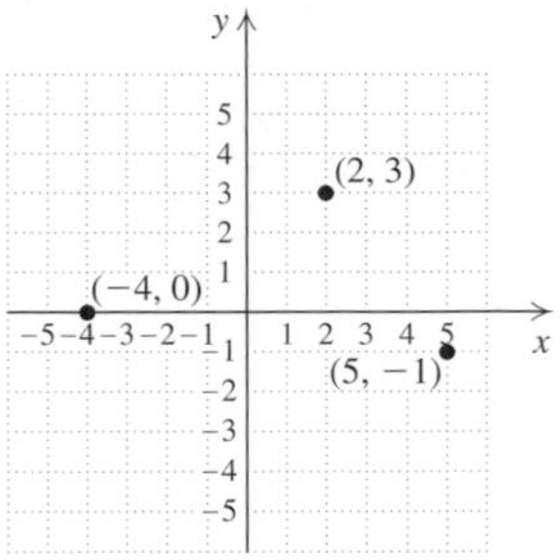

16. IV **17.** III **18.** II **19.** $(-5, -1)$ **20.** $(-2, 5)$ **21.** $(3, 0)$ **22.**

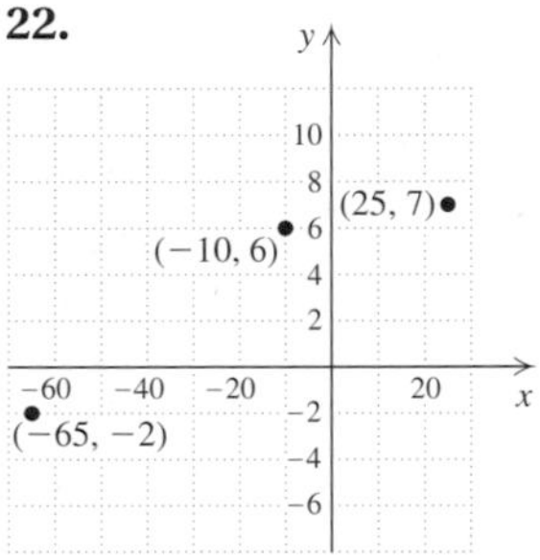

23. **(a)** Yes; **(b)** no

24.

$$\begin{array}{c|c} 2x - y & 3 \\ \hline 2 \cdot 0 - (-3) & 3 \\ 0 + 3 & \\ 3 \stackrel{?}{=} 3 & \text{True} \end{array} \qquad \begin{array}{c|c} 2x - y & 3 \\ \hline 2 \cdot 2 - 1 & 3 \\ 4 - 1 & \\ 3 \stackrel{?}{=} 3 & \text{True} \end{array}$$

$(-1, -5)$; answers may vary

25.

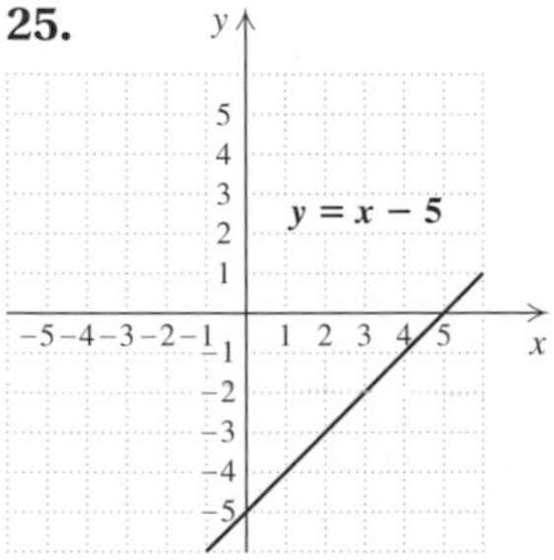

26.

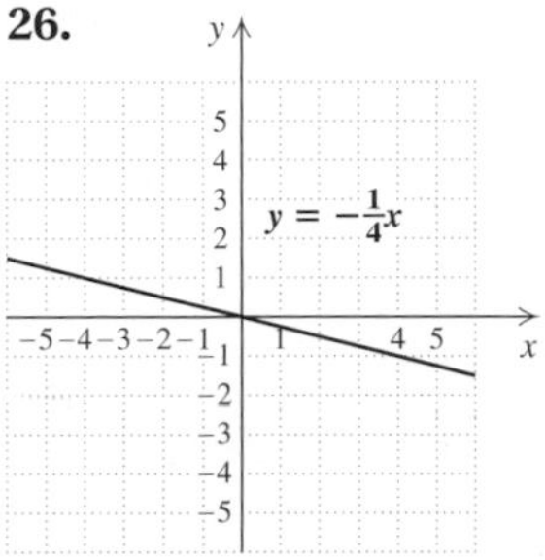

27.

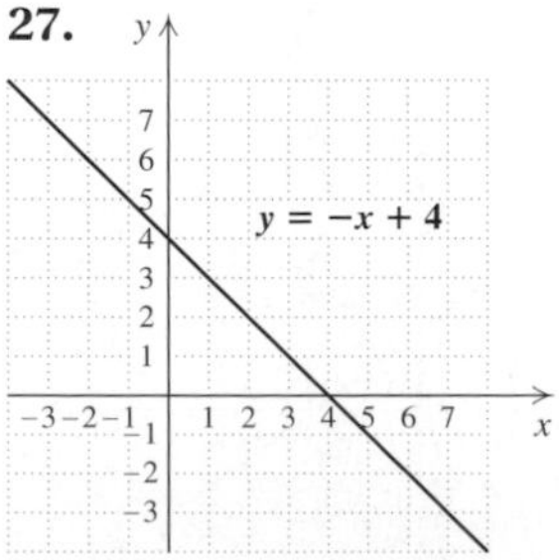

28.

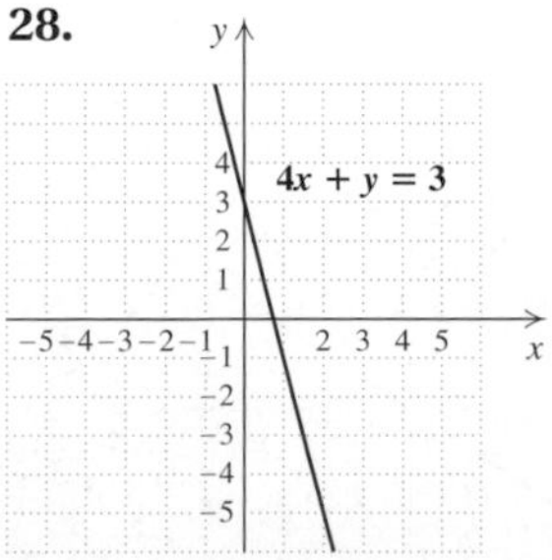

29.

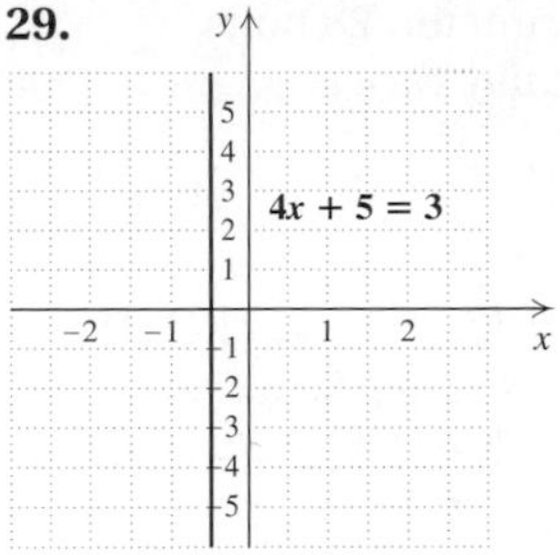

30.

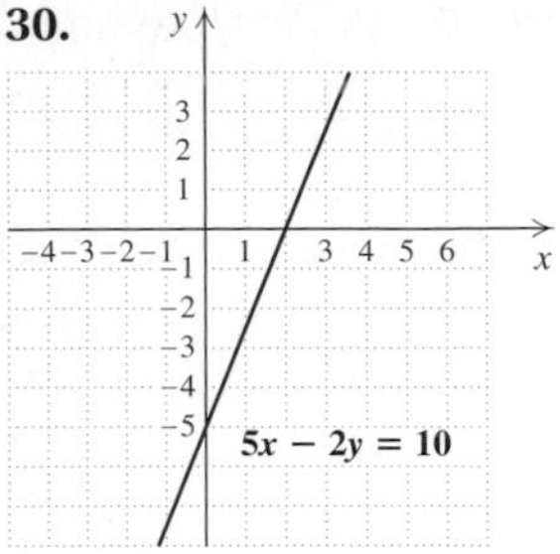

31. **(a)** $\frac{4}{9}$ meal/min; **(b)** $2\frac{1}{4}$ min/meal **32.** 12 mpg **33.** 0 **34.** $\frac{7}{3}$ **35.** $-\frac{3}{7}$ **36.** $\frac{3}{2}$ **37.** 0 **38.** Undefined **39.** 2 **40.** 28% **41.** x-intercept: $(6, 0)$; y-intercept: $(0, 9)$ **42.** $-\frac{1}{2}$; $(0, 5)$ **43.** $y = -\frac{3}{4}x + 6$ **44.** $y - 6 = -\frac{1}{2}(x - 3)$ **45.** **(a)** \$3100; **(b)** \$4900 **46.** $y = 4x + 5$

47.

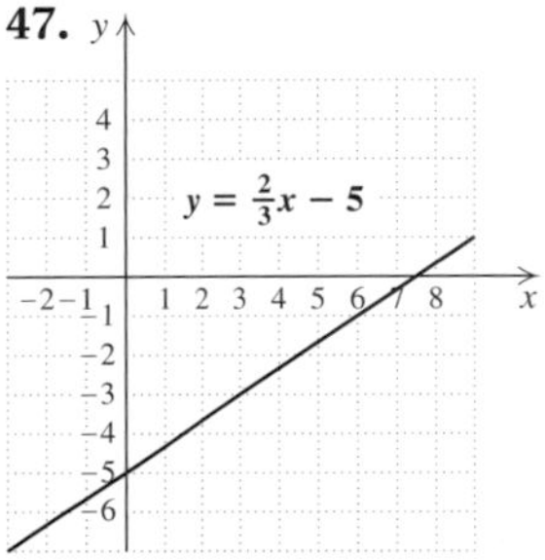

48.

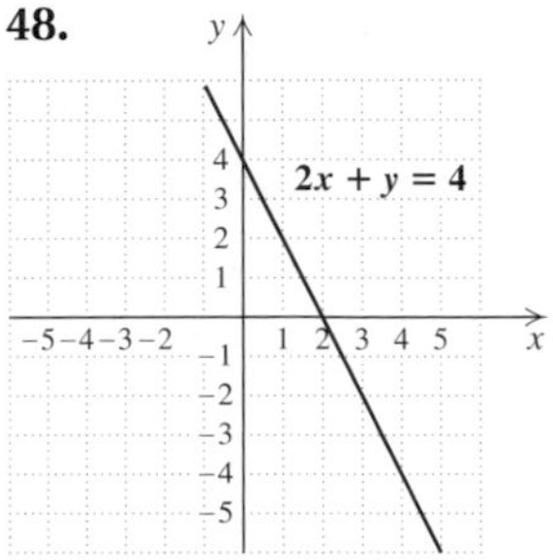

49.

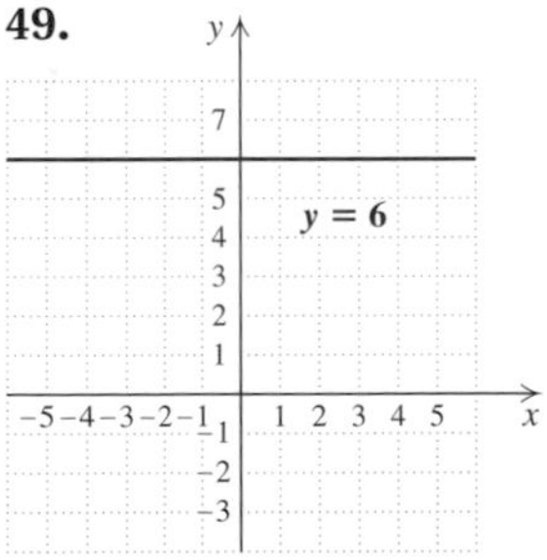

50.

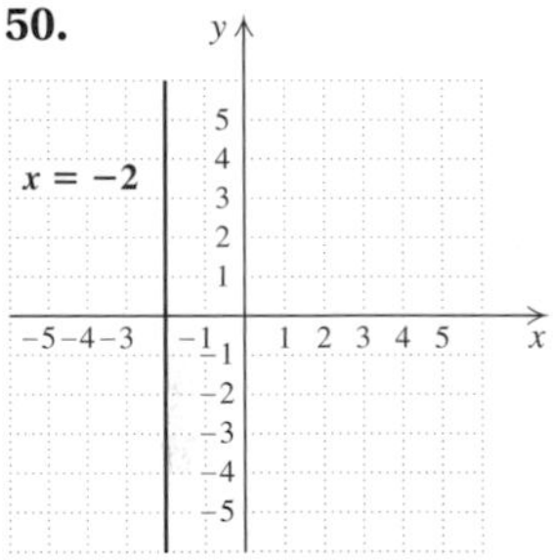

51.

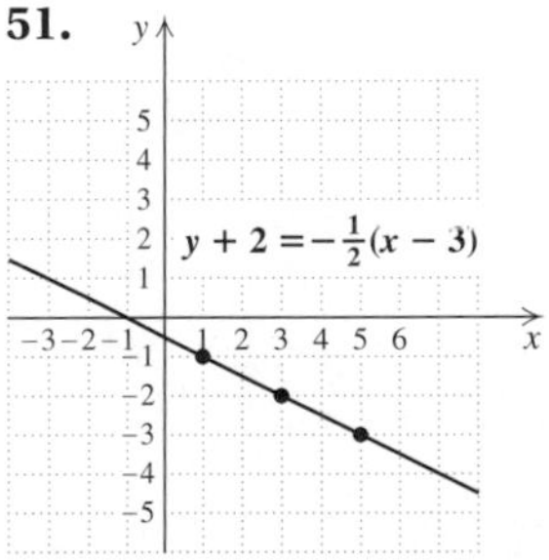

52. Two perpendicular lines share the same y-intercept if their point of intersection is on the y-axis. **53.** The y-intercept is the point at which the graph crosses the y-axis. Since a point on the y-axis is neither left nor right of the origin, the first coordinate of the point is 0. **54.** -1

55. 19 **56.** Area: 45 sq units; perimeter: 28 units
57. (0, 4), (1, 3), (−1, 3); answers may vary

Test: Chapter 3, pp. 222–223

1. [3.1] \$205.20 **2.** [3.1] \$638 **3.** [3.1] II **4.** [3.1] III
5. [3.1] (3, 4) **6.** [3.1] (0, −4) **7.** [3.1] (−5, 2)

8. [3.2]

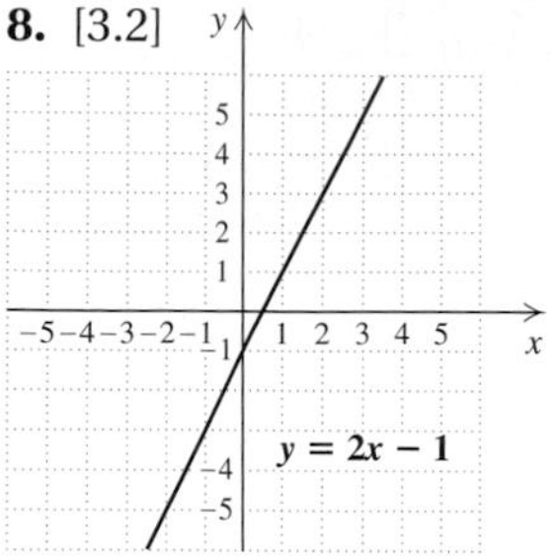

9. [3.3]

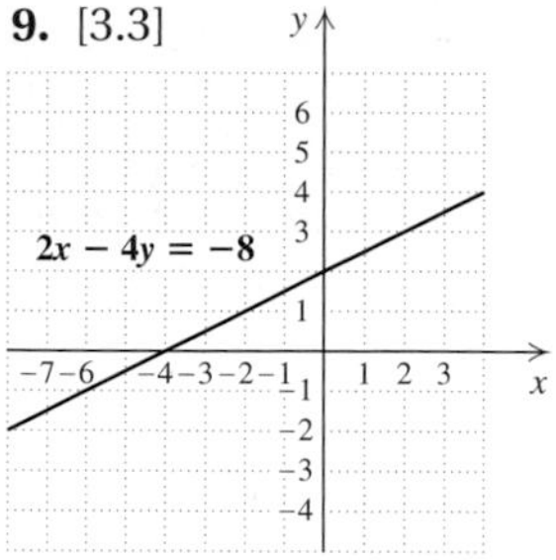

10. [3.3]

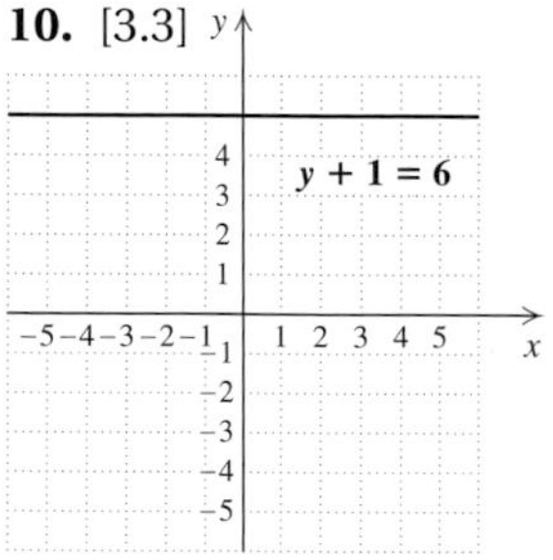

11. [3.2]

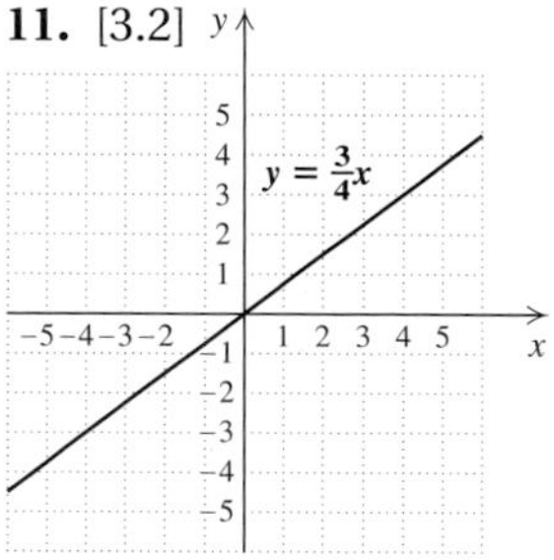

12. [3.3]

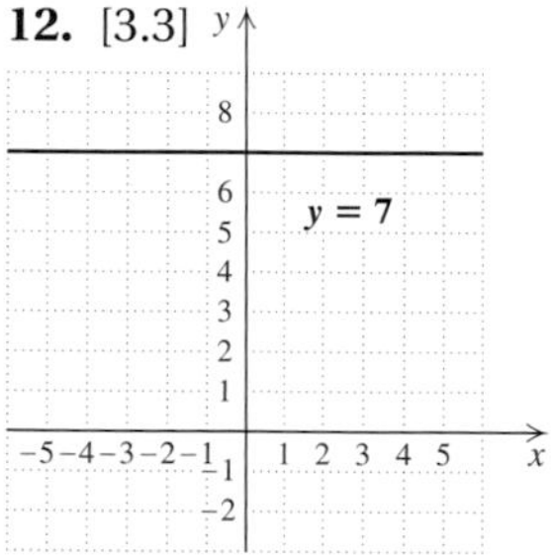

13. [3.2]

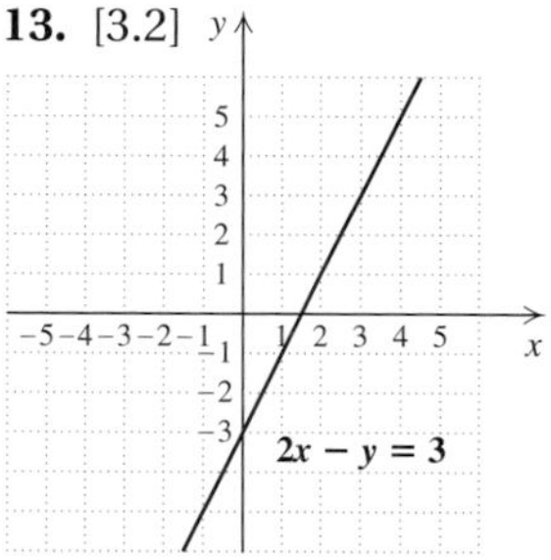

14. [3.3]

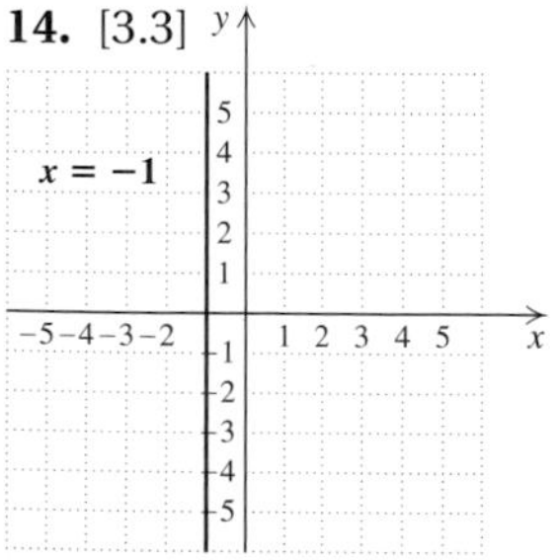

15. [3.3] x-intercept: (6, 0); y-intercept: (0, −10)
16. [3.3] x-intercept: (10, 0); y-intercept: $\left(0, \frac{5}{2}\right)$ **17.** [3.5] $\frac{9}{2}$
18. [3.5] $\frac{7}{12}$ **19.** [3.4] $\frac{1}{3}$ km/min **20.** [3.5] 31.5%
21. [3.6] 3; (0, 7)

22. [3.6]

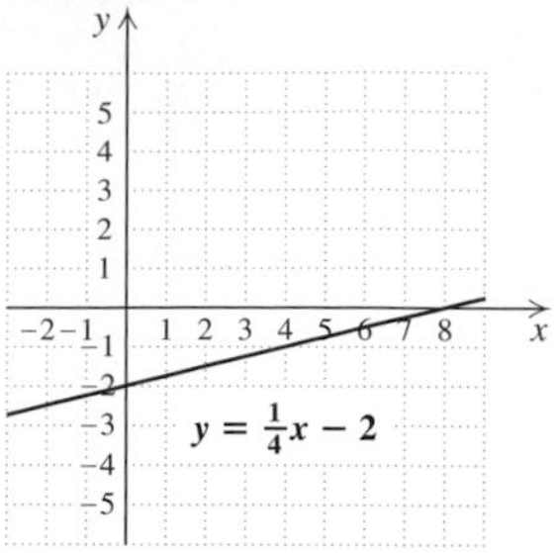

23. [3.7]

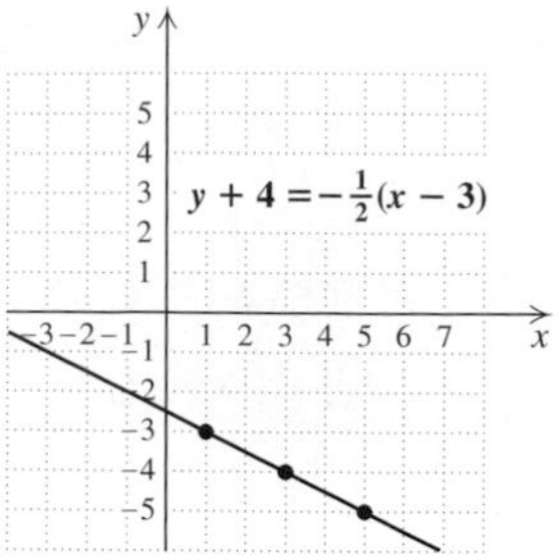

24. [3.7] $y - 8 = -3(x - 6)$ **25.** [3.6] $y = \frac{2}{5}x + 9$
26. [3.1] Area: 25 sq units; perimeter: 20 units **27.** [3.2], [3.7] (0, 12), (−3, 15), (5, 7)

Cumulative Review: Chapters 1–3, pp. 223–224

1. 7 **2.** $12x - 15y + 21$ **3.** $3(5x - 3y + 1)$ **4.** $2 \cdot 3 \cdot 7$
5. 0.45 **6.** 4 **7.** $\frac{1}{4}$ **8.** −4 **9.** $-x - y$ **10.** 0.785
11. $\frac{11}{60}$ **12.** 2.6 **13.** 7.28 **14.** $-\frac{5}{12}$ **15.** −3 **16.** 27
17. $-2y - 7$ **18.** $5x + 11$ **19.** −1.2 **20.** −21 **21.** 9
22. $-\frac{20}{3}$ **23.** 2 **24.** $\frac{13}{8}$ **25.** $-\frac{17}{21}$ **26.** −17 **27.** 2
28. $\{x \mid x < 16\}$ **29.** $\{x \mid x \le -\frac{11}{8}\}$ **30.** $h = \dfrac{A - \pi r^2}{2\pi r}$
31. IV **32.**

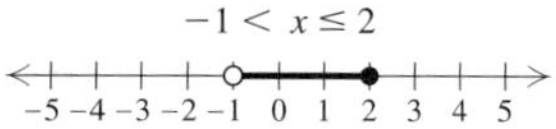

33.

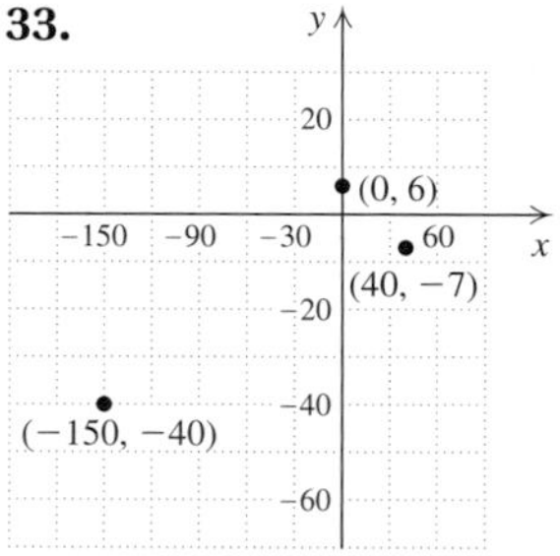

34.

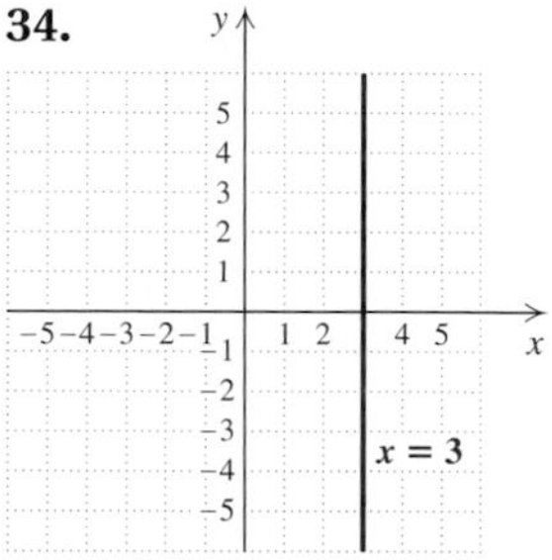

35.

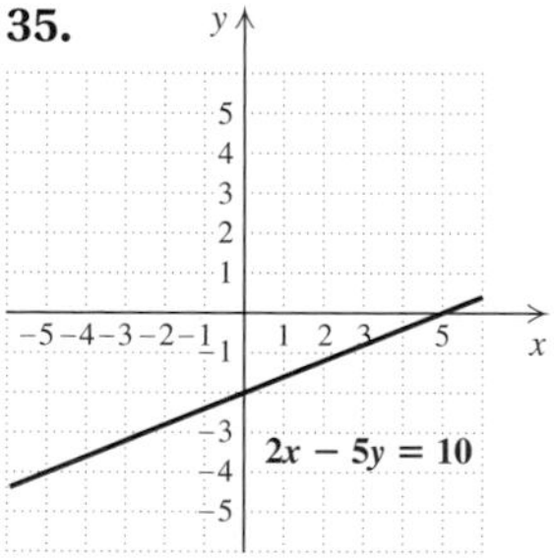

36.

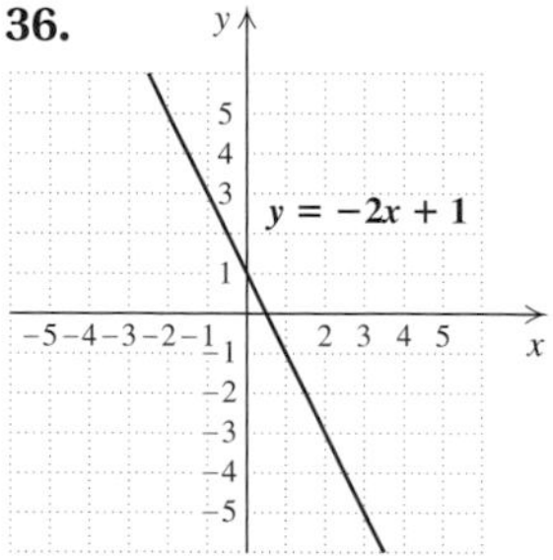

37.

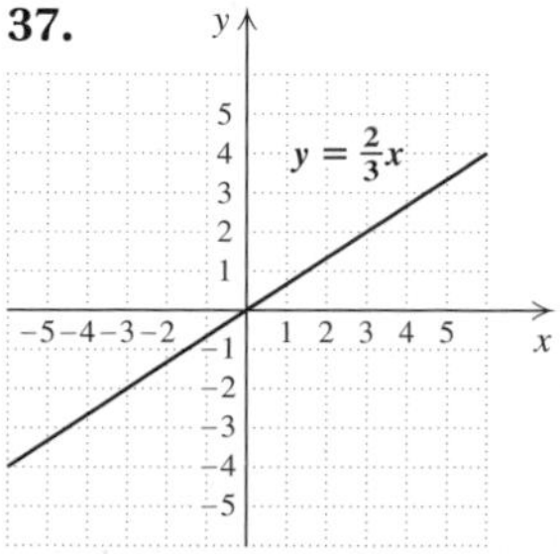

38.

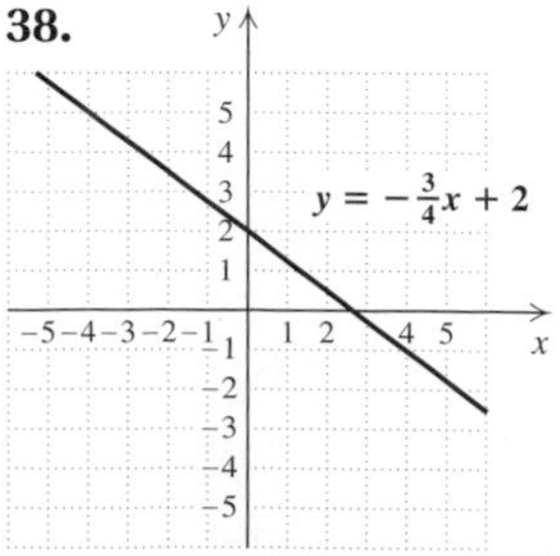

39. (10.5, 0); (0, −3) **40.** (−1.25, 0); (0, 5)
41. 160 million **42.** 15.6 million **43.** \$120
44. 50 m, 53 m, 40 m **45.** No more than 8 hr
46. \$40/person **47.** $-\frac{1}{3}$ **48.** $y = \frac{2}{7}x - 4$
49. $-\frac{1}{3}$; (0, 3) **50.** $y - 4 = -\frac{3}{8}(x - (-6))$
51. \$25,000 **52.** −4, 4 **53.** 2 **54.** −5 **55.** 3
56. No solution **57.** $Q = \dfrac{2 - pm}{p}$
58. $y = -\frac{7}{3}x + 7; y = -\frac{7}{3}x - 7; y = \frac{7}{3}x - 7; y = \frac{7}{3}x + 7$

CHAPTER 4

Exercise Set 4.1, pp. 232–234

1. (b) **3.** (e) **5.** (g) **7.** (c) **9.** r^{10} **11.** 9^8 **13.** a^7
15. 8^{11} **17.** $(3y)^{12}$ **19.** $(5t)^7$ **21.** a^5b^9 **23.** $(x + 1)^{12}$
25. r^{10} **27.** x^4y^7 **29.** 7^3 **31.** x^{12} **33.** t^4 **35.** $5a$
37. 1 **39.** $\frac{3}{4}m^3$ **41.** $4a^7b^6$ **43.** m^9n^4 **45.** 1 **47.** 5
49. 2 **51.** −4 **53.** x^{28} **55.** 5^{16} **57.** m^{35} **59.** t^{80}
61. $49x^2$ **63.** $-8a^3$ **65.** $16m^6$ **67.** $a^{14}b^7$ **69.** x^8y^7
71. $24x^{19}$ **73.** $\dfrac{a^3}{64}$ **75.** $\dfrac{49}{25a^2}$ **77.** $\dfrac{a^{20}}{b^{15}}$ **79.** $\dfrac{y^6}{4}$ **81.** $\dfrac{x^8y^4}{z^{12}}$
83. $\dfrac{a^{12}}{16b^{20}}$ **85.** $\dfrac{125x^{21}y^3}{8z^{12}}$ **87.** 1 **89.** **91.** $3(s - r + t)$
92. $-7(x - y + z)$ **93.** $8x$ **94.** $-3a - 6b$ **95.** $2y + 3x$
96. $5z + 2xy$ **97.** **99.** **101.** Let $a = 1$; then $(a + 5)^2 = 36$, but $a^2 + 5^2 = 26$. **103.** Let $a = 0$; then $\dfrac{a + 7}{7} = 1$, but $a = 0$. **105.** a^{8k} **107.** $\frac{16}{375}$ **109.** 13
111. < **113.** < **115.** > **117.** 4,000,000; 4,194,304; 194,304 **119.** 2,000,000,000; 2,147,483,648; 147,483,648
121. 1,536,000 bytes, or approximately 1,500,000 bytes

Technology Connection, p. 239

1. 79

Exercise Set 4.2, pp. 240–244

1. (b) **3.** (d) **5.** (g) **7.** (c) **9.** $7x^4, x^3, -5x, 8$
11. $-t^4, 7t^3, -3t^2, 6$ **13.** Coefficients: 4, 7; degrees: 5, 1
15. Coefficients: 9, −3, 4; degrees: 2, 1, 0
17. Coefficients: 7, 9, 1; degrees: 4, 1, 3 **19.** Coefficients: 1, −1, 4, −3; degrees: 4, 3, 1, 0 **21.** **(a)** 1, 2, 6; **(b)** $3x^6$, 3; **(c)** 6 **23.** **(a)** 2, 0, 4; **(b)** $2a^4$, 2; **(c)** 4 **25.** **(a)** 0, 2, 1, 5; **(b)** $-x^5$, −1; **(c)** 5

27.

Term	Coefficient	Degree of the Term	Degree of the Polynomial
$8x^5$	8	5	
$-\frac{1}{2}x^4$	$-\frac{1}{2}$	4	
$-4x^3$	−4	3	5
$7x^2$	7	2	
6	6	0	

29. Trinomial **31.** None of these **33.** Binomial
35. Monomial **37.** $11x^2 + 3x$ **39.** $4a^4$ **41.** $6x^2 - 3x$
43. $5x^3 - x + 5$ **45.** $-x^4 - x^3$ **47.** $\frac{1}{15}x^4 + 10$
49. $3.4x^2 + 1.3x + 5.5$ **51.** −17; 25 **53.** 16; 34
55. −67; 17 **57.** −27; 81 **59.** −117; −63
61. \$2.17 trillion **63.** 1112 ft **65.** 62.8 cm
67. 153.86 m² **69.** 5 million gigawatt hours
71. 4.5 million gigawatt hours **73.** About 9 words
75. About 6 **77.** Approximately 1.8 million; approximately 4.4 million **79.** **81.** 5 **82.** −9
83. $5(x + 3)$ **84.** $7(a - 3)$ **85.** 6.25¢/mi **86.** 274 and 275 **87.** **89.** $2x^5 + 4x^4 + 6x^3 + 8$; answers may vary
91. \$2510 **93.** $3x^6$ **95.** 5, 13, 80 **97.** 85.0
99.

t	$-t^2 + 10t - 18$
3	3
4	6
5	7
6	6
7	3

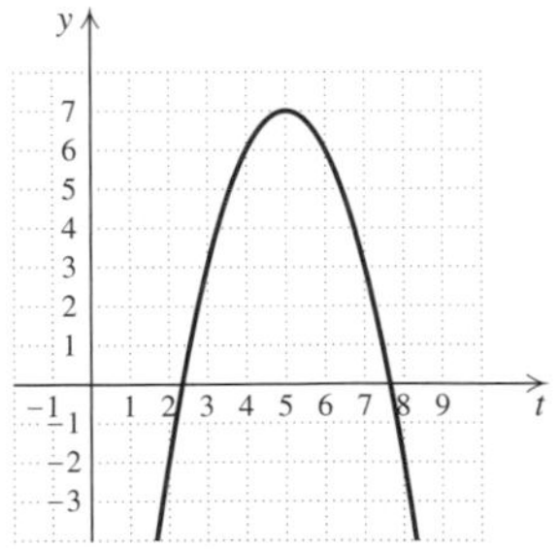

$y = -t^2 + 10t - 18$

Technology Connection, p. 249

1. In each case, let y_1 = the expression before the addition or subtraction has been performed, y_2 = the simplified sum or difference, and $y_3 = y_2 - y_1$; and note that the graph of y_3 coincides with the x-axis. That is, $y_3 = 0$.

Exercise Set 4.3, pp. 250–252

1. $-2x + 6$ **3.** $x^2 - 5x - 1$ **5.** $9t^2 + 5t - 3$
7. $8m^3 + 3m^2 - 3m - 7$ **9.** $7 + 13a + 6a^2 + 14a^3$
11. $9x^8 + 8x^7 - 3x^4 + 2x^2 - 2x + 5$

13. $-\frac{1}{2}x^4 + \frac{2}{3}x^3 + x^2 + 2$
15. $4.2t^3 + 3.5t^2 - 6.4t - 1.8$ **17.** $-3x^4 + 3x^2 + 4x$
19. $1.05x^4 + 0.36x^3 + 14.22x^2 + x + 0.97$
21. $-(-t^3 + 4t^2 - 9)$; $t^3 - 4t^2 + 9$
23. $-(12x^4 - 3x^3 + 3)$; $-12x^4 + 3x^3 - 3$ **25.** $-8x + 9$
27. $-3a^4 + 5a^2 - 9$ **29.** $4x^4 - 6x^2 - \frac{3}{4}x + 8$
31. $9x + 3$ **33.** $-t^2 - 8t + 7$
35. $6x^4 + 3x^3 - 4x^2 + 3x - 4$
37. $4.6x^3 + 9.2x^2 - 3.8x - 23$ **39.** 0
41. $1 + 2a + 7a^2 - 3a^3$ **43.** $\frac{3}{4}x^3 - \frac{1}{2}x$
45. $0.05t^3 - 0.07t^2 + 0.01t + 1$ **47.** $3x + 5$
49. $11x^4 + 12x^3 - 10x^2$ **51.** **(a)** $5x^2 + 4x$; **(b)** 145; 273
53. $\frac{23}{2}a + 12$ **55.** $(r + 11)(r + 9)$; $9r + 99 + 11r + r^2$
57. $(x + 3)^2$; $x^2 + 3x + 9 + 3x$ **59.** $\pi r^2 - 25\pi$
61. $xy - 21$ **63.** $(x^2 - 12)$ ft^2 **65.** $(z^2 - 16\pi)$ ft^2
67. $\left(144 - \frac{d^2}{4}\pi\right)$ m^2 **69.** **71.** 0 **72.** 0
73. $13t + 14$ **74.** $14t - 15$ **75.** $\{x \mid x < \frac{14}{3}\}$
76. $\{x \mid x \leq 12\}$ **77.** **79.** $9t^2 - 20t + 11$
81. $-10y^2 - 2y - 10$ **83.** $250.591x^3 + 2.812x$
85. $20w + 42$ **87.** $2x^2 + 20x$ **89.** $8x + 24$ **91.**

Technology Connection, p. 258

1. Let $y_1 = (-2x^2 - 3)(5x^3 - 3x + 4)$ and $y_2 = -10x^5 - 9x^3 - 8x^2 + 9x - 12$. With the table set in AUTO mode, note that the values in the Y1- and Y2-columns match, regardless of how far we scroll up or down. **2.** Use TRACE, a table, or a boldly drawn graph to confirm that y_3 is always 0.

Exercise Set 4.4, pp. 258–260

1. (b) **3.** (d) **5.** $36x^3$ **7.** $-x^7$ **9.** x^8 **11.** $24a^4$
13. $-0.12x^9$ **15.** $-\frac{1}{20}x^{12}$ **17.** $5n^3$ **19.** $72y^{10}$
21. $8x^2 - 12x$ **23.** $3x^2 + 6x$ **25.** $3a^2 + 27a$
27. $x^5 + x^2$ **29.** $6x^3 - 18x^2 + 3x$ **31.** $15t^3 + 30t^2$
33. $-6x^4 - 6x^3$ **35.** $4a^9 - 8a^7 - \frac{5}{12}a^4$
37. $x^2 + 8x + 12$ **39.** $x^2 + 3x - 10$ **41.** $a^2 - 13a + 42$
43. $x^2 - 9$ **45.** $25 - 15x + 2x^2$ **47.** $t^2 + \frac{17}{6}t + 2$
49. $\frac{3}{16}a^2 + \frac{5}{4}a - 2$ **51.**

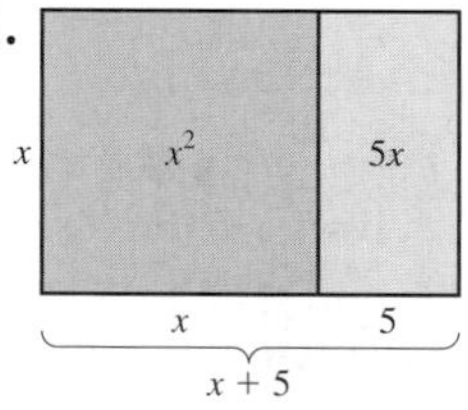

53.

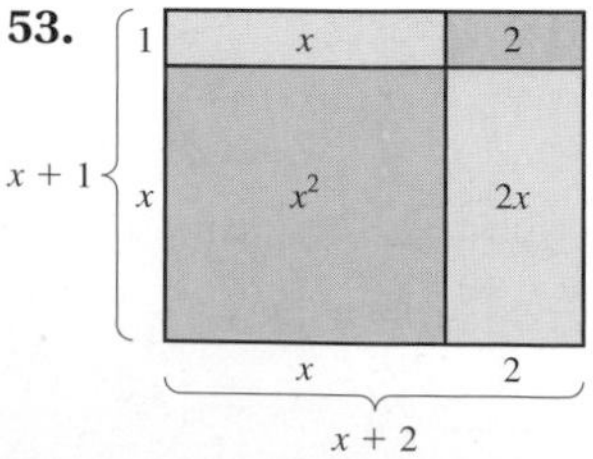

55.

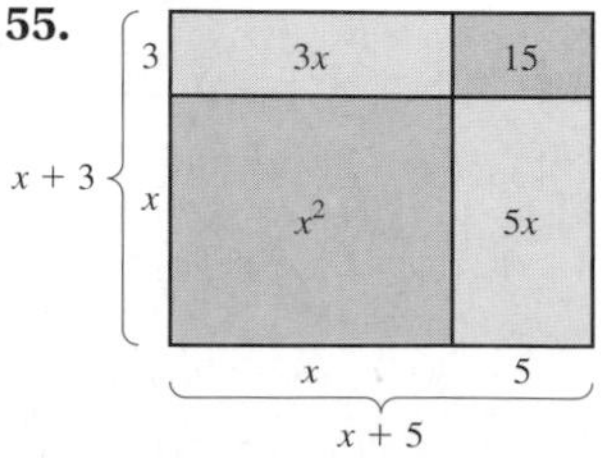

57. $x^3 + 4x + 5$ **59.** $2a^3 - a^2 - 11a + 10$
61. $2y^5 - 13y^3 + y^2 - 7y - 7$ **63.** $27x^2 + 39x + 14$
65. $x^4 - 2x^3 - x + 2$ **67.** $6t^4 - 17t^3 - 6t^2 + \frac{3}{2}t - 2$
69. $x^4 + 8x^3 + 12x^2 + 9x + 4$ **71.** **73.** 6 **74.** 31
75. 0 **76.** 0 **77.** **79.** $75y^2 - 45y$ **81.** 5
83. $V = 4x^3 - 48x^2 + 144x$ in^3; $S = -4x^2 + 144$ in^2
85. $x^3 + 2x^2 - 210$ m^3 **87.** 16 ft by 8 ft **89.** 0 **91.** 0

Exercise Set 4.5, pp. 267–270

1. True **3.** False **5.** $x^3 + 3x^2 + 5x + 15$
7. $x^4 + 2x^3 + 6x + 12$ **9.** $y^2 - y - 6$
11. $9x^2 + 21x + 10$ **13.** $5x^2 + 6x - 8$ **15.** $2 + 3t - 9t^2$
17. $2x^2 - 13x + 20$ **19.** $p^2 - \frac{1}{16}$ **21.** $x^2 - 0.01$
23. $-2x^2 - 11x + 6$ **25.** $a^2 + 18a + 81$
27. $1 - 2t - 15t^2$ **29.** $x^5 + 3x^3 - x^2 - 3$
31. $3x^6 - 2x^4 - 6x^2 + 4$ **33.** $4t^6 + 16t^3 + 15$
35. $8x^5 + 16x^3 + 5x^2 + 10$ **37.** $4x^3 - 12x^2 + 3x - 9$
39. $x^2 - 49$ **41.** $4x^2 - 1$ **43.** $25m^2 - 4$ **45.** $9x^8 - 1$
47. $x^8 - 49$ **49.** $t^2 - \frac{9}{16}$ **51.** $x^2 + 4x + 4$
53. $49x^6 + 14x^3 + 1$ **55.** $a^2 - \frac{4}{5}a + \frac{4}{25}$
57. $t^6 + 10t^3 + 25$ **59.** $4 - 12x^4 + 9x^8$
61. $25 + 60t^2 + 36t^4$ **63.** $49x^2 - 4.2x + 0.09$
65. $10a^5 - 5a^3$ **67.** $a^3 - a^2 - 10a + 12$
69. $9 - 12x^3 + 4x^6$ **71.** $5x^3 + 30x^2 - 10x$
73. $t^6 - 2t^3 + 1$ **75.** $15t^5 - 3t^4 + 3t^3$
77. $36x^8 - 36x^4 + 9$ **79.** $12x^3 + 8x^2 + 15x + 10$
81. $25 - 60x^4 + 36x^8$ **83.** $a^3 + 1$ **85.** $a^2 + 2a + 1$
87. $x^2 + 7x + 10$ **89.** $x^2 + 14x + 49$ **91.** $t^2 + 10t + 24$
93. $t^2 + 13t + 36$ **95.** $9x^2 + 24x + 16$
97.

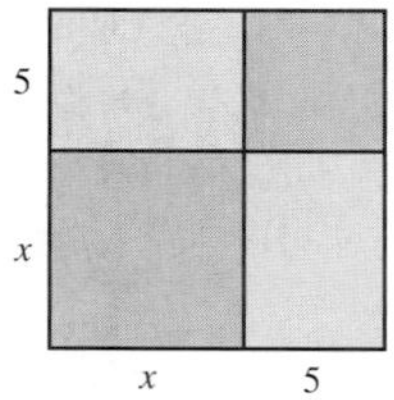

99.

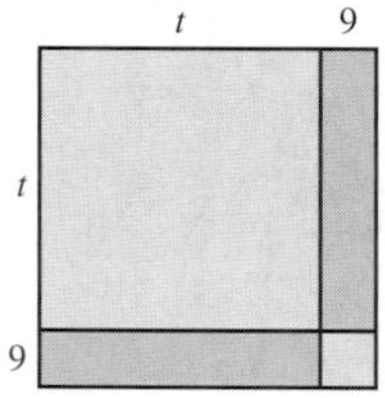

101.

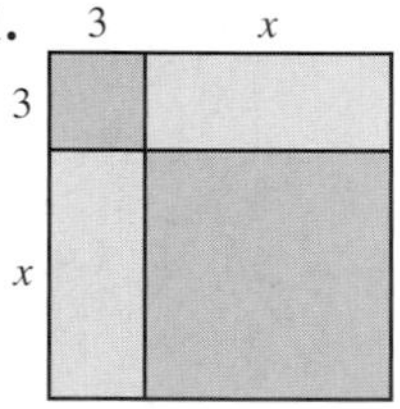

103.

105. Lamps: 500 watts; air conditioner: 2000 watts; television: 50 watts **106.** II **107.** $y = \frac{8}{5x}$ **108.** $a = \frac{c}{3b}$
109. $x = \frac{b + c}{a}$ **110.** $t = \frac{u - r}{s}$ **111.**
113. $16x^4 - 81$ **115.** $81t^4 - 72t^2 + 16$
117. $t^{24} - 4t^{18} + 6t^{12} - 4t^6 + 1$ **119.** 396 **121.** -7
123. $17F + 7(F - 17)$, $F^2 - (F - 17)(F - 7)$; other equivalent expressions are possible.

125. $x^2 - 9, (x - 3)^2 + 3(x - 3) + 3(x - 3)$; other equivalent expressions are possible.
127. $100 - 40x + 4x^2$ **129.**

Technology Connection, p. 274

1. 36.22 **2.** 22,312

Exercise Set 4.6, pp. 274–278

1. (a) **3.** (b) **5.** (c) **7.** (a) **9.** -7 **11.** -92 **13.** 2.97 L **15.** About 2494 calories **17.** 20.60625 in^2 **19.** 66.4 m **21.** Coefficients: 1, -2, 3, -5; degrees: 4, 2, 2, 0; 4 **23.** Coefficients: 17, -3, -7; degrees: 5, 5, 0; 5
25. $3a - 2b$ **27.** $3x^2y - 2xy^2 + x^2 + 5x$
29. $8u^2v - 5uv^2 + 7u^2$ **31.** $6a^2c - 7ab^2 + a^2b$
33. $3x^2 - 4xy + 3y^2$ **35.** $-6a^4 - 8ab + 7ab^2$
37. $-6r^2 - 5rt - t^2$ **39.** $3x^3 - x^2y + xy^2 - 3y^3$
41. $10y^4x^2 - 8y^3x$ **43.** $-8x + 8y$ **45.** $6z^2 + 7uz - 3u^2$
47. $x^2y^2 + 3xy - 28$ **49.** $4a^2 - b^2$ **51.** $15r^2t^2 - rt - 2$
53. $m^6n^2 + 2m^3n - 48$ **55.** $30x^2 - 28xy + 6y^2$
57. $0.01 - p^2q^2$ **59.** $x^2 + 2xh + h^2$
61. $16a^2 + 40ab + 25b^2$ **63.** $c^4 - d^2$ **65.** $a^2b^2 - c^2d^4$
67. $a^2 + 2ab + b^2 - c^2$ **69.** $a^2 - b^2 - 2bc - c^2$
71. $a^2 + ab + ac + bc$ **73.** $x^2 - z^2$
75. $x^2 + y^2 + z^2 + 2xy + 2xz + 2yz$
77. $\frac{1}{2}x^2 + \frac{1}{2}xy - y^2$
79. We draw a rectangle with dimensions $r + s$ by $u + v$.

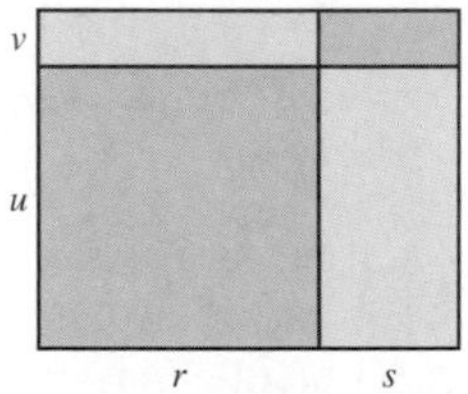

81.

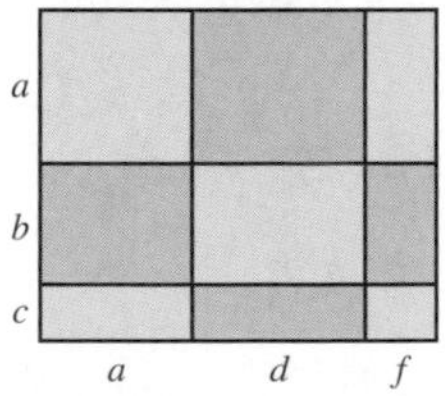

83. **85.** 12 **86.** 5

87. 27 **88.** 36 **89.** 7 **90.** 5 **91.** **93.** $4xy - 4y^2$
95. $2xy + \pi x^2$ **97.** $x^3 + 2y^3 + x^2y + xy^2$
99. $2\pi nh + 2\pi mh + 2\pi n^2 - 2\pi m^2$ **101.**
103. $P + 2Pr + Pr^2$ **105.** \$15,638.03

Exercise Set 4.7, pp. 283–284

1. $4x^5 - 3x$ **3.** $1 - 2u + u^6$ **5.** $6t^2 - 8t + 2$
7. $-5x^4 + 4x^2 + 1$ **9.** $6t^2 - 10t + \frac{3}{2}$
11. $4x^2 - 5x + \frac{1}{2}$ **13.** $x^4 + \frac{3}{2}x^2 + \frac{1}{x}$
15. $-3rs - r + 2s$ **17.** $x + 6$ **19.** $t - 5 + \frac{-45}{t - 5}$
21. $2x - 1 + \frac{1}{x + 6}$ **23.** $a^2 - 2a + 4$ **25.** $t + 4 + \frac{3}{t - 4}$
27. $x + 4$ **29.** $3a + 1 + \frac{3}{2a + 5}$ **31.** $t^2 - 3t + 1$
33. $t^2 - 2t + 3 + \frac{-4}{t + 1}$ **35.** $t^2 + 1 + \frac{4t - 2}{t^2 - 3}$
37. $2x^2 + 1 + \frac{-x}{2x^2 - 3}$ **39.** **41.** -17 **42.** -23
43. -2 **44.** 5 **45.** 167.5 ft **46.** 2
47.

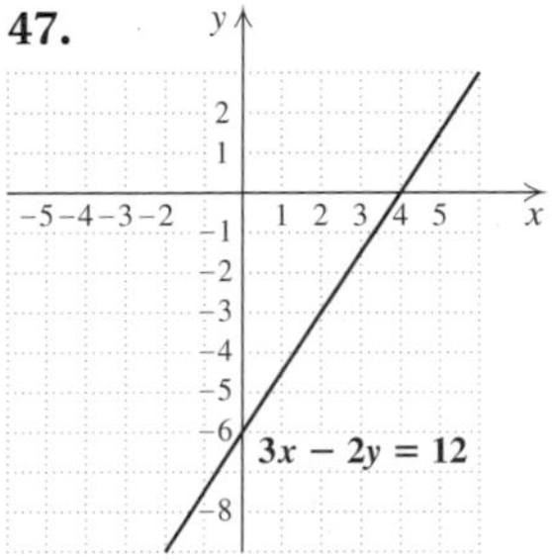

48.

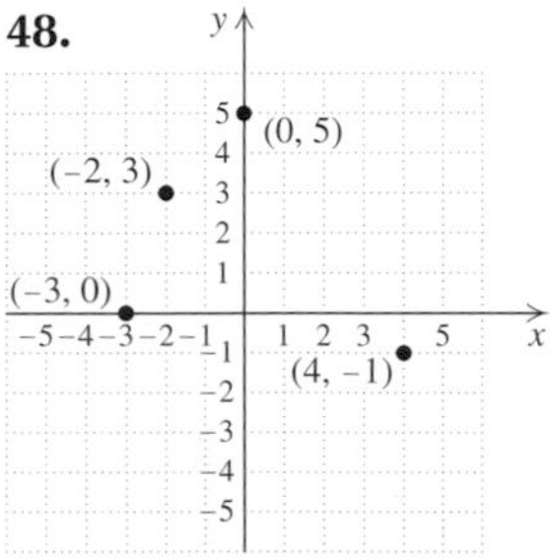

49. **51.** $5x^{6k} - 16x^{3k} + 14$ **53.** $3t^{2h} + 2t^h - 5$
55. $a + 3 + \frac{5}{5a^2 - 7a - 2}$ **57.** $2x^2 + x - 3$ **59.** 3
61. -1

Technology Connection, p. 291

1. 1.71×10^{17} **2.** $5.\overline{370} \times 10^{-15}$ **3.** 3.68×10^{16}

Exercise Set 4.8, pp. 291–293

1. $\frac{1}{7^2} = \frac{1}{49}$ **3.** $\frac{1}{10^4} = \frac{1}{10{,}000}$ **5.** $\frac{1}{(-2)^6} = \frac{1}{64}$ **7.** $\frac{1}{x^8}$
9. $\frac{x}{y^2}$ **11.** $\frac{t}{r^5}$ **13.** t^8 **15.** h^8 **17.** $\frac{1}{7}$ **19.** $\left(\frac{5}{3}\right)^2 = \frac{25}{9}$
21. $\left(\frac{2}{a}\right)^3 = \frac{8}{a^3}$ **23.** $\left(\frac{t}{s}\right)^7 = \frac{t^7}{s^7}$ **25.** 6^{-2} **27.** t^{-6}
29. a^{-4} **31.** p^{-7} **33.** 5^{-1} **35.** t^{-1} **37.** 2^3, or 8
39. $\frac{1}{x^9}$ **41.** $\frac{1}{t^2}$ **43.** $\frac{1}{a^{18}}$ **45.** t^{18} **47.** $\frac{1}{t^{12}}$ **49.** x^8
51. $\frac{1}{a^3b^3}$ **53.** $\frac{1}{m^7n^7}$ **55.** $\frac{9}{x^8}$ **57.** $\frac{25t^6}{r^8}$ **59.** t^{10} **61.** $\frac{1}{y^4}$
63. $3y^5$ **65.** $2x^5$ **67.** $\frac{3b^9}{2a^7}$ **69.** 1 **71.** $\frac{3y^6z^2}{x^5}$
73. $3s^2t^4u^4$ **75.** $\frac{1}{x^{12}y^{15}}$ **77.** $x^{24}y^8$ **79.** $\frac{b^5c^4}{a^8}$ **81.** $\frac{9}{a^8}$
83. $\frac{n^{12}}{m^3}$ **85.** $\frac{27b^{12}}{8a^6}$ **87.** 1 **89.** 71,200 **91.** 0.00892

93. 904,000,000 **95.** 0.0000000002764 **97.** 42,090,000 **99.** 4.9×10^5 **101.** 5.83×10^{-3} **103.** 7.8×10^{10} **105.** 5.27×10^{-7} **107.** 1.8×10^{-8} **109.** 1.094×10^{15} **111.** 8×10^{12} **113.** 2.47×10^8 **115.** 3.915×10^{-16} **117.** 2.5×10^{13} **119.** 5×10^{-4} **121.** 3×10^{-21} **123.** **125.** 15 **126.** 49 **127.** 78 **128.** 6

129.

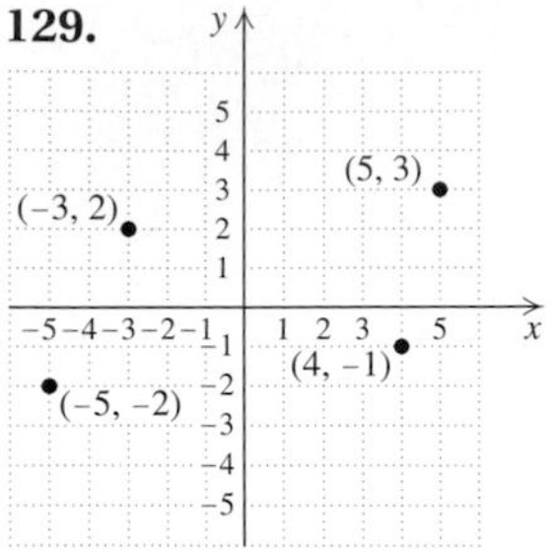

130. $t = \dfrac{r - cx}{b}$ **131.**

133. 8×10^5 **135.** 2^{-12} **137.** 5 **139.** 7×10^{23} **141.** $4.894179894 \times 10^{26}$ **143.** 3.12×10^{43} **145.** **(a)** False; **(b)** false; **(c)** false **147.** 2.5×10^{12} bytes **149.** Approximately 1.15385×10^{12} times

Review Exercises: Chapter 4, pp. 295–297

1. False **2.** True **3.** True **4.** False **5.** True **6.** False **7.** True **8.** True **9.** y^{11} **10.** $(3x)^{14}$ **11.** t^6 **12.** 4^3, or 64 **13.** 1 **14.** $\dfrac{9t^8}{4s^6}$ **15.** $-8x^3y^6$ **16.** $18x^5$ **17.** a^7b^6 **18.** $3x^2, 6x, \frac{1}{2}$ **19.** $-4y^5, 7y^2, -3y, -2$ **20.** $9, -1, 7$ **21.** $4, 6, -5, \frac{5}{3}$ **22.** **(a)** 2, 0, 5; **(b)** $15t^2$, 15; **(c)** 5 **23.** **(a)** 5, 0, 2, 1; **(b)** $-2x^5, -2$; **(c)** 5 **24.** Binomial **25.** None of these **26.** Monomial **27.** $-x^2 + 7x$ **28.** $-\frac{1}{4}x^3 + 4x^2 + 7$ **29.** $-3x^5 + 25$ **30.** $-2x^2 - 3x + 2$ **31.** $10x^4 - 7x^2 - x - \frac{1}{2}$ **32.** -15 **33.** 10 **34.** $x^5 + 8x^4 + 6x^3 - 2x - 9$ **35.** $-x^5 + 3x^4 - x^3 - 2x^2$ **36.** $2x^2 - 4x - 6$ **37.** $x^5 - 3x^3 - 2x^2 + 8$ **38.** $\frac{3}{4}x^4 + \frac{1}{4}x^3 - \frac{1}{3}x^2 - \frac{7}{4}x + \frac{3}{8}$ **39.** $-x^5 + x^4 - 5x^3 - 2x^2 + 2x$ **40.** **(a)** $4w + 6$; **(b)** $w^2 + 3w$ **41.** $-12x^3$ **42.** $49x^2 + 14x + 1$ **43.** $a^2 - 3a - 28$ **44.** $m^2 - 25$ **45.** $12x^3 - 23x^2 + 13x - 2$ **46.** $x^2 - 16x + 64$ **47.** $15t^5 - 6t^4 + 12t^3$ **48.** $a^2 - 81$ **49.** $x^2 - 1.3x + 0.4$ **50.** $x^7 + x^5 - 3x^4 + 3x^3 - 2x^2 + 5x - 3$ **51.** $9x^2 - 30x + 25$ **52.** $2t^4 - 11t^2 - 21$ **53.** $a^2 + \frac{1}{6}a - \frac{1}{3}$ **54.** $9x^2 - 49$ **55.** 49 **56.** Coefficients: $1, -7, 9, -8$; degrees: 6, 2, 2, 0; 6 **57.** Coefficients: $1, -1, 1$; degrees: 16, 40, 23; 40 **58.** $-y + 9w - 5$ **59.** $6m^3 + 4m^2n - mn^2$ **60.** $-x^2 - 10xy$ **61.** $11x^3y^2 - 8x^2y - 6x^2 - 6x + 6$ **62.** $2x^2 - xy - 15y^2$ **63.** $9a^8 - 2a^4b^3 + \frac{1}{9}b^6$ **64.** $\frac{1}{2}x^2 - \frac{1}{2}y^2$ **65.** $5x^2 - \frac{1}{2}x + 4$ **66.** $3x^2 - 7x + 4 + \dfrac{1}{2x + 3}$ **67.** $t^3 + 2t - 3$ **68.** $\dfrac{1}{m^4}$ **69.** a^{-9} **70.** $\dfrac{1}{7^2}$, or $\dfrac{1}{49}$ **71.** $\dfrac{2}{a^{13}b^7}$ **72.** $\dfrac{1}{x^{12}}$ **73.** $\dfrac{x^6}{4y^2}$ **74.** $\dfrac{y^3}{8x^3}$ **75.** 8,300,000 **76.** 3.28×10^{-5} **77.** 2.09×10^4 **78.** 5.12×10^{-5} **79.** 2.28×10^{11} platelets **80.** In the expression $5x^3$, the exponent refers only to the x. In the expression $(5x)^3$, the entire expression $5x$ is the base. **81.** It is possible to determine two possibilities for the binomial that was squared by using the equation $(A - B)^2 = A^2 - 2AB + B^2$ in reverse. Since, in $x^2 - 6x + 9$, $A^2 = x^2$ and $B^2 = 9$, or 3^2, the binomial that was squared was $A - B$, or $x - 3$. If the polynomial is written $9 - 6x + x^2$, then $A^2 = 9$ and $B^2 = x^2$, so the binomial that was squared was $3 - x$. We cannot determine without further information whether the binomial squared was $x - 3$ or $3 - x$. **82.** **(a)** 4; **(b)** 2 **83.** $64x^{16}$ **84.** $8x^4 + 4x^3 + 5x - 2$ **85.** $-16x^6 + x^2 - 10x + 25$ **86.** $\frac{94}{13}$

Test: Chapter 4, p. 298

1. [4.1] a^{10} **2.** [4.1] 4^3, or 64 **3.** [4.1] 1 **4.** [4.1] x^6 **5.** [4.1] $-27y^6$ **6.** [4.1] $\dfrac{25}{16a^6}$ **7.** [4.1] $-24x^{17}$ **8.** [4.1] a^6b^5 **9.** [4.2] Binomial **10.** [4.2] $\frac{1}{3}, -1, 7$ **11.** [4.2] Degrees of terms: 3, 1, 5, 0; leading term: $7t^5$; leading coefficient: 7; degree of polynomial: 5 **12.** [4.2] -7 **13.** [4.2] $5a^2 - 6$ **14.** [4.2] $\frac{7}{4}y^2 - 4y$ **15.** [4.2] $x^5 + 2x^3 + 4x^2 - 8x + 3$ **16.** [4.3] $4x^5 + x^4 + 5x^3 - 8x^2 + 2x - 7$ **17.** [4.3] $5x^4 + 5x^2 + x + 5$ **18.** [4.3] $-4x^4 + x^3 - 8x - 3$ **19.** [4.3] $-x^5 + 1.3x^3 - 0.8x^2 - 3$ **20.** [4.4] $-6x^4 + 6x^3 + 10x^2$ **21.** [4.5] $x^2 - \frac{2}{3}x + \frac{1}{9}$ **22.** [4.5] $25t^2 - 49$ **23.** [4.5] $3b^2 - 4b - 15$ **24.** [4.5] $x^{14} - 4x^8 + 4x^6 - 16$ **25.** [4.5] $48 + 34y - 5y^2$ **26.** [4.4] $6x^3 - 7x^2 - 11x - 3$ **27.** [4.5] $64a^2 + 48a + 9$ **28.** [4.6] 24 **29.** [4.6] $-4x^3y - x^2y^2 + xy^3 - y^3 + 19$ **30.** [4.6] $8a^2b^2 + 6ab + 6ab^2 + ab^3 - 4b^3$ **31.** [4.6] $9x^{10} - y^2$ **32.** [4.7] $4x^2 + 3x - 5$ **33.** [4.7] $2x^2 - 4x - 2 + \dfrac{17}{3x + 2}$ **34.** [4.8] $\dfrac{1}{5^3}$ **35.** [4.8] y^{-8} **36.** [4.8] $\dfrac{1}{t^6}$ **37.** [4.8] $\dfrac{y^5}{x^5}$ **38.** [4.8] $\dfrac{b^4}{16a^{12}}$ **39.** [4.8] $\dfrac{c^3}{a^3b^3}$ **40.** [4.8] 3.9×10^9 **41.** [4.8] 0.00000005 **42.** [4.8] 1.75×10^{17} **43.** [4.8] 1.296×10^{22} **44.** [4.4], [4.5] $V = l(l - 2)(l - 1) = l^3 - 3l^2 + 2l$ **45.** [2.2], [4.5] $\frac{100}{21}$ **46.** [4.8] 3.0×10^5 sound files

CHAPTER 5

Technology Connection, p. 306

1. Correct **2.** Correct **3.** Not correct **4.** Not correct **5.** Not correct **6.** Correct **7.** Not correct **8.** Correct

Exercise Set 5.1, pp. 307–308

1. (h) **3.** (b) **5.** (c) **7.** (d) **9.** Answers may vary. $(10x)(x^2)$, $(5x^2)(2x)$, $(-2)(-5x^3)$ **11.** Answers may vary. $(-15)(a^4)$, $(-5a)(3a^3)$, $(-3a^2)(5a^2)$ **13.** Answers may vary. $(2x)(13x^4)$, $(13x^5)(2)$, $(-x^3)(-26x^2)$ **15.** $7(x-2)$ **17.** $t(3t+1)$ **19.** $-4a(a+2)$, or $4a(-a-2)$ **21.** $x^2(x+6)$ **23.** $8x^2(x^2-3)$ **25.** $2(x^2+x-4)$ **27.** $-a^2(7a^4-10a^2+14)$ **29.** $6x^2(x^6+2x^4-4x^2+5)$ **31.** $x^2y^2(x^3y^3+x^2y+xy-1)$ **33.** $-5a^2b^2(ab^2-2b+3a)$ **35.** $(y-2)(y+7)$ **37.** $(x+3)(x^2-7)$ **39.** $(y+8)(y^2+1)$ **41.** $(x+3)(x^2+4)$ **43.** $(a+3)(5a^2+2)$ **45.** $(3x-4)(3x^2+1)$ **47.** $(t-5)(4t^2+3)$ **49.** $(7x+2)(x^2-2)$ **51.** $(6a-7)(a^2+1)$ **53.** $(x+8)(x^2-3)$ **55.** $(x+6)(2x^2-5)$ **57.** Not factorable by grouping **59.** $(y+8)(y^2-2)$ **61.** $(x-4)(2x^2-9)$ **63.** **65.** $x^2+8x+15$ **66.** $x^2+9x+14$ **67.** $a^2-4a-21$ **68.** $a^2-3a-40$ **69.** $6x^2+7x-20$ **70.** $12t^2-13t-14$ **71.** $9t^2-30t+25$ **72.** $4t^2-36t+81$ **73.** **75.** $(2x^3+3)(2x^2+3)$ **77.** $(x^5+1)(x^7+1)$ **79.** $(x-1)(5x^4+x^2+3)$ **81.** Answers may vary. $8x^4y^3-24x^2y^4+16x^3y^4$

Exercise Set 5.2, pp. 314–315

1. Positive; positive **3.** Negative; positive **5.** Positive **7.** $(x+6)(x+1)$ **9.** $(x+3)(x+4)$ **11.** $(x-3)^2$ **13.** $(x+2)(x+7)$ **15.** $(b-4)(b-1)$ **17.** $(a+6)(a-2)$ **19.** $(d-2)(d-5)$ **21.** $(x-5)(x+3)$ **23.** $(x+5)(x-3)$ **25.** $3(y+4)(y-7)$ **27.** $-x(x+6)(x-7)$ **29.** $(x-5)(x+12)$ **31.** $(x-6)(x+12)$ **33.** $-5(b-3)(b+8)$ **35.** $x^3(x-2)(x+1)$ **37.** Prime **39.** $(t+5)(t+10)$ **41.** $(x+9)(x+11)$ **43.** $2x(x-8)(x-12)$ **45.** $-4(x+5)^2$ **47.** $(y-9)(y-12)$ **49.** $-a^4(a-6)(a+15)$ **51.** $\left(t+\frac{1}{3}\right)^2$ **53.** Prime **55.** $(p+5q)(p-2q)$ **57.** Prime **59.** $(s-5t)(s+3t)$ **61.** $6a^8(a+2)(a-7)$ **63.** **65.** $\frac{8}{3}$ **66.** $-\frac{7}{2}$ **67.** $3x^2+22x+24$ **68.** $49w^2+84w+36$ **69.** 29,443 people **70.** 100°, 25°, 55° **71.** **73.** −5, 5, −23, 23, −49, 49 **75.** $(y+0.2)(y-0.4)$ **77.** $-\frac{1}{3}a(a-3)(a+2)$ **79.** $(x^m+4)(x^m+7)$ **81.** $(a+1)(x+2)(x+1)$ **83.** $(x+3)^3$, or $x^3+9x^2+27x+27$ cubic meters **85.** $x^2(\pi-1)$ **87.** $x^2\left(9-\frac{1}{2}\pi\right)$ **89.** $(x+5)(x+7)$

Exercise Set 5.3, pp. 324–326

1. (c) **3.** (d) **5.** $(2x-1)(x+4)$ **7.** $(3t-5)(t+3)$ **9.** $(3x-1)(2x-7)$ **11.** $(7x+1)(x+2)$ **13.** $(3a+2)(3a-4)$ **15.** $2(3x+1)(x-2)$ **17.** $6(2t+1)(t-1)$ **19.** $(5x+3)(3x+2)$ **21.** $-1(7x+4)(5x+2)$, or $-(7x+4)(5x+2)$ **23.** Prime **25.** $(5x+4)^2$ **27.** $(8a+3)(2a+9)$ **29.** $2(3t-1)(3t+5)$ **31.** $-1(x-3)(2x+5)$, or $-(x-3)(2x+5)$ **33.** $-3(2x+1)(x+5)$ **35.** $5(4x-1)(x-1)$ **37.** $4(3x-1)(x+6)$ **39.** $(3x+1)(x+1)$ **41.** $(y+4)(y-2)$ **43.** $(4t-3)(2t-7)$ **45.** $(3x+2)(2x+3)$ **47.** $(t+3)(2t-1)$ **49.** $(a-4)(3a-1)$ **51.** $(9t+5)(t+1)$ **53.** $-1(4x+1)(4x+7)$, or $-(4x+1)(4x+7)$ **55.** $5(2a-1)(a+3)$ **57.** $3x(3x-1)(2x+3)$ **59.** $(x+1)(25x+64)$ **61.** $3x(7x+1)(8x+1)$ **63.** $-t^2(2t-3)(7t+1)$ **65.** $3(5x-3)(3x+2)$ **67.** $(2a+b)(a+2b)$ **69.** $(2s+3t)(4s+3t)$ **71.** $6(3x-4y)(x+y)$ **73.** $-2(3a-2b)(4a-3b)$ **75.** $x^2(4x+7)(2x+5)$ **77.** $a^6(3a+4)(3a+2)$ **79.** **81.** 6369 km, 3949 mi **82.** 40° **83.** $9x^2+6x+1$ **84.** $25x^2-20x+4$ **85.** $16t^2-40t+25$ **86.** $49a^2+14a+1$ **87.** $25x^2-4$ **88.** $4x^2-9$ **89.** $4t^2-49$ **90.** $16a^2-49$ **91.** **93.** $(3xy+2)(6xy-5)$ **95.** Prime **97.** $(4t^5-1)^2$ **99.** $-1(10x^n+3)(2x^n+1)$, or $-(10x^n+3)(2x^n+1)$ **101.** $a(a^n-1)^2$ **103.** $-2(a+1)^n(a+3)^2(a+6)$

Exercise Set 5.4, pp. 332–333

1. Difference of squares **3.** None of these **5.** Perfect-square trinomial **7.** Prime polynomial **9.** Perfect-square trinomial **11.** Yes **13.** No **15.** No **17.** No **19.** $(x+8)^2$ **21.** $(x-7)^2$ **23.** $3(x+1)^2$ **25.** $(2-x)^2$, or $(x-2)^2$ **27.** $2(3x+1)^2$ **29.** $(7-4y)^2$, or $(4y-7)^2$ **31.** $-x^3(x-9)^2$ **33.** $2x(x-1)^2$ **35.** $5(2x+5)^2$ **37.** $(7-3x)^2$, or $(3x-7)^2$ **39.** $(4x+3)^2$ **41.** $2(1+5x)^2$, or $2(5x+1)^2$ **43.** $(2p+3q)^2$ **45.** Prime **47.** $-1(8m+n)^2$, or $-(8m+n)^2$ **49.** $-2(4s-5t)^2$ **51.** No **53.** Yes **55.** No **57.** $(y+2)(y-2)$ **59.** $(p+3)(p-3)$ **61.** $(7+t)(-7+t)$, or $(t+7)(t-7)$ **63.** $6(a+3)(a-3)$ **65.** $(7x-1)^2$ **67.** $2(10-t)(10+t)$ **69.** $-5(4a-3)(4a+3)$ **71.** $5(t+4)(t-4)$ **73.** $2(2x+7)(2x-7)$ **75.** $x(6+7x)(6-7x)$ **77.** Prime **79.** $(t-1)(t+1)(t^2+1)$ **81.** $-3x(x-4)^2$ **83.** $3(4t+3)(4t-3)$ **85.** $a^6(a-1)^2$ **87.** $7(a+b)(a-b)$ **89.** $(5x+2y)(5x-2y)$ **91.** $2(3t+2s)(3t-2s)$ **93.** **95.** 3.125 L **96.** Scores ≥ 77 **97.** $x^{12}y^{12}$ **98.** $25a^4b^6$

99.

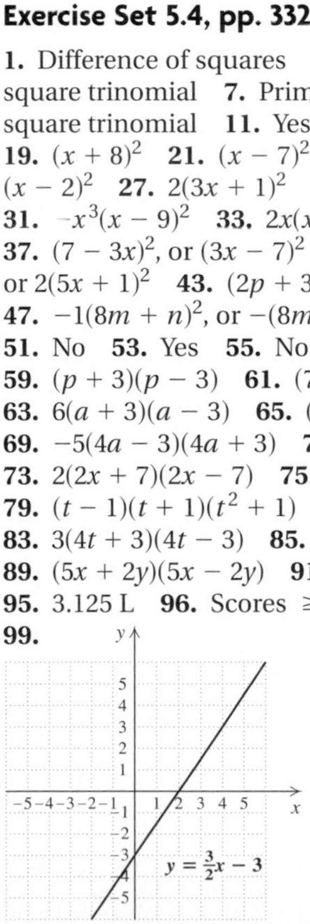

100.

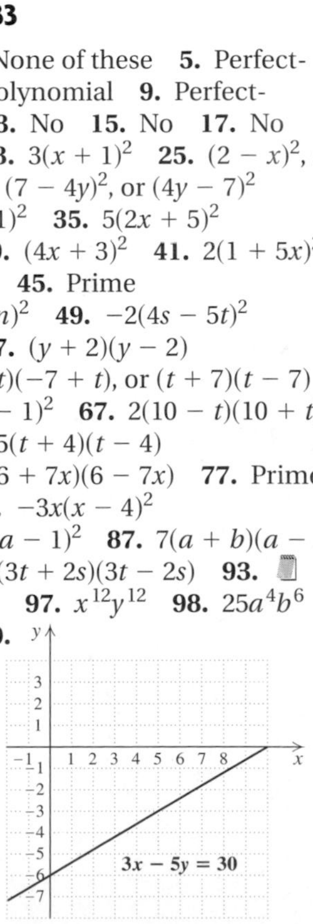

101. **103.** $(x^4 + 2^4)(x^2 + 2^2)(x + 2)(x - 2)$, or $(x^4 + 16)(x^2 + 4)(x + 2)(x - 2)$ **105.** $2x(3x - \frac{2}{5})(3x + \frac{2}{5})$
107. $(y^2 - 10y + 25 + z^4)(y - 5 + z^2)(y - 5 - z^2)$
109. $-1(x^2 + 1)(x + 3)(x - 3)$, or $-(x^2 + 1)(x + 3)(x - 3)$
111. $(y + 4)^2$ **113.** $(3x - 7)^2(3x + 7)$
115. $(9 + b^{2k})(3 + b^k)(3 - b^k)$ **117.** $2x^3 - x^2 - 1$
119. $(y + x + 7)(y - x - 1)$ **121.** 16
123. $(x + 1)^2 - x^2 = [(x + 1) + x][(x + 1) - x] = 2x + 1 = (x + 1) + x$

Exercise Set 5.5, pp. 338–339

1. Common factor **3.** Grouping **5.** $10(a + 8)(a - 8)$
7. $(y - 7)^2$ **9.** $(2t + 3)(t + 4)$ **11.** $x(x - 9)^2$
13. $(x - 5)^2(x + 5)$ **15.** $3t(3t + 1)(3t - 1)$
17. $3x(3x - 5)(x + 3)$ **19.** Prime **21.** $3(x + 3)(2x - 5)$
23. $-2a^4(a - 2)^2$ **25.** $5x(x^2 + 4)(x + 2)(x - 2)$
27. $(t^2 + 3)(t^2 - 3)$ **29.** $-x^4(x^2 - 2x + 7)$
31. $(pq + r)(pq - r)$ **33.** $a(x^2 + y^2)$ **35.** $9mn(4 - mn)$
37. $2\pi r(h + r)$ **39.** $(a + b)(5a + 3b)$ **41.** $(x + 1)(x + y)$
43. $(a - 3)(a + y)$ **45.** $(3x - 2y)(x + 5y)$
47. $(a - 2b)^2$ **49.** $(4x + 3y)^2$ **51.** Prime
53. $(a^2b^2 + 4)(ab + 2)(ab - 2)$ **55.** $p(4p^2 + 4pq - q^2)$
57. $(3b - a)(b + 6a)$ **59.** $-1(xy + 2)(xy + 6)$, or $-(xy + 2)(xy + 6)$ **61.** $(pq + 6)(pq + 1)$
63. $b^4(ab - 4)(ab + 8)$ **65.** $x^4(x + 2y)(x - y)$
67. $(6a - \frac{5}{4})^2$ **69.** $(\frac{1}{9}x - \frac{4}{3})^2$
71. $(1 + 4x^6y^6)(1 + 2x^3y^3)(1 - 2x^3y^3)$ **73.** $(2ab + 3)^2$
75. $a(a^2 + 8)(a + 8)$ **77.**
79. For $(-1, 11)$:

$y = -4x + 7$	
11	$-4(-1) + 7$
	$4 + 7$

$11 \stackrel{?}{=} 11$ True

For $(0, 7)$:

$y = -4x + 7$	
7	$-4 \cdot 0 + 7$
	$0 + 7$

$7 \stackrel{?}{=} 7$ True

For $(3, -5)$:

$y = -4x + 7$	
-5	$-4 \cdot 3 + 7$
	$-12 + 7$

$-5 \stackrel{?}{=} -5$ True

80. $\frac{4}{5}$ **81.** $-\frac{7}{3}$ **82.** $-\frac{9}{2}$ **83.** $\frac{9}{4}$
84.

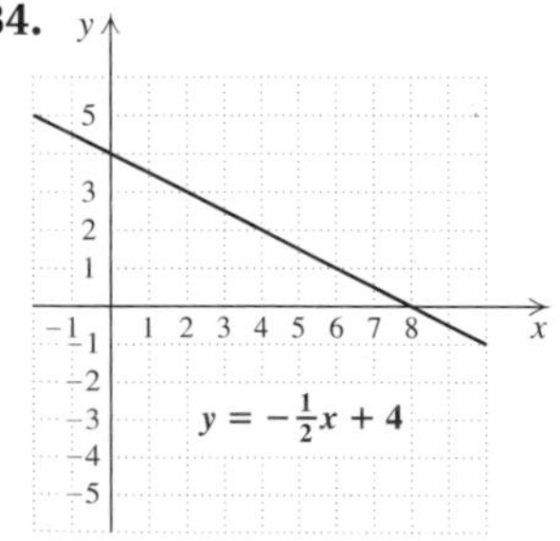

85.
87. $-x(x^2 + 9)(x^2 - 2)$
89. $-3(a + 1)(a - 1)(a + 2)(a - 2)$
91. $(y + 1)(y - 7)(y + 3)$ **93.** $(2x - 2 + 3y)(3x - 3 - y)$
95. $(a + 3)^2(2a + b + 4)(a - b + 5)$

Technology Connection, p. 345

1. −4.65, 0.65 **2.** −0.37, 5.37 **3.** −8.98, −4.56
4. No solution **5.** 0, 2.76

Exercise Set 5.6, pp. 345–347

1. (c) **3.** (a) **5.** −7, −5 **7.** −6, 3 **9.** $-4, \frac{9}{2}$ **11.** $-\frac{7}{4}, \frac{9}{10}$
13. −2, 0 **15.** $\frac{1}{21}, \frac{18}{11}$ **17.** $-\frac{9}{2}, 0$ **19.** 50, 70 **21.** 1, 6
23. −7, 3 **25.** −7, −2 **27.** 0, 6 **29.** −6, 0 **31.** $-\frac{2}{3}, \frac{2}{3}$
33. −5 **35.** 1 **37.** 0, 2 **39.** $-\frac{5}{3}, 4$ **41.** −5, −1
43. 3 **45.** $0, \frac{3}{2}$ **47.** $-\frac{5}{9}, \frac{5}{9}$ **49.** $-1, \frac{6}{5}$ **51.** −2, 9
53. $-\frac{5}{2}, \frac{4}{3}$ **55.** −3, 2 **57.** −1, 3 **59.** (−4, 0), (1, 0)
61. (−3, 0), (5, 0) **63.** $(-\frac{5}{2}, 0)$, (2, 0) **65.** **67.** $(a + b)^2$
68. $a^2 + b^2$ **69.** Let x represent the first integer; $x + (x + 1)$ **70.** Let x represent the number; $2x + 5 < 19$
71. Let x represent the number; $\frac{1}{2}x - 7 > 24$ **72.** Let x represent the number; $x - 3 \geq 34$ **73.** **75.** $-7, -\frac{8}{3}, \frac{5}{2}$
77. **(a)** $x^2 - x - 20 = 0$; **(b)** $x^2 - 6x - 7 = 0$; **(c)** $4x^2 - 13x + 3 = 0$; **(d)** $6x^2 - 5x + 1 = 0$; **(e)** $12x^2 - 17x + 6 = 0$; **(f)** $x^3 - 4x^2 + x + 6 = 0$
79. −5, 4 **81.** $-\frac{3}{5}, \frac{3}{5}$ **83.** −4, 2
85. **(a)** $2x^2 + 20x - 4 = 0$; **(b)** $x^2 - 3x - 18 = 0$; **(c)** $(x + 1)(5x - 5) = 0$; **(d)** $(2x + 8)(2x - 5) = 0$; **(e)** $4x^2 + 8x + 36 = 0$; **(f)** $9x^2 - 12x + 24 = 0$ **87.**
89. −0.25, 0.88 **91.** −3.23, 4.55 **93.** −3.76, 0

Exercise Set 5.7, pp. 354–358

1. −4, 5 **3.** 9 cm, 12 cm, 15 cm **5.** 9, 10 **7.** −17 and −15; 15 and 17 **9.** Length: 12 ft; width: 2 ft
11. Length: 6 cm; width: 4 cm **13.** Base: 14 cm; height: 4 cm **15.** Foot: 7 ft; height: 12 ft **17.** 1 min, 3 min
19. 16 teams **21.** 105 handshakes **23.** 12 players
25. 9 ft **27.** 25 ft **29.** Dining room: 12 ft by 12 ft; kitchen: 12 ft by 10 ft **31.** 20 ft **33.** 1 sec, 2 sec
35. **37.** $-\frac{8}{21}$ **38.** $-\frac{8}{45}$ **39.** $-\frac{35}{54}$ **40.** $-\frac{5}{16}$ **41.** $-\frac{2}{21}$
42. $-\frac{26}{45}$ **43.** $\frac{1}{18}$ **44.** $-\frac{11}{24}$ **45.** **47.** \$1200
49. 39 cm **51.** 15 cm by 30 cm **53.** 35 ft
55. 2 hr, 4.2 hr **57.** 3 hr

Review Exercises: Chapter 5, pp. 360–361

1. False **2.** True **3.** True **4.** False **5.** True **6.** False
7. True **8.** False **9.** Answers may vary. $(12x)(3x^2)$, $(-9x^2)(-4x)$, $(6x)(6x^2)$ **10.** Answers may vary. $(-4x^3)(5x^2)$, $(2x^4)(-10x)$, $(-5x)(4x^4)$ **11.** $6x^3(2x - 3)$
12. $4a(2a - 3)$ **13.** $(2t - 3)(2t + 3)$ **14.** $(x - 2)(x + 6)$
15. $(x + 7)^2$ **16.** $3x(2x + 1)^2$ **17.** $(2x + 3)(3x^2 + 1)$
18. $(6t + 1)(t - 1)$ **19.** $(5t - 3)^2$ **20.** $2(24t^2 - 14t + 3)$
21. $(9a^2 + 1)(3a + 1)(3a - 1)$ **22.** $3x(3x - 5)(x + 3)$

23. $2(x-5)(x+5)$ **24.** $(x+4)(x^3-2)$
25. $(ab^2-6)(ab^2+6)$ **26.** $-4x^4(2x^2-8x+1)$
27. $3(2x-5)^2$ **28.** Prime **29.** $-x(x-6)(x+5)$
30. $(2x+5)(2x-5)$ **31.** $2z(2z-3)$ **32.** $5z(3+2z)$
33. $(4t+5)(t+2)$ **34.** $(2t+1)(t-4)$
35. $7x(x+1)(x+4)$ **36.** $5x(x+2)(x+5)$
37. $2(3x-1)^2$ **38.** $-3(x+3)(x-3)$ **39.** $(5-x)(3-x)$
40. $(5x-2)^2$ **41.** $(xy-3)(xy+4)$ **42.** $3(2a+7b)^2$
43. $(m+5)(m+t)$ **44.** $32(x^2+2y^2z^2)(x^2-2y^2z^2)$
45. $(2m+n)(3m+n)$ **46.** Prime **47.** $-8, 7$ **48.** $-7, 5$
49. $-\frac{1}{3}, \frac{1}{3}$ **50.** $\frac{2}{3}, 1$ **51.** $-\frac{3}{2}, 4$ **52.** $-2, 3$ **53.** $0, \frac{3}{4}$
54. $0, \frac{4}{3}$ **55.** $-3, 4$ **56.** 10 teams **57.** $(-1, 0), (\frac{5}{2}, 0)$
58. Height: 40 cm; base: 40 cm **59.** 24 ft
60. Answers may vary. Because Edith did not first factor out the largest common factor, 4, her factorization will not be "complete" until she removes a common factor of 2 from each binomial. The answer should be $4(x-5)(x+5)$. Awarding 3 to 7 points would seem reasonable.
61. The equations solved in this chapter have an x^2-term (are quadratic), whereas those solved previously have no x^2-term (are linear). The principle of zero products is used to solve quadratic equations and is not used to solve linear equations. **62.** 2.5 cm **63.** 0, 2
64. Length: 12 cm; width: 6 cm **65.** 100 cm², 225 cm²
66. $-3, 2, \frac{5}{2}$ **67.** No real solution

Test: Chapter 5, pp. 361–362

1. [5.1] $(2x)(4x^3), (-4x^2)(-2x^2), (8x)(x^3)$
2. [5.2] $(x-2)(x-5)$ **3.** [5.4] $(x-5)^2$
4. [5.1] $2y^2(2y^2-4y+3)$ **5.** [5.1] $(x+1)(x^2+2)$
6. [5.1] $t^5(t^2-3)$ **7.** [5.2] $x(x+3)(x-1)$
8. [5.3] $2(5x-6)(x+4)$ **9.** [5.4] $(2t+5)(2t-5)$
10. [5.2] $(x-4)(x+3)$ **11.** [5.3] $-3m(2m+1)(m+1)$
12. [5.4] $3(w+5)(w-5)$ **13.** [5.4] $5(3r+2)^2$
14. [5.4] $3(x^2+4)(x+2)(x-2)$ **15.** [5.4] $(7t+6)^2$
16. [5.3] $(5x-1)(x-5)$ **17.** [5.1] $(x+2)(x^3-3)$
18. [5.4] $5(4+x^2)(2+x)(2-x)$
19. [5.3] $(2x+3)(2x-5)$ **20.** [5.3] $3t(2t+5)(t-1)$
21. [5.3] $3(m-5n)(m+2n)$ **22.** [5.6] $-5, 4$
23. [5.6] $-\frac{3}{2}, 5$ **24.** [5.6] $-4, 7$ **25.** [5.6] $(-1, 0), (\frac{8}{3}, 0)$
26. [5.7] Length: 8 m; width: 6 m **27.** [5.7] 5 ft
28. [5.7] 4 in., 6 in. **29.** [5.7] Width: 3; length: 15
30. [5.2] $(a-4)(a+8)$ **31.** [5.6] $-\frac{8}{3}, 0, \frac{2}{5}$

CHAPTER 6

Technology Connection, p. 367

1. Correct **2.** Correct **3.** Not correct **4.** Not correct

Exercise Set 6.1, pp. 369–371

1. (e) **3.** (d) **5.** (c) **7.** 0 **9.** -8 **11.** 4 **13.** $-4, 7$
15. $-6, \frac{1}{2}$ **17.** $\frac{5a}{4b^2}$ **19.** $\frac{4}{3xy^4}$ **21.** $\frac{3}{1}$ **23.** $\frac{a-3}{a+1}$ **25.** $\frac{3}{2x^3}$
27. $\frac{y-3}{4y}$ **29.** $\frac{3(2a-1)}{7(a-1)}$ **31.** $\frac{t+4}{t+5}$ **33.** $\frac{a+4}{2(a-4)}$
35. $\frac{x+4}{x-4}$ **37.** $t-1$ **39.** $\frac{y^2+4}{y+2}$ **41.** $\frac{1}{2}$ **43.** $\frac{y}{2y+1}$
45. $\frac{2x-3}{5x+2}$ **47.** -1 **49.** -7 **51.** $-\frac{1}{3}$ **53.** $-\frac{3}{2}$ **55.** -1
57. **59.** $-\frac{4}{7}$ **60.** $-\frac{10}{33}$ **61.** $-\frac{15}{4}$ **62.** $-\frac{21}{16}$ **63.** $\frac{13}{63}$
64. $\frac{5}{48}$ **65.** **67.** $-(2y+x)$ **69.** $\frac{x^3+4}{(x^3+2)(x^2+2)}$
71. $\frac{(t-1)(t-9)^2}{(t+1)(t^2+9)}$ **73.** $\frac{(x-y)^3}{(x+y)^2(x-5y)}$ **75.**

Technology Connection, p. 374

1. Let $y_1 = ((x^2+3x+2)/(x^2+4))/(5x^2+10x)$ and $y_2 = (x+1)/((x^2+4)(5x))$. With the table set in AUTO mode, note that the values in the Y1- and Y2-columns match except for $x = -2$.
2. ERROR messages occur when division by 0 is attempted. Since the simplified expression has no factor of $x+5$ or $x+1$ in a denominator, no ERROR message occurs in Y2 for $x = -5$ or -1.

Exercise Set 6.2, pp. 374–376

1. $\frac{7x(x-5)}{5(2x+1)}$ **3.** $\frac{(a-4)(a+2)}{(a+6)^2}$ **5.** $\frac{(2x+3)(x+1)}{4(x-5)}$
7. $\frac{(a-4)(a+4)}{(a^2+4)(a^2-4)}$ **9.** $\frac{(x+6)(x-1)}{(3+x)(x+1)}$ **11.** $\frac{5a^2}{3}$
13. $\frac{4}{c^2d}$ **15.** $\frac{x+2}{x-2}$ **17.** $\frac{(a^2+25)(a-5)}{(a-3)(a-1)(a+5)}$
19. $\frac{7(a+3)}{a(a+4)}$ **21.** $\frac{2a}{a-2}$ **23.** $\frac{t-5}{t+5}$ **25.** $\frac{5(a+6)}{a-1}$
27. 1 **29.** $\frac{t+4}{t+2}$ **31.** $\frac{x+2}{x+3}$ **33.** $\frac{7}{3x}$ **35.** $\frac{1}{a^3-8a}$
37. $\frac{x^2-4x+7}{x^2+2x-5}$ **39.** $\frac{35}{24}$ **41.** $\frac{x^2}{20}$ **43.** $\frac{a^3}{b^3}$ **45.** $\frac{y+5}{2y}$
47. $4(y-2)$ **49.** $-\frac{a}{b}$ **51.** $\frac{(y+3)(y^2+1)}{y+1}$ **53.** $\frac{15}{16}$ **55.** $\frac{15}{4}$
57. $\frac{a-5}{3(a-1)}$ **59.** $\frac{(2x-1)(2x+1)}{x-5}$ **61.** $\frac{(a-5)(3a-4)}{(a+4)(2a-7)}$
63. $\frac{1}{(c-5)(5c-3)}$ **65.** $\frac{(x-4y)(x-y)}{(x+y)^3}$ **67.** **69.** $\frac{19}{12}$
70. $\frac{41}{24}$ **71.** $\frac{1}{18}$ **72.** $-\frac{1}{6}$ **73.** $-\frac{37}{20}$ **74.** $\frac{49}{45}$ **75.**
77. $\frac{a}{(c-3d)(2a+5b)}$ **79.** $\frac{1}{b^3(a-3b)}$ **81.** $\frac{a^2-2b}{a^2+3b}$
83. $\frac{(z+4)^3}{3(z-4)^2}$ **85.** $\frac{x(x^2+1)}{3(x+y-1)}$ **87.** $\frac{3(y+2)^3}{y(y-1)}$ **89.**

Exercise Set 6.3, pp. 384–387

1. Numerators; denominator **3.** Least common denominator; LCD **5.** $\frac{10}{x}$ **7.** $\frac{3x+5}{12}$ **9.** $\frac{9}{a+3}$ **11.** $\frac{6}{a+2}$ **13.** $\frac{2y+7}{2y}$ **15.** 11 **17.** $\frac{3x+5}{x+1}$ **19.** $a+5$ **21.** $x-4$ **23.** 0 **25.** $\frac{1}{x+2}$ **27.** $\frac{t-4}{t+3}$ **29.** $\frac{x+5}{x-6}$ **31.** $-\frac{5}{x-4}$, or $\frac{5}{4-x}$ **33.** $-\frac{1}{x-1}$, or $\frac{1}{1-x}$ **35.** 135 **37.** 72 **39.** 126 **41.** $12x^3$ **43.** $30a^4b^8$ **45.** $6(y-3)$ **47.** $(x-2)(x+2)(x+3)$ **49.** $t(t-4)(t+2)^2$ **51.** $30x^2y^2z^3$ **53.** $(a+1)(a-1)^2$ **55.** $(m-3)(m-2)^2$ **57.** $12x^3(x-5)(x-3)(x-1)$ **59.** $\frac{3a^3}{10a^6}, \frac{2b}{10a^6}$ **61.** $\frac{21y}{9x^4y^3}, \frac{4x^3}{9x^4y^3}$ **63.** $\frac{2x(x+3)}{(x-2)(x+2)(x+3)}, \frac{4x(x-2)}{(x-2)(x+2)(x+3)}$ **65.** **67.** $-\frac{7}{9}, \frac{-7}{9}$ **68.** $\frac{-3}{2}, \frac{3}{-2}$ **69.** $-\frac{11}{36}$ **70.** $-\frac{7}{60}$ **71.** $x^2-9x+18$ **72.** $s^2-\pi r^2$ **73.** **75.** $\frac{18x+5}{x-1}$ **77.** $\frac{x}{3x+1}$ **79.** 30 strands **81.** 60 strands **83.** $72(t+1)(t-1)^4$ **85.** 70 minutes **87.** 7:55 A.M. **89.**

Exercise Set 6.4, pp. 393–395

1. LCD **3.** Numerators; LCD **5.** $\frac{4x+9}{x^2}$ **7.** $-\frac{5}{24r}$ **9.** $\frac{2d^2+7c}{c^2d^3}$ **11.** $\frac{-2xy-18}{3x^2y^3}$ **13.** $\frac{5x+7}{18}$ **15.** $\frac{-x-4}{6}$ **17.** $\frac{a^2+16a+16}{16a^2}$ **19.** $\frac{7z-12}{12z}$ **21.** $\frac{x^2+4xy+y^2}{x^2y^2}$ **23.** $\frac{4x^2-13xt+9t^2}{3x^2t^2}$ **25.** $\frac{6x}{(x+2)(x-2)}$ **27.** $\frac{2x-40}{(x-5)(x+5)}$ **29.** $\frac{11x+2}{3x(x+1)}$ **31.** $\frac{3-5t}{2t(t-1)}$ **33.** $\frac{x^2+6x}{(x-4)(x+4)}$ **35.** $\frac{16}{3(z+4)}$ **37.** $\frac{3x-1}{(x-1)^2}$ **39.** $\frac{3x-14}{(x-2)(x+2)}$ **41.** $\frac{9a}{4(a-5)}$ **43.** 0 **45.** $\frac{10}{(a-3)(a+2)}$ **47.** $\frac{x-5}{(x+5)(x+3)}$ **49.** $\frac{3z^2+19z-20}{(z-2)^2(z+3)}$ **51.** $\frac{-5}{x^2+17x+16}$ **53.** $\frac{5x-3}{5}$ **55.** $y+3$ **57.** $\frac{2b-14}{b^2-16}$ **59.** $\frac{p^2+7p+1}{(p-5)(p+5)}$ **61.** $\frac{13x+20}{(4+x)(4-x)}$ **63.** $\frac{-a-2}{(a+1)(a-1)}$, or $\frac{a+2}{(1+a)(1-a)}$ **65.** $\frac{10x+6y}{(x-y)(x+y)}$ **67.** $\frac{2x-3}{2-x}$ **69.** 2 **71.** 0 **73.** **75.** $-\frac{13}{14}$ **76.** $-\frac{5}{9}$ **77.** $\frac{2}{15}$ **78.** $\frac{7}{6}$

79.

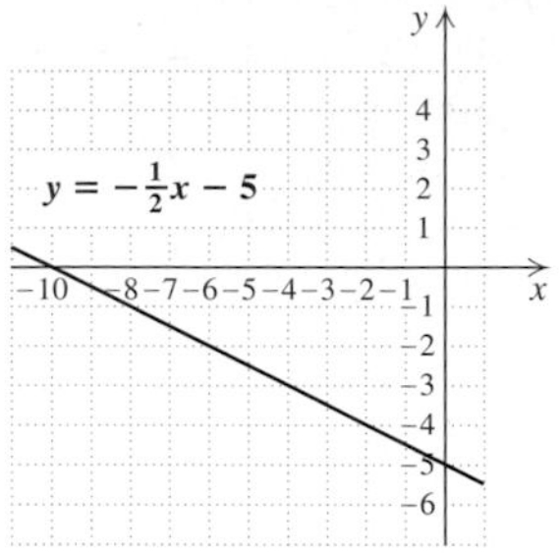

80.

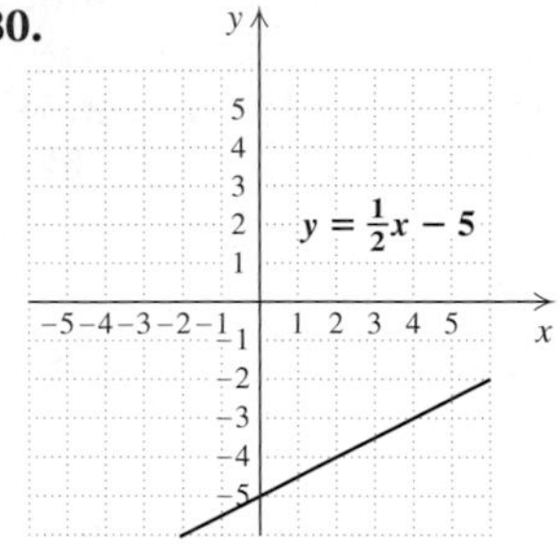

81. **83.** Perimeter: $\frac{10x-14}{(x-5)(x+4)}$; area: $\frac{6}{(x-5)(x+4)}$ **85.** $\frac{30}{(x-3)(x+4)}$ **87.** $\frac{x^4+4x^3-5x^2-126x-441}{(x+2)^2(x+7)^2}$ **89.** $\frac{-x^2-3}{(2x-3)(x-3)}$ **91.** $\frac{a}{a-b}+\frac{3b}{b-a}$; answers may vary. **93.** ,

Technology Connection, p. 400

1. $(1 - 1/x)/(1 - 1/x^2)$ **2.** Parentheses are needed to group separate terms into factors. When a fraction bar is replaced with a division sign, we need parentheses to preserve the groupings that had been created by the fraction bar. This holds for denominators and numerators alike.

Exercise Set 6.5, pp. 400–402

1. (d) **3.** (b) **5.** $\frac{6}{5}$ **7.** $\frac{117}{22}$ **9.** $\frac{4s^2}{9+3s^2}$ **11.** $\frac{4x}{3x+2}$ **13.** $\frac{4a-10}{a-7}$ **15.** $x-4$ **17.** $-\frac{1}{x}$ **19.** $\frac{1+t^2}{t-t^2}$ **21.** $\frac{x}{x-y}$ **23.** $\frac{2a^2+7a}{5-3a^2}$ **25.** $\frac{60-15a^3}{126a^2+28a^3}$ **27.** 1 **29.** $\frac{3a^2+4b^3}{5b^3-3a^2b^3}$ **31.** $\frac{2x^4-3x^2}{2x^4+3}$ **33.** $\frac{t^2-2}{t^2+5}$ **35.** $\frac{3a^2b^3+4a}{3b^2+ab^2}$ **37.** $\frac{t^2+5t+3}{(t+1)^2}$ **39.** $\frac{x^2-2x-1}{x^2-5x-4}$ **41.** **43.** -4 **44.** -4 **45.** $\frac{19}{3}$ **46.** $-\frac{14}{27}$ **47.** $-3, 10$ **48.** $-10, 2$ **49.** **51.** 6, 7, 8 **53.** $-\frac{4}{5}, \frac{9}{2}$ **55.** $\frac{P(i+12)^2}{12(i+24)}$ **57.** $\frac{(x-8)(x-1)(x+1)}{x^2(x-2)(x+2)}$ **59.** 0 **61.** $\frac{2z(5z-2)}{(z+2)(13z-6)}$ **63.**

Exercise Set 6.6, pp. 408–409

1. False **3.** True **5.** $-\frac{1}{2}$ **7.** $\frac{6}{7}$ **9.** $\frac{24}{7}$ **11.** $-5, -1$ **13.** $-6, 6$ **15.** 3 **17.** $\frac{14}{3}$ **19.** $\frac{35}{3}$ **21.** $-4, -3$ **23.** 5 **25.** $\frac{5}{2}$ **27.** -1 **29.** No solution **31.** -10 **33.** $\frac{10}{7}$ **35.** $-2, \frac{7}{3}$ **37.** No solution **39.** 2 **41.** No solution **43.** No solution **45.** **47.** 137, 139 **48.** 14 yd **49.** Base: 9 cm; height: 12 cm **50.** $-8, -6; 6, 8$ **51.** 0.06 cm per day **52.** 0.28 in. per day **53.** **55.** -2 **57.** $-\frac{1}{6}$ **59.** $-1, 0$ **61.** 4 **63.**

Exercise Set 6.7, pp. 417–422

1. 12 min **3.** $\frac{48}{7}$ hr, or 6 hr, $51\frac{3}{7}$ min **5.** $\frac{12}{7}$ hr, or 1 hr, $42\frac{6}{7}$ min **7.** $\frac{144}{7}$ hr, or 20 hr, $34\frac{2}{7}$ min **9.** $\frac{20}{9}$ days, or $2\frac{2}{9}$ days **11.** $\frac{36}{5}$ min, or $7\frac{1}{5}$ min

13.

	Distance (in km)	Speed (in km/h)	Time (in hours)
B & M	330	$r - 14$	$\frac{330}{r - 14}$
AMTRAK	400	r	$\frac{400}{r}$

AMTRAK: 80 km/h; B & M: 66 km/h

15. Bill: 50 mph; Hillary: 80 mph **17.** Ralph: 5 km/h; Bonnie: 8 km/h **19.** 3 hr **21.** 10.5 **23.** $\frac{8}{3}$ **25.** $3\frac{3}{4}$ in. **27.** 20 ft **29.** $2\frac{2}{7}$ ft **31.** 3.75 cm **33.** 12.6 **35.** 105 steps per minute **37.** 560 trees **39.** 1.92 g **41.** \$32,340 **43.** $7\frac{1}{2}$ **45.** 20 duds **47.** 287 **49.** 184 **51.** 40 **53.** **(a)** 1.92 T; **(b)** 28.8 lb **55.**

57.

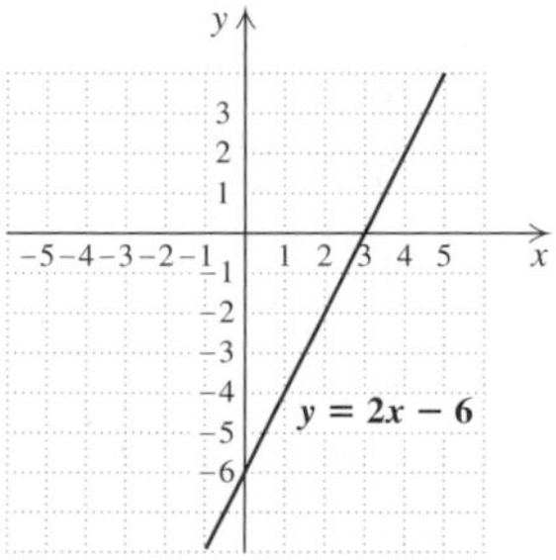

58.

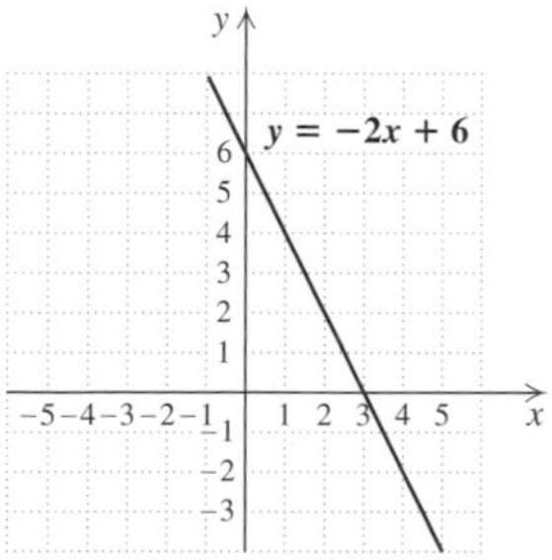

59.

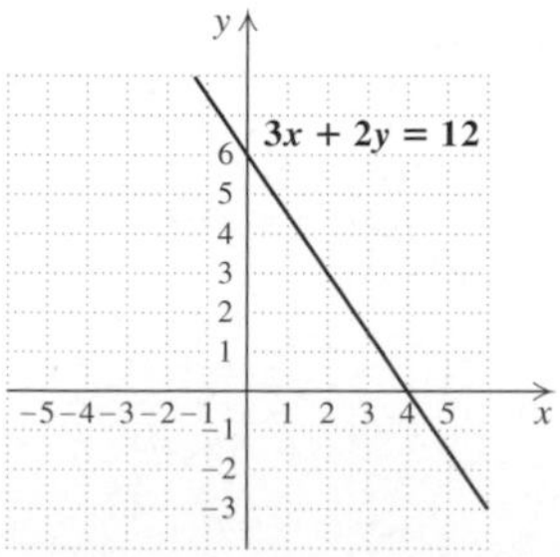

60.

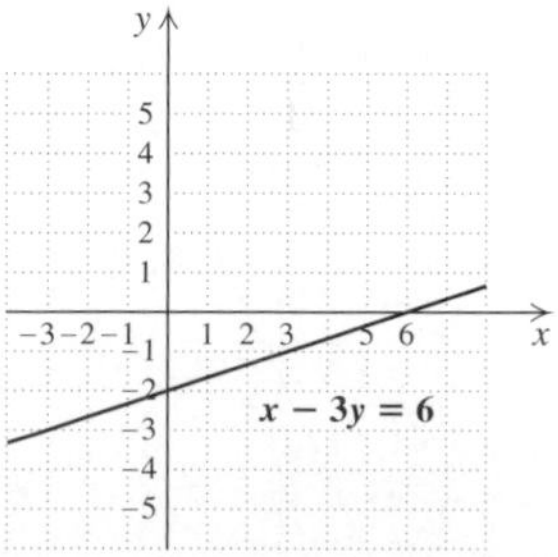

61.

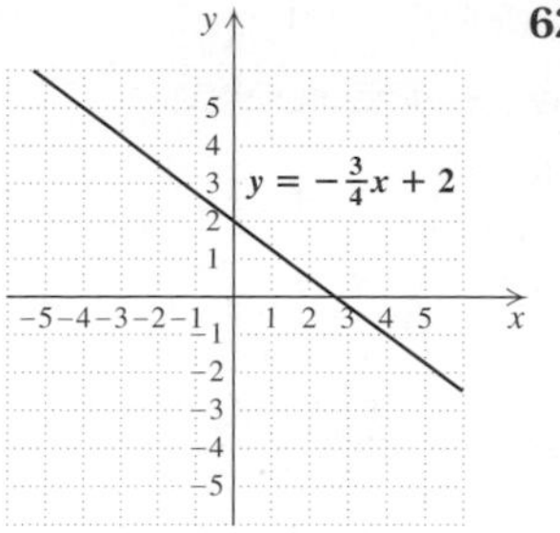

62.

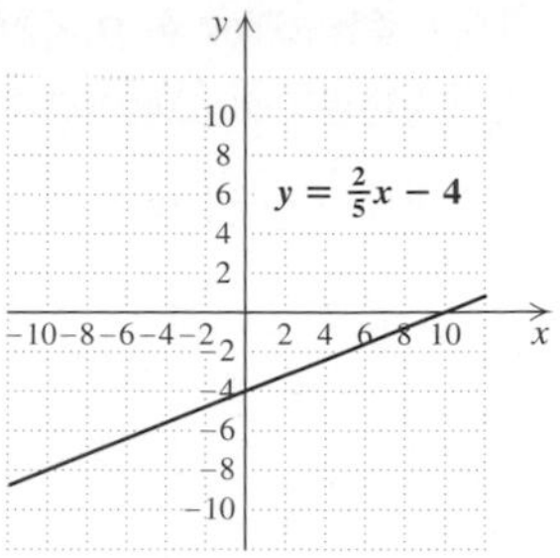

63. **65.** Ricki: 6 hr; Maura: 12 hr **67.** $9\frac{3}{13}$ days **69.** 12 hr **71.** Add 80 oz of gasoline. **73.** 45 mph **75.** $\frac{36}{68}$ **77.** $\frac{B}{A} = \frac{D}{C}; \frac{A}{C} = \frac{B}{D}; \frac{C}{A} = \frac{D}{B}$ **79.**

Review Exercises: Chapter 6, pp. 424–425

1. False **2.** True **3.** False **4.** True **5.** True **6.** False **7.** False **8.** False **9.** 0 **10.** 4 **11.** $-6, 6$ **12.** $-6, 5$ **13.** -2 **14.** $\frac{x-2}{x+1}$ **15.** $\frac{7x+3}{x-3}$ **16.** $\frac{y-5}{y+5}$ **17.** $-5(x+2y)$ **18.** $\frac{a-6}{5}$ **19.** $\frac{8(t+1)}{(2t-1)(t-1)}$ **20.** $-32t$ **21.** $\frac{2x(x-1)}{x+1}$ **22.** $\frac{(x^2+1)(2x+1)}{(x-2)(x+1)}$ **23.** $\frac{(t+4)^2}{t+1}$ **24.** $24a^5b^9$ **25.** $x^4(x-1)(x+1)$ **26.** $(y-2)(y+2)(y+1)$ **27.** $\frac{15-3x}{x+3}$ **28.** -1 **29.** $\frac{4}{x-4}$ **30.** $\frac{x+5}{2x}$ **31.** $\frac{2x+5}{x-2}$ **32.** $\frac{2a}{a-1}$ **33.** $d+c$ **34.** $\frac{-x^2+x+26}{(x+1)(x-5)(x+5)}$ **35.** $\frac{2(x-2)}{x+2}$ **36.** $\frac{19x+8}{10x(x+2)}$ **37.** $\frac{z}{1-z}$ **38.** $\frac{x^3(2xy^2+1)}{y(1+x)}$ **39.** $c-d$ **40.** 8 **41.** $-\frac{1}{2}$ **42.** $-5, 3$ **43.** $5\frac{1}{7}$ hr **44.** Car: 105 km/h; train: 90 km/h **45.** 60 **46.** 6 **47.** 28 doorbells **48.** The LCM of denominators is used to clear fractions when simplifying a complex rational expression using the method of multiplying by the LCD, and when solving rational equations. **49.** Although multiplying the denominators of the expressions being added results in a common denominator, it is often not the *least* common denominator. Using a common denominator other than the LCD makes the expressions more complicated, requires additional simplifying after the addition has been performed, and leaves more room for error. **50.** $\frac{5(a+3)^2}{a}$ **51.** $\frac{10a}{(a-b)(b-c)}$ **52.** 0 **53.** 44%

Test: Chapter 6, p. 426

1. [6.1] 0 **2.** [6.1] -8 **3.** [6.1] $-7, 7$ **4.** [6.1] 1, 2 **5.** [6.1] $\frac{3x+7}{x+3}$ **6.** [6.2] $\frac{-2(a+5)}{3}$ **7.** [6.2] $\frac{(5y+1)(y+1)}{3y(y+2)}$ **8.** [6.2] $\frac{(2x+1)(2x-1)(x^2+1)}{(x-1)^2(x-2)}$ **9.** [6.2] $(x+3)(x-3)$ **10.** [6.3] $(y-3)(y+3)(y+7)$ **11.** [6.3] $\frac{-3x+9}{x^3}$ **12.** [6.3] $\frac{-2t+8}{t^2+1}$ **13.** [6.4] $\frac{3}{3-x}$ **14.** [6.4] $\frac{2x-5}{x-3}$ **15.** [6.4] $\frac{11t-8}{t(t-2)}$ **16.** [6.4] $\frac{-x^2-7x-15}{(x+4)(x-4)(x+1)}$ **17.** [6.4] $\frac{x^2+2x-7}{(x+1)(x-1)^2}$ **18.** [6.5] $\frac{3y+1}{y}$ **19.** [6.5] $\frac{a^2(3b^2-2a)}{b^2(a^3+2)}$ **20.** [6.6] 12 **21.** [6.6] $-3, 5$ **22.** [6.7] 12 min **23.** [6.7] $2\frac{1}{7}$ cups **24.** [6.7] Craig: 65 km/h; Marilyn: 45 km/h **25.** [6.7] Rema: 4 hr; Reggie: 10 hr **26.** [6.5] a **27.** [6.7] -1

Cumulative Review: Chapters 1–6, pp. 427–428

1. $2b + a$ **2.** $>$ **3.** 25 **4.** $-8x + 28$ **5.** $-\frac{43}{8}$ **6.** 1 **7.** -6.2 **8.** 8 **9.** 10 **10.** $-7, 7$ **11.** $-\frac{10}{3}$ **12.** -3 **13.** $\frac{8}{3}$ **14.** $-10, -1$ **15.** -8 **16.** 1, 4 **17.** $\{y \mid y \le -\frac{2}{3}\}$ **18.** -17 **19.** $-4, \frac{1}{2}$ **20.** $\{x \mid x > 43\}$ **21.** 5 **22.** $-\frac{7}{2}, 5$ **23.** -13 **24.** $b = 3a - c + 9$ **25.** $y = \frac{4z-3x}{6}$ **26.** $\frac{3}{2}x + 2y - 3z$ **27.** $-4x^3 - \frac{1}{7}x^2 - 2$

28.

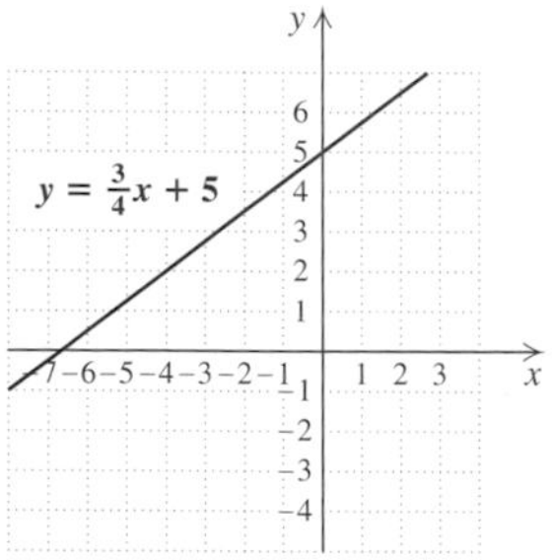

29.

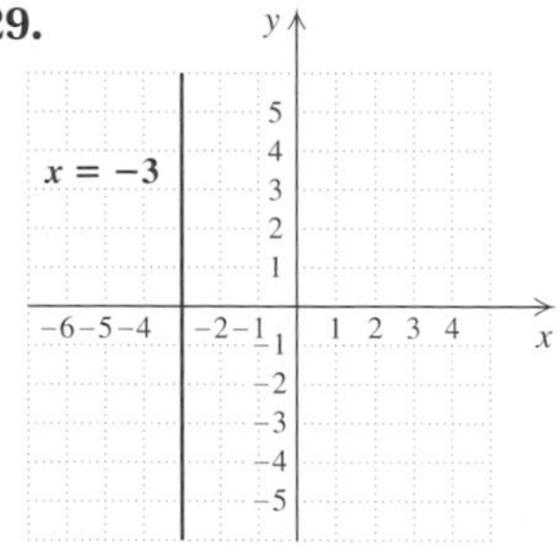

30.

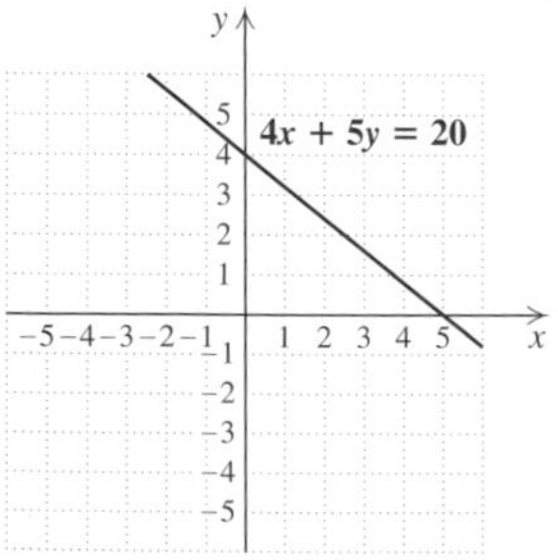

31.

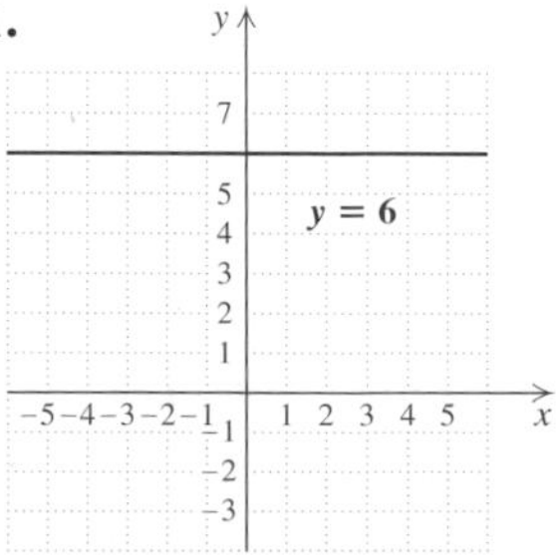

32. -2 **33.** $\frac{1}{x^2}$ **34.** y^{-6}, or $\frac{1}{y^6}$ **35.** $-4a^4b^{14}$ **36.** $-y^3 - 2y^2 - 2y + 7$ **37.** $15a - 10b + 5c$ **38.** $2x^5 + x^3 - 6x^2 - x + 3$ **39.** $36x^2 - 60xy + 25y^2$ **40.** $2x^2 + 11x - 40$ **41.** $4x^6 - 1$ **42.** $2x(3 - x - 12x^3)$ **43.** $(4x+9)(4x-9)$ **44.** $(t-4)(t-6)$ **45.** $(4x+3)(2x+1)$ **46.** $2(3x-2)(x-4)$ **47.** $4(t+3)(t-3)$ **48.** $(5t+4)^2$ **49.** $(3x-2)(x+4)$ **50.** $(x+2)(x^3-3)$ **51.** $\frac{y+6}{2}$ **52.** 1 **53.** $\frac{a^2+7ab+b^2}{(a+b)(a-b)}$ **54.** $\frac{2x+5}{4-x}$ **55.** $\frac{x}{x-2}$ **56.** $\frac{t(2t^2+1)}{t^3-2}$ **57.** $6x^2 - 5x + 2 + \frac{4}{x} + \frac{1}{x^2}$ **58.** $15x^3 - 57x^2 + 177x - 529 + \frac{1605}{x+3}$ **59.** At most 225 sheets **60.** \$3.60 **61.** 14 ft **62.** $-278, -276$ **63.** 30 min **64.** 50 **65.** 26 in. **66.** 12 **67.** $-144, 144$ **68.** $16y^6 - y^4 + 6y^2 - 9$ **69.** $2(a^{16} + 81b^{20})(a^8 + 9b^{10})(a^4 + 3b^5)(a^4 - 3b^5)$ **70.** $-7, 4, 12$ **71.** -7 **72.** 18 **73.** $66\frac{2}{3}\%$

CHAPTER 7

Technology Connection, p. 433

1.  **2.** $y_1 - y_2 = y_3 = -2$

Exercise Set 7.1, pp. 434–436

1. Both **3.** Consistent **5.** Yes **7.** No **9.** Yes **11.** (4, 3) **13.** (1, 3) **15.** (2, -1) **17.** No solution **19.** (6, -1) **21.** (5, -2) **23.** (3, -2) **25.** Infinite number of solutions **27.** (-6, -2) **29.** Infinite number of solutions **31.** (1, -3) **33.** (-8, -7) **35.** (3, -4) **37.** (2, 6)

39. 2;

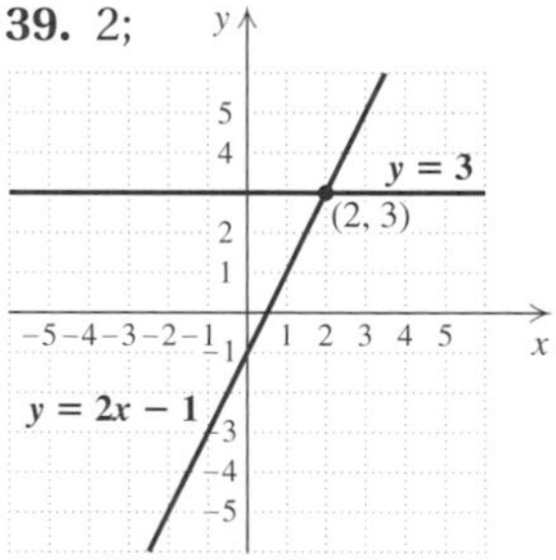

41. 5;

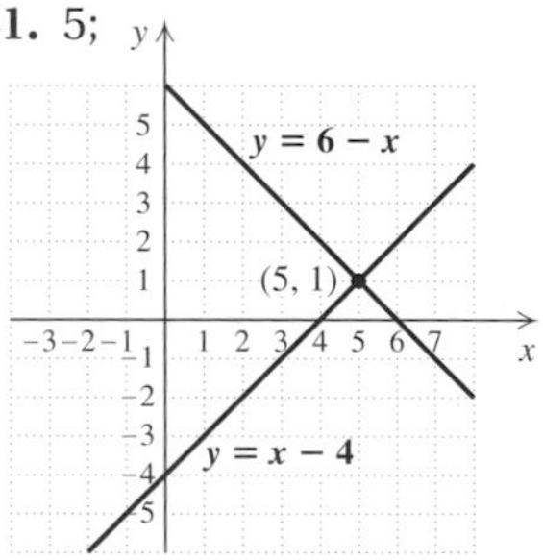

43. 2;

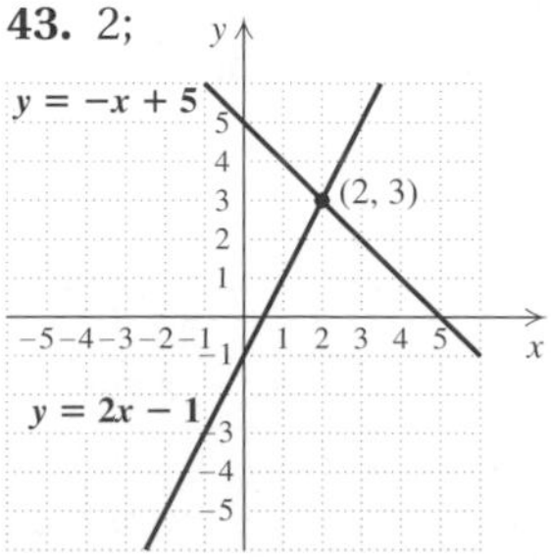

45. -4;

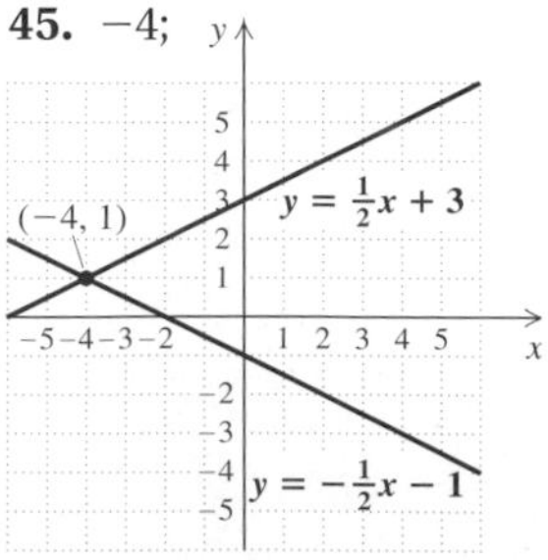

47. [icon] **49.** $\frac{26}{7}$ **50.** $\frac{15}{2}$ **51.** $\frac{6}{11}$ **52.** $\frac{9}{10}$ **53.** $b = \dfrac{3a - 7}{5}$
54. $r = \dfrac{-6s - 8}{5}$ **55.** [icon] **57.** Exercises 18, 25, 26, 29
59. Exercises 17 and 30 **61.** $2x + y = 2$. Answers may vary. **63.** $A = 2$; $B = 2$ **65.** **(a)** Copy card: $y = 20$; per page: $y = 0.06x$; **(b)**

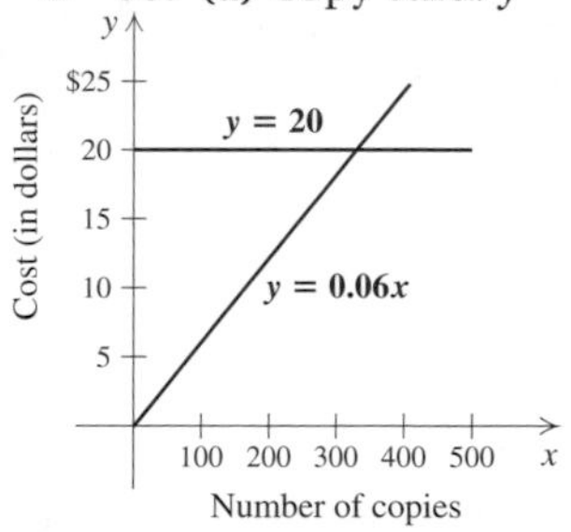

(c) more than 333 copies **67.** **(a)** Filmed: $n = 33.1 - 1.1t$; digital: $n = 2.8 + 2.9t$; **(b)** 2007 **69.** 2.24

Technology Connection, p. 439

1. [icon] **2.** Both equations change: The first becomes $y = 6 - \dfrac{x}{-2}$ and the second becomes $y = 4 - \dfrac{3x}{2}$.

Exercise Set 7.2, pp. 441–444

1. False **3.** True **5.** (2, 5) **7.** (2, 1) **9.** (4, 3) **11.** (2, −4) **13.** (−2, 4) **15.** No solution **17.** (−1, −3) **19.** $\left(\frac{17}{3}, \frac{2}{3}\right)$ **21.** Infinite number of solutions **23.** Infinite number of solutions **25.** $\left(\frac{25}{8}, -\frac{11}{4}\right)$ **27.** (−3, 0) **29.** (6, 3) **31.** No solution **33.** (−3, −4) **35.** No solution **37.** 39, 44 **39.** 42, 51 **41.** 12, 28 **43.** 55°, 125° **45.** 36°, 54° **47.** $1\frac{3}{4}$ in. by $3\frac{1}{2}$ in. **49.** Length: 380 mi; width: 270 mi **51.** Length: 90 yd; width: 50 yd **53.** Height: 20 ft; width: 5 ft **55.** [icon] **57.** $-5x - 3y$ **58.** $-11x$ **59.** $-11y$ **60.** $-6y - 25$ **61.** $-11y$ **62.** $23x$ **63.** [icon] **65.** (7, −1) **67.** (4.38, 4.33) **69.** 34 yr **71.** (30, 50, 100) **73.** [icon]

Exercise Set 7.3, pp. 450–452

1. False **3.** True **5.** (9, 3) **7.** (5, 1) **9.** (2, 7) **11.** (−1, 3) **13.** $\left(-1, \frac{1}{5}\right)$ **15.** Infinite number of solutions **17.** (−3, −5) **19.** (4, 5) **21.** (4, 1) **23.** No solution **25.** (1, −1) **27.** (−3, −1) **29.** No solution **31.** (50, 18) **33.** (−2, 2) **35.** (2, −1) **37.** $\left(\frac{231}{202}, \frac{117}{202}\right)$ **39.** 50 mi **41.** 26°, 64° **43.** 165 min **45.** 37°, 143° **47.** White: 92 loaves; whole-wheat: 83 loaves **49.** Length: 6 ft; width: 3 ft **51.** [icon] **53.** 0.08 **54.** 0.073 **55.** 0.004 **56.** 40% **57.** 31.5 **58.** 16% **59.** [icon] **61.** (2, 5) **63.** $\left(\frac{1}{2}, -\frac{1}{2}\right)$ **65.** (0, 3) **67.** $x = \dfrac{c - b}{a - 1}$; $y = \dfrac{ac - b}{a - 1}$ **69.** Rabbits: 12; pheasants: 23 **71.** Man: 45 yr; his daughter: 10 yr

Exercise Set 7.4, pp. 459–463

1. Two-pointers: 8; three-pointers: 3 **3.** Two-pointers: 38; three-pointers: 4 **5.** 3-credit courses: 19; 4-credit courses: 8 **7.** 5-cent bottles or cans: 336; 10-cent bottles or cans: 94 **9.** 2225 motorcycles **11.** 123 adult admissions **13.** Private lessons: 7 students; group lessons: 5 students **15.** 9 CDs; 5 videos **17.** Brazilian: 200 kg; Turkish: 100 kg **19.** Peanuts: 135 lb; Brazil nuts: 345 lb
21.

Type of Solution	50%-acid	80%-acid	68%-acid mix
Amount of Solution	x	y	200
Percent Acid	50%	80%	68%
Amount of Acid in Solution	$0.5x$	$0.8y$	136

80 mL of 50%; 120 mL of 80%
23. 100 L of 28%; 200 L of 40% **25.** 87-octane: 4 gal; 93-octane: 8 gal **27.** 1300-word pages: 7; 1850-word pages: 5 **29.** Foul shots: 28; two-pointers: 36 **31.** Kinney's: $33\frac{1}{3}$ fl oz; Coppertone: $16\frac{2}{3}$ fl oz **33.** Breadshop Supernatural: 20 lb; New England Natural Bakers Muesli: 20 lb **35.** [icon] **37.** $\{x \mid x > -5\}$ **38.** $\{x \mid x \leq -7\}$

39.

40.
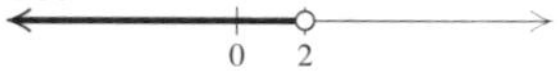

41.

42.

43. [icon] **45.** $19\frac{2}{7}$ lb **47.** 1.8 L **49.** 2.5 gal **51.** $13 **53.** 1300 gal **55.** 54 **57.** Tweedledum: 120 lb; Tweedledee: 121 lb

Technology Connection, p. 467

1.
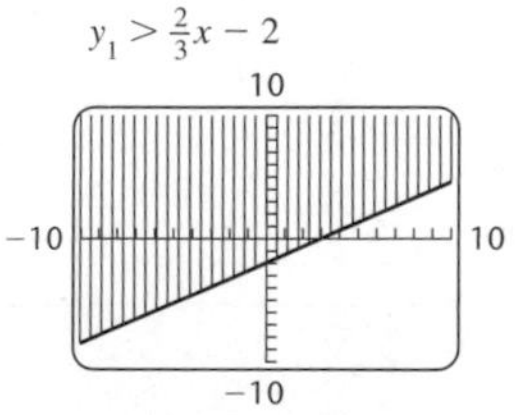

2.
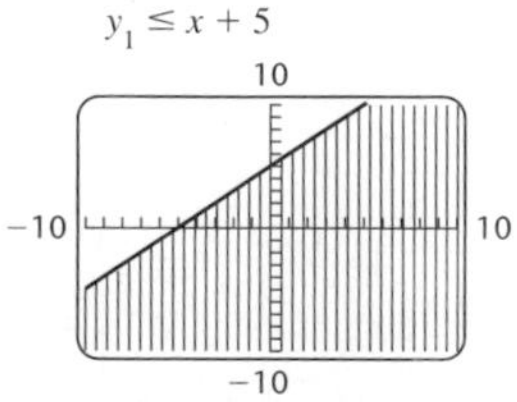

3.
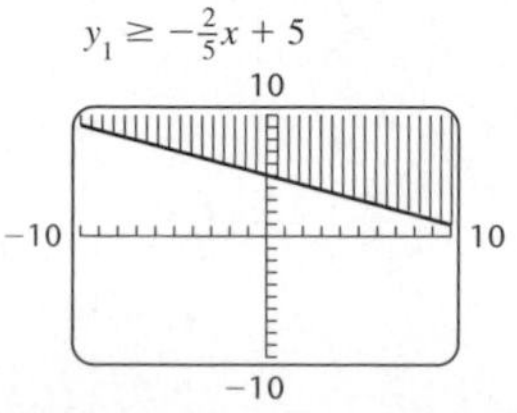

Exercise Set 7.5, pp. 467–468

1. True **3.** True **5.** No **7.** Yes

9.

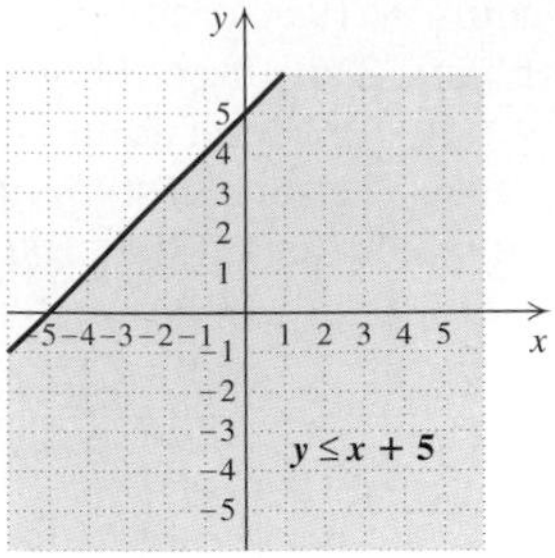

11.

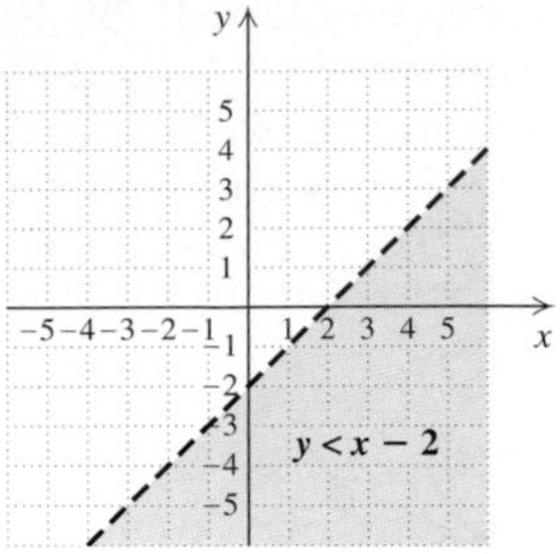

13.

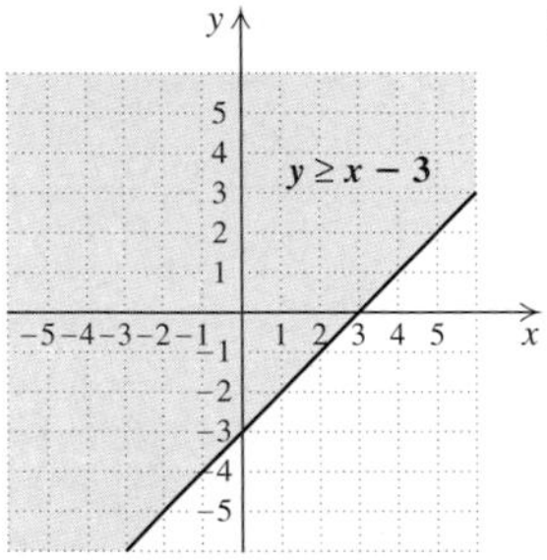

15.

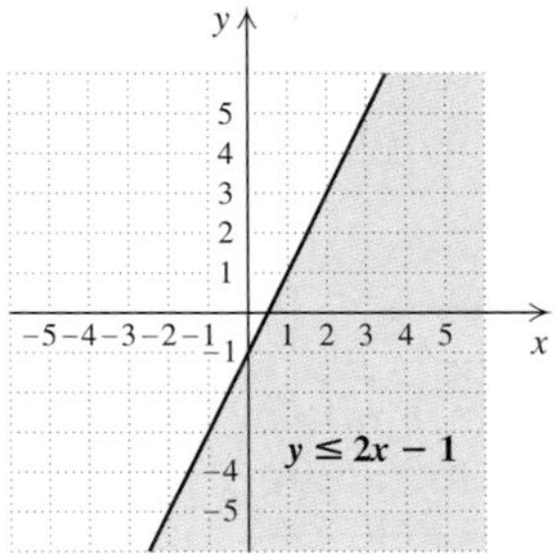

17.

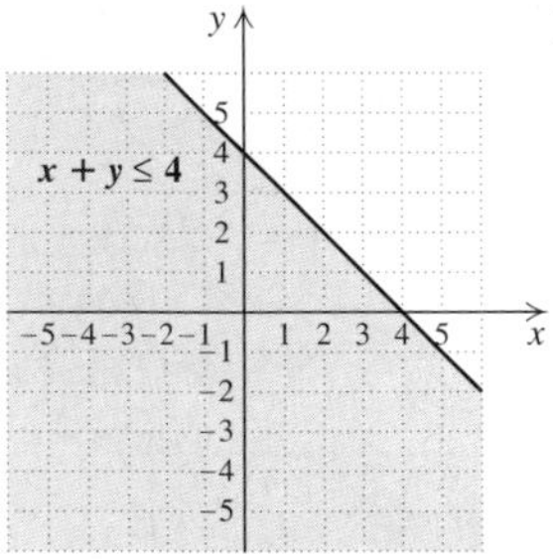

19.

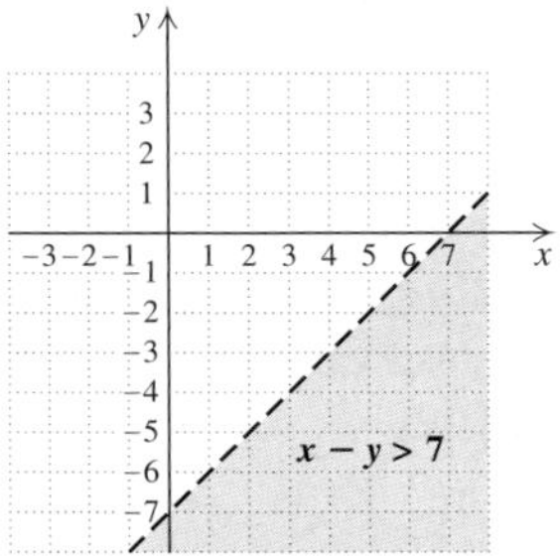

21.

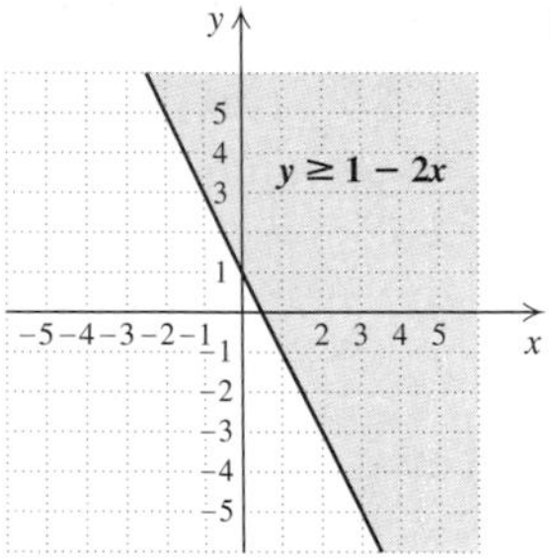

23.

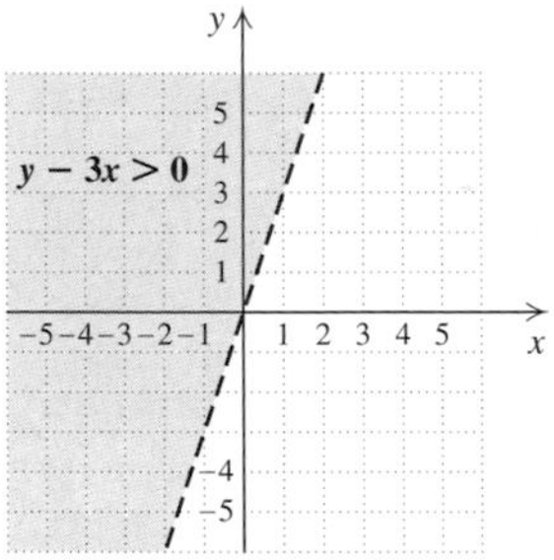

25.

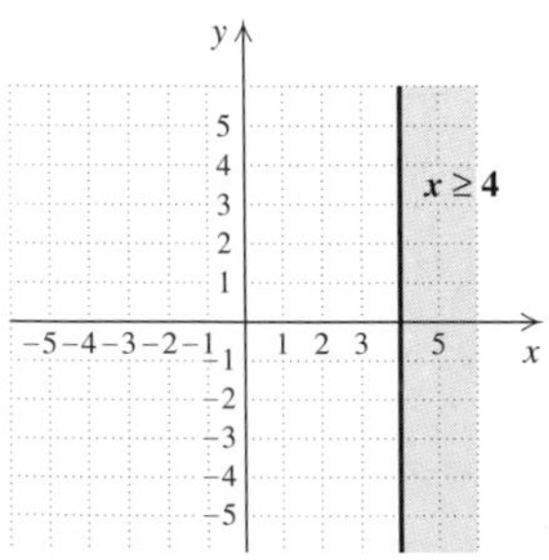

27.

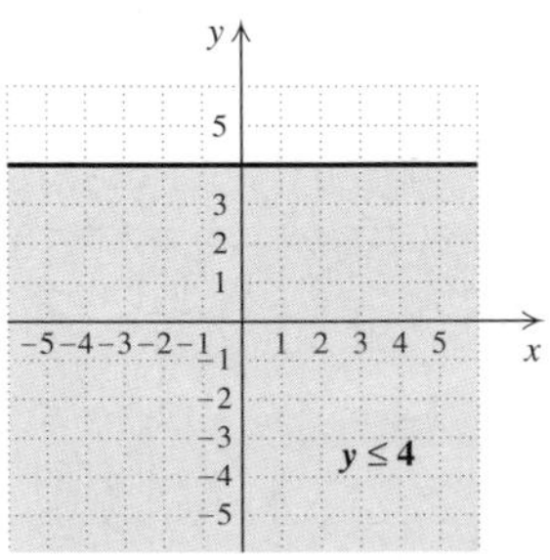

29.

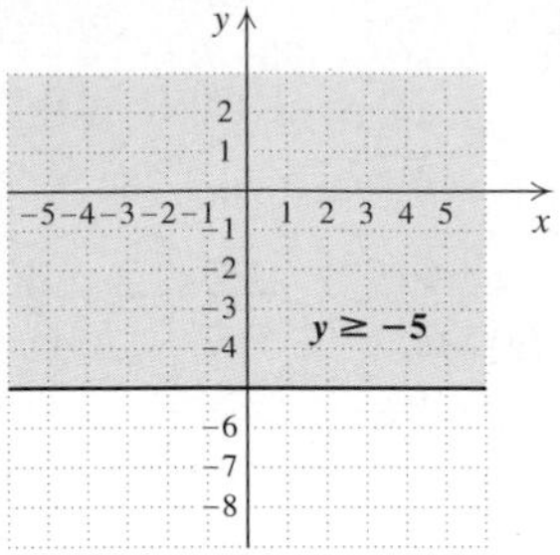

31.

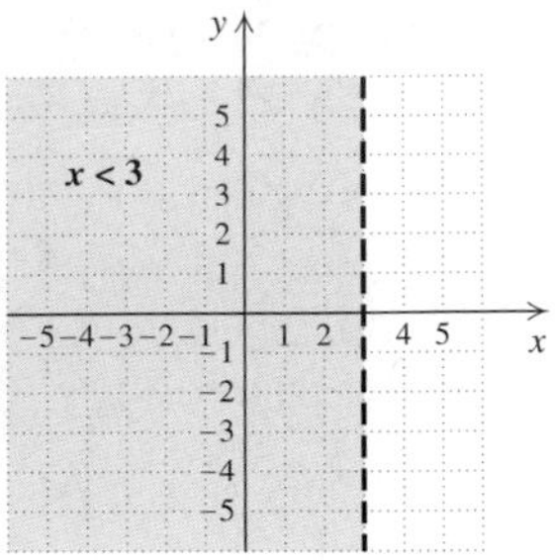

33.

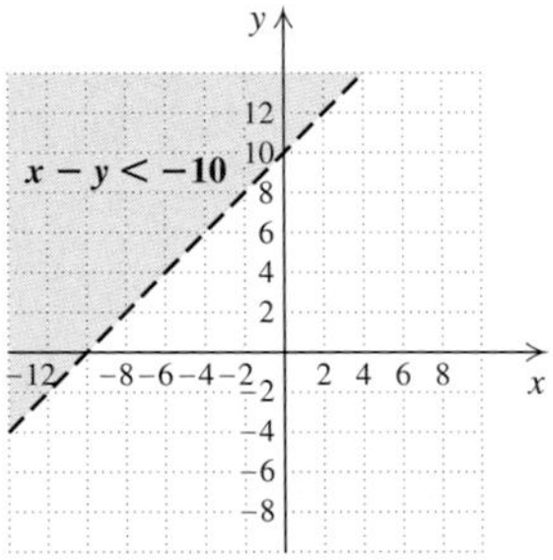

35.

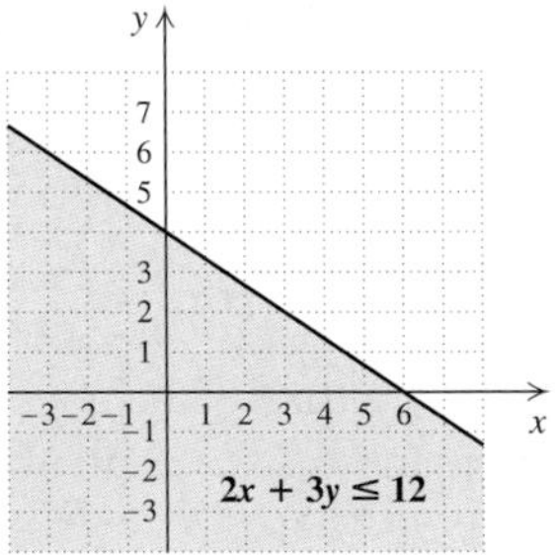

37. **39.** 14 **40.** 2 **41.** About \$100/ton **42.** Between June 1998 and December 1998 **43.** June 2000 **44.** December 1998 **45.** December 2000 to June 2001 and December 2002 to June 2003 **46.** December 2001 to June 2002 **47.** **49.** $75c + 150a > 1000$ **51.** $r + t \geq 17$

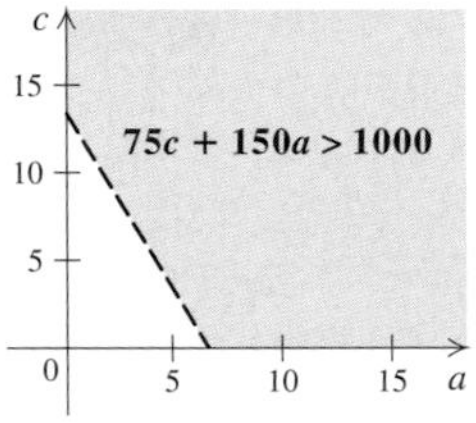

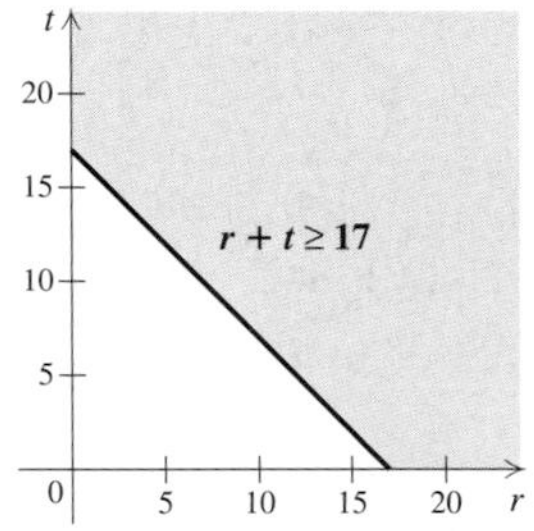

53. $y > x - 2$

55.

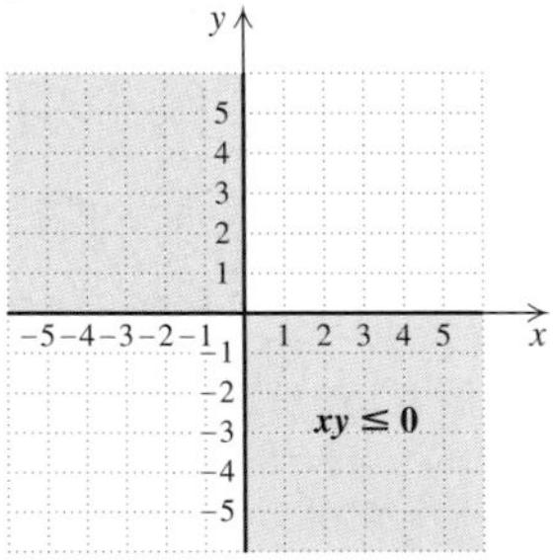

57.

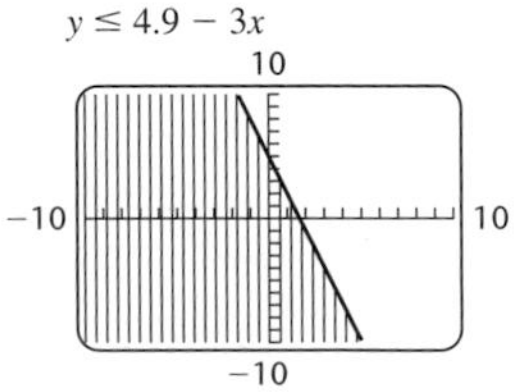

Exercise Set 7.6, p. 471

1.
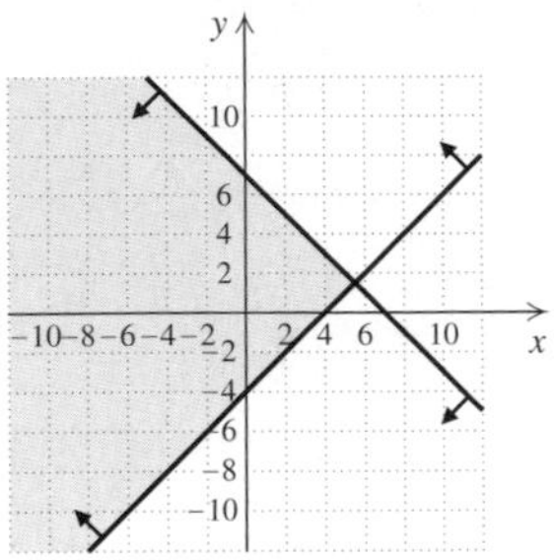

3.
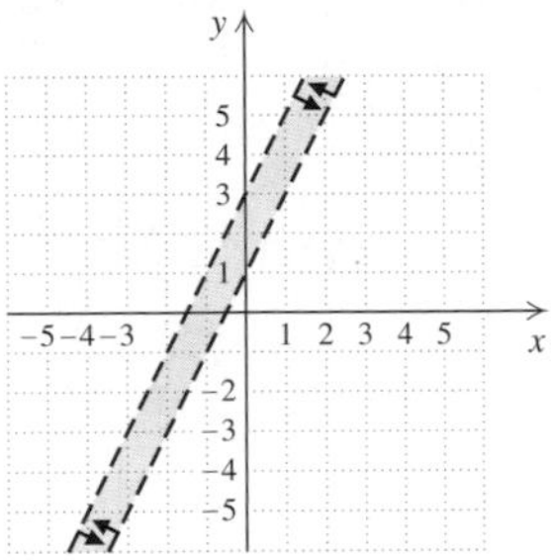

5.
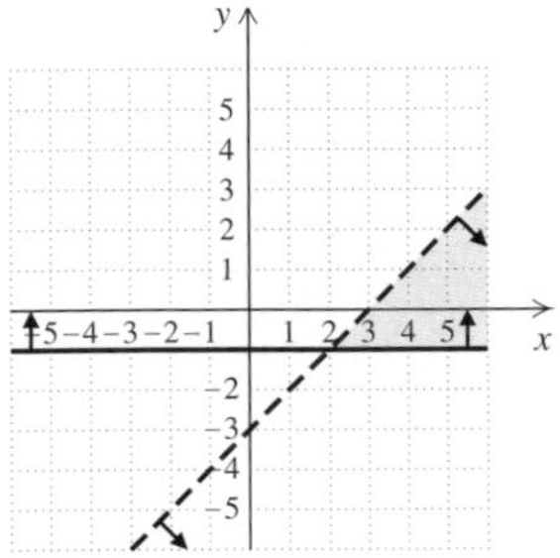

7.
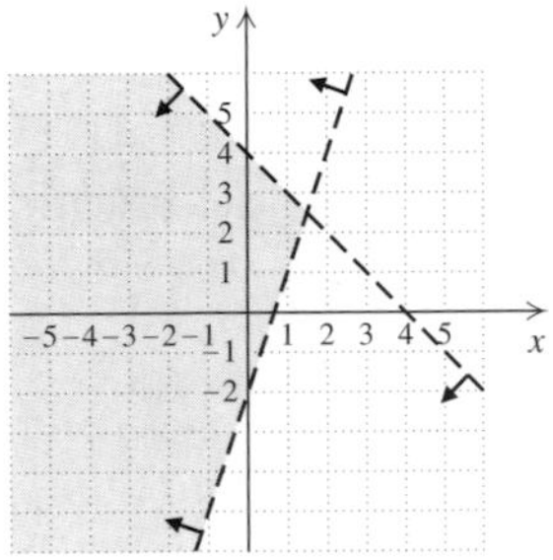

9.
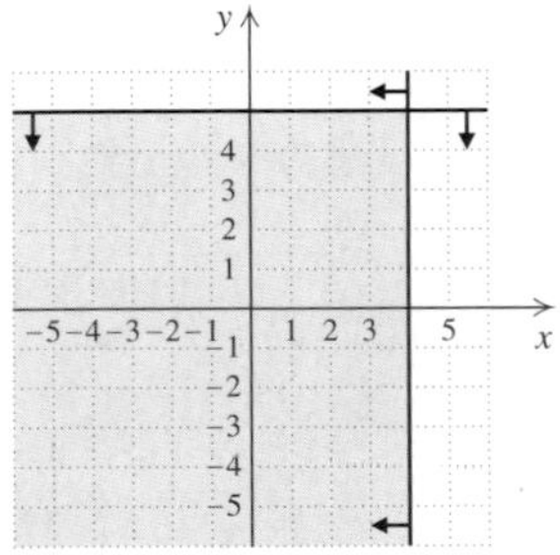

11.
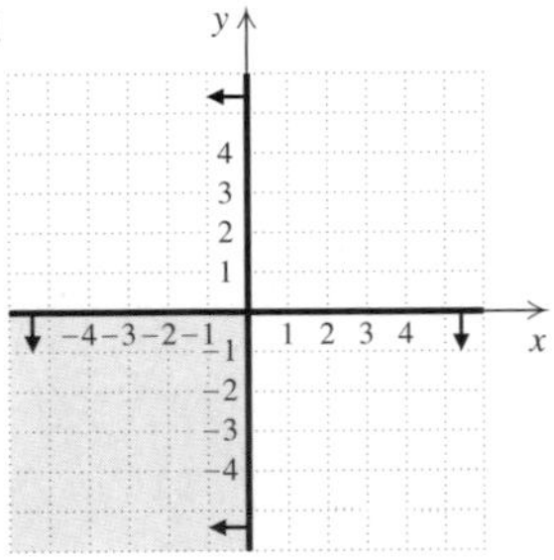

13.
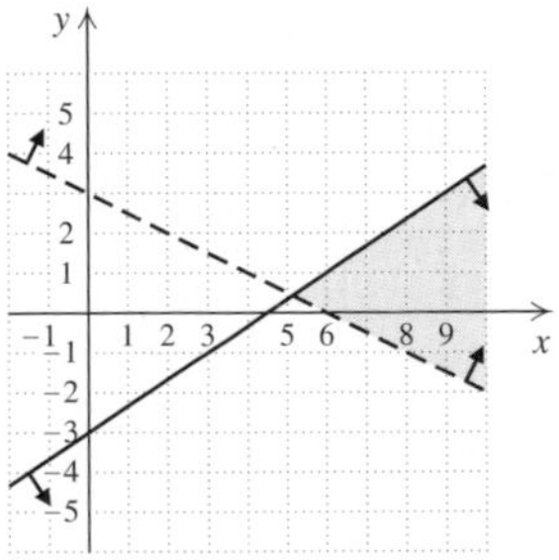

15.
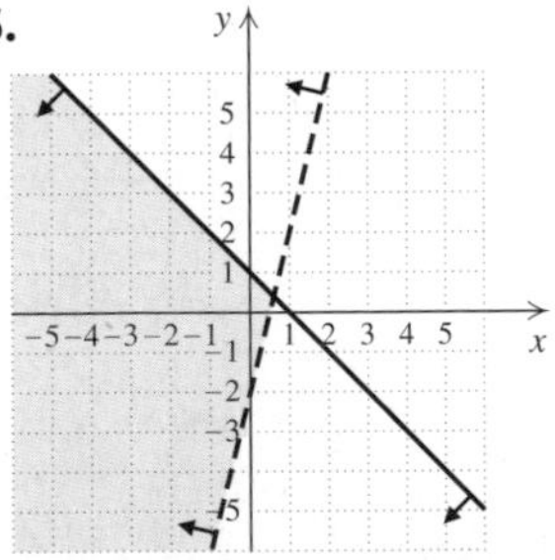

17.
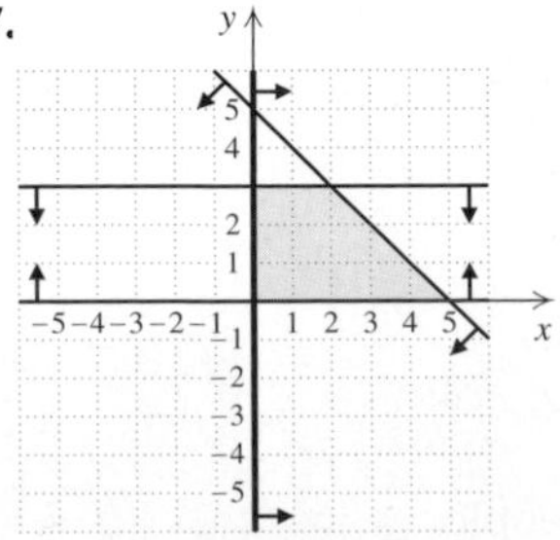

19.
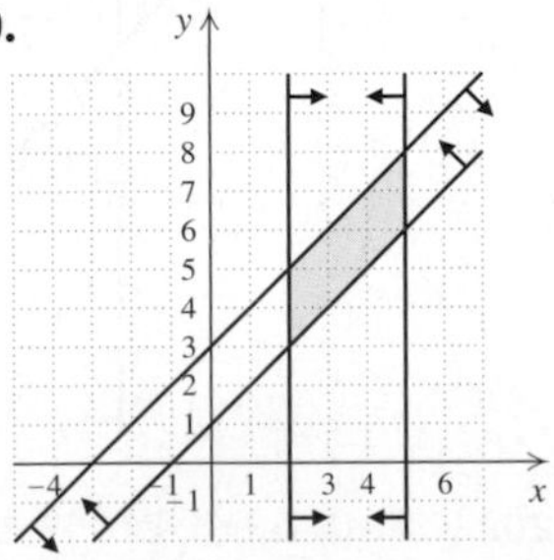

21.
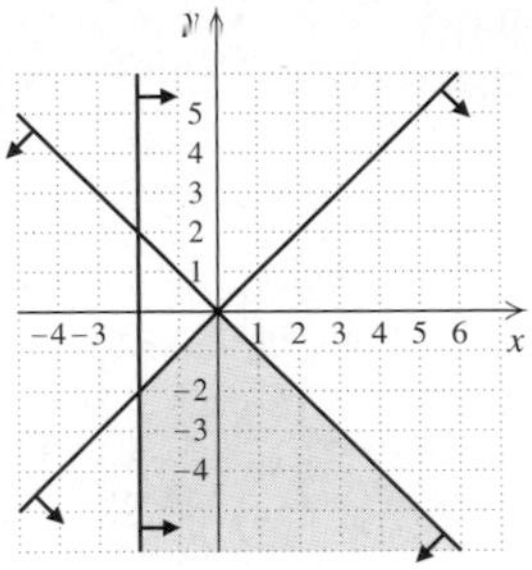

23. **25.** 35 **26.** 24

27. 6 **28.** 5 **29.** $\frac{1}{9}$ **30.** $\frac{1}{3}$ **31.**

33.
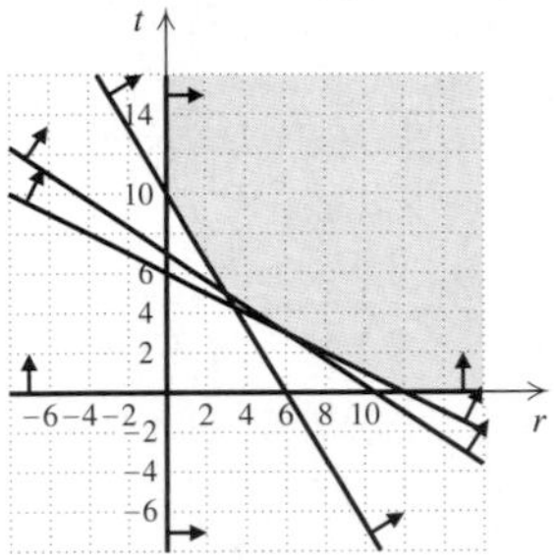

35.
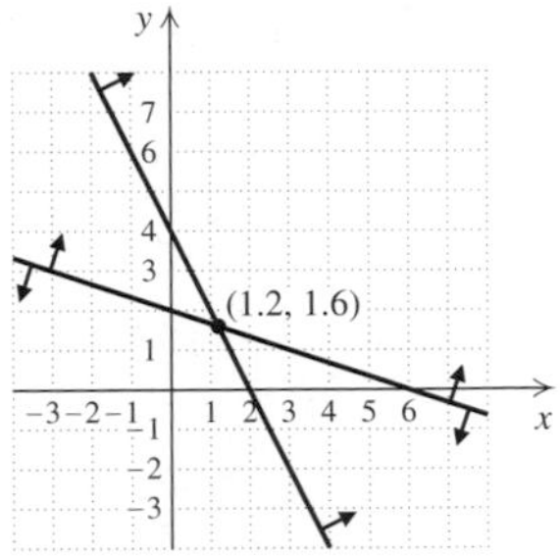

37. No solution **39.** **41.**
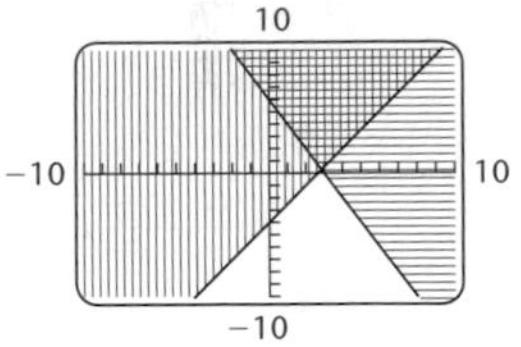

Exercise Set 7.7, pp. 477–478

1. Inverse variation **3.** Direct variation **5.** Inverse variation **7.** $y = 5x$ **9.** $y = \frac{7}{4}x$ **11.** $y = \frac{16}{3}x$ **13.** $y = \frac{2}{3}x$ **15.** $y = \frac{90}{x}$ **17.** $y = \frac{70}{x}$ **19.** $y = \frac{156.25}{x}$ **21.** $y = \frac{210}{x}$ **23.** \$207 **25.** 320 cm^3 **27.** About 30.8 lb **29.** 1.6 ft **31.** 54 min **33.** 15 people **35.** **37.** **39.** 49 **40.** 25 **41.** 169 **42.** 225 **43.** $9x^2$ **44.** $36a^2$ **45.** a^4b^2 **46.** s^6t^2 **47.** **49.** $P = kv^3$ **51.** $P^2 = kt$ **53.** $N = k \cdot \frac{T}{P}$ **55.** $P = 8S$ **57.** $A = \pi r^2$

Review Exercises: Chapter 7, pp. 480–481

1. Ordered **2.** Infinite **3.** Parallel **4.** Inexact **5.** Alone, or Isolated **6.** Coefficients **7.** Below **8.** Decreases **9.** Yes **10.** No **11.** $(1, -1)$ **12.** $(6, -2)$ **13.** No solution **14.** Infinite number of solutions **15.** $(-5, 9)$ **16.** $\left(\frac{10}{3}, \frac{4}{3}\right)$ **17.** No solution **18.** $(-3, 9)$ **19.** $(4, 5)$ **20.** Infinite number of solutions **21.** $\left(\frac{3}{2}, \frac{15}{4}\right)$ **22.** $(5, -3)$ **23.** Infinite number of solutions **24.** $(-2, 4)$ **25.** $(3, 2)$ **26.** $(3, 2)$ **27.** No solution **28.** $(-4, 2)$ **29.** Length: $37\frac{1}{2}$ cm; width: $10\frac{1}{2}$ cm **30.** Two-pointers: 7; three-pointers: 2 **31.** Fajitas: 11; Kid's Meals: 9 **32.** Café Rich: $66\frac{2}{3}$ g; Café Light: $133\frac{1}{3}$ g

33.

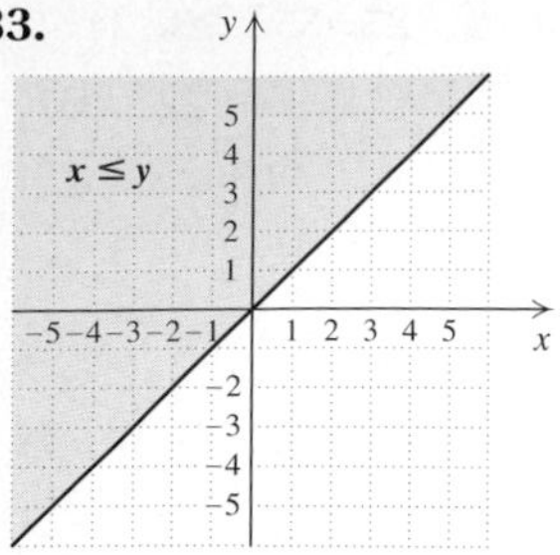

34.

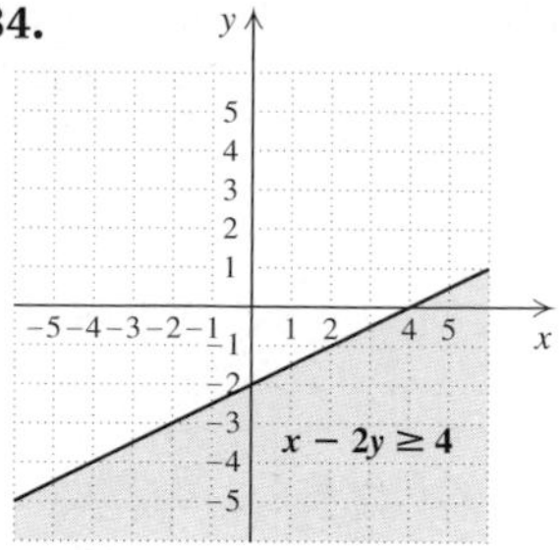

35.

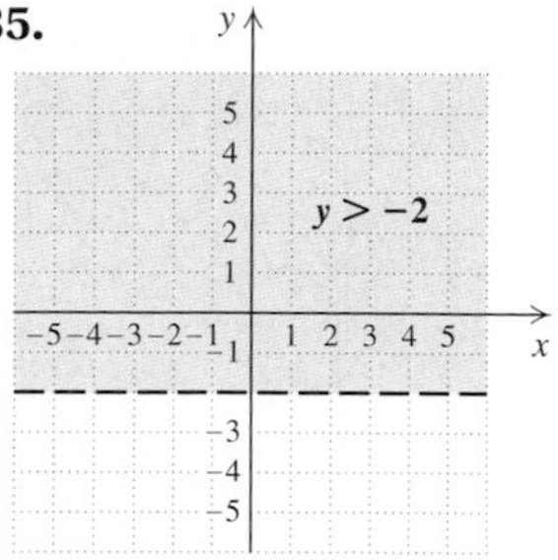

36.

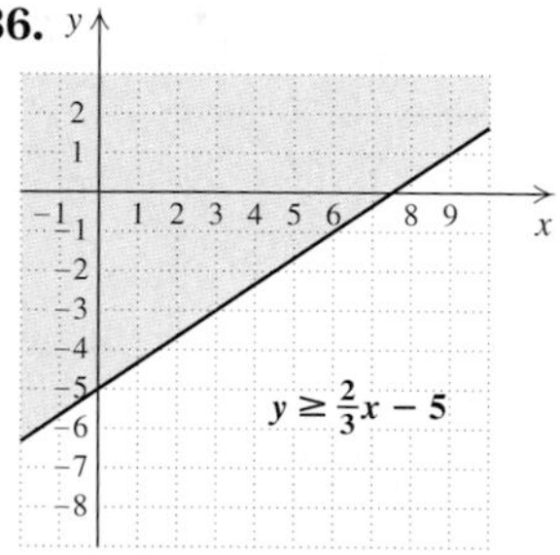

37.

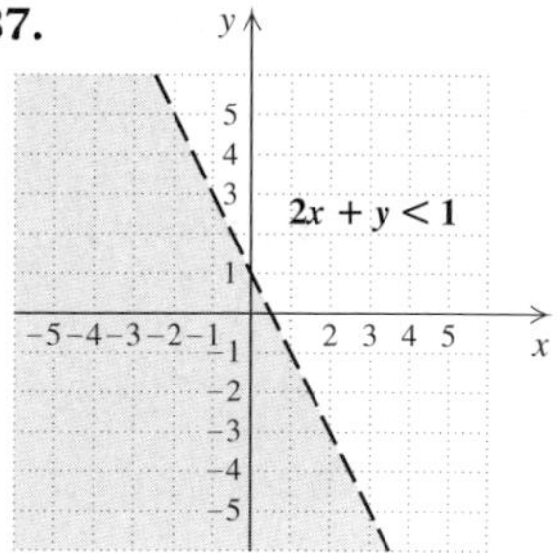

38.

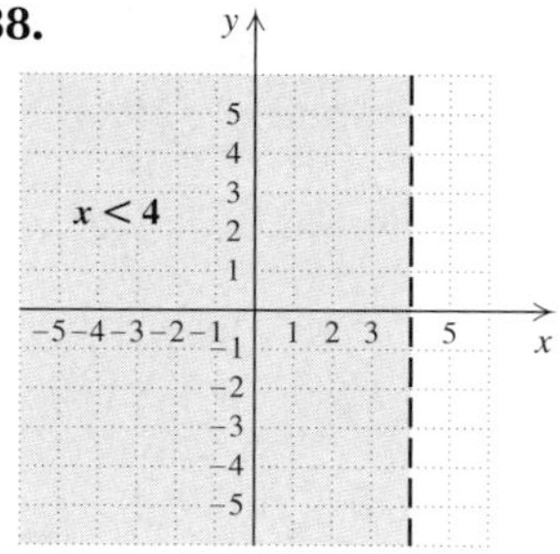

39.

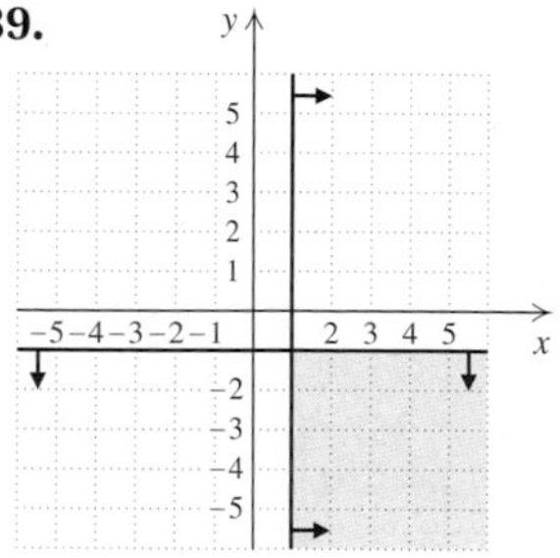

40.

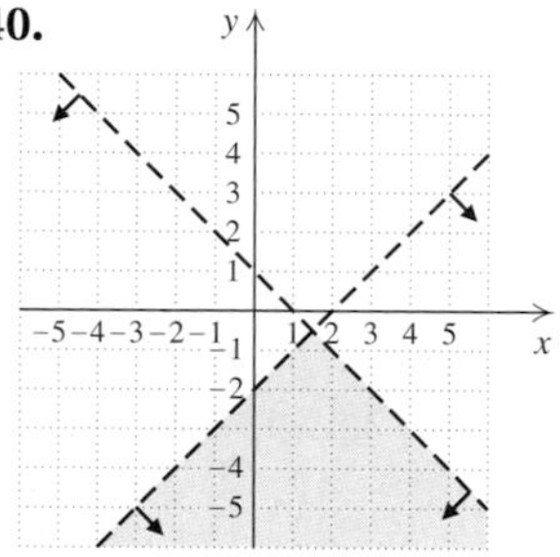

41. $y = \dfrac{243}{x}$ **42.** 9.6 lb

43. A solution of a system of two equations is an ordered pair that makes both equations true. The graph of an equation represents all ordered pairs that make that equation true. So in order for an ordered pair to make *both* equations true, it must be on both graphs. **44.** The solution sets of linear inequalities are regions, not lines. Thus the solution sets can intersect even if the boundary lines do not. **45.** $C = 1, D = 3$ **46.** $(2, 1, -2)$ **47.** $(2, 0)$ **48.** 24 **49.** \$33,600

Test: Chapter 7, p. 482

1. [7.1] Yes **2.** [7.1] (1, 3) **3.** [7.1] No solution **4.** [7.2] (8, −2) **5.** [7.2] (−1, 3) **6.** [7.2] Infinite number of solutions **7.** [7.3] (1, −5) **8.** [7.3] (12, −6) **9.** [7.3] (0, 1) **10.** [7.3] (5, 1) **11.** [7.2] 36°, 54° **12.** [7.4] 40%: 20 L; 25%: 40 L **13.** [7.4] $2\frac{5}{8}$ mi

14. [7.5]

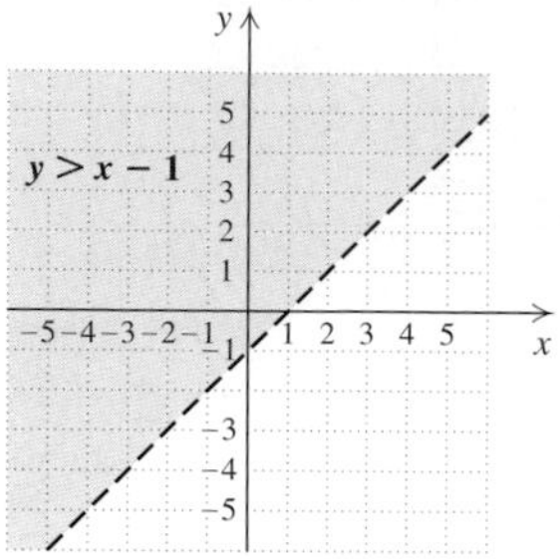

15. [7.5]

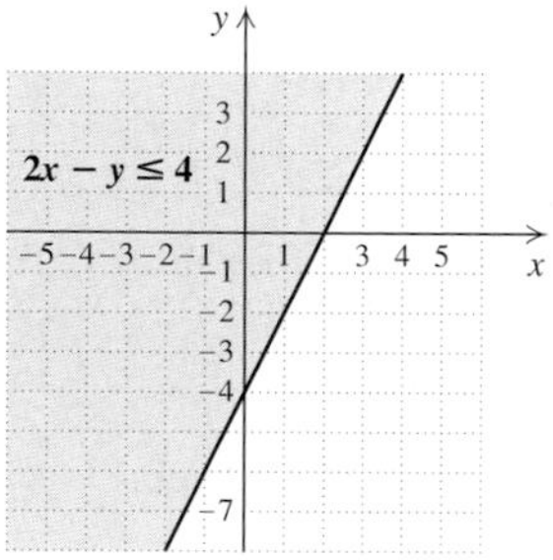

16. [7.5]

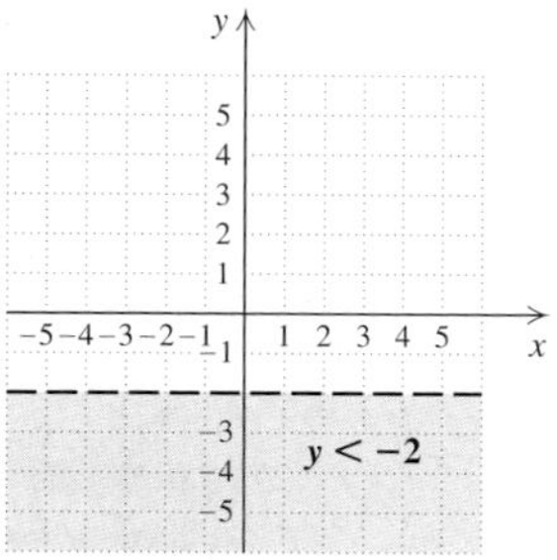

17. [7.6]

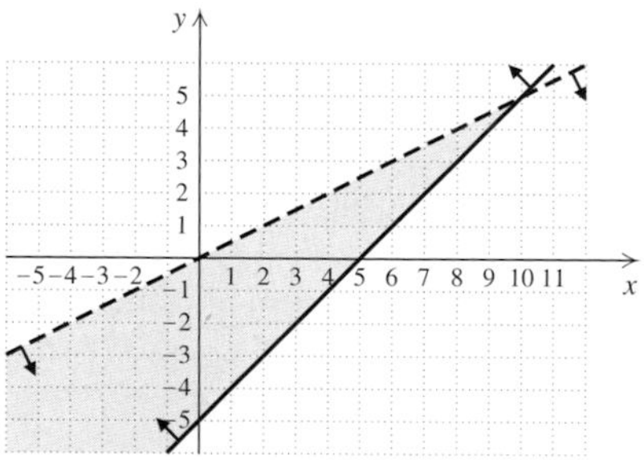

18. [7.6]

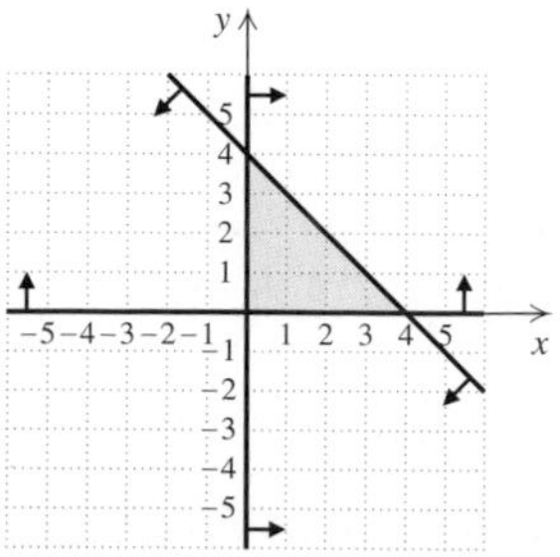

19. [7.7] $y = 4.5x$

20. [7.7] 18 min **21.** [7.4] 9 people

22. [7.6]

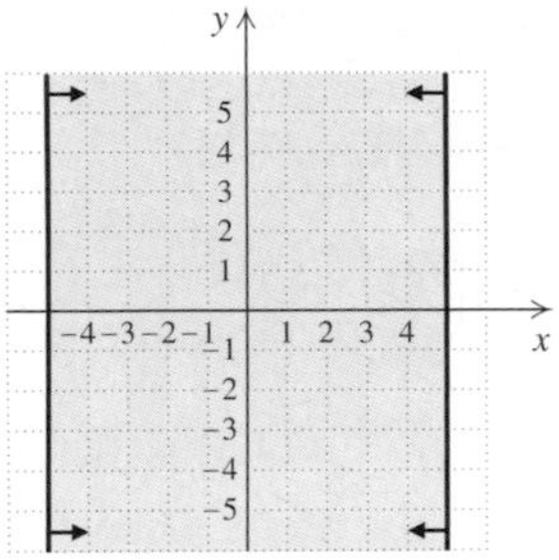

23. [7.1] $C = -\frac{19}{2}, D = \frac{14}{3}$

CHAPTER 8

Technology Connection, p. 486

1. $\sqrt{8} \approx 2.828427125$; $\sqrt{11} \approx 3.31662479$; $\sqrt{48} \approx 6.92820323$

Technology Connection, p. 488

1.

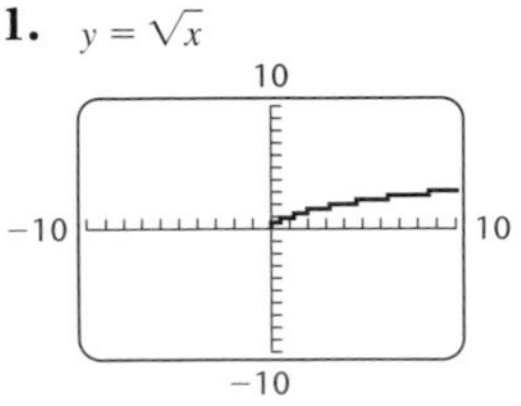

2.

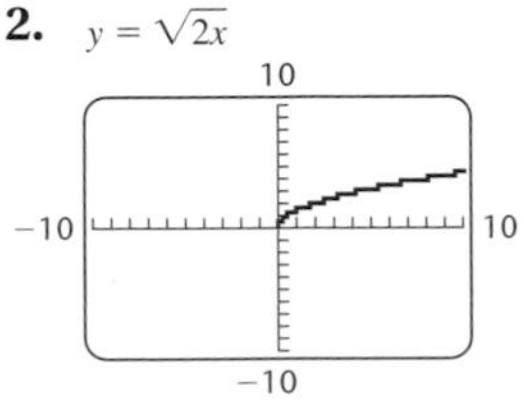

3.

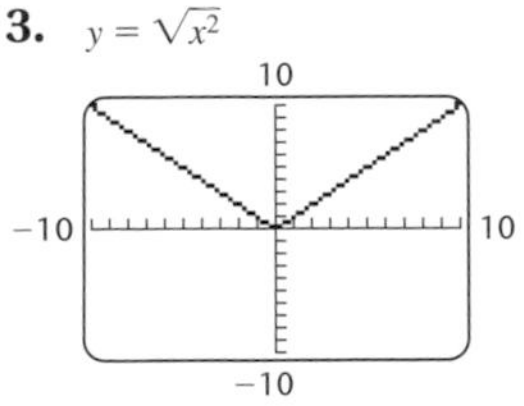

4.

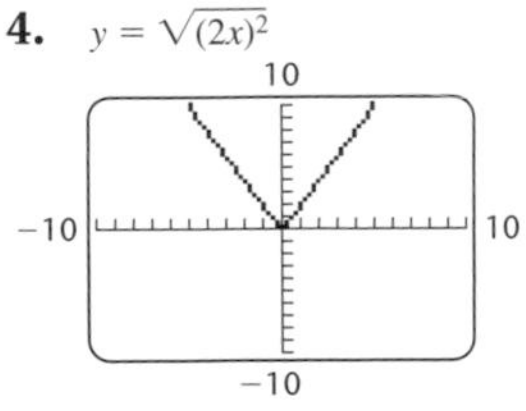

5.

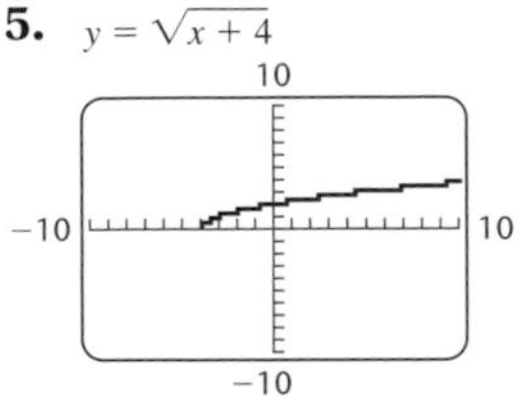

6.

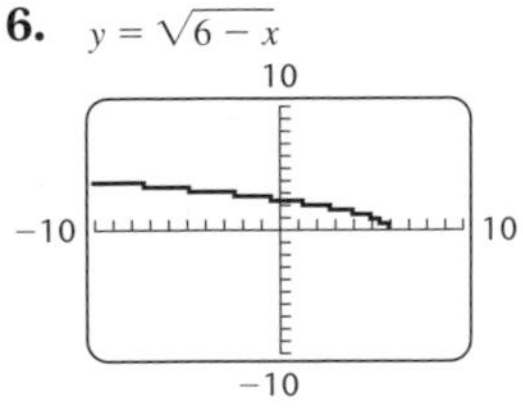

Exercise Set 8.1, pp. 488–490

1. (c) **3.** (a) **5.** (b) **7.** True **9.** False **11.** $-3, 3$ **13.** $-4, 4$ **15.** $-7, 7$ **17.** $-12, 12$ **19.** 2 **21.** -1 **23.** 0 **25.** -11 **27.** 30 **29.** 12 **31.** -25 **33.** $a + 7$ **35.** $t^3 - 2$ **37.** $\frac{7}{x+y}$ **39.** Rational **41.** Irrational **43.** Irrational **45.** Irrational **47.** Rational **49.** Rational **51.** 2.236 **53.** 4.123 **55.** 9.644 **57.** $|x|$ **59.** $|x - 3|$ **61.** $|8x|$, or $8|x|$ **63.** $|2x + 1|$ **65.** t **67.** $3x$ **69.** $7a$ **71.** $x + 1$ **73.** (a) 15; (b) 14 **75.** 0.91 sec **77.** **79.** $49x^2$ **80.** $9a^2$ **81.** $16t^{14}$ **82.** $45x^7$ **83.** $48a^{11}$ **84.** $8t^9u^6$ **85.** **87.** 3 **89.** $-6, -5$ **91.** $-7, 7$ **93.** $-3, 3$ **95.** $\{x \mid x < -5\}$ **97.** $\frac{2x^4}{y^3}$ **99.** $\frac{20}{m^8}$ **101.** (a) 1.7; (b) 2.2; (c) 2.6 **103.** 1097.1 ft/sec

105.

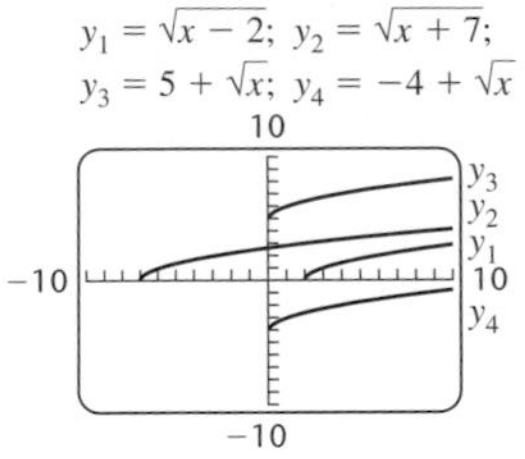

Exercise Set 8.2, pp. 496–498

1. (h) **3.** (f) **5.** (i) **7.** (b) **9.** (c) **11.** $\sqrt{21}$ **13.** $\sqrt{12}$, or $2\sqrt{3}$ **15.** $\sqrt{\frac{3}{10}}$ **17.** 14 **19.** $\sqrt{75}$, or $5\sqrt{3}$ **21.** $\sqrt{2x}$ **23.** $\sqrt{14a}$ **25.** $\sqrt{35x}$ **27.** $\sqrt{6ac}$ **29.** $2\sqrt{5}$ **31.** $5\sqrt{2}$ **33.** $10\sqrt{7}$ **35.** $2\sqrt{t}$ **37.** $5\sqrt{3a}$ **39.** $4\sqrt{a}$ **41.** $8y$ **43.** $x\sqrt{13}$ **45.** $2t\sqrt{7}$ **47.** $2\sqrt{10}$ **49.** 7 **51.** $2\sqrt{21}$ **53.** a^7 **55.** x^8 **57.** $r^3\sqrt{r}$ **59.** $t^9\sqrt{t}$ **61.** $2a\sqrt{10a}$ **63.** $2a^2\sqrt{2a}$ **65.** $2p^8\sqrt{26p}$ **67.** $7\sqrt{2}$ **69.** 9 **71.** $6\sqrt{xy}$ **73.** $17\sqrt{x}$ **75.** $10b\sqrt{5}$ **77.** $8t$ **79.** $a\sqrt{bc}$ **81.** $3x^2\sqrt{2}$ **83.** $xy^3\sqrt{xy}$ **85.** $10ab^4\sqrt{5a}$ **87.** 70.2 million; 83.5 million **89.** 20 mph; 54.8 mph **91.** **93.** a^5b^2 **94.** x^3y^8 **95.** $\frac{6x^2}{35y^2}$ **96.** $\frac{35a^2}{6b^2}$ **97.** $\frac{2r^3}{7t}$ **98.** $\frac{5x^7}{11y}$ **99.** **101.** 0.1 **103.** 0.25 **105.** $<$ **107.** $>$ **109.** $>$ **111.** $18(x + 1)\sqrt{y(x + 1)}$ **113.** $2x^7\sqrt{5x}$ **115.** $\sqrt{14x^{26}}$ **117.** x^{8n} **119.** $y^{(1/2)(n-1)}\sqrt{y}$

Exercise Set 8.3, pp. 501–503

1. True **3.** False **5.** 2 **7.** 5 **9.** $\sqrt{7}$ **11.** $\frac{1}{5}$ **13.** $\frac{3}{4}$ **15.** 2 **17.** $3y$ **19.** $3x^2$ **21.** $a^3\sqrt{3}$ **23.** $\frac{6}{5}$ **25.** $\frac{7}{4}$ **27.** $-\frac{5}{9}$ **29.** $\frac{a^2}{5}$ **31.** $\frac{x^3\sqrt{3}}{4}$ **33.** $\frac{t^3\sqrt{3}}{2}$ **35.** $\frac{5\sqrt{3}}{3}$ **37.** $\frac{\sqrt{21}}{7}$ **39.** $\frac{2\sqrt{3}}{9}$ **41.** $\frac{\sqrt{21}}{3}$ **43.** $\frac{\sqrt{6}}{10}$ **45.** $\frac{\sqrt{10a}}{15}$ **47.** $\frac{2\sqrt{15}}{5}$ **49.** $\frac{\sqrt{5z}}{z}$ **51.** $\frac{\sqrt{2t}}{8}$ **53.** $\frac{\sqrt{10x}}{30}$ **55.** $\frac{\sqrt{3a}}{5}$ **57.** $\frac{x\sqrt{15}}{6}$ **59.** \$10,582 **61.** \$6518 **63.** 6.28 sec; 7.85 sec **65.** 0.5 sec **67.** 9.42 sec **69.** **71.** $12x + 13$ **72.** $10a + 6$ **73.** $-a^3 - 8a^2$ **74.** $-11t^2 + 3t$ **75.** $18x^2 - 63x$ **76.** $6x^2 - 10x$ **77.** $6 + 23x + 20x^2$ **78.** $14 - 13x + 3x^2$ **79.** **81.** $\frac{\sqrt{70}}{100}$ **83.** $\frac{\sqrt{6xy}}{4x^3y^2}$ **85.** $\frac{\sqrt{10abc}}{5b^2c^5}$ **87.** $\frac{3\sqrt{7\sqrt{7}}}{7}$ **89.** $\frac{1}{x} - \frac{1}{y}$ **91.** $\frac{53}{2}$

Technology Connection, p. 506

1. −0.086 **2.** 1.217 **3.** 2.765

Exercise Set 8.4, pp. 507–508

1. (b) **3.** (d) **5.** $6\sqrt{7}$ **7.** $3\sqrt{5}$ **9.** $13\sqrt{x}$ **11.** $-2\sqrt{x}$ **13.** $8\sqrt{2a}$ **15.** $8\sqrt{10y}$ **17.** $12\sqrt{7}$ **19.** $4\sqrt{2}$ **21.** $5\sqrt{3}+2\sqrt{2}$ **23.** $-2\sqrt{x}$ **25.** $-18\sqrt{3}$ **27.** $28\sqrt{2}$ **29.** $13\sqrt{2}$ **31.** $6\sqrt{2}$ **33.** $13\sqrt{3}$ **35.** $\sqrt{x}$ **37.** $\sqrt{35}+\sqrt{14}$ **39.** $\sqrt{30}-5\sqrt{2}$ **41.** $14+7\sqrt{2}$ **43.** $17-7\sqrt{7}$ **45.** −11 **47.** 3 **49.** $7\sqrt{2}$ **51.** $52+14\sqrt{3}$ **53.** $13-4\sqrt{3}$ **55.** $x-2\sqrt{10x}+10$ **57.** $-6+3\sqrt{5}$ **59.** $-4-2\sqrt{7}$ **61.** $\frac{5-\sqrt{7}}{9}$ **63.** $\frac{-6-5\sqrt{6}}{19}$ **65.** $\frac{7+\sqrt{21}}{4}$ **67.** $\frac{\sqrt{15}+3}{2}$ **69.** $\frac{2\sqrt{7}-2\sqrt{2}}{5}$ **71.** $\frac{6-2\sqrt{6x}+x}{6-x}$ **73.** **75.** $\frac{5}{11}$ **76.** $-\frac{38}{13}$ **77.** −1, 6 **78.** 2, 5 **79.** Jolly Juice: 1.6 L; Real Squeeze: 6.4 L **80.** At least 3 hr **81.** **83.** $\frac{11\sqrt{x}-5x\sqrt{2}}{2x}$ **85.** $xy\sqrt{2y}(2x^2-y^2-xy^3)$ **87.** $37xy\sqrt{3x}$ **89.** All three are correct.

Technology Connection, p. 511

1. $y_1=3\sqrt{x},\ y_2=\sqrt{x+32}$

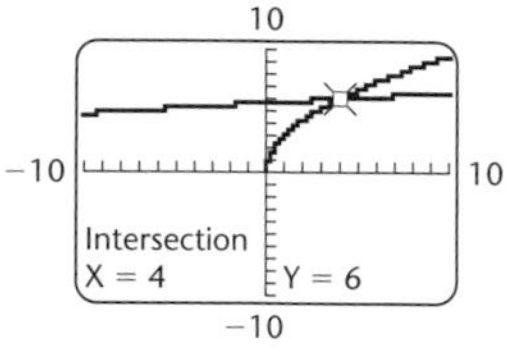

2. $y_1=3+\sqrt{27-3x},\ y_2=x$

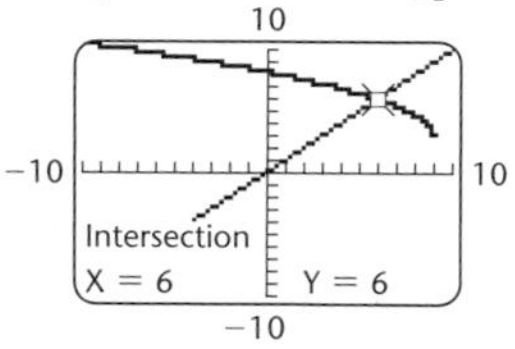

Exercise Set 8.5, pp. 512–514

1. True **3.** False **5.** 49 **7.** 64 **9.** 59 **11.** −46 **13.** $\frac{4}{5}$ **15.** 5 **17.** No solution **19.** −2 **21.** 8 **23.** 12 **25.** 11, 23 **27.** 3 **29.** 0, 8 **31.** No solution **33.** 3 **35.** $-\frac{2}{5}$ **37.** 3 **39.** 80 ft; 180 ft **41.** 25.2°F **43.** 806.56 m **45.** 576 m **47.** 15.71 ft **49.** **51.** Type A: 12; type B: 4 **52.** First type: 45 oz; second type: 15 oz **53.** 168 km **54.** Dimes: 70; quarters: 33 **55.** **57.** 121 **59.** 16 **61.** No solution **63.** 3 **65.** 10 **67.** $34\frac{569}{784}$ m

69.

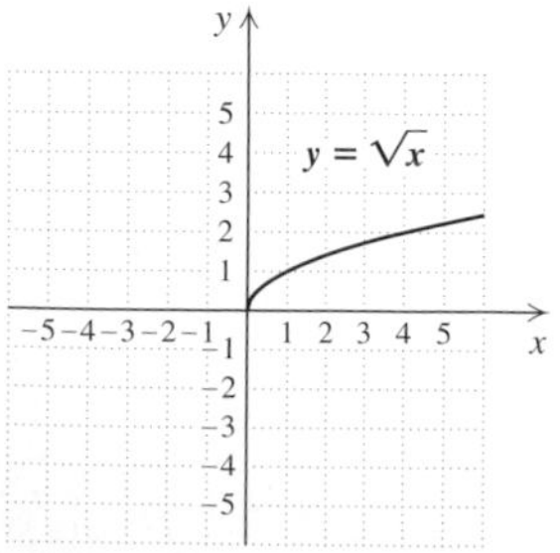

71.

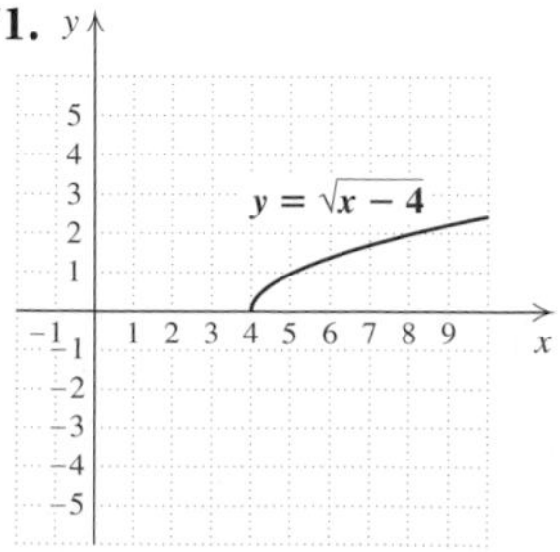

73. 30 mph **75.**

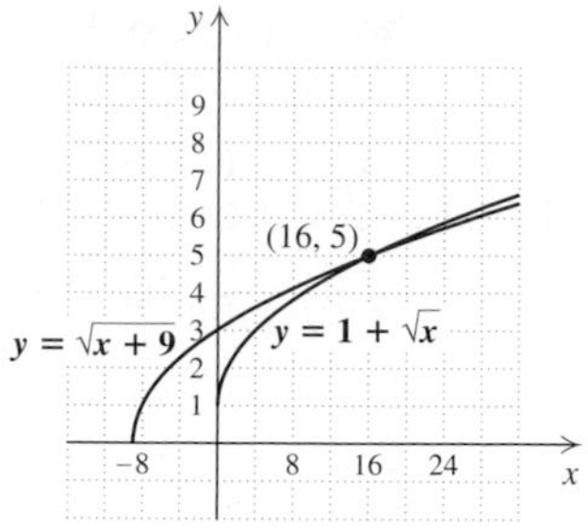

The solution is 16.

77. −0.32

Exercise Set 8.6, pp. 518–522

1. Hypotenuse **3.** Approximation **5.** 17 **7.** $6\sqrt{2}\approx 8.485$ **9.** 12 **11.** $\sqrt{34}\approx 5.831$ **13.** 13 **15.** 12 **17.** 2 **19.** $\sqrt{2}\approx 1.414$ **21.** 5 **23.** 17 ft **25.** $3\sqrt{21}$ in. ≈ 13.748 in. **27.** $4\sqrt{13}$ ft ≈ 14.422 ft **29.** $90\sqrt{2}$ ft ≈ 127.279 ft **31.** $\sqrt{356}$ ft ≈ 18.868 ft **33.** $\sqrt{12{,}500}$ yd ≈ 111.803 yd **35.** $\sqrt{448}$ ft ≈ 21.166 ft **37.** **39.** −45, −9.7, 0, $\frac{2}{7}$, 5.09, 19 **40.** $-\sqrt{5}, \sqrt{7}, \pi$ **41.** −45, −9.7, $-\sqrt{5}$, 0, $\frac{2}{7}$, $\sqrt{7}$, π, 5.09, 19 **42.** −45, 0, 19 **43.** −32 **44.** $\frac{49}{4}$ **45.** $16a^4$ **46.** $-125x^3$ **47.** $(x-5)^2$ **48.** $(t-6)^2$ **49.** **51.** 5 68-ft strands for $59.95 **53.** Yes **55.** 8 ft **57.** 6, 8, 10 **59.** $s\sqrt{3}$ **61.** $\frac{\sqrt{3}a}{2}$ **63.** $\sqrt{1525}$ mi ≈ 39.051 mi **65.** 640 acres

Exercise Set 8.7, p. 528

1. True **3.** True **5.** −2 **7.** −5 **9.** 10 **11.** −6 **13.** 5 **15.** 0 **17.** −1 **19.** Not a real number **21.** 10 **23.** 8 **25.** 2 **27.** a **29.** $3\sqrt[3]{2}$ **31.** $2\sqrt[4]{3}$ **33.** $\frac{4}{5}$ **35.** $\frac{2}{3}$ **37.** $\frac{\sqrt[3]{7}}{2}$ **39.** $\frac{\sqrt[4]{14}}{3}$ **41.** 4 **43.** 5 **45.** 2 **47.** 8 **49.** 243 **51.** 16 **53.** 32 **55.** 32 **57.** $\frac{1}{5}$ **59.** $\frac{1}{4}$ **61.** $\frac{1}{8}$ **63.** $\frac{1}{243}$ **65.** $\frac{1}{4}$ **67.** **69.** −1, 6 **70.** −5, 1 **71.** $-\frac{3}{2}, \frac{3}{2}$ **72.** $-\frac{2}{5}, \frac{2}{5}$ **73.** $-2, -\frac{2}{3}$ **74.** $-3, \frac{2}{5}$ **75.** **77.** 6.310 **79.** 3.834 **81.** $a^{7/4}$ **83.** $m^{13/12}$

85.

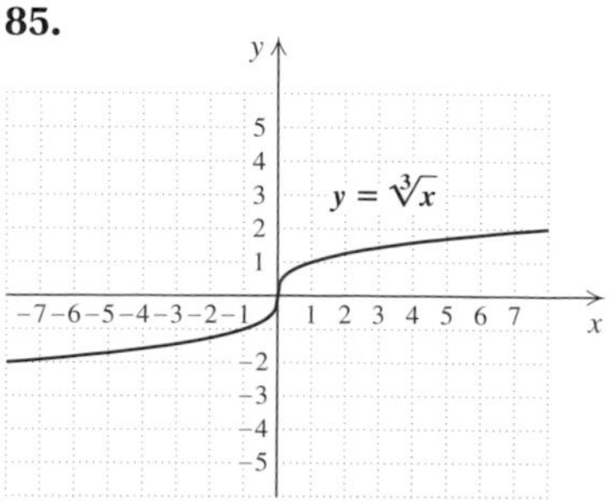

87. $y_1=x^{2/3},\ y_2=x^1,$ $y_3=x^{5/4},\ y_4=x^{3/2}$

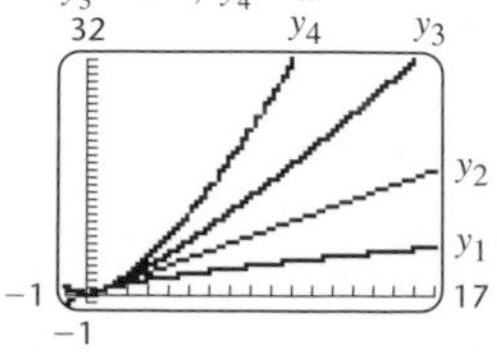

Review Exercises: Chapter 8, pp. 530–531

1. False **2.** True **3.** True **4.** True **5.** False **6.** False **7.** False **8.** True **9.** True **10.** True **11.** 5, −5 **12.** 14, −14 **13.** 20, −20 **14.** 15, −15 **15.** −12 **16.** 9 **17.** 7 **18.** −13 **19.** $2x^2y$ **20.** $\frac{a}{b}$ **21.** Rational **22.** Irrational **23.** Irrational **24.** Rational **25.** 1.732 **26.** 9.950 **27.** $|5x|$, or $5|x|$ **28.** $|x+1|$ **29.** p **30.** $7x$ **31.** $4m$ **32.** ac **33.** $4\sqrt{3}$ **34.** $7t\sqrt{2}$ **35.** $4\sqrt{2p}$ **36.** x^3 **37.** $2a^6\sqrt{3a}$ **38.** $6m^7\sqrt{m}$ **39.** $\sqrt{33}$ **40.** $2\sqrt{15}$ **41.** $\sqrt{35xt}$ **42.** $2a\sqrt{6}$ **43.** $5xy\sqrt{2}$ **44.** $10a^2b\sqrt{ab}$ **45.** $\frac{\sqrt{7}}{3}$ **46.** $\frac{y^4\sqrt{5}}{3}$ **47.** $\frac{7}{8}$ **48.** $\frac{2}{3}$ **49.** $\frac{5}{t}$ **50.** $13\sqrt{5}$ **51.** $\sqrt{5}$ **52.** $-3\sqrt{x}$ **53.** $7+4\sqrt{3}$ **54.** 1 **55.** $-11+5\sqrt{7}$ **56.** $\frac{\sqrt{2}}{2}$ **57.** $\frac{\sqrt{10}}{4}$ **58.** $\frac{\sqrt{7y}}{y}$ **59.** $\frac{2\sqrt{3}}{3}$ **60.** $8-4\sqrt{3}$ **61.** $-7-3\sqrt{5}$ **62.** 54 **63.** No solution **64.** 4 **65.** 0, 3 **66.** 35.344 ft **67.** 20 **68.** $\sqrt{3}\approx 1.732$ **69.** $48\sqrt{2}$ ft $\approx$ 67.882 ft **70.** 2 **71.** Not a real number **72.** −3 **73.** $2\sqrt[4]{2}$ **74.** 10 **75.** $\frac{1}{3}$ **76.** 64 **77.** $\frac{1}{27}$ **78.** He could be mistakenly assuming that negative solutions are not possible because principal square roots are never negative. He could also be assuming that substituting a negative value for the variable in a radicand always produces a negative radicand. **79.** Some radical terms that are like terms may not appear to be so until they are in simplified form. **80.** 2 **81.** No solution **82.** $(x+\sqrt{5})(x-\sqrt{5})$ **83.** $b=\sqrt{A^2-a^2}$ or $b=-\sqrt{A^2-a^2}$

Test: Chapter 8, p. 532

1. [8.1] 9, −9 **2.** [8.1] 8 **3.** [8.1] −5 **4.** [8.1] s^2-3 **5.** [8.1] Irrational **6.** [8.1] Rational **7.** [8.1] 9.327 **8.** [8.1] 2.646 **9.** [8.1] a **10.** [8.1] $7y$ **11.** [8.2] $2\sqrt{10}$ **12.** [8.2] $3x^3\sqrt{3}$ **13.** [8.2] $2t^2\sqrt{t}$ **14.** [8.2] $\sqrt{30}$ **15.** [8.2] $5\sqrt{2}$ **16.** [8.2] $\sqrt{14xy}$ **17.** [8.2] $4t$ **18.** [8.2] $3ab^2\sqrt{2}$ **19.** [8.3] $\frac{3}{4}$ **20.** [8.3] $\frac{\sqrt{7}}{4y}$ **21.** [8.3] $\frac{3}{2}$ **22.** [8.3] $\frac{12}{a}$ **23.** [8.4] $-6\sqrt{2}$ **24.** [8.4] $7\sqrt{3}$ **25.** [8.4] $21-8\sqrt{5}$ **26.** [8.4] 11 **27.** [8.3] $\frac{\sqrt{10}}{5}$ **28.** [8.3] $\frac{2x\sqrt{y}}{y}$ **29.** [8.4] $\frac{40+10\sqrt{5}}{11}$ **30.** [8.6] $\sqrt{10{,}625}$ ft $\approx$ 103.078 ft **31.** [8.5] 48 **32.** [8.5] −2, 2 **33.** [8.5] About 5000 m **34.** [8.7] 2 **35.** [8.7] −1 **36.** [8.7] −4 **37.** [8.7] Not a real number **38.** [8.7] 3 **39.** [8.7] $\frac{1}{3}$ **40.** [8.7] 1000 **41.** [8.7] $\frac{1}{32}$ **42.** [8.5] −3 **43.** [8.2] y^{8n}

CHAPTER 9

Technology Connection, p. 535

1.

$y_1 = 5x^2,\ y_2 = 15$

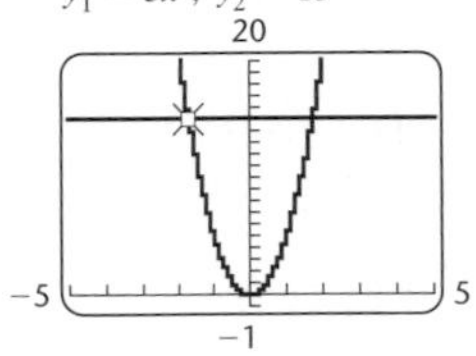

Intersection
X = −1.732051, Y = 15

$y_1 = 5x^2,\ y_2 = 15$

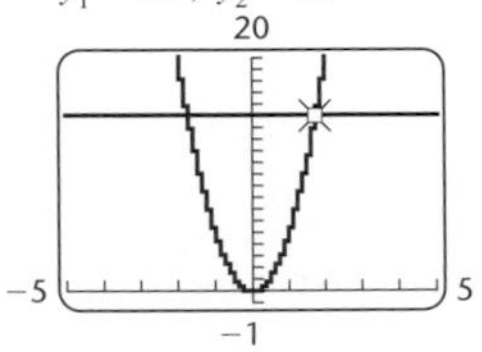

Intersection
X = 1.7320508, Y = 15

$y_1 = -3x^2 + 7,\ y_2 = 0$

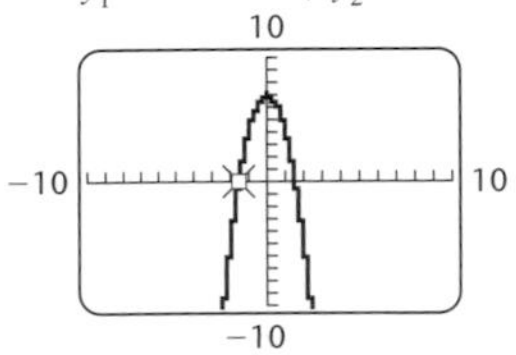

Intersection
X = −1.527525, Y = 0

$y_1 = -3x^2 + 7,\ y_2 = 0$

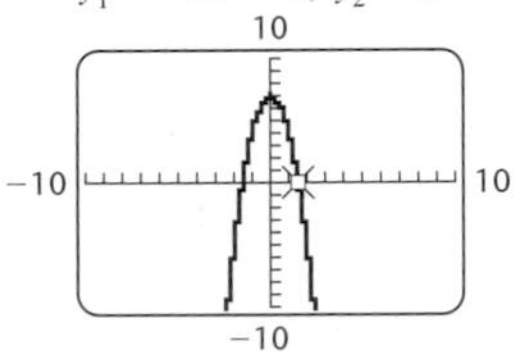

Intersection
X = 1.5275252, Y = 0

Exercise Set 9.1, pp. 537–538

1. True **3.** False **5.** −6, 6 **7.** −5, 5 **9.** $-\sqrt{17}, \sqrt{17}$ **11.** −3, 3 **13.** 0 **15.** $-\frac{2}{3}, \frac{2}{3}$ **17.** $-\frac{2\sqrt{5}}{7}, \frac{2\sqrt{5}}{7}$ **19.** $-\frac{\sqrt{14}}{2}, \frac{\sqrt{14}}{2}$ **21.** −6, 8 **23.** −13, 5 **25.** $-3-\sqrt{6}, -3+\sqrt{6}$, or $-3\pm\sqrt{6}$ **27.** 7 **29.** $5-\sqrt{14}, 5+\sqrt{14}$, or $5\pm\sqrt{14}$ **31.** −2, 0 **33.** $\frac{3}{4}-\frac{\sqrt{17}}{4}, \frac{3}{4}+\frac{\sqrt{17}}{4}$, or $\frac{3}{4}\pm\frac{\sqrt{17}}{4}$ **35.** −5, 15 **37.** −5, −3 **39.** $3-\sqrt{13}, 3+\sqrt{13}$, or $3\pm\sqrt{13}$ **41.** $-6-3\sqrt{2}, -6+3\sqrt{2}$, or $-6\pm3\sqrt{2}$ **43.** **45.** $3(x^2+4x+1)$ **46.** $5(t^2+4t+5)$ **47.** $(t+8)^2$ **48.** $(x+7)^2$ **49.** $(x-5)^2$ **50.** $(t-4)^2$ **51.** **53.** $-\frac{7}{6}-\frac{\sqrt{7}}{6}, -\frac{7}{6}+\frac{\sqrt{7}}{6}$, or $-\frac{7}{6}\pm\frac{\sqrt{7}}{6}$ **55.** $\frac{3}{4}-\frac{\sqrt{17}}{4}, \frac{3}{4}+\frac{\sqrt{17}}{4}$, or $\frac{3}{4}\pm\frac{\sqrt{17}}{4}$ **57.** −4.35, 1.85 **59.** −4, −2 **61.** −6, 0 **63.** $d=\frac{\sqrt{kMmf}}{f}$

Exercise Set 9.2, pp. 544–545

1. (c) **3.** (a) **5.** (d) **7.** $x^2+8x+16$ **9.** $x^2-12x+36$ **11.** $x^2-3x+\frac{9}{4}$ **13.** $t^2+t+\frac{1}{4}$ **15.** $x^2+\frac{5}{4}x+\frac{25}{64}$ **17.** $m^2-\frac{9}{2}m+\frac{81}{16}$ **19.** −6, −2 **21.** $12\pm\sqrt{123}$ **23.** $1\pm\sqrt{6}$ **25.** $11\pm\sqrt{19}$ **27.** $-\frac{3}{2}\pm\frac{\sqrt{21}}{2}$, or $\frac{-3\pm\sqrt{21}}{2}$ **29.** −7, 4

31. $\frac{3}{4} \pm \frac{\sqrt{41}}{4}$, or $\frac{3 \pm \sqrt{41}}{4}$ **33.** $\frac{3}{4} \pm \frac{\sqrt{73}}{4}$, or $\frac{3 \pm \sqrt{73}}{4}$ **35.** $\frac{2}{3} \pm \frac{\sqrt{13}}{3}$, or $\frac{2 \pm \sqrt{13}}{3}$ **37.** $-\frac{1}{2}, 5$ **39.** $-\frac{5}{2}, \frac{2}{3}$ **41.** **43.** $1 + 2x$ **44.** $2 + x$ **45.** $3 - 2x$ **46.** $6 - 5x$ **47.** $\frac{8 - \sqrt{5}}{3}$ **48.** $\frac{5 - \sqrt{6}}{2}$ **49.** **51.** $-12, 12$ **53.** $-6\sqrt{5}, 6\sqrt{5}$ **55.** $-16, 16$ **57.** $-7.61, -0.39$ **59.** $0.91, 23.09$ **61.** $-1.21, 3.71$ **63.**

Technology Connection, p. 548

1. An ERROR message appears. **2.** The graph has no x-intercepts, so there is no value of x for which $x^2 + x + 1 = 0$, or, equivalently, for which $x^2 + x = -1$.

Exercise Set 9.3, pp. 552–555

1. (c) **3.** (b) **5.** $-9, 2$ **7.** 4 **9.** $-\frac{4}{3}, -1$ **11.** $-\frac{1}{2}, \frac{7}{2}$ **13.** $-8, 8$ **15.** $-2 \pm \sqrt{11}$ **17.** $5 \pm \sqrt{6}$ **19.** $-1 \pm \sqrt{7}$ **21.** $-\frac{4}{3} \pm \frac{\sqrt{10}}{3}$, or $\frac{-4 \pm \sqrt{10}}{3}$ **23.** $\frac{5}{4} \pm \frac{\sqrt{33}}{4}$, or $\frac{5 \pm \sqrt{33}}{4}$ **25.** $-\frac{1}{4} \pm \frac{\sqrt{13}}{4}$, or $\frac{-1 \pm \sqrt{13}}{4}$ **27.** No real-number solution **29.** $\frac{5}{6} \pm \frac{\sqrt{73}}{6}$, or $\frac{5 \pm \sqrt{73}}{6}$ **31.** $\frac{3}{2} \pm \frac{\sqrt{29}}{2}$, or $\frac{3 \pm \sqrt{29}}{2}$ **33.** $-5, \frac{2}{3}$ **35.** No real-number solution **37.** $\pm 3\sqrt{2}$ **39.** $-1.317, 5.317$ **41.** $-0.193, 5.193$ **43.** $-1.207, 0.207$ **45.** 10 sides **47.** 9.62 sec **49.** 1.36 sec **51.** 7 ft, 24 ft **53.** Length: 10 cm; width: 6 cm **55.** Length: 24 m; width: 18 m **57.** 6.76 m, 9.16 m **59.** 4.18 in., 7.18 in. **61.** Length: 5.66 m; width: 2.83 m **63.** 20% **65.** 5% **67.** 5.05 km **69.** **71.** 25 **72.** 4 **73.** 15 **74.** 9 **75.** 16 **76.** 50 **77.** **79.** 0, 2 **81.** $\frac{3}{2} \pm \frac{\sqrt{5}}{2}$, or $\frac{3 \pm \sqrt{5}}{2}$ **83.** $-\frac{7}{2} \pm \frac{\sqrt{61}}{2}$, or $\frac{-7 \pm \sqrt{61}}{2}$ **85.** $\pm\sqrt{5}$ **87.** $\frac{5}{2} \pm \frac{\sqrt{37}}{2}$, or $\frac{5 \pm \sqrt{37}}{2}$ **89.** 4.83 cm **91.** Length: 120 m; width: 75 m **93.** 5% **95.** Length: 44.06 in.; width: 19.06 in.

Technology Connection, p. 557

1. 0.88; 5.12 **2.** They are rational approximations of the answers yielded by the quadratic formula.

Exercise Set 9.4, pp. 560–562

1. 1 **3.** 2, 3 **5.** 25 **7.** 4 **9.** $-\frac{1}{6}$ **11.** $\frac{4}{33}$ **13.** $\frac{1}{3}, 2$ **15.** $\frac{16}{3}$ **17.** $\frac{5}{2} \pm \frac{\sqrt{19}}{2}$, or $\frac{5 \pm \sqrt{19}}{2}$ **19.** $\frac{4}{3}$ **21.** No real-number solution **23.** No real-number solution **25.** $\frac{2}{3}$ **27.** $g = \frac{2s}{t^2}$ **29.** $t = \frac{A}{Pr} - \frac{1}{r}$, or $t = \frac{A - P}{Pr}$ **31.** $h = \frac{d^2}{c^2}$ **33.** $R = \frac{r_1 r_2}{r_1 + r_2}$ **35.** $x = \frac{-b \pm \sqrt{b^2 - 4ac}}{2a}$ **37.** $n = \frac{m}{p - q}$ **39.** $y = \frac{C - Ax}{B}$ **41.** $h = \frac{S - 2\pi r^2}{2\pi r}$ **43.** $h = \pm\sqrt{st}$ **45.** $t = \frac{-n \pm \sqrt{n^2 + 4mp}}{2m}$ **47.** $n = \frac{m}{r}$ **49.** $m = \frac{-t \pm \sqrt{t^2 + 4n}}{2}$ **51.** $t = \frac{p^2 - 2pn + n^2 - 9c}{9}$ **53.** $n = m - 3t$ **55.** **57.** $2\sqrt{15}$ **58.** $3\sqrt{35}$ **59.** $5\sqrt{6}$ **60.** $3\sqrt{7}$ **61.** $2a^3b^2\sqrt{a}$ **62.** $3x^4y^2\sqrt{y}$ **63.** **65.** 6 yr **67.** $m = \frac{g \pm \sqrt{g^2 - 4ft}}{2f}$ **69.** $t = -\frac{b}{a} + \frac{k^2}{a(V - c)^2}$ **71.** $-40°$

Exercise Set 9.5, p. 565

1. False **3.** True **5.** i **7.** $9i$ **9.** $5\sqrt{2}i$, or $5i\sqrt{2}$ **11.** $-3\sqrt{5}i$, or $-3i\sqrt{5}$ **13.** $-3\sqrt{2}i$, or $-3i\sqrt{2}$ **15.** $4 + 7i$ **17.** $3 + 3i$ **19.** $5 - 7\sqrt{2}i$, or $5 - 7i\sqrt{2}$ **21.** $\pm 3i$ **23.** $\pm 2\sqrt{7}i$, or $\pm 2i\sqrt{7}$ **25.** $-2 \pm i$ **27.** $-3 \pm 4i$ **29.** $1 \pm 2i$ **31.** $2 \pm \sqrt{3}i$, or $2 \pm i\sqrt{3}$ **33.** $-\frac{3}{2} \pm \frac{1}{2}i$ **35.** $-\frac{1}{3} \pm \frac{\sqrt{2}}{3}i$ **37.**

39.

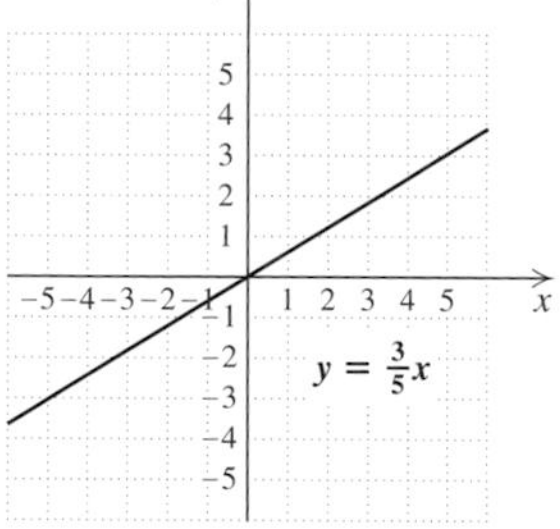

40.

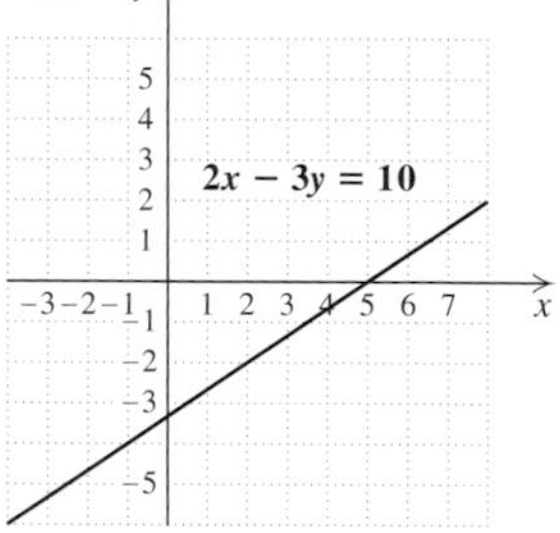

41.

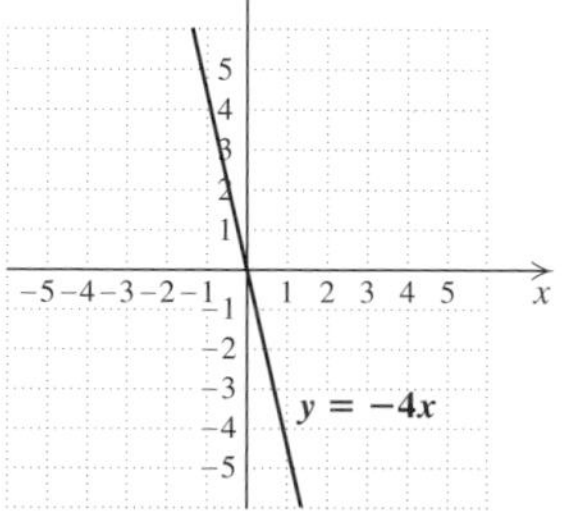

42.

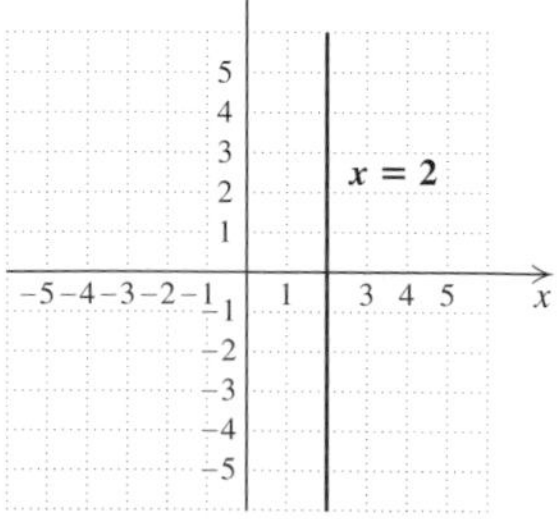

43. 0 **44.** 0 **45.** **47.** $-2 \pm i$ **49.** $-1 \pm \sqrt{19}i$ **51.**

Exercise Set 9.6, pp. 571–572

1.
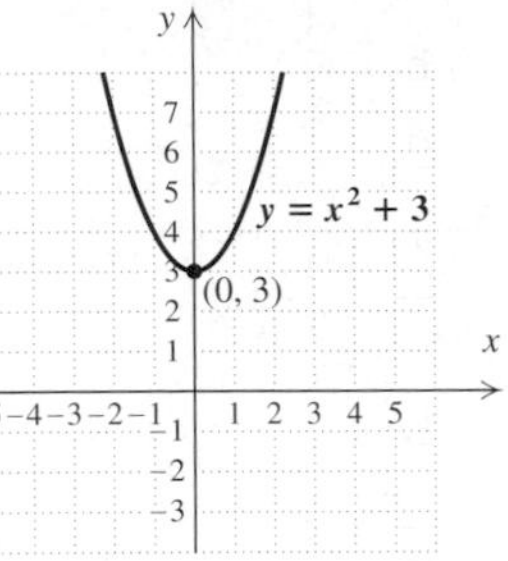

3.
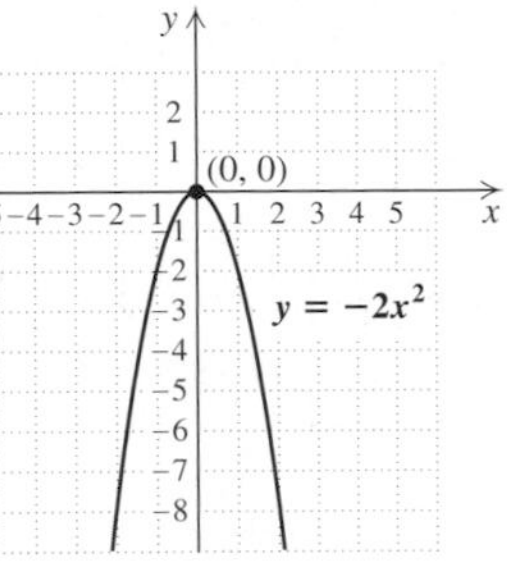

5.
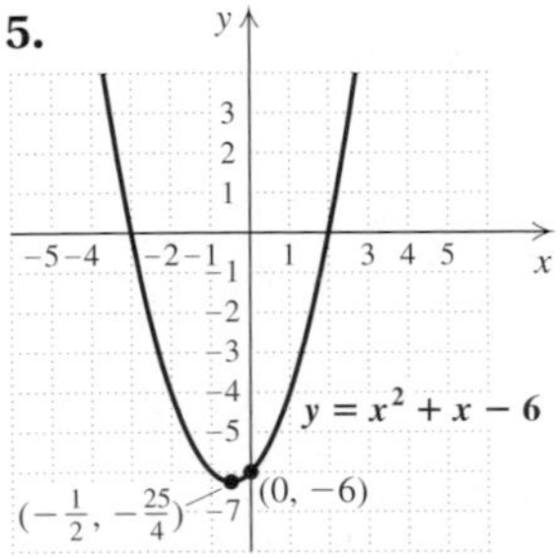

7.
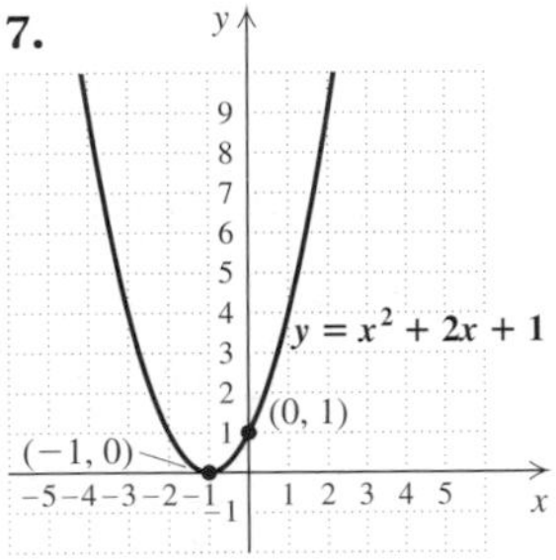

9.
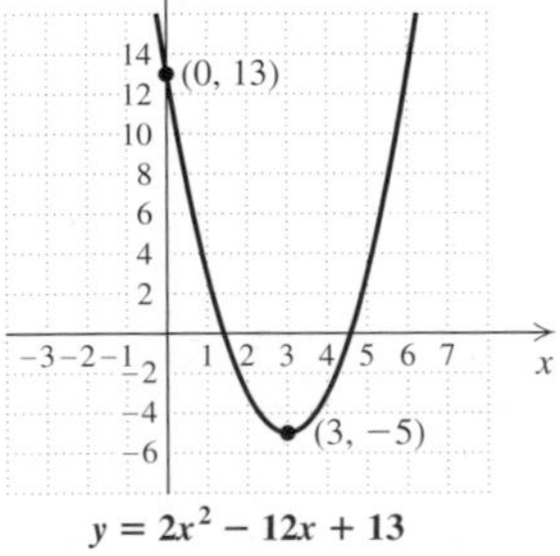

11.
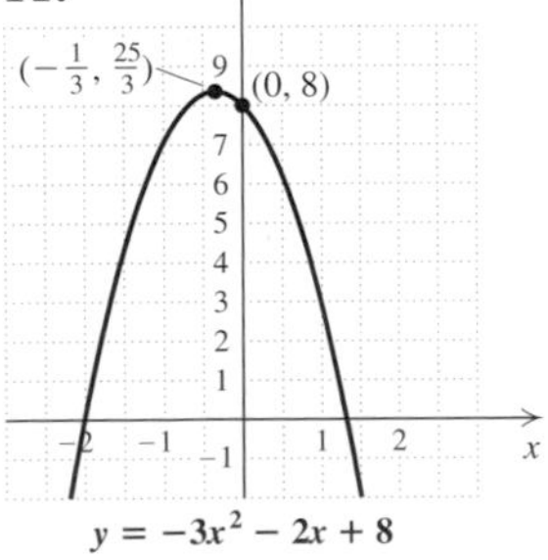

13.
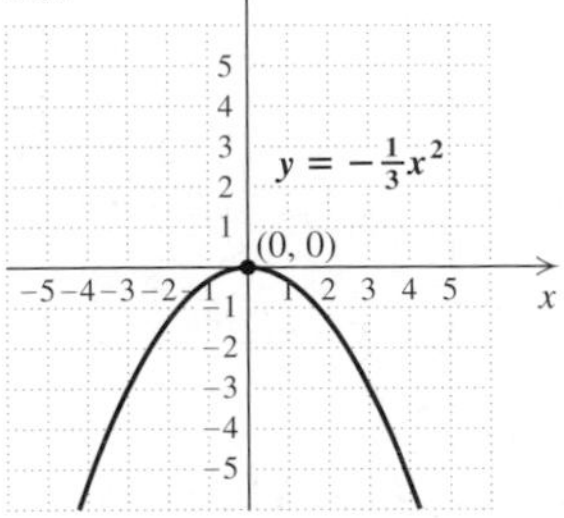

15.
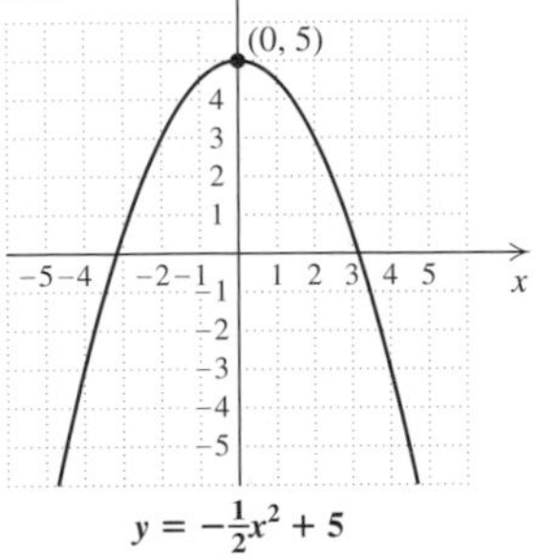

17.
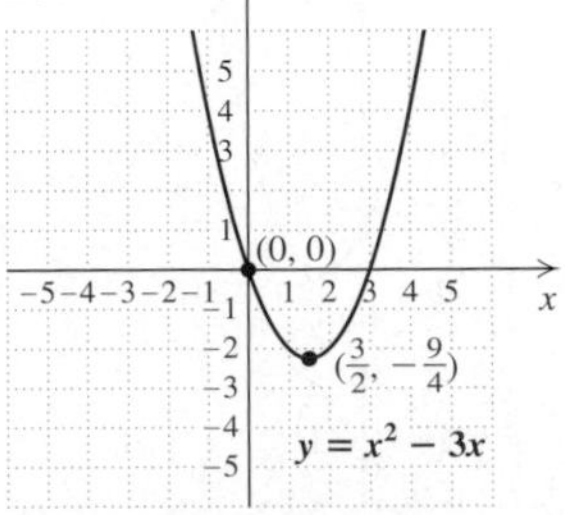

19.
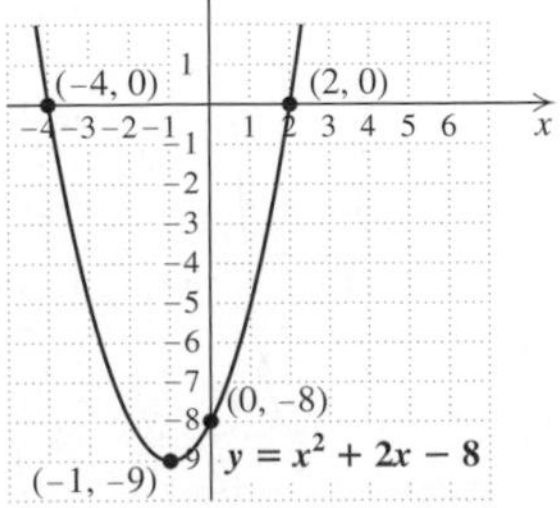

21.
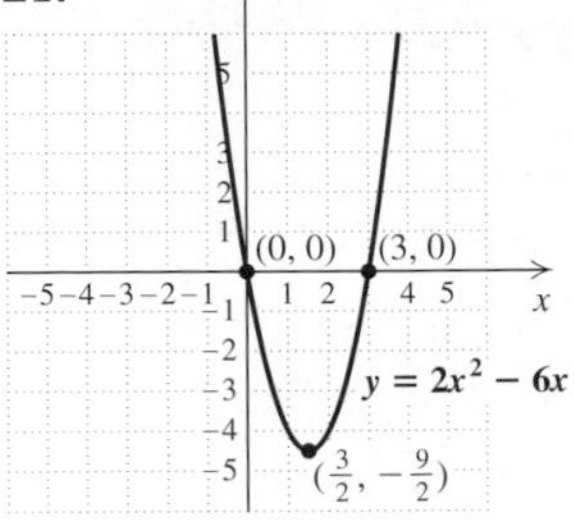

23.
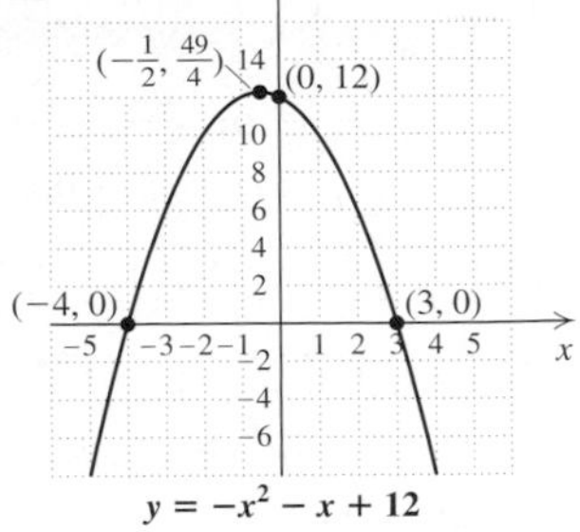

25.
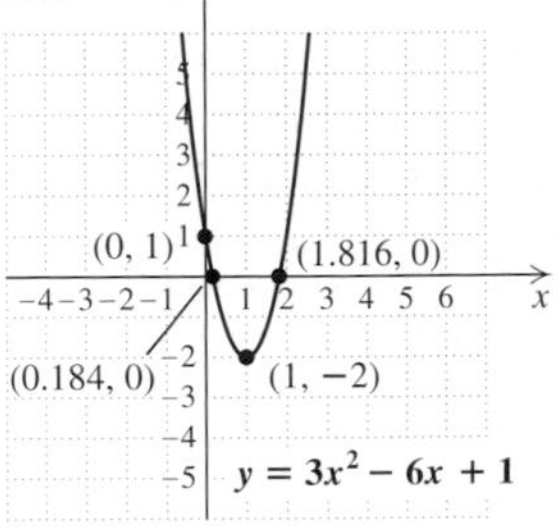

27.
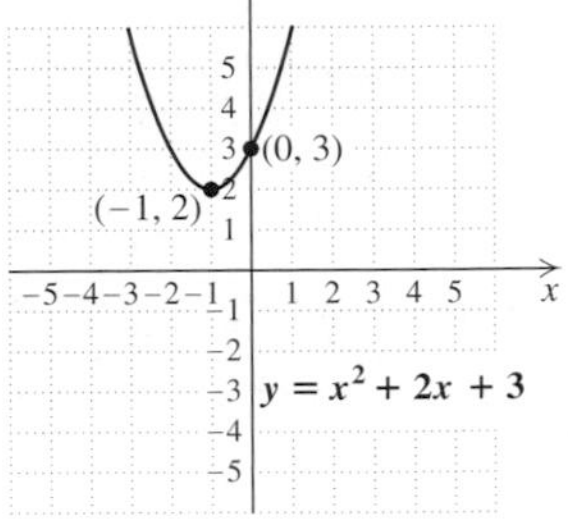

29.
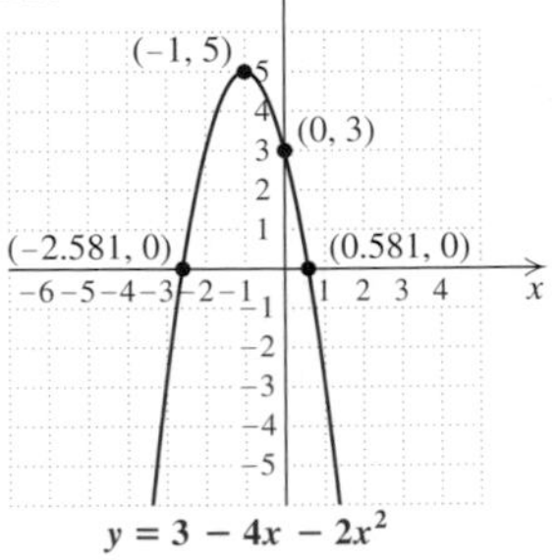

31.

33. 8 **34.** 22 **35.** −3 **36.** 68 **37.** −6.6 **38.** 0
39. **41.** **(a)** 2 sec after launch and 4 sec after launch; **(b)** 3 sec after launch; **(c)** 6 sec after launch
43. **(a)** 56.25 ft, 120 ft, 206.25 ft, 276.25 ft, 356.25 ft, 600 ft;
(b)
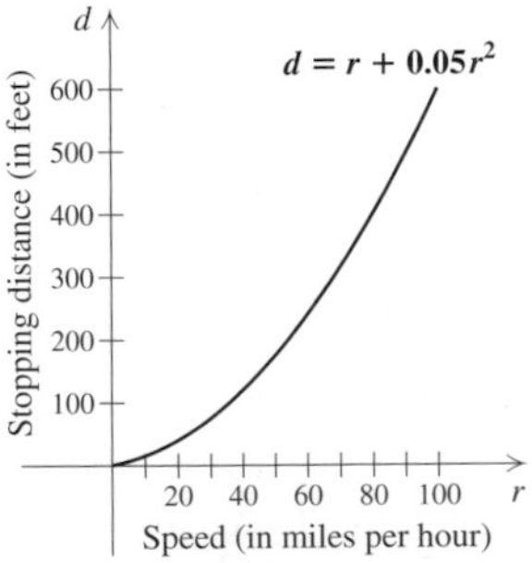

45.
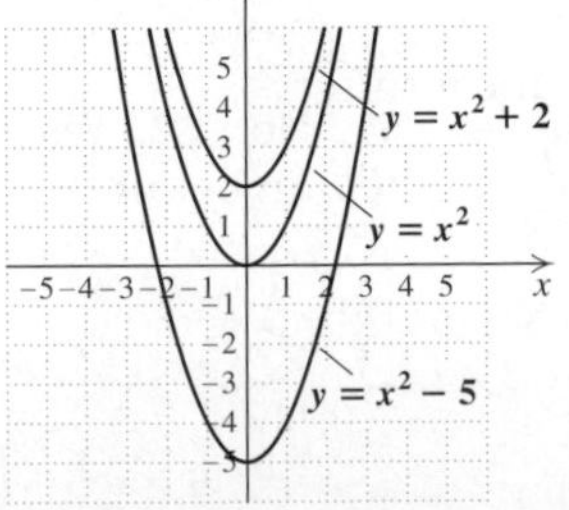

We can move the graph of $y = x^2$ up k units if $k \geq 0$ or down $|k|$ units if $k < 0$ to obtain the graph of $y = x^2 + k$.

47.

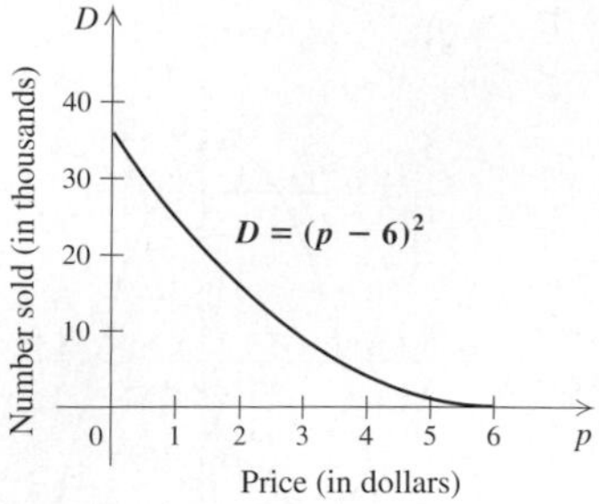

49. 2.2361

Exercise Set 9.7, pp. 580–582

1. True **3.** False **5.** Yes **7.** Yes **9.** No **11.** Yes **13.** 9; 12; 3 **15.** −21; 15; 30 **17.** 7; −11; 24.1 **19.** 0; 5; 2 **21.** 16; 1; $\frac{25}{16}$ **23.** 4; −122; 3 **25.** **(a)** 159.48 cm; **(b)** 153.98 cm **27.** 70°C; 220°C; 10,020°C **29.** $1.\overline{60}$ atm; $1.\overline{90}$ atm; $4.\overline{03}$ atm

31.

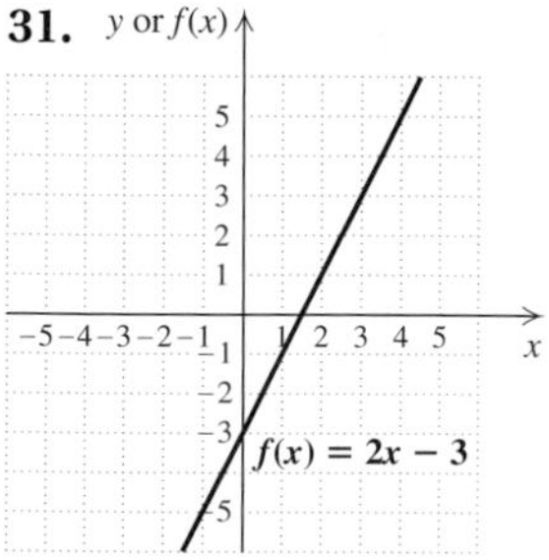

33.

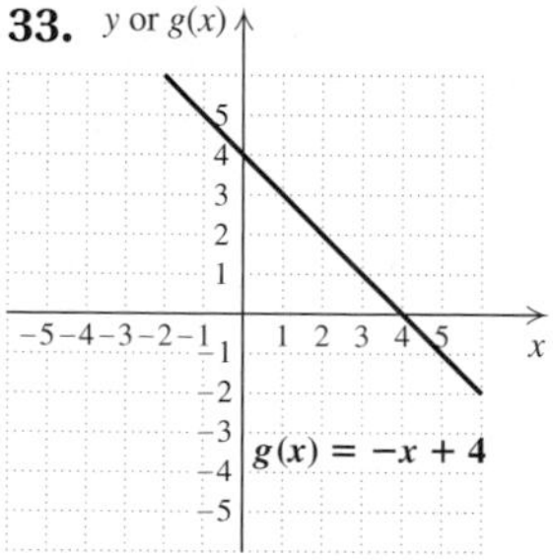

35.

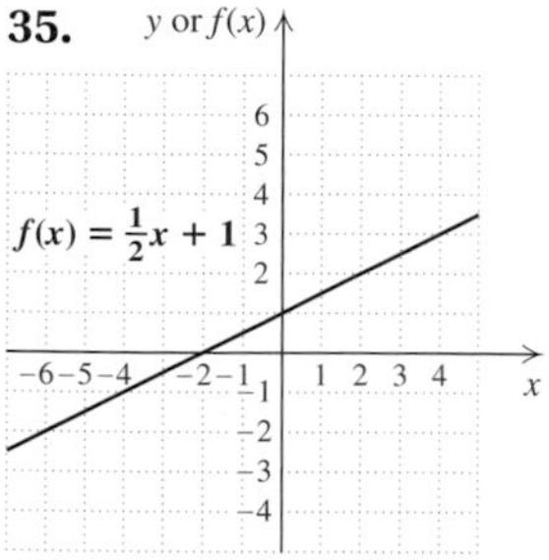

37.

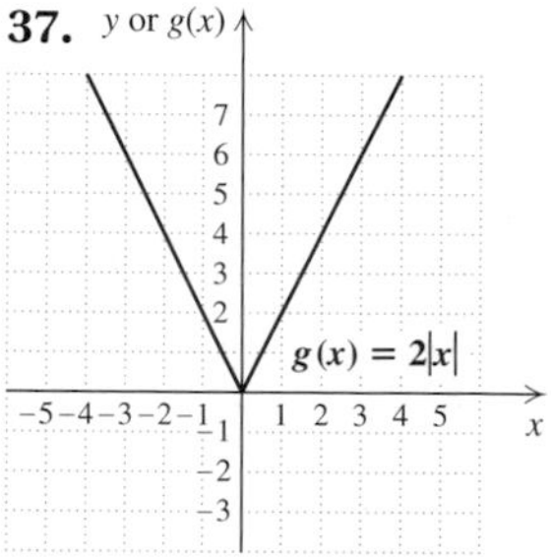

39.

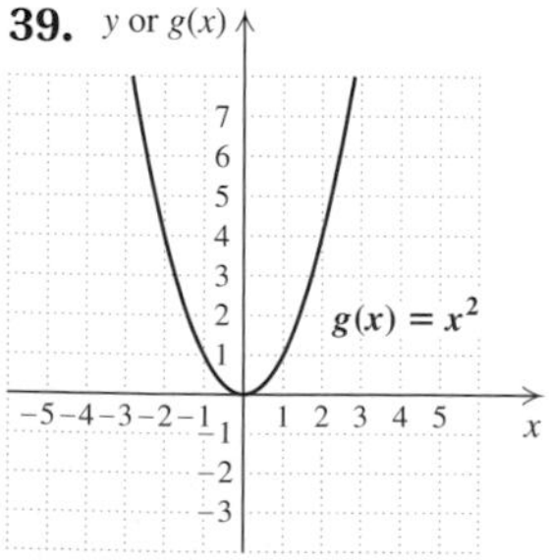

41.

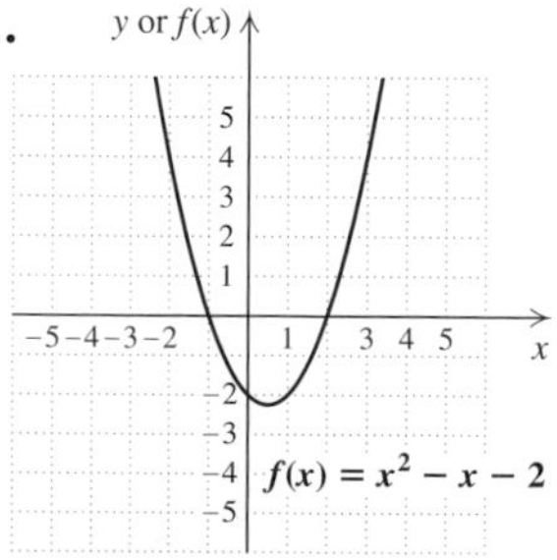

43. Yes **45.** No **47.** Yes **49.** **51.** No **52.** Yes **53.** Yes **54.** No solution **55.** Infinite number of solutions **56.** $\left(\frac{9}{11}, -\frac{5}{11}\right)$ **57.**

59.

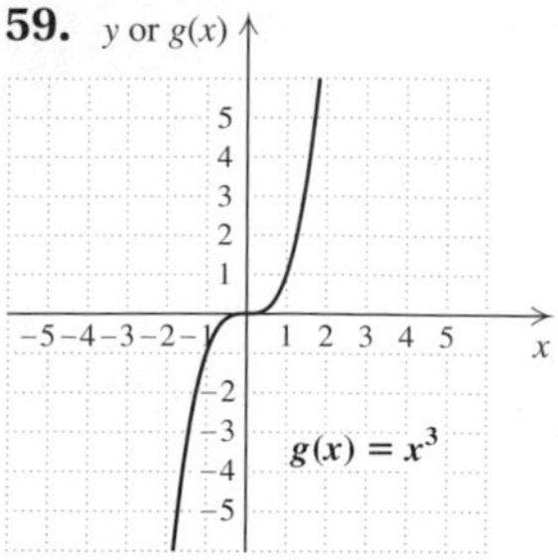

61.

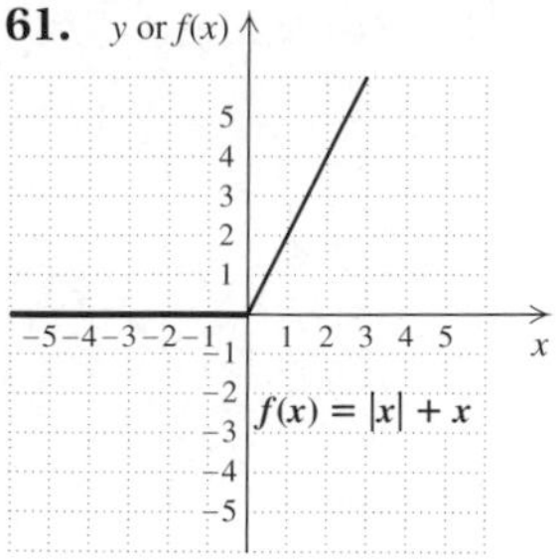

63. Answers may vary. **65.** $g(x) = x^2 - 4$ **67.** $\{-5, -4, -1, 4\}$ **69.** $\{-7, 0, 1, 2, 9\}$

Review Exercises: Chapter 9, pp. 584–585

1. (h) **2.** (f) **3.** (g) **4.** (e) **5.** (b) **6.** (d) **7.** (a) **8.** (c) **9.** $\frac{5}{2} \pm \frac{\sqrt{29}}{2}$, or $\frac{5 \pm \sqrt{29}}{2}$ **10.** $-\frac{5}{3}, 1$ **11.** $\pm\sqrt{3}$ **12.** $\frac{3}{5}, 1$ **13.** $1 \pm \sqrt{11}$ **14.** $\pm 8i$ **15.** $-2, \frac{1}{3}$ **16.** $-8 \pm \sqrt{13}$ **17.** $3 \pm 2i$ **18.** $-1, 3$ **19.** 0 **20.** $-3 \pm 3\sqrt{2}$ **21.** $-\frac{1}{2} \pm \frac{\sqrt{3}}{2}i$ **22.** $1 \pm \frac{\sqrt{3}}{2}$, or $\frac{2 \pm \sqrt{3}}{2}$ **23.** 1 **24.** $\pm 2\sqrt{2}$ **25.** $\frac{3}{10} \pm \frac{\sqrt{71}}{10}i$ **26.** $-\frac{7}{2}, \frac{5}{3}$ **27.** $t = \sqrt{\frac{r+s}{2}}$, or $t = \frac{\sqrt{2(r+s)}}{2}$ **28.** $m = \frac{100 + n}{3}$ **29.** $a = \frac{b+c}{2}$ **30.** $t = \frac{rs}{r+s}$ **31.** 0.382, 2.618 **32.** −1.866, −0.134 **33.** 3.217 m, 6.217 m **34.** 5% **35.** Length: 12 m; width: 9 m **36.** 6.349 sec **37.** $2 - 8i$ **38.** $2\sqrt{6}i$, or $2i\sqrt{6}$

39.

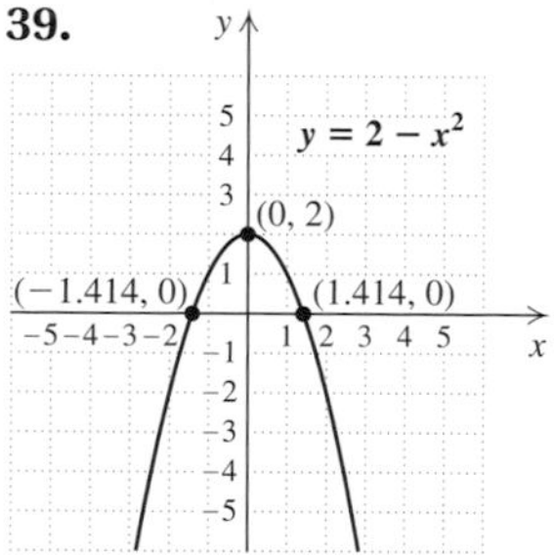

40.

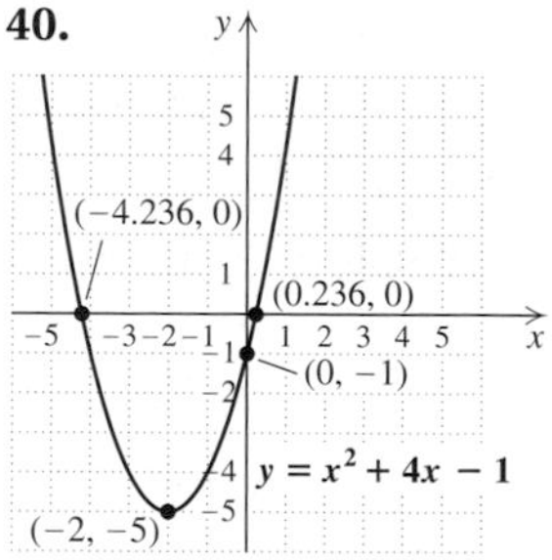

41.

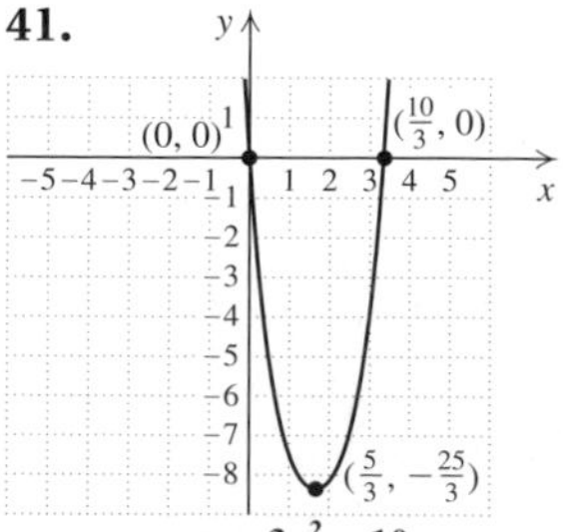

$y = 3x^2 - 10x$

42.

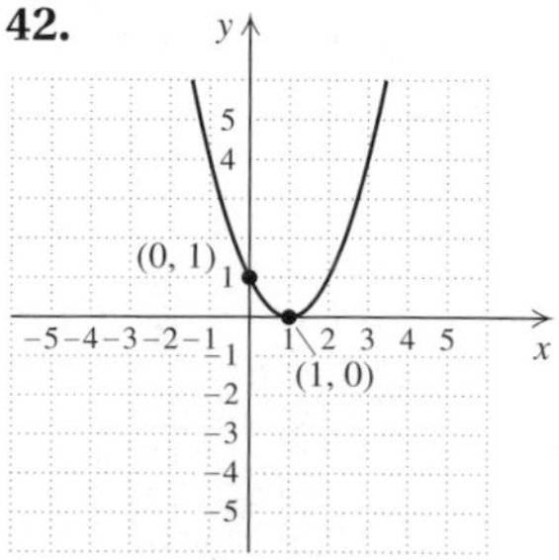

$y = x^2 - 2x + 1$

43. −1; −7; 2 **44.** 0; 0; 19 **45.** 1950 calories

46.

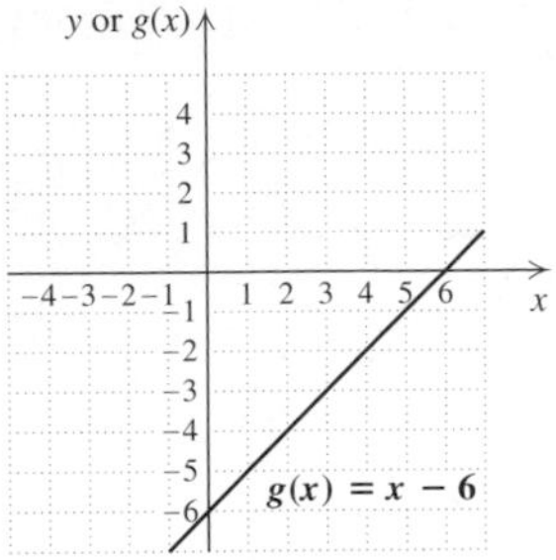

47.

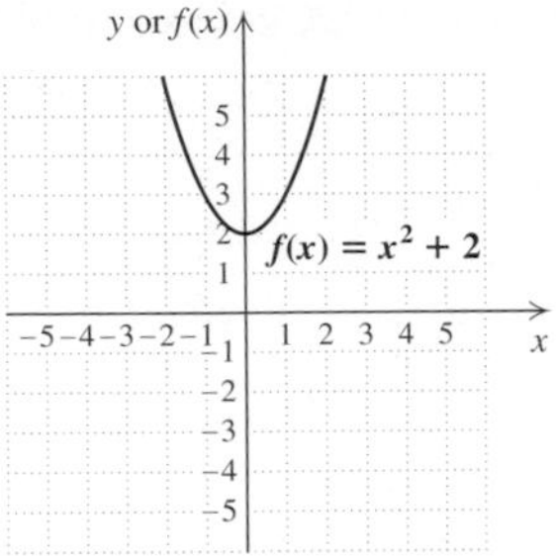

48.

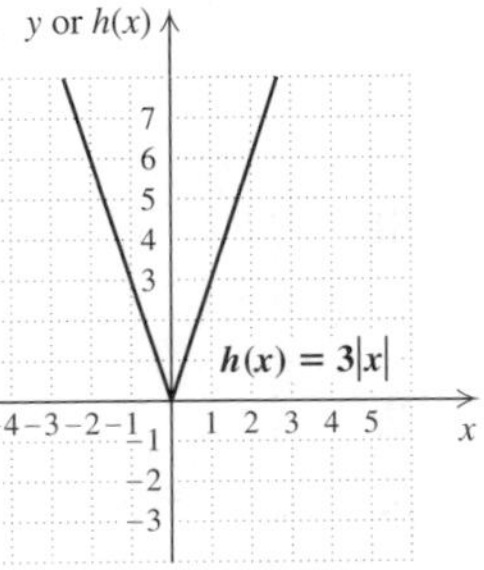

49. No **50.** Yes

51. If $b^2 - 4ac$ is 0, then the quadratic formula becomes $x = -b/(2a)$; thus there is only one x-intercept. If $b^2 - 4ac$ is negative, then there are no real-number solutions and thus no x-intercepts. If $b^2 - 4ac$ is positive, then $x = \dfrac{-b + \sqrt{b^2 - 4ac}}{2a}$ or $x = \dfrac{-b - \sqrt{b^2 - 4ac}}{2a}$ so there must be two x-intercepts.
52. The graph can be drawn more accurately and with fewer points plotted when the general shape is known.
53. Yes; a rational equation like $x + \dfrac{6}{x} = -5$ has two solutions whereas a quadratic equation like $x^2 + 6x + 9 = 0$ has just one solution. **54.** −32 and −31; 31 and 32 **55.** ±14 **56.** 25 **57.** $5\sqrt{\pi}$

Test: Chapter 9, p. 586

1. [9.1] $\pm\sqrt{3}$ **2.** [9.3] $0, \frac{7}{3}$ **3.** [9.3] $\dfrac{1}{2} \pm \dfrac{\sqrt{13}}{2}$, or $\dfrac{1 \pm \sqrt{13}}{2}$
4. [9.3] $-3, \frac{5}{3}$ **5.** [9.3] −8, 6 **6.** [9.5] $\pm 7i$
7. [9.1] $3 \pm \sqrt{7}$ **8.** [9.1] 2 **9.** [9.5] $2 \pm 2i$
10. [9.3] $\dfrac{3}{2} \pm \dfrac{\sqrt{37}}{2}$, or $\dfrac{3 \pm \sqrt{37}}{2}$ **11.** [9.3] $-2 \pm \sqrt{14}$
12. [9.3] $\dfrac{7}{6} \pm \dfrac{\sqrt{37}}{6}$, or $\dfrac{7 \pm \sqrt{37}}{6}$ **13.** [9.2] $2 \pm \sqrt{14}$
14. [9.4] $p = \dfrac{n^2 - 6n - 11}{4}$ **15.** [9.4] $b = \dfrac{a}{1 + t}$
16. [9.3] 4.702, −1.702 **17.** [9.3] 6.5 m, 2.5 m
18. [9.3] 11 **19.** [9.5] $7i$ **20.** [9.5] $3 - 4\sqrt{2}i$

21. [9.6]

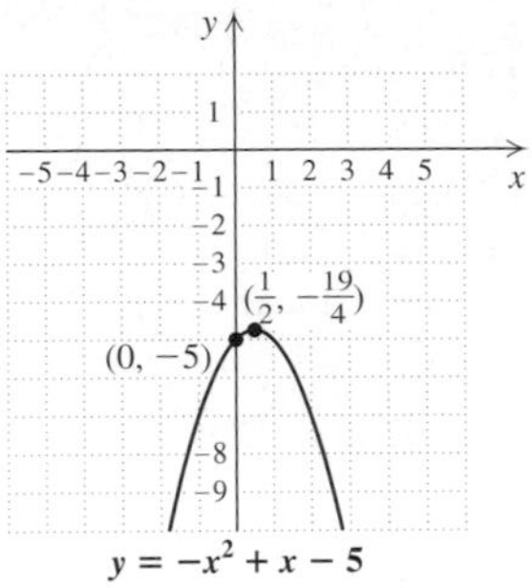

22. [9.6]

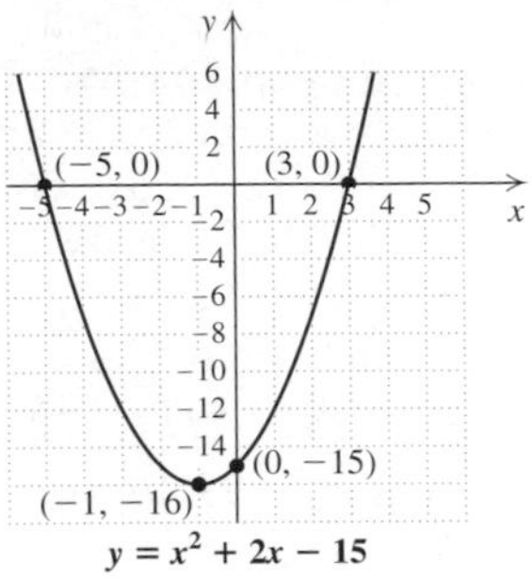

23. [9.7] $1, \frac{3}{2}, 2$ **24.** [9.7] 1, 3, −3 **25.** [9.7] 25.98 min

26. [9.7]

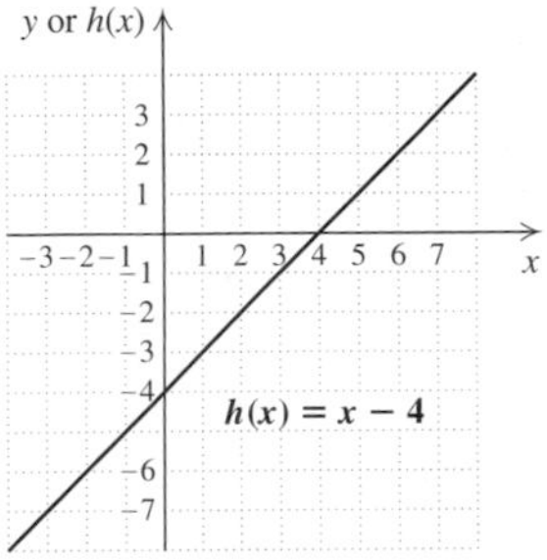

27. [9.7]

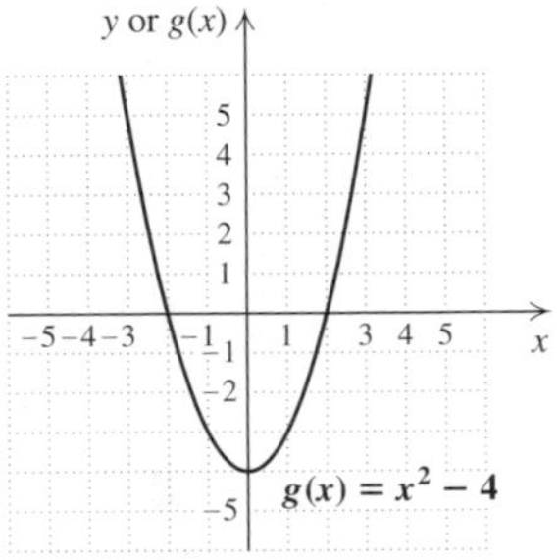

28. [9.7] Yes **29.** [9.7] No
30. [9.3] $75 + 50\sqrt{2} \approx 145.7\text{ ft}^2$ **31.** [9.3] $1 \pm \sqrt{5}$

Cumulative Review: Chapters 1–9/Final Exam, pp. 587–589

1. x^3 **2.** 67 **3.** $(6x)y$, $x(6y)$; there are other answers.
4. 240 **5.** 7 **6.** 9 **7.** 15 **8.** $-\frac{3}{20}$ **9.** 4 **10.** $-2m - 4$
11. −6 **12.** $\{x \mid x < -6\}$ **13.** 7 **14.** 3, 5 **15.** (1, 2)
16. $-\frac{3}{5}$ **17.** (6, 7) **18.** 3, −2 **19.** $-\dfrac{3}{2} \pm \dfrac{\sqrt{29}}{2}$, or $\dfrac{-3 \pm \sqrt{29}}{2}$ **20.** 2 **21.** $\{x \mid x \geq -1\}$ **22.** 8 **23.** −3
24. (15, 0) **25.** $-1 \pm 2i$ **26.** $\pm\sqrt{10}$ **27.** $3 \pm \sqrt{6}$
28. $\frac{2}{9}$ **29.** $\frac{5}{4}, -\frac{4}{3}$ **30.** No solution **31.** 12
32. $t = \dfrac{4s + 3}{A}$ **33.** $m = \dfrac{tn}{t + n}$ **34.** 2.73×10^{-5}
35. 2.0×10^{14} **36.** x^{-4}, or $\dfrac{1}{x^4}$ **37.** y^7 **38.** $4y^{12}$
39. $10x^3 + 3x - 3$ **40.** $7x^3 - 2x^2 + 4x - 17$
41. $8x^2 - 4x - 6$ **42.** $-8y^4 + 6y^3 - 2y^2$
43. $6t^3 - 17t^2 + 16t - 6$ **44.** $t^2 - \frac{1}{16}$
45. $9m^2 - 12m + 4$ **46.** $15x^2y^3 + x^2y^2 + 5xy^2 + 7$
47. $x^4 - 0.04y^2$ **48.** $9p^2 + 24pq^2 + 16q^4$ **49.** $\dfrac{2}{x + 3}$
50. $\dfrac{3a(a - 1)}{2(a + 1)}$ **51.** $\dfrac{27x - 4}{5x(3x - 1)}$ **52.** $\dfrac{-x^2 + x + 2}{(x + 4)(x - 4)(x - 5)}$

53. $x^2 + 9x + 16 + \dfrac{35}{x - 2}$ **54.** $(5x - 3)(5x + 3)$
55. $(x - 8)(x^2 - 5)$ **56.** $x(4x + 1)(4x - 1)$
57. $(m - 4)^2$ **58.** $(5x - 2)(3x + 4)$
59. $2x(9x^4 + 2x^3 - 5)$ **60.** $(3p + 2)(2p - 3)$
61. $(c - 3b)(2a + d)$ **62.** $(3x + 5y)^2$
63. $3(t^2 + 6)(t + 2)(t - 2)$ **64.** $(7ab + 4)(7ab - 4)$
65. $-\frac{42}{5}$ **66.** 7 **67.** -5 **68.** $8x$ **69.** $\sqrt{a^2 - b^2}$
70. $8a^2b\sqrt{3ab}$ **71.** $\frac{1}{4}$ **72.** $9xy\sqrt{3x}$ **73.** $\frac{10}{9}$ **74.** 7
75. $16\sqrt{3}$ **76.** $\dfrac{2\sqrt{10}}{5}$ **77.** 40 cm

78.

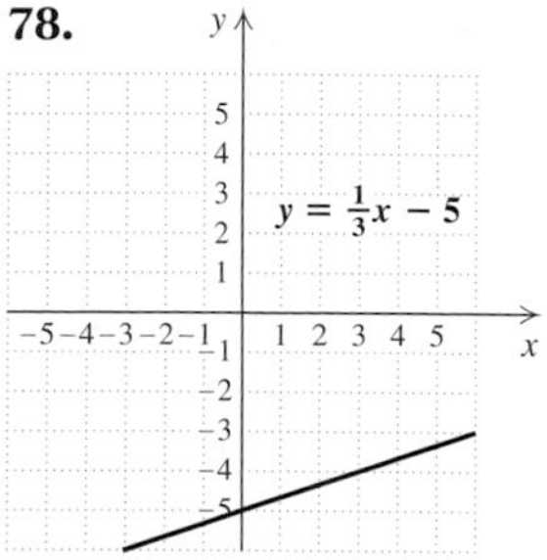

79.

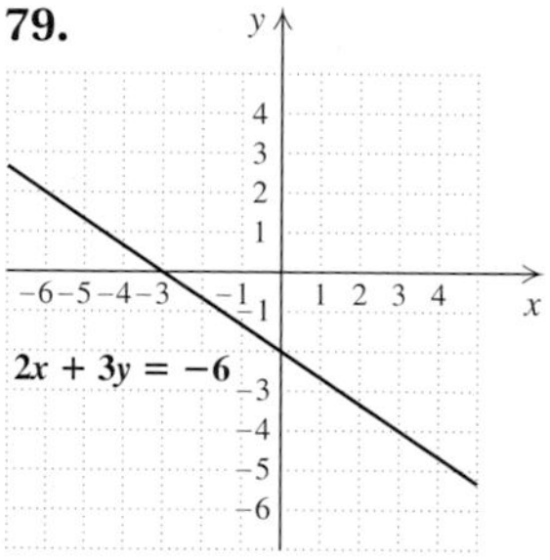

80.

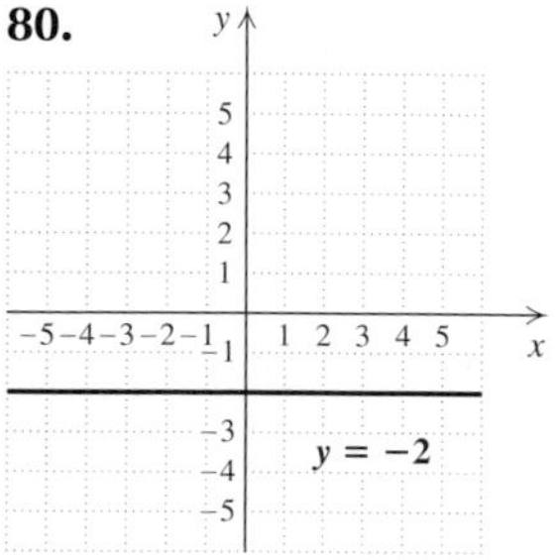

81.

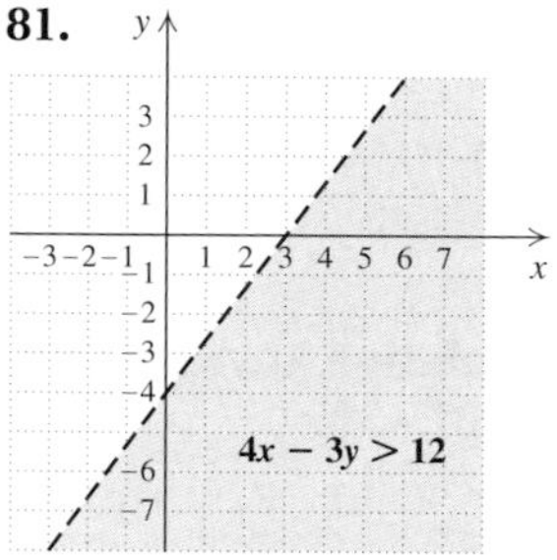

82.

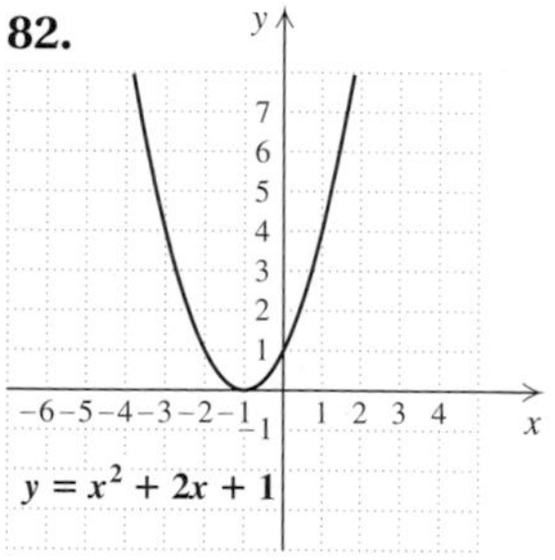

83.

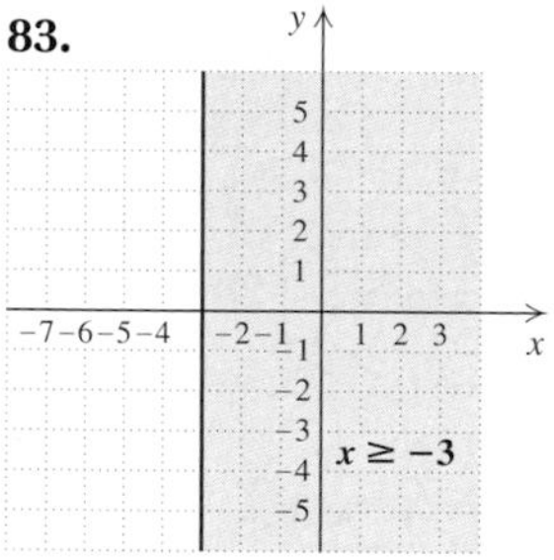

84. $\dfrac{2}{3} \pm \dfrac{\sqrt{6}}{3}$, or $\dfrac{2 \pm \sqrt{6}}{3}$ **85.** 1.207, -0.207

86.

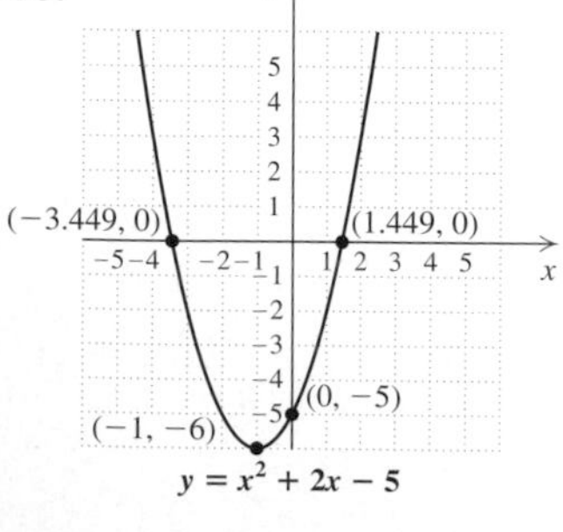

87. 2.145 million women **88.** \$95.14/year
89. 14, 16; -16, -14 **90.** 12 m **91.** 6090 cars
92. Chocolate creams: 19 lb; nut candies: 6 lb **93.** 24 min
94.

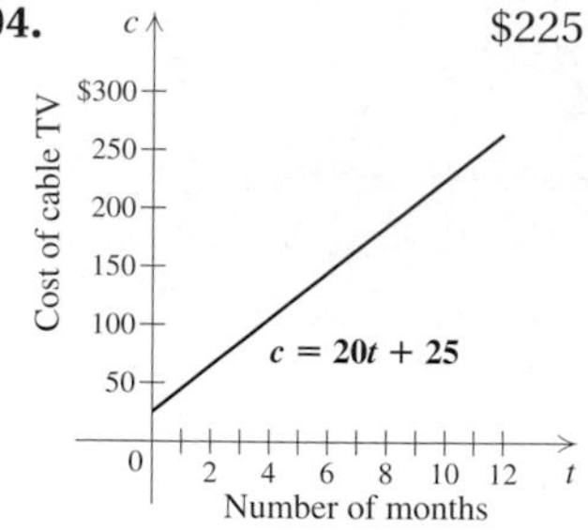

\$225 **95.** $-4, 0, 0$

96. Parallel **97.**

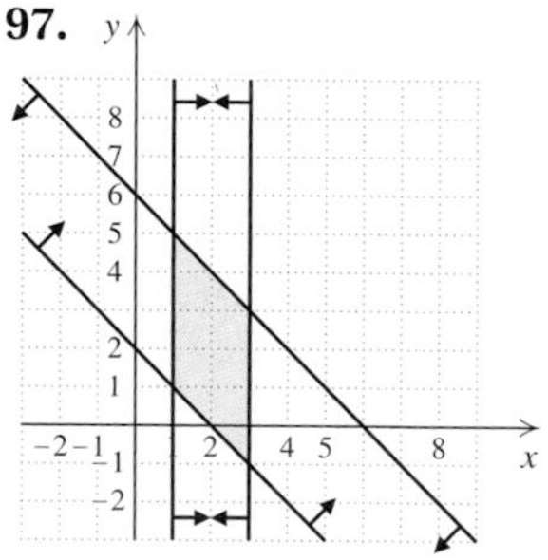

98. 2; $(0, -8)$ **99.** 15 **100.** $y + 3 = -\dfrac{1}{2}(x - 1)$
101. $-5i$ **102.** 30, -30 **103.** $\dfrac{\sqrt{6}}{3}$ **104.** Yes **105.** Yes
106. No **107.** No **108.** Yes

APPENDIXES

Exercise Set A, p. 593

1. $(t + 2)(t^2 - 2t + 4)$ **3.** $(a - 4)(a^2 + 4a + 16)$
5. $(z + 5)(z^2 - 5z + 25)$ **7.** $(2a - 1)(4a^2 + 2a + 1)$
9. $(y - 3)(y^2 + 3y + 9)$ **11.** $(4 + 5x)(16 - 20x + 25x^2)$
13. $(5p - 1)(25p^2 + 5p + 1)$
15. $(3m + 4)(9m^2 - 12m + 16)$
17. $(p - q)(p^2 + pq + q^2)$ **19.** $\left(x + \frac{1}{2}\right)\left(x^2 - \frac{1}{2}x + \frac{1}{4}\right)$
21. $2(y - 4)(y^2 + 4y + 16)$ **23.** $3(2a + 1)(4a^2 - 2a + 1)$
25. $r(s - 4)(s^2 + 4s + 16)$
27. $5(x + 2z)(x^2 - 2xz + 4z^2)$
29. $(x + 0.1)(x^2 - 0.1x + 0.01)$ **31.**
33. $(5c^2 + 2d^2)(25c^4 - 10c^2d^2 + 4d^4)$
35. $3(x^a - 2y^b)(x^{2a} + 2x^ay^b + 4y^{2b})$
37. $\frac{1}{3}\left(\frac{1}{2}xy + z\right)\left(\frac{1}{4}x^2y^2 - \frac{1}{2}xyz + z^2\right)$

Exercise Set B, pp. 596–598

1. Mean: 21; median: 18.5; mode: 29 **3.** Mean: 21; median: 20; mode: 5, 20 **5.** Mean: 5.2; median: 5.7; mode: 7.4 **7.** Mean: 239.5; median: 234; mode: 234 **9.** Average: 23.8; median: 15; mode: 1 **11.** Mean: 897.2;

median: 798, mode: none **13.** Average: \$8.19; median: \$8.49; mode: \$6.99 **15.** 10 home runs **17.** $a = 30, b = 58$

Exercise Set C, pp. 601–602

1. $\{3, 4, 5, 6, 7\}$ **3.** $\{41, 43, 45, 47, 49\}$ **5.** $\{-3, 3\}$ **7.** False **9.** True **11.** True **13.** True **15.** True **17.** False **19.** $\{c, d, e\}$ **21.** $\{1, 10\}$ **23.** $\varnothing$ **25.** $\{a, e, i, o, u, q, c, k\}$ **27.** $\{0, 1, 2, 5, 7, 10\}$ **29.** $\{a, e, i, o, u, m, n, f, g, h\}$ **31.** **33.** The set of integers **35.** The set of real numbers **37.** $\varnothing$ **39.** **(a)** A; **(b)** A; **(c)** A; **(d)** $\varnothing$ **41.** True

Glossary

A

absolute value [1.4] A number's distance from 0 on the number line.

additive inverses [1.6] Two numbers whose sum is 0; opposites.

algebraic expression [1.1] A number or variable or a collection of numbers and variables on which the operations $+, -, \cdot, \div, (\ )^n$, or $\sqrt[n]{(\ )}$ are performed.

ascending order [4.3] A polynomial written with the terms arranged according to the degree of one variable, from least to greatest.

associative law of addition [1.2] The statement that when three numbers are added, regrouping the addends gives the same sum.

associative law of multiplication [1.2] The statement that when three numbers are multiplied, regrouping the factors gives the same product.

average [2.7] Most commonly, the mean of a set of numbers.

axes [3.1] Two perpendicular number lines used to identify points in a plane.

axis of symmetry [9.6] A line that can be drawn through a graph such that the part of the graph on one side of the line is an exact reflection of the part on the other side.

B

bar graph [3.1] A graphic display of data using bars proportional in length to the numbers represented.

base [1.8] In exponential notation, the number being raised to a power.

binomial [4.2] A polynomial composed of two terms.

C

circle graph [3.1] A graphic display of data using sectors of a circle to represent percents.

circumference [2.3], [4.2] The distance around a circle.

coefficient [2.1] The numerical multiplier of a variable.

commutative law of addition [1.2] The statement that when two numbers are added, changing the order in which the numbers are added does not affect the sum.

commutative law of multiplication [1.2] The statement that when two numbers are multiplied, changing the order in which the numbers are multiplied does not affect the product.

completing the square [9.2] To complete the square for an expression like $x^2 + bx$, add half of the coefficient of x, squared.

complex number [9.5] Any number that can be written as $a + bi$, where a and b are real numbers.

complex rational expression [6.5] A rational expression that has one or more rational expressions within its numerator and/or denominator.

composite number [1.3] A natural number that has more than two integers as factors.

conjugates [8.4] Expressions of the form $a\sqrt{b} + c\sqrt{d}$ and $a\sqrt{b} - c\sqrt{d}$ are called conjugates. Their product does not contain a radical term.

consistent system of equations [7.1] A system of equations that has at least one solution.

constant [1.1] A known number.

constant of proportionality [7.7] In an equation of the form $y = kx$ or $y = \frac{k}{x}(k > 0)$, with x and y variables, k is the constant of proportionality.

contradiction [2.1] An equation that has no solution and is never true.

coordinates [3.1] The numbers in an ordered pair.

cube root [8.7] The number c is the cube root of a if $c^3 = a$.

D

degree of a polynomial [4.2] The degree of the term of highest degree of a polynomial.

degree of a term [4.2] The number of variable factors in a term.

denominator [1.3] The number below the fraction bar in a fraction.

dependent equations [7.1] For two equations, when one equation can be obtained by multiplying both sides of the other equation by a constant.

descending order [4.2] A polynomial written with the terms arranged according to the degree of one variable, from greatest to least.

difference of squares [5.4] An expression that can be written in the form $a^2 - b^2$.

direct variation [7.7] A situation that translates to an equation of the form $y = kx$, with k a constant. The equation $y = kx$ is an equation of direct variation.

distributive law [1.2] The statement that multiplying a factor by the sum of two numbers gives the same result as multiplying the factor by each of the two numbers and then adding.

domain [9.7] The set of all first coordinates of the ordered pairs in a function.

E

equation [1.1] A number sentence with the verb =.

equivalent equations [2.1] Equations with the same solutions.

equivalent expressions [1.2] Expressions that have the same value for all allowable replacements.

equivalent inequalities [2.6] Inequalities that have the same solution set.

evaluate [1.1] To substitute a value for each occurrence of a variable in an expression.

exponent [1.8] In expressions of the form a^n, the number n is an exponent. For n a natural number, a^n represents n factors of a.

exponential notation [1.8] A representation of a number using a base raised to an exponent.

extrapolation [3.7] The process of estimating a value that goes beyond the given data.

F

factor [1.2] *Verb*: To write an equivalent expression that is a product. *Noun*: A number being multiplied.

FOIL [4.5] To multiply two binomials by multiplying the **F**irst terms, the **O**utside terms, the **I**nside terms, and the **L**ast terms, and then adding the results.

formula [2.3] An equation that uses numbers or letters to represent a relationship between two or more quantities.

fraction notation [1.3] A quotient represented with a bar under (or slash following) the dividend and over (or before) the divisor.

function [9.7] A correspondence that assigns to each member of a set called the domain exactly one member of a set called the range.

function values [9.7] Outputs from equations in function notation.

G

grade [3.5] The grade of a road is the measure of the road's steepness expressed as a percent.

graph [3.1] A graph can be a picture or diagram of the data in a table. A graph can also be a line or a curve that represents all the solutions of an equation.

greatest common factor [5.1] The common factor of a polynomial with the largest possible coefficient and the largest possible exponent(s).

H

higher roots [8.7] Cube roots, fourth roots, and, in general, roots of the form $\sqrt[n]{\ }$, with n a natural number and $n > 2$.

hypotenuse [5.7] In a right triangle, the side opposite the right angle.

I

identity [2.1] An equation that is always true.

identity property of 0 [1.5] The statement that the sum of a number and 0 is always the original number.

identity property of 1 [1.3] The product of a number and 1 is always the original number.

imaginary number [9.5] A number that can be written in the form $a + bi$, where a and b are real numbers and $b \neq 0$.

imaginary number *i* [9.5] The square root of -1. That is, $i = \sqrt{-1}$ and $i^2 = -1$.

inconsistent system of equations [7.1] A system of equations for which there is no solution.

independent equations [7.1] Equations that are not dependent.

index [8.7] In $\sqrt[n]{a}$, the number n is called the index.

inequality [1.4] A mathematical sentence using $>, <, \geq, \leq$, or $\neq$.

input [9.7] A member of the domain of a function.

integers [1.4] The whole numbers and their opposites.

interpolation [3.7] The process of estimating a value between given values.

inverse variation [7.7] A situation that translates to an equation of the form $y = k/x$, with k a constant. The equation $y = k/x$ is an equation of inverse variation.

irrational number [1.4] A number that cannot be named as a ratio of two integers.

L

leading coefficient [4.2] The coefficient of the term of highest degree in a polynomial.

leading term [4.2] A polynomial's term of highest degree.

least common denominator [6.3] The least common multiple of the denominators.

least common multiple [6.3] The smallest positive number that is a multiple of all the numbers under consideration.

legs [5.7] In a right triangle, the sides that form the right angle.

like radicals [8.4] Radical expressions that have the same common radical factor.

like terms [1.5], [1.8] Terms that have exactly the same variable factors.

line graph [3.1] A graph in which quantities are represented as points connected by straight-line segments.

linear equation [3.2] Any equation that can be written in the form $y = mx + b$ or $Ax + By = C$, where x and y are variables.

linear inequality [7.5] An inequality whose related equation is a linear equation.

M

mean [2.7] The sum of a set of numbers divided by the number of numbers in the set.

monomial [4.2] A constant, a variable, or a product of a constant and one or more variables.

motion problem [6.7] A problem that deals with distance, speed, and time.

multiplicative inverses [1.3] Two numbers whose product is 1; reciprocals.

multiplicative property of zero [1.7] The statement that for any real number a, $0 \cdot a = a \cdot 0 = 0$.

N

natural numbers [1.3] The counting numbers: $1, 2, 3, 4, 5, \ldots$.

nonlinear equation (in two variables) [3.2] An equation that when graphed is not a line.

numerator [1.3] The number above the fraction bar in a fraction.

O

opposites [1.6] Two expressions whose sum is 0; additive inverses.

opposites, law of [1.6] The statement that for any two numbers a and $-a$, $a + (-a) = 0$.

origin [3.1] The point on a coordinate plane where the two axes intersect.

output [9.7] A member of the range of a function.

P

parabola [9.6] The graph of any equation of the form $y = ax^2 + bx + c$.

percent [2.4] A ratio or fraction with a denominator of 100.

perfect square [8.1] Any number that is the square of a rational number.

perfect-square trinomial [5.4] A trinomial that is the square of a binomial.

point–slope equation [3.7] An equation of the form $y - y_1 = m(x - x_1)$, where x and y are variables.

polynomial [4.2] A monomial or a sum of monomials.

prime factorization [1.3] The factorization of a whole number into a product of its prime factors.

prime number [1.3] A natural number that has exactly two different factors: the number itself and 1.

principal square root [8.1] The nonnegative square root of a number.

principle of zero products [5.6] The statement that an equation $AB = 0$ is true if and only if $A = 0$ or $B = 0$.

proportion [6.7] An equation stating that two ratios are equal.

Pythagorean theorem [5.7] In any right triangle, if a and b are the lengths of the legs and c is the length of the hypotenuse, then $a^2 + b^2 = c^2$.

Q

quadrants [3.1] The four regions into which the axes divide a plane.

quadratic equation [5.6] An equation equivalent to one of the form $ax^2 + bx + c = 0$, where $a \neq 0$.

quadratic formula [9.3] For $a \neq 0$, the solutions of $ax^2 + bx + c = 0$ are given by $x = \dfrac{-b \pm \sqrt{b^2 - 4ac}}{2a}$.

R

radical equation [8.5] An equation in which a variable appears in a radicand.

radical expression [8.1] An algebraic expression that contains at least one radical sign.

radical sign [8.1] A symbol, $\sqrt{}$, generally used when finding square roots and indicating the principal root.

radicand [8.1] The expression under the radical sign.

range [9.7] The set of all the second coordinates of the ordered pairs in a function.

rate [3.4] A ratio that indicates how two quantities change with respect to each other.

ratio [6.7] The ratio of a to b is a/b, also written $\dfrac{a}{b}$ or $a{:}b$.

rational equation [6.6] An equation containing one or more rational expressions.

rational expressions [6.1] A quotient of two polynomials.

rational numbers [1.4] Numbers that can be written in the form $\dfrac{a}{b}$, where a and b are integers and $b \neq 0$.

rationalizing the denominator [8.3] A procedure for finding an equivalent expression without a radical in the denominator.

real number [1.4] Any number that is either rational or irrational.

reciprocals [1.3] Any two numbers whose product is 1; multiplicative inverses.

repeating decimal [1.4] A decimal in which a number pattern repeats indefinitely.

right triangle [5.7] A triangle that includes a 90° angle.

S

scientific notation [4.8] A number written in the form $N \times 10^m$, where m is an integer, $1 \leq N < 10$, and N is expressed in decimal notation.

set [1.4] A collection of objects.

set-builder notation [2.6] A set named by describing basic characteristics of the elements in the set.

similar triangles [6.7] Triangles in which corresponding angles have the same measure and corresponding sides are proportional.

slope [3.5] The ratio of the rise to the run for any two points on a line.

slope–intercept equation [3.6] An equation of the form $y = mx + b$, where x and y are variables.

solution [1.1] A replacement or substitution that makes an equation or inequality true.

solution set [2.6] The set of all solutions of an equation or inequality.

solve [2.1] To find all solutions of the equation, inequality, or problem.

square root [8.1] The number c is a square root of a if $c^2 = a$.

substitute [1.1] To replace a variable with a number or an expression that represents a number.

system of equations [7.1] A set of two or more equations that are to be solved simultaneously.

system of linear inequalities [7.6] A set of two or more linear inequalities that are to be solved simultaneously.

T

term [1.2] A number, a variable, a product, or a quotient of numbers and/or variables.

terminating decimal [1.4] A decimal that can be written using a finite number of decimal places.

trinomial [4.2] A polynomial that is composed of three terms.

U

undefined [1.7] An expression that has no meaning attached to it.

V

variable [1.1] A letter that represents an unknown number.

vertex [9.6] The point at which a parabola crosses its axis of symmetry.

vertical-line test [9.7] The statement that a graph represents a function if it is impossible to draw a vertical line that intersects the graph more than once.

W

whole number [1.3] The set of numbers: 0, 1, 2, 3, 4, ...

X

***x*-intercept** [3.3] A point at which a graph crosses the x-axis.

Y

***y*-intercept** [3.3] A point at which a graph crosses the y-axis.

Index

H

I

K

L

M

N

INDEX OF APPLICATIONS

Health/Medicine

Labor

Miscellaneous

Physics

Social Sciences

Sports/Entertainment

Statistics/Demographics

Technology

Transportation

For Extra Practice

MyMathLab

The following sections feature extra practice problems available when you register for MyMathLab.com. For your convenience, these exercises are also printed in the *Instructor's Resource Guide*. Please contact your instructor for assistance.

Section 1.5	Addition of Real Numbers
Section 1.6	Subtraction of Real Numbers
Section 1.7	Multiplication and Division of Real Numbers
Section 1.8	Exponential Notation and Order of Operations
Section 2.5	Problem Solving
Section 2.6	Solving Inequalities
Section 3.2	Graphing Linear Equations
Section 3.3	Graphing and Intercepts
Section 3.6	Slope–Intercept Form
Section 3.7	Point–Slope Form
Section 4.4	Multiplication of Polynomials
Section 4.7	Division of Polynomials
Section 5.1	Introduction to Factoring
Section 5.2	Factoring Trinomials of the Type $x^2 + bx + c$
Section 5.3	Factoring Trinomials of the Type $ax^2 + bx + c$
Section 5.4	Factoring Perfect-Square Trinomials and Differences of Squares
Section 5.5	Factoring: A General Strategy
Section 5.7	Solving Applications
Section 6.1	Rational Expressions
Section 6.2	Multiplication and Division
Section 6.3	Addition, Subtraction, and Least Common Denominators
Section 6.4	Addition and Subtraction with Unlike Denominators
Section 6.5	Complex Rational Expressions
Section 6.6	Solving Rational Equations
Section 6.7	Applications Using Rational Equations and Proportions
Section 7.2	Systems of Equations and Substitution
Section 7.3	Systems of Equations and Elimination
Section 7.4	More Applications Using Systems
Section 7.5	Linear Inequalities in Two Variables
Section 7.6	Systems of Linear Inequalities
Section 8.2	Multiplying and Simplifying Radical Expressions
Section 8.3	Quotients Involving Square Roots
Section 8.4	Radical Expressions with Several Terms
Section 8.5	Radical Equations
Section 8.6	Applications Using Right Triangles
Section 8.7	Higher Roots and Rational Exponents
Section 9.3	The Quadratic Formula and Applications
Section 9.6	Graphs of Quadratic Equations
Section 9.7	Functions

Selected Keys of the Scientific Calculator

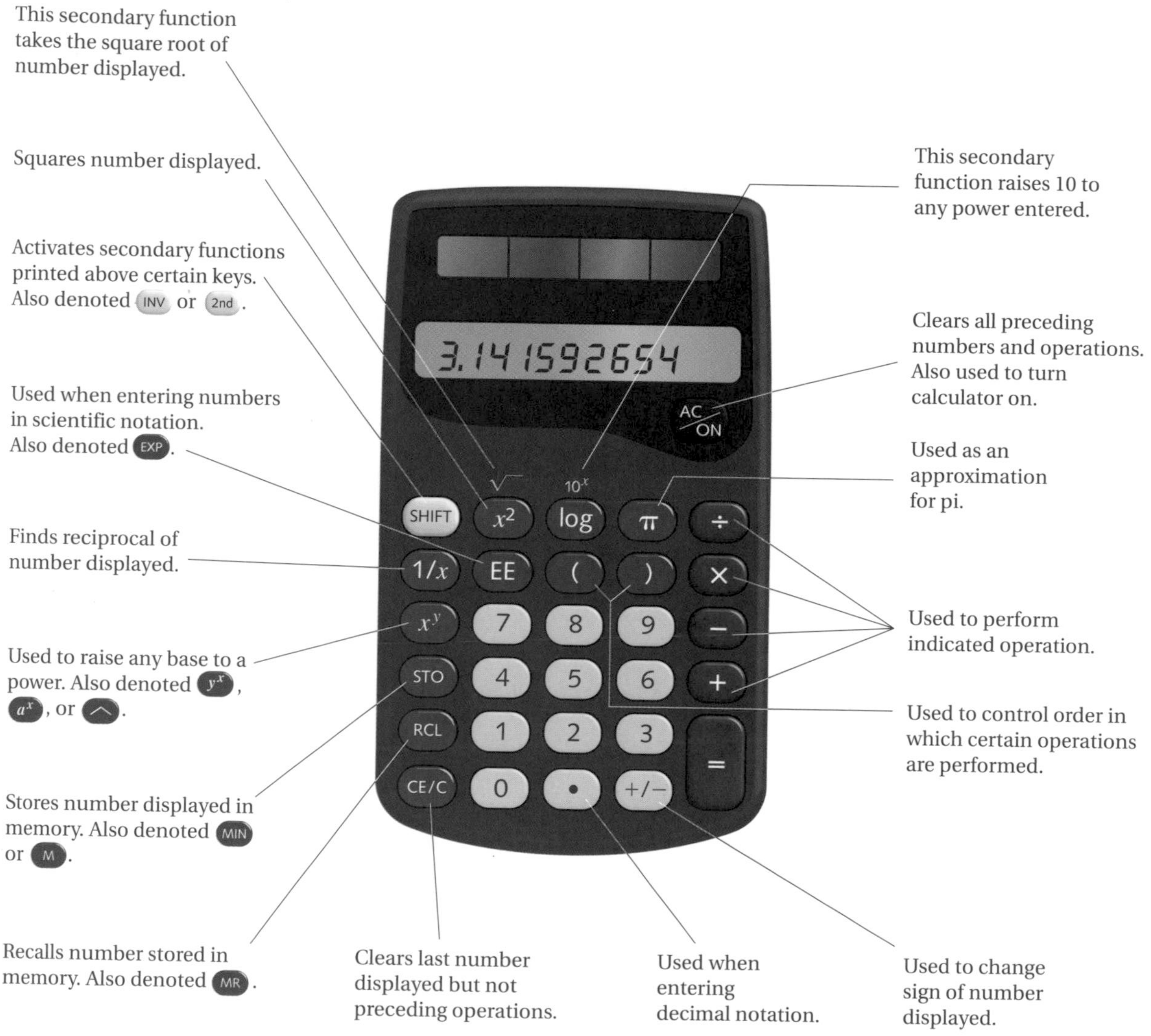